CAMPERSTOP
EUROPE
2016

motorhome stopovers in

Albania
Austria
Belgium
Bosnia-Herzegovina
Croatia
Czech Republiek
Denmark
Finland
France
Germany
Greece
Hungary
Ireland
Italy
Luxemburg

Montenegro
Netherlands
Norway
United Kingdom
Poland
Portugal
Romania
Slovenia
Slowakia
Spain
Sweden
Switzerland

Publisher - Herausgeber - Éditeur - Editore

Facile
Media

Reliable information

Every summer, 50 teams of Facile Media drive all across Europe to inspect the motorhome stopovers. The inspections take place according to predefined guidelines. The inspections by these specially trained motorhome enthusiasts have made it possible to make the information in the guide as up-to-date as possible. Almost 9000 motorhome stopovers and 7000 illustrative photos are the result.

Unique way to find the motorhome sites

The motorhome stopovers can be easily located on the 38 maps. Below each map, you'll find a location name index with map referral and a page number where the location can be found in the guide. In addition, the type of motorhome stopover is indicated. In a glance, you'll be able to see whether it is the type of stopover you had in mind. In order to provide you with additional information, the location is described extensively on the relevant page, usually with a picture.

GPS-data sets on your navigation system

In addition to this guide, you can order datasets online, which you can download. The sets can be uploaded to the most common navigation systems. This allows you to drive to the motorhome stopovers listed in this guide without any effort. More information about this is available on page 6.

For more information: camperstop.com/app

Preface

COLOPHON

A publication of:

Facile Media, Oss
Landweerstraat-Zuid 109
5349 AK Oss
Postbus 555
NL-5340 AN Oss
tel: +31 412 65 68 85
E-mail: info@camperstop.com
Internet: www.camperstop.com

Chief editor
Anne van den Dobbelsteen

The draft of this version is saved
in October 2015

Comments or suggestions can
be sent to the publisher:

Facile Media
Postbus 555, NL-5340 AN Oss
Tel.: +31 412 65 68 85
E-mail: info@camperstop.com

ISBN 978-90-76080-44-4

Copyright 2015 Facile Media

This latest motorhome guide publication has undergone a transformation. We've had to bid farewell to the old, trusted format as each year the countless additional motorhome stopovers just couldn't be fitted in. This year the guide also includes the Scandinavian countries and Eastern Europe.

Besides the weather, travel is the most popular topic of conversation: at get-togethers, amongst friends or simply during a lunch break at work. Recently I've found people are listening with increasing interest to our motorhome trip tales. This is almost always followed up with: 'I'm considering a trip in a motorhome'. Our stories enthuse friends and family, who also wish to go motorhoming. Do you find the same? But how does one become a motorhomer? It seems relatively simple: you hire or buy a motorhome.

Wrong; that's just the beginning. The anticipation can start. A novice motorhomer still has a lot to discover and learn in order to make the trip a success. In order to enjoy the freedom a motorhome offers to the max, one must 'practise'. How do I plan my trip, do I work it out down to the finest detail in advance, or go off the cuff? What do I need to bear in mind? You've selected a motorhome stopover to overnight at but you might receive a horrible surprise upon arrival to find it fully booked. Make sure that you have a number of alternatives in mind. Do you have enough water onboard and if the tank for your waste water and toilet is empty there's no need to find a site with exhaustive facilities. As a novice it's also advisable to go on a trip with an experienced motorhomer; there's no doubt you'll learn a great deal.

Heading off to Greece with the motorhome is on many a wish list. We made our first trip to Greece with the motorhome eighteen years ago, along with our two little girls. Taking the boat from Venice was pretty much the only way to get to Greece back then. It became a memorable trip that we often recall to this day. Greece is one of our top motorhoming countries. We made the trip again last year but this time overland rather than by ferry. Via coastal routes in Croatia, Bosnia-Herzegovina, Montenegro and Albania, we arrived in Igoumenitsa in the north-west of Greece on 29 May 2015. We covered many kilometres but it was worth it. As before, Greece was relaxed, with a pleasant climate, delicious food and fascinating places of interest. There aren't that many official motorhome stopovers, but rather an increasing number of tavernas that offer motorhomes a pitch, often right on the beach. Motorhome park Aphrodite Waters in Ancient Corinth, one of the few official motorhome stopovers, deserves an extra mention. A hospitable welcome means you'll really enjoy your stay. It is located a couple of hundred metres from the famous antiquities and the compact centre with its convivial eateries. From here it's also a quick and easy train ride to Athens. In addition, we found the city of Ioannina to be a pleasant surprise. It's teeming with young people and boasts a pleasant historic centre with numerous shops, pavement cafés and restaurants. If you're planning on going to Greece, I say, DO IT!

On behalf of the editorial team and our inspectors, I wish you a splendid and pleasurable motorhoming season in 2016!

Anne van den Dobbelsteen
Chief editor

Table of contents

Table of contents

GPS - convenience

Downloading GPS-coordinates

Downloads of the gps-coordinates for the motorhome stopovers listed in this guide are available from www.camperstop.com. The files are suitable for most navigation systems. The data that appears on the screen gives the town name and page number in this guide so you can look up the details of the facilities very easily.

The downloadable files list the stopovers and most of the other facilities mentioned in the guide. Therefore it could be a stopover with or without service facilities, a place with service facilities only, but also a tourist information office or a campsite.

You can easily check for your nearest stopover, the navigation system will list the stopovers by distance. Use the guide to see what facilities are available. Once a choice has been made you can navigate to there without a problem.

The costs for downloading are € 3.25 per country/dataset. The Netherlands/Belgium/Luxembourg are sold as one country, also Austria/Switzerland and Spain/Portugal are treated the same.

Full downloading instructions are found on at www.camperstop.com. There are different downloads of several navigation systems.

You are driving in the region of St. Tropez, South of France
As you drive along the cost road near Fréjus in the direction of Saint Tropez, you would like to find a suitable stopover; click on the motorhome facilities in France and a list of the nearest places will appear each with the page number in the guide.

p 392 - Ramatuelle, Pal	5.1ᵏₘ	E
p 392 - Ramatuelle, Pal	6.0ᵏₘ	SE
p 395- St.Tropez, Aire c	6.6ᵏₘ	NE
p 396 - Ste.Maxime, Pal	8.1ᵏₘ	N
p 396 - Ste.Maxime, D2	9.0ᵏₘ	N
Back	Spell	▲ ▼

Look them up in the guide
You look in the guide on the page numbers given and select the place, which interests you most. In this example we want to go to the Camperpark in Saint Tropez.

Make the sat nav ready to go
Once the stopover has been chosen, click on your selection and the information will appear. Then click on Go!

p 395- St.Tropez, Aire camping-car, Chemin Fontaine du pin, Chemin de la Moutte

Go!

Map

Back ▲ ▼ Save

Navigate easily to place of destination
Your sat nav shows and tells you the way to your chosen stopover.

p 395- St.Tropez, Aire ca

Back 200ᵐ

6

How to use the guide

Searching in a region
In the table of contents, at the beginning of the guide, one can search a region in preferred country. On the page of the region a map indicates the different departments/provinces with a reference to the pages.

Maps
On pages 10-11 the countries are divided into sections. The number in each box is the number of the map. On the map the red dots indicate the location of the town. Next to each map an index is published with the places on maps. The index shows the name, type of stopover, map code and page number of each location. This way the description of the motorhome stopover can be found quickly and easy.

Searching for a town
Places identified in this guide can be found under the name of the local town in the alphabetical index at the back. Use the index like a dictionary to look for specific towns, the facilities offered, map references and relevant page numbers.

Country specific rules
When travelling you have to take into account that each country has its own rules and regulations. These rules are written on the first page of each countries section.

Advise
It is recommended not to wait to long to look for an overnight stop. It could be that chosen motorhome stopover is already full and you have to go looking for an alternative.

Other symbols

🛏 Motorhome stopover, number of pitches and rate

⬆ Signposted on the spot
➡ Signposted in town
⬆ No signs to indicate the motorhome stopover

Payment
💶 Collector parking fee
🅿 Parking meter
💳 Payment only with a credit/debit card
💳 Payment with cash and credit/debit card

S Service facilities
This symbol indicates that there are service facilities available.

🚰 drinking water
🪣 grey water dump
Ch chemical toilet disposal point
🔋 charging battery
⚡ electricity available
WC toilets
🚿 showers
🧺 washing machine/ dryer on the spot
📶 wifi access point

Description motorhome stopover

The information per motorhome stopover always begins with a colored block containing the type of stopover, town name and reference to the map. Directly below the name, address, GPS coordinates mostly followed by a picture. Beneath the picture you find the following information: number of pitches, rate, facilities and opening period. After that, if known, distances to city centre, shop, restaurant etc. Specific information of the motorhome stopover and a brief route description.

Motorhome facilities

🚐 MOTORHOME PARK
This symbol indicates a motorhome park, a park designed for motorhomes with a range of facilities.

🚚 OFFICIAL MOTORHOME STOPOVER
This symbol indicates an area suitable for overnight parking

🚛 OVERNIGHT PARKING TOLERATED
In some countries tolerated places are mentioned. This means that it is officially prohibited but is being tolerated by local authorities. Therefore the local or national situation may change at any time. Nevertheless these places are listed because they were frequently being used by motorhomes at the time of writing.

⚓ OVERNIGHT STAY IN HARBOUR/MARINA
Motorhome stopover in or near harbour or marina, often with a beautiful view.

🍇 OVERNIGHT STAY AT FARM/VINEYARD
Farms and vineyards that welcome motorhomes, you may be encouraged to sample and buy their fare.

🍽 OVERNIGHT STAY AT RESTAURANT
Motorhomes are allowed to stopover on the car park of a hotel, restaurant or bar. You should expect to dine or drink in the bar. Some restaurants insist on you having dinner. Sometimes a nominal charge is asked for the overnight stay.

♨ OVERNIGHT STAY AT SPA
A growing number of spas and thermal baths offer stopovers to motorhomes.

😀 OVERNIGHT STAY AT ZOO/MUSEUM/ AMUSEMENT PARK
Motorhomes are allowed to stopover on the car park of a zoo, museum or amusement park. Entrance is not always obligated.

🏭 OVERNIGHT STAY AT COMPANY/ ENTERPRISE
Overnight stay, mostly inside the gates, at companies/enterprises.

🏕 OVERNIGHT STAY OUTSIDE THE CAMPSITE
Motorhomes are allowed to stopover on the parking place outside the gate of a campsite.

🔺 CAMPSITE
Overnight stay on a campsite.

🅿 CAR-PARK
Motorhome parking bays, suitable for daytime use only. Often in large cities and/or tourist towns, charges may apply.

Driving regulations in Europe

Each country has different driving rules. For motorhomes sometimes there are different regulations. Here below an overview with maximum speed limits for motorhomes.

Per country there are also different rules as for warning triangles, security vests or driving with daily lights. Here below this information at a glance.

	within towns	single carriageway		expressway		motorway		compulsory in your vehicle:
		<3,5T	>3,5T	<3,5T	>3,5T	<3,5T	>3,5T	
(AL) Albania	40	80		90	70	110	80	triangle, first aid
(A) Austria	50	100	70			130	80	triangle, vest, first aid — A10-A12-A13-en A14 : 22-05h max. 110km/h.
(B) Belgium	50	90				120	90	triangle, vest, extinguisher, first aid
(BIH) Bosnia and Herzegovina	50	80		100	80	130	80	triangle, vest, extinguisher, first aid, spare
(CH) Switzerland	50	80		100	80	120	80	triangle, vest, spare
(CZ) Czech Republic	50	90		120	80	130	80	triangle, vest, first aid, spare
(D) Germany	50	100	80	130	100	130	100	triangle, vest, first aid, spare — 130km/h is a recommended speed limit.
(DK) Denmark	50	80	70	110	80	130	80	triangle, vest, extinguisher, spare
(ES) Spain	50	80		90	80	100	90	triangle, vest — Set of spare bulbs.
(FIN) Finland	50	80		100	80	100	80	triangle, vest, spare
(F) France	50	90	80	110	100	130	110	triangle, vest — Speed limits on a dry road. Safety vest also for bicycles.
(GB) Great Britain	30	60	50	70	60	70		30mph=48km 50mph=80km / 60mph=96km 70mph=112km / Speed limits in mph.
(GR) Greece	50	90		110	90	120	90	triangle, extinguisher, first aid
(HR) Croatia	50	90	80	110	90	130	90	triangle, vest, first aid — Set of spare bulbs.
(HU) Hungary	50	90		110	70	130	80	triangle, vest, extinguisher, first aid, spare

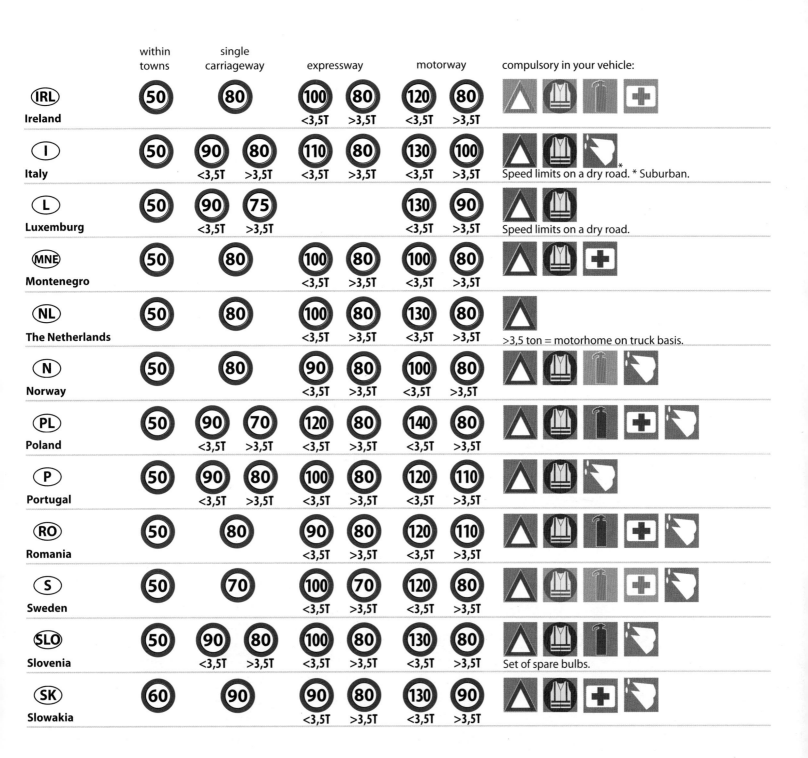

	within towns	single carriageway		expressway		motorway		compulsory in your vehicle:
		<3,5T	>3,5T	<3,5T	>3,5T	<3,5T	>3,5T	
(IRL) Ireland	50	80		100	80	120	80	warning triangle, security vest, fire extinguisher, first aid kit
(I) Italy	50	90	80	110	80	130	100	warning triangle, security vest, daily lights. Speed limits on a dry road. * Suburban.
(L) Luxemburg	50	90	75			130	90	warning triangle, security vest. Speed limits on a dry road.
(MNE) Montenegro	50	80		100	80	100	80	warning triangle, security vest, first aid kit
(NL) The Netherlands	50	80		100	80	130	80	warning triangle. >3,5 ton = motorhome on truck basis.
(N) Norway	50	80		90	80	100	80	warning triangle, security vest, fire extinguisher, daily lights
(PL) Poland	50	90	70	120	80	140	80	warning triangle, security vest, fire extinguisher, first aid kit, daily lights
(P) Portugal	50	90	80	100	80	120	110	warning triangle, security vest, daily lights
(RO) Romania	50	80		90	80	120	110	warning triangle, security vest, fire extinguisher, first aid kit, daily lights
(S) Sweden	50	70		100	70	120	80	warning triangle, security vest, fire extinguisher, first aid kit, daily lights
(SLO) Slovenia	50	90	80	100	80	130	80	warning triangle, security vest, fire extinguisher, daily lights. Set of spare bulbs.
(SK) Slowakia	60	90		90	80	130	90	warning triangle, security vest, first aid kit, daily lights

warning triangle

security vest

fire extinguisher

first aid kit

daily lights

recommended

Information is based on information available in November 2015.

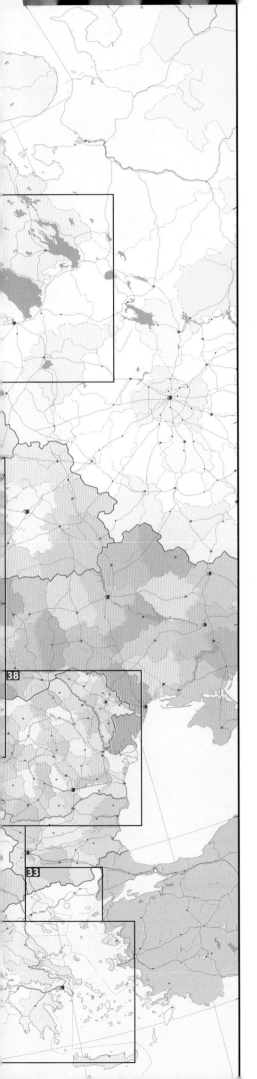

Overview map

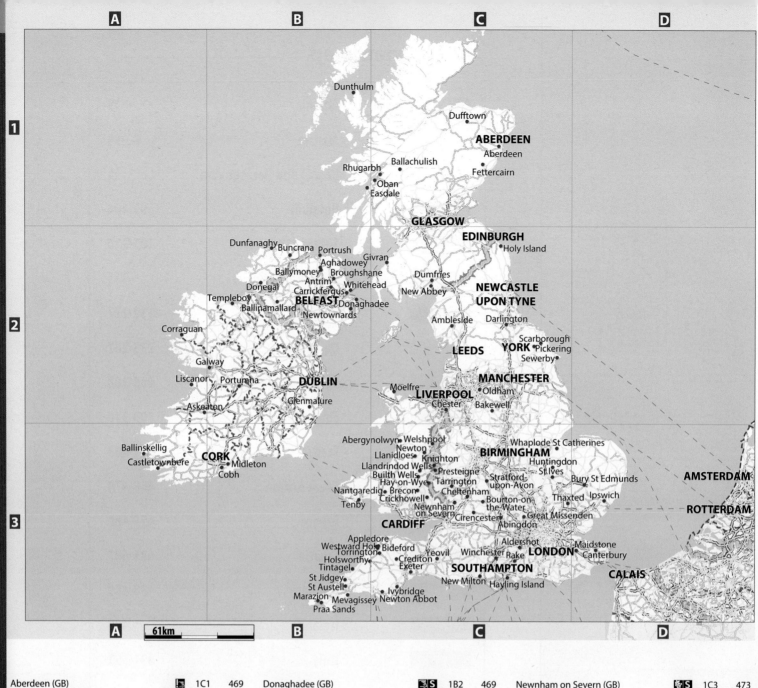

Scale: **61km**

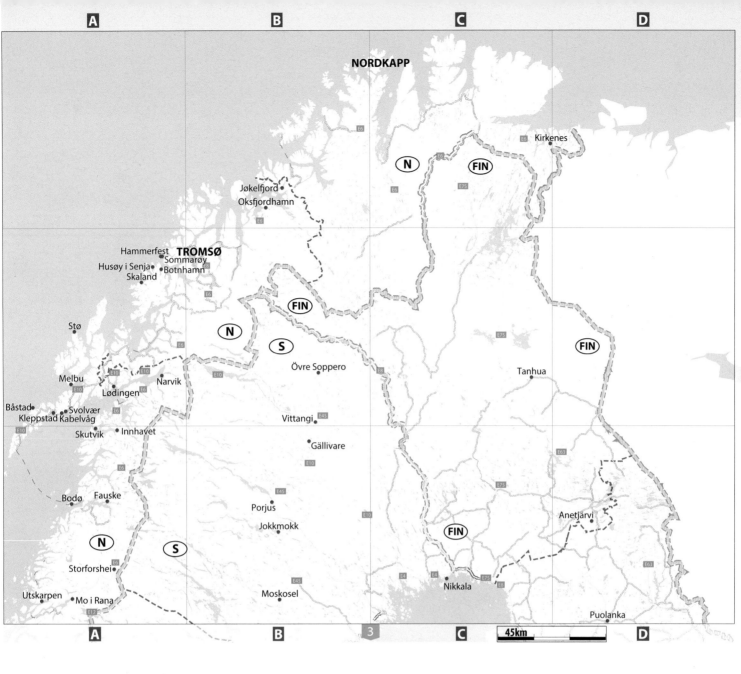

Anetjärvi (FI)	⚙S	2D3	310		Tanhua (FI)	⚙S	2C2	310
Båstad (NO)	⚙S	2A2	584		Utskarpen (NO)	⚙	2A3	585
Bodø (NO)	⚙S	2A3	584		Vittangi (SE)	⚙	2B2	610
Botnhamn (NO)	⚓S	2A2	584					
Fauske (NO)	⚙S	2A3	584					
Gällivare (SE)	⚙S	2B3	610					
Hammerfest (NO)	🍴	2A2	584					
Husøy i Senja (NO)	⚙	2A2	584					
Innhavet (NO)	⚙S	2A3	584					
Jokkmokk (SE)	⚙⚙S	2B3	610					
Jøkelfjord (NO)	⚙S	2B1	584					
Kabelvåg (NO)	⚙S	2A2	584					
Kirkenes (NO)	⚙S	2C1	584					
Kleppstad (NO)	⚙S	2A2	584					
Lødingen (NO)	⚓S	2A2	584					
Melbu (NO)	⚓S	2A2	584					
Mo i Rana (NO)	S	2A3	584					
Moskosel (SE)	⚙S	2B3	610					
Narvik (NO)	⚙	2A2	584					
Nikkala (SE)	⚓S	2C3	610					
Oksfjordhamn (NO)	⚓S	2B1	584					
Övre Soppero (SE)	⚙	2B2	610					
Porjus (SE)	⚙	2B3	610					
Puolanka (FI)	⚙S	2D3	310					
Skaland (NO)	⚙S	2A2	584					
Skutvik (NO)	⚓	2A3	584					
Sommarøy (NO)	⚙S	2A2	584					
Storforshei (NO)	⚙	2A3	584					
Stø (NO)	⚙S	2A2	584					
Svolvær (NO)	⚓S	2A2	585					

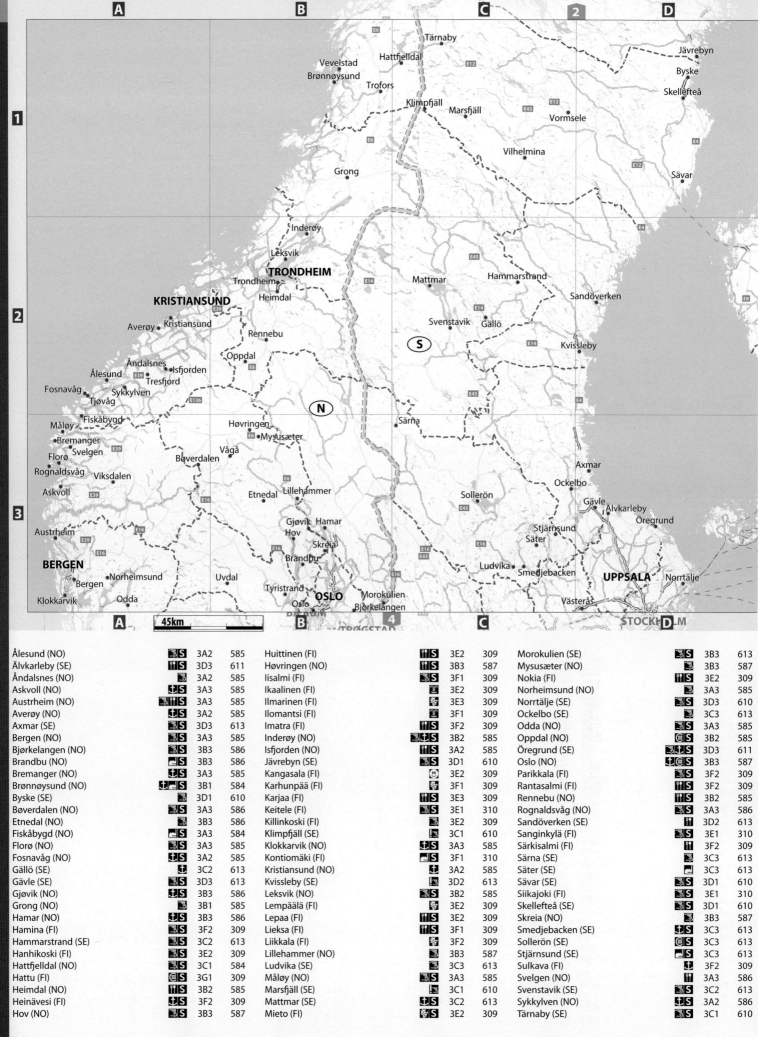

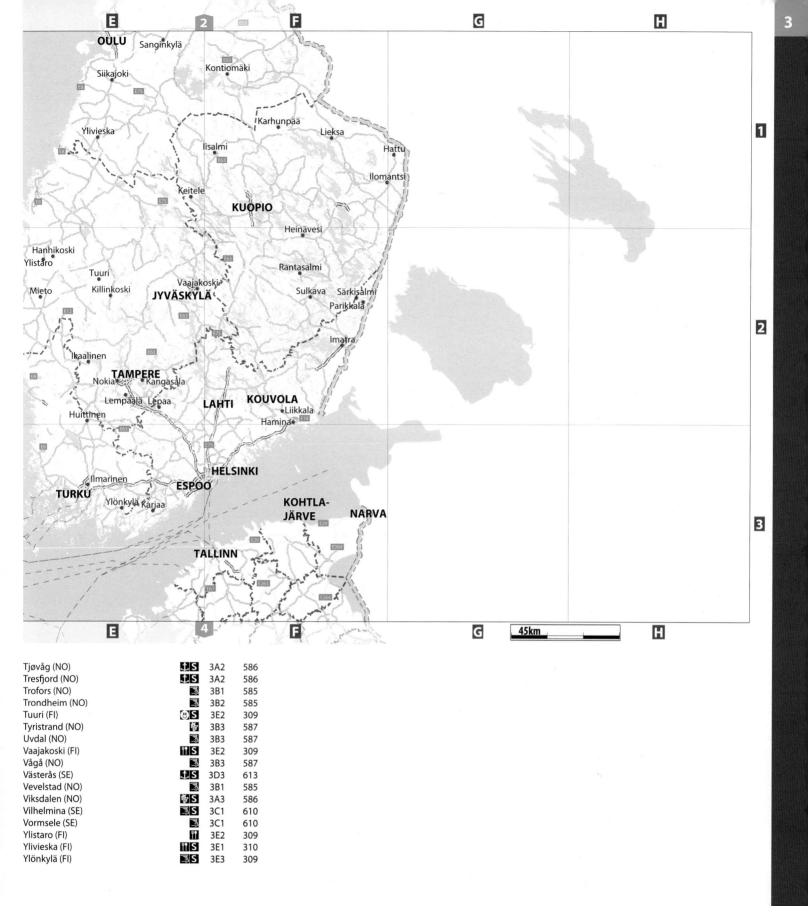

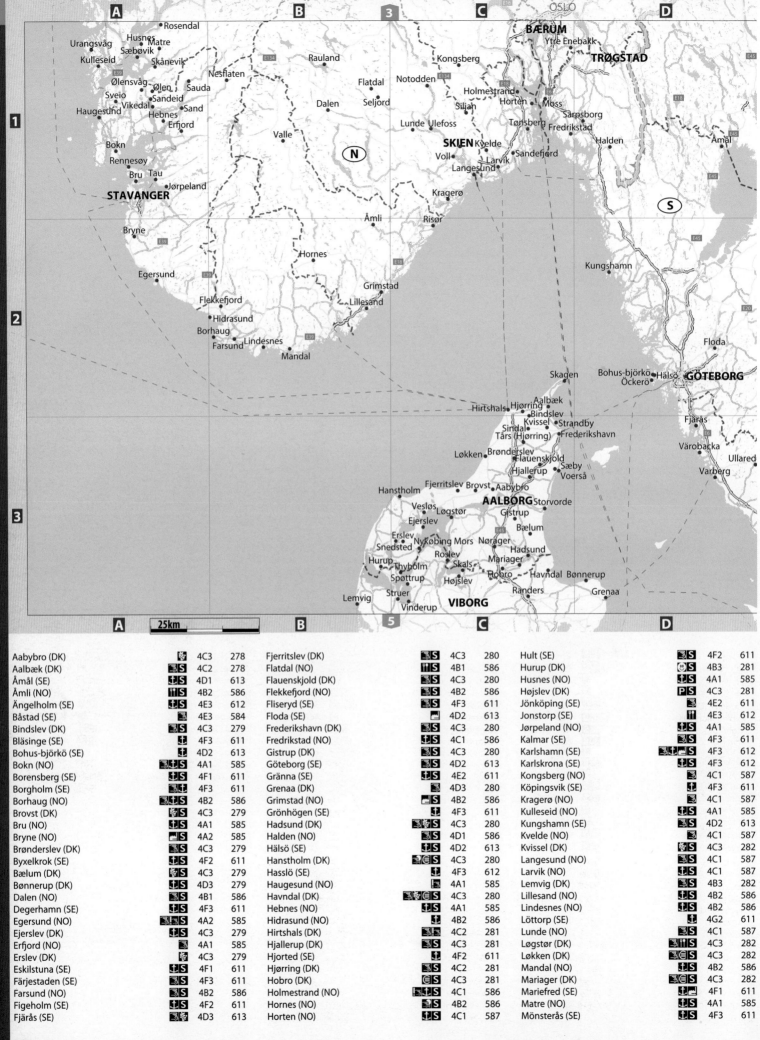

Map labels (selection): Rosendal, Urangsvåg, Husnes, Matre, Sæbøvik, Kulleseid, Skånevik, Ølensvåg, Ølen, Sauda, Nesflaten, Sveio, Sandeid, Haugesund, Vikedal, Hebnes, Sand, Erfjord, Bokn, Rennesøy, Bru, Tau, Jørpeland, STAVANGER, Bryne, Egersund, Hornes, Flekkefjord, Hidrasund, Borhaug, Farsund, Lindesnes, Mandal, Rauland, Flatdal, Dalen, Seljord, Valle, Åmli, Grimstad, Lillesand, Notodden, Lunde, Ulefoss, SKIEN, Voll, Langesund, Kragerø, Risør, Kongsberg, Holmestrand, Siljan, Horten, Tønsberg, Kvelde, Larvik, Sandefjord, BÆRUM, Ytre Enebakk, TRØGSTAD, Møss, Sarpsborg, Fredrikstad, Halden, Åmål, Kungshamn, Floda, Skagen, Bohus-björkö, Öckerö, Hälsö, GÖTEBORG, Fjärås, Värobacka, Varberg, Ullared, Hirtshals, Hjørring, Aalbæk, Bindslev, Kvissel, Strandby, Sindal, Tårs (Hjørring), Frederikshavn, Løkken, Brønderslev, Flauenskjold, Sæby, Hjallerup, Voerså, Hanstholm, Fjerritslev, Brovst, Aabybro, Storvorde, AALBORG, Gistrup, Vesløs, Løgstør, Ejerslev, Bælum, Erslev, Nykøbing Mors, Nørager, Hadsund, Snedsted, Roslev, Mariager, Havndal, Bønnerup, Hurup, Skals, Hobro, Thyholm, Højslev, Randers, Grenaa, Spøttrup, Struer, Lemvig, Vinderup, VIBORG, N, S

25km

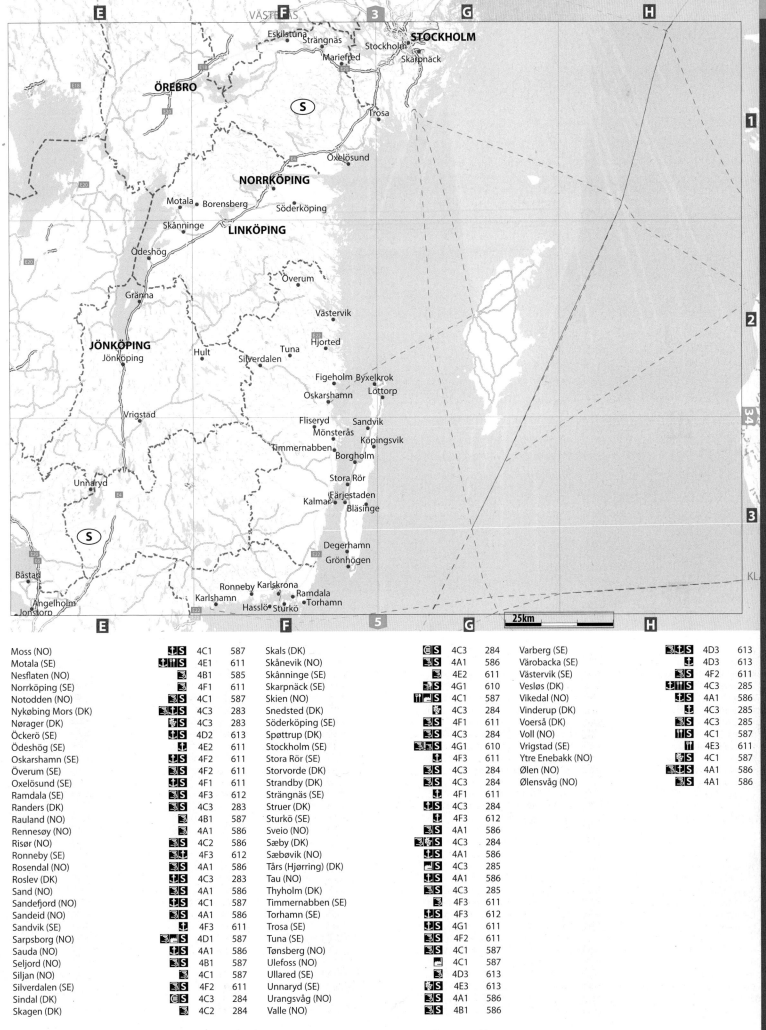

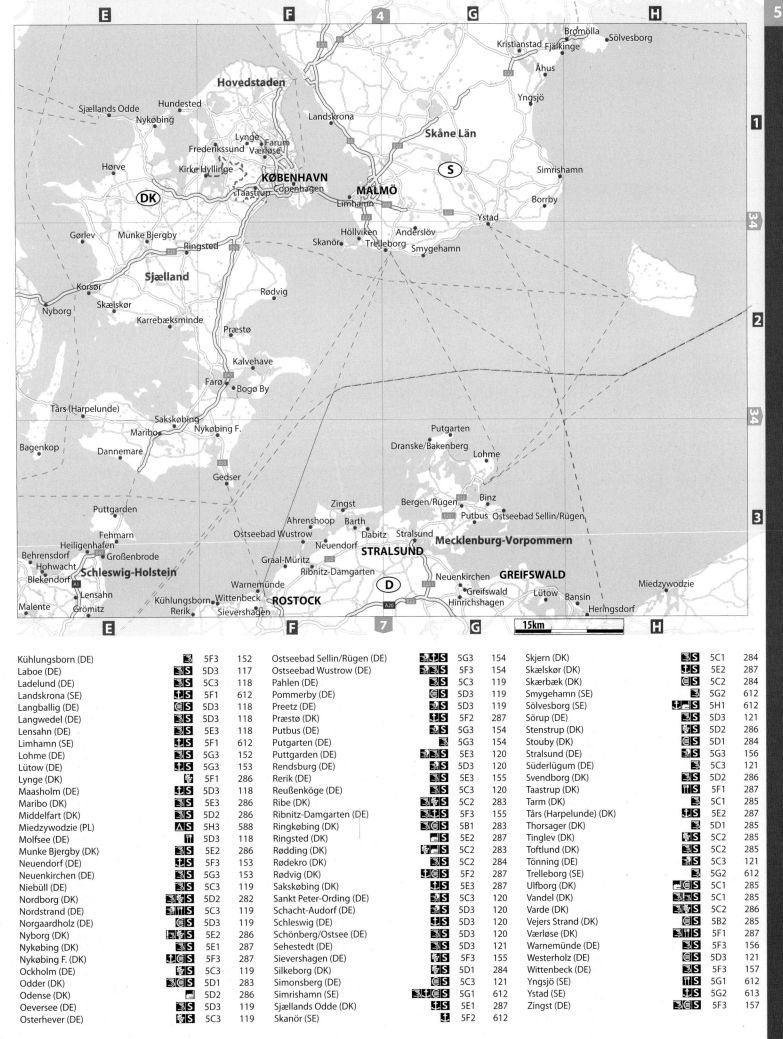

Place	Grid	Page	Place	Grid	Page	Place	Grid	Page
Kühlungsborn (DE)	5F3	152	Ostseebad Sellin/Rügen (DE)	5G3	154	Skjern (DK)	5C1	284
Laboe (DE)	5D3	117	Ostseebad Wustrow (DE)	5F3	154	Skælskør (DK)	5E2	287
Ladelund (DE)	5C3	118	Pahlen (DE)	5C3	119	Skærbæk (DK)	5C2	284
Landskrona (SE)	5F1	612	Pommerby (DE)	5D3	119	Smygehamn (SE)	5G2	612
Langballig (DE)	5D3	118	Preetz (DE)	5D3	119	Sölvesborg (SE)	5H1	612
Langwedel (DE)	5D3	118	Præstø (DK)	5F2	287	Sörup (DE)	5D3	121
Lensahn (DE)	5E3	118	Putbus (DE)	5G3	154	Stenstrup (DK)	5D2	286
Limhamn (SE)	5F1	612	Putgarten (DE)	5G3	154	Stouby (DK)	5D1	284
Lohme (DE)	5G3	152	Puttgarden (DE)	5E3	120	Stralsund (DE)	5G3	156
Lütow (DE)	5G3	153	Rendsburg (DE)	5D3	120	Süderlügum (DE)	5C3	121
Lynge (DK)	5F1	286	Rerik (DE)	5E3	155	Svendborg (DK)	5D2	286
Maasholm (DE)	5D3	118	Reußenköge (DE)	5C3	120	Taastrup (DK)	5F1	287
Maribo (DK)	5E3	286	Ribe (DK)	5C2	283	Tarm (DK)	5C1	285
Middelfart (DK)	5D2	286	Ribnitz-Damgarten (DE)	5F3	155	Tårs (Harpelunde) (DK)	5E2	287
Miedzywodzie (PL)	5H3	588	Ringkøbing (DK)	5B1	283	Thorsager (DK)	5D1	285
Molfsee (DE)	5D3	118	Ringsted (DK)	5E2	287	Tinglev (DK)	5C2	285
Munke Bjergby (DK)	5E2	286	Rødding (DK)	5C2	283	Toftlund (DK)	5C2	285
Neuendorf (DE)	5F3	153	Rødekro (DK)	5C2	284	Tönning (DE)	5C3	121
Neuenkirchen (DE)	5G3	153	Rødvig (DK)	5F2	287	Trelleborg (SE)	5G2	612
Niebüll (DE)	5C3	119	Sakskøbing (DK)	5E3	287	Ulfborg (DK)	5C1	285
Nordborg (DK)	5D2	282	Sankt Peter-Ording (DE)	5C3	120	Vandel (DK)	5C1	285
Nordstrand (DE)	5C3	119	Schacht-Audorf (DE)	5D3	120	Varde (DK)	5C2	286
Norgaardholz (DE)	5D3	119	Schleswig (DE)	5D3	120	Vejers Strand (DK)	5B2	285
Nyborg (DK)	5E2	286	Schönberg/Ostsee (DE)	5D3	120	Værløse (DK)	5F1	287
Nykøbing (DK)	5E1	287	Sehestedt (DE)	5D3	121	Warnemünde (DE)	5F3	156
Nykøbing F. (DK)	5F3	287	Sievershagen (DE)	5F3	155	Westerholz (DE)	5D3	121
Ockholm (DE)	5C3	119	Silkeborg (DK)	5D1	284	Wittenbeck (DE)	5F3	157
Odder (DK)	5D1	283	Simonsberg (DE)	5C3	121	Yngsjö (SE)	5G1	612
Odense (DK)	5D2	286	Simrishamn (SE)	5G1	612	Ystad (SE)	5G2	613
Oeversee (DE)	5D3	119	Sjællands Odde (DK)	5E1	287	Zingst (DE)	5F3	157
Osterhever (DE)	5C3	119	Skanör (SE)	5F2	612			

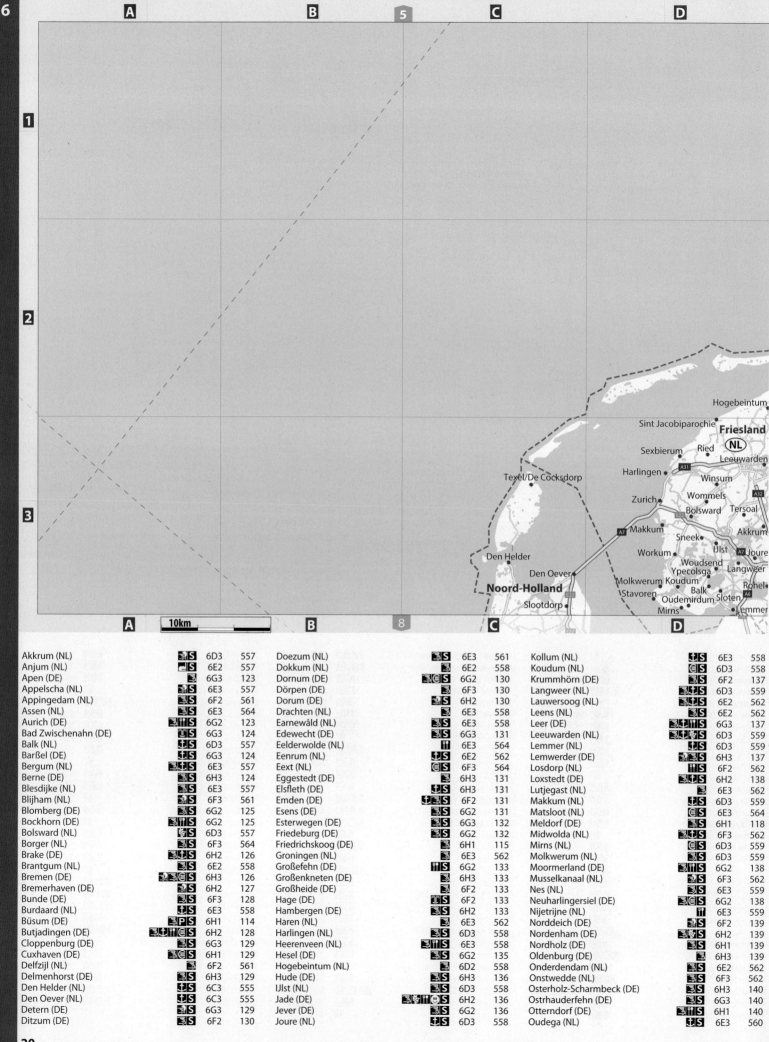

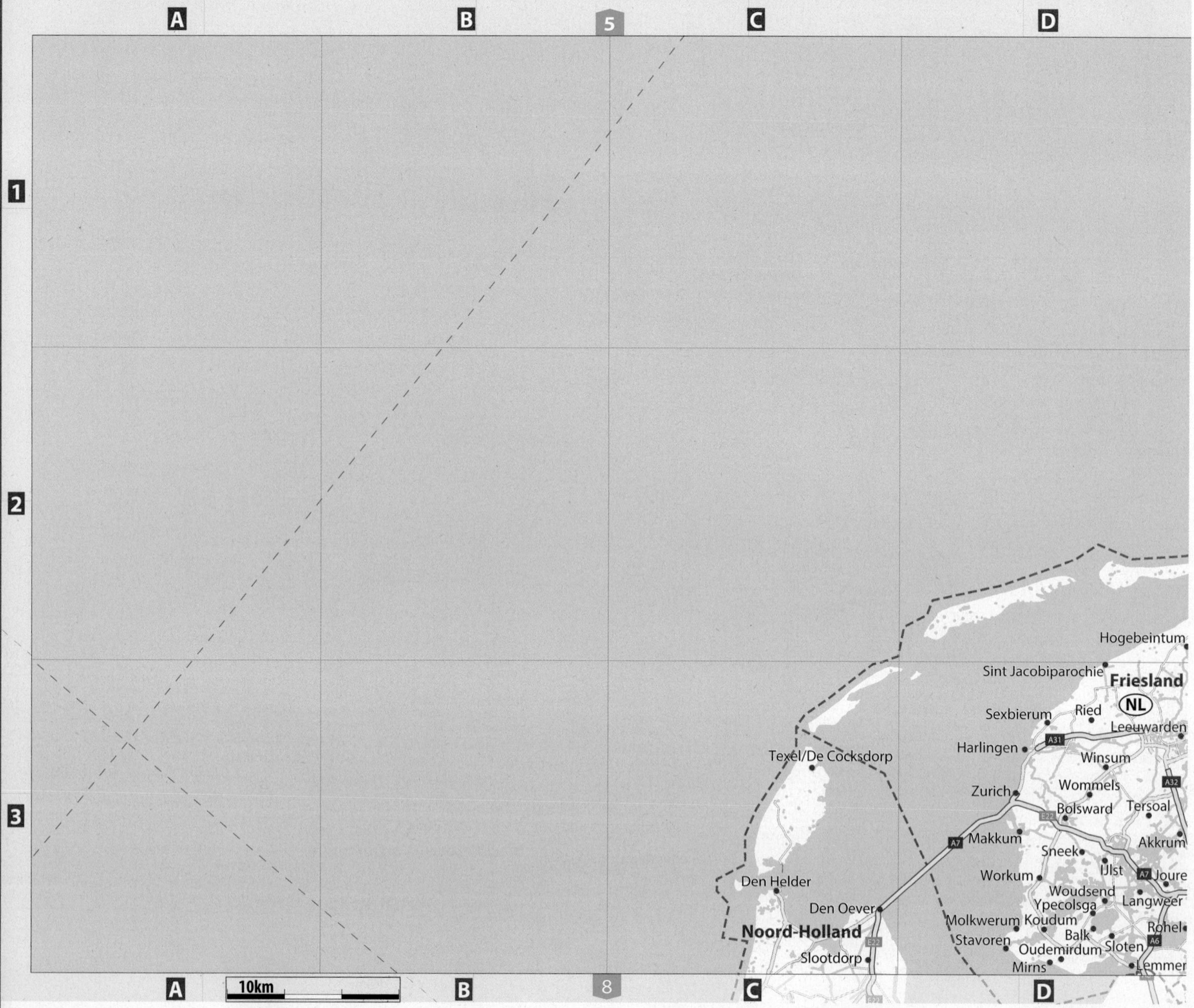
A
B
5
C
D
1
2
3
Hogebeintum
Sint Jacobiparochie
Friesland
NL
Sexbierum
Ried
Leeuwarden
Harlingen
A31
Texel/De Cocksdorp
Winsum
A32
Zurich
Wommels
Bolsward
Tersoal
E22
A7
Makkum
Sneek
Akkrum
Den Helder
Workum
IJlst
A7
Joure
Woudsend
Ypecolsga
Langweer
Den Oever
Molkwerum
Koudum
Noord-Holland
Balk
Rohel
Stavoren
Oudemirdum
Sloten
A6
E22
Slootdorp
Mirns
Lemmer
10km
A
B
8
C
D

Akkrum (NL)	6D3	557
Anjum (NL)	6E2	557
Apen (DE)	6G3	123
Appelscha (NL)	6E3	557
Appingedam (NL)	6F2	561
Assen (NL)	6E3	564
Aurich (DE)	6G2	123
Bad Zwischenahn (DE)	6G3	124
Balk (NL)	6D3	557
Barßel (DE)	6G3	124
Bergum (NL)	6E3	557
Berne (DE)	6H3	124
Blesdijke (NL)	6E3	557
Blijham (NL)	6F3	561
Blomberg (DE)	6G2	125
Bockhorn (DE)	6G2	125
Bolsward (NL)	6D3	557
Borger (NL)	6F3	564
Brake (DE)	6H2	126
Brantgum (NL)	6E2	558
Bremen (DE)	6H3	126
Bremerhaven (DE)	6H2	127
Bunde (DE)	6F3	128
Burdaard (NL)	6E3	558
Büsum (DE)	6H1	114
Butjadingen (DE)	6H2	128
Cloppenburg (DE)	6G3	129
Cuxhaven (DE)	6H1	129
Delfzijl (NL)	6F2	561
Delmenhorst (DE)	6H3	129
Den Helder (NL)	6C3	555
Den Oever (NL)	6C3	555
Detern (DE)	6G3	129
Ditzum (DE)	6F2	130
Doezum (NL)	6E3	561
Dokkum (NL)	6E2	558
Dornum (DE)	6G2	130
Dörpen (DE)	6F3	130
Dorum (DE)	6H2	130
Drachten (NL)	6E3	558
Earnewâld (NL)	6E3	558
Edewecht (DE)	6G3	131
Eelderwolde (NL)	6E3	564
Eenrum (NL)	6E2	562
Eext (NL)	6F3	564
Eggestedt (DE)	6H3	131
Elsfleth (DE)	6H3	131
Emden (DE)	6F2	131
Esens (DE)	6G2	131
Esterwegen (DE)	6G3	132
Friedeburg (DE)	6G2	132
Friedrichskoog (DE)	6H1	115
Groningen (NL)	6E3	562
Großefehn (DE)	6G2	133
Großenkneten (DE)	6H3	133
Großheide (DE)	6F2	133
Hage (DE)	6F2	133
Hambergen (DE)	6H2	133
Haren (NL)	6E3	562
Harlingen (NL)	6D3	558
Heerenveen (NL)	6E3	558
Hesel (DE)	6G2	135
Hogebeintum (NL)	6D2	558
Hude (DE)	6H3	136
IJlst (NL)	6D3	558
Jade (DE)	6H2	136
Jever (DE)	6G2	136
Joure (NL)	6D3	558
Kollum (NL)	6E3	558
Koudum (NL)	6D3	558
Krummhörn (DE)	6F2	137
Langweer (NL)	6D3	559
Lauwersoog (NL)	6E2	562
Leens (NL)	6E2	562
Leer (DE)	6G3	137
Leeuwarden (NL)	6D3	559
Lemmer (NL)	6D3	559
Lemwerder (DE)	6H3	137
Losdorp (NL)	6F2	562
Loxstedt (DE)	6H2	138
Lutjegast (NL)	6E3	562
Makkum (NL)	6D3	559
Matsloot (NL)	6E3	564
Meldorf (DE)	6H1	118
Midwolda (NL)	6F3	562
Mirns (NL)	6D3	559
Molkwerum (NL)	6D3	559
Moormerland (DE)	6G2	138
Musselkanaal (NL)	6F3	562
Nes (NL)	6E3	559
Neuharlingersiel (DE)	6G2	138
Nijetrijne (NL)	6E3	559
Norddeich (DE)	6F2	139
Nordenham (DE)	6H2	139
Nordholz (DE)	6H1	139
Oldenburg (DE)	6H3	139
Onderdendam (NL)	6E2	562
Onstwedde (NL)	6F3	562
Osterholz-Scharmbeck (DE)	6H3	140
Ostrhauderfehn (DE)	6G3	140
Otterndorf (DE)	6H1	140
Oudega (NL)	6E3	560

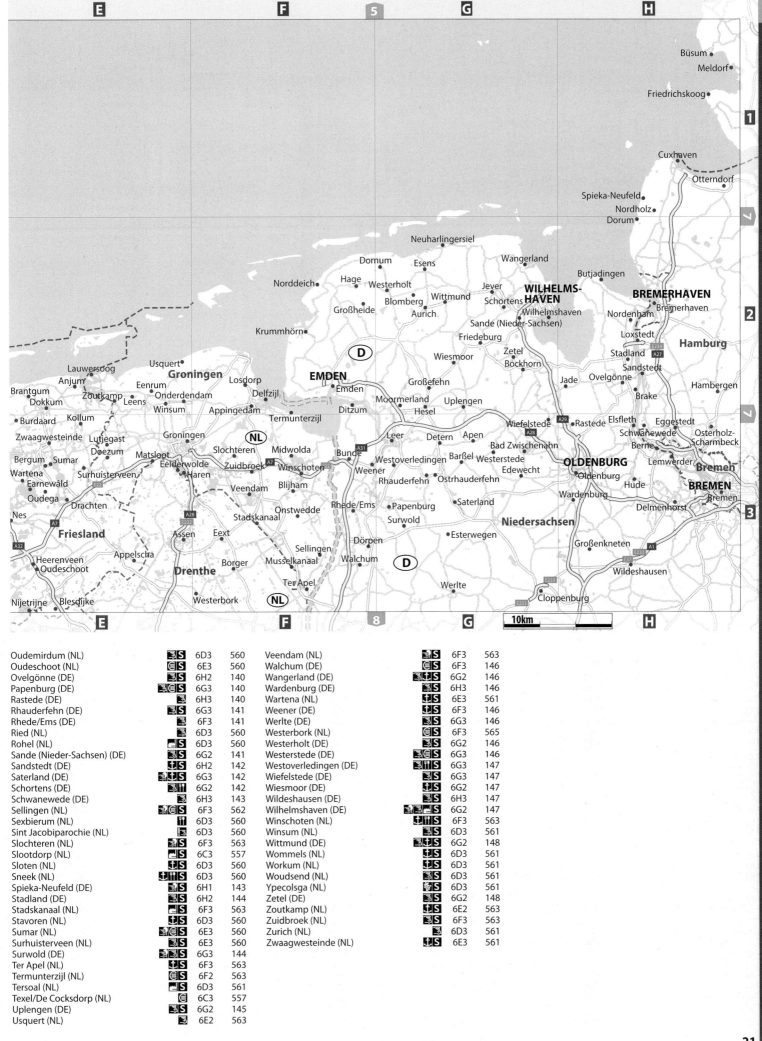

Oudemirdum (NL)		6D3	560	Veendam (NL)		6F3	563
Oudeschoot (NL)		6E3	560	Walchum (DE)		6F3	146
Ovelgönne (DE)		6H2	140	Wangerland (DE)		6G2	146
Papenburg (DE)		6G3	140	Wardenburg (DE)		6H3	146
Rastede (DE)		6H3	140	Wartena (NL)		6E3	561
Rhauderfehn (DE)		6G3	141	Weener (DE)		6F3	146
Rhede/Ems (DE)		6F3	141	Werlte (DE)		6G3	146
Ried (NL)		6D3	560	Westerbork (NL)		6F3	565
Rohel (NL)		6D3	560	Westerholt (DE)		6G2	146
Sande (Nieder-Sachsen) (DE)		6G2	141	Westerstede (DE)		6G3	146
Sandstedt (DE)		6H2	142	Westoverledingen (DE)		6G3	147
Saterland (DE)		6G3	142	Wiefelstede (DE)		6G3	147
Schortens (DE)		6G2	142	Wiesmoor (DE)		6G2	147
Schwanewede (DE)		6H3	143	Wildeshausen (DE)		6H3	147
Sellingen (NL)		6F3	562	Wilhelmshaven (DE)		6G2	147
Sexbierum (NL)		6D3	560	Winschoten (NL)		6F3	563
Sint Jacobiparochie (NL)		6D3	560	Winsum (NL)		6D3	561
Slochteren (NL)		6F3	560	Wittmund (DE)		6G2	148
Slootdorp (NL)		6C3	557	Wommels (NL)		6D3	561
Sloten (NL)		6D3	560	Workum (NL)		6D3	561
Sneek (NL)		6D3	560	Woudsend (NL)		6D3	561
Spieka-Neufeld (DE)		6H1	143	Ypecolsga (NL)		6D3	561
Stadland (DE)		6H2	144	Zetel (DE)		6G2	148
Stadskanaal (NL)		6F3	563	Zoutkamp (NL)		6E2	563
Stavoren (NL)		6D3	560	Zuidbroek (NL)		6F3	563
Sumar (NL)		6E3	560	Zurich (NL)		6D3	561
Surhuisterveen (NL)		6E3	560	Zwaagwesteinde (NL)		6E3	561
Surwold (DE)		6G3	144				
Ter Apel (NL)		6F3	563				
Termunterzijl (NL)		6F2	563				
Tersoal (NL)		6D3	561				
Texel/De Cocksdorp (NL)		6C3	557				
Uplengen (DE)		6G2	145				
Usquert (NL)		6E2	563				

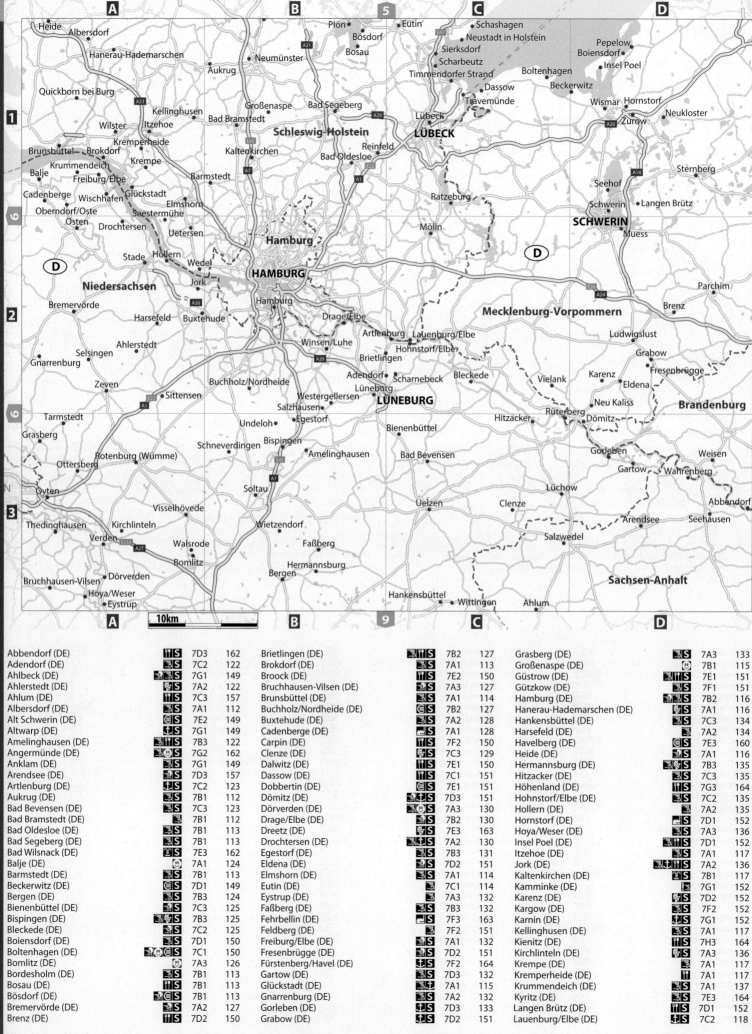

Name	Grid	Page	Name	Grid	Page	Name	Grid	Page
Abbendorf (DE)	7D3	162	Brietlingen (DE)	7B2	127	Grasberg (DE)	7A3	133
Adendorf (DE)	7C2	122	Brokdorf (DE)	7A1	113	Großenaspe (DE)	7B1	115
Ahlbeck (DE)	7G1	149	Broock (DE)	7E2	150	Güstrow (DE)	7E1	151
Ahlerstedt (DE)	7A2	122	Bruchhausen-Vilsen (DE)	7A3	127	Gützkow (DE)	7F1	151
Ahlum (DE)	7C3	157	Brunsbüttel (DE)	7A1	114	Hamburg (DE)	7B2	116
Albersdorf (DE)	7A1	112	Buchholz/Nordheide (DE)	7B2	127	Hanerau-Hademarschen (DE)	7A1	116
Alt Schwerin (DE)	7E2	149	Buxtehude (DE)	7A2	128	Hankensbüttel (DE)	7C3	134
Altwarp (DE)	7G1	149	Cadenberge (DE)	7A1	128	Harsefeld (DE)	7A2	134
Amelinghausen (DE)	7B3	122	Carpin (DE)	7F2	150	Havelberg (DE)	7E3	160
Angermünde (DE)	7G2	162	Clenze (DE)	7C3	129	Heide (DE)	7A1	116
Anklam (DE)	7G1	149	Dalwitz (DE)	7E1	150	Hermannsburg (DE)	7B3	135
Arendsee (DE)	7D3	157	Dassow (DE)	7C1	151	Hitzacker (DE)	7C3	135
Artlenburg (DE)	7C2	123	Dobbertin (DE)	7E1	151	Höhenland (DE)	7G3	164
Aukrug (DE)	7B1	112	Dömitz (DE)	7D3	151	Hohnstorf/Elbe (DE)	7C2	135
Bad Bevensen (DE)	7C3	123	Dörverden (DE)	7A3	130	Hollern (DE)	7A2	135
Bad Bramstedt (DE)	7B1	112	Drage/Elbe (DE)	7B2	130	Hornstorf (DE)	7D1	152
Bad Oldesloe (DE)	7B1	113	Dreetz (DE)	7E3	163	Hoya/Weser (DE)	7A3	136
Bad Segeberg (DE)	7B1	113	Drochtersen (DE)	7A2	130	Insel Poel (DE)	7D1	152
Bad Wilsnack (DE)	7E3	162	Egestorf (DE)	7B3	131	Itzehoe (DE)	7A1	117
Balje (DE)	7A1	124	Eldena (DE)	7D2	151	Jork (DE)	7A2	136
Barmstedt (DE)	7B1	113	Elmshorn (DE)	7A1	114	Kaltenkirchen (DE)	7B1	117
Beckerwitz (DE)	7D1	149	Eutin (DE)	7C1	114	Kamminke (DE)	7G1	152
Bergen (DE)	7B3	125	Eystrup (DE)	7A3	132	Karenz (DE)	7D2	152
Bienenbüttel (DE)	7C3	125	Faßberg (DE)	7B3	132	Kargow (DE)	7E2	152
Bispingen (DE)	7B3	125	Fehrbellin (DE)	7F3	163	Karnin (DE)	7G1	152
Bleckede (DE)	7C2	125	Feldberg (DE)	7F2	151	Kellinghusen (DE)	7A1	117
Boiensdorf (DE)	7D1	150	Freiburg/Elbe (DE)	7A1	132	Kienitz (DE)	7H3	164
Boltenhagen (DE)	7C1	150	Fresenbrügge (DE)	7D2	151	Kirchlinteln (DE)	7A3	136
Bomlitz (DE)	7A3	126	Fürstenberg/Havel (DE)	7F2	164	Krempe (DE)	7A1	117
Bordesholm (DE)	7B1	113	Gartow (DE)	7D3	132	Kremperheide (DE)	7A1	117
Bosau (DE)	7B1	113	Glückstadt (DE)	7A1	115	Krummendeich (DE)	7A1	137
Bösdorf (DE)	7B1	113	Gnarrenburg (DE)	7A2	132	Kyritz (DE)	7E3	164
Bremervörde (DE)	7A2	127	Gorleben (DE)	7D3	133	Langen Brütz (DE)	7D1	152
Brenz (DE)	7D2	150	Grabow (DE)	7D2	151	Lauenburg/Elbe (DE)	7C2	118

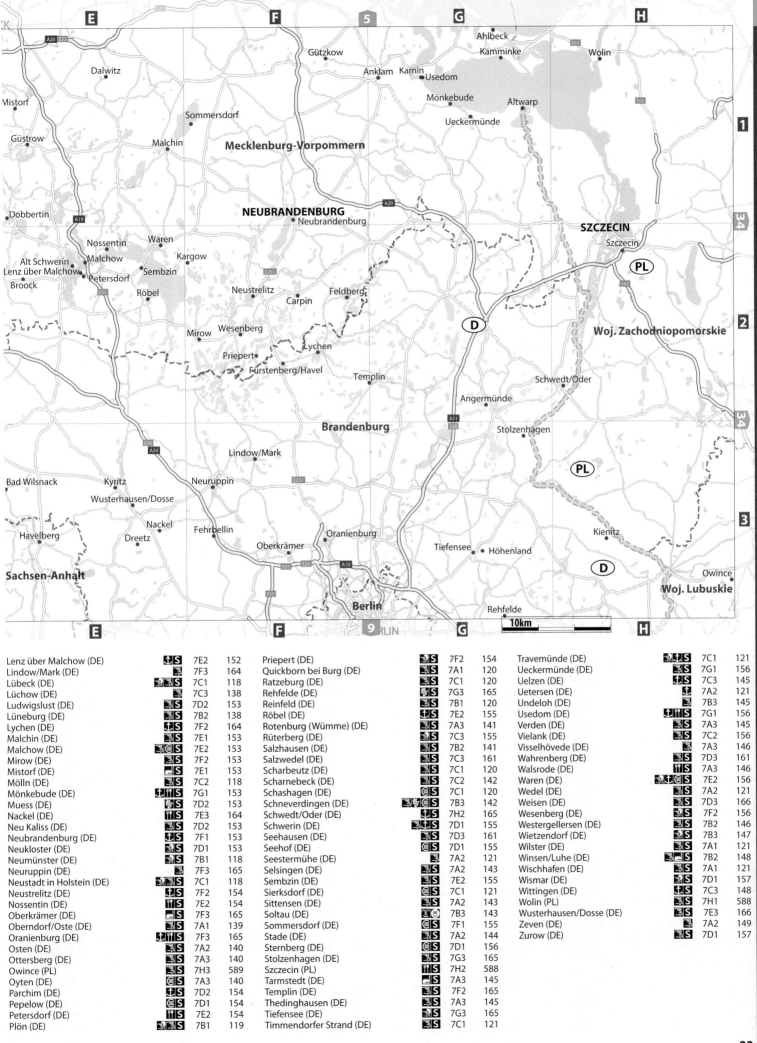

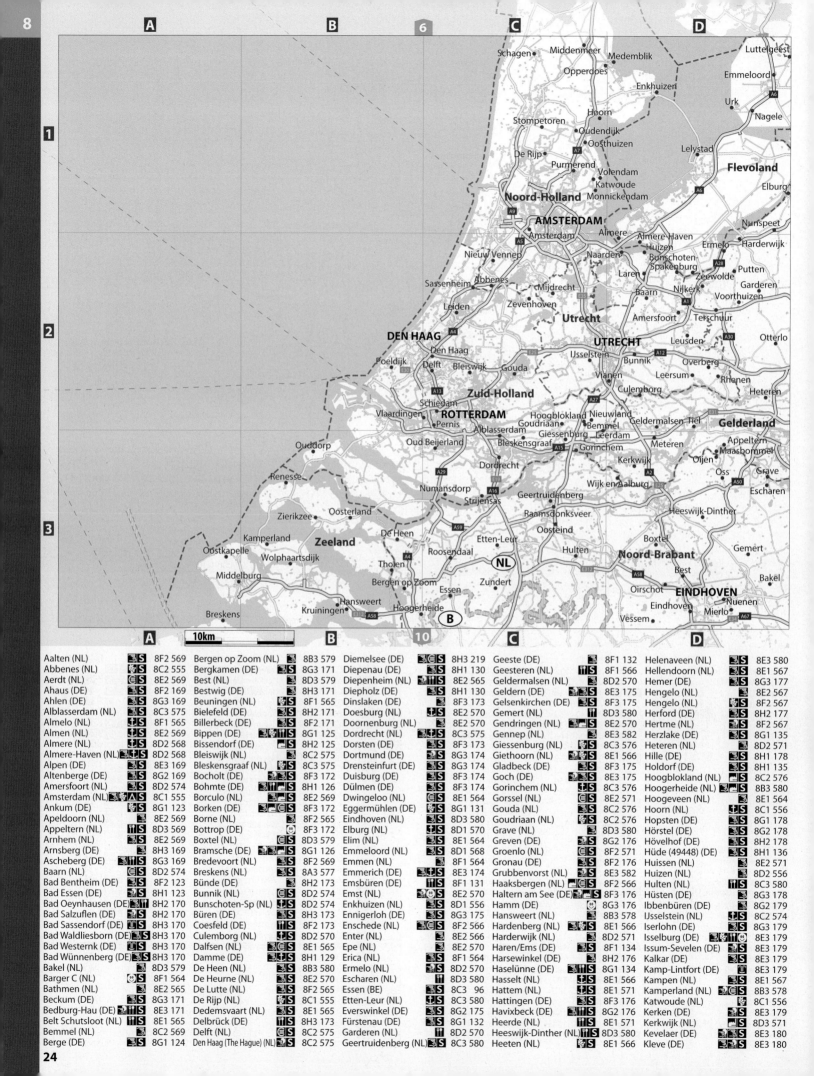

Map: Netherlands / Germany border region (Noord-Holland, Zuid-Holland, Utrecht, Gelderland, Flevoland, Zeeland, Noord-Brabant) — scale 10km

Index

Place	Grid ref.
Aalten (NL)	8F2 569
Abbenes (NL)	8C2 555
Aerdt (NL)	8E2 569
Ahaus (DE)	8F2 169
Ahlen (DE)	8G3 169
Alblasserdam (NL)	8C3 575
Almelo (NL)	8F1 565
Almen (NL)	8E2 569
Almere (NL)	8D2 568
Almere-Haven (NL)	8D2 568
Alpen (DE)	8E3 169
Altenberge (DE)	8G2 169
Amersfoort (NL)	8D2 574
Amsterdam (NL)	8C1 555
Ankum (DE)	8G1 123
Apeldoorn (NL)	8E2 569
Appeltern (NL)	8D3 569
Arnhem (NL)	8E2 569
Arnsberg (DE)	8H3 169
Ascheberg (DE)	8G3 169
Baarn (NL)	8D2 574
Bad Bentheim (DE)	8F2 123
Bad Essen (DE)	8H1 123
Bad Oeynhausen (DE)	8H2 170
Bad Salzuflen (DE)	8H2 170
Bad Sassendorf (DE)	8H3 170
Bad Waldliesborn (DE)	8H3 170
Bad Westernk (DE)	8H3 170
Bad Wünnenberg (DE)	8H3 170
Bakel (NL)	8D3 579
Barger C (NL)	8F1 564
Bathmen (NL)	8E2 565
Beckum (DE)	8G3 171
Bedburg-Hau (DE)	8E3 171
Belt Schutsloot (NL)	8E1 565
Bemmel (NL)	8C2 569
Berge (DE)	8G1 124
Bergen op Zoom (NL)	8B3 579
Bergkamen (DE)	8G3 171
Best (NL)	8D3 579
Bestwig (DE)	8H3 171
Beuningen (NL)	8F1 565
Bielefeld (DE)	8H2 171
Billerbeck (DE)	8F2 171
Bippen (DE)	8G1 125
Bissendorf (DE)	8H2 125
Bleiswijk (NL)	8C2 575
Bleskensgraaf (NL)	8C3 575
Bocholt (DE)	8F3 172
Bohmte (DE)	8H1 126
Borculo (NL)	8E2 569
Borken (DE)	8F3 172
Borne (NL)	8F2 565
Bottrop (DE)	8F3 172
Boxtel (NL)	8D3 579
Bramsche (DE)	8G1 126
Bredevoort (NL)	8F2 569
Breskens (NL)	8A3 577
Bünde (DE)	8H2 173
Bunnik (NL)	8D2 574
Bunschoten-Sp (NL)	8D2 574
Büren (DE)	8H3 173
Coesfeld (DE)	8F2 173
Culemborg (NL)	8D2 570
Dalfsen (NL)	8E1 565
Damme (DE)	8H1 129
De Heen (NL)	8B3 580
De Heurne (NL)	8E2 570
De Lutte (NL)	8F2 565
De Rijp (NL)	8C1 555
Dedemsvaart (NL)	8E1 565
Delbrück (DE)	8H3 173
Delft (NL)	8C2 575
Den Haag (The Hague) (NL)	8C2 575
Diemelsee (DE)	8H3 219
Diepenau (DE)	8H1 130
Diepenheim (NL)	8E2 565
Diepholz (DE)	8H1 130
Dinslaken (DE)	8F3 173
Doesburg (NL)	8E2 570
Doornenburg (NL)	8E2 570
Dordrecht (NL)	8C3 575
Dorsten (DE)	8F3 173
Dortmund (DE)	8G3 174
Drensteinfurt (DE)	8G3 174
Duisburg (DE)	8F3 174
Dülmen (DE)	8G3 174
Dwingeloo (NL)	8E1 564
Eggermühlen (DE)	8G1 131
Eindhoven (NL)	8D3 580
Elburg (NL)	8D1 570
Elim (NL)	8E1 564
Emmeloord (NL)	8D1 568
Emmen (NL)	8F1 564
Emmerich (DE)	8E3 174
Emsbüren (DE)	8F1 131
Emst (NL)	8E2 570
Enkhuizen (NL)	8D1 556
Ennigerloh (DE)	8G3 175
Enschede (NL)	8F2 566
Enter (NL)	8E2 566
Epe (NL)	8E2 570
Erica (NL)	8F1 564
Ermelo (NL)	8D2 570
Escharen (NL)	8D3 580
Essen (BE)	8C3 96
Etten-Leur (NL)	8C3 580
Everswinkel (DE)	8G2 175
Fürstenau (DE)	8G1 132
Garderen (NL)	8D2 570
Geertruidenberg (NL)	8C3 580
Geeste (DE)	8F1 132
Geesteren (NL)	8F1 566
Geldermalsen (NL)	8D2 570
Geldern (DE)	8E3 175
Gelsenkirchen (DE)	8F3 175
Gemert (NL)	8D3 580
Gendringen (NL)	8E2 570
Gennep (NL)	8E3 582
Giessenburg (NL)	8C3 576
Giethoorn (NL)	8E1 566
Gladbeck (DE)	8F3 175
Goch (DE)	8E3 175
Gorinchem (NL)	8C3 576
Gorssel (NL)	8E2 571
Gouda (NL)	8C2 576
Goudriaan (NL)	8C2 576
Grave (NL)	8D3 580
Greven (DE)	8G2 176
Groenlo (NL)	8F2 571
Gronau (DE)	8F2 176
Grubbenvorst (NL)	8E3 582
Haaksbergen (NL)	8F2 566
Haltern am See (DE)	8F3 176
Hamm (DE)	8G3 176
Hansweert (NL)	8B3 578
Hardenberg (NL)	8E1 566
Harderwijk (NL)	8D2 571
Haren/Ems (DE)	8F1 134
Harsewinkel (DE)	8H2 176
Haselünne (DE)	8G1 134
Hasselt (NL)	8E1 566
Hattem (NL)	8E1 571
Hattingen (DE)	8F3 176
Havixbeck (DE)	8G2 175
Heerde (NL)	8E1 571
Heeswijk-Dinther (NL)	8D3 580
Heeten (NL)	8E1 566
Helenaveen (NL)	8E3 580
Hellendoorn (NL)	8E1 567
Hemer (DE)	8G3 177
Hengelo (NL)	8E2 567
Hengelo (NL)	8F2 567
Herford (DE)	8H2 171
Hertme (NL)	8F2 567
Herzlake (DE)	8G1 135
Hille (DE)	8H1 178
Holdorf (DE)	8H1 135
Hoogblokland (NL)	8C2 576
Hoogerheide (NL)	8B3 580
Hoogeveen (NL)	8E1 564
Hoorn (NL)	8C1 556
Hopsten (DE)	8G1 178
Hörstel (DE)	8G2 178
Hövelhof (DE)	8H2 178
Hüde (49448) (DE)	8H1 136
Huissen (NL)	8E2 571
Huizen (NL)	8D2 556
Hulten (NL)	8C3 580
Hüsten (DE)	8G3 178
Ibbenbüren (DE)	8G2 179
IJsselstein (NL)	8C2 574
Iserlohn (DE)	8G3 178
Isselburg (DE)	8E3 179
Issum-Sevelen (DE)	8E3 179
Kalkar (DE)	8E3 179
Kamp-Lintfort (DE)	8E3 179
Kampen (NL)	8E1 567
Kamperland (NL)	8B3 578
Katwoude (NL)	8C1 556
Kerken (DE)	8E3 179
Kerkwijk (NL)	8D3 571
Kevelaer (DE)	8E3 180
Kleve (DE)	8E3 180

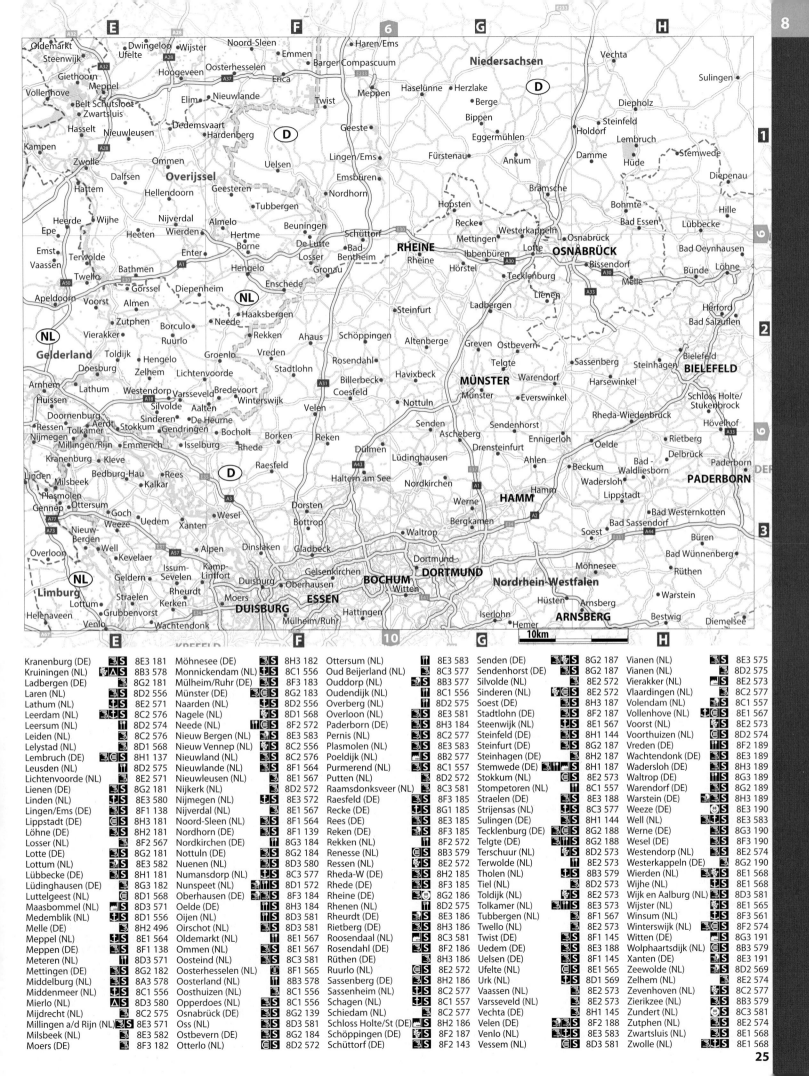

Index

Place	Grid		Place	Grid		Place	Grid		Place	Grid		Place	Grid
Kranenburg (DE)	8E3 181		Möhnesee (DE)	8H3 182		Ottersum (NL)	8E3 583		Senden (DE)	8G2 187		Vianen (NL)	8E3 575
Kruiningen (NL)	8B3 578		Monnickendam (NL)	8C1 556		Oud Beijerland (NL)	8C3 577		Sendenhorst (DE)	8G2 187		Vianen (NL)	8D2 575
Ladbergen (DE)	8G2 181		Mülheim/Ruhr (DE)	8F3 183		Ouddorp (NL)	8B3 577		Silvolde (NL)	8E2 572		Vierakker (NL)	8E2 573
Laren (NL)	8D2 556		Münster (DE)	8G2 183		Oudendijk (NL)	8C1 556		Sinderen (NL)	8E2 572		Vlaardingen (NL)	8C2 577
Lathum (NL)	8E2 571		Naarden (NL)	8D2 556		Overberg (NL)	8D2 575		Soest (DE)	8H3 187		Volendam (NL)	8C1 557
Leerdam (NL)	8C2 576		Nagele (NL)	8D1 568		Overloon (NL)	8E3 581		Stadtlohn (DE)	8F2 187		Vollenhove (NL)	8E1 567
Leersum (NL)	8D2 574		Neede (NL)	8F2 572		Paderborn (DE)	8H3 184		Steenwijk (NL)	8E1 567		Voorst (NL)	8E2 573
Leiden (NL)	8C2 576		Nieuw Bergen (NL)	8E3 583		Pernis (NL)	8C2 577		Steinfeld (DE)	8H1 144		Voorthuizen (NL)	8D2 574
Lelystad (NL)	8D1 568		Nieuw Vennep (NL)	8C2 556		Plasmolen (NL)	8E3 583		Steinfurt (DE)	8G2 187		Vreden (DE)	8F2 189
Lembruch (DE)	8H1 137		Nieuwland (NL)	8C2 576		Poeldijk (NL)	8B2 577		Steinhagen (DE)	8H2 187		Wachtendonk (DE)	8E3 189
Leusden (NL)	8D2 575		Nieuwlande (NL)	8F1 564		Purmerend (NL)	8C1 557		Stemwede (DE)	8H1 187		Wadersloh (DE)	8H3 189
Lichtenvoorde (NL)	8E2 571		Nieuwleusen (NL)	8E1 567		Putten (NL)	8D2 572		Stokkum (NL)	8E2 573		Waltrop (DE)	8G3 189
Lienen (DE)	8G2 181		Nijkerk (NL)	8D2 572		Raamsdonksveer (NL)	8C3 581		Stompetoren (NL)	8C1 557		Warendorf (DE)	8G2 189
Linden (NL)	8E3 580		Nijmegen (NL)	8E3 572		Raesfeld (DE)	8F3 185		Straelen (DE)	8E3 188		Warstein (DE)	8H3 189
Lingen/Ems (DE)	8F1 138		Nijverdal (NL)	8E1 567		Recke (DE)	8G1 185		Strijensas (NL)	8C3 577		Weeze (DE)	8E3 190
Lippstadt (DE)	8H3 181		Noord-Sleen (NL)	8F1 564		Rees (DE)	8E3 185		Sulingen (DE)	8H1 144		Well (NL)	8E3 583
Löhne (DE)	8H2 181		Nordhorn (DE)	8F1 139		Reken (DE)	8G3 184		Tecklenburg (DE)	8G2 188		Wesel (DE)	8F3 190
Losser (NL)	8F2 567		Nordkirchen (DE)	8G3 184		Rekken (NL)	8F2 572		Telgte (DE)	8G2 188		Westendorp (NL)	8E2 574
Lotte (DE)	8G2 181		Nottuln (DE)	8G2 184		Renesse (NL)	8B3 579		Terschuur (NL)	8D2 573		Westerkappeln (DE)	8G2 190
Lottum (NL)	8E3 582		Nuenen (NL)	8D3 580		Ressen (NL)	8E2 572		Terwolde (NL)	8E2 573		Wierden (NL)	8E1 568
Lübbecke (DE)	8H1 181		Numansdorp (NL)	8C3 577		Rheda-W (DE)	8H2 185		Tiel (NL)	8D2 573		Wijhe (NL)	8E1 568
Lüdinghausen (DE)	8G3 182		Nunspeet (NL)	8D1 572		Rhede (DE)	8F3 185		Toldijk (NL)	8E2 573		Wijk en Aalburg (NL)	8D3 581
Luttelgeest (NL)	8D1 568		Oberhausen (DE)	8F3 184		Rheine (DE)	8G2 186		Tolkamer (NL)	8E3 573		Wijster (NL)	8E1 565
Maasbommel (NL)	8D3 571		Oelde (DE)	8H3 184		Rhenen (NL)	8D2 575		Tubbergen (NL)	8F1 567		Winsum (NL)	8D1 556
Medemblik (NL)	8C1 556		Oijen (NL)	8D3 581		Rheurdt (NL)	8E3 186		Twello (NL)	8E2 573		Winterswijk (NL)	8F2 574
Melle (NL)	8H2 496		Oirschot (NL)	8C3 581		Rietberg (DE)	8H3 186		Twist (DE)	8F1 145		Witten (DE)	8G3 191
Meppel (NL)	8E1 564		Oldemarkt (NL)	8E1 567		Roosendaal (NL)	8C3 581		Uedem (DE)	8E3 188		Wolphaartsdijk (NL)	8B3 579
Meppen (DE)	8F1 138		Ommen (NL)	8E1 567		Rosendahl (DE)	8F2 186		Uelsen (DE)	8F1 145		Xanten (DE)	8E3 191
Meteren (NL)	8D3 571		Oosteind (NL)	8C3 581		Rüthen (DE)	8H3 186		Ufelte (NL)	8E1 565		Zeewolde (NL)	8D2 569
Mettingen (DE)	8G2 182		Oosterhesselen (NL)	8F1 565		Ruurlo (NL)	8E2 572		Urk (NL)	8D1 569		Zelhem (NL)	8E2 574
Middelburg (NL)	8A3 578		Oosterland (NL)	8B3 578		Sassenberg (DE)	8H2 186		Vaassen (NL)	8E2 573		Zevenhoven (NL)	8C2 577
Middenmeer (NL)	8C1 556		Oosthuizen (NL)	8C1 556		Sassenheim (NL)	8C2 577		Varsseveld (NL)	8E2 573		Zierikzee (NL)	8B3 579
Mierlo (NL)	8D3 580		Opperdoes (NL)	8C1 556		Schagen (NL)	8C1 557		Vechta (DE)	8H1 145		Zundert (NL)	8C3 581
Mijdrecht (NL)	8C2 576		Osnabrück (DE)	8G2 184		Schiedam (NL)	8C2 577		Velen (DE)	8F2 188		Zutphen (NL)	8E2 574
Millingen a/d Rijn (NL)	8E3 571		Oss (NL)	8D3 581		Schloss Holte/St (DE)	8H2 186		Venlo (NL)	8E3 583		Zwartsluis (NL)	8E1 568
Milsbeek (NL)	8E3 582		Ostbevern (DE)	8G2 184		Schöppingen (DE)	8F2 187		Vessem (NL)	8D3 581		Zwolle (NL)	8E1 568
Moers (DE)	8F3 182		Otterlo (NL)	8D2 572		Schüttorf (DE)	8F2 143						

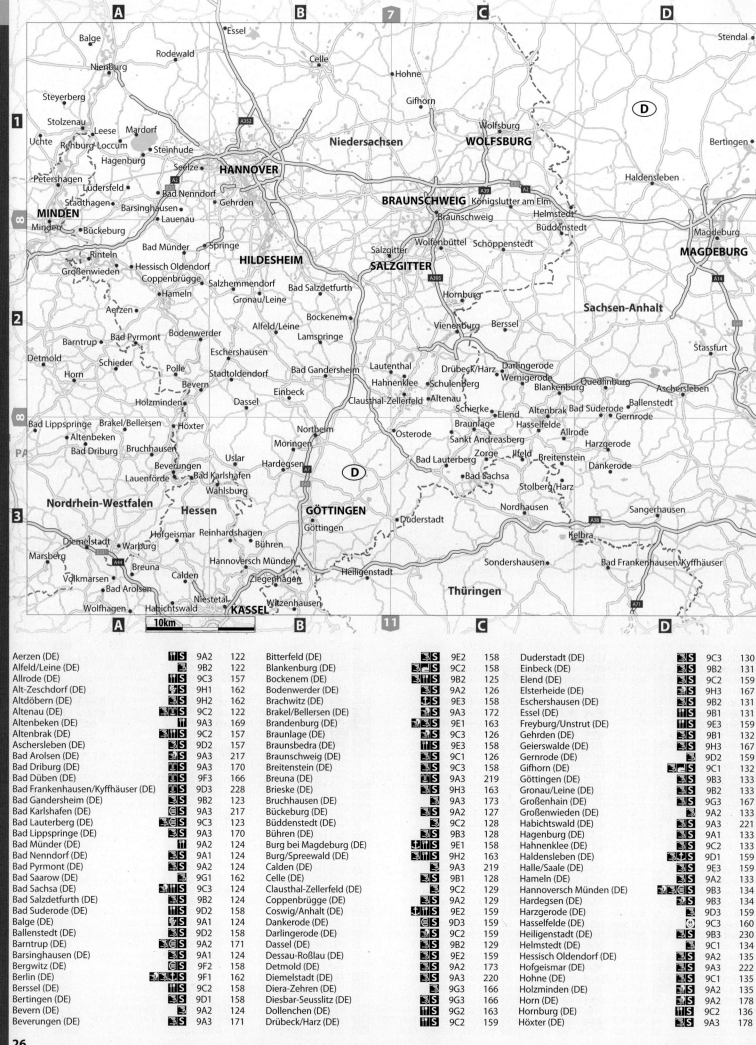

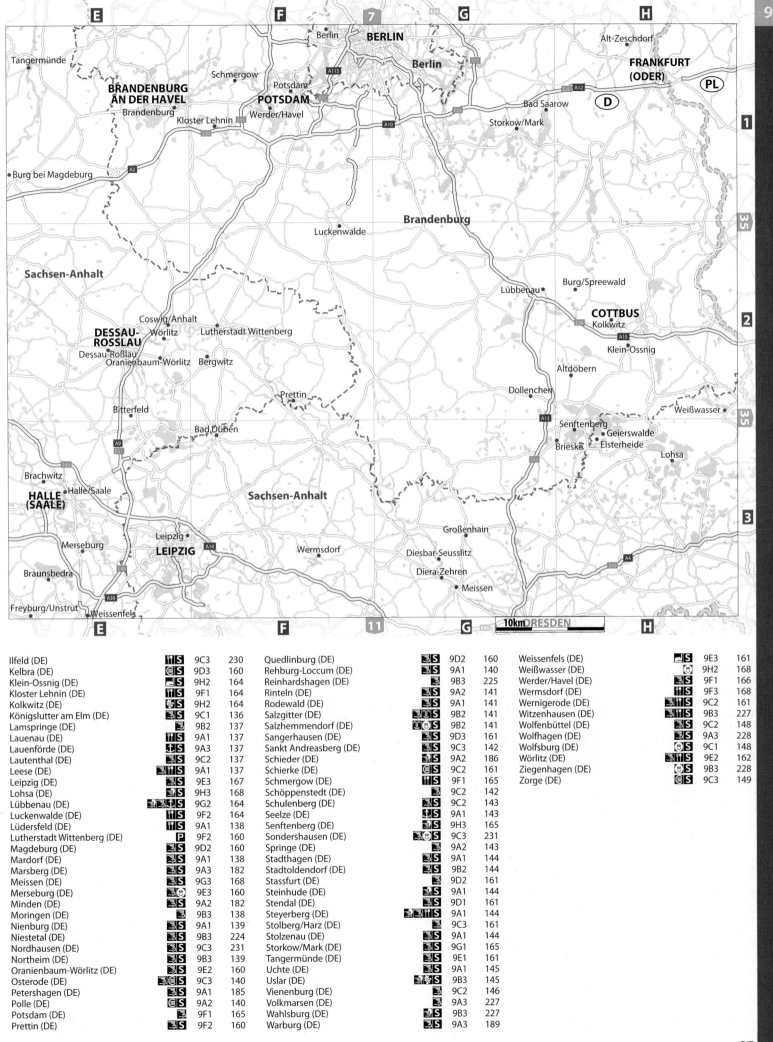

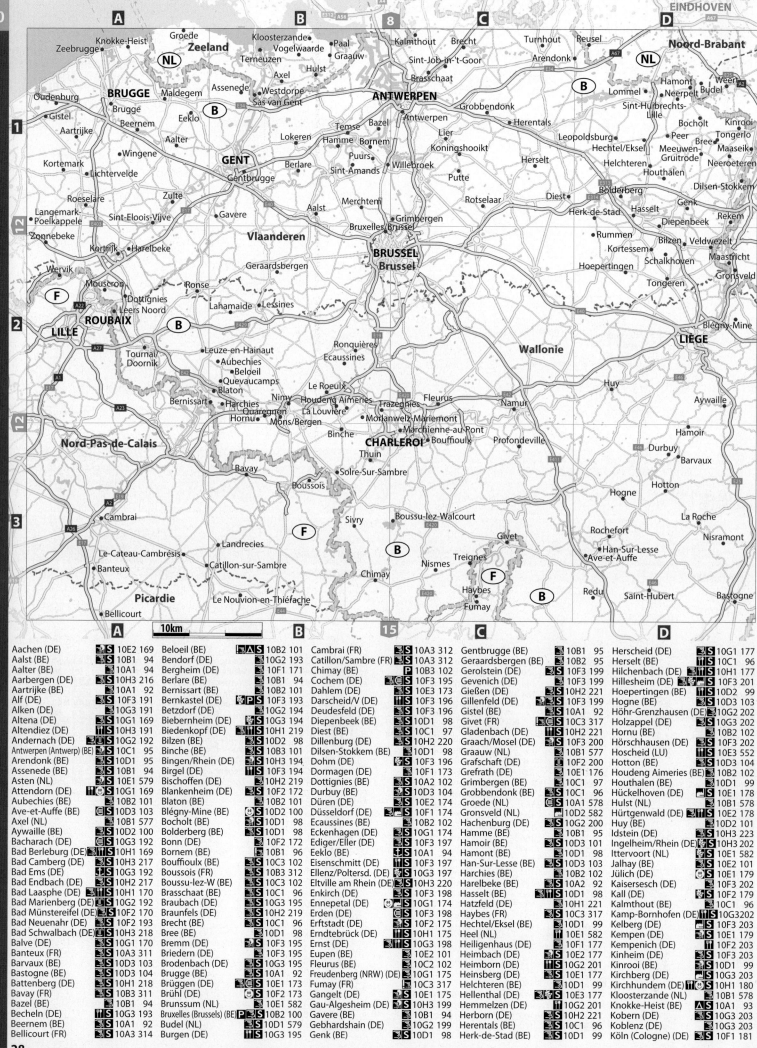

Scale: 10km

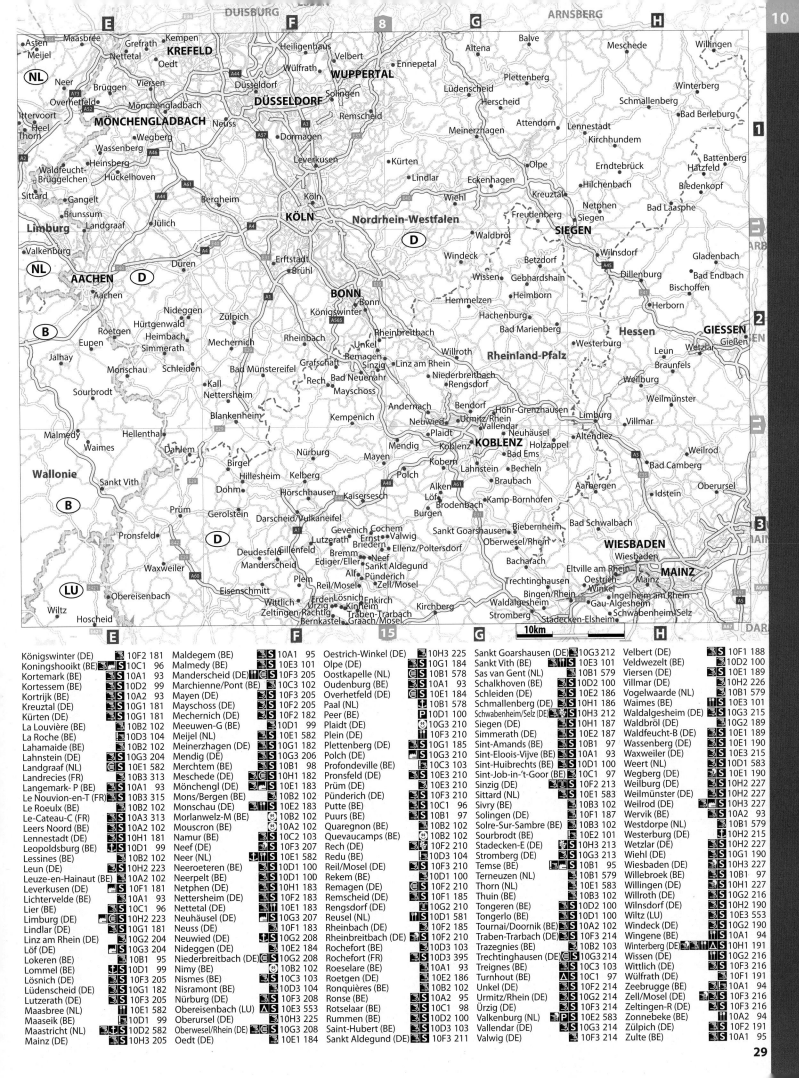

Königswinter (DE) 10F2 181
Koningshooikt (BE) 10C1 96
Kortemark (BE) 10A1 93
Kortessem (BE) 10D2 99
Kortrijk (BE) 10A2 93
Kreuztal (DE) 10G1 181
Kürten (DE) 10G2 181
La Louvière (BE) 10B2 102
La Roche (BE) 10D3 104
Lahamaide (BE) 10B2 102
Lahnstein (DE) 10G3 204
Landgraaf (NL) 10E1 582
Landrecies (FR) 10B3 313
Langemark- P (BE) 10A1 93
Le Nouvion-en-T (FR) 10B3 315
Le Roeulx (BE) 10B2 102
Le-Cateau-C (FR) 10A3 313
Leers Noord (BE) 10A2 102
Lennestadt (DE) 10H1 181
Leopoldsburg (BE) 10D1 99
Lessines (BE) 10B2 102
Leun (DE) 10H2 223
Leuze-en-Hainaut (BE) 10A2 102
Leverkusen (DE) 10F1 181
Lichtervelde (BE) 10A1 93
Lier (BE) 10C1 96
Limburg (DE) 10H2 223
Lindlar (DE) 10G2 181
Linz am Rhein (DE) 10G2 204
Löf (DE) 10G3 204
Lokeren (BE) 10B1 95
Lommel (BE) 10D1 99
Lösnich (DE) 10F3 205
Lüdenscheid (DE) 10G1 182
Lutzerath (DE) 10F3 205
Maasbree (NL) 10E1 582
Maaseik (BE) 10D1 99
Maastricht (NL) 10D2 582
Mainz (DE) 10H3 205

Maldegem (BE) 10A1 95
Malmedy (BE) 10E3 101
Manderscheid (DE) 10F3 205
Marchienne/Pont (BE) 10C3 102
Mayen (DE) 10F3 205
Mayschoss (DE) 10F2 205
Mechernich (DE) 10E2 182
Meeuwen-G (BE) 10D1 99
Meijel (NL) 10E1 582
Meinerzhagen (DE) 10G1 182
Mendig (DE) 10G3 206
Merchtem (BE) 10B1 98
Meschede (DE) 10H1 182
Mönchengl (DE) 10E1 183
Mons/Bergen (BE) 10B2 102
Monschau (DE) 10E2 183
Morlanwelz-M (BE) 10C3 102
Mouscron (BE) 10A2 102
Namur (BE) 10C2 103
Neef (DE) 10F3 207
Neer (NL) 10E1 582
Neeroeteren (BE) 10D1 100
Neerpelt (BE) 10D1 100
Netphen (DE) 10H1 183
Nettersheim (DE) 10E2 183
Neuhäusel (DE) 10G3 207
Neuss (DE) 10E1 183
Neuwied (DE) 10G2 208
Nideggen (DE) 10E2 184
Niederbreitbach (DE) 10G2 208
Nimy (BE) 10B2 102
Nismes (BE) 10C3 103
Nisramont (BE) 10D3 104
Nürburg (DE) 10F3 210
Obereisenbach (LU) 10E3 553
Oberursel (DE) 10H3 225
Oberwesel/Rhein (DE) 10G3 208
Oedt (DE) 10E1 184

Oestrich-Winkel (DE) 10H3 225
Olpe (DE) 10G1 184
Oostkapelle (NL) 10B1 578
Oudenburg (BE) 10A1 93
Overhetfeld (DE) 10E1 184
Paal (NL) 10D1 578
Peer (BE) 10D1 99
Plaidt (DE) 10G3 210
Plein (DE) 10F3 210
Plettenberg (DE) 10G1 185
Polch (DE) 10G3 210
Profondeville (BE) 10C3 103
Pronsfeld (DE) 10E3 210
Prüm (DE) 10E3 210
Putte (BE) 10C1 96
Puurs (BE) 10B1 97
Quaregnon (BE) 10B2 102
Quevaucamps (BE) 10B2 102
Rech (DE) 10F2 210
Redu (BE) 10C3 104
Reil/Mosel (DE) 10F3 210
Rekem (BE) 10D1 100
Remagen (DE) 10F2 210
Remscheid (DE) 10F1 185
Rengsdorf (DE) 10G2 210
Reusel (NL) 10D1 581
Rheinbach (DE) 10F2 185
Rheinbreitbach (DE) 10F2 210
Rochefort (BE) 10D3 103
Rochefort (FR) 10D3 395
Roeselare (BE) 10A1 93
Roetgen (DE) 10E2 186
Ronquières (BE) 10B2 102
Ronse (BE) 10A2 95
Rotselaar (BE) 10C1 98
Rummen (BE) 10D2 100
Saint-Hubert (BE) 10D3 103
Sankt Aldegund (DE) 10F3 211

Sankt Goarshausen (DE) 10G3 212
Sankt Vith (BE) 10E3 101
Sas van Gent (NL) 10B1 579
Schalkhoven (BE) 10D2 100
Schleiden (DE) 10E2 186
Schmallenberg (DE) 10H1 186
Schwabenheim/Selz (DE) 10H3 212
Siegen (DE) 10H1 187
Simmerath (DE) 10E2 187
Sint-Amands (BE) 10B1 97
Sint-Eloois-Vijve (BE) 10A1 93
Sint-Huibrechts (BE) 10D1 100
Sint-Job-in-'t-Goor (BE) 10C1 97
Sinzig (DE) 10F2 213
Sittard (NL) 10E1 583
Sivry (BE) 10B3 102
Solingen (DE) 10F1 187
Solre-Sur-Sambre (BE) 10B3 102
Sourbrodt (BE) 10E2 101
Stadecken-E (DE) 10H3 213
Stromberg (DE) 10G3 213
Temse (BE) 10B1 95
Terneuzen (NL) 10B1 579
Thorn (NL) 10E1 583
Thuin (BE) 10B3 102
Tongeren (BE) 10D2 100
Tongerlo (BE) 10D1 100
Tournai/Doornik (BE) 10A2 102
Traben-Trarbach (DE) 10F3 214
Trazegnies (BE) 10B2 103
Trechtinghausen (DE) 10G3 214
Treignes (BE) 10C3 103
Turnhout (BE) 10C1 97
Unkel (DE) 10F2 214
Urmitz/Rhein (DE) 10G2 214
Ürzig (DE) 10F3 214
Valkenburg (NL) 10E2 583
Vallendar (DE) 10G3 214
Valwig (DE) 10F3 214

Velbert (DE) 10F1 188
Veldwezelt (BE) 10D2 100
Viersen (DE) 10E1 189
Villmar (DE) 10H2 226
Vogelwaarde (NL) 10B1 579
Waimes (BE) 10E3 101
Waldalgesheim (DE) 10G3 215
Waldbröl (DE) 10G2 189
Waldfeucht-B (BE) 10E1 189
Wassenberg (DE) 10E1 190
Waxweiler (DE) 10E3 215
Weert (NL) 10D1 583
Wegberg (DE) 10E1 190
Weilburg (DE) 10H2 227
Weilmünster (DE) 10H2 227
Weilrod (DE) 10H2 227
Wervik (BE) 10A2 93
Westdorpe (NL) 10B1 579
Westerburg (DE) 10H2 215
Wetzlar (DE) 10H2 227
Wiehl (DE) 10G1 190
Wiesbaden (DE) 10H3 227
Willebroek (BE) 10B1 97
Willingen (DE) 10H1 191
Willroth (DE) 10G2 216
Wilnsdorf (DE) 10H2 190
Wiltz (LU) 10E3 553
Windeck (DE) 10G2 216
Wingene (BE) 10A1 94
Winterberg (DE) 10H1 191
Wissen (DE) 10G2 216
Wittlich (DE) 10F3 216
Wülfrath (DE) 10F1 191
Zeebrugge (BE) 10A1 94
Zell/Mosel (DE) 10F3 216
Zeltingen-R (DE) 10F3 216
Zonnebeke (BE) 10A2 94
Zülpich (DE) 10F2 191
Zulte (BE) 10A1 95

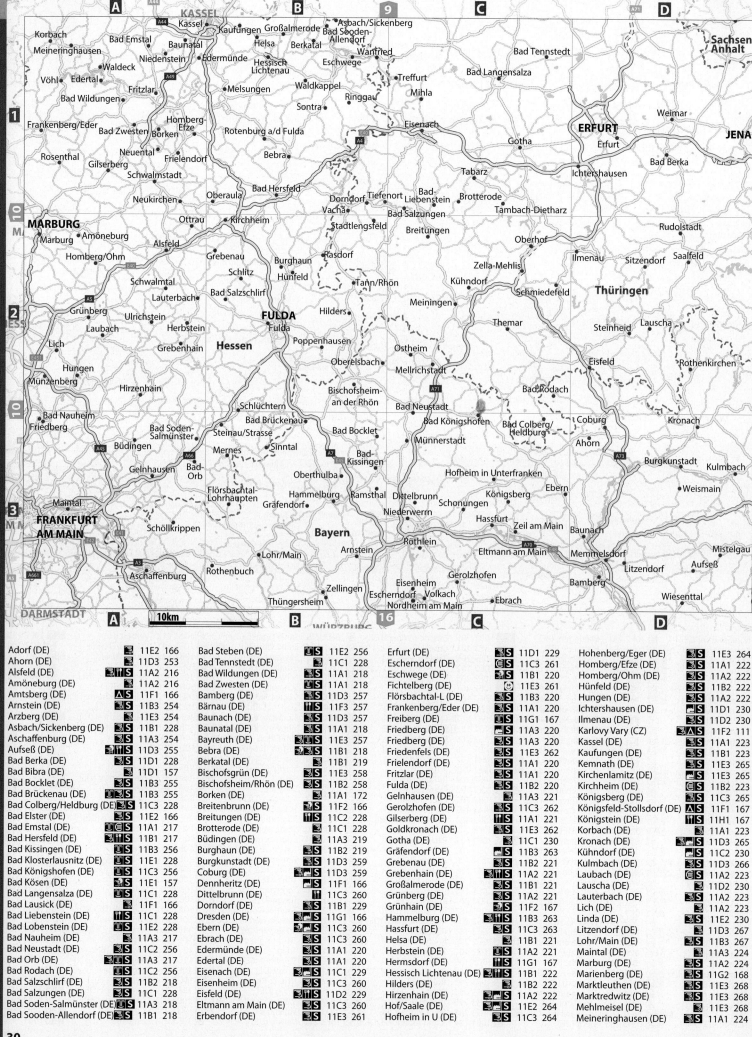

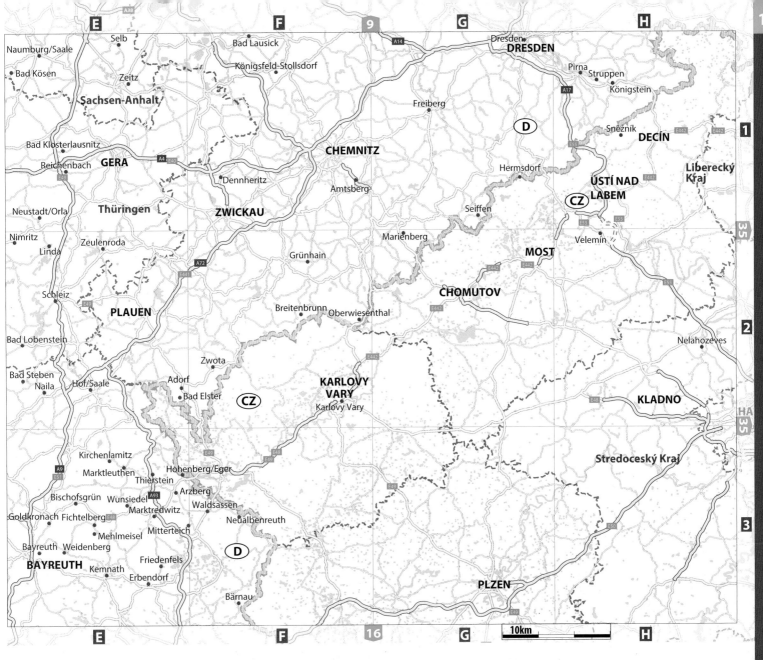

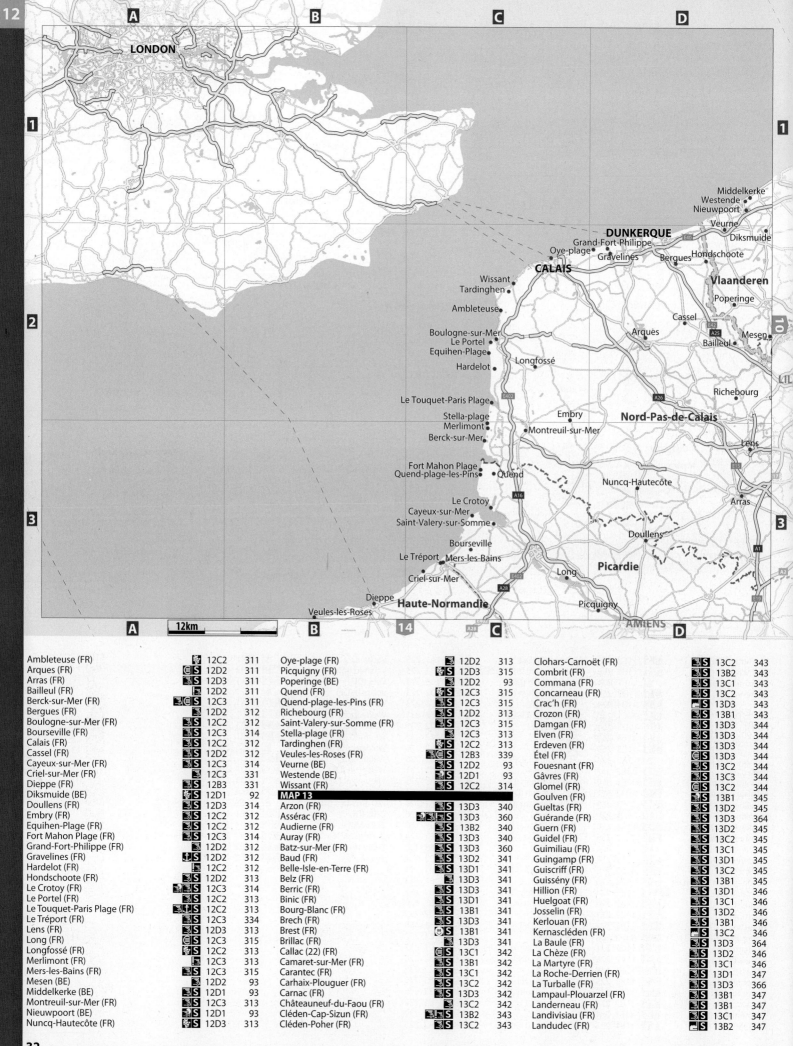

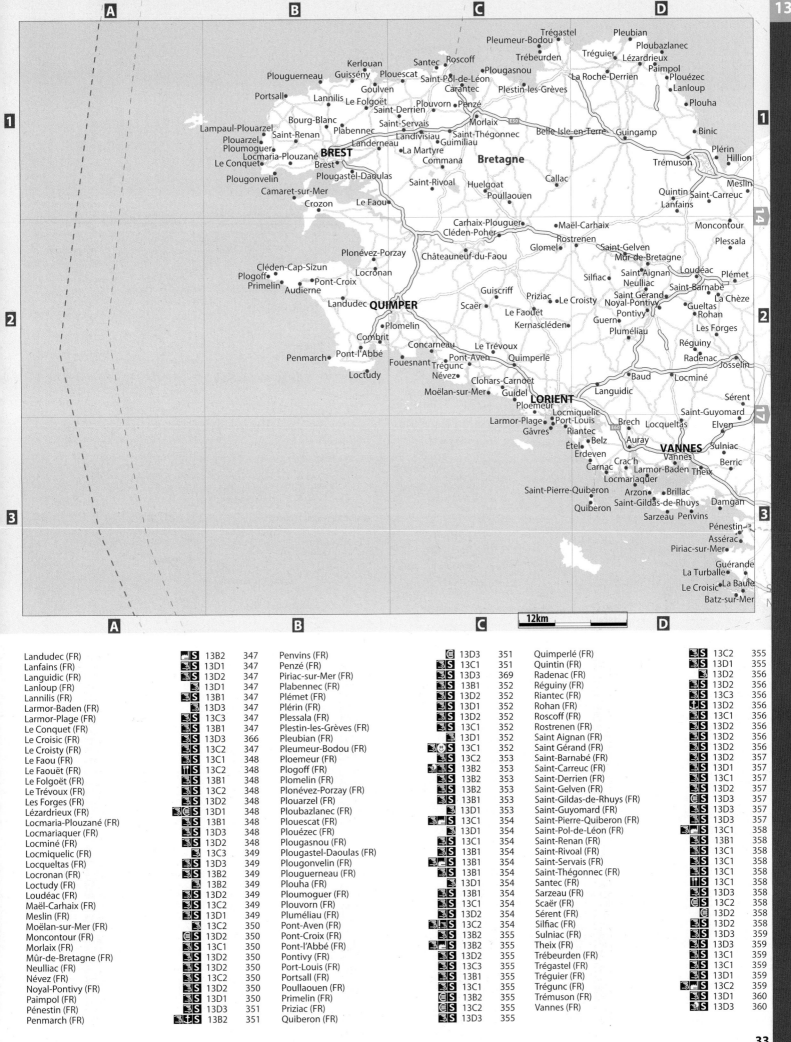

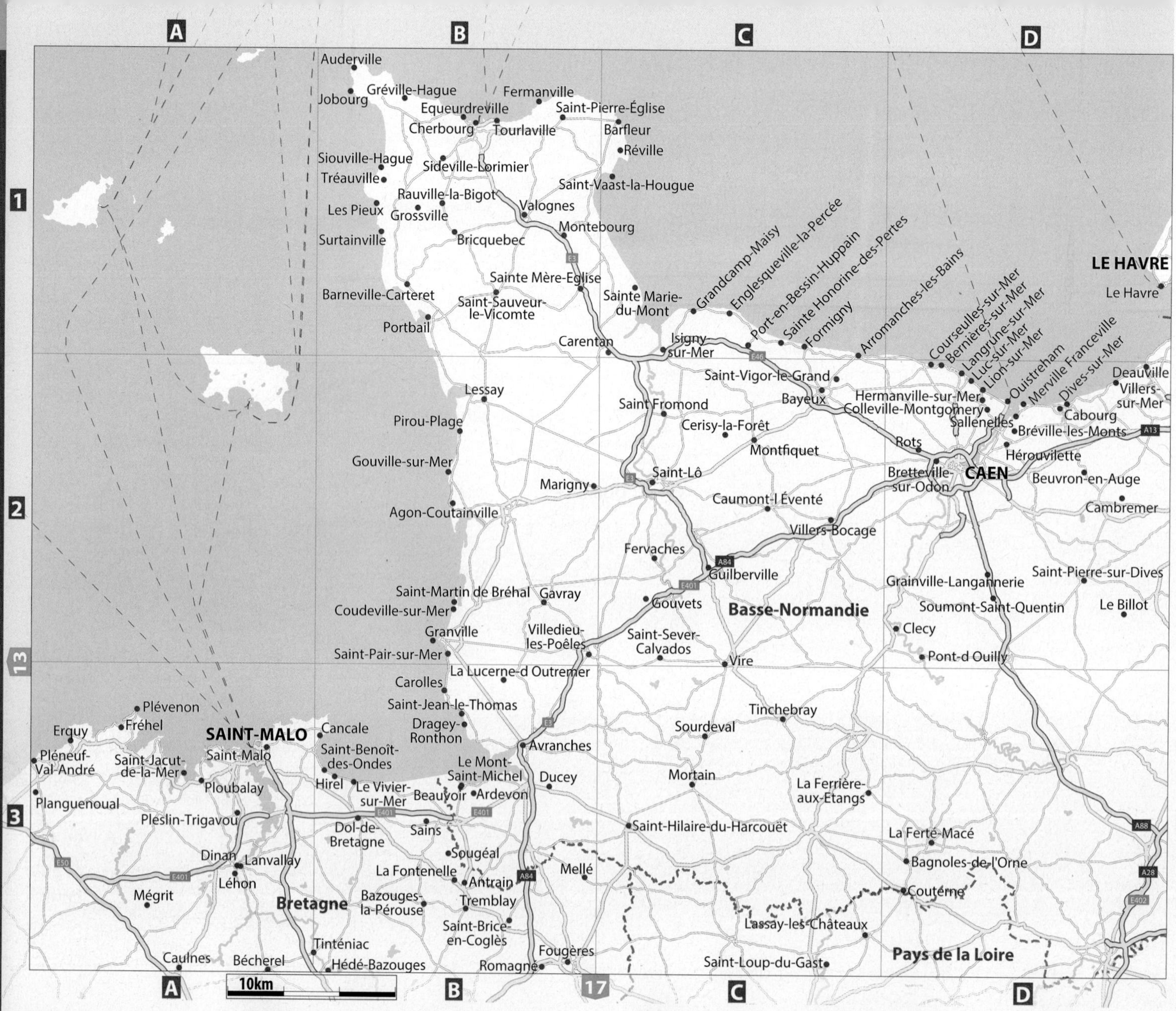

A B C D

LE HAVRE

1

Auderville
Gréville-Hague
Jobourg
Fermanville
Equeurdreville
Saint-Pierre-Église
Cherbourg Tourlaville
Barfleur
Réville
Siouville-Hague
Sideville-Lorimier
Tréauville
Rauville-la-Bigot
Saint-Vaast-la-Hougue
Les Pieux
Grossville
Valognes
Surtainville
Montebourg
Bricquebec
Sainte Mère-Eglise
Barneville-Carteret
Saint-Sauveur-du-Mont
Saint-Sauveur-le-Vicomte
Sainte Marie-du-Mont
Portbail
Carentan
Isigny-sur-Mer
Grandcamp-Maisy
Englesqueville-la-Percée
Port-en-Bessin-Huppain
Sainte Honorine-des-Pertes
Formigny
Arromanches-les-Bains
Courseulles-sur-Mer
Bernières-sur-Mer
Langrune-sur-Mer
Luc-sur-Mer
Lion-sur-Mer
Le Havre
Saint-Vigor-le-Grand
Bayeux
Quistreham
Merville Franceville
Deauville
Villers-sur-Mer
Lessay
Hermanville-sur-Mer
Colleville-Montgomery
Cabourg
Saint-Fromond
Sallenelles
Bréville-les-Monts
Pirou-Plage
Cerisy-la-Forêt
Rots
Hérouvilette
Gouville-sur-Mer
Montfiquet
Bretteville-sur-Odon
CAEN
Beuvron-en-Auge
Marigny
Saint-Lô
Cambremer
Agon-Coutainville
Caumont-l'Éventé
Fervaches
Villers-Bocage
Saint-Pierre-sur-Dives

2

Guilberville
Grainville-Langannerie
Le Billot
Saint-Martin de Bréhal
Gavray
Gouvets
Basse-Normandie
Soumont-Saint-Quentin
Coudeville-sur-Mer
Clecy
Granville
Villedieu-les-Poêles
Saint-Sever-Calvados
Pont-d Ouilly
Saint-Pair-sur-Mer
Vire
La Lucerne-d'Outremer
Carolles
Saint-Jean-le-Thomas
Tinchebray
Dragey-Ronthon
Avranches
Sourdeval
Plévenon
Cancale
Frehel
Erquy
Pléneuf-Val-André
Saint-Jacut-de-la-Mer
SAINT-MALO
Saint-Malo
Saint-Benoît-des-Ondes
Le Mont-Saint-Michel
Ducey
Mortain
La Ferrière-aux-Etangs
Planguenoual
Ploubalay
Hirel
Le Vivier-sur-Mer
Beauvoir Ardevon
La Ferté-Macé
Pleslin-Trigavou
Dol-de-Bretagne
Sains
Saint-Hilaire-du-Harcouët
Bagnoles-de-l'Orne
Dinan Lanvallay
Sougéal
Coutĕrne
Léhon
La Fontenelle
Mellé
Mégrit
Bazouges-la-Pérouse
Antrain
Bretagne
Tremblay
Lassay-les-Châteaux
Pays de la Loire
Caulnes
Bécherel
Saint-Brice-en-Coglès
Fougères
Tinténiac
Romagné
Saint-Loup-du-Gast
Hédé-Bazouges

10km

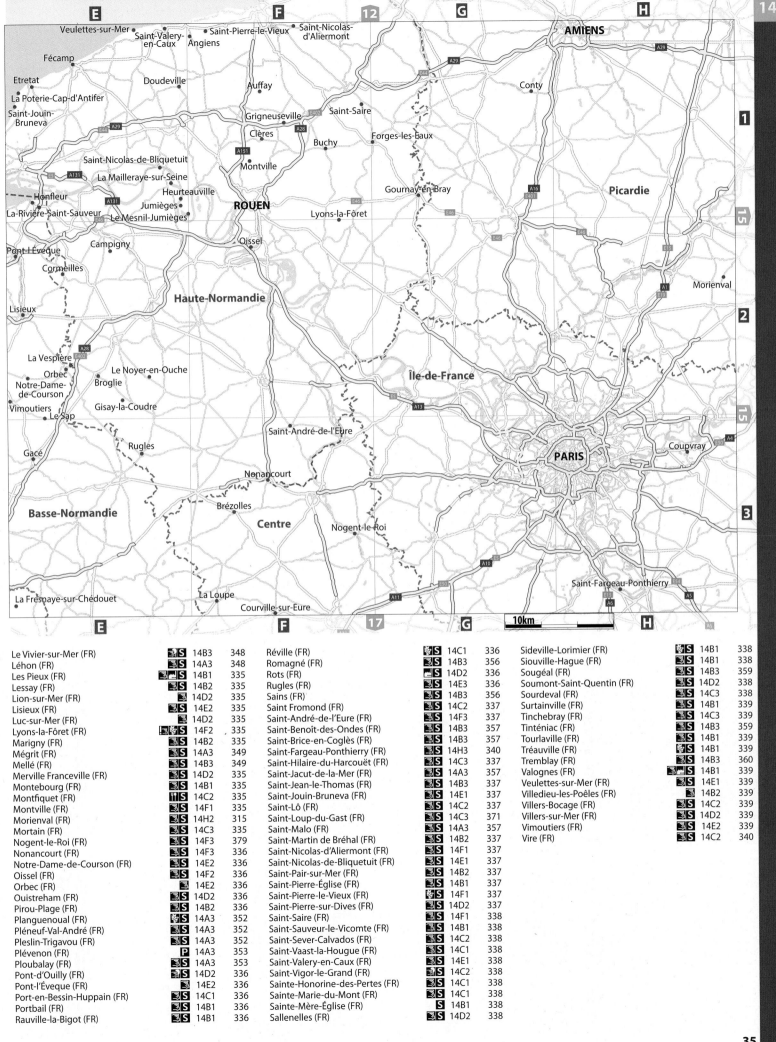

Le Vivier-sur-Mer (FR)	14B3 348	Réville (FR)	14C1 336
Léhon (FR)	14A3 348	Romagné (FR)	14B3 356
Les Pieux (FR)	14B1 335	Rots (FR)	14D2 336
Lessay (FR)	14B2 335	Rugles (FR)	14E3 336
Lion-sur-Mer (FR)	14D2 335	Sains (FR)	14B3 356
Lisieux (FR)	14E2 335	Saint Fromond (FR)	14C2 337
Luc-sur-Mer (FR)	14D2 335	Saint-André-de-l'Eure (FR)	14F3 337
Lyons-la-Fôret (FR)	14F2 335	Saint-Benoît-des-Ondes (FR)	14B3 357
Marigny (FR)	14B2 335	Saint-Brice-en-Coglès (FR)	14B3 357
Mégrit (FR)	14A3 349	Saint-Fargeau-Ponthierry (FR)	14H3 340
Mellé (FR)	14B3 349	Saint-Hilaire-du-Harcouët (FR)	14C3 337
Merville Franceville (FR)	14D2 335	Saint-Jacut-de-la-Mer (FR)	14A3 357
Montebourg (FR)	14B1 335	Saint-Jean-le-Thomas (FR)	14B3 337
Montfiquet (FR)	14C2 335	Saint-Jouin-Bruneva (FR)	14E1 337
Montville (FR)	14F1 335	Saint-Lô (FR)	14C2 337
Morienval (FR)	14H2 315	Saint-Loup-du-Gast (FR)	14C3 371
Mortain (FR)	14C3 335	Saint-Malo (FR)	14A3 357
Nogent-le-Roi (FR)	14F3 379	Saint-Martin de Bréhal (FR)	14B2 337
Nonancourt (FR)	14F3 336	Saint-Nicolas-d'Aliermont (FR)	14F1 337
Notre-Dame-de-Courson (FR)	14E2 336	Saint-Nicolas-de-Bliquetuit (FR)	14E1 337
Oissel (FR)	14F2 336	Saint-Pair-sur-Mer (FR)	14B2 337
Orbec (FR)	14E2 336	Saint-Pierre-Église (FR)	14B1 337
Ouistreham (FR)	14D2 336	Saint-Pierre-le-Vieux (FR)	14F1 337
Pirou-Plage (FR)	14B2 336	Saint-Pierre-sur-Dives (FR)	14D2 337
Planguenoual (FR)	14A3 352	Saint-Saire (FR)	14F1 338
Pléneuf-Val-André (FR)	14A3 352	Saint-Sauveur-le-Vicomte (FR)	14B1 338
Pleslin-Trigavou (FR)	14A3 352	Saint-Sever-Calvados (FR)	14C2 338
Plévenon (FR)	14A3 353	Saint-Vaast-la-Hougue (FR)	14C1 338
Ploubalay (FR)	14A3 353	Saint-Valery-en-Caux (FR)	14E1 338
Pont-d'Ouilly (FR)	14D2 336	Saint-Vigor-le-Grand (FR)	14C2 338
Pont-l'Évêque (FR)	14E2 336	Sainte-Honorine-des-Pertes (FR)	14C1 338
Port-en-Bessin-Huppain (FR)	14C1 336	Sainte-Marie-du-Mont (FR)	14C1 338
Portbail (FR)	14B1 336	Sainte-Mère-Église (FR)	14B1 338
Rauville-la-Bigot (FR)	14B1 336	Sallenelles (FR)	14D2 338

Sideville-Lorimier (FR)	14B1 338
Siouville-Hague (FR)	14B1 338
Sougéal (FR)	14B3 359
Soumont-Saint-Quentin (FR)	14D2 338
Sourdeval (FR)	14C3 338
Surtainville (FR)	14B1 339
Tinchebray (FR)	14C3 339
Tinténiac (FR)	14B3 359
Tourlaville (FR)	14B1 339
Tréauville (FR)	14B1 339
Tremblay (FR)	14B3 360
Valognes (FR)	14B1 339
Veulettes-sur-Mer (FR)	14E1 339
Villedieu-les-Poêles (FR)	14B2 339
Villers-Bocage (FR)	14C2 339
Villers-sur-Mer (FR)	14D2 339
Vimoutiers (FR)	14E2 339
Vire (FR)	14C2 340

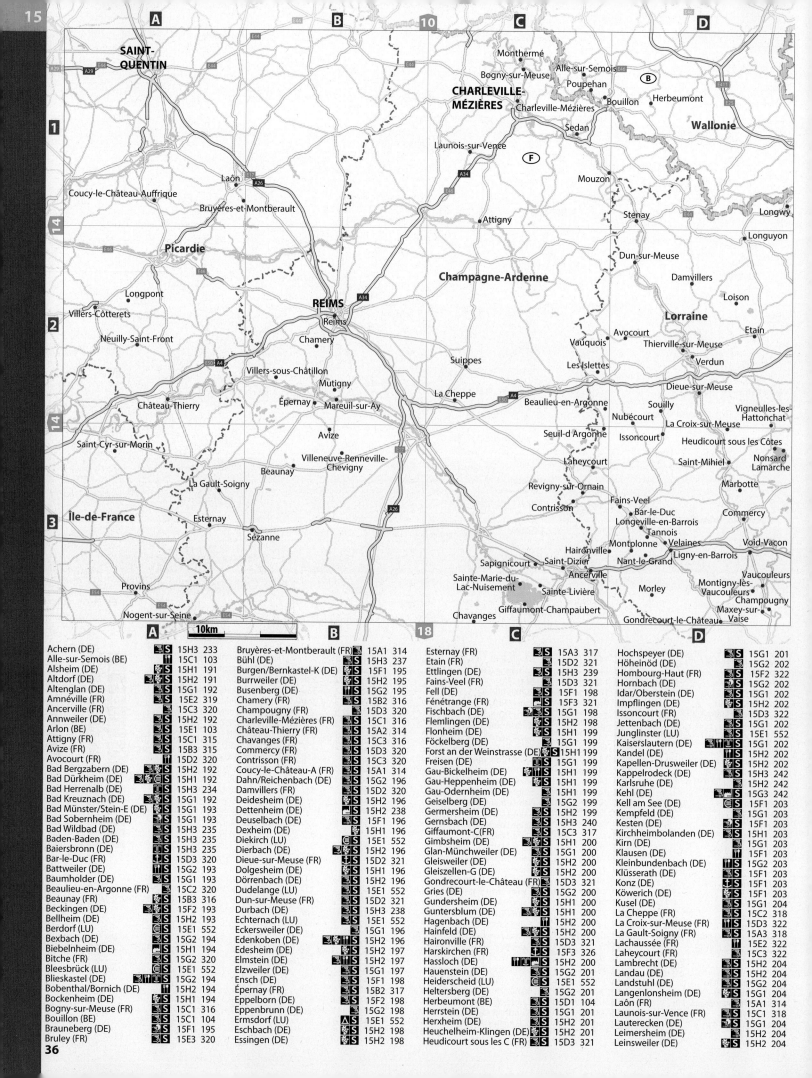

10km

A		
Achern (DE)	15H3	233
Alle-sur-Semois (BE)	15C1	103
Alsheim (DE)	15H1	191
Altdorf (DE)	15H2	191
Altenglan (DE)	15G1	192
Amnéville (FR)	15E2	319
Ancerville (FR)	15C3	320
Annweiler (DE)	15H2	192
Arlon (BE)	15E1	103
Attigny (FR)	15C1	315
Avize (FR)	15B3	315
Avocourt (FR)	15D2	320
Bad Bergzabern (DE)	15H2	192
Bad Dürkheim (DE)	15H1	192
Bad Herrenalb (DE)	15H3	234
Bad Kreuznach (DE)	15G1	192
Bad Münster/Stein-E (DE)	15G1	193
Bad Sobernheim (DE)	15G1	193
Bad Wildbad (DE)	15H3	235
Baden-Baden (DE)	15H3	235
Baiersbronn (DE)	15H3	235
Bar-le-Duc (FR)	15D3	320
Battweiler (DE)	15G2	193
Baumholder (DE)	15G1	193
Beaulieu-en-Argonne (FR)	15C2	320
Beaunay (FR)	15B3	316
Beckingen (DE)	15F2	193
Bellheim (DE)	15H2	193
Berdorf (LU)	15E1	552
Bexbach (DE)	15G2	194
Biebelnheim (DE)	15H1	194
Bitche (FR)	15G2	320
Bleesbrück (LU)	15E1	552
Blieskastel (DE)	15G2	194
Bobenthal/Bornich (DE)	15H2	194
Bockenheim (DE)	15H1	194
Bogny-sur-Meuse (FR)	15C1	316
Bouillon (BE)	15C1	104
Brauneberg (DE)	15F1	195
Bruley (FR)	15E3	320

B		
Bruyères-et-Montberault (FR)	15A1	314
Bühl (DE)	15H3	237
Burgen/Bernkastel-K (DE)	15F1	195
Burrweiler (DE)	15H2	195
Busenberg (DE)	15G2	195
Chamery (FR)	15B2	316
Champougny (FR)	15D3	320
Charleville-Mézières (FR)	15C1	316
Château-Thierry (FR)	15A2	314
Chavanges (FR)	15C3	316
Commercy (FR)	15D3	320
Contrisson (FR)	15C3	320
Coucy-le-Château-A (FR)	15A1	314
Dahn/Reichenbach (DE)	15G2	196
Damvillers (FR)	15D2	320
Deidesheim (DE)	15H1	196
Dettenheim (DE)	15H2	238
Deuselbach (DE)	15F1	196
Dexheim (DE)	15H1	196
Diekirch (LU)	15E1	552
Dierbach (DE)	15H2	196
Dieue-sur-Meuse (FR)	15D2	321
Dolgesheim (DE)	15H1	196
Dörrenbach (DE)	15H2	196
Dudelange (LU)	15E1	552
Dun-sur-Meuse (FR)	15D2	321
Durbach (DE)	15H3	238
Echternach (LU)	15E1	552
Eckersweiler (DE)	15G1	196
Edenkoben (DE)	15H2	196
Edesheim (DE)	15H2	197
Elmstein (DE)	15H2	197
Elzweiler (DE)	15G1	197
Ensch (DE)	15F1	198
Épernay (FR)	15B2	317
Eppelborn (DE)	15F2	198
Eppenbrunn (DE)	15G2	198
Ermsdorf (LU)	15E1	552
Eschbach (DE)	15H2	198
Essingen (DE)	15H2	198

C		
Esternay (FR)	15A3	317
Etain (FR)	15D2	321
Ettlingen (DE)	15H3	239
Fains-Veel (FR)	15D3	321
Fell (DE)	15F1	198
Fénétrange (FR)	15F3	321
Fischbach (DE)	15G1	198
Flemlingen (DE)	15H2	198
Flonheim (DE)	15H1	199
Föckelberg (DE)	15G1	199
Forst an der Weinstrasse (DE)	15H1	199
Freisen (DE)	15G1	199
Gau-Bickelheim (DE)	15H1	199
Gau-Heppenheim (DE)	15H1	199
Gau-Odernheim (DE)	15H1	199
Geiselberg (DE)	15G2	199
Germersheim (DE)	15H2	199
Gernsbach (DE)	15H3	240
Giffaumont-C (FR)	15C3	317
Gimbsheim (DE)	15H1	200
Glan-Münchweiler (DE)	15G1	200
Gleisweiler (DE)	15H2	200
Gleiszellen-G (DE)	15H2	200
Gondrecourt-le-Château (FR)	15D3	321
Gries (DE)	15G2	200
Gundersheim (DE)	15H1	200
Guntersblum (DE)	15H1	200
Hagenbach (DE)	15H2	200
Hainfeld (DE)	15H2	200
Haironville (FR)	15D3	321
Harskirchen (FR)	15F3	326
Hassloch (DE)	15H2	200
Hauenstein (DE)	15G2	201
Heiderscheid (LU)	15E1	552
Heltersberg (DE)	15G2	201
Herbeumont (BE)	15D1	104
Herrstein (DE)	15G1	201
Herxheim (DE)	15H2	201
Heuchelheim-Klingen (DE)	15H2	201
Heudicourt sous les C (FR)	15D3	321

D		
Hochspeyer (DE)	15G1	201
Höheinöd (DE)	15G2	202
Hombourg-Haut (FR)	15F2	322
Hornbach (DE)	15G1	202
Idar/Oberstein (DE)	15G1	202
Impflingen (DE)	15H2	202
Issoncourt (FR)	15D3	322
Jettenbach (DE)	15G1	202
Junglinster (LU)	15E1	552
Kaiserslautern (DE)	15G1	202
Kandel (DE)	15H2	202
Kapellen-Drusweiler (DE)	15H2	202
Kappelrodeck (DE)	15H3	242
Karlsruhe (DE)	15H2	242
Kehl (DE)	15G3	242
Kell am See (DE)	15F1	203
Kempfeld (DE)	15G1	203
Kesten (DE)	15F1	203
Kirchheimbolanden (DE)	15H1	203
Kirn (DE)	15G1	203
Klausen (DE)	15F1	203
Kleinbundenbach (DE)	15G2	203
Klüsserath (DE)	15F1	203
Konz (DE)	15F1	203
Köwerich (DE)	15F1	203
Kusel (DE)	15G1	204
La Cheppe (FR)	15C2	318
La Croix-sur-Meuse (FR)	15D3	322
La Gault-Soigny (FR)	15A3	318
Lachaussée (FR)	15E2	322
Laheycourt (FR)	15C3	322
Lambrecht (DE)	15H2	204
Landau (DE)	15H2	204
Landstuhl (DE)	15G1	204
Langenlonsheim (DE)	15G1	204
Laôn (FR)	15A1	314
Launois-sur-Vence (FR)	15C1	318
Lauterecken (DE)	15G1	204
Leimersheim (DE)	15H2	204
Leinsweiler (DE)	15H2	204

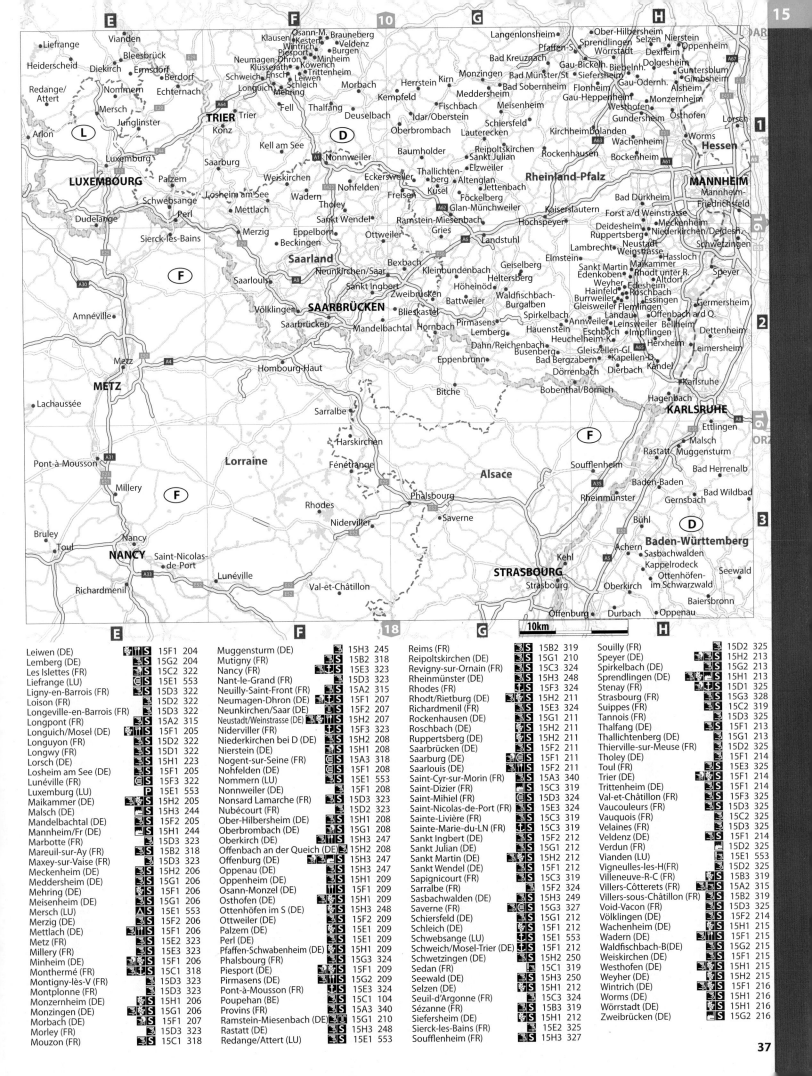

Map labels

DARMSTADT, Breuberg, Klingenberg, Markheidenfeld, Veitshöchheim, Dettelbach, Prichsenstadt, Schlüsselfeld, Ebermannstadt, Gößweinstein, Pottenstein

Bad König, Großheubach, Freudenberg, Wertheim, Würzburg, Albertshofen, Mainstockheim, Kitzingen, Burghaslach, Forchheim, Adelsdorf

Reichelsheim/Odenwald, Michelstadt, Bürgstadt, Miltenberg, Külsheim, Kreuzwertheim, Eibelstadt, Mainbernheim, Iphofen, Scheinfeld, Herzogenaurach, Hersbruck

Lindenfels, Erbach, Amorbach, Tauberbischofsheim, Segnitz, Marktbreit, Neustadt/Aisch, NÜRNBERG

Hessen, Hardheim, Ippesheim, Burgbernheim, Zirndorf, Feucht

Beerfelden, Walldürn, Lauda-Königshofen, Bad Windsheim, Cadolzburg

Ladenburg, Hirschhorn, Buchen/Odenwald, Röttingen, Tauberrettersheim,

Eberbach, Neunkirchen, Mosbach, Boxberg, Bad Mergentheim, Markelsheim, Weikersheim, Rothenburg ob der Tauber, Geslau, Ansbach, Hilpoltstein

Baden-Württemberg, Langenburg, Herrieden, Bayern

Sinsheim, Bad Wimpfen, Langenbrettach, Kirchberg/Jagst, Schnelldorf, Enderndorf, Absberg, Greding

Bad Rappenau, Neckarsulm, Öhringen, Untermünkheim, Crailsheim, Gunzenhausen

Bad Schönborn, HEILBRONN, Weinsberg, Schwäbisch Hall, Dinkelsbühl, Wassertrüdingen, Weissenburg

Bruchsal, Eppingen, Schwaigern, Heilbronn, Nordheim

Brackenheim, Güglingen, Neckarwestheim, Oberstenfeld, Gaildorf, Ellwangen, Oettingen, Treuchtlingen, Eichstätt

Bretten, Bönnigheim, Hessigheim, Aspach, Murrhardt, Gschwend, Mörnsheim

Cleebronn, Besigheim, Grossbottwar, Oppenweiler, Backnang, Kaisersbach, Deiningen, Huisheim, Monheim

Bietigheim-Bissingen, Benningen am Neckar, Marbach am Neckar, Welzheim, Aalen, Bopfingen, Nördlingen

Pforzheim, Korb, Schorndorf, Heubach, Neresheim, Neuburg/Donau

PFORZHEIM, Waiblingen, Schwäbisch Gmünd

Leonberg, Rechberghausen, Nattheim, Donauwörth, Rain/Lech

Bad Liebenzell, Weil der Stadt, STUTTGART, Esslingen am Neckar, Göppingen, Heidenheim, Schrobenhausen

Calw, Sindelfingen, Filderstadt, Kirchheim unter Teck, Herbrechtingen, Wertingen

Böblingen, Nürtingen, Holzmaden, Giengen

Bad Teinach, Bad Ditzenbach, Öllingen, Aichach

Wildberg, Metzingen, Beuren, Neuffen, Hülben, Langenau

Nagold, REUTLINGEN, Bad Urach, Günzburg

Rottenburg/Neckar, Reutlingen, Neusäß, AUGSBURG

Bad Niedernau, Pfullingen, Blaubeuren, Blaustein, ULM, Augsburg, Friedberg

10km

Index

Place	Grid	Page
Aalen (DE)	16C3	232
Absberg (DE)	16D2	253
Adelsdorf (DE)	16D1	253
Aichach (DE)	16D3	253
Albertshofen (DE)	16C1	254
Altmannstein (DE)	16E2	254
Amberg (DE)	16E1	254
Amorbach (DE)	16A1	254
Ansbach (DE)	16C2	254
Arnbruck (DE)	16G2	254
Aspach (DE)	16B2	233
Auerbach (DE)	16E1	254
Augsburg (DE)	16D3	255
Backnang (DE)	16B2	233
Bad Abbach (DE)	16E2	255
Bad Birnbach (DE)	16G3	255
Bad Ditzenbach (DE)	16B3	234
Bad Füssing (DE)	16G3	255
Bad Gögging (DE)	16E2	256
Bad Griesbach (DE)	16G3	256
Bad König (DE)	16A1	217
Bad Kötztingen (DE)	16G2	256
Bad Liebenzell (DE)	16A3	234
Bad Mergentheim (DE)	16B1	234
Bad Niedernau (DE)	16A3	234
Bad Rappenau (DE)	16A2	234
Bad Schönborn (DE)	16A2	234
Bad Teinach (DE)	16A3	235
Bad Urach (DE)	16B3	235
Bad Wimpfen (DE)	16A2	235
Bad Windsheim (DE)	16C1	257
Bayerbach (DE)	16G3	257
Beerfelden (DE)	16A1	219
Beilngries (DE)	16E2	257
Benningen am Neckar (DE)	16A2	235
Beratzhausen (DE)	16E2	258
Berching (DE)	16E2	258
Bernried (DE)	16G2	258
Besigheim (DE)	16A2	236
Beuren (DE)	16B3	236
Bietigheim-Bissingen (DE)	16A2	236
Blaubeuren (DE)	16B3	236
Blaustein (DE)	16B3	236
Böblingen (DE)	16A3	236
Bodenmais (DE)	16G2	258
Bodenwöhr (DE)	16F1	258
Bogen (DE)	16F2	258
Bönnigheim (DE)	16A2	237
Bopfingen (DE)	16C3	237
Boxberg (DE)	16B1	237
Brackenheim (DE)	16A2	237
Bretten (DE)	16A2	237
Breuberg (DE)	16A1	219
Bruchsal (DE)	16A2	237
Buchen/Odenwald (DE)	16A1	237
Burgbernheim (DE)	16C1	258
Burghaslach (DE)	16C1	259
Bürgstadt (DE)	16A1	259
Cadolzburg (DE)	16D1	259
Calw (DE)	16A3	237
Cleebronn/Tripsdrill (DE)	16A2	238
Crailsheim (DE)	16C2	238
Deggendorf (DE)	16G2	259
Deining (DE)	16E2	259
Denkendorf (DE)	16E2	259
Dettelbach (DE)	16C1	259
Dingolfing (DE)	16F3	259
Dinkelsbühl (DE)	16C2	259
Donauwörth (DE)	16D3	260
Eberbach (DE)	16A1	238
Ebermannstadt (DE)	16D1	260
Eferding (AT)	16H3	80
Eggenfelden (DE)	16G3	260
Eging am See (DE)	16G2	260
Eibelstadt (DE)	16B1	260
Eichstätt (DE)	16D2	260
Ellwangen (DE)	16C2	238
Enderndorf (DE)	16D2	261
Eppingen (DE)	16A2	239
Erbach (DE)	16A1	220
Esslingen am Neckar (DE)	16B3	239
Feucht (DE)	16D1	261
Filderstadt (DE)	16A3	239
Forchheim (DE)	16D1	261
Freudenberg (DE)	16A1	239
Freyung (DE)	16H2	261
Gaildorf (DE)	16B2	239
Geslau (DE)	16C2	262
Giengen (DE)	16C3	240
Göppingen (DE)	16B3	240
Gößweinstein (DE)	16D1	262
Grafenau (DE)	16G2	262
Greding (DE)	16D2	263
Großheubach (DE)	16A1	240
Grossbottwar (DE)	16B2	240
Gschwend (DE)	16B2	240
Güglingen (DE)	16A2	240
Günzburg (DE)	16C3	263
Gunzenhausen (DE)	16D2	263
Hardheim (DE)	16B1	241
Haslach (AT)	16H3	80
Heidenheim (DE)	16C3	241
Heilbronn (DE)	16A2	241
Herbrechtingen (DE)	16C3	241
Herrieden (DE)	16C2	263
Hersbruck (DE)	16D1	264
Herzogenaurach (DE)	16D1	264
Hessigheim (DE)	16A2	241
Heubach (DE)	16B3	241
Hilpoltstein (DE)	16D2	264
Hirschhorn (DE)	16A1	222
Hohenburg (DE)	16E1	264
Holzmaden (DE)	16B3	242
Huisheim (DE)	16D2	242
Hülben (DE)	16B3	242
Ingolstadt (DE)	16E3	264
Iphofen (DE)	16C1	264
Ippesheim (DE)	16C1	265
Kaisersbach (DE)	16B2	
Kastl/Oberpfalz (DE)	16E1	265
Kelheim (DE)	16E2	265
Kirchberg/Jagst (DE)	16B2	243
Kirchham (DE)	16G3	265
Kirchheim unter Teck (DE)	16B3	243
Kitzingen (DE)	16C1	265
Klingenberg (DE)	16A1	265
Korb (DE)	16B3	243
Kreuzwertheim (DE)	16B1	265
Külsheim (DE)	16B1	243
Kümmersbruck (DE)	16E1	266
Ladenburg (DE)	16A1	243
Lalling (DE)	16G2	266
Landau/Isar (DE)	16F3	266
Langenau (DE)	16C3	242
Langenbrettach (DE)	16B2	243
Langenburg (DE)	16B2	243

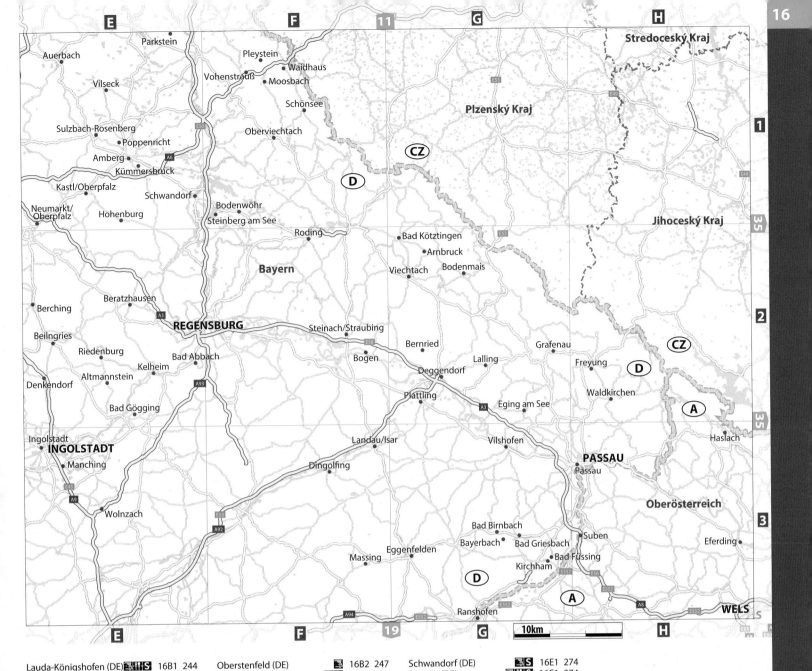

Map region including Bretagne, Pays de la Loire, Centre, Poitou-Charentes — cities RENNES, LAVAL, LE MANS, NANTES, SAINT-NAZAIRE, ANGERS, CHOLET. Scale 10km. Grid columns A–D, rows 1–3, index tabs 14, 20, 13.

Place	Grid	Page
Allogny (FR)	17G3	373
Amboise (FR)	17E3	373
Angé (FR)	17F3	373
Angers (FR)	17C2	360
Angliers (FR)	17D3	389
Angrie (FR)	17C2	360
Arnage (FR)	17D1	360
Arzal (FR)	17A2	340
Athée-sur-Cher (FR)	17E3	374
Aubigné-sur-Layon (FR)	17C3	360
Aubigny-sur-Nère (FR)	17H3	374
Availles-sur-Seiche (FR)	17B1	341
Averton (FR)	17D1	360
Avoine (FR)	17D3	374
Azay-le-Rideau (FR)	17E3	374
Azé (FR)	17F2	374
Barlieu (FR)	17H3	374
Baugé (FR)	17D2	360
Bazouges-sur-le-Loir (FR)	17D2	361
Beauvoir-sur-Mer (FR)	17A3	361
Bédée (FR)	17A1	341
Blain (FR)	17A2	361
Blaison-Gohier (FR)	17E3	361
Blois (FR)	17F2	374
Bonneval (FR)	17F1	375
Bonny-sur-Loire (FR)	17H2	374
Bouchemaine (FR)	17C2	361
Bouin (FR)	17A3	361
Boulleret (FR)	17H3	374
Bourges (FR)	17H3	374
Bourgneuf-en-Retz (FR)	17A3	361
Boussay (FR)	17B3	361
Bréal-sous-Montfort (FR)	17A1	341
Briare-le-Canal (FR)	17H2	375
Briollay (FR)	17C2	361
Brissac-Quincé (FR)	17C3	361
Brou (FR)	17F1	375
Campénéac (FR)	17A1	342
Cesson-Sévigné (FR)	17B1	342
Chabris (FR)	17F3	375
Chailland (FR)	17C1	362
Challans (FR)	17A3	362
Chalonnes-sur-Loire (FR)	17C3	362
Chambord (FR)	17F2	375
Chambretaud (FR)	17C3	362
Champigny-sur-Veude (FR)	17D3	375
Champtocé-sur-Loire (FR)	17C2	362
Champtoceaux (FR)	17B3	362
Changé (FR)	17C1	362
Chanzeaux (FR)	17C3	362
Chaon (FR)	17G2	375
Château-Gontier (FR)	17C2	362
Châteaudun (FR)	17F1	375
Châtillon-en-Vendelais (FR)	17B1	343
Châtillon-sur-Loire (FR)	17H2	375
Chavagne-en-Paillers (FR)	17B3	362
Chavagnes les Eaux (FR)	17C3	363
Chênehutte-Trèves-C (FR)	17D3	363
Chenillé-Changé (FR)	17C2	363
Chenonceaux (FR)	17F3	375
Cheverny (FR)	17F2	375
Chouzé-sur-Loire (FR)	17D3	375
Cloyes-sur-le-Loir (FR)	17F1	376
Combrée (FR)	17C2	363
Concourson-sur-Layon (FR)	17C3	363
Coullons (FR)	17H2	376
Dampierre-en-Burly (FR)	17H2	376
Dampierre-sur-Loire (FR)	17D3	363
Deux-Evailles (FR)	17C1	363
Doué-la-Fontaine (FR)	17D3	363
Dry (FR)	17G2	376
Durtal (FR)	17D2	363
Ernée (FR)	17C1	363
Esvres-sur-Indre (FR)	17E3	376
Faye d'Anjou (FR)	17C3	363
Feneu (FR)	17C2	363
Fontevraud l'Abbaye (FR)	17D3	364
Fresnay-sur-Sarthe (FR)	17D1	364
Gené (FR)	17C2	364
Genillé (FR)	17F3	376
Germigny-des-Prés (FR)	17G2	376
Gien (FR)	17H2	376
Gizeux (FR)	17D3	376
Grand-Fougeray (FR)	17B2	345
Grez-en-Bouère (FR)	17C2	364
Grez-Neuville (FR)	17C2	364
Guenrouet (FR)	17A2	364
Guichen (FR)	17B1	345
Guilly (FR)	17G3	376
Humbligny (FR)	17H3	376
Jans (FR)	17B2	364
Janzé (FR)	17B1	346
Juvigné (FR)	17C1	364
La Baconnière (FR)	17C1	364
La Bernerie-en-Retz (FR)	17A3	365
La Chapelle-St-Florent (FR)	17B3	365
La Chapelle-St-M (FR)	17G2	376
La Charité-sur-Loire (FR)	17H3	383
La Daguenière (FR)	17C2	365
La Ferté-Beauharnais (FR)	17G2	377
La Ferté-Saint-Cyr (FR)	17G2	377
La Flèche (FR)	17D2	365
La Plaine-sur-Mer (FR)	17A3	365
La Poitevinière (FR)	17C3	365
La Roche-Bernard (FR)	17A2	346
La Séguinière (FR)	17C3	365
La Suze-sur-Sarthe (FR)	17D2	365
Lailly-en-Val (FR)	17G2	377
Lamotte-Beuvron (FR)	17G2	377
Langon (Loir-et-Cher) (FR)	17G3	377
Laval (FR)	17C1	366
Le Coudray Macouard (FR)	17D3	366
Le Guédéniau (FR)	17D2	366
Le Mans (FR)	17D1	366
Le Pallet (FR)	17B3	366
Le Puy-Notre-Dame (FR)	17D3	366
Le Vaudelnay (FR)	17D3	367
Léré (FR)	17H3	377
Les Bordes (FR)	17H2	377
Les Montils (FR)	17F2	377
Liffré (FR)	17B1	348
Liré (FR)	17B3	367
Loches (FR)	17E3	377
Longué-Jumelles (FR)	17D3	367
Loudun (FR)	17D3	393
Louzouer (FR)	17H1	377
Maisdon-sur-Sèvre (FR)	17B3	368
Malansac (FR)	17A2	349
Malestroit (FR)	17A1	349
Mamers (FR)	17E1	368
Marboué (FR)	17F1	378
Marcilly-en-Villette (FR)	17G2	378
Martigné-Briand (FR)	17C3	368
Marzan (FR)	17A2	349
Mauléon (FR)	17C3	393
Maure-de-Bretagne (FR)	17A1	349

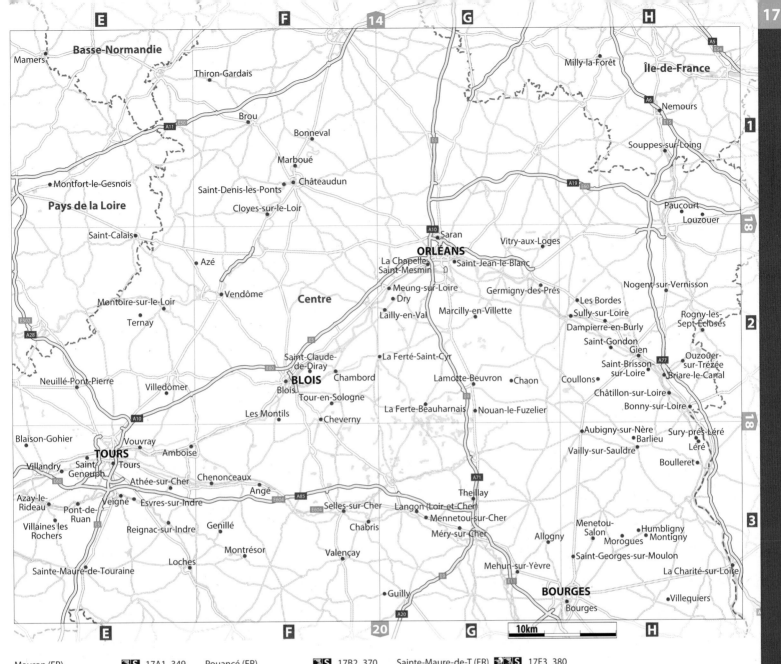

Mauron (FR)	17A1 349	Pouancé (FR)	17B2 370	Sainte-Maure-de-T (FR)	17E3 380
Mayenne (FR)	17C1 368	Préfailles (FR)	17A3 370	Saran (FR)	17G2 380
Mehun-sur-Yèvre (FR)	17G3 378	Rablay sur Layon (FR)	17C3 370	Saulgé l'Hôpital (FR)	17C3 372
Menetou-Salon (FR)	17H3 378	Redon (FR)	17A2 356	Segré (FR)	17C2 372
Mennetou-sur-Cher (FR)	17G3 378	Reignac-sur-Indre (FR)	17E3 379	Selles-sur-Cher (FR)	17F3 380
Méry-sur-Cher (FR)	17G3 378	Rennes (FR)	17B1 356	Sillé-le-Guillaume (FR)	17D1 372
Meung-sur-Loire (FR)	17G2 378	Restigné (FR)	17D3 379	Souppes-sur-Loing (FR)	17H1 340
Mezeray (FR)	17D2 368	Riaille (FR)	17B2 370	Sully-sur-Loire (FR)	17H2 380
Milly-la-Forêt (FR)	17H1 340	Rochefort-en-Terre (FR)	17A2 356	Sury-prés-Léré (FR)	17H3 380
Montfort-le-Gesnois (FR)	17E1 368	Rogny-les-Sept-É (FR)	17H2 384	Ternay (FR)	17E2 380
Montigny (FR)	17H3 378	Rouans (FR)	17A3 370	Theillay (FR)	17G3 381
Montoire-sur-le-Loir (FR)	17E2 378	Saint-Aubin-d'Aubigné (FR)	17B1 357	Thiron-Gardais (FR)	17F1 381
Montrésor (FR)	17F3 378	Saint-Aubin-de-Luigné (FR)	17C3 370	Thouars (FR)	17D3 397
Montreuil-Bellay (FR)	17D3 368	Saint-Brisson-sur-Loire (FR)	17H2 379	Tour-en-Sologne (FR)	17F2 381
Montreuil-Juigné (FR)	17C2 368	Saint-Calais (FR)	17E2 370	Tours (FR)	17E3 381
Montsoreau (FR)	17D3 368	Saint-Claude-de-Diray (FR)	17F2 379	Turquant (FR)	17D3 373
Morogues (FR)	17H3 378	Saint-Clément-des-L (FR)	17D3 370	Vaiges (FR)	17C1 373
Mouzillon (FR)	17B3 368	Saint-Cyr-en-Bourg (FR)	17D3 370	Vailly-sur-Sauldre (FR)	17H3 381
Nantes (FR)	17B3 369	Saint-Denis-les-Ponts (FR)	17F1 379	Val-d'Izé (FR)	17B1 360
Nemours (FR)	17H1 340	Saint-Genouph (FR)	17E3 379	Valanjou (FR)	17C3 373
Neuillé-Pont-Pierre (FR)	17E2 378	St-Georges-sur-Loire (FR)	17C2 370	Valençay (FR)	17F3 381
Nogent-sur-Vernisson (FR)	17H2 379	St-Georges/Moulon (FR)	17H3 380	Veigné (FR)	17E3 381
Noirmoutier-en-l'Ile (FR)	17A3 369	Saint-Gondon (FR)	17H2 380	Vendôme (FR)	17F2 381
Nort-sur-Erdre (FR)	17B2 369	St-Hilaire-de-Chaléons (FR)	17A3 371	Vihiers (FR)	17C3 373
Notre-Dame-de-Monts (FR)	17A3 369	Saint-Jean-le-Blanc (FR)	17G2 380	Villaines les Rochers (FR)	17E3 381
Nouan-le-Fuzelier (FR)	17G2 379	St-Jean-sur-Mayenne (FR)	17C1 371	Villandry (FR)	17E3 381
Nozay (FR)	17B2 369	St-Léonard-des-Bois (FR)	17D1 371	Villedômer (FR)	17E2 381
Ouzouer-sur-Trézée (FR)	17H2 379	St-Mars-la-Jaille (FR)	17B2 371	Villequiers (FR)	17H3 381
Paimpont (FR)	17A1 351	Saint-Michel-C-C (FR)	17A3 371	Villeveque (FR)	17C2 373
Paucourt (FR)	17H1 379	Saint-Nazaire (FR)	17A3 371	Villiers-Charlemagne (FR)	17C1 373
Pellouailles-les-Vignes (FR)	17C2 369	Saint-Philbert-de-G-L (FR)	17B3 372	Vitry-aux-Loges (FR)	17G2 381
Piré-sur-Seiche (FR)	17B1 351	Saint-Rémy-la-Varenne (FR)	17D3 372	Vouvray (FR)	17E3 381
Pont-de-Ruan (FR)	17E3 379	Saint-Saturnin-sur-Loire (FR)	17C3 372		
Pornic (FR)	17A3 370	Saint-Viaud (FR)	17A3 372		

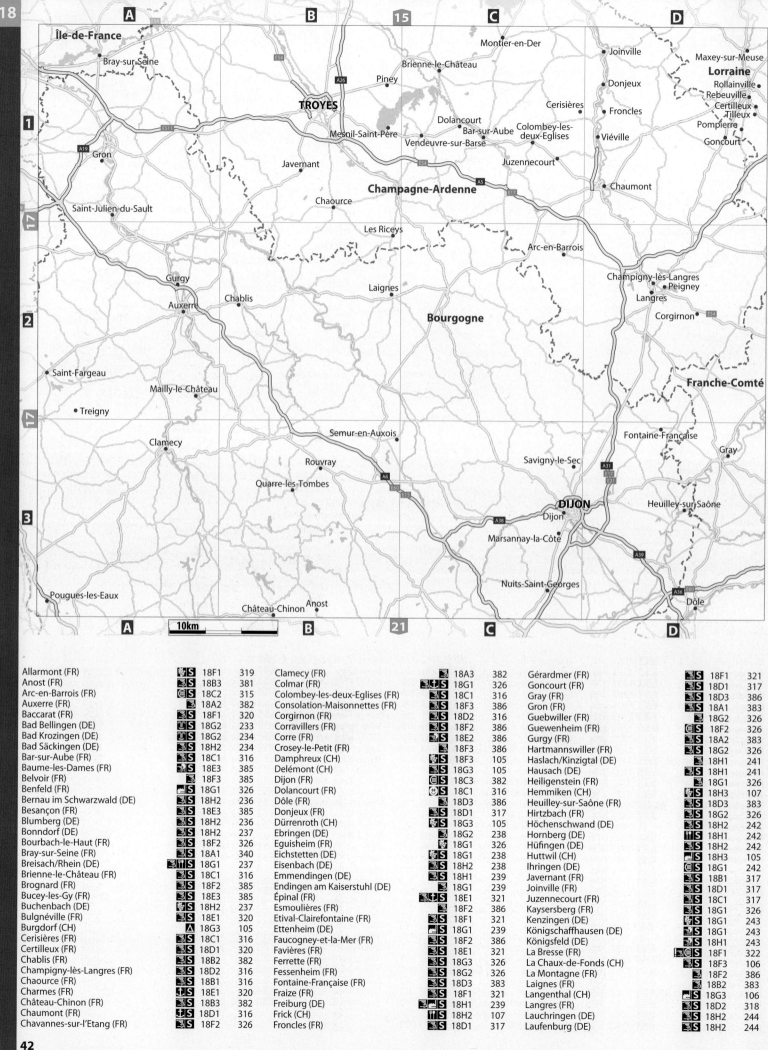

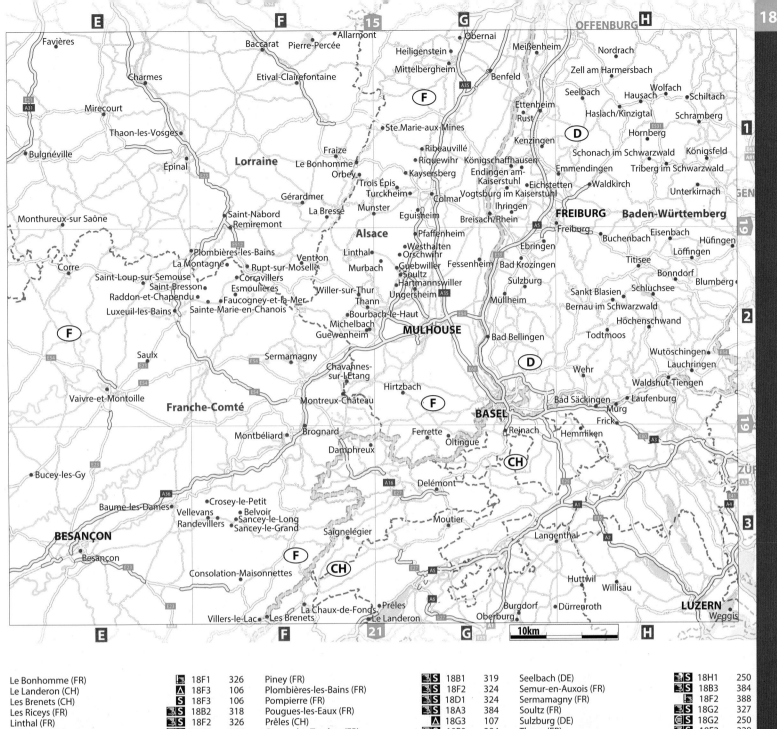

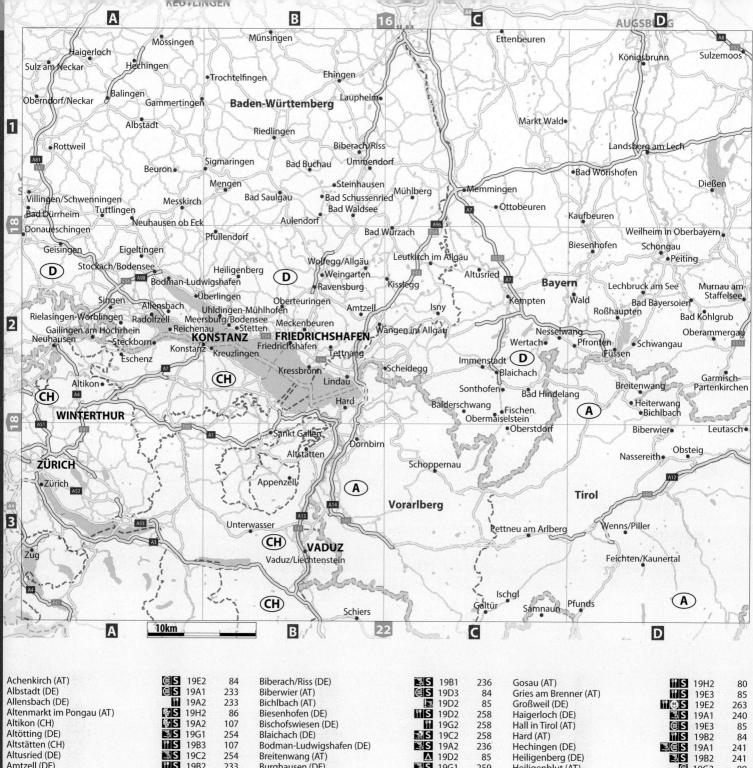

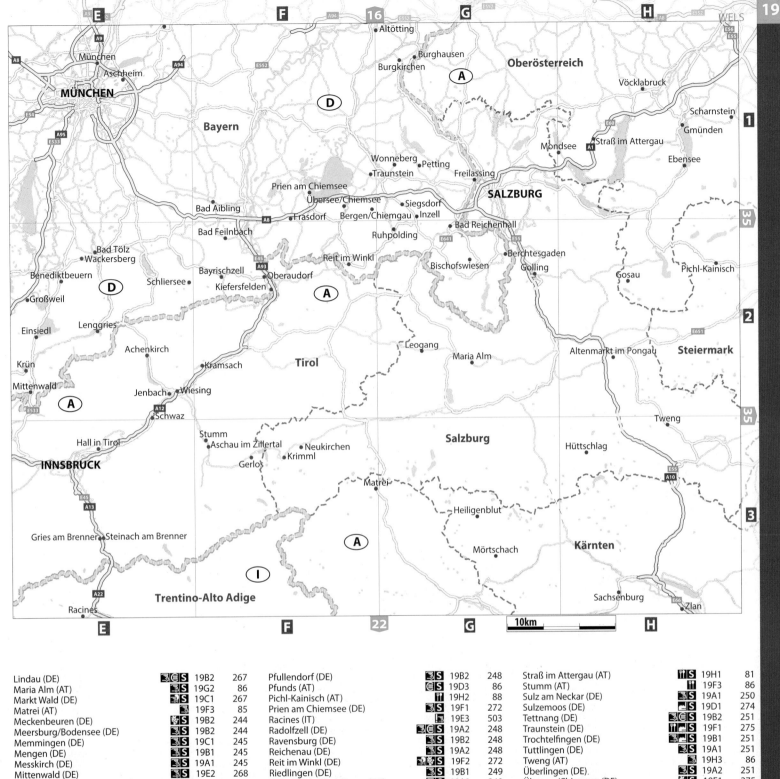

WELS

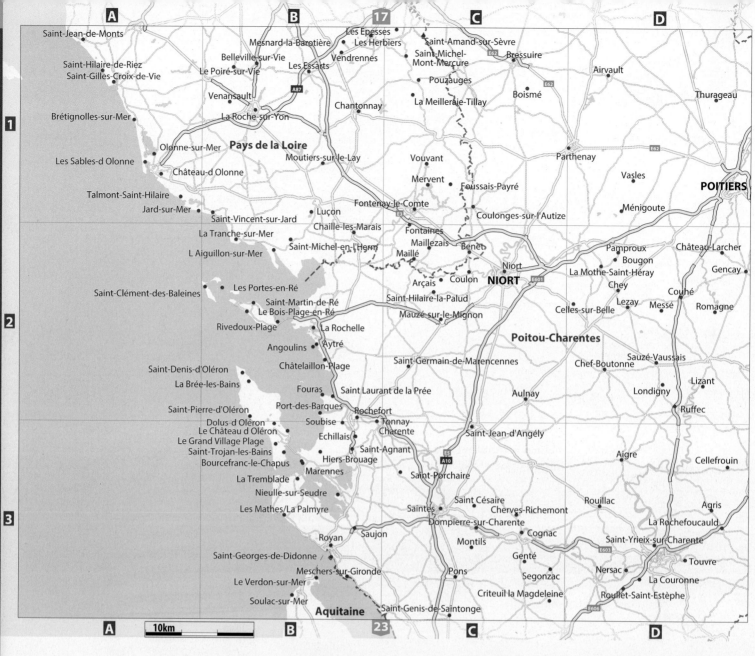

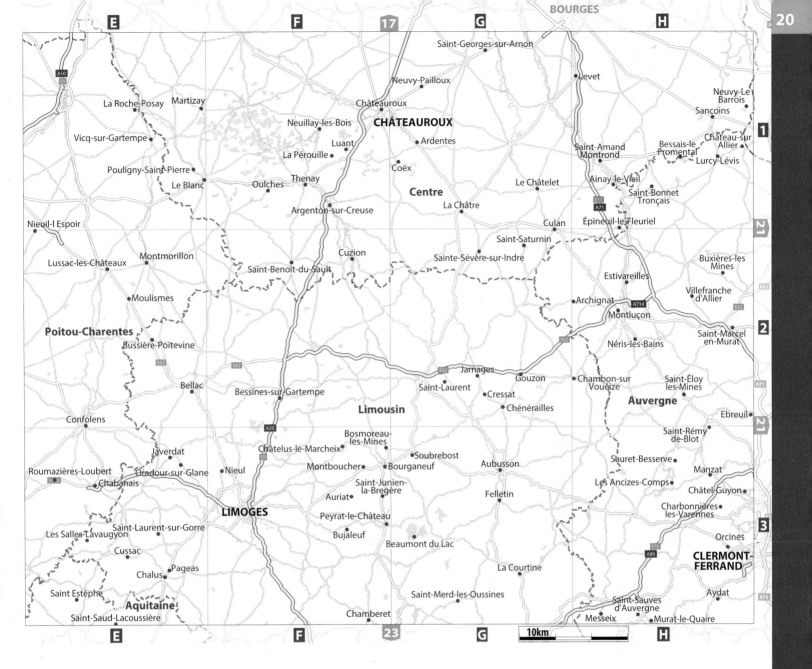

Map labels (Auvergne / Bourgogne / Rhône-Alpes / Franche-Comté region)

Centre · Châtillon-en-Bazois · Autun · Beaune · Seurre · Nolay · Saint-Honoré-les-Bains · Chiddes · Étang-sur-Arroux · Saint-Léger-sur-Dheune · CHALON-SUR-SAÔNE · Fours · Luzy · Ecuisses · Givry · Chalon-sur-Saône · Le Vernois · Baume-les-Messieurs · Beaurepaire-en-Bresse · Conliège · Paray-le-Frésil · Bourgogne · Chevagnes · Beaulon · Saint-Gengoux-le-National · Louhans · Cousance · Franche-Comté · Moulins · Génelard · Thiel-sur-Acolin · Diou · Gilly-sur-Loire · Orgelet · Maisod · Digoin · Arinthod · Jeurre · Saint-Gérand-de-Vaux · Charolles · Jaligny-sur-Besbre · Treteau · Le Donjon · Prissé · Saint-Pourçain-sur-Sioule · Montoldre · Varennes-sur-Allier · Vinzelles · Thoirette · Billy · Périgny · Lapalisse · Pruzilly · Pont-de-Veyle · Izernore · Charix · La Chapelle-de-Guinchay · Illiat · Bourg-en-Bresse · Nantua · Auvergne · Pouilly-sous-Charlieu · Belmont-de-la-Loire · Rhône-Alpes · Bellerive-sur-Allier · Ambierle · Saint-Germain-Lespinasse · Charlieu · Cours-la-Ville · Belleville · Aigueperse · Saint-Haon-le-Châtel · Renaison · Roanne · Saint-Étienne-la-Varenne · Randan · Les Noës · Saint-André-d'Apchon · Lamure-sur-Azergues · Laprugne · Arçon · Amplepuis · Villars-les-Dombes · Le Cheix-sur-Morge · Villerest · Villefranche-sur-Saône · Riom · Saint-Just-en-Chevalet · Les Sauvages · Trévoux · Thiers · Joux · Pontcharra-sur-Turdine · Montalieu-Vercieu · Lezoux · Noirétable · Violay · Saint-Forgeux · Clermont Ferrand · Bibost · Cournon d'Auvergne · Aubusson-d'Auvergne · Panissières · Belley · La Roche-Blanche · Boën · LYON · Crémieu · Courtenay · Chalmazel · Montpeyroux · Saint-Symphorien-sur-Coise · Saint-Martin-en-Haut

Scale: 10km

Index

Place	Grid	Page
Aeschi (CH)	21G1	105
Aigueperse (FR)	21A3	401
Aix-les-Bains (FR)	21E3	410
Albertville (FR)	21F3	410
Ambierle (FR)	21B2	411
Amplepuis (FR)	21B3	411
Annecy (FR)	21E3	411
Antey-Saint-André (IT)	21G3	491
Anthy-sur-Léman (FR)	21F2	411
Aosta (IT)	21G3	491
Arc-et-Senans (FR)	21E1	385
Arçon (FR)	21B3	411
Arinthod (FR)	21D2	385
Arsure-Arsurette (FR)	21E1	385
Aubusson-d'Auvergne (FR)	21A3	401
Autun (FR)	21B1	381
Avenches (CH)	21F1	105
Aymavilles (IT)	21G3	491
Baume-les-Messieurs (FR)	21D1	385
Beaulon (FR)	21A1	402
Beaune (FR)	21C1	382
Beaurepaire-en-Bresse (FR)	21D1	382
Bellerive-sur-Allier (FR)	21A2	402
Belleville (FR)	21C2	411
Belley (FR)	21D3	411
Belmont-de-la-Loire (FR)	21B2	411
Bibost (FR)	21C3	412
Bielmonte (IT)	21H3	493
Billy (FR)	21A2	402
Bionaz (IT)	21G3	491
Boën (FR)	21B3	412
Bois-d'Amont (FR)	21E2	385
Boltigen (CH)	21G1	105
Böningen (CH)	21H1	105
Borgosesia (IT)	21H3	493
Bourg-en-Bresse (FR)	21D2	412
Bourget-du-Lac (FR)	21E3	412
Bouveret (CH)	21F2	109
Brienz (CH)	21H1	105
Brig (CH)	21H2	109
Brusson (IT)	21H3	491
Bullet (CH)	21F1	105
Carcoforo (IT)	21H3	493
Cervinia/Breuil (IT)	21G3	491
Chalmazel (FR)	21B3	412
Chalon-sur-Saône (FR)	21C1	382
Chamonix-Mont-Blanc (FR)	21F3	412
Champagnole (FR)	21E1	385
Champéry (CH)	21F2	109
Champorcher (IT)	21G3	491
Charix (FR)	21D2	412
Charlieu (FR)	21B2	411
Charolles (FR)	21B2	382
Château-d'Oex (CH)	21G2	105
Chatillon (IT)	21G3	491
Châtillon-en-Bazois (FR)	21A1	382
Chevagnes (FR)	21A1	402
Cheyres (CH)	21F1	105
Chiddes (FR)	21B1	382
Clairvaux-les-Lacs (FR)	21E1	385
Clermont Ferrand (FR)	21A3	403
Cogne (IT)	21G3	491
Conliège (FR)	21D1	386
Courmayeur (IT)	21F3	491
Cournon d'Auvergne (FR)	21A3	403
Cours-la-Ville (FR)	21B2	413
Courtenay (FR)	21D3	413
Cousance (FR)	21D2	386
Cravagliana (IT)	21H3	495
Crémieu (FR)	21D3	413
Cudrefin (CH)	21F1	105
Digoin (FR)	21B2	382
Diou (FR)	21B2	403
Echallens (CH)	21F1	105
Ecuisses (FR)	21C1	382
Engelberg (CH)	21H1	107
Estavayer-le-Lac (CH)	21F1	105
Étang-sur-Arroux (FR)	21B1	383
Evolène (CH)	21G2	109
Faverges (FR)	21E3	414
Flaine (FR)	21F3	414
Fours (FR)	21A1	383
Frutigen (CH)	21G1	105
Gampelen (CH)	21F1	105
Génelard (FR)	21B2	383
Gilly-sur-Loire (FR)	21B2	383
Giswil (CH)	21H1	107
Givry (FR)	21C1	383
Grandson (CH)	21F1	105
Gressoney (IT)	21H3	492
Grimentz (CH)	21G2	109
Grimselpas (CH)	21H1	109
Grindelwald (CH)	21H1	105
Gryon (CH)	21G2	105
Gstaad (CH)	21G2	105
Gündlischwand (CH)	21H1	105
Gwatt-Thun (CH)	21G1	105
Hauteluce (FR)	21F3	414
Hérémence (CH)	21G2	109
Hinterkappelen (CH)	21G1	105
Hône (IT)	21H3	492
Horw (CH)	21H1	107
Illiat (FR)	21C2	414
Interlaken (CH)	21H1	106
Izernore (FR)	21D2	414
Jaligny-sur-Besbre (FR)	21A2	404
Jeurre (FR)	21D2	386
Joux (FR)	21B3	414
La Balme de Sillingy (FR)	21E3	414
La Brévine (CH)	21F1	106
La Chapelle des Bois (FR)	21E1	386
La Chapelle-de-G (FR)	21C2	383
La Clusaz (FR)	21F3	414
La Féclaz (FR)	21E3	414
La Fouly (CH)	21G3	109
La Pesse (FR)	21E2	386
La Roche-Blanche (FR)	21A3	404
La Thuile (IT)	21F3	492
Lamoura (FR)	21E2	387
Lamure-sur-Azergues (FR)	21C3	415
Lapalisse (FR)	21A2	404
Laprugne (FR)	21A3	404
Lathuile (FR)	21E3	414
Lausanne (CH)	21F2	106
Lauterbrunnen (CH)	21H1	106
Le Cheix-sur-Morge (FR)	21A3	404
Le Donjon (FR)	21B2	404
Le Grand Bornand (FR)	21F3	415
Le Reposoir (FR)	21F3	415
Le Vernois (FR)	21D1	387
Les Carroz-Arâches (FR)	21F3	415
Les Gets (FR)	21F2	416

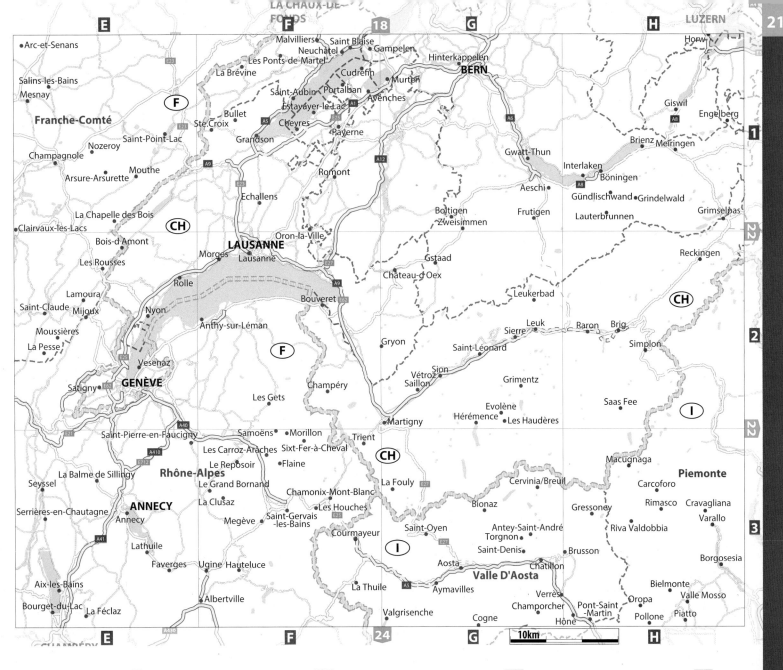

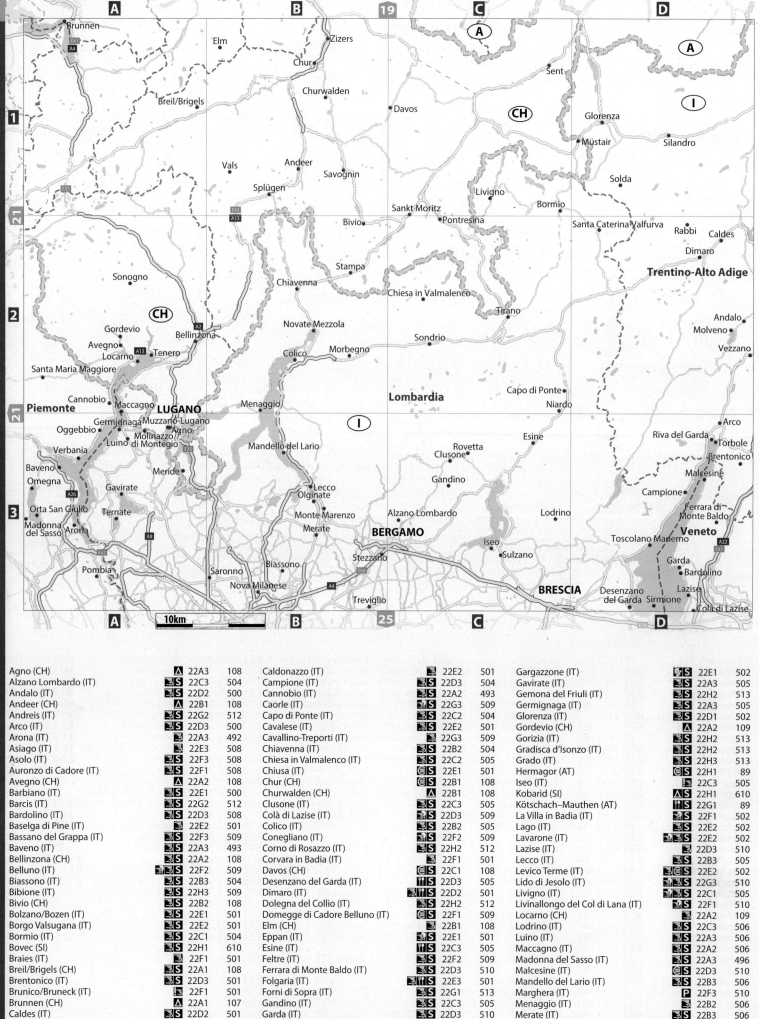

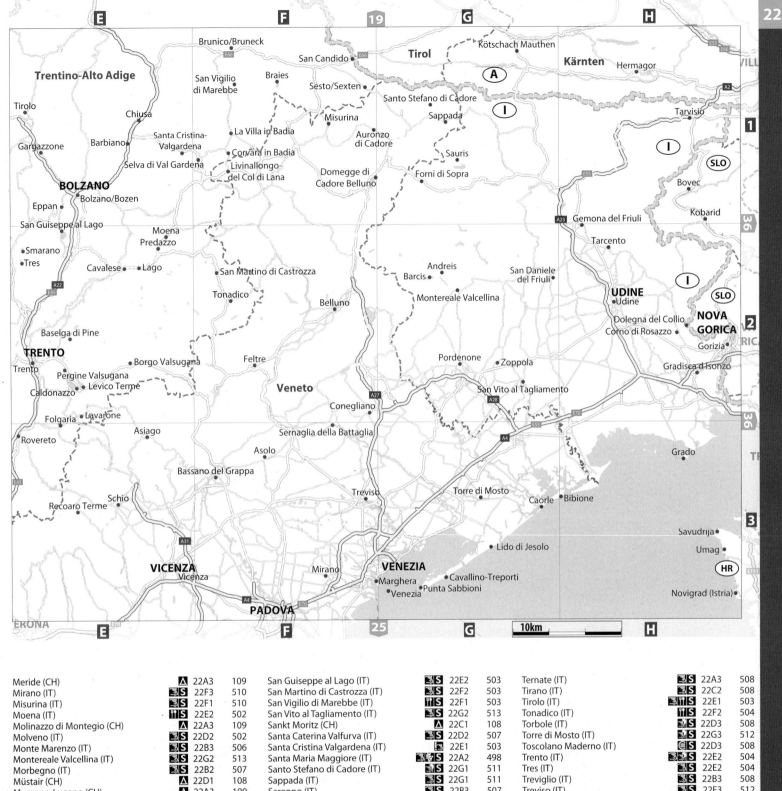

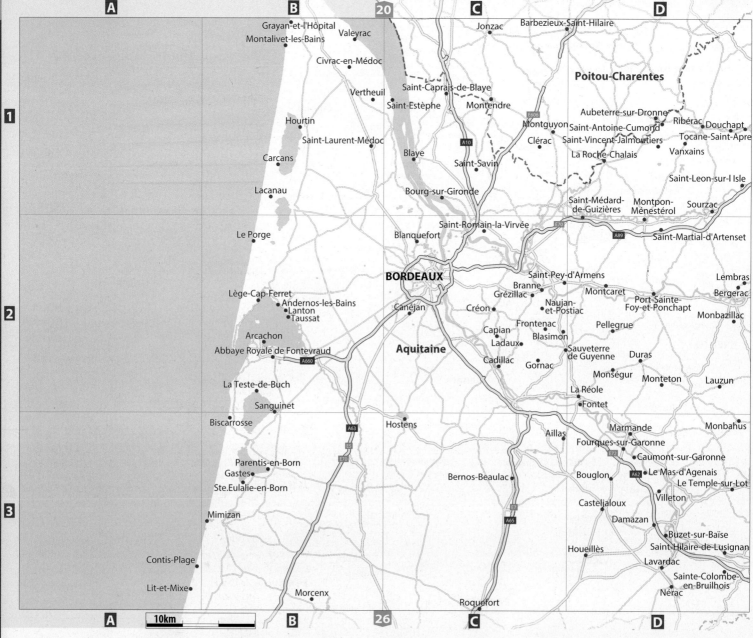

Map labels: Grayan-et-l'Hôpital, Valeyrac, Montalivet-les-Bains, Civrac-en-Médoc, Vertheuil, Saint-Caprais-de-Blaye, Jonzac, Barbezieux-Saint-Hilaire, Poitou-Charentes, Saint-Estèphe, Montendre, Aubeterre-sur-Dronne, Ribérac, Douchapt, Hourtin, Montguyon, Saint-Antoine-Cumond, Tocane-Saint-Apre, Clérac, Saint-Vincent-Jalmoutiers, Saint-Laurent-Médoc, Blaye, La Roche-Chalais, Vanxains, Carcans, Saint-Savin, Saint-Leon-sur-I Isle, Lacanau, Bourg-sur-Gironde, Saint-Médard-de-Guizières, Montpon-Ménestérol, Sourzac, Le Porge, Saint-Romain-la-Virvée, Saint-Martial-d'Artenset, Blanquefort, BORDEAUX, Saint-Pey-d'Armens, Lembras, Lège-Cap-Ferret, Branne, Montcaret, Bergerac, Andernos-les-Bains, Canéjan, Grézillac, Port-Sainte-Foy-et-Ponchapt, Lanton, Créon, Naujan-et-Postiac, Pellegrue, Monbazillac, Taussat, Capian, Frontenac, Arcachon, Ladaux, Blasimon, Sauveterre de Guyenne, Duras, Abbaye Royale de Fontevraud, Aquitaine, Cadillac, Gornac, Monségur, Monteton, Lauzun, La Teste-de-Buch, Monségur, La Réole, Sanguinet, Fontet, Biscarrosse, Hostens, Marmande, Monbahus, Aillas, Fourques-sur-Garonne, Parentis-en-Born, Caumont-sur-Garonne, Gastes, Bouglon, Le Mas-d'Agenais, Ste.Eulalie-en-Born, Bernos-Beaulac, Le Temple-sur-Lot, Castbeljaloux, Villeton, Mimizan, Damazan, Houeillès, Buzet-sur-Baïse, Contis-Plage, Saint-Hilaire-de-Lusignan, Lit-et-Mixe, Morcenx, Lavardac, Roquefort, Sainte-Colombe-en-Bruilhois, Nérac

Scale: 10km

Abbaye Royale dF (FR) 23B2 360	Bouillac (FR) 23G3 439	Coltines (FR) 23H2 403	Hostens (FR) 23C3 427	Le Porge (FR) 23B2 429				
Aillas (FR) 23C3 422	Bourdeilles (FR) 23E1 424	Concèze (FR) 23F1 398	Houeillès (FR) 23D3 427	Le Temple/Lot (FR) 23D3 429				
Alblas (FR) 23F3 438	Bourg/Gironde (FR) 23C1 424	Condat (FR) 23H1 403	Hourtin (FR) 23B1 427	Lège-Cap-Ferret (FR) 23B2 429				
Allanche (FR) 23H1 401	Branne (FR) 23C2 424	Contis-Plage (FR) 23A3 425	Jonzac (FR) 23C1 392	Léguillac/l'Auche (FR) 23E1 429				
Allassac (FR) 23F1 397	Brantôme (FR) 23E1 424	Crandelles (FR) 23G2 403	Jumilhac-le-G (FR) 23E1 429	Lembras (FR) 23E2 429				
Alvignac (FR) 23F2 438	Buzet-sur-Baïse (FR) 23D3 424	Cransac (FR) 23G3 441	La Bourboule (FR) 23H1 404	Les Eyzies (FR) 23E2 429				
Andernos-les-B (FR) 23B2 422	Cadillac (FR) 23C2 425	Créon (FR) 23C2 426	La Coquille (FR) 23E1 427	Liginiac (FR) 23G1 399				
Angoisse (FR) 23E1 423	Cahors (FR) 23F3 439	Damazan (FR) 23D3 426	La Réole (FR) 23D2 427	Limeuil (FR) 23E2 430				
Arcachon (FR) 23B2 423	Cajarc (FR) 23F3 440	Dampniat (FR) 23F1 399	La Roche-C (FR) 23D1 428	Lit-et-Mixe (FR) 23A3 430				
Arnac (Cantal) (FR) 23G2 401	Calvinet (FR) 23G2 402	Domme (FR) 23F2 426	La Roque-G (FR) 23E2 428	Luzech (FR) 23F3 444				
Arvieu (FR) 23H3 438	Campagnac (FR) 23H3 440	Donzac (FR) 23E3 441	La Teste-de-B (FR) 23B2 428	Mandailles-St-J (FR) 23H2 405				
Aubeterre/Dr (FR) 23D1 389	Campuac (FR) 23H3 440	Donzenac (FR) 23F1 399	La Tour-d'A (FR) 23H1 404	Marcolès (FR) 23G2 405				
Aubrac (FR) 23H3 438	Cancon (FR) 23E3 425	Douchapt (FR) 23D1 426	Labastide-Murat (FR) 23F2 442	Marmande (FR) 23D3 430				
Aurillac (FR) 23G2 401	Canéjan (FR) 23C2 425	Douelle (FR) 23F3 441	Lacanau (FR) 23B1 428	Marquay (FR) 23E2 430				
Ayen (FR) 23F1 398	Capian (FR) 23C2 425	Drugeac (FR) 23G1 403	Lacapelle M (FR) 23G2 442	Martel (FR) 23F2 444				
Azerat (FR) 23E1 423	Carcans (FR) 23B1 425	Duras (FR) 23D2 426	Lacapelle-V (FR) 23G2 404	Mauriac (FR) 23G1 405				
Badefols-sur-D (FR) 23E2 423	Cardaillac (FR) 23G2 440	Egletons (FR) 23G1 399	Lacroix-Barrez (FR) 23H2 442	Maurs (FR) 23G2 405				
Baraqueville (FR) 23G3 439	Cassaniouze (FR) 23G2 402	Entraygues/Tr (FR) 23H2 441	Laguepie (FR) 23G2 442	Mensignac (FR) 23E1 430				
Barbezieux-St-H (FR) 23C1 389	Casseneuil (FR) 23E3 425	Excideuil (FR) 23E1 426	Laguepie (FR) 23G3 442	Meuzac (FR) 23F1 399				
Beaumont du P (FR) 23E2 423	Castanet (FR) 23G3 440	Figeac (FR) 23G3 441	Laguiole (FR) 23H2 443	Meymac (FR) 23G1 399				
Bellas (FR) 23H3 439	Castelculier (FR) 23E3 425	Fontet (FR) 23D2 426	Laissac (FR) 23H3 443	Mimizan (FR) 23B3 430				
Bergerac (FR) 23D2 423	Casteljaloux (FR) 23D3 425	Fourques-sur-G (FR) 23D3 426	Lalinde (FR) 23E2 428	Mirandol-B (FR) 23G3 444				
Bernos-Beaulac (FR) 23C3 424	Caumont-sur-G (FR) 23D3 425	Frontenac (FR) 23C2 426	Lanouaille (FR) 23E1 428	Monbahus (FR) 23D2 430				
Beynac-et-Cazenac (FR) 23E2 423	Caylus (FR) 23F3 441	Fumel (FR) 23E3 426	Lanton (FR) 23B2 428	Monbazillac (FR) 23D2 430				
Biron (FR) 23E2 423	Cayrols (FR) 23G2 402	Gastes (FR) 23B3 426	Lanuéjouls (FR) 23G3 443	Monflanquin (FR) 23E3 430				
Biscarrosse (FR) 23B3 424	Chambon/Lac (FR) 23H1 402	Gignac (FR) 23F2 442	Latronquière (FR) 23G2 443	Monpazier (FR) 23E2 430				
Blanquefort (FR) 23C2 424	Chastreix (FR) 23H1 403	Gornac (FR) 23C2 427	Lauzerte (FR) 23E3 443	Monségur (FR) 23D2 431				
Blasimon (FR) 23C2 424	Château-l'Evêque (FR) 23E1 425	Gourdon (FR) 23F2 442	Lauzun (FR) 23D2 428	Montalivet-les-B (FR) 23B1 431				
Blaye (FR) 23C1 424	Chaudes-Aigues (FR) 23H2 403	Gramat (FR) 23F2 442	Lavardac (FR) 23D3 428	Montcaret (FR) 23D2 431				
Boisse Penchot (FR) 23G3 439	Civrac-en-Médoc (FR) 23B1 425	Grayan-et-l'H (FR) 23B1 427	Layrac (FR) 23E3 429	Montcuq (FR) 23E3 445				
Bort-les-Orgues (FR) 23H1 398	Clérac (FR) 23C1 390	Grézillac (FR) 23C2 427	Le Bugue (FR) 23E2 429	Monteils (FR) 23G3 445				
Bouglon (FR) 23D3 424	Collonges-la-R (FR) 23F2 398	Hautefort (FR) 23E1 427	Le Mas-d'AFR	Montendre (FR) 23C1 393				

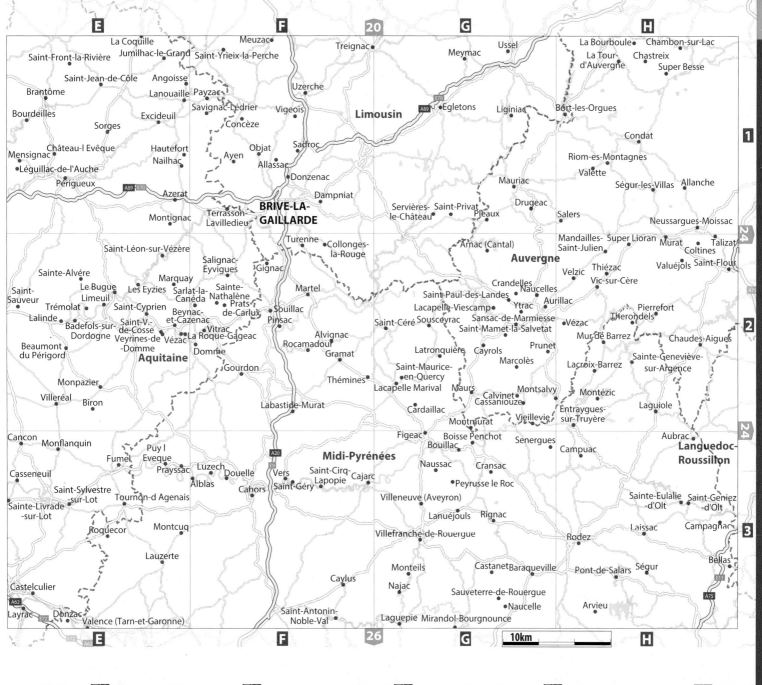

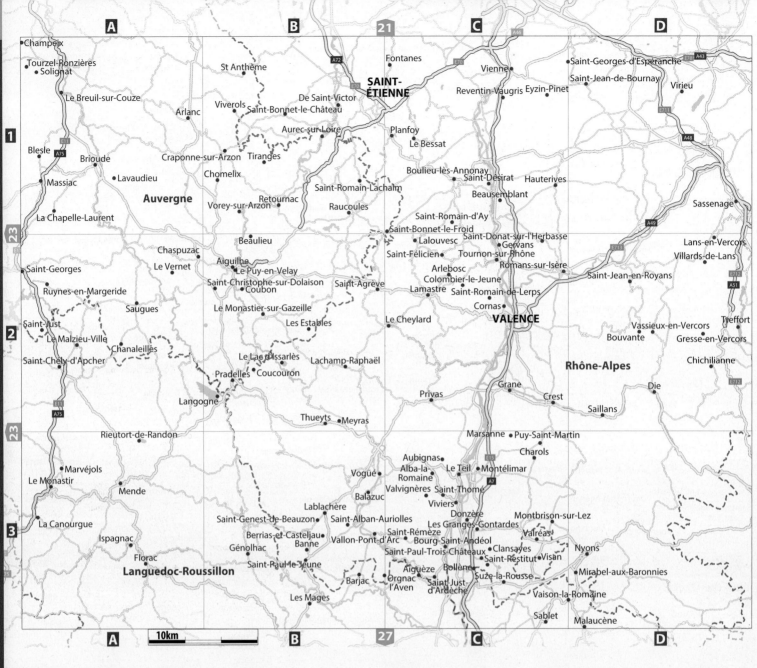

10km

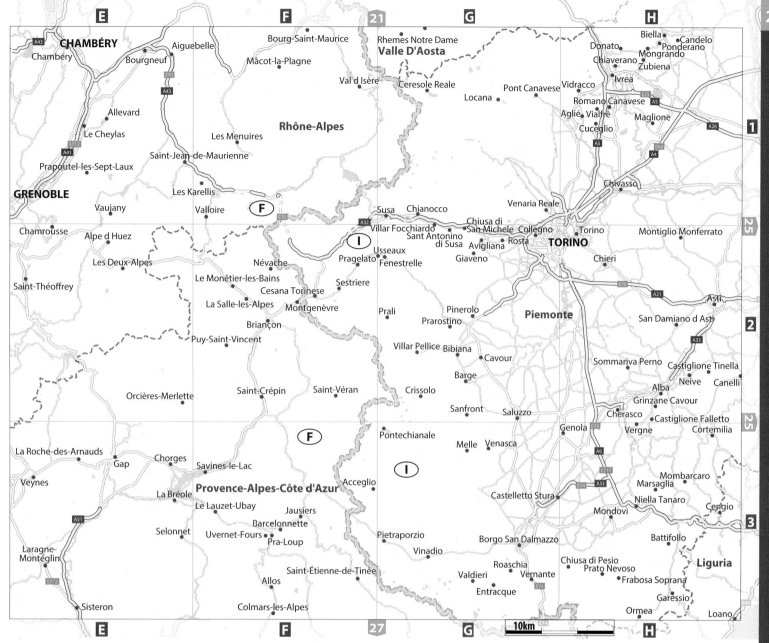

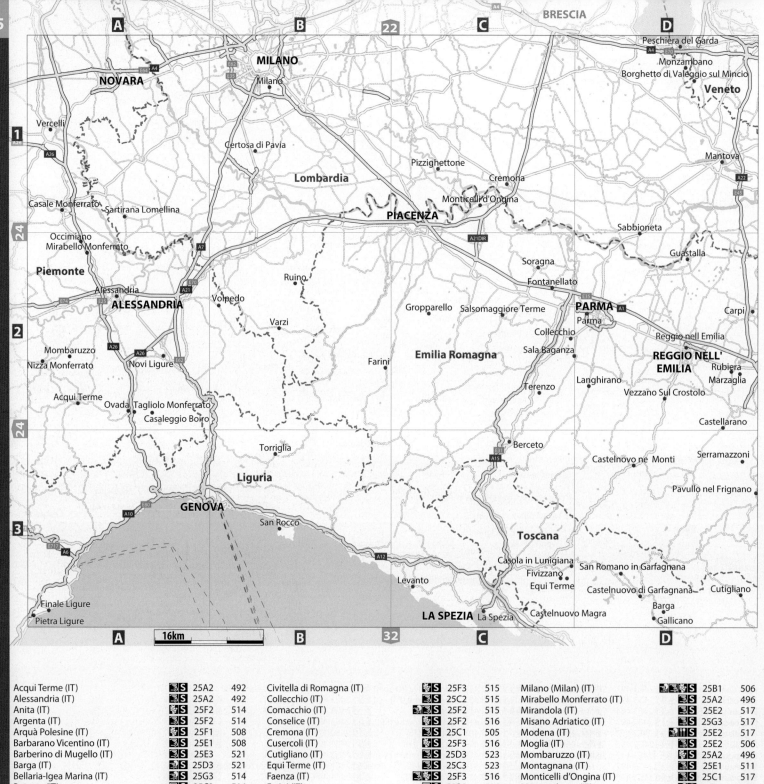

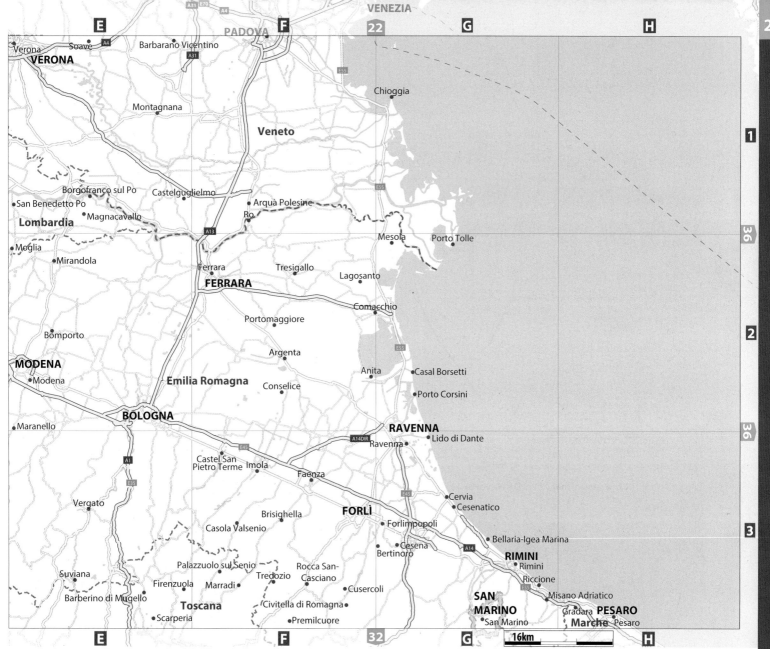

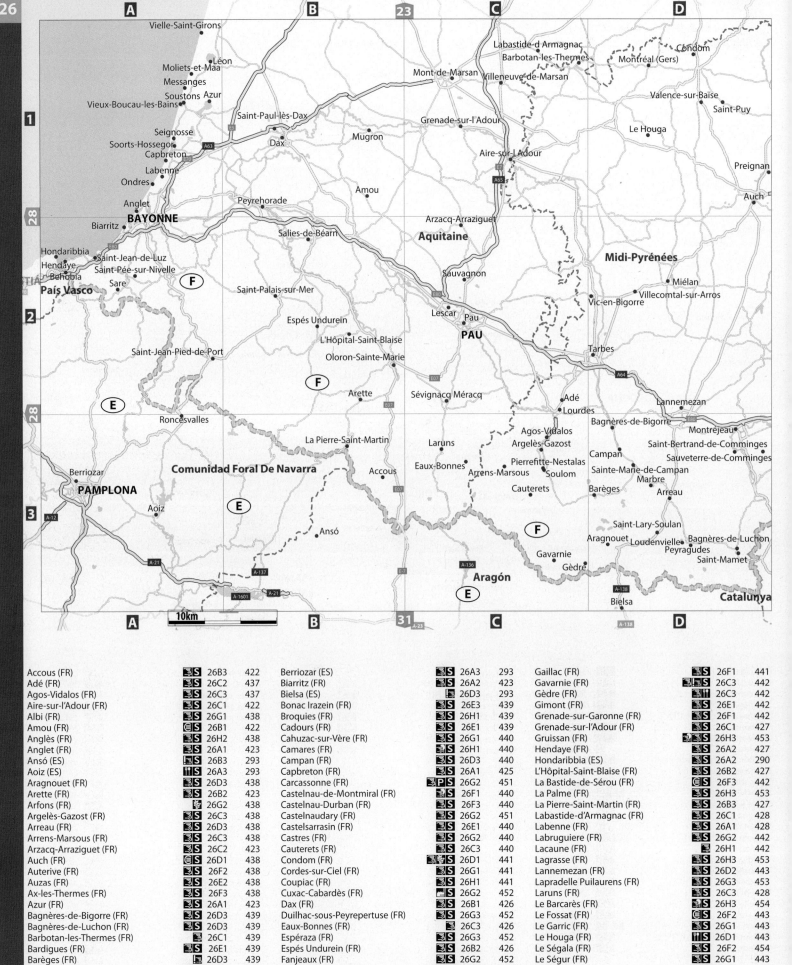

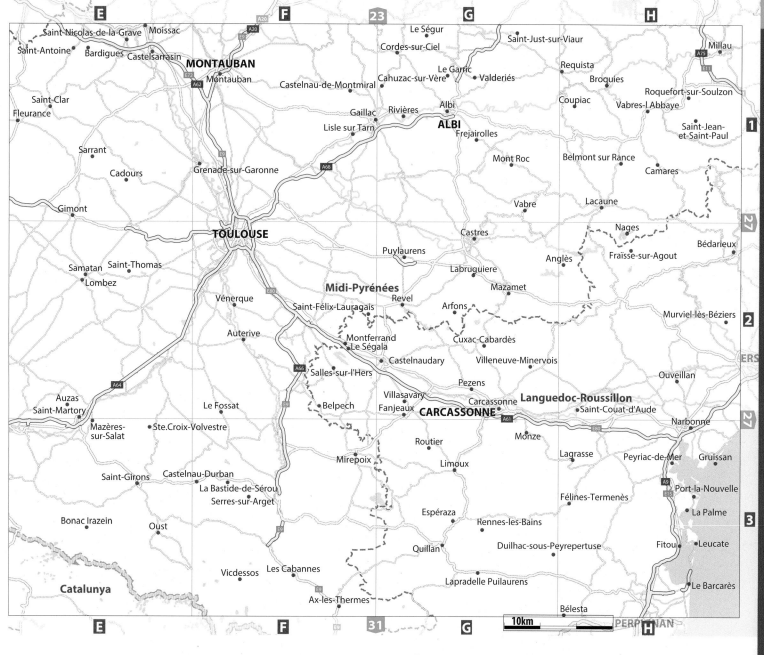

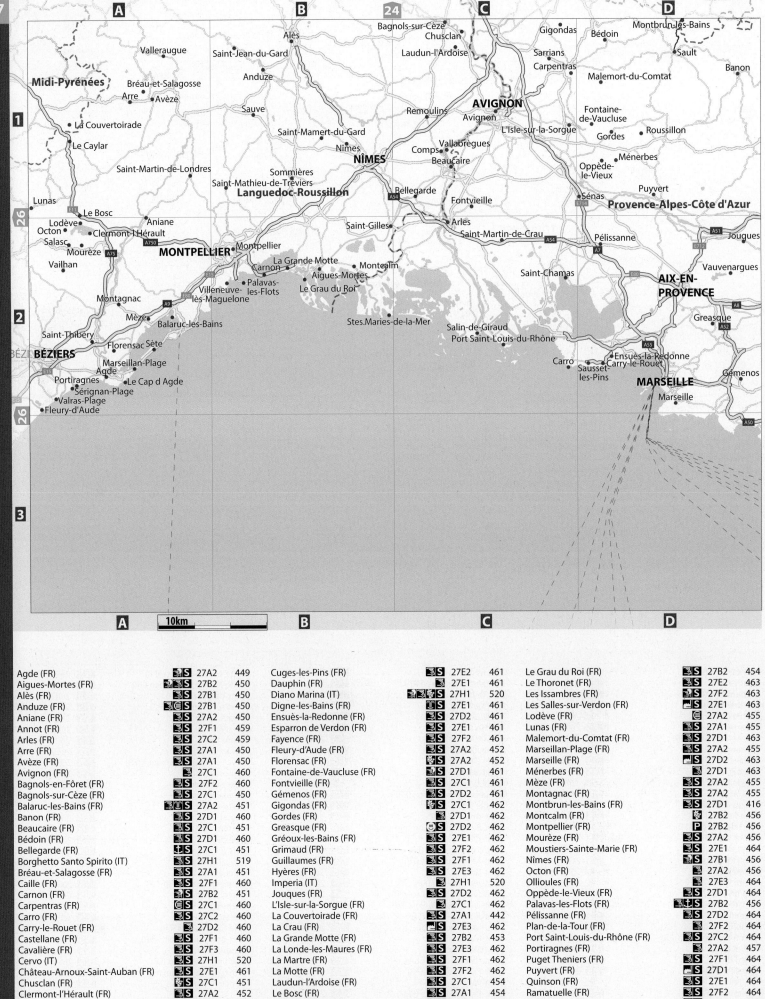

Map legend: **A** | **B** | 24 | **C** | **D**

10km

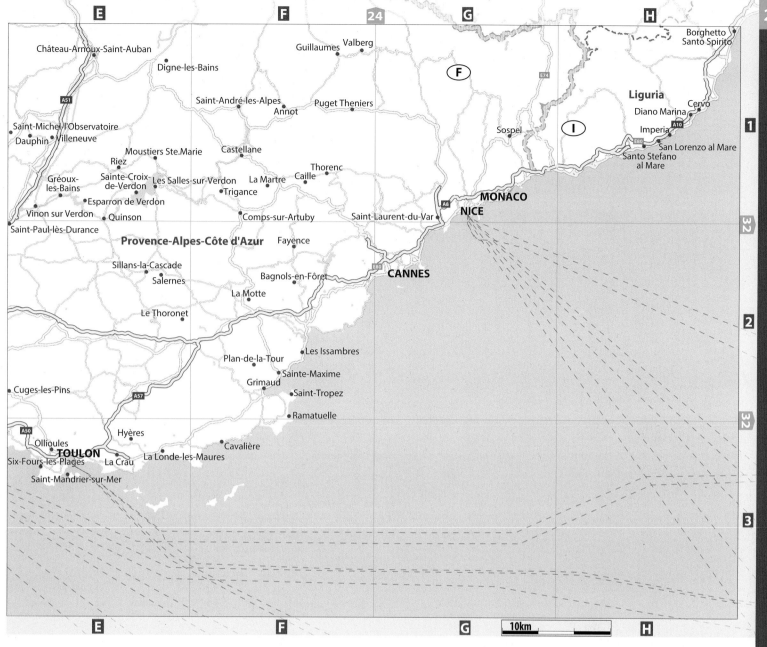

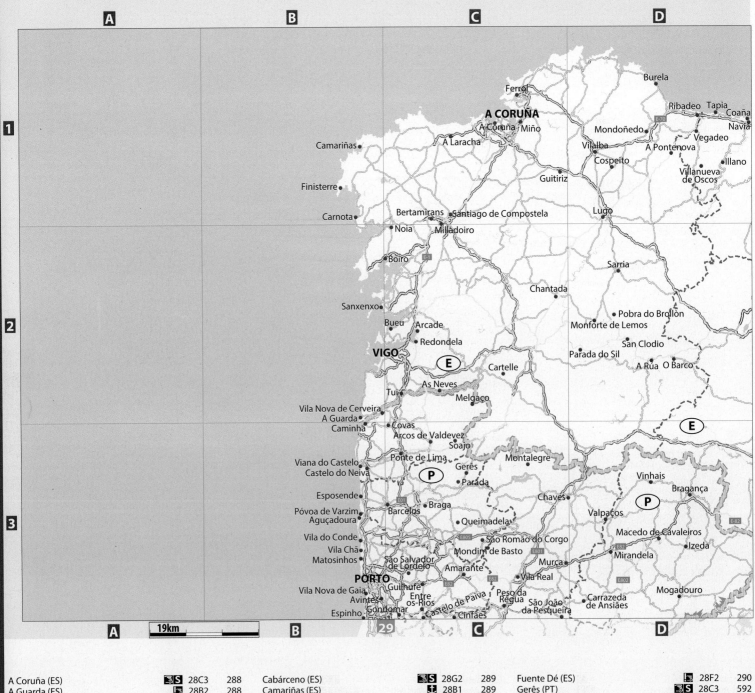

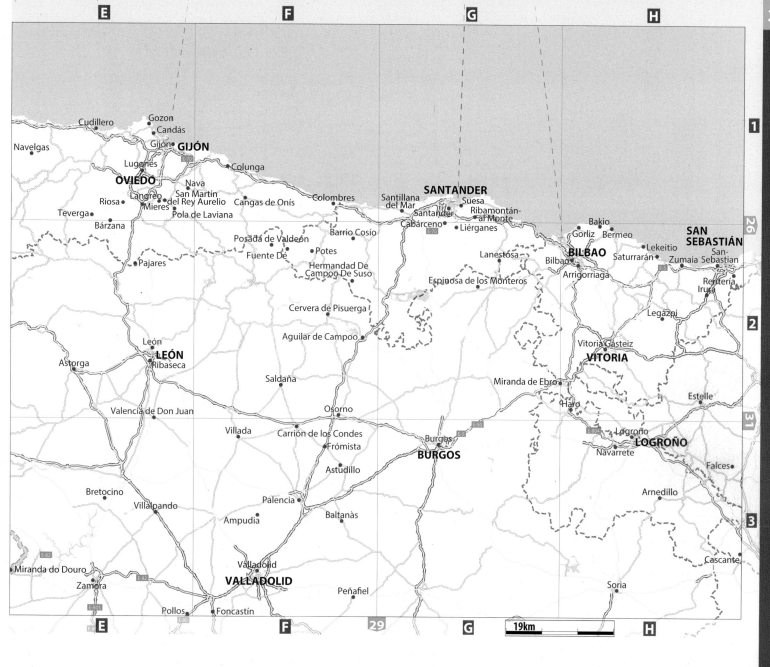

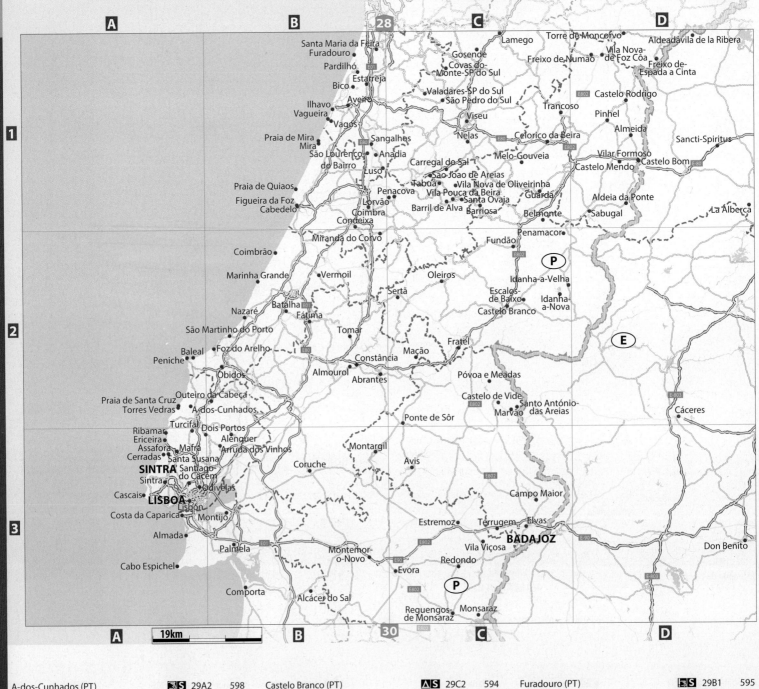

19km

64

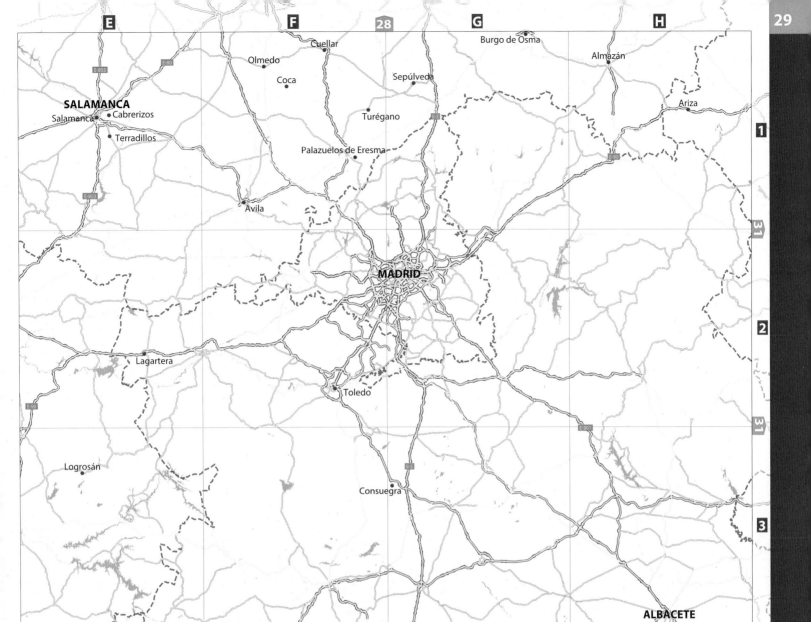

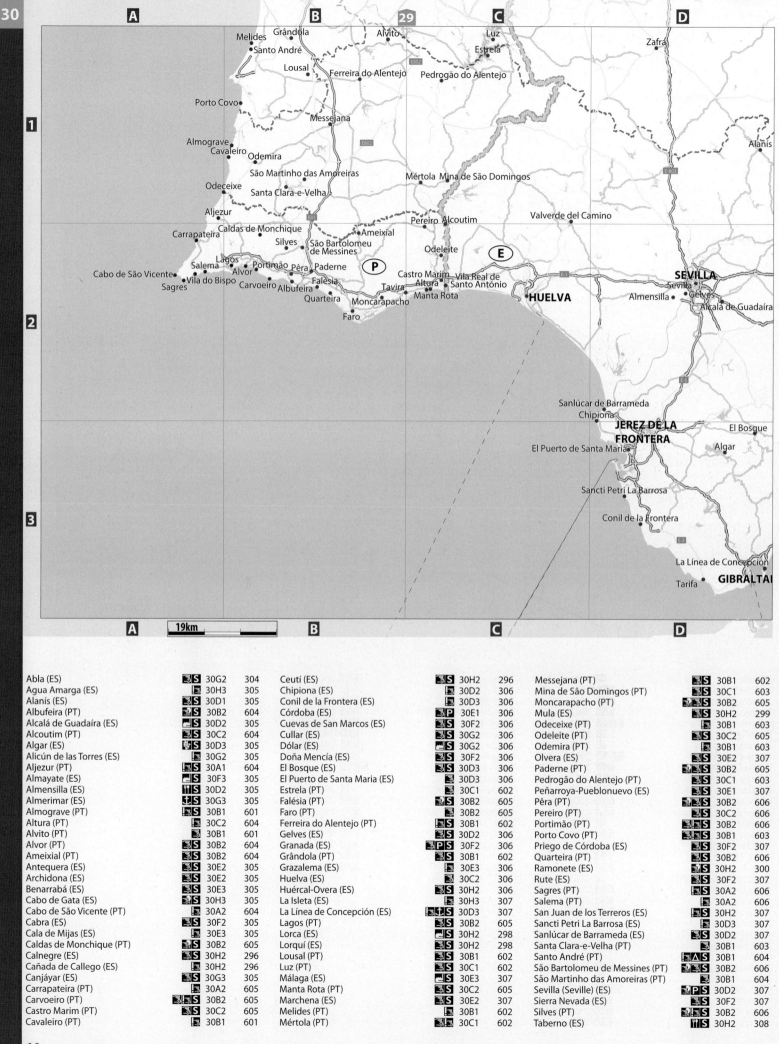

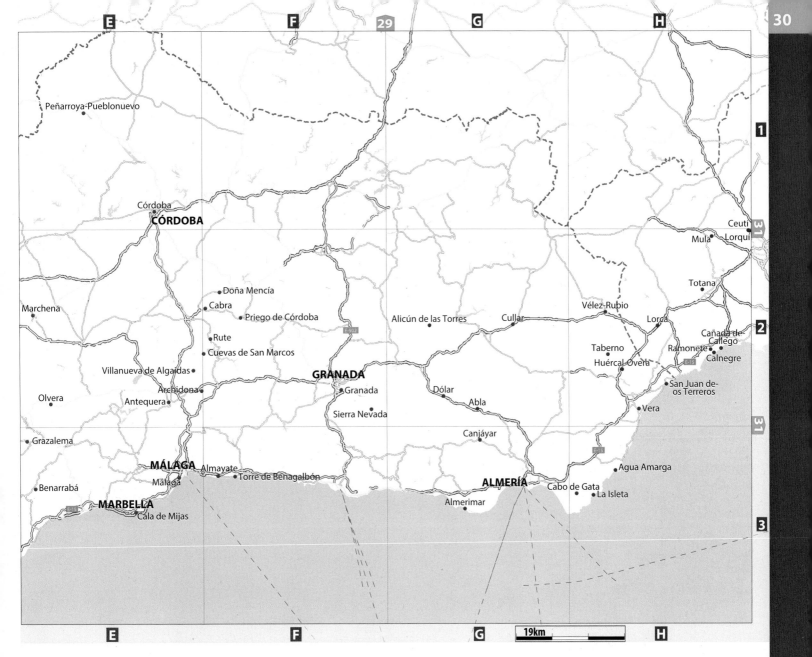

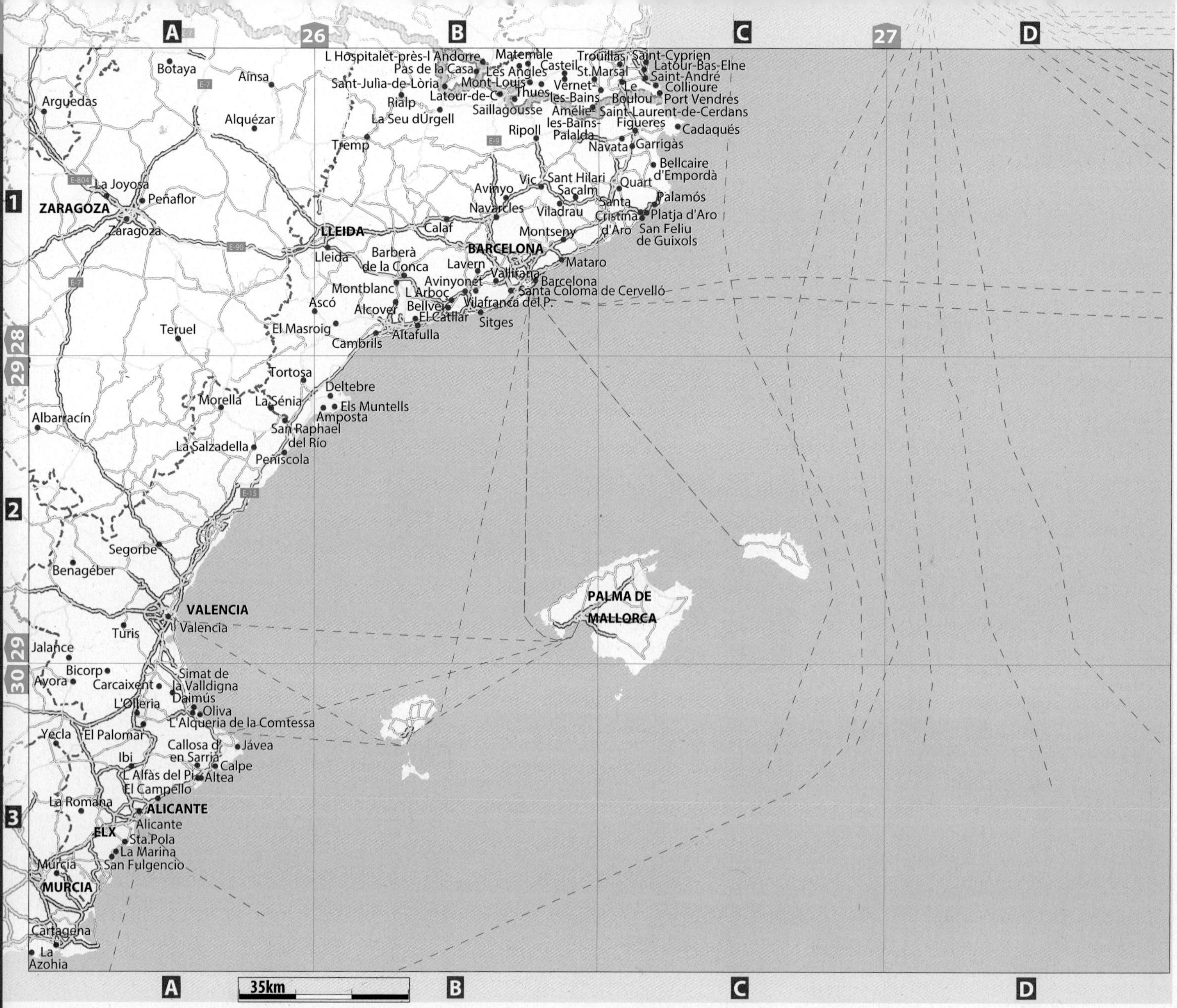

Map labels (geographic):

A 26 B 27 C D

Botaya · Aínsa · Alquézar · Arguedas · La Joyosa · Peñaflor · ZARAGOZA · Zaragoza · Teruel · Albarracín · Morella · La Salzadella · Peñíscola · La Sénia · Amposta · San Raphael del Río · Deltebre · Els Muntells · Tortosa · El Masroig · Cambrils · Altafulla · Alcover · Bellvei · El Catllar · Ascó · Montblanc · Barberà de la Conca · Lleida · LLEIDA · Calaf · Tremp · La Seu d'Úrgell · Rialp · Saillagousse · Latour-de-C · Mont-Louis · L'Hospitalet-près-l'Andorre · Pas de la Casa · Sant-Julià-de-Lòria · Les Angles · Ripoll · Thues · Vernet-les-Bains · Amélie-les-Bains-Palalda · Casteil · Matemale · Trouillas · St.Marsal · Le Boulou · Saint-Cyprien · Latour-Bas-Elne · Saint-André · Collioure · Port Vendres · Saint-Laurent-de-Cerdans · Figueres · Cadaqués · Navata · Garrigàs · Bellcaire d'Empordà · Vic · Sant Hilari Sacalm · Quart · Palamós · Avinyo · Navarcles · Viladrau · Santa Cristina d'Aro · Platja d'Aro · San Feliu de Guixols · Montseny · Lavern · BARCELONA · Barcelona · Mataro · Avinyonet · L'Arboç · Santa Coloma de Cervelló · Vilafranca del P. · Vallirana · Sitges · VALENCIA · Valencia · Turis · Segorbe · Benagéber · Jalance · Bicorp · Ayora · Carcaixent · Simat de la Valldigna · Daimús · L'Olleria · Oliva · L'Alqueria de la Comtessa · Yecla · El Palomar · Callosa d'en Sarrià · Jávea · Ibi · Calpe · L'Alfàs del Pi · Altea · El Campello · La Romana · ALICANTE · Alicante · ELX · Sta.Pola · La Marina · San Fulgencio · Murcia · MURCIA · Cartagena · La Azohia · PALMA DE MALLORCA

35km

A B C D

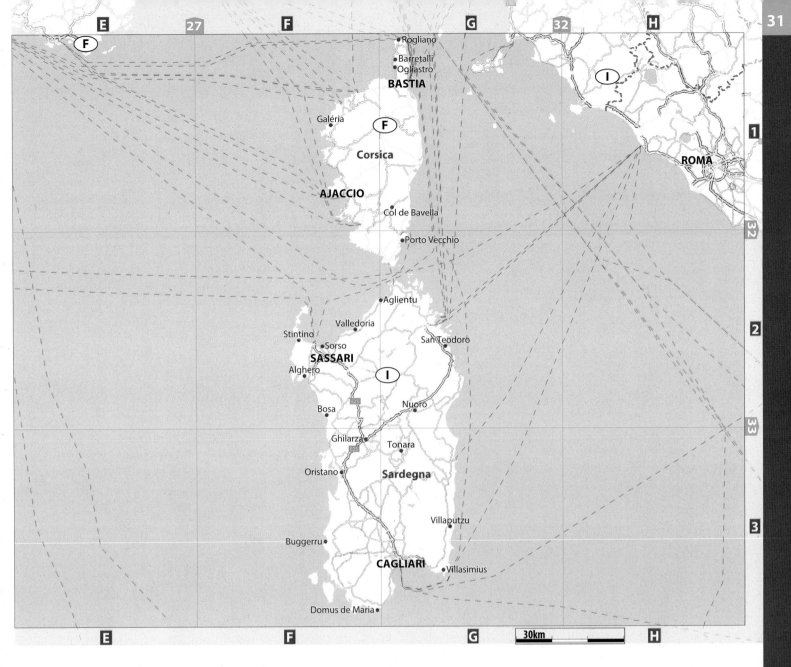

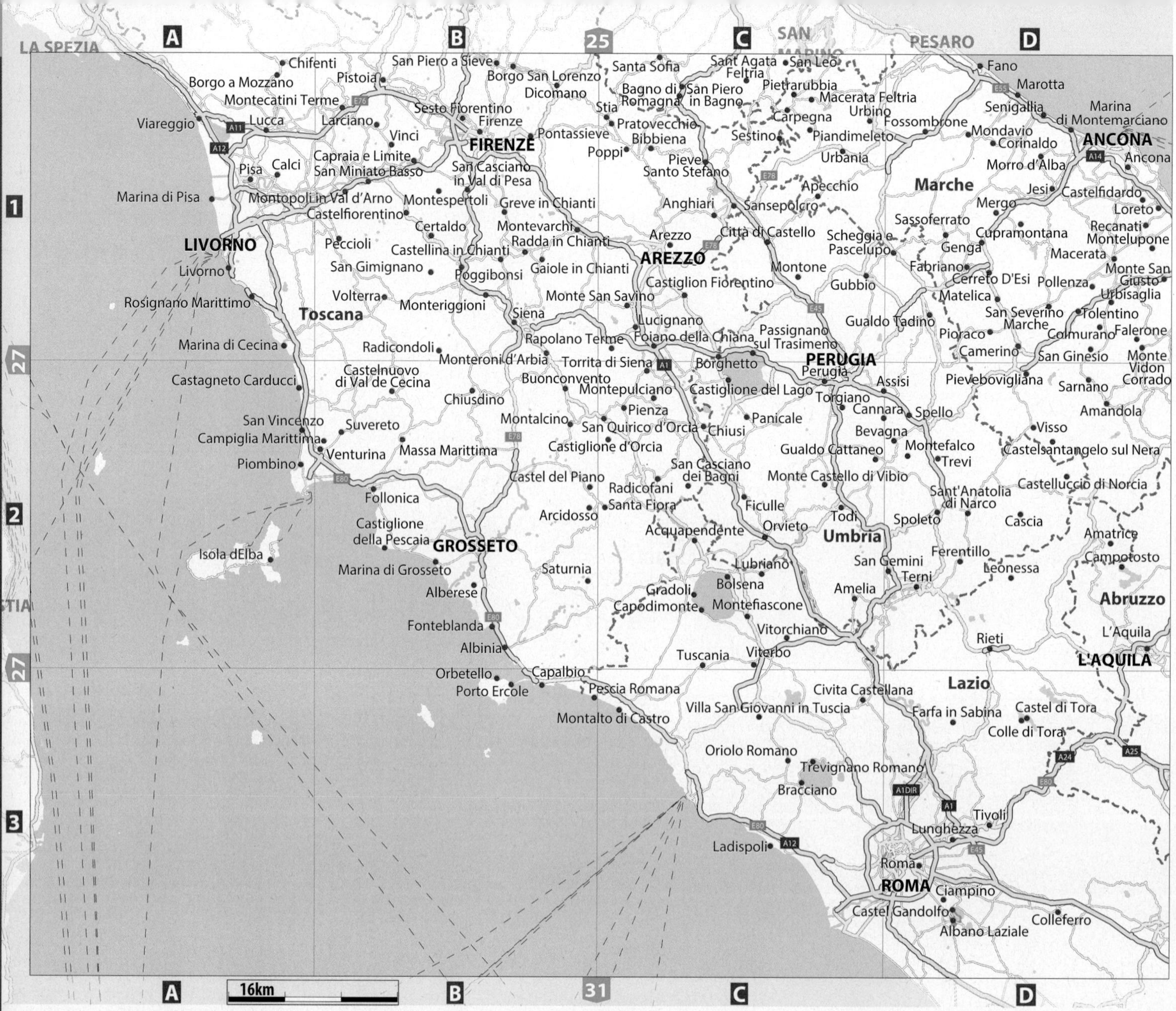

LA SPEZIA · A · B · 25 · C · SAN MARINO · PESARO · D

Map region (Toscana, Umbria, Marche, Lazio, Abruzzo):

Chifenti · San Piero a Sieve · Santa Sofia · Sant'Agata Feltria · San Leo · Fano · Marotta
Borgo a Mozzano · Pistoia · Borgo San Lorenzo · Dicomano · Bagno di Romagna · San Piero in Bagno · Pietrarubbia · Macerata Feltria · Senigallia · Marina di Montemarciano
Montecatini Terme · Sesto Fiorentino · Stia · Pratovecchio · Carpegna · Urbino · Fossombrone · Mondavio · Corinaldo
Viareggio · Lucca · Larciano · Vinci · Firenze · Pontassieve · Bibbiena · Pieve Santo Stefano · Sestino · Piandimeleto · Urbania · ANCONA · Ancona
Pisa · Calci · Capraia e Limite · San Miniato Basso · San Casciano in Val di Pesa · Poppi · Apecchio · Sansepolcro · Marche · Morro d'Alba · Jesi · Castelfidardo
Marina di Pisa · Montopoli in Val d'Arno · Montespertoli · Greve in Chianti · Anghiari · Città di Castello · Mergo · Recanati · Loreto
LIVORNO · Certaldo · Castelfiorentino · Montevarchi · Radda in Chianti · Arezzo · Montone · Sassoferrato · Cupramontana · Montelupone
Livorno · Peccioli · Castellina in Chianti · Poggibonsi · Castiglion Fiorentino · Genga · Fabriano · Cerreto D'Esi · Monte San Giusto
Rosignano Marittimo · San Gimignano · Gaiole in Chianti · Monte San Savino · Matelica · San Severino Marche · Urbisaglia
Toscana · Volterra · Monteriggioni · Siena · Lucignano · Passignano sul Trasimeno · PERUGIA · Pioraco · Camerino · San Ginesio · Tolentino
Marina di Cecina · Radicondoli · Rapolano Terme · Foiano della Chiana · Borghetto · Perugia · Assisi · Pievebovigliana · Falerone · Monte Vidon Corrado
Castagneto Carducci · Castelnuovo di Val de Cecina · Monteroni d'Arbia · Torrita di Siena · Castiglione del Lago · Cannara · Spello · Sarnano · Amandola
Chiusdino · Buonconvento · Montepulciano · Torgiano · Bevagna · Montefalco · Trevi · Castelsantangelo sul Nera
San Vincenzo · Suvereto · Montalcino · Pienza · Chiusi · Panicale · Gualdo Cattaneo · Visso · Castelluccio di Norcia
Campiglia Marittima · Venturina · Massa Marittima · San Quirico d'Orcia · Monte Castello di Vibio
Piombino · Castiglione d'Orcia · San Casciano dei Bagni · Sant'Anatolia di Narco
Follonica · Castel del Piano · Radicofani · Santa Fiora · Todi · Spoleto · Cascia · Amatrice
GROSSETO · Arcidosso · Acquapendente · Orvieto · Umbria · Ferentillo · Leonessa · Campotosto
Castiglione della Pescaia · Saturnia · Lubriano · Bolsena · San Gemini · Terni · Abruzzo
Marina di Grosseto · Alberese · Gradoli · Capodimonte · Montefiascone · Amelia · Rieti · L'Aquila
Fonteblanda · Vitorchiano · L'AQUILA
Albinia · Tuscania · Viterbo · Lazio
Orbetello · Capalbio · Pescia Romana · Civita Castellana · Farfa in Sabina · Castel di Tora
Porto Ercole · Montalto di Castro · Villa San Giovanni in Tuscia · Colle di Tora
Oriolo Romano · Trevignano Romano · Tivoli
Bracciano · Lunghezza
Ladispoli · Roma · ROMA · Ciampino
Castel Gandolfo · Albano Laziale · Colleferro

Scale: 16km

A · B · 31 · C · D

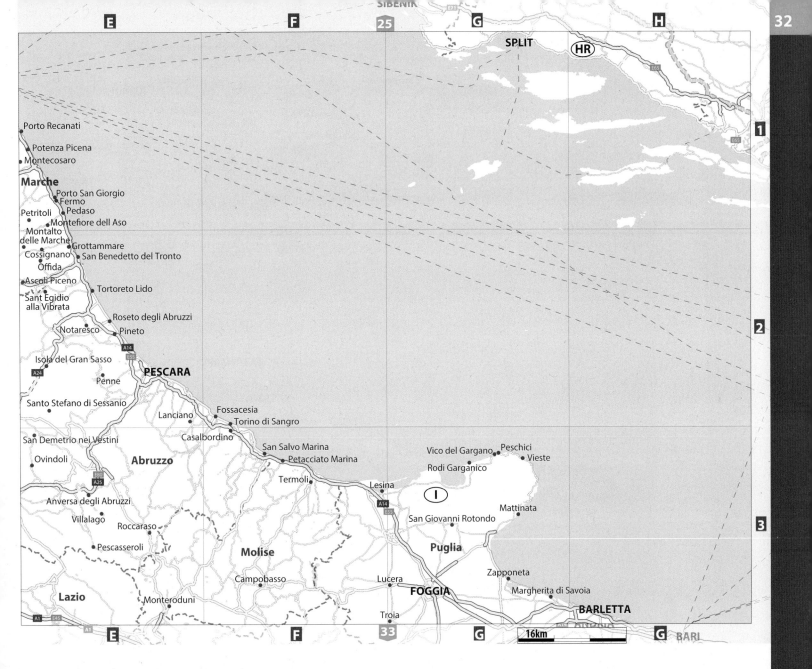

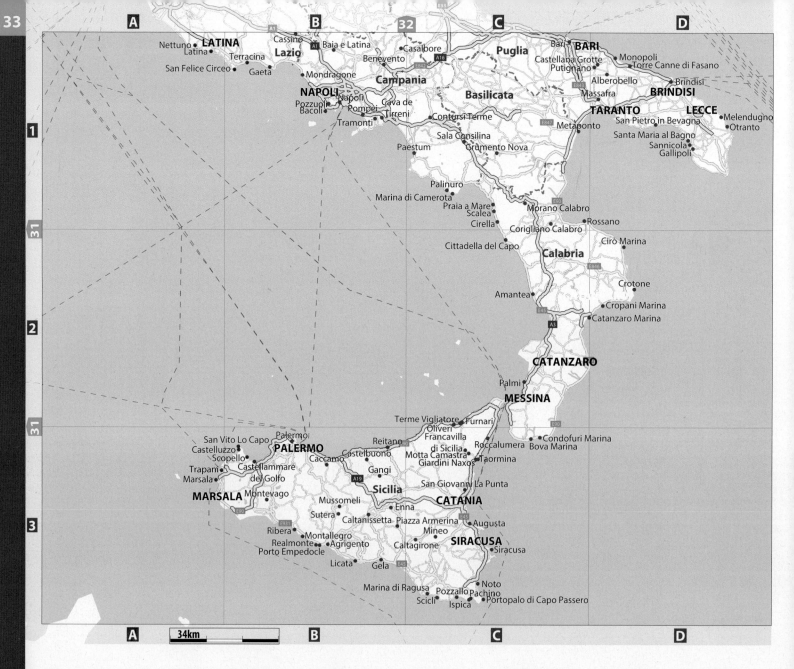

Place	Grid	Page
Achillio (GR)	33G1	475
Ag.Mamas Moudania (GR)	33G1	480
Agia Kyriaki (GR)	33G3	476
Agios Andreas (GR)	33G2	476
Agios Fokas (GR)	33G3	477
Agios Kiriaki (GR)	33F3	477
Agios Nikolaos (GR)	33F2	475
Agrigento (IT)	33B3	548
Akt Armenistis Sithonia (GR)	33H1	480
Alberobello (IT)	33D1	543
Alexandroúpoli (GR)	33H1	480
Amantea (IT)	33C2	546
Ammoudia (GR)	33E1	475
Arahova (GR)	33G2	475
Arillas (GR)	33E1	475
Assini (GR)	33G2	477
Athens (GR)	33G2	477
Augusta (IT)	33C3	548
Bacoli (IT)	33B1	545
Baia e Latina (IT)	33B1	545
Bari (IT)	33C1	543
Benevento (IT)	33B1	545
Boukka (GR)	33F1	475
Bova Marina (IT)	33C3	546
Bozas (GR)	33G3	477
Brindisi (IT)	33D1	543
Caccamo (IT)	33B3	548
Caltagirone (IT)	33C3	548
Caltanissetta (IT)	33B3	548
Casalbore (IT)	33B1	545
Cassino (IT)	33B1	536
Castelbuono (IT)	33B3	548
Castellammare del Golfo (IT)	33B3	548
Castellana Grotte (IT)	33D1	544
Castelluzzo (IT)	33B3	548
Catanzaro Marina (IT)	33C2	546
Cava de'Tirreni (IT)	33B1	545
Cirella (IT)	33C1	547
Cirò Marina (IT)	33D2	547
Cittadella del Capo (IT)	33C2	547
Condofuri Marina (IT)	33C3	547
Contursi Terme (IT)	33C1	546
Corfu (GR)	33E1	475
Corigliano Calabro (IT)	33C1	547
Cropani Marina (IT)	33D2	547
Crotone (IT)	33D2	547
Delphi (GR)	33F2	475
Diakofto (GR)	33F2	477
Dimitsána (GR)	33F2	477
Elefsina (GR)	33G2	477
Enna (IT)	33B3	548
Epidaurus (GR)	33G2	477
Eratini (GR)	33F2	475
Erétria (GR)	33G2	475
Ermioni (GR)	33G2	477
Francavilla di Sicilia (IT)	33C3	548
Furnari (IT)	33C2	546
Gaeta (IT)	33B1	537
Galatas (GR)	33G2	477
Gallipoli (IT)	33D1	544
Gangi (IT)	33B3	549
Gela (IT)	33B3	549
Gerakani (GR)	33H1	480
Gerolimenas (GR)	33G3	477
Gialova Pylou (GR)	33F3	477
Giardini Naxos (IT)	33C3	549
Gjirokaster (AL)	33E1	79
Glifa Kyllini (GR)	33F2	477
Gliki (GR)	33E1	475
Grumento Nova (IT)	33C1	546
Gythion (GR)	33G3	477
Hiliadou (GR)	33F2	475
Himarë (AL)	33E1	79
Igoumenítsa (GR)	33E1	476
Ioánnina (GR)	33E1	476
Ispica (IT)	33C3	549
Itea (GR)	33F2	476
Kakovatos (GR)	33F2	477
Kalamaria (GR)	33G1	480
Kalo Nero (GR)	33F2	477
Kalogria (GR)	33F2	477
Kamares (GR)	33G3	477
Kameras Irion (GR)	33G3	477
Karathona (GR)	33G2	477
Karavostasi (GR)	33G3	477
Kastoriá (GR)	33F1	480
Kastro (GR)	33F2	478
Kato Alissos (GR)	33F2	478
Kifisiá (GR)	33G2	478
Killini (GR)	33F2	478
Kiveri (GR)	33G2	478
Kokkinia (GR)	33G3	478
Korfos (GR)	33G2	478
Korinthos (GR)	33G2	478
Koroni (GR)	33F3	478
Kosmas (GR)	33G2	478
Kotronas (GR)	33G3	478
Krioneri (GR)	33F2	476
Ksamil (AL)	33E1	79
Lambiri (GR)	33F2	478
Latina (IT)	33A1	537
Legrena (GR)	33G2	478
Leskovik (AL)	33E1	79
Levkas (Lefkada) (GR)	33E1	476
Licata (IT)	33B3	549
Llogara (AL)	33E1	79
Marathon (GR)	33G2	478
Marina di Camerota (IT)	33C1	546
Marina di Ragusa (IT)	33C3	549
Marsala (IT)	33A3	549
Massafra (IT)	33D1	544
Mayroyouni/Gythion (GR)	33G3	478
Melendugno (IT)	33D1	544
Mesolóngi (GR)	33F2	476
Metamorphosi (GR)	33H1	480
Metaponto (IT)	33C1	546
Metéora (GR)	33F1	476
Métsovo (GR)	33F1	476
Mineo (IT)	33C3	549
Mondragone (IT)	33B1	546

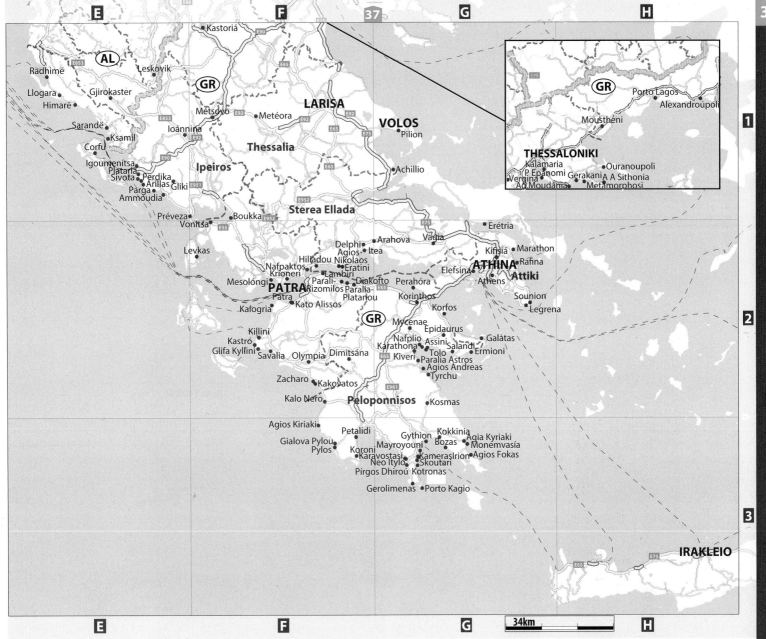

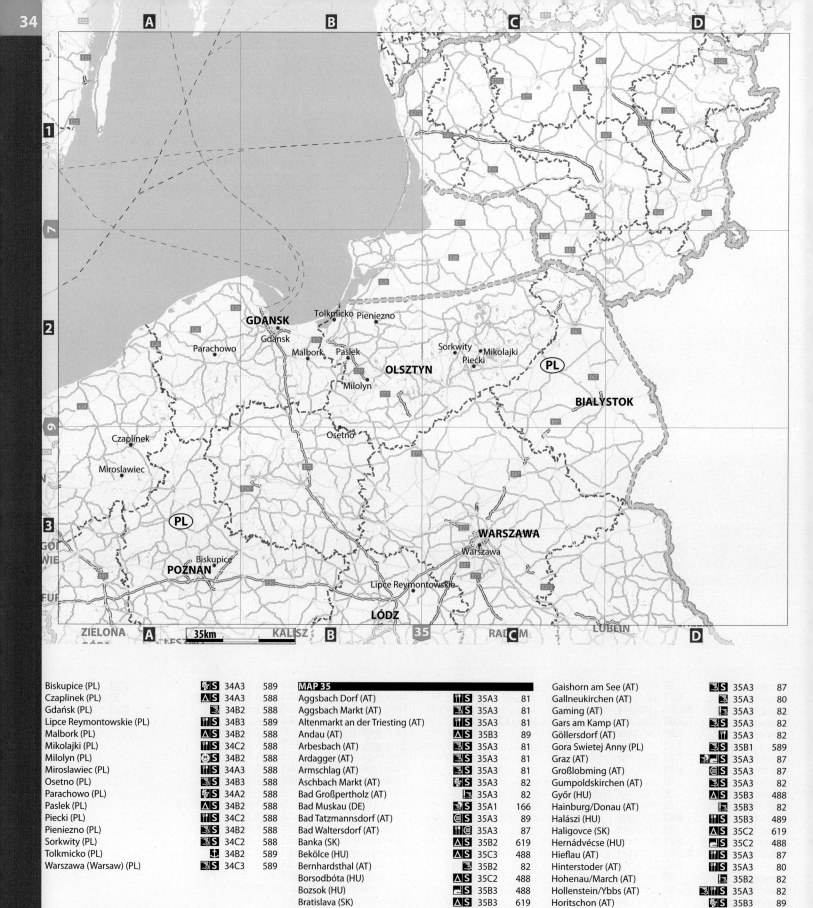

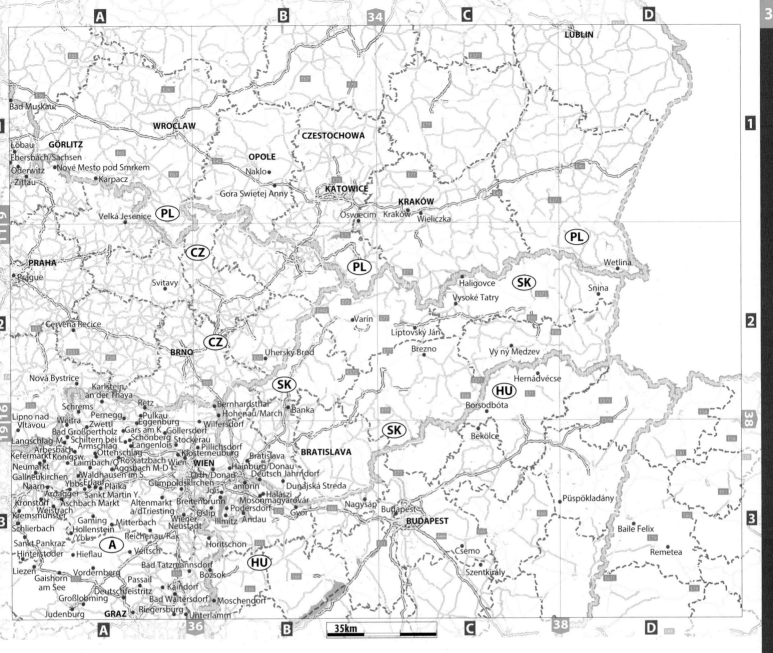

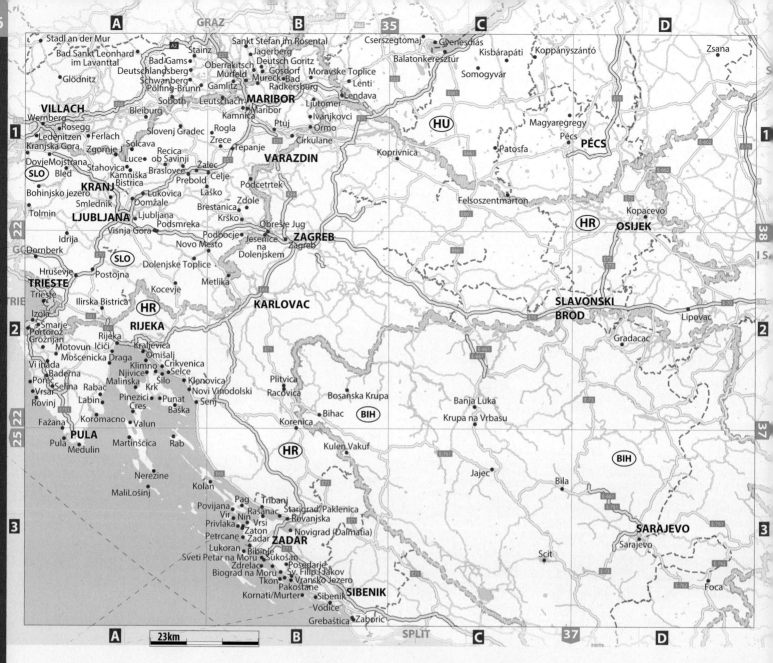

Name	Grid	Page
Bad Gams (AT)	36A1	86
Bad Radkersburg (AT)	36B1	87
Bad Sankt Leonhard im Lavanttal (AT)	36A1	89
Baderna (HR)	36A2	481
Balatonkeresztúr (HU)	36C1	488
Banja Luka (BA)	36C2	91
Bibinje (HR)	36B3	483
Bihać (BA)	36B2	91
Bila (BA)	36C3	91
Biograd na Moru (HR)	36B3	483
Bled (SI)	36A1	614
Bleiburg (AT)	36A1	89
Bohinjsko jezero (SI)	36A1	614
Bosanska Krupa (BA)	36B2	91
Braslovče (SI)	36A1	615
Brestanica (SI)	36B1	615
Celje (SI)	36B1	616
Cirkulane (SI)	36B1	616
Cres/Cres (HR)	36A2	481
Cres/Martinščica (HR)	36A3	481
Cres/Nerezine (HR)	36A3	481
Cres/Valun (HR)	36A2	481
Crikvenica (HR)	36A2	481
Cserszegtomaj (HU)	36C1	488
Deutsch Goritz (AT)	36B1	87
Deutschlandsberg (AT)	36A1	87
Dolenjske Toplice (SI)	36A2	614
Domžale (SI)	36A1	614
Dornberk (SI)	36A2	614
DovjeMojstrana (SI)	36A1	614
Fažana (HR)	36A3	481
Felsőszentmárton (HU)	36C1	488
Ferlach (AT)	36A1	89
Gamlitz (AT)	36B1	87
Glödnitz (AT)	36A1	89
Gosdorf (AT)	36B1	87
Gradacac (BA)	36D2	91
Grožnjan (HR)	36A2	481
Gyenesdiás (HU)	36C1	488
Hruševje (SI)	36A2	614
Ičiči (HR)	36A2	481
Idrija (SI)	36A2	614
Ilirska Bistrica (SI)	36A2	614
Ivanjkovci (SI)	36B1	616
Izola (SI)	36A2	614
Jagerberg (AT)	36B1	87
Jajec (BA)	36C3	91
Jesenice na Dolenjskem (SI)	36B2	616
Kamnica (SI)	36B1	616
Kamniška Bistrica (SI)	36B1	616
Kisbárapáti (HU)	36C1	488
Klenovica (HR)	36A2	481
Kocevje (SI)	36A2	616
Kolan (HR)	36B3	484
Kopačevo (HR)	36D1	486
Koppányszántó (HU)	36C1	488
Koprivnica (HR)	36C1	486
Korenica (HR)	36B2	484
Kornati/Murter (HR)	36B3	484
Koromačno (HR)	36A2	481
Kraljevica (HR)	36A2	481
Kranjska Gora (SI)	36A1	615
Krk/Baška (HR)	36A2	481
Krk/Klimno (HR)	36A2	481
Krk/Krk (HR)	36A2	481
Krk/Malinska (HR)	36A2	482
Krk/Njivice (HR)	36A2	482
Krk/Pinezici (HR)	36A2	482
Krk/Punat (HR)	36A2	482
Krk/Šilo (HR)	36A2	482
Krško (SI)	36B1	616
Krupa na Vrbasu (BA)	36C2	91
Kulen Vakuf (BA)	36B3	91
Labin (HR)	36A2	482
Laško (SI)	36A1	616
Ledenitzen (AT)	36A1	89
Lendava (SI)	36B1	617
Lenti (HU)	36B1	489
Leutschach (AT)	36B1	87
Lipovac (HR)	36D2	487
Ljubljana (SI)	36A1	615
Ljutomer (SI)	36B1	617
Lošinj/Mali Lošinj (HR)	36A3	482
Luče (SI)	36A1	615
Lukoran (HR)	36B3	484
Lukovica (SI)	36A1	615
Magyaregregy (HU)	36C1	489
Maribor (SI)	36B1	617
Medulin (HR)	36A3	482
Metlika (SI)	36B2	617
Moravske Toplice (SI)	36B1	617
Mošćenička Draga (HR)	36A2	482
Motovun (HR)	36A2	482
Mureck (AT)	36B1	88
Murfeld (AT)	36B1	88
Nin (HR)	36B3	484
Novi Vinodolski (HR)	36A2	482
Novigrad (Dalmatia) (HR)	36B3	484
Novo Mesto (SI)	36B2	617
Oberrakitsch (AT)	36B1	88
Obrežje Jug (SI)	36B2	617
Ormož (SI)	36B1	617
Pag (HR)	36B3	484
Pakoštane (HR)	36B3	484
Patosfa (HU)	36C1	489
Pécs (HU)	36C1	488
Petrcane (HR)	36B3	485
Plitviča (HR)	36B2	487
Podbočje (SI)	36B2	617
Podčetrtek (SI)	36B1	617
Podsmreka (SI)	36A2	617
Pölfing-Brunn (AT)	36A1	88
Poreč (HR)	36A2	482
Portorož (SI)	36A2	615
Posedarje (HR)	36B3	485
Postojna (SI)	36A2	615
Povijana (HR)	36B3	485
Prebold (SI)	36A1	617
Privlaka (HR)	36B3	485

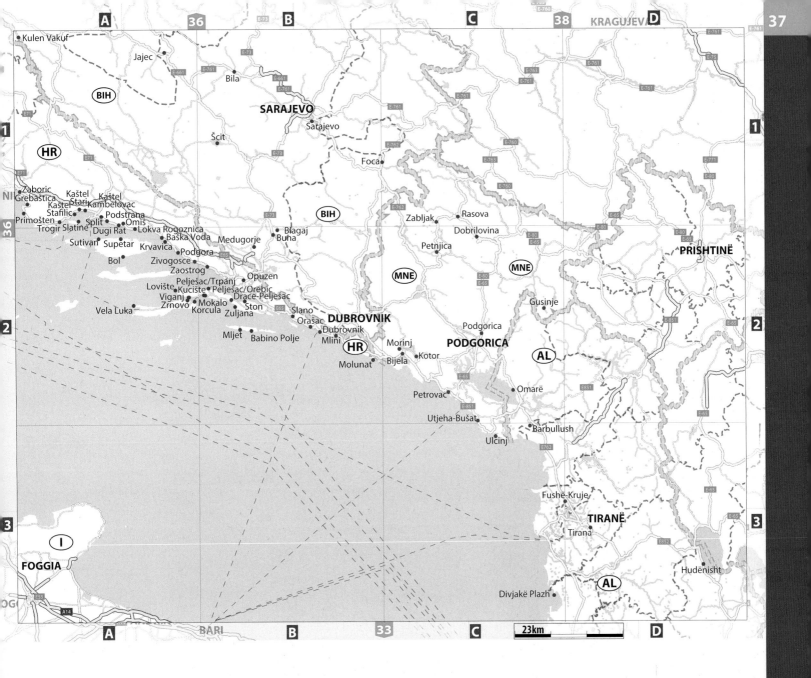

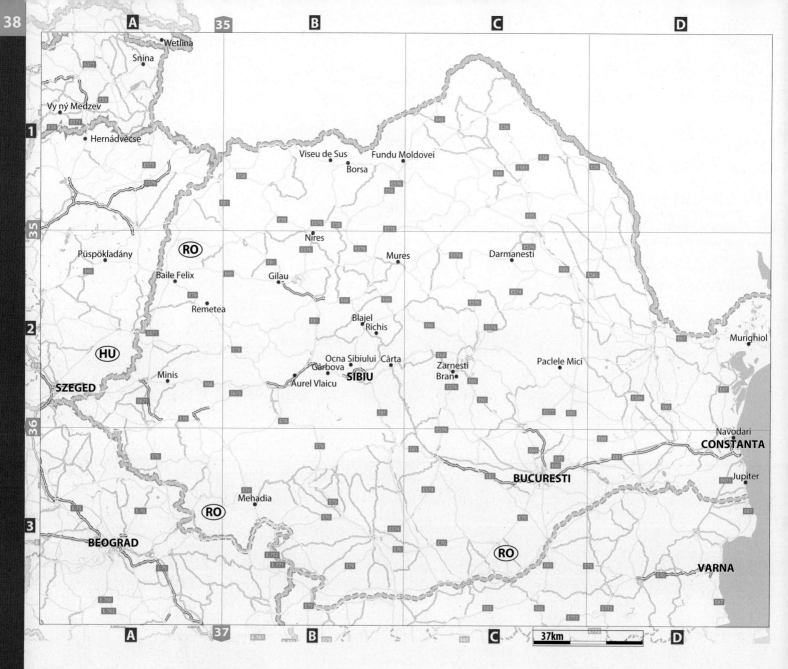

Aurel Vlaicu (RO)	⚠S	38B2	608
Baile Felix (RO)	⚠S	38A2	608
Blăjel (RO)	⚠S	38B2	608
Borşa (RO)	⚠S	38B1	608
Bran (RO)	⚠S	38C2	608
Cârţa (RO)	⚠S	38C2	608
Dărmăneşti (RO)	⚘S	38C2	609
Fundu Moldovei (RO)	⚠S	38B1	609
Gârbova (RO)	⚠S	38B2	608
Gilău (RO)	⚠S	38B2	608
Jupiter (RO)	⚠S	38D3	609
Mehadia (RO)	⚠S	38B3	609
Miniş (RO)	⚠S	38A2	608
Mureş (RO)	⚠S	38B2	608
Murighiol (RO)	⚘♦S	38D2	609
Navodari (RO)	⚠S	38D3	609
Nireş (RO)	⚠S	38B2	608
Ocna Sibiului (RO)	⚘S	38B2	608
Paclele Mici (RO)	⚠S	38C2	609
Remetea (RO)	⚠S	38A2	608
Richis (RO)	⚠S	38B2	608
Vişeu de Sus (RO)	⚘S	38B1	608
Zărneşti (RO)	⚠S	38C2	609

🇦🇱 Albania

Capital: Tirana
Government: parliamentarian republic
Official Language:
Population 3.020.000 (2014)
Area: 28.748 Km²

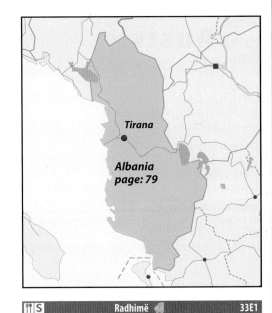

Tirana

Albania
page: 79

General information
Dialling code: 0355
General emergency: 112
Currency: Lek (ALL) € 1 = 140 ALL, 10 ALL = € 0,07
£ 1 = 193 ALL, 10 ALL = £ 0,05 (October 2015)
Credit cards are accepted in the main cities.

Regulations for overnight stays
Wild camping is allowed with permission from
land owner/manager or local government.

Additional public holidays 2016
March 14 Summer Day
March 21 Nowruz
March 25 Good Friday
October 19 Mother Teresa Day
November 28 Independence Day
November 29 Liberation Day

Time Zone
Winter (Standard Time) GMT+1
Summer (DST) GMT+2

🏕 S — Barbullush — 37C3
Restaurant/Camping Albania, Barbullush 4022.
GPS: n41,92386 e19,54186. ⬆➡

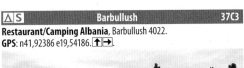

€ 10/night 🚰🔌Ch🚿WC €3,50 📶included.
Location: Rural. **Surface:** grassy. 🅿 01/01-31/12
Distance: Skodër 20km.

Divjakë Plazh — 37C3
Bar/Rest/Hotel Adrian Satka. GPS: n40,97156 e19,48036.

.

🏕 S — Fushë-Kruje — 37D3
Hotel Nordpark. GPS: n41,47078 e19,69875.

€ 19 🚰🔌Ch🚿WC included.
Remarks: Incl. access swimming pool.

Gjirokaster 🌿🍴 — 33E1
Viroi, SH4. **GPS:** n40,10308 e20,12289.

---

2 free.
Distance: 3km on the spot.

🏕 S — Himarë — 33E1
Camping Kranea, Livadh Beach. **GPS:** n40,10734 e19,72739.

€ 14 €2 €3.

🏕 S — Hudënisht — 37D3
Peshku, SH3. **GPS:** n40,96725 e20,64274.
€ 5-12 🚰🔌Ch🚿WC included €2.
Surface: grassy.
🅿 01/01-31/12
Distance: 100m.
Remarks: Lake Ohrid, free use of sun beds and beach chairs.

🏕 S — Ksamil — 33E1
Sunset, SH81. **GPS:** n39,77908 e20,00831. ⬆
20 € 10 🚰🔌Ch🚿📶included.
Surface: unpaved. 🅿 01/01-31/12
Distance: Sarandë 10km on the spot on the spot.

🏕 S — Leskovik 🏔🍴 — 33E1
Farma Sotira, SH75, Leskovik > Ersekë 15km.
GPS: n40,21477 e20,64611. ⬆

20 € 10 🚰🔌Ch🚿WC 📶included. **Location:** Rural, isolated.
Surface: grassy. 🅿 01/04-01/11
Distance: on the spot on the spot on the spot on the spot.

🏕 — Llogara 🏔🍴 — 33E1
Hotel Hamiti, SH8. **GPS:** n40,21035 e19,57924.
€ 5.

🏕 S — Omarë — 37C2
Lake Shkodra Resort, Rruga E Liqenit.
GPS: n42,13836 e19,46562. ⬆➡
€ 12, Jul/Aug € 14 🚰🔌Ch🚿€2 WC €3,95 📶included.
Surface: grassy. 🅿 01/04-15/11
Distance: Skodër 10km lake with sandy beach on the spot on the spot.
Remarks: Free use of sun beds and beach chairs, canoe and bicycle rental.

🍴 S — Radhimë — 33E1
Recidenca Cedochima, SH8. **GPS:** n40,37706 e19,47872. ⬆

20 € 15 🚰🚿WC 📶.
Surface: gravel. 🅿 01/01-31/12
Distance: pebbled beach on the spot.

🍴 S — Sarandë 🏔🍴 — 33E1
Hotel Mediterrane, Rruga Skënderbeu. **GPS:** n39,87041 e20,01854. ⬆

AL

10 € 10 🚰🚿included WC 📶.
Location: Urban. **Surface:** asphalted. 🅿 01/01-31/12
Distance: city centre 1km 600m on the spot.

🍴 S — Tirana — 37D3
Hotel Baron, Rruga e Elbasanit. **GPS:** n41,29947 e19,85012.
6 € 17,50 🔌Ch🚿WC included.
Surface: metalled.
Distance: centre 4km on the spot.

Austria

Capital: Vienna
Government: federal, parliamentarian, democratic republic
Official Language: German
Population: 8,660,000 (2014)
Area: 83,857 km²

General information
Dialling code: 0043
General emergency: 112
Currency: Euro

Regulations for overnight stays
In general overnight parking is allowed, except: Tyrol, Vienna, nature reserves and in areas where locally prohibited. No "camping" activities allowed and disposal wastewater must be at official places.

Additional public holidays 2016
January 6 Epiphany
May 1 Labor Day
Mai 26 Corpus Christi
August 15 Assumption of the Virgin Mary
October 26 National Holiday
November 1 All Saints' Day
December 8 Immaculate Conception

Time Zone
Winter (Standard Time) GMT+1
Summer (DST) GMT+2

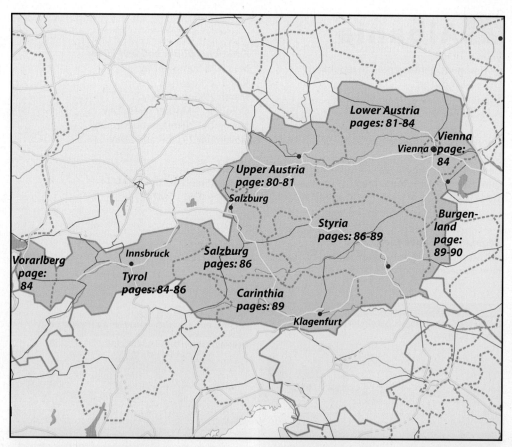

Lower Austria pages: 81-84
Vienna page: 84
Upper Austria page: 80-81
Salzburg
Styria pages: 86-89
Burgenland page: 89-90
Vorarlberg page: 84
Innsbruck
Salzburg pages: 86
Tyrol pages: 84-86
Carinthia pages: 89
Klagenfurt

Upper Austria

Ebensee 19H1
Am Traunsee, Trauneck. **GPS:** n47,81283 e13,77730.

5 ⧈free ⌁€0,50/50liter ⧉Ch ⧈(12x)€3 WC.
Location: Rural, simple, quiet. **Surface:** asphalted.
Distance: ⛱500m ⚓on the spot ⧈300m.
Remarks: At lake.

Ebensee 19H1
Freizeitanlage Rindbach, Strandbadstraße.
GPS: n47,80934 e13,79002.

30 ⧈€ 12 ⌁€1/25liter ⧈(4x)€1/h. ⧈
Location: Rural, simple, quiet. **Surface:** grassy. **□** 01/04-31/10
Distance: ⛱1,4km.
Remarks: At lake.

Eferding 16H3
Brandstatt, Pupping. **GPS:** n48,33503 e14,02698.
⧈.
Remarks: On the Danube river.

Gallneukirchen 35A3
Freizeitcentrum, Veitsdorfer Weg 10. **GPS:** n48,36045 e14,40797.

10 ⧈free. **Location:** Rural, simple. **Surface:** asphalted.
□ 01/01-31/12
Distance: ⛱1km ⚓on the spot ⧈1km.

Gmünden 19H1
Parkplatz des Toscanapark, Scharnsteiner Straße.
GPS: n47,91186 e13,78708.
5 ⧈free. **Surface:** asphalted. **□** 01/01-31/12
Distance: ⛱1km ⧈200m.

Gosau 19H2
Gasthaus Echo, Gosau 614. **GPS:** n47,55171 e13,51345.
10 ⧈free ⌁€5 ⧈. **Location:** Rural, simple, isolated, quiet.
Surface: asphalted. **□** 01/05-31/10
Distance: ⛱400m ⚓on the spot.

Gosau 19H2
Hotel Gosauschmied, Gosau 57. **GPS:** n47,55072 e13,51607.
10 ⧈€ 10 ⧈Ch ⧈on demand. **Surface:** asphalted.
□ 01/01-31/12
Distance: ⛱3km ⚓on the spot ⧈3km ⧈on the spot ⧈500m
⧈on the spot.

Haslach 16H3
Gasthof Furtmühle, Schwackerreith 20, St.Oswald.
GPS: n48,60497 e14,01967.
15 ⧈free ⌁⧈against payment. **□** 01/01-31/12 **●** Tue

Hinterstoder 35A3
Gasthof Baumschlagerreith. **GPS:** n47,64525 e14,09632.
10 ⧈€ 8, guests free ⌁⧈. **Location:** Rural, simple, isolated, quiet.
□ 01/01-31/12
Distance: ⛱9km ⚓on the spot.

Kefermarkt 35A3
Schloßbrauerei Weinberg, Weinberg 2. **GPS:** n48,44856 e14,53957.

5 ⧈guests free. **Location:** Rural, simple. **Surface:** asphalted.
□ 01/01-31/12
Distance: ⛱800m ⚓on the spot.

Königswiesen 35A3
Freibad, Badgasse 4. **GPS:** n48,40450 e14,84080.

3 ⧈€ 2 + € 2/pp ⌁Ch ⧈WCfree. **Location:** Rural, simple, quiet.
Surface: asphalted. **□** 01/04-31/10
Distance: ⛱500m ⚓10m Freibadbuffet ⧈300m.
Remarks: Parking swimming pool.

Kremsmünster 35A3
Parkplatz Benediktiner Stift, Fuxjägerstraße.
GPS: n48,05407 e14,12607.
⧈.
Distance: ⛱500m ⚓500m.

Kronstorf 35A3
Stellplatz Metzenhof, Dörfling 2. **GPS:** n48,12828 e14,43432.

AT

10 🛏€ 18, 2 pers.incl 🚿 💧 WC 📶included.
Location: Rural, comfortable, isolated, quiet.
Surface: gravel/metalled. 🅾 01/03-30/11
Distance: ⚓on the spot ⊗on the spot.
Remarks: At golf court.

Mondsee 🚤 19H1
Geflügelhof Schweighofer, Schwand 10.
GPS: n47,88186 e13,31105. 🔼.

5 🛏€ 13, 2 pers incl 🚿 Ch 💧 included.
Location: Rural, quiet. **Surface:** grassy. 🅾 01/01-31/12
Distance: 🚶3km ⊗2km 🛒3km.

Naarn 35A3
Bauernhof Mostschenke, Dirnwagram 1.
GPS: n48,21750 e14,61972. 🔼.

5 🛏€ 10 🚿 Ch 💧€2/day WCincluded.
Location: Rural, simple. **Surface:** asphalted.
Distance: 🚶2km on the spot 🛒2km.
Remarks: Arrival <19.30h, max. 4 days.

Naarn 35A3
Gasthof zur Post, Marktplatz 1. **GPS:** n48,22579 e14,60662.

5 🛏€ 6, 2 pers.incl.
Location: Simple, noisy. **Surface:** asphalted. 🅾 Thu
Distance: 🚶on the spot ⊗on the spot.

Neumarkt 35A3
Stellplatz Einfach Ausspannen, Seisenbachweg 12.
GPS: n48,43457 e14,47739. 🔼.
2 🛏€ 10 🚿 💧 WC included.
Location: Rural, isolated, quiet. **Surface:** grassy.
Distance: 🚶1km on the spot ⊗1km.

Ranshofen 16G3
Vereinslokal, Scheuhub 2. **GPS:** n48,23228 e12,99893.
10 🛏free 🚿 Ch 💧. **Surface:** grassy. 🅾 01/01-31/12
Distance: 🚶2km on the spot 🛒2km 🚌2km.

Sankt Pankraz 35A3
Parkplatz Klauser Stausee, Klaus an der Pyhrnbahn.
GPS: n47,82733 e14,15703.
🛏.
Remarks: Along river.

Scharnstein 🏛 19H1
Camping Schatzlmühle, Viechtwang 1A.
GPS: n47,91578 e13,97353. ➡️.

5 🛏€ 10 🚿 🔌 Ch included. 💧€3 🛏€2 🗑€2.
Location: Rural, quiet. **Surface:** grassy/gravel. 🅾 01/05-31/10
Distance: 🚶2km ⊗on the spot 🛒600m 🚌on the spot 🎣on the spot 🏊on the spot.

Schlierbach 35A3
Bauernhof Eisterer, Föhrenweg 7. **GPS:** n47,95083 e14,08639. 🔼.
3 🛏€ 6 + € 4/pp 🚿 Ch 💧€2,50/day 🛏.
Location: Rural, comfortable. **Surface:** grassy.

Straß im Attergau 🏛 19H1
Landgasthof Rosslwirt, Halt 4. **GPS:** n47,90488 e13,44677. ➡️.

6 🛏guests free 🚿 🔌 💧free.
Location: Rural, simple, quiet. **Surface:** grassy/gravel. 🅾 01/01-31/12
Distance: ⊗on the spot.

Suben 16H3
Hotel Suben, Etzelshofen 125. **GPS:** n48,40149 e13,42582. 🔼.
40 🛏€ 10 🚿 🔌 Ch 💧included.
Location: Simple, noisy. 🅾 01/01-31/12
Distance: 💧on the spot ⊗on the spot.

Vöcklabruck 19H1
Hallenbad am Freizeitgelände, Hausruckstraße.
GPS: n48,01107 e13,65299. 🔼.

6 🛏free 🚿 🔌 Ch 💧.
Location: Rural, simple. **Surface:** metalled. 🅾 01/01-31/12
Distance: 🚶500m.
Remarks: Max. 48h.

Waldhausen im Strudengau 35A3
Badesee, Schloßberg. **GPS:** n48,28420 e14,95883. ➡️.

6 🛏voluntary contribution 🚿€1/10minutes 🔌 Ch 💧€1/8h.
Location: Rural, isolated, quiet. **Surface:** gravel.
🅾 01/01-31/12
Distance: 🚶2km ⚓on the spot ⊗on the spot 🛒2km 🚌2km.

Lower Austria

Aggsbach Dorf 35A3
Gasthof Pension zur Kartause, Aggsbach-Dorf 38.
GPS: n48,29638 e15,42604. 🔼.

10 🛏free 🚿.
Location: Rural, isolated, quiet. **Surface:** grassy. 🅾 01/01-31/12
Distance: ⊗on the spot.

Aggsbach Markt 🏖 35A3
Badestrand. GPS: n48,29814 e15,40497. 🔼.

26 🛏voluntary contribution 🚿 🔌 Ch 💧€1,50/24h.
Location: Comfortable. **Surface:** gravel. 🅾 01/03-31/10
Distance: 🚶500m 50m Donaustüberl 🛒500m.
Remarks: On the Danube river.

Altenmarkt an der Triesting 35A3
Gasthof Zum Kleinen Semmering, Hafnerberg 15.
GPS: n48,01762 e16,01383. 🔼.

10 🛏free 🚿 WC.
Location: Rural, simple. **Surface:** gravel.
Distance: 🚶2,3km ⊗on the spot 🛒2,3km.

Arbesbach 🏛 35A3
Am Ganser. **GPS:** n48,49123 e14,95683. 🔼.

15 🛏€ 5 🚿 🔌 Ch 💧included.
Location: Rural, simple. **Surface:** gravel. 🅾 01/01-31/12
Distance: 🚶500m ⚓on the spot ⊗500m 🛒500m 🚌500m.
Remarks: Check in at town hall.

Ardagger 35A3
Stellplatz am Donauwellenpark, Markt 39.
GPS: n48,17981 e14,82579. 🔼.

10 🛏free 🚿€2 🔌 Ch 💧(6x)€1/kWh.
Location: Rural, simple. 🅾 01/01-31/12
Distance: 🚶100m 🚲7km ⊗100m 🛒100m 🏊on the spot.
Remarks: At Danube cycle route.

Armschlag 35A3
Mohndorf. **GPS:** n48,45222 e15,21944. 🔼.

AT

5 ③ € 7, 2 pers.incl. ⌐⌐☐Ch.✎included.
Location: Rural, simple. **Surface:** asphalted. ☐ 01/01-31/12
Distance: ⌁on the spot ⊗on the spot ☖2km
⚐Mohnstrudelwandernetz.

| 🏷🅂 | Aschbach Markt | 35A3 |

Fam. Edtbauer, Auckental 1 u. 2. **GPS:** n48,10682 e14,69988.⬆.

8 ③free ⌐✎€2. **Location:** Rural, quiet. ☐ 15/04-30/10
Distance: ⌁7km ⚐3km ☖7km.

| 🏷 | Bad Großpertholz | 35A3 |

Busparkplatz Naturpark Nordwald, Scheiben.
GPS: n48,61765 e14,81548.
③. **Location:** Rural. **Surface:** asphalted.

| 🏷 | Bernhardsthal | 35B2 |

Am Bernhardsthaler Teich, Schulstrasse.
GPS: n48,69402 e16,87481.⬆→.

5 ③free. **Surface:** grassy.
☐ 01/01-31/12
Distance: ⌁500m ⚲on the spot ⚐on the spot ⊗weekends only.

| 🏷🅂 | Eggenburg ⚐⚐ | 35A3 |

Stellplatz an der Stadtmauer, Erzherzog-Karl-Ring 19.
GPS: n48,64513 e15,81745.⬆→.

8 ③€ 4 ⌐€1/10minutes ☐Ch.✎(8x)€1/8h.
Location: Rural, comfortable. **Surface:** gravel. ☐ 01/04-31/10
Distance: ⌁on the spot ⚐4km ⚲creek ⊗300m ☖200m ⚲500m
on the spot ⚐300m.

| 🍴🅂 | Erlauf | 35A3 |

Gasthof Plaika Wirt, Plaika 1. **GPS:** n48,16866 e15,16436.⬆.

10 ③guests free ⌐€2/100liter ✎€2/24h.
Location: Rural, quiet. **Surface:** asphalted. ◐ Mo

Distance: ⌁2km ⊗2km ☖on the spot.

| 🏷 | Gaming | 35A3 |

Kartause. GPS: n47,92463 e15,08223.

| 🏷🅂 | Gars am Kamp | 35A3 |

Sport- und Erlebnisbad, Gföhler Strasse/Strandgasse, Thunau am
Kamp. **GPS:** n48,59300 e15,65723.⬆.

5 ③€ 16 ⌐☐Ch.✎WCincluded.
Location: Comfortable. ☐ 01/01-31/12
Distance: ⌁200m ⊗on the spot ☖200m.
Remarks: At swimming pool.

| 🍴 | Göllersdorf ⚐ | 35A3 |

Parkplatz Barbara Heuriger, Spitalgasse 467.
GPS: n48,49667 e16,11171.⬆.

10 ③free. **Location:** Rural, simple. **Surface:** gravel.
Distance: ⌁500m ⚲1km ⊗on the spot ☖1km.

| 🏷 | Gumpoldskirchen | 35A3 |

Brunngasse. GPS: n48,04212 e16,27820.⬆.

10 ③free. **Location:** Rural, simple. **Surface:** asphalted.
Distance: ⌁500m ⊗500m.
Remarks: Max. 8M.

| 🅂 | Gumpoldskirchen | 35A3 |

Neustiftgasse. GPS: n48,04423 e16,27552.
⌐☐Ch.

| 🏷 | Hainburg/Donau | 35B3 |

Parkplatz an der Donau, Parkweg. **GPS:** n48,15110 e16,94440.

③. **Surface:** asphalted. ☐ 01/01-31/12
Distance: ⌁500m ⊗on the spot.

| 🏷 | Hohenau/March | 35B2 |

Freizeitzentrum, Kindergartenstrasse. **GPS:** n48,61095 e16,91010.

③free. **Surface:** asphalted. ☐ 01/01-31/12
Remarks: Swimming pool 200m.

| 🍴🅂 | Hollenstein/Ybbs | 35A3 |

Naturpark Hollenstein, Wenten 1. **GPS:** n47,76884 e14,77270.
3 ③€ 5 ⌐☐Ch.✎. **Location:** Rural, isolated, quiet.
☐ 01/01-31/12
Distance: ⌁4km.

| 🍴🅂 | Hollenstein/Ybbs | 35A3 |

Gasthof Staudach, Walcherbauer 5. **GPS:** n47,80703 e14,76687.
4 ③€ 14, 4 pers.incl ⌐☐Ch.✎.
Distance: ⌁200m ⊗10m ☖200m ⚐on the spot.

| 🏷 | Karlstein an der Thaya | 35A2 |

Sieghartser Straße. GPS: n48,88186 e15,40442.⬆.
③. **Surface:** grassy. ☐ 01/01-31/12
Distance: ⌁200m ☖200m.
Remarks: At tennis-court.

| 🏷🅂 | Klosterneuburg | 35A3 |

Euromobil Campers, Bahnhofplatz 16, Kritzendorf.
GPS: n48,33582 e16,29863.⬆→.

4 ③free ⌐☐Ch.
Location: Simple. **Surface:** asphalted. ☐ 01/01-31/12
Distance: ⚲12,5km ⊗300m ☖500m.
Remarks: Lock-up parking, guarded.

| 🏷🅂 | Laimbach am Ostrong | 35A3 |

Bauernhof Stoiber, Wagmühle 34. **GPS:** n48,31711 e15,12565.⬆.

5 ③€ 12 ⌐☐Ch.✎included.
Location: Rural, simple. **Surface:** grassy.
Distance: ⌁300m ⊗300m ☖300m.

| 🏷🅂 | Langenlois ⚐ | 35A3 |

Reisemobilstellplatz Langenlois, Krumpöckallee 21.
GPS: n48,47063 e15,69782.⬆.

7 ③€ 8+ € 1,50/pp ⌐€1/10minutes ☐Ch.✎(7x)€1/8h.
Location: Rural, simple, quiet. **Surface:** metalled.
Distance: ⌁1,5km ⊗1km ☖1km.

| 🏷 | Langschlag-Mitterschlag | 35A3 |

Freizeitanlage Frauenwieserteich, Böhmerwald-Bundesstraße.
GPS: n48,58038 e14,83507.⬆.

AT

10 ⌂free. **Location:** Rural, simple, isolated, quiet.
Surface: grassy/gravel.
◻ 01/01-31/12
Distance: ⌐5km ⌐on the spot ⌐on the spot ⌐on the spot ⌐5km.

| ⌐S | Mitterbach | 35A3 |

Biobauernhof Sepplbauer, Bergstraße 11. **GPS:** n47,83216 e15,30648.
10 ⌂€ 6 ⌐€ 2. **Location:** Rural, isolated, quiet. **Surface:** grassy.
◻ 01/05-30/09
Distance: ⌐4km.

| | Orth/Donau | 35B3 |

P2, Am Rosenhügel. **GPS:** n48,14523 e16,70383. ⌐.

⌂free. **Surface:** metalled. ◻ 01/01-31/12
Distance: ⌐on the spot ⌐250m ⌐1,2km.

| ⌐S | Ottenschlag | 35A3 |

Florianigasse. **GPS:** n48,42361 e15,22750. ⌐.

8-10 ⌂€ 5 ⌐€ 1/10minutes ⌐Ch ⌐€ 1/8h.
Location: Rural, simple. **Surface:** gravel.
Distance: ⌐500m ⌐Gaststätte ⌐500m.

| ⌐S | Pernegg | 35A2 |

Freizeitanlage Gallien, Gallien 1. **GPS:** n48,71333 e15,66139. ⌐⌐.
20 ⌂€ 15 + € 5/pp ⌐⌐Ch ⌐WC⌐included.
Location: Rural, comfortable.
Distance: ⌐on the spot ⌐on the spot.

| ⌐S | Pillichsdorf | 35B3 |

Am Tennisclub, Bahnstraße 8A. **GPS:** n48,36167 e16,53750. ⌐⌐.

8 ⌂free, use facilities € 10 ⌐Ch ⌐WC⌐.
Location: Simple. ◻ 01/01-31/12
Distance: ⌐500m, Vienna 15km ⌐300m ⌐500m ⌐on the spot.
Remarks: Use facilities clubhouse possible.

| ⌐S | Plaika | 35A3 |

Gasthaus zum Plaikawirt, Plaika 1. **GPS:** n48,16878 e15,16416. ⌐.
5 ⌂free ⌐⌐. ◻ 01/01-31/12
Distance: ⌐5km ⌐on the spot.

| ⌐S | Pulkau | 35A2 |

Rat-Cumfe Straße. **GPS:** n48,70430 e15,86637. ⌐⌐.

8 ⌂€ 5 ⌐€ 1/10minutes ⌐Ch ⌐€ 1/6h.
Location: Urban, simple. **Surface:** gravel. ◻ 01/01-31/12
Distance: ⌐500m ⌐300m ⌐on the spot ⌐on the spot.

| ⌐⌐S | Reichenau/Rax | 35A3 |

Kaiserbrunn, Bundesstraße Höllental 27. **GPS:** n47,73480 e15,79188.

⌂free. **Surface:** metalled.

| ⌐⌐S | Reichenau/Rax | 35A3 |

Gasthof Flackl Wirt, Hinterleiten 12. **GPS:** n47,69056 e15,82778.

5 ⌂€ 14 breakfast incl ⌐⌐according consumption ⌐WC⌐at restaurant.
Distance: ⌐1,5km ⌐on the spot.

| ⌐S | Retz | 35A2 |

Parkplatz Alter Sportplatz, Jahnstraße. **GPS:** n48,75382 e15,95105.

2 ⌂€ 3 ⌐€ 1/10minutes ⌐Ch ⌐€ 1/8h. **Location:** Simple.
Surface: asphalted. ◻ 01/04-31/10 ⌐ last weekend of Sep
Distance: ⌐500m ⌐500m.

| ⌐S | Rossatzbach | 35A3 |

Wohnmobilplatz Artner, Aggsteiner-Bundesstraße.
GPS: n48,38750 e15,51722. ⌐⌐.

⌂free ⌐⌐(2x)€ 1/8h.
Location: Rural, simple, quiet. **Surface:** grasstiles. ◻ 01/01-31/12
Distance: ⌐on the spot.
Remarks: Parking in front of church.

| ⌐ | Schiltern bei Langenlois | 35A3 |

Erlebnisgärtner Kittenberger, Laabergstraße 15.
GPS: n48,51180 e15,63277. ⌐.

3 ⌂free. **Location:** Simple, isolated. ◻ 01/01-31/12
Distance: ⌐500m.

| ⌐S | Schönberg ⌐ | 35A3 |

Freizeitzentrum, Badgasse. **GPS:** n48,52063 e15,69377. ⌐.

5 ⌂€ 5, first night free ⌐WC⌐.
Location: Rural, simple. **Surface:** asphalted. ◻ 15/5-31/08
Distance: ⌐200m ⌐300m ⌐200m ⌐Kamptalradweg.
Remarks: Use sanitary only during opening hours swimming pool.
Along river.

| ⌐ | Schrems | 35A2 |

Parkplatz Stadthalle, Doktor-Karl-Renner-Straße.
GPS: n48,79167 e15,07120. ⌐.

3 ⌂free. **Location:** Urban, simple, central. **Surface:** asphalted.
◻ 01/01-31/12
Distance: ⌐on the spot ⌐on the spot ⌐100m.

| ⌐S | Stockerau | 35A3 |

Hallenbad Wellness Oase, Pestalozzigasse.
GPS: n48,39385 e16,21912. ⌐⌐.

6 ⌂free ⌐€ 2 ⌐ChWC⌐sanitary in swimming pool.
Location: Comfortable. **Surface:** gravel. ◻ 01/01-31/12
Distance: ⌐1,5km ⌐500m ⌐50m.

AT

| | Sankt Martin am Ybbsfelde ⌐ | 35A3 |

Gemeindeparkplatz, St. Martin. **GPS:** n48,16465 e15,01995. ⌐.

12 ⌂€ 10 ⌐⌐Ch ⌐(12x)WC⌐included.
Location: Rural, comfortable. **Surface:** gravel. ◻ 01/01-31/12
Distance: ⌐300m ⌐on the spot ⌐100m ⌐1,5km.
Remarks: Vinotheek 300m.

Stockerau 35A3

Alte Au, Zum Spitzgarten. **GPS:** n48,38366 e16,20394.⬆️

3 🏕free. **Location:** Urban, simple. **Surface:** asphalted.
📅 01/01-31/12
Distance: 🚶1km ⊗50m.
Remarks: At sports centre.

Weistrach 35A3

Parkplatz Sportplatz. GPS: n48,05475 e14,58167.⬆️

10 🏕free. **Location:** Rural, simple. **Surface:** asphalted.
📅 01/01-31/12
Distance: 🚶200m ⊗on the spot 🚊200m.
Remarks: Near sports fields.

Weitra 35A3

Freizeitzentrum Hausschachen, Promenade.
GPS: n48,70414 e14,89343.⬆️

10 🏕free. **Location:** Simple, quiet. **Surface:** gravel.
📅 01/01-31/12
Distance: 🚶600m ⊗600m.
Remarks: Max. 1 night.

Wiener Neustadt 35A3

Parkplatz Stadion, Stadionstrasse. **GPS:** n47,82156 e16,25629.⬆️

20 🏕. **Location:** Urban. **Surface:** asphalted. 📅 01/01-31/12
Distance: 🚶500m 🚊on the spot.

Wilfersdorf 35B3

Schloss Wilfersdorf, Parkplatz am Schloss.
GPS: n48,58600 e16,64514.⬆️

3 🏕€ 4 🚰WC. 📅 01/01-31/12
Distance: 🚶100m ⊗300m 🚊on the spot.
Remarks: Check in at Schloss, 10-16h tue/su.

Ybbs an der Donau 35A3

Donauufer, Donaulände. **GPS:** n48,17979 e15,08387.⬆️
5 🏕free. **Surface:** metalled. 📅 01/01-31/12
Distance: 🚶700m ⊗700m.

Zwettl 35A3

Wirtshaus zur Minidampfbahn, 47, Teichhäuser bei Zwettl.
GPS: n48,66278 e15,15444.⬆️➡️

10 🏕€ 5 🚰Ch 🚿€2,50. **Location:** Rural, simple, quiet.
Surface: grassy. 📅 01/01-31/12
Distance: 🚶2km 🏊200m ⊗on the spot 🚊2,5km.

Vienna

Wien 35A3

Reisemobil Stellplatz Wien
- ■ **Excellent location for city visit**
- ■ **Open all year**
- ■ **Bread-service**

www.reisemobilstellplatz-wien.at
office@reisemobilstellplatz-wien.at

Reisemobilstellplatz Wien, Perfektastraße 49-53, Vienna (Wien).
GPS: n48,13698 e16,31582.⬆️➡️
167 🏕€ 21 🚰Ch 🚿(167x)WC included 📶€2/24h.
Location: Urban, luxurious. **Surface:** grassy/gravel. 📅 01/01-31/12
Distance: 🚶on the spot 🚲4km ⊗30m 🚊30m 🚌metro 150m
🚊100m.

Wien 35A3

Kurpark Oberlaa, Filmteichstrasse 5, Vienna (Wien).
GPS: n48,15211 e16,39767.
🏕free. **Surface:** grassy/metalled.
📅 01/01-31/12
Distance: 🚌centre > bus 68A Reumannplatz > tram U1 Stefansdom.
Remarks: No camping activities.

Wien 35A3

Weingut Heuriger Schilling, Langenzersdorferstraße 54, Wien-
Strebersdorf, Vienna (Wien). **GPS:** n48,29856 e16,38421.

2 🏕€ 5, guests free 🚰Ch 🚿WC. **Surface:** grassy/gravel.
📅 Feb, Apr, Jun. Aug, Oct 📅 other months
Distance: 🚶Vienna 15km 🚌on the spot.
Remarks: Max. 3 days.

Tourist information Vienna (Wien):
ℹ️ Overnight parking prohibited.
ℹ️ Tourist-Info, Albertinaplatz 1, info.wien.at/. Imperial city, many
curiosities, capital of the classic music.
ℹ️ Wien-Karte. Card gives 72h entrance to public transport and
discounts on museums, curiosities. Available at Tourist-Info and hotels.
🎫 € 19,90.

👁 Spanische Hofreitschule, Michaelerplatz 1. Spanish Riding School,
morning-training can be visited without reservation. 📅 9.40-12.30h.
Ⓜ Kunsthistorisches Museum, Maria Theresien-Platz. Important painting collection. 📅 Tue-Su 10-18h, Thu 10-21h. 🎫 € 14.
☺ Wurstelprater. Amusement park. 📅 15/03-15/10 10-24h.

Vorarlberg

Dornbirn 19B3

Stellplatz Mathis, Obere Härte 27. **GPS:** n47,40577 e9,72492.
3 (7-8-10m) 🏕€ 15 + tourist tax € 1/pp 🚰Ch 🔌included.
Location: Comfortable. **Surface:** grasstiles.
📅 01/01-31/12
Distance: 🚶on the spot 🚲2km 🏊on the spot 🚶on the spot.

Hard 19B2

Gasthaus Sternen, Landstraße 49. **GPS:** n47,48442 e9,68698.
8 🏕customers free 🚰. **Surface:** asphalted. 📅 Mo
Distance: 🚶Bregenz 4,5km ⊗on the spot.

Schoppernau 19C3

Breganzerwaldstrasse. **GPS:** n47,31674 e10,00835.

10 🏕free. **Surface:** metalled.
Distance: 🚶600m ⊗on the spot 🚊600m 🚌on the spot
🚲on the spot.
Remarks: Parking ski-lifts. .

Tyrol

Achenkirch 19E2

Wohnmobilhafen Achensee, Achenkirch 17.
GPS: n47,49947 e11,70655.

10 🏕from € 14 + € 1,50/pp tourist tax, € 1 Umwelttaxe 🚰Ch 🚿
3,50/24h WC included. **Location:** Rural, comfortable, luxurious, quiet.
Surface: grasstiles/metalled. 📅 01/01-31/12
Distance: 🏊on the spot 🚌on the spot.
Remarks: Max. 1 night, dog € 4,50, extra pers € 7, electricity winter €
0,70/kWh.

Aschau im Zillertal 19F3

Reisemobilhafen Aufenfeld, Aufenfeldweg.
GPS: n47,26318 e11,90063.

10 🏕€ 17 🚰Ch 🚿WC.
Location: Rural. **Surface:** grassy. 📅 01/01-31/12
Remarks: Quick-Stop: >19h - <9h.

Biberwier 19D3

Wohnmobilhafen Arienberg, Marienbergstrasse 15.
GPS: n47,37472 e10,89223.⬆️➡️

AT

18 ⛺€ 15, 2 pers.incl, tourist tax € 2/pp 🚰🔌Ch.🚿€2,50/24 ⬛included. **Location:** Rural, comfortable. **Surface:** grassy/gravel. 🅿 01/01-31/12
Distance: 🛒on the spot 🚉2km 🏊on the spot 🚌on the spot.

| 🅰 | Bichlbach | 19D2 |

Almkopfbahn. GPS: n47,42367 e10,78116.

15 ⛺. 🅿 01/01-31/12
Distance: 🛒5km ⊗on the spot 🚞on the spot 🏊on the spot.
Remarks: Parking next to valley station.

| 🅰 | Breitenwang | 19D2 |

Seespitze. GPS: n47,47417 e10,78472.
⛺. 🅿 01/05-15/10

| 🅰 | Breitenwang | 19D2 |

Sennalpe. GPS: n47,48639 e10,83972.
⛺. 🅿 15/12-15/10

| 🅰 | Feichten/Kaunertal | 19D3 |

Kaunertal. GPS: n47,05333 e10,75056.
⛺. 🅿 01/05-30/09

| 🅰🅂 | Galtür ⛷❄ | 19C3 |

Bergbahnen, Silvretta-Bundesstraße, B188, Wirl.
GPS: n46,96570 e10,16390.🚟.

⛺€ 20, summer free 🚰🔌Ch.
Location: Rural. **Surface:** gravel. 🅿 winter
Distance: ⊗100m 🚞on the spot 🏊on the spot 🚌on the spot.
Remarks: Free skibus to Ischgl.

| 🍴🅂 | Galtür ⛷❄ | 19C3 |

Zeinissee, Zeinisjochstrasse. **GPS:** n46,97824 e10,12738.🚟.

⛺€ 23-25,50 incl. 2 pers, dog € 3 🚰🔌🚿€0,70/kWh WC⬛included ⤵against payment. **Location:** Rural. **Surface:** grassy/gravel.
🅿 Whitsuntide-05/10
Distance: 🛒Galtür 8,5km ⊗on the spot.
Remarks: Silvrettacard incl., one night stay + € 5.

| 🍴🅂 | Gerlos ⛷⛰❄ | 19F3 |

Bauernhof Schönachhof, Schönachtal 242. **GPS:** n47,22639 e12,05476.

24 ⛺€ 20, winter € 30 + tourist tax, dog € 4 🚰🔌Ch.🚿WC⬛.
Location: Isolated. 🅿 01/01-31/12
Tourist information Gerlos:
☺ Activ Wellness. Free wellness program. 🅿 01/07-30/09.

| 🍴🅂 | Gries am Brenner | 19E3 |

Gasthof Humler-Hof, Nößlach 483. **GPS:** n47,06660 e11,47187.
50 ⛺free 🚰WCfree. 🅿 01/01-31/12
Distance: 🛒Gries 5km 🚢1km.

| 🅲🅂 | Hall in Tirol ⛷⛰❄ | 19E3 |

Wohnmobilpark, Scheidensteinstraße 24.
GPS: n47,28444 e11,49665.🚟.

10 ⛺€ 10-15 + € 1/pp + tourist tax 🚰🔌Ch.🚿included.
Location: Urban. **Surface:** metalled. 🅿 01/01-31/12
Distance: 🛒400m ⊗200m Gaststätte 🚉300m.
Remarks: Max. 1 night.

| 🍴🅂 | Heiterwang ⛰❄ | 19D2 |

Ferienhof Sunnawirt, Mühle 4. **GPS:** n47,44951 e10,74812.🚟.

30 ⛺€ 7 + tourist tax € 2/pp 🚰🔌Ch.🚿€3 ⤵.
Surface: grassy/gravel.
Distance: 🛒200m 🚣Heiterwanger See 1,6km ⊗200m 🚉200m 🚶on the spot 🚞3km 🏊on the spot.
Remarks: Bread-service.

| 🍴🅂 | Ischgl ⛰⛷❄ | 19C3 |

Mathoner Straße 5, Ischgl-Mathon. **GPS:** n46,98967 e10,24751.🚟.

8 ⛺€ 15 + tourist tax 🚰🔌Ch.🚿(8x)⬛.
Location: Rural, simple. **Surface:** gravel. 🅿 01/01-31/12
Distance: 🛒1km ⊗100m.
Remarks: Free skibus to Ischgl and Galtür.

| 🍴🅂 | Jenbach | 19E2 |

Gasthof Rieder, Fischl 3. **GPS:** n47,40131 e11,77500.🚟.

3 ⛺free 🚰. **Location:** Rural, simple, isolated.
Surface: asphalted.
Remarks: Guests only.

| 🅲🅂 | Kramsach | 19F2 |

Camping Seehof, Moosen 42. **GPS:** n47,46138 e11,90685.

10+10 ⛺€ 13,20-18,20, 2 pers.incl, tourist tax € 2/pp, dog € 3 🚰🔌Ch.🚿€2,80/4kWh WC⬛included ⤵against payment.
Location: Rural. 🅿 01/01-31/12
Distance: 🚣Reintalersee ⊗on the spot 🚞free 🏊on the spot.
Remarks: 10 overnight pitches outside side + 10 special motorhome pitches on campsite (same price).

| 🍴🅂 | Leutasch ⛰ | 19D3 |

Am Kreithlift, Weidach 381. **GPS:** n47,36392 e11,16657.🚟.
20 ⛺€ 26, 2 pers.incl 🚰🔌Ch.🚿WC⬛included 🔌.
Surface: asphalted/gravel. 🅿 15/12-15/03
Distance: 🛒1,5km ⊗on the spot 🚞on the spot 🏊on the spot.
Remarks: Loipenplakette, drying room for skis and sauna included.

| 🅰 | Matrei | 19F3 |

Matreier Tauernhaus, Nähe Tauer 22. **GPS:** n47,11833 e12,49778.
20 ⛺€ 5/24h. **Surface:** gravel. 🅿 01/05-30/11
Distance: ⊗on the spot.

| 🅰🅂 | Nassereith | 19D3 |

Roßbach, Roßbach 325. **GPS:** n47,31153 e10,85270.

⛺€ 20,50 🚰🔌Ch.🚿included. **Surface:** grassy. 🅿 01/01-31/12
Distance: 🚉500m.

| 🍴🅂 | Obsteig ⛰ | 19D3 |

Gasthof zum Lenz, Gschwent 282. **GPS:** n47,30930 e10,94482.🚟.

6 ⛺€ 15 🚰🔌Ch.🚿included. **Location:** Rural, simple, isolated.
Surface: grassy/gravel. 🅿 01/01-31/12
Distance: 🚶on the spot 🏊on the spot.

| 🅲🅂 | Pettneu am Arlberg ⛰ | 19C3 |

Camping Arlberg, Pettneu am Arlberg 235. **GPS:** n47,14506 e10,33816.

54 🛏€ 15, winter € 23 + tourist tax, dog € 3 🚰🔌Ch included 🔌 €1/2kWh 📶. **Location:** Luxurious. **Surface:** grassy/metalled. 🅿 01/01-31/12
Distance: 🚶1km 🏊250m 🚌on the spot.
Remarks: Bread-service, winter: skibus, summer: hiking bus.

| 🅲 S | Pfunds ☕ 📶 ❄ ❄ | 19D3 |

Wohnmobilplatz Via Claudiasee, Rauth 714.
GPS: n46,95429 e10,51171. ⬆.

10 🛏€ 10 + € 1,50/pp tourist tax, dog € 1,50 🚰 €1/80liter 🔌Ch 🔌 0,60/kWh WC 🚽sanitary €3/pp 🚿from €0,50.
Location: Rural, comfortable.
Surface: grassy/metalled.
🅿 01/01-31/12
Distance: 🚶2km 🚌on the spot ⊗200m 🏊on the spot 🧍on the spot.
Remarks: Bread-service.

| 🅿 S | Schwaz ☕ | 19E2 |

Wohnmobilstellplatz Königfeld, Königfeldweg.
GPS: n47,34655 e11,70436. ⬆.

10 🛏€ 4 🚰€2 🔌Ch.
Location: Urban, simple, central. **Surface:** asphalted.
🅿 01/01-31/12
Distance: 🚶500m 🏊1,9km Gaststätte 50m 🚉50m.
Tourist information Schwaz:
👁 Schwazer Silberbergwerk. 🅿 01/05-31/10.

| 🍴 S | Steinach am Brenner | 19E3 |

Gasthaus Wolf, Brennerstraße 36. **GPS:** n47,06704 e11,48574.
5 🛏guests free 🚰. **Surface:** asphalted.
Distance: 🚶2km ⊗on the spot.
Remarks: At the old Brennerstraße.

| 🍴 | Stumm 👣 | 19F3 |

Gasthof Rißbacher Hof, Ahrnbachstraße 37.
GPS: n47,27951 e11,89347. ⬆.

3 🛏€ 15 WC 📶. **Location:** Rural, simple. **Surface:** asphalted.
🅿 Wed

| 🍴 S | Wenns/Piller ❄ ❄ | 19D3 |

Gasthof Sonne, Piller 41. **GPS:** n47,13581 e10,69390. ⬆.

3 🛏€ 5, guests free. **Location:** Rural, simple, isolated. **Surface:** gravel.
🅿 01/01-31/12
Distance: ⊗on the spot 🚉50m.
Remarks: Altitude 1350m.

| ⛺ | Wiesing | 19E2 |

Inntal. **GPS:** n47,40585 e11,80536.

🛏. 🅿 01/01-31/12

Salzburg

| ⚒ S | Altenmarkt im Pongau | 19H2 |

Bauernhof Kellerbauer, Kellerdörfl Palfen 7.
GPS: n47,37015 e13,42923.
10 🛏€ 10 🚰🔌Ch 🔌€2. **Location:** Simple, isolated, quiet.
Surface: grassy/gravel. 🅿 01/01-31/12
Distance: 🚶1,5km.

| ⚒ S | Golling | 19G2 |

Wohnmobil-Park Aqua Salza, Möslstraße 199.
GPS: n47,59543 e13,17222. ⬆.

15 🛏€ 9,90 + € 1/pp tourist tax 🚰€1/80liter 🔌Ch 🔌€0,50/kWh.
Location: Rural, quiet. **Surface:** asphalted. 🅿 01/01-31/12
Distance: 🚶500m ⊗300m 🚉300m 🚌200m.
Remarks: Max. 5 days, check in on arrival.

| 🍴 S | Hüttschlag | 19H3 |

Bauernhof Stockham-Camping, See 5. **GPS:** n47,14775 e13,28947. ⬆.
5 🛏€ 15,60, 2 pers.incl 🚰🔌Ch 🔌€1,50 WC 🚽€1. 🅿 01/04-31/10
Distance: 🚶6km ⊗150m 🚉6km.

| 🍴 S | Krimml 🌲 👣 | 19F3 |

Hotel Krimmlerfälle, Wasserfallstraße 42.
GPS: n47,21827 e12,17543. ⬆ ➡.

10 🛏€ 20, dog € 4 🚰🔌Ch included 🔌(4x).
Location: Rural, simple. **Surface:** grassy/gravel. 🅿 15/05-25/10
Distance: 🚶500m ⊗on the spot.

| ⚒ S | Leogang 🌲 👣 ❄ ❄ | 19G2 |

Leoganger Bergbahnen, Hütten 39. **GPS:** n47,43963 e12,72040. ⬆.

50 🛏€ 8 + € 1,50/pp tourist tax 🚰🔌Ch 🔌(50x)€2/24h WC.
Location: Rural, comfortable, quiet. **Surface:** grassy/gravel.
Distance: 🚶3,5km ⊗on the spot 🚲on the spot.

| ⚒ S | Maria Alm | 19G2 |

Wohnmobilstellplatz Stegerbauer, Stegen 16.
GPS: n47,39765 e12,90350.

10 🛏€ 10-12 + tourist tax € 1/pp 🚰🔌Ch 🔌(10x)€2,50.
Surface: gravel. 🅿 01/01-31/12
Distance: 🚶1km 🚌on the spot ⊗500m 🚉1km 🚌200m 🧍on the spot 🚲1km 🏊on the spot.

| 🍴 S | Neukirchen 👣 | 19F3 |

Panoramastellplatz, Scheffau 96. **GPS:** n47,23862 e12,24083.

17 🛏€ 7, guests free 🚰🔌Ch 🔌€2 WC 📶.
Location: Rural, isolated, quiet. **Surface:** gravel.
🅿 01/01-31/12
Distance: 🚶4km ⊗on the spot 🚲Tauernradweg 🧍on the spot 🚲on the spot 🚲on the spot.
Remarks: Bread-service.

| ⚒ | Tweng | 19H3 |

Landhotel Postgut, Tweng 2. **GPS:** n47,19058 e13,60210.

5 🛏€ 10. **Surface:** metalled. 🅿 01/01-31/12
Distance: 🚶on the spot ⊗on the spot.

Styria

| ⚒ S | Bad Gams 🌲 👣 ⛲ | 36A1 |

Freizeitzentrums GamsBad, Bad Gams 2.
GPS: n46,86730 e15,22743. ⬆.

6 🛏€ 5 🚰🔌Ch. **Surface:** grasstiles/metalled. 🅿 01/01-31/12
Distance: 🚶200m 🏊on the spot ⊗200m 🚉100m 🚌200m.

AT

Remarks: Check in at Gamsbad.

Bad Radkersburg `36B1`

Camping Alt-Weindörfl, Altneudörfl 144. **GPS:** n46,69444 e15,98991. €4 + €3/pp WC included. **Surface:** gravel.
Distance: 750m on the spot 750m.

Bad Waltersdorf `35A3`

Gasthof Erhardt, Am Waltersdorfberg 99.
GPS: n47,16687 e15,98921.

4 €8, guests free. **Location:** Rural, simple. **Surface:** grasstiles.
01/01-31/12
Distance: 1,8km 3,2km on the spot.

Bad Waltersdorf `35A3`

Thermenland Camping, Campingplatzweg 316.
GPS: n47,16246 e16,02296.
10 Mondscheinplätze €9,50/18-9h, 2 pers. incl. + tourist tax.
01/01-31/12
Distance: 1,6km 3km Stüberl.

Deutsch Goritz `36B1`

Pechmann's Alte Ölmühle, Ratschendorf 188.
GPS: n46,75072 e15,81337.
15 customers free according consumption.
Surface: metalled. **Distance:** 850m on the spot.

Deutschfeistritz `35A3`

Sportclub Union. GPS: n47,20116 e15,32710.

20 €11, 2 pers.incl Ch €2 WC included.
Surface: grassy. 01/04-01/11
Remarks: At manege, check in on arrival, bread-service.

Deutschlandsberg `36A1`

Koralmhalle, Höhe Frauentalerstraße 51.
GPS: n46,81783 e15,22248.

2 free. **Surface:** asphalted. 01/01-31/12
Distance: 200m on the spot 100m on the spot.
Remarks: Max. 3 days.

Gaishorn am See `35A3`

Sportzentrum, Sieberer Weg, B113. **GPS:** n47,48583 e14,54803.
10 €11, 2 pers.incl (6x)€4 WC included.
Surface: gravel. 15/04-30/09
Distance: 500m 4,6km Gaishorner See 100m.

Gamlitz `36B1`

Wohnmobilstellplatz Gamlitz, Untere Hauptstraße 455.
GPS: n46,72028 e15,56833.

30 €20 liter Ch stay €1/2kWh WC included.
Location: Rural, comfortable. **Surface:** gravel.
01/04-31/10
Distance: 1km 5km on the spot on the spot on the spot.
Remarks: Parking at Motorikpark.

Gamlitz `36B1`

Buschenschank Loar-Moar, Untere Hauptstraße 21.
GPS: n46,72196 e15,56495.

9 €22 Ch included. **Location:** Rural. **Surface:** grassy.
01/05-31/10
Distance: 900m 5,5km.

Gosdorf `36B1`

Hof Schönwetter, Haus 5. **GPS:** n46,72630 e15,79652.
6 €10 . **Surface:** grassy. 01/01-31/12
Distance: 500m 2km.

Graz `35A3`

Reisemobil Stellplatz Graz

Excellent location for city visit

Open all year

Located in a quiet area

www.reisemobilstellplatz-graz.at
office@reisemobilstellplatz-graz.at

Reisemobil Stellplatz Graz, Martinhofstraße 3.
GPS: n47,02472 e15,39694.
160 €21 Ch (160x) WC included €2/2 €2/day.
Location: Urban. **Surface:** grassy/gravel. 01/01-31/12
Distance: on the spot 3,5km on the spot on the spot
200m 250m 200m on the spot on the spot.
Remarks: Video surveillance.

Graz `35A3`

Stellplatz Wölfl, Steinfeldgasse 47. **GPS:** n47,06527 e15,42046.
5 €12 €2/day.
Location: Simple. **Surface:** asphalted. 01/01-31/12 Sa-Su
Distance: 1,5km 3,7km.
Remarks: At motorhome dealer, check in during opening hours.

Tourist information Graz:
Freilichtmuseum, Stübing. Open air museum. 01/04-31/10.
Schloß Eggenberg, Eggenberger Allee 90. 01/04-31/10 Tue-Su 10-17h. €6.
Schlossbergbahn, Kaiser-Franz-Josef-Kai. Mountain railway, gradient 61%. €1,70.

Großlobming `35A3`

Murinsel, Teichweg 1. **GPS:** n47,19326 e14,80422.
16 €9/18-10h 2 pers,incl, 1 hour €1 Ch included.
Surface: grassy. 01/01-31/12
Remarks: Reservation in winter peak season.

Hieflau `35A3`

Gasthaus zum Harmonika Wald, Wandau 9.
GPS: n47,62255 e14,75411.
5 guests free included. **Surface:** asphalted.
01/01-31/12 Wed
Distance: 1,8km on the spot.

Jagerberg `36B1`

Am Freibad. GPS: n46,85152 e15,74655.

6 free €0,50/60liter Ch.
Location: Rural, simple. **Surface:** asphalted/gravel.
Distance: 500m 500m 500m.

Jagerberg `36B1`

Kindergarten Vorplatz, Jagerberg 98.
GPS: n46,85692 e15,74292.

15 free liter (1x). **Location:** Rural, simple. **Surface:** gravel.
01/01-31/12
Distance: 400m 400m 400m 400m.

Judenburg `35A3`

Erlebnisbad, Fichtenhainstraße. **GPS:** n47,16407 e14,65308.

5 €5 Ch WC free. **Surface:** gravel. 01/01-31/12
Distance: 500m 200m 200m.
Remarks: Check in at swimming pool.

Kaindorf `35A3`

Buschenschank Schleiss, Obertiefenbach 42.
GPS: n47,23839 e15,84498.

4 €6, guests free Ch. **Location:** Rural, simple.
Surface: asphalted. 01/03-15/12
Distance: on the spot.

Leutschach `36B1`

Buschenschank Krampl, Schloßberg 9. **GPS:** n46,63898 e15,45872.
10 Ch . 01/03-30/11
Distance: 6km.

Leutschach `36B1`

Ölpresse Resch, Schlossberg 89. **GPS:** n46,65170 e15,47114.
6 €13 WC included. **Location:** Rural, simple.
Surface: asphalted. 01/04-30/11
Distance: 2km.

AT

Leutschach 36B1

Weinbau Peter Grill, Kranach 48. **GPS**: n46,68478 e15,47191.
4 free included €3. **Surface**: grassy. Easter-01/11
Distance: 4,5km.

Liezen 35A3

Sportzentrum, Friedau. **GPS**: n47,56500 e14,23333.

3 free €1. **Surface**: gravel. 01/01-31/12
Distance: 1km 5,3km 300m 1km on the spot.

Mureck 36B1

Wohnmobilstellplätze Mureck, Hauptplatz 30.
GPS: n46,70489 e15,77240.

5 € 12,40-19. **Location**: Urban, simple. **Surface**: metalled.
01/04-01/11
Distance: 350m 10km.
Remarks: Max. 5 days.

Murfeld 36B1

Gasthof Dorfheuriger Rom Thomas, Dorfstrasse 1, Unterschwarza.
GPS: n46,71557 e15,67624.

40 € 10 Ch WC included.
Location: Comfortable. **Surface**: grassy. 01/01-31/12
Distance: 200m 2,5km on the spot.
Remarks: Check in at restaurant, bread-service,
wifi code: Camping01, entrance code: camp1.

Oberrakitsch 36B1

Ölmühle Sixt, Oberrakitsch 115. **GPS**: n46,73863 e15,74605.

10 € 10 Ch WC included. **Location**: Rural, simple.
Surface: gravel. 01/01-31/12
Distance: 1km on the spot 1km 3km 4km.
Remarks: Bread-service.

Passail 35A3

Almenland Stellplatz, Auen 61. **GPS**: n47,28217 e15,55711.

4 free €0,50/60liter Ch €0,50/kWh. **Location**: Rural,
comfortable. **Surface**: asphalted. 01/01-31/12
Distance: Passail 3,5km.

Pichl-Kainisch 19H2

Sportstüberl Andrea, Pichl 57. **GPS**: n47,56711 e13,85207.
3 guests free. **Surface**: metalled. 01/01-31/12 Wed

Pölfing-Brunn 36A1

Kipferlbad, Badstraße 13. **GPS**: n46,72422 e15,29268.

10 free. **Location**: Rural, simple. **Surface**: grassy.
01/01-31/12
Distance: 1km on the spot on the spot 1km 1km.

Riegersburg 35A3

P Seebad. **GPS**: n46,99677 e15,94107.

10 free. **Location**: Rural, simple. **Surface**: asphalted.
01/01-31/12
Distance: 500m on the spot 500m.
Remarks: Swimming pool available.

Sankt Stefan im Rosental 36B1

Schichenauerstraße 6. GPS: n46,90634 e15,71431.

15 free €1/100liter Ch (6x)€0,50/kWh.
Location: Rural, comfortable. **Surface**: gravel. 01/01-31/12
Distance: 200m 200m 200m.

Schwanberg 36A1

Freibad, Badstraße. **GPS**: n46,76361 e15,20639.

4 free, 16/05-14/09 € 6 Ch included.
Surface: gravel. 01/01-31/12
Distance: 500m on the spot on the spot 500m 500m.

Soboth 36A1

Parkplatz Soboth-Stausee. GPS: n46,68142 e15,03805.

free. **Location**: Rural, simple. **Surface**: asphalted.
Distance: 5km on the spot 200m on the spot.
Remarks: Parking at artificial lake.

Stadl an der Mur 36A1

Da' Bräuhauser, Steindorf 23. **GPS**: n47,08885 e13,98824.
15 € 14-18, 2 pers.incl, tourist tax € 1/pp Ch included
€0,60/kWh. **Surface**: grassy. 01/01-31/12
Distance: 500m.

Stainz 36A1

Parkplatz 3, Ettendorfer Straße. **GPS**: n46,89377 e15,26823.

3 free. **Surface**: metalled.
01/01-31/12
Distance: 100m 100m 100m.

Tourist information Stainz:

Region Süd-Weststeiermark, Hauptplatz 34, www.stainz.at.
Das Land des Schilcher, country of the Austrian rosé wine.
Der Stainzer Flascherlzug. Narrow-gauge steam train. 01/05-31/10 Sa-Su 15h.
Ren(nt)a Traktor, Anton Nettwall, Sommereben 95, St. Stefan ob Stainz. With a tractor through Schilcherland. € 50 1/2 day.

Unterlamm 35A3

Sieglhof, Magland 44. **GPS**: n46,98152 e16,09172.

10 € 5 on demand. **Location**: Rural, simple.
Surface: grassy/gravel. 01/01-31/12 Tue + Wed
Distance: 4km on the spot 1,5km on the spot.

Veitsch 35A3

Marktgemeindeamt, Obere Hauptstraße 18.
GPS: n47,57896 e15,48961.

2 free. **Surface**: asphalted. 01/01-31/12
Distance: 300m 100m 100m 100m.

Vordernberg 35A3

Hauptplatz 2. GPS: n47,48617 e14,99202.

AT

6 ⛺ 🚰 €1/10minutes 🔲Ch 🔧€1/8h. **Surface:** gravel.
🅾 01/04-31/10
Distance: 🛒500m ⊗500m 💧500m 🚌on the spot.

Vordernberg — 35A3

Traktormuseum, Böhlerstraße 8. **GPS:** n47,47364 e14,98741.
5 ⛺ € 5, free with a meal 🚰.
Surface: grassy. 🅾 01/01-31/12 🍴 Restaurant: Mo-Tue
Distance: 🔧13km ⊗on the spot.
Remarks: Parking nearby museum.

Carinthia

Bad Sankt Leonhard im Lavanttal — 36A1

Bachwegbrücke. GPS: n46,96037 e14,79358.

8 ⛺free. 🅾 01/01-31/12
Remarks: Parking behind Spar-supermarket.

Bleiburg — 36A1

Grabenstraße. **GPS:** n46,59095 e14,79550.

4 ⛺free. **Surface:** grasstiles. 🅾 01/01-31/12
Distance: ⊗100m 💧on the spot 🚌200m.

Ferlach — 36A1

Messeparkplatz Schloß Ferlach. GPS: n46,52633 e14,29750.

30 ⛺€ 4/24h 🚰 €1/10minutes 🔲Ch 🔧(10x)€1/10h. 📶
Location: Urban, simple. **Surface:** metalled. 🅾 01/01-31/12
Distance: 🛒500m ⊠on the spot ⊗300m 💧300m 🚌300m.
Remarks: Max. 24h, no camping activities.

Glödnitz — 36A1

Gasthof Hochsteiner, Laas Straß2 9. **GPS:** n46,87226 e14,11655.
20 ⛺€ 3, guests free.
Surface: asphalted. 🅾 01/01-31/12 🍴 Restaurant: Mo
Distance: ⊗on the spot.

Heiligenblut — 19G3

Möllfluss-Camping, Pockhorn 30. **GPS:** n47,02371 e12,86180.
⛺ € 16 2p incl. + tourist tax. **Surface:** asphalted.
🅾 15/06-01/09

Hermagor — 22H1

Schluga, Vellach 15. **GPS:** n46,63147 e13,39532.

6 ⛺€ 14 2 pers.incl, dog € 3,10 🚰🔲Ch 🔧(6x)€2,72 WC⌐included.
Surface: gravel. 🅾 01/01-31/12
Distance: 🚌winter free shuttle to piste.
Remarks: Peak season max. 3 days, max. 7 days.
Tourist information Hermagor:
🖐 Presseggersee. Nature reserve, no motor boats allowed.

Kötschach–Mauthen — 22G1

Gasthof Gailberghöhe, Gailberg 3. **GPS:** n46,71525 e12,96753.

70 ⛺€ 14,50, 2 pers.incl. 🚰🔲Ch 🔧WC⌐included.
Surface: asphalted/gravel. 🅾 01/05-15/11, 15/12-15/03
Distance: 🛒7km ⊗on the spot 💧7km 🔧2km 🚌7km.

Ledenitzen — 36A1

Ferien am Walde. GPS: n46,57046 e13,95161.
⛺. 🅾 01/05-01/10

Mörtschach — 19G3

Gasthaus Schwaiger, Mörtschach 35. **GPS:** n46,92287 e12,91348.

4 ⛺guests free 🚰🔧. **Surface:** grassy.

Rosegg — 36A1

Gasthof Roseggerhof, Schulweg 4. **GPS:** n46,59026 e14,02037.

10 ⛺guests free. **Location:** Rural, simple. **Surface:** gravel.
🅾 01/01-31/12 🍴 week after Easter, week after All Saints' Day
Distance: 🔧9km ⊗on the spot.

30 ⛺€ 10,50-12 + € 1,20/pp tourist tax 🚰🔲🔧included ⌐€2.
Location: Rural, simple. **Surface:** grassy. 🅾 01/04-01/11
Distance: 🔧8km ⊗on the spot 💧bakery 150m.

Sachsenburg — 19H3

Restaurant Auszeit, Obergottesfeld 79. **GPS:** n46,79959 e13,35137.

Wernberg — 36A1

Landgasthof Fruhmann, Triester Straße 1.
GPS: n46,62501 e13,92933.

5 ⛺guests free. **Location:** Rural, simple. **Surface:** gravel.
🅾 01/01-31/12
Distance: 🛒Villach 6,5km 🔧1,2km ⊗on the spot 💧bakery + butcher.

Zlan — 19H3

Nagelerhof, Ziebl 4. **GPS:** n46,74042 e13,57707.

8 ⛺€ 17,20 + € 1,50/pp tourist tax 🚰🔲Ch 🔧€1,50 WC⌐included.
🚿 **Location:** Simple. **Surface:** grassy.
🅾 01/03-31/10
Distance: 🔧8km.
Remarks: Not suitable for motorhomes +7m.

Burgenland

Andau — 35B3

Pusztasee. GPS: n47,77536 e17,03265.
⛺€ 17 🚰🔲Ch🔧. 🅾 15/04-15/10

Bad Tatzmannsdorf — 35A3

Thermencamping, Am Campingplatz 1, Oberschützen.
GPS: n47,33912 e16,21892.
15 ⛺€ 13-19,40 + € 1,50/pp tourist tax 🚰🔲Ch 🔧according consumption WC⌐included ⊡. **Surface:** gravel.

Breitenbrunn am Neusiedlersee — 35B3

Parkplatz Yachthafen und Bad. GPS: n47,91806 e16,76314.
12 ⛺€ 3,20, € 3,20/pp 🚰🔲Ch.
Location: Isolated. **Surface:** gravel. 🅾 01/04-31/10
Distance: 🛒Breitenbrunn 3,8km 🔧14km ⛵on the spot.
Remarks: Service on campsite.

Deutsch Jahrndorf — 35B3

Söldnergasse 19. **GPS:** n48,00777 e17,11073.

17 ⛺voluntary contribution 🚰🔲Ch. **Surface:** grassy.
🅾 01/04-31/10
Distance: 🛒500m ⊗500m 💧on the spot.
Remarks: Max. 3 nights.

Horitschon — 35B3

Weingut Duschanek, Hauptstraße 104. **GPS:** n47,59162 e16,53493.

10 ⛺€ 5, guests free 🚰🔲Ch 🔧€3 WC. **Surface:** metalled.

AT

☐ 01/01-31/12
Distance: 🚶600m ⊗on the spot 🍺600m 🚃on the spot.

Wohnmobilstellplatz Pustablick, Ufergasse 42.
GPS: n47,75851 e16,79606.⬆️.

5 🚐voluntary contribution 🚰🔌€2.
Location: Rural, simple. **Surface:** grassy. ☐ 01/04-01/11
Distance: 🚶900m ⊗900m 🍺bakery 500m.

11 🚐€ 10 🚰🔌Ch🔌 WCincluded.
Location: Rural, comfortable, quiet. **Surface:** grassy. ☐ 01/03-31/10
Distance: 🚶500m 🚴13,5km ⚓500m Neusiedler See ⊗on the spot 🍺1km.
Remarks: When buying wine 1 night free.

Bioweingut Edelhof, Hauptplatz 6. **GPS:** n47,95922 e16,79012.⬆️.

3 🚐€ 15 🚰🔌Ch🔌included.
Location: Rural, simple. **Surface:** grassy/gravel. ☐ 01/03-31/10
Remarks: In the courtyard of a medieval farmstead.

P Weinmuseum-Kulturverein Moschendorf, Moschendorf 95.
GPS: n47,05784 e16,47713.
🚐. **Surface:** asphalted. ☐ 01/01-31/12

Kulturzentrum Gasthof Cselly Mühle, Sachsenweg 63.
GPS: n47,84119 e16,62510.⬆️.

10 🚐free. **Location:** Rural, simple, isolated. **Surface:** grassy.
☐ 01/01-31/12
Distance: 🚶1,2km ⊗on the spot.
Remarks: Check in on arrival.

Weingut Schaller, Frauenkirchnerstraße 20.
GPS: n47,85032 e16,83934.⬆️.

8 🚐€ 8 🚰🔌Chincluded 🔌€2/24h.
Location: Rural, simple. **Surface:** grassy.
Distance: 🚶300m.
Remarks: When buying wine 1 night free.

Weingut Sloboda, Alte Satz 1. **GPS:** n47,85020 e16,83091.⬆️.

AT

Bosnia and Herzegovina

Capital: Sarajevo
Government: Federation
Official Language: Bosnien, Croatien and Serbian
Population 3,871,000 (2014)
Area: 51,209 Km²

General information
Dialling code: 0387
General emergency: 112
Currency: convertible Mark (BAM) also the Euro is accepted as currency.
Credit cards are accepted in the main cities.

Regulations for overnight stays
Wild camping is not allowed.

Additional public holidays 2016
March 1 Independence Day
May 1 Labour Day
May 9 Victory Day
November 25 Statehood Day

Time Zone
Winter (Standard Time) GMT+1
Summer (DST) GMT+2

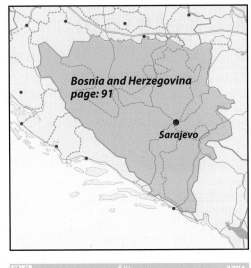

Bosnia and Herzegovina page: 91

Sarajevo

BA

Banja Luka — 36C2
Kamp Olimp. GPS: n44,71114 e17,16642.
10 🏕 €15 🚰🍽Ch🧺 included. **Surface:** grassy. 🅾 01/01-31/12
Distance: 🚶8km ⊘on the spot 🛒on the spot.

Bihać — 36B2
Kamp Orljani. GPS: n44,80145 e15,90643.
120 🏕 €18,50 🚰🍽Ch🧺 included 📺. **Surface:** grassy/gravel.
🅾 01/05-01/11
Distance: 🚶3,5km ⊘on the spot ⊗100m.

Bihać — 36B2
Una Kiro Rafting, Golubić. **GPS:** n44,78250 e15,92472.
9 🏕 €17 🚰🍽Ch🧺 included. **Surface:** grassy. 🅾 01/04-01/11
Distance: 🚶5km ⊘on the spot 🛒on the spot ⊗on the spot.

Bila — 36C3
Motel Carousel. GPS: n44,17886 e17,75475.
15 🏕 €15 🚰🍽Ch🧺 included. **Surface:** grassy. 🅾 01/01-31/12
Distance: 🚶1km ⊘on the spot.

Blagaj — 37B2
Autocam Blagaj. GPS: n43,25682 e17,87936.
25 🏕 €20 🚰🍽Ch🧺📶included.
Surface: grassy. 🅾 01/04-01/10
Distance: 🚶Mostar 12km ⊘on the spot.

Blagaj — 37B2
Mail Wimbledon. GPS: n43,26317 e17,87799.
60 🏕 €18 🚰🍽Ch🧺€3 📶included.
Surface: grassy/gravel. 🅾 01/01-31/12
Distance: 🚶Mostar 10km ⊗150m ⚓100m.

Blagaj — 37B2
River Camp Aganovac. GPS: n43,25724 e17,88774.
8 🏕 €20 🚰🍽Ch🧺📶included.
Surface: grassy/sand. 🅾 01/01-31/12
Distance: ⊘on the spot 🛒on the spot ⊗200m 🚌150m.

Bosanska Krupa — 36B2
Una Camping. GPS: n44,91484 e16,15696.
🏕 €16 🚰🍽Ch🧺 included. **Surface:** grassy. 🅾 01/05-01/10
Distance: ⊘on the spot 🛒on the spot.

Buna — 37B2
River Camp Half Island. GPS: n43,24166 e17,83861.

20 🏕 €17 🚰🍽Ch🧺📶included.
Surface: grassy. 🅾 01/04-01/10
Distance: ⊘on the spot 🛒on the spot ⊗500m 🚌500m.
Remarks: Only cash payment.

Foča — 37C1
Auto Camp Drina. GPS: n43,52948 e18,78254.
15 🏕 €17 🚰🍽Ch🧺📶included. **Surface:** grassy.
🅾 01/05-15/09
Distance: 🚶3km ⊘on the spot 🛒on the spot ⊗on the spot.

Gradačac — 36D2
Hipodrom Vuković. GPS: n44,91860 e18,41893.
🏕 €20 🍽Ch🧺 included. **Location:** Rural. **Surface:** grassy/sand.
🅾 01/04-01/11
Distance: ⊘on the spot.

Jajec — 36C3
Autocamp Plivsko Jezero. GPS: n44,35103 e17,22682.

40 🏕 €21 🍽Ch🧺included 📺. **Surface:** grassy. 🅾 15/04-31/10
Distance: 🚶5km ⊘100m 🛒100m ⊗on the spot.

Krupa na Vrbasu — 36C2
Camp Krupa. GPS: n44,61616 e17,14837.
80 🏕 €12 🚰🍽Ch🧺 included. **Surface:** grassy. 🅾 01/05-01/10
Distance: ⊘on the spot 🛒on the spot ⊗200m.

Kulen Vakuf — 36B3
RC Discover Bihac. GPS: n44,56909 e16,08338.

25 🏕 €5 + €5/pp 🚰🍽Ch🧺 WC 📶included.
Surface: grassy/gravel. 🅾 01/04-30/10
Distance: ⊘on the spot 🚵on the spot 🚶on the spot.

Medugorje — 37B2
Camp Zemo. GPS: n43,19432 e17,67612.
45 🏕 €10 🚰🍽Ch🧺 included. **Surface:** gravel. 🅾 01/01-31/12
Distance: 🚶100m ⊗100m.

Sarajevo — 37B1
Oaza. GPS: n43,82799 e18,29659.

350 🏕 €20,90 🍽Ch included 🧺 €2,60.
Surface: grassy. 🅾 01/01-31/12
Distance: 🚶10km ⊗100m 🚌800m.

Ščit — 37B1
Konoba Gaj. GPS: n43,80230 e17,52560.
5 🏕 €10 🚰🍽Ch🧺 included. **Location:** Rural. 🅾 01/01-31/12
Distance: ⊘on the spot 🛒on the spot ⊗on the spot.

Belgium

Capital: Brussels
Government: Constitutional monarchy
Official Language: Dutch/Flemish, French and German
Population: 11.324.000 (2015)
Area: 30,518 km²

General information
Dialling code: 0032
General emergency: 112
Currency: Euro

Regulations for overnight stays
Wild camping is forbidden.

Additional public holidays 2016
May 1 Labour Day
July 11 Feast Flemish Community
July 21 National Day
August 15 Assumption Day
September 27 Feast of the Walloon Region
November 1 All Saints' Day
November 11 Armistice Day 1918

Time Zone
Winter (Standard Time) GMT+1
Summer (DST) GMT+2

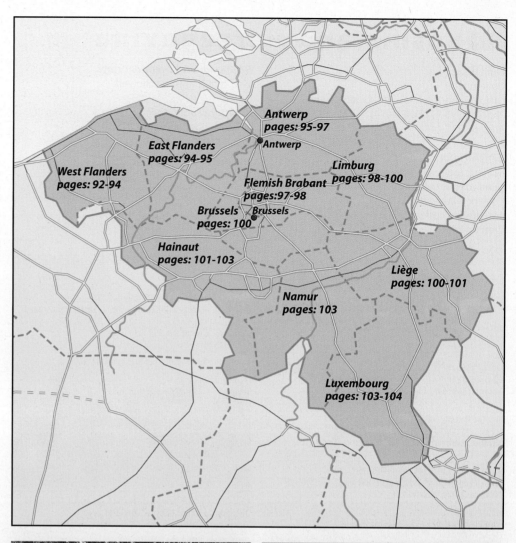

Antwerp pages: 95-97
Antwerp
East Flanders pages: 94-95
West Flanders pages: 92-94
Limburg pages: 98-100
Flemish Brabant pages:97-98
Brussels pages: 100
Brussels
Hainaut pages: 101-103
Liège pages: 100-101
Namur pages: 103
Luxembourg pages: 103-104

West Flanders

Aartrijke   10A1
Sint-Aarnoutstraat. **GPS:** n51,11341 e3,08983.

3 free. **Surface:** asphalted. 01/01-31/12
Distance: 400m 80m 50m.

Beernem   10A1
Kanaaloever Beernem, Oude Vaartstraat.
GPS: n51,13482 e3,33427.

6 € 10/24h Ch (4x)WC included,sanitary at harbour building. **Location:** Rural. **Surface:** metalled.
01/01-31/12
Distance: 1,9km.
Remarks: Max. 72h, only exact change.

Brugge   10A1
Bargeweg. **GPS:** n51,19633 e3,22544.

59 € 15, € 22,50 01/04-30/09 €0,50 Ch included.
Location: Urban, simple, central. **Surface:** metalled.
01/01-31/12
Distance: within walking distance on the spot.
Remarks: Max 3,5t, monitored parking.

Tourist information Brugge:
ℹ Brugge City Card gives for free entrance on among other things 27 museums, boat trips and many discounts on purchases. € 43.
ℹ Toerisme Brugge, 't Zand 34, www.brugge.be. City with medieval character, hiking itinerary available at Tourist office.
👁 Boat excursion from Bruges to Damme with the `Lamme Goedzak', departure Noorweegse Kaai.
👁 Brouwerij Halve Maan, Walplein 26. Town brewery. 10-18h. € 7,50.
Ⓜ Diamantmuseum, Katelijnestraat 43. Diamond museum. 10.30-17.30h.
☻ Boudewijnpark, Alfons De Baeckerstraat 12, Sint-Michiels. Attractions park with dolphinarium, seal island etc., in winter large skating rink covered.

Diksmuide   12D1
't Nesthof, Zijdelingstraat 2a. **GPS:** n51,07178 e2,86422.

14 € 9/night Ch €2. **Location:** Rural, isolated, quiet.
Surface: grassy. 01/04-01/10
Distance: 5km.
Remarks: Bread-service.

Gistel   10A1
Sportstraat. **GPS:** n51,16112 e2,96495.

2 free Ch free. **Surface:** metalled.
Distance: 1km 3,3km on the spot on the spot.
Remarks: Parking behind swimming pool, key service at swimming pool, many walking and bicycle area.

Harelbeke   10A2
Kampeerautoterrein De Dageraad, Stasegemsesteenweg 21.
GPS: n50,84396 e3,31057.

8 🏕️ €5 🔌 💧 Ch 💧 included WC 🚻 €1,25 📶 free. 🚐
Surface: metalled. 🅿️ 01/01-31/12
Distance: 🚂 1,6km 🚴 4,5km 🏊 700m 🚌 100m.
Remarks: Parking next to midget golf, service during opening hours: 8-20h.

⛺ S | Knokke-Heist | 10A1
Holiday, Natiënlaan 72. **GPS:** n51,33612 e3,28666.
10 🏕️ € 18 01/10-30/06 € 20 01/07-30/09 🔌 💧 Ch 💧 WC 🚻 included.
Surface: metalled. 🅿️ 01/10-28/10
Distance: 🚂 1km.

⛺ S | Kortemark | 10A1
Sporthal Kortemark, Ichtegemstraat 2a. **GPS:** n51,03201 e3,04168. ⬆️

2 🏕️ free 🔌 €2 💧 €2 Ch. **Surface:** metalled. 🅿️ 01/01-31/12
Distance: 🚂 500m 🚌 on the spot.
Remarks: Max. 48h.

⛺ S | Kortrijk | 10A2
Kampeerautoterrein Broeltorens, Damkaai.
GPS: n50,83120 e3,26818. ⬆️

8 🏕️ € 10/24h 🔌 💧 Ch 💧 included. 🚐 📖 **Location:** Urban.
Surface: metalled. 🅿️ 01/01-31/12
Distance: 🚂 centre 400m 🛒 100m.
Tourist information Kortrijk:
ℹ️ Dienst Toerisme, Begijnhofpark, www.kortrijk.be. Historical little town with Beguine convent.

⛺ S | Langemark- Poelkappele | 10A1
Boezingestraat 51a. **GPS:** n50,90944 e2,91763. ⬆️

8 🏕️ € 12 🔌 💧 Ch 💧 (4x)included 🚻 €1/time. 🚐
Location: Urban, simple. **Surface:** grasstiles. 🅿️ 01/01-31/12
Distance: 🛒 on the spot 🚶 on the spot.
Remarks: Max. 72h, check in at reception sports centre.

⛺ | Lichtervelde | 10A1
O.C. De Schouw, Twee Lindenstraat. **GPS:** n51,02389 e3,13493. ⬆️
2 🏕️ free. **Surface:** metalled. 🅿️ 01/01-31/12
Distance: 🚂 600m 🛒 600m 🛒 300m 🔌 on the spot 🚶 on the spot.
Remarks: Max. 48h.

⛺ | Mesen | 12D2
Kerkstraat. **GPS:** n50,76391 e2,89825. ⬆️

3 🏕️ free. **Surface:** metalled. 🅿️ 01/01-31/12
Distance: 🚂 on the spot 🍴 frituur 200m 🛒 100m.
Remarks: In front of church, max. 24h.

⛺ S | Middelkerke | 12D1
Camperpark Poldervallei, Westendelaan 178.
GPS: n51,16684 e2,78246. ⬆️
16 🏕️ € 15-22 🔌 💧 Ch 💧 included. **Surface:** asphalted.
🅿️ 01/01-31/12
Remarks: Nearby camp site.

⛺ S | Nieuwpoort 🌿🏖️ | 12D1
De Zwerver, Brugsesteenweg 29, N367. **GPS:** n51,12988 e2,76576. ⬆️

28 🏕️ €0,50/h 🔌 €0,50/50liter 💧 Ch 💧 included,10Amp WC 🚻 💡 €4/time. 🚐 **Surface:** grassy. 🅿️ 01/01-31/12
Distance: 🚂 within walking distance 🚴 3,3km.

⛺ | Oudenburg | 10A1
Carpool, Stationsstraat. **GPS:** n51,19387 e3,00567.

🏕️ free 🔌 €2 💧 €2 Ch. **Surface:** metalled.
Distance: 🚴 800m.
Remarks: P service max. 30 min.
Tourist information Oudenburg:
⛲ 🅿️ Wed-afternoon.

⛺ | Poperinge 🌿 | 12D2
Oudstrijdersplein. **GPS:** n50,85300 e2,72300.

🏕️ 💡 Fri
Distance: 🚂 500m 🛒 50m.

⛺ | Roeselare | 10A1
O.L. Vrouwenmarkt. **GPS:** n50,94786 e3,13450. ⬆️

1 🏕️ free. **Surface:** metalled. 🅿️ 18-9h, 01/01-31/12h

Distance: 🚂 200m 🚌 on the spot.
Remarks: Max. 1 night.

⛺ | Roeselare | 10A1
Trakelweg. **GPS:** n50,94438 e3,13320. ⬆️

10 🏕️ free. **Location:** Urban. **Surface:** asphalted. 🅿️ 01/01-31/12
Distance: 🚂 1km 🔌 on the spot 🚶 on the spot.
Remarks: No camping activities.

⛺ S | Sint-Eloois-Vijve | 10A1
Kampeerautoterrein Leiekamper, Leiesas 15.
GPS: n50,90879 e3,40468.

8 🏕️ € 5 🔌 €1/100liter 💧 💧 included,16Amp. 🚐 🅿️ 01/01-31/12
Distance: 🚂 400m 🛒 400m 🛒 1km 🔌 on the spot 🚶 on the spot.
Remarks: Max. 72h.

⛺ S | Veurne 🌿 | 12D2
Kaaiplaats/Lindendreef. **GPS:** n51,07052 e2,66484. ⬆️

6 🏕️ free WC €0,50 🚻 €1,50,sanitary at harbour building.
Surface: metalled.
Distance: 🚂 on the spot 🚴 2km.
Remarks: Max. 6,5m.

⛺ S | Wervik 🏖️ | 10A2
Kampeerautoterrein De Balokken, De Balokken.
GPS: n50,77456 e3,03705. ⬆️

8 🏕️ € 10/72h 🔌 €1/100liter 💧 Ch 💧 included. 🅿️ 01/01-31/12
Distance: 🚂 1km 🏊 on the spot 🔌 on the spot 🍴 cafetaria 🛒 700m bakery.
Remarks: On leisure island, max. 72h.

⛺ S | Westende 🏖️ | 12D1
Camperpark Westende, Heidestraat 18. **GPS:** n51,15597 e2,76623.

30 🏕️ € 18, 2 pers.incl 🔌 💧 Ch 💧 WC 🚻 📶 included. 🚐

BE

⬛ 01/01-31/12
Distance: 🛒on the spot 🏊1km ⊗on the spot.
Remarks: Discount longer stays, swimming pool.

🛁S	**Westende** 🛶🏖	12D1

Kompas kampeerautoterrein, Strandjuttersdreef.
GPS: n51,15594 e2,76019.⬆.

35 🅿20h € 11-16,50, 44h € 19,50-29,50 ⛽🗑Ch⚡included ♻.
Surface: grasstiles/metalled. ⬛ 01/01-31/12
Distance: 🛒on the spot 🏊1km ⊗Taverne, Frituur 🍴on the spot.

🍴S	**Wingene**	10A1

Smart - ijs BVBA, Noordakkerstraat 1a. **GPS**: n51,07377 e3,26515.⬆.

6 🅿€ 6, guests Bistro free ⛽🗑Ch⚡📶included. 🚿
Location: Rural. **Surface:** gravel.
Distance: 🛒2km 🚴 bike junction.
Remarks: Max. 72h.

🛁	**Zeebrugge**	10A1

Baron de Maerelaan. **GPS**: n51,32821 e3,18452.⬆.

9 🅿free. **Surface:** metalled.
Distance: 🛒on the spot 🏊350m ⊗100m.

🛁	**Zeebrugge**	10A1

Kustlaan. **GPS**: n51,33350 e3,20777.⬆.

7 🅿free. **Location:** Simple. **Surface:** asphalted. ⬛ 01/01-31/12
Distance: ⊗snack 500m 🍴1,5km 🚌200m.

Tourist information Zeebrugge:
👁 Havenrondvaart. ⬛ 01/07-30/09 11h, 14h, 16h, Easter, 01/05-30/06 Su.
Ⓜ Seafront maritiem museum, Albertdok, Vismijnstraat 7. Maritime museum. ⬛ 10-18h.
😊 Boudewijn Seapark, St. Michiels. Amusement park with dolphinarium. ⬛ 01/05-31/08 10-18h.

🍴S	**Zonnebeke**	10A2

Café De Dreve, Lange Dreef 16. **GPS**: n50,85410 e2,97924.

🅿free. **Surface:** gravel. ⬛ 01/01-31/12
Distance: 🛒Zonnebeke 2,7km 🛣3,5km A19 ⊗snacks 🚴on the spot 🚶on the spot.
Remarks: Passendalemuseum-Zonnebeke.

East Flanders

🛁S	**Aalst** 🌿	10B1

Zwembadlaan 2. **GPS**: n50,93825 e4,05829.

2 🅿free 🚰100liter 🗑Ch🚽included1h ⚡€5.
Surface: metalled.
Distance: 🛒city centre ± 1km 🛣3,8km 🍴on the spot.
Remarks: Only 2 plots indicated, more plots permitted.

Tourist information Aalst:
🚶 ⬛ Thu-morning.

🛁	**Aalter**	10A1

Vaart-Zuid, Bellem. **GPS**: n51,09821 e3,49365.⬆.

25 🅿free. **Surface:** asphalted.
Distance: 🏊Canal.

🛁	**Aalter**	10A1

Vaart-Noord, Bellem. **GPS**: n51,09875 e3,49468.⬆.

25 🅿free. **Surface:** asphalted.
Distance: 🍴600m 🏊500m.

🍴	**Aalter**	10A1

Bellemdorpweg, Bellem. **GPS**: n51,09323 e3,48308.⬆.

2 🅿free. **Surface:** asphalted.
Distance: 🛒500m.
Remarks: At football ground.

Tourist information Aalter:

🏰 Kasteel Poeke, Kasteelstraat 26, Poeke. ⬛ weekend, holidays, 01/04-31/10 Su 14-17h.
🚶 ⬛ Wed-morning.

🛁S	**Assenede**	10B1

Kapelledreef. **GPS**: n51,23067 e3,74891.⬆➡.

5 🅿€ 5/72h ⛽€1/60 🗑Ch🚿 WCfree 🗑€1/1.🚰 **Location:** Urban, comfortable, quiet. **Surface:** grassy. ⬛ 01/01-31/12 ⚫ Service: winter
Distance: 🛒500m ⊗600m 🚴on the spot 🚶on the spot.
Remarks: Behind gymnasium, max. 72h, sanitary during opening hours gymnasium.

🛁	**Bazel** 🌿	10B1

Sporthal De Dulpop, Beekdam 1. **GPS**: n51,14778 e4,30583.⬆.

10 🅿free. **Location:** Rural, simple. **Surface:** asphalted.
Distance: 🛒200m 🛣6km 🚉3km 🍴500m 🚌500 m 🚴on the spot 🚶on the spot.
Remarks: Barn-museum 200m.

🛁	**Berlare** 🍴🏖	10B1

Donklaan, Berlare-Overmere. **GPS**: n51,04258 e3,98293.⬆➡.

4 🅿free. **Surface:** grasstiles. ⬛ 01/01-31/12
Distance: 🛣9km 🏊Donkmeer ⊗on the spot.

⚓S	**Eeklo** 🌿	10A1

Jachthaven Eeklo, Nijverheidskaai. **GPS**: n51,17884 e3,54959.⬆.

12 🅿€ 10/24h ⛽€0,50/130liter 🗑Ch⚡€5/24h,6Amp WC🚿
Surface: grasstiles/metalled. ⬛ 01/01-31/12
Distance: 🛒1,5km ⊗1,5km 🍴800m.
Remarks: Check in at harbourmaster, use sanitary only during opening hours.

Tourist information Eeklo:
👁 Provinciaal Domein "Het Leen", Gentsesteenweg 80. Nature reserve. ⬛ 9-12h, 13-17h ⚫ Mo.

🛁	**Gavere** 🌿	10B1

Sportdreef. **GPS**: n50,92823 e3,65810.⬆.

12 ⌁free. **Surface:** asphalted. ◘ 01/01-31/12
Distance: 🚾on the spot.
Remarks: Behind sports complex.

| 🅿️ | Gentbrugge | | 10B1 |

Sportcentrum Driebeek, Driebeekstraat 22.
GPS: n51,03762 e3,76628.⬆️➡️

5 ⌁free ⚡Chfree. **Surface:** asphalted. ◘ 01/01-31/12
Distance: 🚾900m, Gent 4,5km 🚲1,5km 🚃 Tram Ghent-centre.
Remarks: Ghent Festival the week of July 21.

Tourist information Gentbrugge:
⛲ Ledebergplein, Ledeberg. ◘ Su 7.30-13h.
⛲ Schooldreef. ◘ Mo 7.30-13h.
🎭 Lazy River, Arsenaal. Jazz festival and village fair. ◘ Whitsuntide.

| 🅿️ | Geraardsbergen 〰️ | | 10B2 |

Jeugherberg 't Schipken, Kampstraat 59, N460, dir Ninove.
GPS: n50,79500 e3,90412.⬆️➡️

4 ⌁free. **Surface:** grassy. ◘ 01/01-31/12
Distance: 🚾Geraardsbergen 3,7km 🚲on the spot.
Remarks: Max. 1 night.

Tourist information Geraardsbergen:
⛲ Provinciaal Domein "de Gavers", Onkelzelestraat 280. Recreation area; swimming, watersports, fishing, boat trips and tennis.Free entrance, payment per attraction.

| Hamme | | 10B1 |

Camperplaats Hamme, Mirabrug, Hamveer.
GPS: n51,10418 e4,14246.⬆️

2 ⌁free. **Location:** Rural, simple, quiet.
Surface: metalled.
Distance: 🚾1km 🚲400m 🚌500m 🚲 on the spot 🚶on the spot.
Remarks: Max. 48h.

| 🅿️ | Lokeren 〰️ | | 10B1 |

Veerstraat. **GPS:** n51,11013 e3,97163.⬆️

5 ⌁free. **Location:** Urban, noisy. **Surface:** metalled.
◘ 01/01-31/12
Distance: 🚃1,5km, bakery 500m.
Remarks: Parking in front of church, max. 48h.

| 🅿️ | Lokeren 〰️ | | 10B1 |

Verloren Bos, Aardeken. **GPS:** n51,10981 e3,99525.⬆️

2 ⌁free. **Location:** Rural, simple. **Surface:** unpaved.
◘ 01/01-31/12
Distance: 🚾500m 🚌600m.

Tourist information Lokeren:
⛲ Stationsplein. Flea market. ◘ Su 7-12h.
〰️ Molsbroek. Protected European Nature Reserve, 80ha marsh area with many birds, asphalted hiking trail. ◘ Su 14-17h, 01/07-31/08 Wed-Su 14-17h.

| 🅿️ S | Maldegem 〰️ | | 10A1 |

Zwembad St.Anna, Gidsenlaan. **GPS:** n51,21160 e3,44172.⬆️

⌁free 🚰. **Location:** Urban. **Surface:** asphalted/metalled.
Distance: 🚾700m 🚌700m.
Remarks: Check in at swimming pool, water on demand.

| 🅿️ S | Ronse | | 10A2 |

Engelsenlaan/Boulevard des Anglais. **GPS:** n50,74447 e3,58794.

4 ⌁free 🚰⚡free. **Surface:** asphalted.
Distance: 🚾1km 🚌200m 🚌on the spot.
Remarks: Behind swimming pool.

| 🅿️ | Temse 〰️ | | 10B1 |

De Zaat, Nagelheetmakerslaan1. **GPS:** n51,12466 e4,21007.⬆️

⌁free. **Location:** Urban. **Surface:** asphalted. ◘ 01/01-31/12
Distance: 🚾400m 🚌250m.
Remarks: Behind police station, temporary stopover.

| 🅿️ S | Temse 〰️ | | 10B1 |

Camperbedrijf Alpha Motorhomes, Kapelanielaan 13a, N16.
GPS: n51,13699 e4,18017.⬆️

⌁free 🚰⚡Chfree. **Surface:** metalled.
Distance: 🚾city centre 3km.

Tourist information Temse:
⛲ Grote Markt. ◘ Fri-morning.

| 🅿️ S | Zulte 〰️ 🚲 | | 10A1 |

Leihoekstraat, Machelen. **GPS:** n50,96095 e3,48305.⬆️

8 ⌁€8/72h 🚰€1 ⚡Ch 🔌included. **Surface:** metalled.
◘ 01/01-31/12
Distance: 🚾150m 🚌50m 🚌150m 🚲on the spot.
Remarks: Max. 72h.

Antwerp

| 🅿️ S | Antwerpen 〰️ 🚲 🛒 | | 10C1 |

Vogelzang, Vogelzanglaan 7-9, **GPS:** n51,18983 e4,40074.⬆️

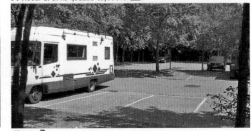

140 ⌁€ 8,50, July-Aug € 10,50 🚰included ⚡Ch 🔌(30x)€1/kWh.
Location: Simple. **Surface:** grassy/metalled.
◘ 01/01-31/12
◙ 31/10-11/11, 04/01-19/01
Distance: 🚾city centre 3km 🚲1km 🏊3km 🚌500m 🚃1km 🎬3km 🚌150m.

Tourist information Antwerp (Antwerpen):
ℹ️ Antwerp City Card gives free City tour, entrance to museums, churches and many discounts on purchases. 🎫 € 19.
ℹ️ Toerisme Antwerpen, Grote Markt, 13, www.visitantwerpen.be.
Large port city, worth seeing is the city centre.
⛲ Dageraadsplaats. ◘ Thu 8-13h.
⛲ Lijnwaadmarkt. Antiques market. ◘ Easter-Oct Sa 9-17h.
⛲ St. Andriesplaats. ◘ Tue 8-13h.
⛲ St. Jansplein. ◘ Wed, Fri 8-13h.
⛲ St. Jansvliet. Bric-a-brac market. ◘ Su 9-17h.
⛲ Theaterplein. Exotic market. ◘ Sa.
⛲ Vogelenmarkt, Theaterplein. Famous flea market. ◘ Su-morning.

| 🅿️ S | Arendonk | | 10D1 |

De Vloed. **GPS:** n51,32253 e5,08610.⬆️

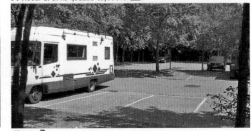

⌁free 🚰
Distance: 🚾400m 🚌on the spot 🚃100m.
Remarks: Parking in front of swimming pool, max. 24h, water during

BE

openinghours swimming pool.

BE

Bornem 10B1
Kasteel d'Ursel, Koningin Astridlaan. **GPS**: n51,10294 e4,27261.

5 free. **Location**: Rural. **Surface**: unpaved.
01/01-31/12
Remarks: Parking next to castle, open 8-21h.

Brasschaat 10C1
P5b, Elshoutbaan 17. **GPS**: n51,28555 e4,50325.

15 free €1/100liter Chfree €0,50/kWh.
Location: Rural. **Surface**: metalled/sand. 01/01-31/12
Distance: 1,7km 6km 500m 500m on the spot on the spot.
Remarks: Parking sports and recreation centre, max. 72h.

Tourist information Brasschaat:
Armand Reusensplein. Mo 8-13h.

Brecht 10C1
Mudeausstraat. **GPS**: n51,34814 e4,64123.

2 free At townhall. **Location**: Urban. **Surface**: metalled.
01/01-31/12
Distance: on the spot 1,2km 150m 150m.
Remarks: Max. 48h.

Brecht 10C1
Schoolstraat. **GPS**: n51,34992 e4,64577.

10 free. **Surface**: grassy.
Distance: 800m 1,5km.

Essen 8C3
Kerkeneind, N133. **GPS**: n51,47086 e4,46401.

2 free Chfree. **Location**: Urban, simple, central, quiet.

Surface: metalled. 01/01-31/12
Distance: on the spot 150m on the spot on the spot.
Remarks: Max. 24h.

Grobbendonk 10C1
Vaartkom. **GPS**: n51,18954 e4,73638.

6 free €1/5minutes free Ch€1 (6x)€1.
Surface: asphalted.
Distance: 200m 3,6km frituur 200m.

Herentals 10C1
Herenhoutseweg. **GPS**: n51,16586 e4,82664.

Surface: asphalted.
Distance: 1,5km 2,8km bakery 200m.
Remarks: Parking multipurpose area, next to footballstadium VC Herentals.

Herentals 10C1
BLOSO centrum Netepark, Vorselaarsebaan.
GPS: n51,18937 e4,82899. 15 free. **Surface**: asphalted.

Tourist information Herentals:
Augustijnenlaan. Su-morning.
Grote Markt. Fri-morning.

Herselt 10C1
Taverne Herberg Mie Maan, Diestsebaan 28.
GPS: n51,06025 e4,92897.

6 free. **Surface**: gravel. 01/01-31/12
Distance: 3km on the spot 3km.
Remarks: Restaurant visit appreciated, intersection hiking and biking trails.

Kalmthout 10C1
Kalmthoutse Heide, Heibloemlaan. **GPS**: n51,37688 e4,44911.

2 free. **Location**: Rural, simple, isolated, quiet. **Surface**: grasstiles.
01/01-31/12
Distance: city centre 2km 50m on the spot on the spot.
Remarks: Parking nature reserve, max. 24h.

Koningshooikt 10C1
Donderheide. **GPS**: n51,08439 e4,56541.

free. **Surface**: unpaved.
Distance: on the spot.
Remarks: In front of 'Het Fort'.

Koningshooikt 10C1
Motorhomes Konings, Sander de Vosstraat 141.
GPS: n51,08774 e4,62816.

€2,50 €2 €2,50. **Surface**: asphalted.
Remarks: Apply during openinghours.

Lier 10C1
Parking Mol Poort, Aarschotsesteenweg. **GPS**: n51,12525 e4,57332.

3 €1 Ch . 01/01-31/12

Lier 10C1
Zaat, Leuvense Poort. **GPS**: n51,13020 e4,58212.

2 free. **Surface**: metalled.
01/01-31/12

Tourist information Lier:
Dienst Toerisme, Grote Markt 57.
City with old centre worth a visit.
City walls, prison tower and Zimmertoren. 10-12h, 14-17/18h.
Grote Markt/Eikelstraat. Sa 8-13h.
Kerststallentocht. Dec.

Putte 10C1
Ixenheuvel, Heuvel. **GPS**: n51,04678 e4,62564.

2 free Chfree. **Location**: Simple. **Surface**: asphalted.
01/01-31/12
Distance: 1,5km.
Remarks: Max. 48h.

ⓈPuurs 10B1
Eeuwfeeststraat/ Kerkhofstraat. **GPS:** n51,07476 e4,28337.⬆️➡️.

2 free ⚡Chfree. **Surface:** metalled. 🅿 01/01-31/12
Distance: 5,3km.
Remarks: Max. 48h, intersection hiking and biking trails.

ⓈSint-Amands 10B1
Parking Noord, Emile Verhaerenstraat. **GPS:** n51,05906 e4,20206.⬆️.

2 free ⚡Chfree. **Surface:** metalled. 🅿 01/01-31/12
Distance: ⊗200m 200m on the spot on the spot.

ⓈSint-Job-in-'t-Goor 10C1
Vaartlaan. **GPS:** n51,30151 e4,56888.⬆️.

2 free. **Location:** Urban. **Surface:** metalled. 🅿 01/01-31/12
Distance: on the spot ⊗50m 50m.
Remarks: Max. 48h.

Turnhout 10C1
Baalse Hei, Roodhuisstraat. **GPS:** n51,35385 e4,95591.⬆️.
7 € 19 - € 25 Ch €1,20 WC free.
Location: Rural. 🅿 15/01-15/12
Distance: 3km on the spot on the spot ⊗on the spot.
Tourist information Turnhout:
👁 Begijnhof. Beguine convent. 🅿 Tue-Sa 14-17h, Su 11-17h
◉ Christmas. 🅃 € 1,75.

ⓈWillebroek 10B1
Dijlelaan. **GPS:** n51,06028 e4,34472.⬆️.

3 free €1 €1 Ch. **Surface:** metalled. 🅿 01/01-31/12
Distance: 300m.
Remarks: Max. 2 nights.

Flemish Brabant

ⓈDiest 10C1
De Halve Maan, Omer Vanaudenhovelaan 48.
GPS: n50,98607 e5,06373.⬆️⬆️.

4 € 15 ⚡Ch (4x)included. **Location:** Comfortable, quiet.
Surface: grassy/gravel. 🅿 01/11-28/02
Distance: 1,2km, beguine convent 350m 20m ⊗200m 100m 100m.
Remarks: Check in at pay desk recreation centre, max. 72h.
Tourist information Diest:
👁 Begijnhof. Beguine convent. Art studios open: sa/so afternoon and in july/aug each afternoon. 🅿 Beguine convent daily, Angel convent Sa/Su 14.30-17h, church Easter-Oct Su 14-17h.

Grimbergen 10C1
K.S.C. Grimbergen, Brusselsesteenweg. **GPS:** n50,92787 e4,36610.⬆️.

10 free. **Location:** Simple. **Surface:** asphalted.
🅿 01/01-31/12
Distance: 1km 1km > Brussels.

BE

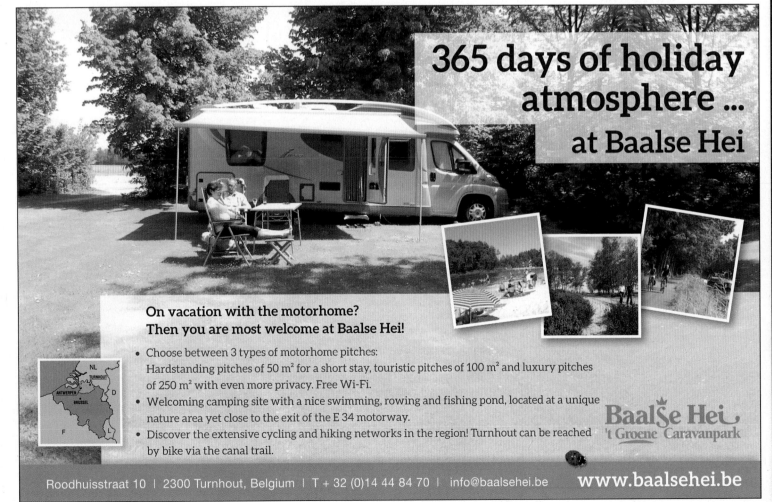

Tourist information Grimbergen:

🛈 Gemeentelijke Dienst voor Toerisme, Prinsenstraat 22. Well-known for the Abbey beer, info at the beer museum.
👁 Abdijkerk. Abbey-church. ⏱ 10-12h, 13-17h.
🎇 Jaarmarkt. Village festival with among other things fair, cattle market. ⏱ 1st weekend Sep.

| ♿ S | Merchtem | 10B1 |

Brusselsesteenweg. **GPS:** n50,95553 e4,24011. ⬆.

4 🍴free 🚿free.
Surface: metalled.
Distance: 🚌300m Good bus connection for Brussels.
Remarks: Next to cemetery and sports fields, no camping activities.

| ♿ S | Rotselaar | 10C1 |

Recreatiedomein Sportoase Ter Heide, Vakenstraat 18. **GPS:** n50,96217 e4,72288.

4 🍴free 🚰€1 🗑Chfree 🚿€1 WC🚽.
Surface: gravel. ⏱ 01/01-31/12
Distance: 🚌2km ⛱100m 🚲100m ⊗500m 🍺2km 🚗200m 🚴on the spot 🚶on the spot.

Limburg

| ♿ S | Bilzen 🌿 🚂 | 10D2 |

Parking Lanakerdij, Lanakerdij. **GPS:** n50,86985 e5,52215. ⬆.

7 🍴free 🚰€2 🗑Ch (5x). **Surface:** asphalted. ⏱ 01/01-31/12
Distance: 🚌300m ⚓3km ⊗300m 🍺300m 🚴on the spot 🚶on the spot.
Remarks: Max. 24h.

Tourist information Bilzen:

👁 Landcommanderij Alden Biesen, Rijkhoven. ⏱ 10-17h. 🎫 free.
👁 Zuivelhoeve 't Wanthof. Dairy farm. ⏱ Tue-Fri 10-22h, Sa-Su 9-23h.
🛒 Markt. ⏱ Wed.

| ♿ S | Bocholt 🌿 | 10D1 |

Heuvelzicht, Schipperstraat 1. **GPS:** n51,17722 e5,58500.

7 🍴€ 6,50/24h 🚰🗑Ch 🚿WCincluded 🔌€1.
Surface: asphalted.
⏱ 01/01-31/12
Distance: 🚌on the spot ⊗50m 🍺100m 🛒50m 🚗50m.
Remarks: Parking marina at Zuidwillemsvaart, max. 48h.

| ♿ S | Bolderberg | 10D1 |

Domein Bovy, Galgeneinde. **GPS:** n50,98690 e5,27048. ⬆.

3 🍴free 🚰€2 Ch 🔌€2/1h.
Location: Rural.
Surface: metalled.
Distance: 🚌500m ⊗150m 🍺500m 🚲bike junction 🚶on the spot.
Remarks: Estate with i.e. restaurant, bar, brasserie, marked hiking trails, herb garden, petting zoo, old tools.

| ♿ | Bree 🌿 | 10D1 |

N721, Opitter. **GPS:** n51,11788 e5,64524. ⬆.

5 🍴free. ⏱ 01/01-31/12
Remarks: Parking next to church, in front of petrol station, max. 48h.

Tourist information Bree:

🛒 Vrijthof. ⏱ Fri.
🎇 Sint-Antoniuskapel, Opitter.

| ♿ S | Diepenbeek | 10D1 |

Demerstrand, Stationsstraat. **GPS:** n50,91392 e5,42209. ⬆.

4 🍴free 🚰€2/100liter 🗑Ch 🚿€2/8h. **Surface:** asphalted.
⏱ 01/01-31/12
Distance: 🚌500m ⊗250m 🍺1km.
Remarks: At gymnasium, video surveillance.

| ♿ S | Dilsen-Stokkem | 10D1 |

De Wissen, Maaspark 3. **GPS:** n51,02361 e5,74945. ⬆.

3 🍴free. **Surface:** metalled. ⏱ 01/01-31/12
Distance: 🚌500m ⛱on the spot 🚲on the spot ⊗Taverne Maascentrum 🍺500m 🚗on the spot.
Remarks: Parking at tourist office De Wissen, starting point of cycle routes.

| ♿ S | Genk 🌿 | 10D1 |

Parking Kattevennen, Kattevennen. **GPS:** n50,95728 e5,53337.

8 🍴€ 5 🚰🗑Ch 🚿included.
Surface: asphalted.
Distance: 🚌3km ⊗taverne 🚗on the spot 🚴on the spot 🚶on the spot.
Remarks: Max. 24h, mountainbike and hiking trails, national park Hoge Kempen.

Tourist information Genk:

🛒 Zondagsmarkten. Flea market. ⏱ 01/06-31/08 9-13h.

| ♿ | Hamont | 10D1 |

Kerkplein. **GPS:** n51,25152 e5,54612. ⬆.

5 🍴free. **Surface:** metalled. ⏱ 01/01-31/12
Distance: 🚌on the spot ⊗50m 🍺50m 🚗50m.
Remarks: Behind church, max. 24h.

| ♿ | Hamont | 10D1 |

Michielsplein, Achel. **GPS:** n51,25423 e5,47985.

🍴free.
Distance: 🚌on the spot ⊗on the spot 🍺on the spot.
Remarks: At bicycle trail Limburgse Kempen, behind church of Achel, max. 24h, market Tuesday 8-13h.

| ♿ | Hamont | 10D1 |

Stadpark. **GPS:** n51,25085 e5,55200.

🍴free. **Surface:** unpaved.
Remarks: Large parking in the centre behind tennis-courts, max. 24h.

Tourist information Hamont:

🛈 VVV,
Generaal Dempseylaan 1, www.hamontachel.com. Historical little town. ⏱ Mo-Fri 9-12h, 13-16h, Sa 9-12h.

| ♿ S | Hasselt | 10D1 |

Sporthal Alverberg, Herkenrodesingel. **GPS:** n50,93998 e5,32072. ⬆.

>5 ⌹free ⛽€2 🚽Ch. **Surface:** metalled. ⬛ 01/01-31/12
Distance: 🚲city centre 3km 🛒Carrefour 🚐on the spot.

🏕 **Hasselt** 10D1
Bakkerslaan. **GPS:** n50,92141 e5,32562.⬆.

3 ⌹free. **Location:** Urban, simple. **Surface:** grasstiles/grassy.
⬛ 01/01-31/12
Distance: 🚲2km 🚴600m ⊗500m 🍽500m 🚐on the spot.

🍴 **Hasselt** 10D1
Restaurant Myosotis, Overdemerstraat 20, Kuringen.
GPS: n50,94663 e5,30877.⬆.

8 ⌹guests free.
Distance: ⊗on the spot 🍽bakery 50m.

🏕 **Hechtel/Eksel** 10D1
In den Brand. **GPS:** n51,12673 e5,35090.⬆.

⌹free. **Surface:** sand.
Distance: 🚲1,5km.

🏕 **Hechtel/Eksel** 10D1
Parking CC De Schans, Rode Kruisplein 10, Hechtel.
GPS: n51,12391 e5,36271.⬆.

⌹free. **Surface:** asphalted.
Distance: 🚲400m.

🏕 **Hechtel/Eksel** 10D1
Pijnven, Bosmuseum, Kiefhoekstraat. **GPS:** n51,16133 e5,31091.⬆.

⌹free. **Surface:** asphalted.
Distance: 🚲4km.
Remarks: Parking forest.

🏕 **Helchteren** 10D1
Parking de Dool, Sportstraat. **GPS:** n51,06087 e5,38650.⬆.

10 ⌹free. **Surface:** asphalted. ⬛ 01/01-31/12
Distance: 🚲1km ⊗500m 🚐500m.
Remarks: Next to castle.

🏕 **Herk-de-Stad** 10D1
Park Olmenhof, Pikkeleerstraat. **GPS:** n50,93361 e5,16654.

7 ⌹free 🚰€1/100liter 🚽Ch ⚡€0,60/kWh WC. **Location:** Rural,
simple. **Surface:** asphalted. ⬛ 01/01-31/12
Distance: 🚲400m 🚴7km ⊗50m 🍽300m.
Remarks: Max. 48h.

🍴🏕 **Hoepertingen** 10D2
De Verborgen Parel, Hoenshovenstraat 5.
GPS: n50,80170 e5,28944.⬆.

6 ⌹€7,50 🚰🚽Ch⚡. **Location:** Simple. **Surface:** gravel.
⬛ 01/01-31/12
Distance: 🚲1,5km 🍽1,5km 🚴on the spot 🚶on the spot.

🏕 **Houthalen** 10D1
De Dool, Sportstraat. **GPS:** n51,06143 e5,38670.⬆.

5 ⌹free. **Surface:** asphalted. ⬛ 01/01-31/12
Distance: 🚲Helchteren 800m 🚴5,6km ⊗800m.

🏕 **Houthalen** 10D1
Parking Kelchterhoef, Kelchterhoefstraat.
GPS: n51,03015 e5,44063.⬆.

6 ⌹free. **Surface:** metalled. ⬛ 01/01-31/12
Distance: 🚲6km ⊗on the spot.
Remarks: In front of abbey farm.

🏕 **Kinrooi** 10D1
Bomerhof, Bomerstraat 13. **GPS:** n51,15201 e5,74064.
25 ⌹€10 🚰🚽Ch⚡ WC included. **Surface:** grassy.
⬛ 01/01-31/12

Distance: 🚲800m ⊗800m 🚴on the spot 🚶on the spot.
Remarks: Check in on arrival.

🏕 **Kortessem** 10D2
Kapittelstraat. **GPS:** n50,85724 e5,39126.⬆→.

5 ⌹free 🚰. **Surface:** asphalted. ⬛ 01/01-31/12
Distance: 🚲200m ⊗200m 🍽bakery 200m 🚴on the spot.
Remarks: At gymnasium, max. 2 nights.

Tourist information Kortessem:
⚔ 't Rood Kasteel, Guigoven. Former medieval water castle.

⚓🏕 **Leopoldsburg** 10D1
Jachthaven, Antwerpsesteenweg 129. **GPS:** n51,12892 e5,25028.⬆.

22 ⌹€10 🚰included WC🚽€1. **Surface:** asphalted.
⬛ 01/01-31/12
Distance: 🚲2km 🏊on the spot ⊗on the spot 🍽2km.
Remarks: Check in at harbourmaster.

⚓🏕 **Lommel** 10D1
Taverne Haven de Meerpaal, Boskantstraat 60.
GPS: n51,24266 e5,36891.⬆.

15 ⌹€10 🚰€0,50 🚽Ch⚡(6x)€1 WC🚽€1. **Surface:** asphalted.
Distance: ⊗on the spot.
Remarks: Near marina.

🏕 **Maaseik** 10D1
Sportlaan P4. **GPS:** n51,10108 e5,78964.⬆.

20 ⌹free. **Surface:** asphalted. ⬛ 01/01-31/12
Distance: 🚲historical centre 200m.

Tourist information Maaseik:
⚔ Marktplein. ⬛ Wed 9-12h.

🏕 **Meeuwen-Gruitrode** 10D1
CC Gruitrode, Royerplein 1, Gruitrode. **GPS:** n51,08939 e5,58949.⬆⬆.

8 ⛺free. **Surface:** metalled. ⬛ 01/01-31/12
Distance: 🚶200m ⊗on the spot 🍴200m 🛒200m.
Remarks: Max. 24h.

⬛S Neeroeteren 🌿 10D1

Komweg. **GPS:** n51,08375 e5,70284.

10 ⛺€ 5 🚰⬛Ch 🔌 **Surface:** asphalted.
Remarks: At football ground.

⬛S Neerpelt 10D1

De Welvaart, Jaak Tassetstraat. **GPS:** n51,23333 e5,43164.⬆.

10 ⛺€ 6/24h 🚰⬛Ch 🔌free. 🚲 📋
Surface: metalled. ⬛ 01/01-31/12
Distance: 🚶500m.
Remarks: At the canal, parking marina, max. 48h, checked, coin waste dump € 1.

P Peer 10D1

P1 Aan den Boogaard. **GPS:** n51,13193 e5,45741.
⛺free.
Distance: 🚶100m.
Remarks: Max. 24h.

P Peer 10D1

P2 Noordervest. **GPS:** n51,13422 e5,45511.
⛺free.
Distance: 🚶150m.
Remarks: Max. 24h.

⬛ Rekem 🌿 10D1

Kanaalstraat. **GPS:** n50,92297 e5,70622.⬆.

⛺free. **Surface:** unpaved.
Distance: 🚶1km 🏊on the spot 🚂on the spot ⊗500m 🍴1km
🛒100m 🚲on the spot.
Remarks: Max. 48h, walking and bicycle area.

Tourist information Rekem:
ℹ Oud-Rekem with museum-church, city walls and castle, marked walking route 2km.

⬛S Rummen 10D2

Ketelstraat. **GPS:** n50,89280 e5,16140.

2 ⛺free ⬛Chfree. ⬛ 01/01-31/12
Distance: 🚶on the spot ⊗300m 🍴250m 🚲on the spot
🚶on the spot.

⬛S Schalkhoven 10D2

Nollekes Winning, Schalkhovenstraat 79. **GPS:** n50,84531 e5,44687.

4 ⛺ 🚰WC⬛. **Surface:** gravel. ⬛ 01/01-31/12
Distance: 🚶200m ⊗on the spot.

⬛S Sint-Huibrechts-Lille 10D1

De Bosuil, Bosuilstraat 4. **GPS:** n51,22371 e5,49502.

20 ⛺€ 5 🚰⬛Ch 🔌included. **Surface:** grassy.
Distance: 🚶1,5km ⊗on the spot 🚲on the spot 🚶on the spot.
Remarks: Check in on arrival.

⬛S Tongeren 🌿 10D2

Pliniuspark, Fonteindreef. **GPS:** n50,78626 e5,45256.⬆➡.
24 ⛺€ 10/24h 🚰€0,50/100liter ⛺free Ch 🔌€0,50/kWh. 🚲 📋
Surface: metalled. ⬛ 01/01-31/12
Distance: 🚶2 km 🚲on the spot 🚶on the spot.

Tourist information Tongeren:
ℹ Dienst Toerisme, Stadhuisplein 9, www.tongeren.be. Oldest city of Belgium with numerous historico-cultural heritage.
🛍 Maastrichterstraat, Schiervelstraat, Clarissenstraat. Biggest antique market in the Benelux, also all antique stores open. ⬛ Su 6-13h.

⬛S Tongerlo 10D1

De Kieper, Keyartstraat. **GPS:** n51,12397 e5,65449.

5 ⛺free 🚰€1/100liter 🔌€1. **Surface:** metalled.
Distance: 🚶10 min walking 🚂on the spot 🚲on the spot.

⬛ Veldwezelt 🌿 10D2

Omstraat 20. **GPS:** n50,86195 e5,62696.⬆.

---

2 ⛺free. **Surface:** metalled. ⬛ 01/01-31/12
Distance: 🚶800m ⊗200m 🍴500m.
Remarks: Parking gymnasium.

Brussels

P Bruxelles/Brussel 🌿🚰🗑 10B2

Bruparck, Wemmel/Heizel, Brussels (Bruxelles/Brussel).
GPS: n50,89745 e4,33826.
🚲.
Remarks: Ring road Brussels exit 8.

⬛S Bruxelles/Brussel 🌿🚰🗑 10B2

Jeugdherberg Génération Europe, Rue de l'Eléphant 4, Brussels (Bruxelles/Brussel). **GPS:** n50,85317 e4,33479.
5 ⛺€ 30 🚰⬛Ch 🔌🚿WC⬛🛜. ⬛ 01/01-31/12
Distance: 🚶on the spot.

P Bruxelles/Brussel 🌿🚰🗑 10B2

Heizel/Heysel Metro, Brussels (Bruxelles/Brussel) .
GPS: n50,89736 e4,33827.
🚲.
Remarks: Nearby Bruparck.

Tourist information Brussels (Bruxelles/Brussel):
ℹ Brussels City Card gives for free entrance on public transport and museums and many discounts on purchases. 🎫 € 24.
ℹ Bureau van Toerisme, Office de Tourisme, Grote Markt 1, Grand Place, www.brucity.be. Capital of Belgium, with a history of more than 1000 years. A lot of buildings worth seeing and historical places.
👁 Koninklijke Serres van Laken, Les serres royales à Laeken. Park, garden, nature area.
🏛 Autoworld, Jubelpark, Parc du Cinquantenaire. Motorcar history from 1886 up to 1970s. ⬛ 01/04-30/09 10-18h, 01/10-31/03 10-17h.
🏛 Museum van de stad Brussel Broodhuis, Musée de la ville Bruxelles, Grote Markt 44, Grand Place. History of the city. ⬛ Tue-Su 10-17h.
✝ Basiliek van Koekelberg, basilique de Koekelberg. The fifth largest church of the world. ⬛ 01/10-18/10 Su 14-17.45h, 01/07-31/08 Sa-Su. 🎫 € 2,50.
🛍 Grote Markt, Grand place. Flowers and plant market. ⬛ 8-18h.
🛍 Grote Zavel, Place du Grand Sablon. Antiques and book market. ⬛ Sa 9-17h, Su 9-13h.
🛍 Vossenplein. ⬛ 7-14h.
🛍 Kunstmarkt, marché d'art, Boterstraat, rue au Beurre. Painters and portraitists. ⬛ 11-18h.
🎡 Atomium, Bruparck, Boulevard du Centenaire, Laeken. Built for the occasion of the 1958 Brussels World Fair, symbolising a crystallised iron molecule to the scale of its atoms enlarged 160 thousand million times. ⬛ 10-18h, 01/04-31/08 9-20h. 🎫 € 5.
🎡 Bruparck, Boulevard du Centenaire 20, Laeken. Family park with among other things Mini-Europe, paradise pool and The Village with restaurants, cafés and shops. ⬛ 01/01-31/12.
🎡 Mini-Europe, Bruparck, Boulevard du Centenaire, Laeken. Europe in miniature, 300 monuments. ⬛ 30/03-03/01.
🎡 Oceade, Bruparck, Boulevard du Centenaire, Laeken. Subtropical leisure pool park. ⬛ holidays, Sa-Su 10-22h.

Liège

⬛S Aywaille 🚰🗑 10D2

Esplanade du Fair-Play, Rue de la Heid. **GPS:** n50,47583 e5,67809.⬆➡.

8 ⛺€ 8/48h, incl. 1 coin (water or 2h electricity) 🚰€2 ⬛Ch 🔌(4x)
€ 1/h. **Surface:** metalled. ⬛ 01/01-31/12
Distance: 🚶300m 🍴200m.
Remarks: At recreation area.

⊙S Blégny-Mine 10D2

Domaine de Blégny-Mine, Rue Lambert Marlet.
GPS: n50,68617 e5,72367.⬆.

8 ⛺free 🚿 ♻Chfree ⚡(8x)€2/12h. **Location:** Rural, comfortable, isolated, quiet. **Surface:** gravel. 📅 01/01-31/12
Distance: 🚲4,6km ⊗on the spot 🚴on the spot 🏕on the spot.
Remarks: At former coalmine, UNESCO World Heritage, access € 9,30, 1 day all inclusive € 29,50, coins electricity at reception park.

Eupen 🌼 10E2
Langesthal 164. **GPS:** n50,62180 e6,09148.

⛺free. **Surface:** asphalted. 📅 18-10h
Distance: 🚲Eupen 4km ⊗150m Taverne.
Remarks: At weir, isolated.

Tourist information Eupen:
🏕 Benedenstad. 📅 Wed 7-12.30h.
🏕 Eupen/Keltenis. Flea market. 📅 Su 7-16h.

Hamoir 🏔🍴 10D3
Complexe Sportif, Quai du Batty. **GPS:** n50,42463 e5,53522. ➡

10 ⛺€ 8/24h 🚿 ♻Chfree. 🚽 ♻ **Location:** Urban, comfortable.
Surface: grassy/gravel. 📅 01/01-31/12
Distance: 🚲200m 🛒on the spot ⛽on the spot ⊗200m ⛴200m.
Remarks: Along the Ourthe river.

Huy 🌼 10D2
Avenue Godin Parnajon. **GPS:** n50,52379 e5,24310. ⬆

2 ⛺free. **Location:** Urban, central, noisy. **Surface:** asphalted.
📅 01/01-31/12
Distance: 🚲500m ⊗on the spot ⛴500m.
Remarks: Parking in front of restaurant Quick.

Huy 🌼 10D2
Quai de Namur. **GPS:** n50,51673 e5,23453. ⬆

2 ⛺free. **Location:** Urban, central, noisy. **Surface:** asphalted.
📅 01/01-31/12

Distance: 🚲500m ⊗on the spot ⊗on the spot ⛴500m.
Remarks: Under the citadel, along the Meuse River, in front of Hôtel du Fort to the right to the quay.

Tourist information Huy:
ℹ Office du Tourisme, Quai de Namur,1, www.huy.be. Tourist town, citadel above the city.
🏛🏕 Fort en museum. 📅 Easter-Sep 10-17/18/19h.

Jalhay 10E2
Baraque de La Gileppe. **GPS:** n50,58759 e5,96980. ⬆
4 ⛺free 🚿free.
Distance: 🚲3,5km.
Remarks: At artificial lake.

Malmedy 🌼❄ 10E3
Avenue de la Gare, N62. **GPS:** n50,42282 e6,03080. ⬆➡

30 ⛺€ 5/24h 🚿 ♻Ch ⚡(8x)included. 🚽 **Surface:** gravel/metalled.
📅 01/01-31/12
Distance: 🚲300m ⊗300m ⛴bakery 100m, supermarket 800m
🛒on the spot 🚴on the spot 🏕on the spot 🚂Waimes 5km.
Remarks: At cycle route (former railroad).

Tourist information Malmedy:
🏕 Place St. Géréon. 📅 Fri 7-13h.
❄ Hautes Fagnes. Nature reserve Hautes Fagnes.

Sankt Vith 10E3
An den Weyern, Rodter Strasse 9a. **GPS:** n50,28091 e6,12240. ⬆➡

20 ⛺free 🚿€1/4minutes 🚽. **Location:** Urban, simple.
Surface: asphalted. 📅 01/01-31/12
Distance: 🚲500m ⊗on the spot ⛴on the spot.
Remarks: At sports centre.

Sankt Vith 🍴 10E3
Skihütte-Biermuseum, Rodt 89/A. **GPS:** n50,29720 e6,06193.

10 ⛺free. **Location:** Rural, isolated, quiet. **Surface:** asphalted/gravel.
📅 01/01-31/12
Distance: 🚲5km ⚓3km ⊗on the spot ⛴5km 🏕on the spot
🚂on the spot.

Sourbrodt 🍴❄ 10E2
Signal de Botrange, Rue de Botrange. **GPS:** n50,50148 e6,09312. ⬆

20 ⛺free. **Location:** Rural, simple, noisy. **Surface:** gravel.
📅 01/01-31/12
Distance: ⚓on the spot ⊗on the spot 🏕on the spot 🚂on the spot.

Waimes 👣 10E3
La Faitafondue, Rue de Merkem 4. **GPS:** n50,39532 e6,07024. ⬆

10 ⛺€ 9, free with a meal 🚿♻ ⚡ WC 🔌. **Location:** Rural, comfortable. **Surface:** gravel. 📅 01/01-31/12 🔵 Wed
Distance: 🚲4km ⚓6km 🚴on the spot 🏕on the spot 🚂200m.

Hainaut

Aubechies 10B2
Parking Archéosite, Rue de l'Abbaye 1Y. **GPS:** n50,57419 e3,67546.
⛺.

Tourist information Aubechies:
ℹ Archéosite d'Aubechies. Archeological open air museum.
📅 Easter-01/11 Mo-Fri 9-17h, Sa, Su 14-18h.

Beloeil 🌼 10B2
Château Beloeil. **GPS:** n50,55000 e3,73242.
⛺free. 📅 01/01-31/12
Remarks: Parking castle.

Beloeil 🌼 10B2
Camping à la Ferme, Rue de la Hunelle 16. **GPS:** n50,55165 e3,73275.
12 ⛺€ 6 + € 2/pp 🚿 ♻Ch ⚡€1 WC 🔌. 📅 15/03-15/11

Tourist information Beloeil:
🏛 Château de Beloeil, www.beloeil.be/. 📅 01/06-30/09 10-19h, 01/04-31/05 Sa,Su 10-19h.

Bernissart 🌼 10B2
Musée de l'Iguanodon, Ruelle des Médecins. **GPS:** n50,47530 e3,64958.

⛺free.
Distance: ⚓6km.
Remarks: Parking 100m of dinosaur museum.

Binche 🌼 10B3
Pastures, Rue des Pastures. **GPS:** n50,41413 e4,17070.

50 ⛺free ♻Ch 🚿(2x). **Surface:** asphalted. 📅 01/01-31/12
Distance: 🚲on the spot.
Remarks: Parking just outside centre.

Tourist information Binche:
ℹ Office du Tourisme, Parc communal, rue des Promenades, 2, www.binche.be. Medieval city with ramparts.

Blaton 10B2
Place de Feignies. **GPS:** n50,50179 e3,66135.

BE

🛏free.
Distance: [icon]200m.
Remarks: Nearby Romanesque church.

Bouffioulx 10C3 [S]
Rue du Général Jacques. GPS: n50,39024 e4,51406.
[icons]Ch [icon]against payment. Surface: metalled.
Remarks: Next to Centre d'Interprétation de la Poterie, coins at Maison de la Poterie.

Boussu-lez-Walcourt 10C3 [S]
Les Lacs de l'Eau d'Heure, Route de la Plate Taille.
GPS: n50,19265 e4,37958. [icon].

20 🛏free [icons]Chfree. Surface: asphalted. 01/01-31/12
Distance: [icon]on the spot [icon]on the spot [icon]on the spot [icon]on the spot.

Chimay 10B3 [P]
Place Froissart. GPS: n50,04728 e4,31307.
🛏.

Chimay 10B3 [P]
Place Léopold. GPS: n50,04747 e4,31784.
🛏. [icon] Fri

Dottignies 10A2 [S]
Rue des Écoles 75b. GPS: n50,72821 e3,30011.
🛏[icon]free. 01/01-31/12
Distance: [icon]500m [icon]1,3km.
Remarks: Square behind fire-station.

Ecaussines 10B2
Château de la Folie, Rue de la Folie. GPS: n50,57443 e4,17851.
🛏free.
Distance: [icon]800m.

Ecaussines 10B2
Eglise Sainte Aldegonde, Rue Jacquemart Boulle 28, Ecaussines-Lalaing. GPS: n50,57085 e4,18107.
🛏free.
Distance: [icon]500m.

Fleurus 10C2
Parking Gare, Avenue de la Gare. GPS: n50,48215 e4,54433.
🛏.

Fleurus 10C2
Stade Communal, Rue de Fleurjoux. GPS: n50,47852 e4,55237.

🛏free.

Harchies 10B2
Place du Rivage. GPS: n50,47106 e3,69619.
🛏.

Hornu 10B2
Le Site du Grand Hornu, Rue Sainte-Louise 82.
GPS: n50,43488 e3,83707. [icon].

🛏free.
Distance: [icon]1km.
Tourist information Hornu:

[icon] Grand-Hornu. Old industrial mining complex, a remarkable reminder of the Industrial Revolution.
[icon] Tue-Fri 10-18h. [icon] € 6.

Houdeng Aimeries 10B2
Musée de la Mine de Bois-du-Luc, Rue Saint-Patrice.
GPS: n50,47081 e4,14952.
🛏free.

La Louvière 10B2
Boulevard de Roi Baudouin. GPS: n50,46619 e4,19055.
🛏.
Remarks: P Station Sud.
Tourist information La Louvière:
[M] Ascenseur Funiculaire de Strépy-Thieu, Strépy-Bracquegnies. Draw-works, 19th century. 01/02-27/11 9.30-18.30.
[icon] Rue du Marché. [icon] Sa 8-13h.

Lahamaide 10B2
Place Plada. GPS: n50,69465 e3,72202.
🛏.
Remarks: At Ecomuseum.

Le Roeulx 10B2
Grand Place. GPS: n50,50019 e4,10919.
🛏.

Le Roeulx 10B2
Place de la Chapelle. GPS: n50,50294 e4,10874.
🛏.
Distance: [icon]100m.
Remarks: Next to church.

Le Roeulx 10B2
Place de la Tannée. GPS: n50,50339 e4,10819.
🛏.

Le Roeulx 10B2
Place du Château. GPS: n50,50406 e4,11024.
🛏.
Remarks: Parking at castle.

Leers Noord 7C5 [S]
La Maison du Canal, Rue du Canal 6. GPS: n50,69089 e3,25728. [icon].

3 🛏free [icons]Chfree. Location: Rural, quiet. Surface: gravel.
01/01-31/12
Distance: [icon]on the spot [icon]on the spot [icon]on the spot [icon]on the spot.
Remarks: Taverne closed on Monday.

Lessines 10B2
Rue des 4 fils Aymon. GPS: n50,71280 e3,83403.
🛏free.
Distance: [icon]400m.

Leuze-en-Hainaut 10A2
Rue du Pont de la Cure. GPS: n50,59924 e3,61347.
🛏free.

Marchienne-au-Pont 10C3
Musée d'Histoire et d'Archéologie Industrielle, 134 rue de la Providence. GPS: n50,41301 e4,40450.
🛏free.
Remarks: In front of museum.

Mons/Bergen 10B2
Maison Van Gogh,
Rue de Pavillon 3, Cuesmes, Mons (Mons/Bergen).
GPS: n50,44174 e3,92630.
🛏free.
Remarks: In case of city-visit use parking nearby station or bypass.
Tourist information Mons (Mons/Bergen):
[M] Maison Van Gogh, Rue du Pavillon 3, Cuesmes. Former place of residence of painter Van Gogh 1879/80, exhibition of reproductions. 10-18h Mo.
[icon] Château Havré, Havré. Castle, 12-13th century.

Morlanwelz-Mariemont 10B2
Musée Alex Louis Martin, Place de Carnières, 52, Carnières.
GPS: n50,44402 e4,25416.
10 🛏free.

Mouscron 10A2 [icon]
Musée du Folklore
Rue des Brasseurs, 3. GPS: n50,74217 e3,21795.
Remarks: Possibility make a reservation tel 02.56.33.23.36.

Nimy 10B2 [icon]
Musée de la Pipe et du Vieux Nimy, Rue Mouzin.
GPS: n50,47499 e3,95853.
🛏free. Surface: metalled.
Remarks: Museum closed: Nov-Mar.

Quaregnon 10B2
La Grand Place. GPS: n50,44369 e3,86428.
2 🛏.

Quevaucamps 10B2 [icon]
Musée de la Bonneterie, Rue Paul Pastur.
GPS: n50,52671 e3,68776. [icons].

2 🛏free. 01/01-31/12
Remarks: Parking in front of museum, via N527.

Ronquières 10B2
Grande tour et promenade en Bateau Mouche, Rue Rosemont.
GPS: n50,60636 e4,22249.

20 🛏free.
Distance: [icon]on the spot [icon]on the spot.

Sivry 10B3
Observatoire de Sivry, Route de Mons 52. GPS: n50,17897 e4,22646.
2 🛏.
Remarks: Centre for nature studies.

Solre-Sur-Sambre 10B3
Château-Fort, Rue du Chateau Fort. GPS: n50,30918 e4,15585.
🛏free.
Remarks: At castle.

Thuin 10B3
Drève des Alliés. GPS: n50,33951 e4,29860.
🛏.
Remarks: Max. 24h.

Thuin 10B3
L'Abbaye d'Aulnes, Rue Vandervelde. GPS: n50,36592 e4,33324.
🛏free.
Remarks: Near abbey, max. 24h.

Thuin 10B3
Place du Chapitre. GPS: n50,33980 e4,28724.
🛏.
Remarks: Max. 24h.

Tournai/Doornik 10A2 [S]
Maison de la Culture, Boulevard Frère Rimbaud, Tournai (Tournai/Doornik). GPS: n50,60432 e3,38199. [icon].

15-20 🛏free [icons]Chfree. Surface: metalled. 01/01-31/12
Distance: [icon]5 min walking [icon]5 min walking [icon]5 min walking

🚐 on the spot.

| 🏕 | Trazegnies | 10B2 |

Place Albert I 32. **GPS:** n50,46248 e4,33025.
🚐.
Distance: 🚶 1,5km.
Remarks: Parking at castle.

Namur

| 🏕 | Alle-sur-Semois 🌿🚣🌳〰 | 15C1 |

Recreatiecentrum Recrealle, restaurant les Pierres du Diable,
Rue Léon Henrard 16. **GPS:** n49,84648 e4,97579. ⬆.

10 🚐 free. **Location:** Rural, simple. **Surface:** unpaved.
⏱ 01/01-31/12
Distance: 🚶 700m 🛥 on the spot 🎣 fishing permit obligatory
⊗ on the spot 🛒 700m.

Tourist information Alle-sur-Semois:
ℹ Recrealle. Canoe rent; departures for canoe and kayaks, fishing and swimming possibilities, bowling, tennis, play ground, restaurant.

| 📷 S | Ave-et-Auffe 🏘 | 10D3 |

Le Roptai, Rue du Roptai 34. **GPS:** n50,11144 e5,13373. ➡.

10 🚐 € 16-19 🚰🗑 Ch 🚿 (10x)€3/24h WC included 🗑 €1 🔌 €4
📶 €1/3h. **Location:** Rural, comfortable, quiet. **Surface:** grassy/gravel.
⏱ 08/01-31/12
Distance: 🚶 4km 🚲 2km ⊗ 1km 🛒 5km 🚐 1km 🚶 on the spot.
Remarks: Bread-service, Han 5km.

| 🏕 S | Han-Sur-Lesse 🌿🏞 | 10D3 |

Rue de la Lesse. **GPS:** n50,12751 e5,18819. ⬆.

40 🚐 € 7,50, Jul/Aug € 10 🚰🗑 Ch 🚿 WC included. 🚻
Location: Urban. **Surface:** asphalted. ⏱ 01/01-31/12
Distance: 🚶 200m ⊗ 200m 🛒 200m 🚐 on the spot.
Remarks: Parking nearby caves and centre.

Tourist information Han-Sur-Lesse:
🚹 Tourist centre around the caves.
👁 Grottes de Han. Caves, son-et-lumière and boat trip on underground river. ⏱ 01/04-31/10 10-16/18h, 01/11-31/03 11.30-16h.
🐾 Réserve d'Animaux. European animals alive today and those which lived previously in this area. ⏱ 01/03-31/12 10-17h, 01/07-31/08 9.30-18h

| 🏕 S | Hogne | 10D3 |

Aire del Foy, 16 rue de Serinchamps. **GPS:** n50,24981 e5,27933.
25 🚐 € 5-10 🚰🗑 🚿 16Amp WC 📶. **Surface:** grassy.
Distance: ⊗ on the spot.

| 🏕 S | Namur | 10C2 |

Tabora, Place André Ryckmans. **GPS:** n50,46770 e4,85056. ⬆.

8 🚐 free 🚰🗑 Ch €7,50. **Surface:** asphalted. ⏱ 01/01-31/12
Distance: 🚶 1km ⊗ 1km 🛒 1km 🚐 200m.
Remarks: Behind gymnasium.

| 🏕 S | Nismes | 10C3 |

Rue Longue. **GPS:** n50,07387 e4,54863. ⬆.

± 8 🚐 free 🚰 €2/100liter 🗑 Ch 🚻 €2/h. **Surface:** asphalted.
⏱ 01/01-31/12
Distance: 🚶 on the spot ⊗ 100m 🛒 bakery 100m 🚲 on the spot
🚶 on the spot.
Remarks: Coins at tourist info.

| 🅿 | Profondeville | 10C3 |

Chaussée de Namur. **GPS:** n50,37644 e4,87106. ⬆.

4 🚐 free. **Surface:** asphalted. ⏱ 01/01-31/12
Distance: 🚶 50m 🚐 150m 🛒 50m.
Remarks: Max. 24h.

| 🏕 S | Rochefort ✈ | 10D3 |

Route de Marche. **GPS:** n50,15800 e5,22639. ➡.

10 🚐 free. **Location:** Urban, simple. **Surface:** metalled.
⏱ 01/01-31/12
Distance: 🚶 200m ⊗ 200m 🛒 200m.

| 🏕 S | Saint-Hubert 🏘 | 10D3 |

Chemin des Etangs/ Rue de Lavaux. **GPS:** n50,02689 e5,38088. ⬆ ➡.

3 🚐 free 🚰 free. **Location:** Urban, simple. **Surface:** gravel.
⏱ 01/01-31/12
Distance: 🚶 500m ⊗ 500m 🛒 500m 🚲 on the spot 🚶 on the spot.
Remarks: Max. 48h, 10 parking places tolerated, European capmital of hunting, events: 1st weekend September and November 1st Saint Hubert.

| 🏕 S | Saint-Hubert 🏘 | 10D3 |

Fourneau Saint Michel, Rue Saint Hubert.
GPS: n50,08480 e5,33902. ⬆.

10 🚐 free 🚰🗑 Ch free 🚿 (4x)€1/h. **Location:** Rural, simple.
Surface: asphalted/grassy. ⏱ 01/01-31/12
Distance: 🚶 St Hubert 9km 🛒 200m 🚶 on the spot.
Remarks: At open air museum from Fourneau Saint-Michel.

| 🏕 S | Treignes 🏘 | 10C3 |

Rue de la Gare. **GPS:** n50,09085 e4,68182. ⬆.

3 🚐 free 🚰 €2 🗑 Ch 🚻 €2. **Surface:** gravel. ⏱ 01/01-31/12
Distance: 🚶 900m.
Remarks: At former station, coins at tourist info Nismes, steam train museum.

Luxembourg

| 🏕 S | Arlon 🌿🍽 | 15E1 |

Casserne Callemeyn, Drève des Espagnols, N882.
GPS: n49,68990 e5,81929. ➡.

5 🚐 free 🚰🗑 🚿 free.
Location: Urban, simple. **Surface:** asphalted. ⏱ 01/01-31/12
Distance: 🚶 600m 🚲 5,8km.
Remarks: At fire-station.

Tourist information Arlon:
⛏ Parc Archéologique, Rue des Thermes. Archeological site. ⏱ 9-12h, 14-17h.
🎪 Flea market. ⏱ 01/03-31/10 1st Su of the month 7-19h.

| 🏕 S | Barvaux ✈ | 10D3 |

Petit Barvaux. **GPS:** n50,35223 e5,49501. ⬆.

20 🚐 € 10/24h 🚰 €2 🗑 Ch 🚻
Surface: grasstiles.
⏱ 01/01-31/12
Distance: 🚶 300m 🛒 Delhaize 50m 🚲 Ravel-route 🚶 on the spot.
Remarks: Along the Ourthe river, max. 24h, coins at tourist info.

Tourist information Barvaux:
👁 Labyrinthus, Rue Basse Commene. Labyrinth park.
⏱ 01/07-31/08 10.30-19.30h. 🎫 € 7,50.
🌿 Domaine de Hottemme. Nature reserve with visitor centre.
⏱ 10.30-17h, summer 10.30-18h.

BE

⬛S Bastogne 🌿🍽 10D3

Avenue Albert I. **GPS:** n49,99825 e5,71526.➡️

10 free 🔧🔌free. **Location:** Urban, simple, central.
Surface: asphalted. 🔲 01/01-31/12
Distance: 🚶300m 🚲3km ⊗300m 🍺300m.

⬛S Bouillon 🌿 15C1

Parking du stade, Rue de la Poulie. **GPS:** n49,79106 e5,05767.

10 free 🔧🔌Ch. **Surface:** gravel. 🔲 01/01-31/12
Distance: 🚶1,3km ⊗1,3km 🍺1,5km.

⬛S Durbuy 🌿🏛🎭🏞 10D3

P Mobilhome Le Vedeur, Rue Fond de Vedeur.
GPS: n50,35780 e5,45672.⬆️➡️

50 €21, 2 pers.incl 🔧🔌Ch 🚿WC 🔊included.
Location: Comfortable. **Surface:** gravel. 🔲 01/01-31/12
Distance: 🚶750m 🏊on the spot 🎣fishing permit obligatory ⊗750m
🍺750m 🏃on the spot.

Tourist information Durbuy:

👁 Confiturerie Saint Amour, Rue St Amour 13. Production of traditional
products. 🔲 10-18h 🔳 01/10-31/03 Mo. 🎫 free.

👁 Diamour, Rue de la Prevoté. Centre of diamonds and goldsmithing.
🔲 10.30-19.30h 🔳 Tue-Wed. 🎫 free.

👁 Parc des Topiaires, Rue Haie Himbe. Model garden. 🔲 10-18h
🔳 01/01-31/01. 🎫 €4,50. 🪁 Antiques and flea market.
🔲 01/03-30/09, 9-17h, 2nd Sa of the month.

⬛S Herbeumont 🌿🎭 15D1

Avenue de Combattants. **GPS:** n49,77729 e5,23700.⬆️

50 free 🔧Chfree. **Location:** Rural.
Surface: asphalted/grassy.
Distance: 🚶500m 🍺500m.
Remarks: Parking of old station.

Tourist information Herbeumont:

ℹ️ Royal Syndicat d'Initiative, Avenue des Combattants, 7, www.
herbeumont.be. Beautiful position in the Ardennes landscape. Ruins of
medieval castle, free entry.

👁 Grottes, 7 km di Bertrix. Caves.
🔲 01/04-30/09 daily, 01/11-31/03 Sa-Su. 🎫 €7.

⬛S Hotton 🌿 10D3

Rue du Batty. **GPS:** n50,26873 e5,44417.⬆️.

3 free 🔌Ch. **Location:** Urban, simple. 🔲 01/01-31/12
Distance: 🚶300m 🔌on the spot ⊗300m 🍺300m.
Tourist information Hotton: 👁 Grottes de Hotton. Caves.
🔲 01/04-31/10 10-17h, 01/07-31/08 10-18h.

⬛ La Roche 🌿🏞 10D3

Rue du Harzé. **GPS:** n50,19075 e5,57432.⬆️.

5 free. **Location:** Urban, simple. **Surface:** asphalted.
🔲 01/01-31/12
Distance: 🚶500m ⊗500m 🍺500m 🔌on the spot.
Remarks: Parking at sports park.

Tourist information La Roche:

ℹ️ Syndicat d'Initiative, Place du Marché, 15, www.la-roche-tourisme.
com. Small town totally destroyed during the battle of the Ardennes,
1944/45. ⚔️ Medieval citadel. 🔲 10-12h, 14-17h, 01/07-31/08 10-19h,
winter Sa-Su 🔳 frost.

⬛ Nisramont 🎭🏞 10D3

Barrage de Nisramont, Rue de barrage. **GPS:** n50,14089 e5,67118.⬆️.

10 free. **Location:** Simple, isolated, quiet. **Surface:** metalled.
🔲 01/01-31/12
Distance: 🚶3,7km 🚲15km 🏊on the spot 🔌on the spot
⊗on the spot 🏃on the spot.
Remarks: At artificial lake.

⬛ Poupehan 🌿🏛🎭🏞 15C1

Rue du Pont. **GPS:** n49,80886 e5,00418.⬆️.

20 free 🔧🔌Chfree. **Location:** Rural, simple, quiet.
Surface: gravel. 🔲 01/01-31/12
Distance: 🏊on the spot 🔌on the spot ⊗200m 🍺300m.
Remarks: Along the Semois river, next to sports fields, max. 24h, canoe
rental.

⬛ Redu 10D3

Rue de Saint Hubert. **GPS:** n50,00877 e5,16348.⬆️.

10 free. **Location:** Rural, simple. **Surface:** gravel. 🔲 01/01-31/12
Distance: 🚶on the spot.

🇨🇭 Switzerland

Capital: Bern
Government: Direct democracy, Federal republic
Official Language: German, French, Italian, Romansh
Population: 8,100,000 (2014)
Area: 41,284 km²

General information
Dialling code: 0041
General emergency: 112
Currency: Swiss franc (CHF)
1 CHF = € 0,92, € 1 = 1,08 CHF (October 2015)
1 CHF = £ 0,66, £ 1 = CHF 1,50 (October 2015)

Regulations for overnight stays
Overnight parking is allowed, max 15 hours.

Additional public holidays 2016
August 1 National Day

Time Zone
Winter (Standard Time) GMT+1
Summer (DST) GMT+2

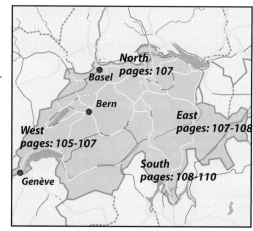

North pages: 107
Basel
Bern
East pages: 107-108
West pages: 105-107
Genève
South pages: 108-110

CH

Switzerland West

| | Aeschi | 21G1 |
Panorama, Scheidgasse 272. GPS: n46,65399 e7,70070.
🏞️ 🅿️ 15/05-15/10

| | Avenches | 21F1 |
Port-Plage. GPS: n46,90351 e7,04918.
🅿️ 01/04-01/10

| | Boltigen | 21G1 |
Jaunpass. GPS: n46,59208 e7,33758.
🏞️ 🅿️ 01/01-31/12

| | Böningen | 21H1 |
Seeblick, Campingstrasse 14. GPS: n46,68987 e7,89398.
🏞️ 🅿️ Easter-01/10

| | Brienz | 21H1 |
Aaregg. GPS: n46,74634 e8,04844.
🏞️.
🅿️ 01/04-01/11
Tourist information Brienz:
ℹ️ Alpen Region Brienz-Meiringen-Hasliberg, Bahnhofstrasse 22, Meiringen, www.alpenregion.ch. Village of wood-cutters.
🅿️ during school hours 📷 01/07-31/08.
👁️ Brienz Rothorn Bahn. Steam rack-railway.
🅿️ 01/06-31/10 8.45h. 🎫 CHF 46.
🏛️ Freilichtmuseum Ballenberg. Open air museum.
🅿️ 15/04-31/10 10-17h.

| | Bullet | 21F1 |
Restaurant Les Cluds, Les Cluds. GPS: n46,84248 e6,55991. ⬆️➡️.

4 🏞️ CHF 10 🔌🍽️ Ch 🚿 (4x) included.
Location: Rural, simple, isolated, quiet. **Surface:** asphalted.
🅿️ 01/01-31/12 📷 Restaurant: Mo
Distance: ⊗ on the spot.
Remarks: Max. 2 nights, pay at restaurant.

| | Burgdorf | 18G3 |
Waldegg, Waldeggweg. GPS: n47,05407 e7,62895.
🏞️ 🅿️ 01/04-31/10

| | Château-d'Oex | 21G2 |
Le Berceau. GPS: n46,46673 e7,12529.
🏞️ 🅿️ 01/01-31/12

| | Cheyres | 21F1 |
Route de Crevel. GPS: n46,81651 e6,78501. ⬆️.
🔌 10minutes 🍽️ Ch 🚿 (2x) against paymenth.
Location: Simple. 🅿️ 01/01-31/12
Tourist information Cheyres:
🍇 Fête de vendanges. Wine festivals. 🅿️ beginning Oct.

| | Cudrefin | 21F1 |
Route de Neuchâtel. GPS: n46,96000 e7,02750. ⬆️.
🔌🍽️ Ch free.

Remarks: In front of camping Le Chablais.

| | Damphreux | 18F3 |
Stellplatz Forest-Ranch, Sur la Côte 21. GPS: n47,47588 e7,09978.
20 🏞️ CHF 20 🔌 Ch WC 📷 included. 🚿
Location: Rural. **Surface:** grassy.
Distance: 🚶 300m ⊗ 300m 🛒 300m 🏍️ on the spot 🚶 on the spot.

| | Delémont | 18G3 |
Place de Parc Gros-Pré Monsieur, Route de Porrentruy.
GPS: n47,36289 e7,34008. ⬆️➡️.

10 🏞️ free 🔌🍽️ Ch 🚰 free. **Surface:** gravel. 🅿️ 01/01-31/12
Distance: 🚶 200m.

| | Dürrenroth | 18G3 |
Reisemobilstellplatz Blueberry Hill, Brunnen.
GPS: n47,06563 e7,76553. ⬆️.

4 🏞️ CHF 10 🚿 CHF 2. **Location:** Rural, comfortable, quiet.
Surface: gravel. 🅿️ 01/01-31/12
Distance: 🚶 Dürrenroth 3,5km 🏍️ on the spot 🚶 on the spot.
Remarks: Panoramic view.

| | Echallens | 21F1 |
Chemin du Pont. GPS: n46,63945 e6,64096. ⬆️➡️.

5 🏞️ free 🔌🍽️ Ch free. **Location:** Rural, simple. **Surface:** asphalted.
🅿️ 01/01-31/12
Distance: 🚶 700m ⊗ 300m 🛒 700m.

| | Estavayer-le-Lac | 21F1 |
Nouvelle-Plage. GPS: n46,85602 e6,84801.
🏞️ 🅿️ 01/04-01/10

| | Frutigen | 21G1 |
Grassi. GPS: n46,58178 e7,64213.
🏞️ 🅿️ 01/01-31/12

| | Gampelen | 21F1 |
Fanel, Seestraße. GPS: n47,00702 e7,05973.
🏞️ 🅿️ Easter-01/10

| | Grandson | 21F1 |
Le Pécos, Rue du Pécos. GPS: n46,80371 e6,63575.
4 🏞️ 🔌 Ch. 🅿️ 01/04-01/10
Remarks: Next to campsite.

| | Grindelwald | 21H1 |
Eigernordwand. GPS: n46,62135 e8,01683.
🏞️.
🅿️ 01/01-31/12
Tourist information Grindelwald:
👁️ Jungfraubahn. Train journey to the highest train station of Europe.

| | Gryon | 21G2 |
Place de la Barboleuse. GPS: n46,28222 e7,07028. ⬆️.

4 🏞️ CHF 2,80/pp, Summer CHF 5,30/pp 🔌🍽️ Ch 🚿 (4x) CHF 5.
Location: Rural, simple, quiet. **Surface:** asphalted.
Distance: 🚶 200m 🚲 3,5km 🚌 on the spot 🏍️ 100m.
Remarks: To be paid at office de tourisme.

| | Gstaad | 21G2 |
Bellerive. GPS: n46,48106 e7,27328.
🏞️ 🅿️ 01/01-31/12

| | Gündlischwand | 21H1 |
Säumertaverne, Am Chienbach 96. GPS: n46,63692 e7,92636.
🏞️ guests free 🚿. **Location:** Rural, central. **Surface:** asphalted.
📷 Restaurant: Mo
Distance: 🚲 7km 🏊 on the spot 🚂 on the spot ⊗ on the spot
🍽️ on the spot 🚌 6km 🚠 on the spot.

| | Gwatt-Thun | 21G1 |
Betlireiche. GPS: n46,72749 e7,62760.
🏞️ 🅿️ 01/04-01/10

| | Hinterkappelen | 21G1 |
Kappelenbrucke, Wohlenstrasse 62. GPS: n46,96433 e7,38361.
🏞️ 🅿️ 01/01-31/12

| | Huttwil | 18H3 |
Firma Flyer E-Bike, Luzernstrasse. GPS: n47,11527 e7,86795. ⬆️.

20 🏞️ free 🔌🍽️ Ch 🚰 free. **Location:** Rural. **Surface:** gravel.
🅿️ 01/01-31/12
Distance: 🚶 500m.
Remarks: E-bike factory, guided tour Tuesdays 14.30h.

Interlaken 21H1
Hobby, Lehnweg 16. **GPS:** n46,68079 e7,82793.
🚐 ⭕ 01/04-01/10

Interlaken 21H1
Jungfr+ublick, Gsteigstraße 80. **GPS:** n46,67581 e7,86597.
🚐 ⭕ 01/05-01/10

Interlaken 21H1
Lazy-Rancho, Lehnweg 6. **GPS:** n46,68079 e7,82793.
🚐 ⭕ 01/04-01/10

Tourist information Interlaken:
👁 Heimwehfluhbahn. Telpher carrier from 1906. ⭕ 01/04-31/10.
🎡 Mistery Park. Attractions and themepark. ⭕ 10-18h ⚫ 25/12-01/01.

La Brévine 21F1
Les Varodes. **GPS:** n46,97195 e6,58860. ⬆.

10 🚐free 🔌🍴Ch🚿(2x)WCfree. **Location:** Rural, simple, isolated, quiet. **Surface:** asphalted. ⭕ 01/01-31/12
Distance: 🚶3km ⛴on the spot ✕1,5km 🚴on the spot 🎣on the spot 🏊on the spot.
Remarks: Parking at Lac des Tailleres.

La Chaux-de-Fonds ❄ 18F3
Bois du Couvent. **GPS:** n47,09334 e6,83593. ⬆.

2 🚐free 🔌🍴Ch🚿(4x)free.
Location: Rural, simple. **Surface:** gravel. ⭕ 01/05-30-09
Distance: 🚶1,3km ✕350m 🎣700m 🏊on the spot.
Remarks: In front of campsite du Bois du Couvent.

Tourist information La Chaux-de-Fonds:
ℹ️ Tourisme neuchâtelois - Montagnes, Espacité 1, Place Le Corbusier. Capital of the clock industry.
Ⓜ Musée International d'Horlogerie, Rue des Musée 29. Watch museum. ⭕ 10-17h ⚫ Mo, 25/12-01/01.

Langenthal 18G3
Lexa-Wohnmobile, Bern-Zürichstrasse 49b.
GPS: n47,22461 e7,77944. ⬆.

5 🚐free 🔌🍴Ch🚿free. **Surface:** asphalted. ⭕ 01/01-31/12
Distance: 🚶2km.
Remarks: At motorhome dealer.

Lausanne 21F2
Vidy, Chemin du Camping 3. **GPS:** n46,51734 e6,59777. ⬆➡.

10 🚐CHF 23,10 or € 20 🔌🍴Ch🚿WC included 🔵CHF 4,35/4h.

Location: Urban, simple, central.
Surface: grassy/metalled.
⭕ 01/01-31/12
Distance: ⛴on the spot ✕on the spot.
Remarks: Next to campsite the Vidy, pay at reception, service passerby CHF 3, free bus to centre.

Tourist information Lausanne:
ℹ️ Lausanne Tourisme, Avenue de Rhodanie 2, www.lausanne-tourisme.ch. Parking at the port, rack-railway to city centre.
Ⓜ Musée Olympique, Quai d'Ouchy 1. All about the Olympic games.
⭕ 01/05-14/10 9-18h, 14/10-30/04 10-18h ⚫ Mo, 01/10-30/04.

Lauterbrunnen ❄ 21H1
Jungfrau. GPS: n46,58834 e7,90882.
🚐 ⭕ 01/01-31/12

Lauterbrunnen ❄ 21H1
Schützenbach. GPS: n46,59047 e7,91194.
🚐 ⭕ 01/01-31/12

Tourist information Lauterbrunnen:
👁 Jungfraubahn, Grindelwald. Train journey to the highest train station of Europe.
👁 Klöppelstube, Altes Schulhaus. Making of bobbin lace.
⭕ Tue 14-17h. 🎟 free.
👁 Trümmelbachfälle, Lauterbrunnen dir Stechelberg. Underground waterfalls.
⭕ 01/04-30/11 9-17h.

Le Landeron 18F3
Camp des Pêches. GPS: n47,05257 e7,06993.
🚐 ⭕ 01/04-15/10

Tourist information Le Landeron:
✕ Restaurant Le Carnotzet, Rue de la Gare 22. Restaurant with regional specialities. ⭕ Tue-Sa 11-14h, 17-23h ⚫ Mo, Su.

Les Brenets 18F3
Champ de la Fontaine. GPS: n47,06588 e6,69898.

🔌CHF5 🍴Ch🚿. ⭕ 01/01-31/12
Remarks: Nearby campsite Lac de Brenets.

Les Ponts-de-Martel 21F1
Rue du Bugnon. **GPS:** n46,99644 e6,73065. ➡.

3 🚐free 🔌🍴Ch🚿(2x)free. **Location:** Rural, simple.
Surface: asphalted.
Distance: 🚶600m ✕700m.
Remarks: At community centre.

Malvilliers 21F1
Hotel-Restaurant La Croisée, Route de Neuchâtel.
GPS: n47,03200 e6,86779. ⬆➡.

5 🚐CHF5 🍴Ch🚿(4x)included.
Location: Simple, noisy. **Surface:** asphalted. ⭕ 01/01-31/12
Distance: 🚶100m 🏊on the spot.

Meiringen 21H1
Alpencamping, Brüningstrasse 46. **GPS:** n46,73448 e8,17122.

8 🚐CHF 27,90 🔌🍴Ch🚿WC📶🔵🔵included. **Surface:** grassy.
Distance: 🚶1km ✕1km.
Remarks: Max. 3 nights.

Morges 21F2
Le Petit Bois. GPS: n46,50446 e6,48894.
🚐🔌🍴Chagainst payment. ⭕ 01/04-01/10
Remarks: Service at entrance campsite.

Moutier 18G3
Chemin de la Piscine. **GPS:** n47,27365 e7,37923. ⬆➡.

5 🚐free 🔌🍴Chfree.
Location: Urban, simple, quiet. **Surface:** asphalted.
Distance: 🚶1km.
Remarks: At swimming pool.

Murten 21G1
Lac de Morat, Ryf. **GPS:** n46,93240 e7,11967. ⬆.

30 🚐CHF 1/h, overnight stay free. 🚐 **Location:** Urban, simple, central.
Surface: grasstiles. ⭕ 01/01-31/12
Distance: 🚶on the spot ⛴on the spot ✕on the spot.

Neuchâtel 21F1
Route des Falaises. **GPS:** n47,00145 e6,95735. ⬆.

8 🚐free 🔌🍴Ch🚿(4x)free.
Location: Simple, noisy.
Surface: grasstiles.
Distance: 🚶city centre 2km ⛴300m 🚉100m.
Remarks: Max. 2 days, max. 7m.

Tourist information Neuchâtel:
🌿 Le Creux-du-Van, Val-de-Travers. Nature reserve. ⭕ 01/01-31/12.

Nyon 21E2
Piscine de Colovray, Chemin de la Piscine. **GPS:** n46,36989 e6,22842.

10 🚐free 🔌🍴Ch🚿WC free. **Surface:** asphalted.
⭕ 01/01-31/12
Distance: 🚶1km ⛴150m ✕1km 🎣1km.
Remarks: Max. 15h.

Oberburg 18G3
Reisemobilstellplätze Kürbishof, Krauchthalstrasse 40.
GPS: n47,03807 e7,62079.
5 🚐CHF 13 or € 9 🔌🍴Ch🚿WCagainst payment. ⭕ 01/01-31/12
Distance: 🚶600m ✕300m.
Remarks: Payment also in euros.

Oron-la-Ville 21F1
Chemin de Botollie. **GPS:** n46,57191 e6,82199.

3 free ⌖ Ch. **Surface:** gravel/metalled. 01/01-31/12
Distance: on the spot on the spot on the spot.

Payerne 21F1
Place de la Concorde. **GPS:** n46,81976 e6,93757.

2 free ⌖ Ch (2x)free. **Location:** Urban, simple, central, noisy. **Surface:** asphalted. 01/01-31/12
Distance: on the spot on the spot on the spot.

Portalban 21F1
Route du Port. **GPS:** n46,92131 e6,95614.

26 CHF 20, 2 pers.incl ⌖ Ch (30x)WC included.
Location: Rural, simple. **Surface:** grasstiles.
01/01-31/12
Distance: on the spot 200m on the spot on the spot.
Remarks: In harbour, near campsite, check in at reception.

Prêles 18G3
Prêles, Route de la Neuveville 61. **GPS:** n47,08404 e7,11262.
01/04-15/10

Rolle 21E2
Camping de Rolle Aux Vernes, Chemin de la Plage.
GPS: n46,46191 e6,34630.
5 CHF 18-30 + CHF 8,50-10/pp tourist tax CHF 3.
Surface: asphalted. 01/03-01/10
Distance: 500m.
Remarks: Max. 48h.

Romont 21F1
Promenade des Avoines. **GPS:** n46,69753 e6,91774.

2 free ⌖ Ch (4x)free. **Location:** Rural, simple, noisy.
Surface: grasstiles. 01/01-31/12
Distance: on the spot 100m 700m.
Remarks: Max. 24h.

Saignelégier 18F3
Chemin de la Tuilerie. **GPS:** n47,25223 e7,00347.

10 free ⌖ Ch free. **Location:** Rural, simple, noisy.
Surface: grasstiles. 01/01-31/12
Distance: 700m on the spot 200m.

Saint Blaise 21F1
Chemin des Pêcheurs. **GPS:** n47,01139 e6,98778.

12 CHF 16/24h ⌖ Ch (4x)WC included.
Location: Urban, simple, central, noisy.
Surface: asphalted.
Distance: Neuchâtel 5km 300m 250m 500m 600m.

Saint-Aubin 21F1
Port de St-Aubin-Sauges. **GPS:** n46,89181 e6,77427.

10 CHF 20 ⌖ Ch (6x)WC included.
Location: Simple, quiet. **Surface:** asphalted. 01/01-31/12
Distance: 600m on the spot on the spot 400m 400m.
Remarks: Parking port, nearby the capitainerie.

Sainte-Croix 21F1
Grand-Rue, L'Auberson. **GPS:** n46,82019 e6,47230.

4 free ⌖ Ch (4x)free. **Location:** Rural, simple.
Surface: asphalted.
Distance: 2km on the spot 3km.

Satigny 21E2
Bois de Bay, Route du Bois-de-Bay 19. **GPS:** n46,19856 e6,04724.
01/01-31/12

Vesenaz 21E2
Pointe a la Bise. **GPS:** n46,24517 e6,19331.
01/01-31/12

Zweisimmen 21G1
Vermeille, Eygässli 2. **GPS:** n46,56265 e7,37766.
01/01-31/12

Switzerland North

Altikon 19A2
Stellplatz auf dem Bauernhof, Feldistrasse 18.
GPS: n47,57337 e8,78391.
3 CHF 10 CHF 1 Ch CHF 4 CHF 2. **Surface:** metalled.
01/01-31/12
Distance: 200m 200m.
Remarks: Max. 48h.

Brunnen 22A1
Hopfraeben. **GPS:** n46,99700 e8,59300.
01/05-01/10

Engelberg 21H1
Eienwäldli, Wasserfallstraße 108. **GPS:** n46,81009 e8,42243.
01/11-30/11

Frick 18H2
Hotel Engel, Hauptstraße 101. **GPS:** n47,50576 e8,02430.

20 free WC. **Surface:** gravel. 01/01-31/12
Distance: 300m 1,6km on the spot 50m 50m.
Remarks: Behind the hotel.

Giswil 21H1
Stellplatz an der Kirche, Panoramastrasse. **GPS:** n46,83230 e8,17900.
3 free. **Surface:** asphalted. 01/01-31/12
Distance: on the spot on the spot on the spot.
Remarks: Max. 1 night.

Hemmiken 18H3
Stellplatz Bauernhof, Asphof 50. **GPS:** n47,49682 e7,88749.
3 CHF 20 ⌖ Ch.
Location: Isolated. **Surface:** unpaved. 01/01-31/12
Distance: 1,4km.

Horw 21H1
Steinibachried. **GPS:** n47,01100 e8,31100.
01/04-01/10

Reinach 18G3
Waldhort, Heideweg 16. **GPS:** n47,49923 e7,60296.
15/03-15/10

Weggis 18H3
Bauernhof Gerberweid, Eichistrasse 2. **GPS:** n47,03888 e8,41446.

15 CHF 6-10 + CHF 6/pp + CHF 2,70/pp tourist tax CHF 1
Ch CHF 3 CHF 2. **Surface:** grassy. 01/04-15/10
Distance: 2km 1km 1km 500m on the spot.

Willisau 18H3
Bisangmatt. **GPS:** n47,11937 e7,99829.

4 CHF 5 ⌖ (4x)free. **Surface:** metalled. 01/01-31/12
Distance: 800m 800m 800m.
Remarks: At fire-station.

Zug 19A3
Zugersee, Chamer Fussweg 36. **GPS:** n47,17758 e8,49358.
01/04-01/10
Remarks: Max. ^3.17m.

Switzerland East

Altstätten 19B3
Gasthausziel, Trogenerstrasse 99. **GPS:** n47,38892 e9,53457.
6 CHF 10, guests free ⌖ Ch CHF 5/day. 01/01-31/12
Wed-Thu
Distance: 3km on the spot.

Andeer — 22B1

Sut Baselgia. GPS: n46,60651 e9,42630.

Appenzell — 19B3

Restaurant Eggli, Egglistrasse. GPS: n47,32104 e9,46565.
10 ⚡ Ch guests free. **Surface:** asphalted.
01/01-31/12
Remarks: The most beautiful panorama of Appenzell.

Bivio — 22B2

Wohnmobil-Stellplatz Tua. GPS: n46,46304 e9,65597.

20 ⚡ CHF 10-15 + CHF 2,50/pp tourist tax ⚡ Ch ⚡ CHF 7/day.
Surface: grasstiles. 01/01-31/12
Distance: 🚶 Savognin 18km ⊗ on the spot 🍴 Savognin 18km
🎿 on the spot.
Remarks: Parking ski-lifts.

Breil/Brigels — 22A1

Parkplatz der Bergbahnen. GPS: n46,77104 e9,06770. ⬆

20 ⚡ CHF 7 + CHF 3/pp tourist tax ⚡ CHF 2/50liter ⚡ Ch ⚡ CHF 3/day.
Surface: metalled. 01/04-30/11
Distance: 🚶 600m 🛁 on the spot Imbiss on the spot, restaurants
600m 🍴 600m 🚌 on the spot 🎿 nearby.
Remarks: At Brigeler See.

Chur — 22B1

Stellplätze Camp Au, Felsenaustrasse 61. GPS: n46,86187 e9,50756.
⚡ CHF 15 + CHF 1,20/pp tourist tax ⚡ Ch WC.
01/01-31/12
Distance: 🚶 3km 🛁 2km ⊗ on the spot 🍴 on the spot.
Remarks: Max. 1 night, oldest city of Switzerland.

Churwalden — 22B1

Pradafenz, Girabodawag 34. GPS: n46,77636 e9,54178.
01/01-31/12

Davos — 22C1

Rinerlodge Talstation, Rinerhornbahn, Davos Glaris.
GPS: n46,74150 e9,77814.
10 ⚡ CHF 29 ⚡ Ch ⚡ CHF 2.
Surface: gravel.
Distance: 🚶 1km 🛁 on the spot ⊗ on the spot 🎿 on the spot
🚠 on the spot.
Remarks: Max. 24h.

Tourist information Davos:
👁 Davos Alpengarten. Botanical garden.
01/05-30/09 9-17h.
⊗ Berghaus Stafelalp, Frauenkirch. 250 Year old inn where they still cook on a wood oven and shimmer paraffin lamps are lit.

Elm — 22B1

Sportbahnen Elm, Schiesserblock. GPS: n46,91332 e9,16228.
50 ⚡ free. **Surface:** asphalted. 01/03-30/11
Distance: ⊗ 650m 🍴 650m 🎿 on the spot 🎿 on the spot.

Eschenz — 19A2

Hüttenberg. GPS: n47,64436 e8,85935.
8 ⚡ CHF 20 ⚡ Ch ⚡ WC included. **Location:** Rural.
Surface: grassy/metalled. 01/01-31/12
Remarks: Payment also in euros.

Kreuzlingen — 19B2

Fischerhaus, Promenadestraße 52. GPS: n47,64745 e9,19898.
01/04-01/11

Müstair — 22D1

Clenga. GPS: n46,62900 e10,45400.
01/05-20/10

Neuhausen — 19A2

Parkplatz Fischacker, Nohlstrasse. GPS: n47,67373 e8,60866.

50 ⚡ € 15 ⚡ Ch WC. **Surface:** grassy/metalled.
Distance: 🚶 200m 🛁 on the spot ⊗ 200m 🍴 1km.

Tourist information Neuhausen:
👁 Der Rheinfall. Water falls.

Pontresina — 22C2

Plauns. GPS: n46,46200 e9,93400.
01/06-15/10, 15/12-15/04

Samnaun — 19C3

Wohnmobilstellplatz Samnaun-Ravaisch, Sportplatzweg 13.
GPS: n46,94906 e10,36705.

18 ⚡ CHF 18-39/day, CHF 6,20/pp ⚡ Ch ⚡ WC included.
01/01-31/12
Distance: ⊗ 750m 🚌 200m 🎿 on the spot.
Remarks: At football ground.

Sankt Gallen — 19B3

Paul-Grüninger-Stadion, Grütlistrasse. GPS: n47,43361 e9,40464.
2 ⚡ CHF 2/9-19h, CHF 1/19-8h ⚡ CHF 1/100liter ⚡ CHF 0,50/kWh.
Surface: asphalted. 01/01-31/12
Distance: 🚶 2km ⊗ 300m.
Remarks: Next to sports fields.

Sankt Moritz — 22C1

Olympiaschanze. GPS: n46,47800 e9,82600.
15/05-01/10

Tourist information Sankt Moritz:
⚡ Clean Energy Tour. Hiking trail, nature, energy, climate and weather adventure. Sign up at Kur- und Verkehrsverein St. Moritz. 15/06-01/10 Wed 13.45h duration 2,5 hours.

Savognin — 22B1

Veia Sandeilas. GPS: n46,59660 e9,59226.
15 ⚡ CHF 15 + CHF 8/pp ⚡ CHF 1 ⚡ Ch ⚡ CHF 2,50.
Surface: gravel. 01/01-31/12
Distance: 🚶 500m.
Remarks: Near the chair-lift, summer: parking at campsite Julia.

Schiers — 19B3

Restaurant Prättigauerhof, Flurystrasse 19. GPS: n46,97034 e9,68752.
2 ⚡ free, use of a meal obligated ⚡.
Surface: metalled. 01/01-31/12 Sa + Su
Distance: 🚶 300m ⊗ on the spot 🍴 100m.

Sent — 22C1

Camping Sur En. GPS: n46,81852 e10,36596.
10 ⚡ CHF 15 + CHF 2,50/pp tourist tax ⚡ CHF 3.
01/01-31/12
Distance: ⊗ on the spot.
Remarks: Max. 1 night, 17-10h.

Splügen — 22B1

Auf dem Sand. GPS: n46,54922 e9,31399.
01/01-31/12

Steckborn — 19A2

Wohnmobilplatz Steckborn, Schützengraben.
GPS: n47,66813 e8,98462. ⬆

8 ⚡ CHF 12/24h ⚡ Ch (8x) included.
Surface: gravel. 01/01-31/12
Distance: 🚶 400m 🛁 200m ⊗ 400m 🍴 300m.

Unterwasser — 19B3

Hotel Restaurant Post, Postplatz. GPS: n47,19673 e9,30949.
6 ⚡ CHF 15 + CHF 3/pp tourist tax, guests free ⚡ (6x).
01/01-31/12
Distance: 🚶 300m ⊗ on the spot 🍴 300m 🚶 on the spot.

Vaduz/Liechtenstein — 19B3

Rheinparkstadion, Rheindamm. GPS: n47,14022 e9,50945. ⬆

10 ⚡ CHF 4,50, 19-07h free ⚡ Ch WC free.
Surface: asphalted. 01/01-31/12
Distance: ⚡ 1,8km 🚌 on the spot.
Remarks: Along the Rhine river, parking near stadium, max. 24h.

Tourist information Vaduz/Liechtenstein:
ℹ Liechtenstein Tourismus, Städtle 37, www.vaduz.li. Monarchy on the Austrian-Swiss border.
🏛 Skimuseum, Fabrikstrasse 5. 100 years ski history. Mo-Fri 14-18h.
☺ Erlebniswelt Neuguthof, Neugutweg 30. Maize labyrinth with wild-west city. 15/06-30/09 Wed 13-18h, Sa-Su 10-20h, holidays Mo-Fri 10-20h, Sa-Su 10-22h.

Vals — 22B1

Stellplatz Vals, Vallée. GPS: n46,60891 e9,17438.

10 ⚡ CHF 17 + CHF 2,80/pp tourist tax ⚡ WC.
Surface: metalled. summer
Distance: 🚶 300m 🛁 on the spot ⊗ 300m 🍴 300m 🎿 on the spot.
Remarks: Parking funicular railway.

Zizers — 22B1

K. Lüthi, Rappagugg. GPS: n46,91937 e9,56270.
5 ⚡ free ⚡ Ch. **Surface:** metalled.
Distance: 🚶 1,6km ⚡ on the spot.
Remarks: At motorhome dealer.

Zürich — 19A3

Seeburcht, Seestrasse 559. GPS: n47,33641 e8,53960.
01/05-01/10

Tourist information Zürich:
ℹ Zürich Tourismus, Im Hauptbahnhof, www.zuerich.com. Historical city with large pedestrian area.

Switzerland South

Agno — 22A3

Eurocampo, Via di Molinnazzo. GPS: n45,99547 e8,90063.
01/04-01/10

Avegno — 22A2

Piccolo Paradiso. GPS: n46,20100 e8,74300.
01/03-01/11

Bellinzona — 22A2

Centro Sportivo, Viale Giuseppe Motta. GPS: n46,20116 e9,01729. ⬆

7 CHF 20 CHF 1/20liter Ch.
Surface: asphalted. 01/01-31/12
Distance: 1,5km 4km.
Remarks: Max. 48h.

Tourist information Bellinzona:
Castelgrande. 01/01-31/12 10-18h.
Castello di Montebello. 01/03-30/11 10-18h.
Castello di Sasso Corbaro. 01/03-30/11 10-18h.
Palestra di Roccia San Paolo, Palazo Civico. Climbing garden for beginners and experienced, 30.000²m, 23 climbing trails.

| | Bouveret | 21F2 |

Rive Bleue. GPS: n46,38645 e6,86041.
01/04-30/09

| | Brig | 21H2 |

Brigerbad. GPS: n46,29995 e7,93617.

| | Champéry | 21F2 |

Route de la Fin. GPS: n46,17592 e6,87076.

6 CHF 18 + 2,20/pp Ch (4x)included.
Location: Rural, simple. **Surface:** asphalted. 01/01-31/12
Distance: 100m on the spot 200m 200m.
Remarks: Parking supermarket, nearby the télepherique.

| | Evolène | 21G2 |

Evolène. GPS: n46,11075 e7,49654.
01/01-31/12

| | Gordevio | 22A2 |

Bella Riva. GPS: n46,22293 e8,74313.
01/04-01/10

| | Grimentz | 21G2 |

Aire camping-car l'Ilôt Bosquet, Route de Moiry.
GPS: n46,17432 e7,57271.

20 CHF 15 Ch CHF 3.
Location: Rural, simple, quiet. **Surface:** asphalted. 01/01-31/12
Distance: on the spot on the spot on the spot on the spot nearby nearby.
Remarks: Pay and coins at tourist office, public transport, free entrance swimming pool (summer).

Tourist information Grimentz:
Grimentz/St.Jean Tourisme, www.grimentz.ch. Many signposted cycle and hiking routes.
La Maison bourgeoisiale. Life of the citizens of Grimentz. guided tour Mo. free.

| | Grimselpas | 21H1 |

Hotel Grimselblick, Totensee. **GPS:** n46,56115 e8,33673.
20 CHF 10. **Surface:** asphalted.
Distance: on the spot.
Remarks: Service at hotel.

| | Hérémence | 21G2 |

Val des Hérémence, Parking B,C,D en E, Le Chargeur.
GPS: n46,08882 e7,40362.

15 free. **Surface:** unpaved. 01/01-31/12
Remarks: At artificial lake.

| | La Fouly | 21G3 |

Les Glaciers. GPS: n45,93351 e7,09361.
15/05-30/09

| | Les Haudères | 21G2 |

Molignon. GPS: n46,09061 e7,50776.
01/01-31/12

| | Leuk | 21G2 |

Hexenplatzstrasse. **GPS:** n46,31082 e7,63436.
4 CHF 15/24h Ch. **Surface:** asphalted. 01/01-31/12
Distance: 400m on the spot on the spot 400m 400m.

| | Leukerbad | 21G2 |

Winterstellplatz, Parkplatz Fischweiher. **GPS:** n46,38215 e7,63232.

30 CHF 10/24h. **Location:** Rural, simple. **Surface:** gravel/sand.
01/11-15/04
Distance: 150m 600m 100m.
Remarks: Payment only with coins.

| | Locarno | 22A2 |

Parco della Pace, Via Gioacchino Respini.
GPS: n46,16011 e8,80255.

50 CHF 5/6h. **Surface:** gravel. 01/01-31/12
Distance: 900m 100m 100m.
Remarks: Max. 24h.

Tourist information Locarno:
Rasa. Touristic car-free miniature village, can be reached by first taking the Centrovall-track, till Verdasio, then the small telpher carrier to Rasa.
Tenero-Locarno-Tenero. Free boat service. 31/05-30/09.

| | Martigny | 21G2 |

P1, Place de la Fondation Gianadda. **GPS:** n46,09585 e7,07143.

5 free. **Location:** Urban, simple. **Surface:** asphalted.

| | Martigny | 21G2 |

Les Neuvilles, Rue du Levant 68. **GPS:** n46,09787 e7,07930.
01/02-31/12

Tourist information Martigny:
Gorges du Durnand. Hiking trail through the gorge of the river Durnand.

| | Meride | 22A3 |

Parco al Sole. GPS: n45,88806 e8,94944.
01/05-01/10

| | Molinazzo di Montegio | 22A3 |

Tresiana. GPS: n45,98990 e8,81576.
Easter-01/11

| | Muzzano-Lugano | 22A3 |

Piodella di Agnuzzo. GPS: n45,99463 e8,90857.
01/01-31/12

| | Raron | 21H2 |

Santa Monica, Kantonstrasse 56. **GPS:** n46,30007 e7,82374.
01/01-31/12

| | Reckingen | 21H2 |

Camping Augenstern, Im Ellbogen 21. **GPS:** n46,46500 e8,24500.
01/05-18/10 and 15/12-15/03

| | Saas Fee | 21H2 |

Parkplatz P4. GPS: n46,11090 e7,93208.

50 CHF 26/24h Chincluded CHF 2 WC. **Location:** Rural, simple, isolated, quiet. **Surface:** grassy/gravel. 01/01-31/12
service in winter
Distance: 100m 200m 900m 200m.

| | Saillon | 21G2 |

Bains de Saillon, Route du Centre Thermal 16. **GPS:** n46,17353 e7,19372.
12 free. **Surface:** grassy.
01/01-31/12
Distance: 4km.
Remarks: Max. 48h.

Tourist information Saillon:
Sentier des Vitraux. Hiking trail, 45 minutes, through wine region.

| | Saint-Léonard | 21G2 |

Place du Lac Souterrain. GPS: n46,25564 e7,42600.

15 CHF 10/night Ch (4x) WC included. **Location:** Rural, simple, central, quiet. **Surface:** asphalted/grassy. service: 01/11-19/03
Distance: 5,5km 300m.
Remarks: Pay in at kiosk.

| | Sierre | 21G2 |

Chemin Du Grand-Lac. **GPS:** n46,28597 e7,54013.

4 . **Location:** Rural, simple. **Surface:** grassy.
Distance: on the spot 100m on the spot.
Remarks: Max. 1 night.

| | Sierre | 21G2 |

Bois de Finges. GPS: n46,29362 e7,55777.
01/05-01/10

Tourist information Sierre:
Happyland New, Route Foulon, Granges. Amusement park.

☐ 01/03-31/10 11-18h.

Simplon 21H2
Col du Simplon, Simplonstrasse. **GPS**: n46,24944 e8,03056.⬆.

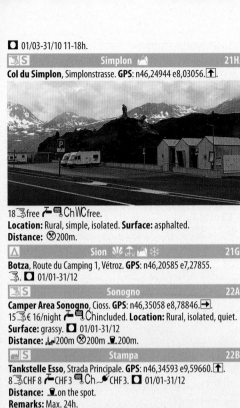

18 free ⌐ Ch WC free.
Location: Rural, simple, isolated. **Surface:** asphalted.
Distance: ⊗200m.

Sion 21G2
Botza, Route du Camping 1, Vétroz. **GPS**: n46,20585 e7,27855.
. ☐ 01/01-31/12

Sonogno 22A2
Camper Area Sonogno, Cioss. **GPS**: n46,35058 e8,78846.➡.
15 € 16/night ⌐ Ch included. **Location:** Rural, isolated, quiet.
Surface: grassy. ☐ 01/01-31/12
Distance: 200m ⊗200m 200m.

Stampa 22B2
Tankstelle Esso, Strada Principale. **GPS**: n46,34593 e9,59660.⬆.
8 CHF 8 ⌐ CHF 3 Ch CHF 3. ☐ 01/01-31/12
Distance: on the spot.
Remarks: Max. 24h.

Tenero 22A2
Campofelice, Via Alle Brere 7. **GPS**: n46,17353 e8,85401.
. ☐ 01/04-27/10

Tenero 22A2
Lido Mappo, Via Mappo. **GPS**: n46,17850 e8,84519.
. ☐ 15/03-01/11

Tenero 22A2
Tamaro, Via Mappo 32. **GPS**: n46,17525 e8,84779.
. ☐ 15/03-01/11

Trient 21F3
Place de Repos Du Peuty, Le Peuty. **GPS**: n46,04645 e6,99499.⬆.

6 CHF 3/pp ⌐ free.
Location: Rural, simple, isolated, quiet. **Surface:** grassy.
Distance: ⊗1,5km on the spot.

Vétroz 21G2
Restaurant L'As de Pique. **GPS**: n46,20556 e7,27833.
⌐ Ch CHF 15, guests free.

Czech Republic

Capital: Prague
Government: parliamentary constitutional republic
Official Language: Czech
Population 10,627,000 (2014)
Area: 78,866 Km²

General information
Dialling code: 0048
General emergency: 112
Currency: Koruna(CZK)
€ 1 = 27 CZK, 10 CZK = € 0,40 (October 2015)
£ 1 = 37,55 CZK, 10 CZK = £ 0,26 (October 2015)
Credit cards are accepted almost everywhere.

Regulations for overnight stays
Wild camping is not allowed.

Additional public holidays 2016
May 1 Labour Day
May 8 Liberation Day
July 5 St. Cyril & St. Methodius Day
July 6 Jan Hus Day
September 28 St. Wenceslas Day
October 28 Independent Czechoslavak State Day
November 17 Freedom and Democracy Day

Time Zone
Winter (Standard Time) GMT+1
Summer (DST) GMT+2

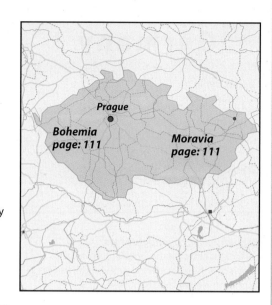

Bohemia

Karlovy Vary · 11F2
Nakladni. **GPS**: n50,23438 e12,86782.⬆.
15 🛏 € 20 🚰🔌Ch ⚡included 📶€1. **Surface**: metalled.
⭕ 01/03-01/11
Distance: 🚃500m ⊗200m 🍴600m.

Karlovy Vary · 11F2
U. Podjezdu 1616/5. **GPS**: n50,21992 e12,83688.⬆.
10 🛏 🚰🔌Chincluded ⚡€2,50. **Surface**: grassy.
⭕ 01/03-01/11
Distance: ⊗400m.

Lipno nad Vltavou · 35A3
Camping Hotel Panorama, Lipno nad Vltavou 22.
GPS: n48,63869 e14,22484.⬆.
40 🛏 € 10,50-17,50 🚰🔌Ch ⚡ WC 🔲📶included.
Location: Rural. **Surface**: grassy/metalled. ⭕ 01/04-01/10
Distance: 🏊on the spot ⊗on the spot 🚴on the spot 🚶on the spot.
Remarks: Bread-service.

Nelahozeves · 11H2
Marina Vltava, Dvořákova stezka. **GPS**: n50,25898 e14,30230.
15 🛏 € 6 🚰€2/100liter 🔌€2 ⚡€2. 🛶 **Surface**: grasstiles.
⭕ 01/01-31/12
Distance: 🏊on the spot ⊗on the spot 🍺300m.

Nová Bystřice · 35A2
Farma Alpaka, Dobrá Voda čp 20. **GPS**: n49,06400 e15,10481.
10 🛏 € 8 🚰🔌Ch ⚡. **Location**: Rural. **Surface**: gravel.
⭕ 01/01-31/12
Distance: 🚃6km.
Remarks: Bread-service.

Nové Město pod Smrkem · 35A1
Ludvíkov Horses&Holiday, Ludvíkov pod Smrkem 9.
GPS: n50,91579 e15,20486.⬆.
15 🛏 € 13 🚰🔌Ch ⚡included WC 🔲📶.
Location: Rural. **Surface**: grassy. ⭕ 01/01-31/12
Distance: 🚴on the spot 🚶on the spot 🎿10km.

Prague · 35A2
Caravan Camping Císařská Louka, Císařská louka 16.
GPS: n50,05584 e14,41336.⬆.
40 🛏 € 16,50 🚰🔌ChWC€3,50 🔲📶included.
Location: Urban. **Surface**: grassy. ⭕ 01/01-31/12
Distance: 🚃4km 🚆750m.

Prague · 35A2
Camp Herzog, Trojská 602/161. **GPS**: n50,11719 e14,42717.
20 🛏 € 14 🚰🔌Ch ⚡€3,50 WC 🔲📶included.
Location: Urban. **Surface**: grassy.
⭕ 01/01-31/12
Distance: 🚃4,2km 🚆500m.

Prague · 35A2
Dana Troja, Trojská 357/129. **GPS**: n50,11716 e14,43176.⬆.
15 🛏 € 19 🚰🔌Ch ⚡€3 WC 🔲📶€2,50📶included.
Location: Urban. **Surface**: grassy.
⭕ 01/01-31/12
Distance: 🚃4km 🚆200m.

Sněžník · 11H1
Stellplatz Sněžník, Jílové. **GPS**: n50,79647 e14,08425.⬆.

15 🛏 € 5/5h, then € 0,60/h 🚰€0,10/10liter 🔌Ch ⚡€0,60/kWh.
⭕ 01/01-31/12
Distance: ⊗50m.

Svitavy · 35A2
U Stadion, U Stadionu. **GPS**: n49,75146 e16,46521.⬆.
6 🛏free 🚰🔌Chfree ⚡€0,25/kWh. **Location**: Urban.
Surface: metalled. ⭕ 01/01-31/12
Distance: ⊗on the spot.
Remarks: At stadium.

Velemín · 11H2
Finaso, Velemín 198. **GPS**: n50,53639 e13,97333.⬆.

6 🛏free 🚰🔌Chfree ⚡€0,50/kWh. **Location**: Simple.
Surface: metalled. ⭕ 01/01-31/12

Velká Jesenice · 35A1
Stellplatz Rozkoš, Vodní nádrž Rozkoš. **GPS**: n50,36444 e16,05944.
16 🛏 € 11 🚰🔌Ch ⚡📶included. 🚐 **Location**: Rural.
⭕ 01/01-31/12
Distance: 🏊on the spot 🚣on the spot.

Moravia

Červená Řečice · 35A2
Camping Kovarna, Červená Řečice 63. **GPS**: n49,51922 e15,15661.⬆.
39 🛏 € 15 🚰🔌Ch ⚡€3,75 WC 📶included. **Location**: Rural.
Surface: grassy. ⭕ 01/06-26/08
Distance: 🏊on the spot ⊗5km 🍺2km 🚴on the spot 🚶on the spot.
Remarks: Bread-service.

Uherský Brod · 35B2
Aquapark Delfin, Slovácké náměstí 2377.
GPS: n49,01960 e17,64828.⬆.
2 🛏free. **Location**: Urban. **Surface**: metalled. ⭕ 01/01-31/12
Distance: ⊗100m 🍺150m.

Germany

Capital: Berlin
Government: Federal republic
Official Language: Germany
Population: 82,000,000 (2014)
Area: 356,970 km²

General information
Dialling code: 0049
General emergency: 112
Currency: Euro

Regulations for overnight stays
Overnight stays on the public highway are allowed, if there is no local prohibition, but no "camping" activities are allowed.

Additional public holidays 2016
January 6 Epiphany
March 25 Good Friday
March 28 Eastermonday
May 1 Labor Day
May 15 White Monday
May 26 Corpus Christi
August 15 Assumption of the Virgin Mary
October 3 Day of German Unity
November 1 All Saints' Day

Time Zone
Winter (Standard Time) GMT+1
Summer (DST) GMT+2

DE

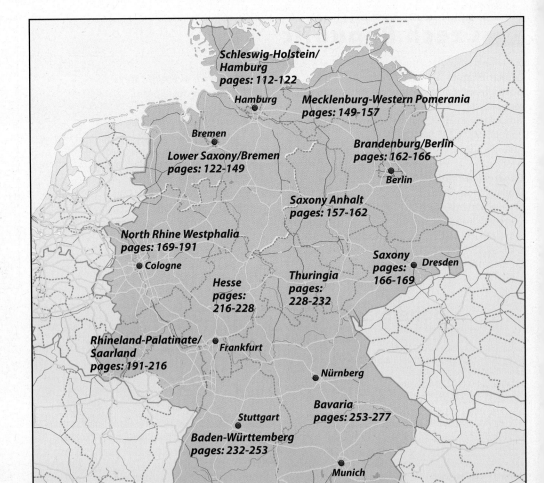

Schleswig-Holstein/Hamburg pages: 112-122

Hamburg

Mecklenburg-Western Pomerania pages: 149-157

Bremen

Lower Saxony/Bremen pages: 122-149

Brandenburg/Berlin pages: 162-166

Berlin

Saxony Anhalt pages: 157-162

North Rhine Westphalia pages: 169-191

Cologne

Hesse pages: 216-228

Thuringia pages: 228-232

Saxony pages: 166-169

Dresden

Rhineland-Palatinate/Saarland pages: 191-216

Frankfurt

Nürnberg

Bavaria pages: 253-277

Stuttgart

Baden-Württemberg pages: 232-253

Munich

Schleswig-Holstein /Hamburg

Albersdorf 7A1
Freitzeitbad Albersdorf, Weg zur Badeanstalt 18. **GPS**: n54,15350 e9,28055.

6 �\€ 15 swimming pool incl ⌐□Ch⌐ (6x)included. **Location**: Rural, isolated, quiet. **Surface**: grassy.
🗓 01/05-31/08
Distance: ⌐1km ⊗100m ⌐300m on the spot ⌐on the spot.
Remarks: Parking at swimming pool, max. 3 days.

Altenhof 5D3
Wohnmobilpark Ostsee 'Grüner Jäger', Grünen Jäger. **GPS**: n54,44392 e9,90526.⬆➡

80 ⌐\€8 ⌐□Ch⌐€3/24h WC⌐€1 **Location**: Rural, simple, isolated, quiet. **Surface**: grassy. 🗓 01/01-31/12
Distance: ⌐Eckernförde 6km ⌐2km ⊗on the spot ⌐6km ⌐200m

busstop -> Kiel on the spot on the spot.
Remarks: Check in at restaurant Grüner, bread-service.

Aukrug 7B1
Zum Sportplatz 1. **GPS**: n54,07441 e9,79160.⬆➡

8 ⌐\€8 ⌐□Ch⌐ included. **Location**: Rural.
Surface: grassy/metalled. 🗓 01/01-31/12
Distance: ⌐1km ⊗800m ⌐1km on the spot ⌐on the spot.
Remarks: Max. 3 days, check in and key service at pay-desk of swimming pool.

Aventoft 5C3
Bauernhof Clausen, Gotteskoogstrasse 5. **GPS**: n54,88250 e8,80722.⬆➡

5 ⌐\€6 ⌐\€2 WC⌐€2. **Location**: Rural, simple, isolated, quiet.
Surface: grassy. 🗓 01/01-31/12
Distance: ⌐5km ⌐5km.
Remarks: <3000kg.

Aventoft 5C3
Wohnmobilstellplatz Zu den Fuchswiesen, Revtoftweg 1. **GPS**: n54,87661 e8,84562.⬆.

15 ⌐\€ 5, dog € 1 ⌐□Ch⌐€1,50. **Location**: Rural, simple, isolated, quiet. **Surface**: asphalted/grassy.
🗓 01/01-31/12
Distance: ⌐3km ⊗3km ⌐3km on the spot.
Remarks: Bread-service.

Bad Bramstedt 7B1
Parkplatz P7, Am Bahnhof, König Christian Strasse. **GPS**: n53,92167 e9,88967.⬆➡

5 ⌐free. **Location**: Urban, simple, central, noisy. **Surface**: metalled.
🗓 01/01-31/12
Distance: ⌐centre 500m ⊗500m ⌐500m ⌐on the spot.
Remarks: At station, max. 1 night, service at camping Roland, Kielerstrasse.

Bad Malente 5E3
Parkplatz Krützen, Sebastian Kneipp strasse.
GPS: n54,17198 e10,54919.

8 €2/pp €1 €1 Ch. **Location:** Rural, simple.
Surface: metalled. 01/01-31/12
Distance: on the spot 500m 1km.

Bad Oldesloe 7B1
Wohnmobilplatz Exer, Am Bürgerpark.
GPS: n53,81101 e10,36915.

8 free €1/10minutes Ch. (8x)€2/10h WC.
Location: Urban, simple, quiet. **Surface:** metalled.
01/01-31/12
Distance: on the spot 3km on the spot 400m.

Bad Segeberg 7B1
Kalkbergblick, Kastanienweg 1b. GPS: n53,93872 e10,31423.

25 €8 Chincluded (15x)€3/night,6 Amp.
Location: Rural, comfortable, quiet. **Surface:** gravel.
01/01-31/12
Distance: 500m A7 3km 600m Segerberger See 600m
500m 500m on the spot on the spot.
Remarks: Jun/Aug Karl May Spiele, open air theater.

Barmstedt 7B1
Am Rantzauer See, Seestrasse 12. GPS: n53,78640 e9,76420.

5 €5 Ch. WC included. **Surface:** metalled.
01/01-31/12
Distance: on the spot on the spot 500m.

Behrensdorf 5E3
Campingpark Waldesruh, Neuland. GPS: n54,35754 e10,60216.

18 €10-12 2 pers.incl, dog €1,50 Ch. €1/24h WC.

Location: Rural, comfortable. **Surface:** grassy. 01/04-31/10
Distance: 2km on the spot on the spot on the spot on the spot.

Bistensee 5D3
Ferienplatz bei Matz, Mühlenweg 1. GPS: n54,39538 e9,71386.

5 €3 + €3/pp included WC. **Location:** Rural, simple,
isolated, quiet. **Surface:** grassy. 01/01-31/12
Distance: 500m 600m Bistensee on the spot 2km 1km
on the spot on the spot.

Blekendorf 5E3
Am Sehlendorfer Strand, Strandstrasse 24.
GPS: n54,30571 e10,69358.

40 €15,50 €1 Ch. included WC. **Location:** Rural,
comfortable. **Surface:** grassy.
01/01-31/12
Distance: 1km on the spot on the spot on the spot 5km.

Bordesholm 7B1
Festplatz, Kielerstrasse. GPS: n54,18389 e10,02667.

6 free. **Location:** Rural, simple, quiet. **Surface:** grassy/sand.
01/01-31/12
Distance: 1,5km 4km.
Remarks: Max. 18h, service at petrol station.

Bordesholm 7B1
Shell tankstelle, Bahnofstrasse 78. GPS: n54,17343 e10,03497.
Ch. 01/01-31/12

Bosau 7B1
Dat Gröne Huus, Stadtbeker Strasse 97. GPS: n54,09198 e10,42886.

3 €5, guests free €3. **Location:** Rural, simple, quiet.
Surface: gravel. 01/04-30/11
Distance: 100m Großer Plöner See on the spot on the spot
1km.
Remarks: Bread-service.

Bösdorf 7B1
Wohnmobilcamp Augustfelde, Vierer See, Augustfelde.
GPS: n54,12898 e10,45506.

---

16 €11,50-13,50 Ch. (16x) WC included €0,75.
Surface: grassy. 01/04-25/10
Distance: on the spot on the spot on the spot on the spot.

Bösdorf 7B1
Campingpark Gut Ruhleben, Missionsweg 2, Ruhleben.
GPS: n54,14308 e10,45021.

10 €10,50-13,50 Ch. included. **Location:** Rural,
simple. **Surface:** grassy/gravel. 01/04-30/09
Remarks: Max. 3 nights.

Bredstedt 5C3
Süderstraße. GPS: n54,61307 e8,97082.

5 free. **Location:** Rural. **Surface:** asphalted. 01/01-31/12
Distance: 900m Aldi 650m.
Remarks: Nearby swimming pool.

Brodersby 5D3
Ferienhof Lassen, Grossbrodersbyer weg 5.
GPS: n54,53829 e9,71443.

3 €10 Ch. included. **Location:** Rural, simple, quiet.
Surface: grassy.
Distance: 500m 2km 500m.

Brodersby 5D3
Camping Am Mussinder Fährhaus, Mussinder Fahrstrasse 33.
GPS: n54,52500 e9,71583.

20 €12 Ch. WC. **Surface:** grassy. 01/04-31/10

Brokdorf 7A1
Parkplatz, Dorfstrasse. GPS: n53,86417 e9,31667.

DE

30 ⬛free ⌁€1/5minutes ⬛€1 Ch ⚡(30x)€0,50/kWh WC ⬛€0,50. **Location:** Rural, comfortable. **Surface:** metalled. ⬛ 01/01-31/12
Distance: 🚂800m 🏊400m ⊗on the spot 🏪500m 🚲on the spot 🏕 on the spot.

⬛S Brunsbüttel ⬛ 7A1
An der Braake, Am Freizeitbad. **GPS:** n53,89832 e9,13138.⬆

12 ⬛free ⌁€1 Ch. **Location:** Rural, comfortable, central, quiet. **Surface:** grassy/metalled. ⬛ 01/01-31/12
Distance: 🚂500m ⊗500m 🏪500m on the spot.

⬛ Büdelsdorf 5D3
Hermann-Ehlers-Platz, Agnes Miegel Strasse. **GPS:** n54,31583 e9,69306.⬆➡

10 ⬛free. **Location:** Simple, central. **Surface:** metalled. ⬛ 01/01-31/12
Distance: 🚂on the spot ⊗1km 🏪1,5km.
Remarks: Max. 1 night.

⬛S Büsum 6H1
Wohnmobilstellplatz Nordsee, Dr. Martin Bahr Strasse. **GPS:** n54,12889 e8,86889.⬆➡

100 ⬛1/11-28/2 € 10, 1/3-31/10 € 13 ⌁€0,50/50liter ⬛ Ch ⬛WC ⬛€0,50/day. ⚡ **Location:** Rural, comfortable, isolated, quiet. **Surface:** grassy. ⬛ 01/01-31/12
Distance: 🚂1km 🏊500m ⊗300m.

P Büsum 6H1
Deichmuseum P2, Westereck 2. **GPS:** n54,14210 e8,84212.⬆

50 ⬛free. **Location:** Simple, isolated, quiet.
Distance: 🚂500m 🏊500m.

⬛S Dagebüll ⬛ 5C3
Am Nordseedeich, Am Badedeich 15. **GPS:** n54,72666 e8,69527.⬆

10 ⬛€ 6 ⌁€2. ⚡ **Location:** Rural. **Surface:** grassy. ⬛ 01/01-31/12
Distance: 🚂5km 🏊100m 🛒100m ⊗on the spot 🥖bakery 300m.

⬛S Damp ⬛⬛ 5D3
Wohnmobilpark Damp, Parkstrasse 2. **GPS:** n54,57750 e10,01667.⬆➡

70 ⬛€ 12 ⌁€1/100liter ⬛Ch ⚡(60x)€0,60/kWh WC ⬛€1/3minutes ⬛⬛⚡ **Location:** Rural, comfortable, quiet. **Surface:** grassy/gravel. ⬛ 01/01-31/12
Distance: 🏊on the spot ⊗on the spot 🏪on the spot 🚌150m.

⬛S Drelsdorf 5C3
Drelsdörper Krog, Dorfstrasse 23. **GPS:** n54,60555 e9,03555.⬆

15 ⬛€ 5, guests free ⌁€2 WC. **Location:** Simple, central, noisy. **Surface:** grassy. ⬛ 01/01-31/12
Distance: 🚂200m 🏪2km.
Remarks: Along through road.

⬛S Eckernförde ⚡⬛⬛ 5D3
Parkplatz P1, Grüner Weg, B76. **GPS:** n54,46549 e9,83574.⬆➡

46 ⬛€ 1,60/h 10-20h, overnight stay free ⌁€0,50/120liter ⬛€ 0,50 Ch€0,50 ⚡€0,50/kWh. ⬛ **Location:** Urban, simple, central. **Surface:** metalled. ⬛ 01/01-31/12
Distance: 🚂200m 🏊250m ⊗300m 🏪300m 🛒200m 🚲on the spot 🏕on the spot.
Remarks: Along busy through road, parking nearby centre and beach.

⬛S Eckernförde ⚡⬛⬛ 5D3
Wohnmobilstellplatz am Noor, Kakabellenweg. **GPS:** n54,46443 e9,83402.⬆
49 ⬛€ 12 + € 2/pp tourist tax ⌁€1/100liter ⬛Ch ⚡€0,50/kWh WC ⬛⬛€2/2 ⬛ ⬛ ⬛ 01/01-31/12
Distance: 🚂1km 🏊on the spot 🛒on the spot 🏪500m 🏪on the spot.

⬛S Elmshorn ⬛⬛ 7A1
Stellplatz Elmshorn, Nordufer. **GPS:** n53,75157 e9,65268.⬆

6 ⬛free ⌁€1/80liter ⬛ChWC. **Location:** Urban, simple, central, quiet. **Surface:** metalled. ⬛ 01/01-31/12
Distance: 🚂800m 🏊on the spot 🛒on the spot.

⬛ Eutin 7C1
Elisabethstrasse. **GPS:** n54,13507 e10,60935.⬆

5+3 ⬛free. **Location:** Urban. **Surface:** metalled. ⬛ 01/01-31/12
Distance: 🚂on the spot.
Remarks: Parking at station.

⬛ Eutin 7C1
Schloss-Parkplatz P11, Schlossstraße. **GPS:** n54,13828 e10,61990.⬆
5 ⬛free. **Surface:** metalled. ⬛ 01/01-31/12
Distance: 🏊Großer Eutiner See.

⬛S Fehmarn 5E3
Wohnmobilpark Wulfener Hals, Wulfener-Hals-Weg 16, Wulfen. **GPS:** n54,40687 e11,17489.⬆

100 ⬛from € 11,80-27,40 ⌁€ ⬛Ch ⚡€2,10 WC ⬛€0,90 ⬛ ⬛ ⬛ **Location:** Rural, luxurious. **Surface:** grassy. ⬛ 01/01-31/12
Distance: 🏊on the spot.

⬛S Fehmarn 5E3
Hintz-Heizungsbau, Landkirchenerweg 1b, Burg. **GPS:** n54,44228 e11,18967.⬆

16 ⬛€ 10 ⌁€1 ⬛Ch ⚡(16x)€5. **Location:** Simple, quiet. **Surface:** metalled. ⬛ 01/01-31/12
Distance: 🚂on the spot.

⬛ Fehmarn 5E3
Parkplatz Ost, Osterstrasse, Burg. **GPS:** n54,43754 e11,19990.⬆

30 ⬛€ 8 (21-8h). ⬛ **Location:** Urban, simple. **Surface:** metalled. ⬛ 01/01-31/12

Distance: 100m.

Fehmarn 5E3

Kommunal- und Yachthafen Burgstaaken, Burgstaaken/am Binnensee, Burgstaaken. **GPS**: n54,42028 e11,19224.

15 € 10 21-08h. **Location:** Rural, simple. **Surface:** metalled.
01/01-31/12
Distance: 100m 100m.

Fehmarn 5E3

Camping Strukkamphuk, Strukkamp. **GPS**: n54,41239 e11,10223.

21 € 14,50-31 Ch WC included. **Location:** Rural.
Surface: grassy. 01/01-31/12
Distance: 10m.

Flensburg 5D3

Am Industriehafen, dir Flensburg Mürwick. **GPS**: n54,80444 e9,44388.

20 free. **Location:** Urban, simple, isolated, quiet.
Surface: gravel.
Distance: 1,5km on the spot on the spot.

Fockbek 5D3

Am Freibad, Grosse Rheie 17. **GPS**: n54,30190 e9,60331.

3 free Ch WC. **Location:** Rural, quiet. **Surface:** grassy/sand.
01/01-31/12
Distance: 800m 800m 800m on the spot on the spot.
Remarks: Parking swimming pool, max. 24h.

Friedrichskoog 6H1

P2, Nordseestrasse. **GPS**: n54,03272 e8,84833.

30 € 2, overnight stay free. **Location:** Rural, comfortable, isolated, quiet. **Surface:** asphalted/grassy. 01/03-31/10
Distance: 1km 550m 800m.
Remarks: Bread-service.

Gelting 5D3

Hafen Wackerballig, Strandweg, Wackerballig.
GPS: n54,75564 e9,87842.

18 € 8 €0,50/40liter Ch €1,50/day WC €0,50.
Location: Rural, simple. **Surface:** grassy/gravel.
01/04-31/10
Distance: 1,5km on the spot 2km.
Remarks: Key sanitary building/waste dump at harbour master, caution € 20.

Glückstadt 7A1

Park & Ride platz, Bahnhofstrasse. **GPS**: n53,78776 e9,43145.

10 free. **Location:** Urban, simple. **Surface:** asphalted.
01/01-31/12
Distance: 900m 200m on the spot on the spot.

Glückstadt 7A1

Am Außenhafen, Am Hafen. **GPS**: n53,78560 e9,41088.

16 € 5. **Location:** Rural, comfortable. **Surface:** metalled.
01/01-31/12 high water
Distance: 1km on the spot on the spot on the spot on the spot on the spot.
Remarks: Along the river Elbe.

Grödersby 5D3

WSG Arin/Grödersby, Friedenshöher Straße 21.
GPS: n54,63444 e9,92944.

15 € 15 Ch WC €3/2 included.
Location: Rural, simple, quiet. **Surface:** gravel/metalled.
01/05-30/09
Distance: 200m on the spot on the spot 200m on the spot.

Grömitz 5E3

Wohnmobilstellplatz am Lensterstrand, Blankwasserweg.
GPS: n54,15650 e10,99134.

50 winter free, summer € 7,50 WC. **Location:** Rural.
Surface: grassy. 01/01-31/12 water disconnected in winter
Distance: on the spot on the spot.

Grömitz 5E3

Wohnmobilstellplatz, Gildestraße 14.
GPS: n54,14490 e10,95262.

60 winter € 6, summer € 12 €0,50 Ch (20x)€1/kWh.
Location: Rural, comfortable. **Surface:** metalled.
01/01-31/12
Distance: 200m on the spot 200m.

Großenaspe 7B1

Wildpark Eekholt, Eekhol 1. **GPS**: n53,94819 e10,02916.

10 free. **Location:** Rural, simple, isolated, quiet.
Surface: grassy/sand. 01/01-31/12
Distance: 4km Grossenaspe Kiek ut Stuben, Game preserve > Wildpark.

Großenbrode 5E3

Wassersportzentrum, Am Kai 29. **GPS**: n54,35583 e11,07798.

50 € 8-10 €0,50/100liter Ch €1/kWh WC €0,50.
Location: Rural. **Surface:** grassy/metalled. 01/01-31/12
Distance: 300m on the spot 2km.

Großenbrode 5E3

Wohnmobilhafen Reise, Südstrand 1.
GPS: n54,36170 e11,08567.

36 € 10-14 Ch WC €0,50. **Location:** Rural, comfortable. **Surface:** gravel. 01/01-31/12
Distance: on the spot 500m on the spot.

Großsolt 5D3

Stellplatz Mühlenbrück, Flensburger strasse, Mühlenbrück.
GPS: n54,70853 e9,52243.

50 €10 Ch (13x)€2/day WC €0,50. **Location**: Rural, comfortable, quiet. **Surface**: gravel. 01/03-01/10
Distance: 200m.

Hamburg 7B2

Wohnmobilhafen Hamburg, Grüner Deich 8, Hammerbrook.
GPS: n53,54303 e10,02814.

60 €19 Ch WC. **Location**: Urban, simple, central, noisy. **Surface**: gravel. 01/01-31/12
Distance: 4km 200m.

Hamburg 7B2

Wohnmobilplatz Hamburg Süd, Finkenrieker Hauptdeich 5.
GPS: n53,47440 e10,00134.

80 €12 €1 €1 Ch€1 (10x)€1/2kWh WC €1. **Location**: Urban, simple, noisy. **Surface**: metalled. 01/01-31/12
Distance: 14km 100m 100m 5 min.

Hamburg 7B2

Am Strand Pauli, St. Pauli Hafenstraße.
GPS: n53,54598 e9,96099.
20 €8,50, weekend €13.
Surface: asphalted.
01/01-31/12
Distance: Hamburg Altstadt 2,4km on the spot many restaurant 100m 600m.

Tourist information Hamburg:
Hamburg-card. Card offers free entrance to public transport and museums, discounts on boat trips, zoo etc. Available at Tourist Information. €9,50/1 day, €22,90/3 days, 1 adult + max. 3 children.
Sankt Pauli. City district with well-known Reeperbahn.
Flohschanze, Rinderschlachthalle St Pauli. Antiques and flea market. Sa 8-16h.
Tierpark Hagenbeck, Stellingen. Zoo.
Antikpassage, Klosterwall 9-21. Arcade with 39 antique stores. Tue-Fri 12-18h, Sa 10-16h.

Hanerau-Hademarschen 7A1

Ferienhof Sievers, Wilhelmsburg. **GPS**: n54,12360 e9,38627.

6 €10 Ch (6x) WC. **Location**: Rural, comfortable, isolated, quiet. **Surface**: grassy. 01/01-31/12
Distance: 2km.

Harrislee 5D3

Skandic Camping, Am Oxer 17a. **GPS**: n54,79800 e9,36960.

5 €5 Ch included WC€1. **Location**: Urban, simple, isolated. **Surface**: metalled. 01/01-31/12
Distance: 6km.
Remarks: Motorhome dealer, accessory shop.

Hasselberg 5D3

Camping Oehe-Draecht, Drecht. **GPS**: n54,71590 e9,99030.

10 €11 Ch €3 WC included. **Location**: Rural, simple, quiet. **Surface**: grassy. 01/04-30/09
Distance: 3km on the spot on the spot.

Heide 7A1

Wohnmobilplatz Heide, Langvogt-Johannsen-strasse.
GPS: n54,20181 e9,11319.

16 €5/€7 €1/100liter €1 Ch €1/2kWh.
Surface: grasstiles/metalled. 01/01-31/12
Distance: 800m 5,5km 100m 300m.

Heiligenhafen 5E3

Parkplatz Steinwarder, B207 Abfahrt Heiligenhafen.
GPS: n54,37896 e10,97875.

90 €7,50, peak season €12/24h €0,50 Ch (42x)€2 WC.
Surface: asphalted. 01/01-31/12
Distance: 400m on the spot on the spot.
Remarks: Direct access to the beach.

Heiligenhafen 5E3

Reisemobilstellplatz Binnensee, Eichholzweg.
GPS: n54,37721 e10,95548.

20 €7,50-10 (21x)€2. **Location**: Urban. **Surface**: metalled.
01/01-31/12
Distance: 1km on the spot.
Remarks: Max. 24h.

Hohenfelde 5D3

Campingpark Ostseestrand, Strandstraße.
GPS: n54,38588 e10,49152.

25 €15 Ch WC included. **Location**: Rural, luxurious.
Surface: grassy. 01/04-15/10
Distance: 1km beach 150m 150m on the spot on the spot.

Hohenfelde 5D3

Wohnmobilplatz Radeland, Strandstraße 18.
GPS: n54,38278 e10,49295.

20 €5 Ch €0,60/kWh WC €3/day. **Location**: Rural.
Surface: grassy/sand. 01/04-30/09
Distance: 300m.

Hohwacht 5E3

Parkplatz Alt-Hohwacht, Strandstrasse.
GPS: n54,31902 e10,67529.

20 €10 €1/80liter €1 Ch (20x)€1/kWh.
Location: Urban. **Surface**: metalled. 01/01-31/12
Distance: on the spot on the spot.

Husum 5C3

Loof's Wohnmobilhafen, Dockoogstrasse 7. **GPS**: n54,47451 e9,04249.

30 €12 €1 €2 Ch€2 (30x)€3 WC €0,50. **Location**: Rural, simple, central, quiet. **Surface**: gravel.
01/01-31/12
Distance: 200m 200m 200m 200m 200m on the

spot ⋏ on the spot.

ⒸⓈ Husum ≋🏖🌊 5C3
Wohnmobilplatz Am Dockkoog, Dockoogstrasse 17.
GPS: n54,47888 e9,01138.⬆️.

40 🍴€ 12 2 pers.incl, dog € 1 🚰🔌ChWCincluded 🗑€ 1.♨️
Location: Rural, simple, quiet. **Surface:** grassy.
🅿️ Easter-31/10
Distance: 🛒500m ⚓200m 🚤200m on the spot 🚴 on the spot
⋏ on the spot.
Remarks: Max. 3 nights.

🅂Ⓢ Itzehoe 7A1
Malzmüllerwiesen, Schuhmacherallee.
GPS: n53,91970 e9,51815.⬆️➡️.

5 🍴free 🚰€1/100liter 🔌€1 Ch€1. **Location:** Rural, simple, central,
quiet. **Surface:** metalled/sand.
🅿️ 01/01-31/12 🅟 during event
Distance: 🛒600m ⚓20m 🚴 on the spot ⋏ on the spot.

🅂Ⓢ Jagel 5D3
Wohnmobilhafen Jagel, Bundesstrasse 13.
GPS: n54,45388 e9,53416.⬆️.

31 🍴€ 10 🚰🔌Ch🔌day WC🗑. **Location:** Rural, comfortable, quiet.
Surface: grassy. 🅿️ 01/01-31/12
Distance: 🛒250m ⚓4,5km.

ⓊⓈ Kaltenkirchen ♉ 7B1
Reisemobilstellplatz Holstentherme, Norderstrasse 8.
GPS: n53,84056 e9,94650.⬆️➡️.

20 🍴free 🚰€1/80liter 🔌€1 Ch€1 ♨️. **Location:** Quiet.
Surface: grassy/gravel. 🅿️ 01/01-31/12
Distance: 🛒1,5km ⚓1km ⊗on the spot 🍽1,5km 🚌on the spot.
Remarks: Coins available at pay-desk of theTherme.

🅂Ⓢ Kappeln 🌊 5D3
Aral-Tankstelle, Eckernförder Strasse 9/B. **GPS:** n54,65688 e9,94480.

10 🍴free 🚰🔌Ch🗑€5/day. **Location:** Urban, simple.
Surface: metalled. 🅿️ 01/01-31/12
Distance: 🛒300m ⚓2km ⊗on the spot.
Remarks: Caution key electricity € 25.

⚓Ⓢ Kappeln 🌊 5D3
Anker Yachting, Am Hafen. **GPS:** n54,66715 e9,93718.⬆️.
20 🍴€ 10-14 🚰🔌Ch🔌€0,50/kWh🗑€1. 🅿️ 01/01-31/12
Distance: 🛒1km ⊗1km 🍽1km.
Remarks: Near marina.

🅂Ⓢ Kellinghusen 🌳 7A1
Am Freibad, Jacob-Fleischer-Strasse 6. **GPS:** n53,94715 e9,71035.⬆️➡️.

10 🍴free 🚰€0,50/100liter 🔌€0,50 Ch🗑(4x)€1/h WC🗑use sanitary
facilities at swimming pool. **Location:** Rural, quiet. **Surface:** gravel.
🅿️ 01/01-31/12
Distance: 🛒centre 500m ⊗500m 🍽500m.
Remarks: Check in at swimming pool.

🅂Ⓢ Kiel ≋🏖🌊 5D3
Wohnmobilstellplatz Kiel, Förde und Kanalblick, Mecklenburg-
strasse 58. Kiel-Wik. **GPS:** n54,36362 e10,14705.⬆️➡️.

30 🍴€ 11-13 🚰🔌Ch🔌(33x)€3,50/24h WC🗑€1/5minutes 🚿€3/1.
Location: Urban, simple, central, noisy.
Surface: metalled.
🅿️ 01/01-31/12
Distance: 🛒6,5km ⊗Imbiss on the spot 🍽1,5km 🚴 on the spot ⋏on
the spot.
Remarks: Check in and pay at reception, bread-service.

⚓Ⓢ Kiel ≋🏖🌊 5D3
Olympiahafen Schilksee, Soling 26. **GPS:** n54,43033 e10,16634.⬆️.

20 🍴€ 10 🚰€0,50/3minutes 🔌€1 Ch🔌WC🗑.
Surface: metalled.
🅿️ 01/01-31/12
🅟 last 2 weeks of Jun
Distance: 🛒13km ⚓400m 🚤400m.
Remarks: Check in and coins service at harbourmaster.
Tourist information Kiel:
Ⓜ Schleswig-Holsteinisches Freilichtmuseum, Molfsee. Open air
museum. 🅿️ 01/04-31/10 daily 9-18h, 01/11-31/03 Su 11-16h. 🎫 €
4,50, family card € 11.

🅂Ⓢ Krempe 7A1
Am Schul- und Sportzentrum, Am Freibad.
GPS: n53,83356 e9,49447.⬆️.

3 🍴free. **Location:** Rural, simple, quiet. **Surface:** gravel.
🅿️ 01/01-31/12
Distance: 🛒200m.

🚻 Kremperheide 7A1
Heidekrug, Dorfstraße. **GPS:** n53,88006 e9,47967.
4 🍴€ 5, guests free. 🅿️ 01/01-31/12
Distance: ⊗on the spot.
Remarks: In front of restaurant.

🍴🅂Ⓢ Kropp 5D3
Hotel Wikingerhof, Tetenhusener Chaussee 1.
GPS: n54,40638 e9,51055.⬆️.

8 🍴€ 5, guests free 🔌WC🗑🔊. **Location:** Urban, simple, quiet.
Surface: metalled. 🅿️ 01/01-31/12
Distance: 🛒300m ⊗on the spot 🍽300m.

🍴🅂Ⓢ Kropp 5D3
Restaurant Rosengarten, Rheiderweg 7.
GPS: n54,41388 e9,50138.⬆️.

5 🍴€ 5 WC. **Location:** Urban, simple, quiet. **Surface:** metalled.
🅿️ 01/01-31/12
Distance: 🛒200m ⊗on the spot 🍽200m.

🅂Ⓢ Kropp 5D3
Garage Audi-VW Thomsen, Werkstrasse 2. **GPS:** n54,41361 e9,52833.

5 🍴€ 5 🚰🔌Ch🔌. **Location:** Urban, simple, noisy.
Surface: metalled. 🅿️ 01/01-31/12
Distance: 🛒300m ⊗300m 🍽300m.

🅂Ⓢ Laboe 5D3
Ostseebad Laboe Ehrenmal, Steinerweg/Prof. Munzerring.
GPS: n54,41029 e10,23289.⬆️.

DE

18 🏕€ 12 🚰€1/5minutes 🔌€1 Ch. 🏠 **Location:** Urban, simple. **Surface:** metalled. ⬛ 01/01-31/12 **Distance:** 🚲1km ⛱400m ⌒400m 🐟on the spot 🛒1km.

🏕🅂 **Ladelund** 5C3
Am Naturbad, Stato. **GPS:** n54,84919 e9,03629.⬆.

4 🏕€ 5, € 10 swimming pool incl 🚰🔌Ch🛁 WC 🔲included. 🏊 **Location:** Rural, comfortable, isolated, quiet. **Surface:** grassy. ⬛ 01/01-31/12 **Distance:** 🚲1km ⛱on the spot.

🄲🅂 **Langballig** ⚓ 5D3
Campingplatz Langballigau, Strandweg 3, Langballigau. **GPS:** n54,82234 e9,65969.

50 🏕€ 10, dog € 1 🚰🔌Ch🛁€2,50/night WC included 🔲€1/time. 🏊 **Location:** Rural, simple. **Surface:** grassy/gravel. ⬛ 01/01-31/12 **Distance:** ⛱100m 🐟on the spot.

🏕🅂 **Langwedel** 🌿 🚣 5D3
Caravanpark am Brahmsee, Mühlenstraße 30a. **GPS:** n54,21462 e9,91943.⬆➡.

20 🏕€ 10 🚰€1/80liter 🔌Ch🛁€2,50/24h,6 Amp WC 🔲sanitary at campsite. **Location:** Rural, comfortable, quiet. **Surface:** grassy/gravel. ⬛ 01/01-31/12 **Distance:** 🚲600m 🛣A7 3 km ⛱Brahmsee 500m ⌒500m 🛒7km. **Remarks:** Check in at reception campsite, bread-service.

⚓🅂 **Lauenburg/Elbe** 🌿⚓🚣 7C2
Marina Lauenburg/Yachthafen, Hafenstrasse 14. **GPS:** n53,37156 e10,56527.⬆.

10 🏕€ 7 🚰€1/100liter 🛁(8x)€1/kWh WC€0,50 🔲€1 🔌€4/4.

Location: Rural, comfortable. **Surface:** metalled. ⬛ 01/01-31/12 **Distance:** 🚲10 min walking 🐟on the spot 🛒10 min walking.

🏕🅂 **Lensahn** 5E3
Reisemobilplatz Lensahn, Dr. Julius-Stinde strasse. **GPS:** n54,21446 e10,87745.⬆➡.

15 🏕€ 8 🚰€1/80liter 🔌Ch🛁(4x)€2. 🏊 **Location:** Rural, simple. **Surface:** grasstiles. ⬛ 01/01-31/12 **Distance:** 🚲1,5km ⛱on the spot 🐟200m 🛒2,5km.

🏕🅂 **Lübeck** 🌿🚣 7C1
Wohnmobil Treff Lübeck, An der Hülshorst 11. **GPS:** n53,89510 e10,71088.⬆.

40 🏕€ 9/day 🚰🔌Ch🛁 WC 🔲€1/5minutes 📶€1,50. 🏊 **Location:** Urban, luxurious, quiet. **Surface:** gravel. ⬛ 02/01-31/10 **Distance:** 🚲4,5km 🛣5km 🐟on the spot 🚌50m.

🏕🅂 **Lübeck** 🌿🚤🚣 7C1
Wohnmobilstellplatz Lübeck Marienbrücke P4, Lastadie. **GPS:** n53,87147 e10,67904.⬆➡.

16 🏕free, 18-10h. **Location:** Urban, simple. **Surface:** asphalted. ⬛ 01/01-31/12 **Distance:** 🚲500m 🛣2km ⛱on the spot ⌒on the spot.

Tourist information Lübeck:
Ⓜ Museum Holstentor, Holstentorplatz. Historical museum. ⬛ 10-16/17h. 🎟 € 4 (incl. 3 children).
Ⓜ Niederegger Einkaufserlebnis, Café und Marzipan-Museum, Breite strasse 89. Marzipan, Lübecker speciality, museum, café and shop.

⚓🅂 **Maasholm** 🌿🚤🚣 5D3
Stellplatz am Yachthafen, Uleweg 31. **GPS:** n54,68334 e9,99436.⬆.

80 🏕€ 10 🚰🔌Ch🛁€2/day WC 🔲€0,50 🔌€2 📶. 🏊 **Location:** Rural, comfortable, quiet. **Surface:** grassy/gravel. ⬛ 01/01-31/12 **Distance:** 🚲100m 🛣5km ⛱on the spot ⌒on the spot 🐟100m. **Remarks:** Parking marina.

🏕🅂 **Meldorf** 6H1
Reisemobil-Stellplatz am Deich, Deichstraße 2. **GPS:** n54,09409 e8,95070.⬆.

80 🏕€ 7, only overnight stay € 3,50 🚰🔌Ch🛁(18x)€3 WC€2. 🏊 **Location:** Rural, comfortable, isolated, quiet. **Surface:** grassy/metalled. ⬛ Easter-31/10 **Distance:** 🚲7km ⛱on the spot 🐟Imbiss 10-18 uur 🚴on the spot 🚶on the spot.

🏛 **Molfsee** 🌿 5D3
Freilichtmuseum/Restaurant Drathenhof, Hamburger Landstrasse 99. **GPS:** n54,27411 e10,07571.⬆.

20 🏕free, use of a meal desired WC at restaurant. **Location:** Central. **Surface:** gravel. ⬛ 01/01-31/12 **Distance:** 🚲on the spot 🐟on the spot 🚌on the spot 🚴on the spot 🚶on the spot. **Remarks:** At open air museum.

🏕🅂 **Mölln** 7C2
Alt Möllner strasse. **GPS:** n53,62564 e10,68314.⬆.

20 🏕€ 7/24h 🛁(20x)included. 🏠 **Location:** Rural. **Surface:** gravel. ⬛ 01/01-31/12 **Distance:** 🚲1km 🐟250m 🛒300m. **Remarks:** Service: Vorkamp 19, GPS n53,62024, o10,67701.

🏕🅂 **Neumünster** 🐑 7B1
Bad am Stadtwald, Hansaring 177. **GPS:** n54,08078 e9,96064.⬆➡.

22 🏕€ 10 🚰€0,50/100liter 🔌€0,50 Ch🛁(22x)€0,50/kWh WC 🔲€0,50 📶. **Location:** Rural, comfortable, central, quiet. **Surface:** grassy/gravel. ⬛ 01/01-31/12 **Distance:** 🚲2km 🛣A7 1 km 🐟on the spot 🛒300m 🚌on the spot. **Remarks:** Check in at swimming pool.

🏕🅂 **Neustadt in Holstein** 🚣 7C1
Wohnmobilstellplatz Ostsee, Auf der Pelzer Wiese 45, Pelzerhaken. **GPS:** n54,08889 e10,87250.⬆➡.

DE

90 ⌷€ 12 + tourist tax (summer) ⟶€1 ▦€1 Ch ⟋(90x)€1/2kWh WC⌷▣€2. ▣ Location: Rural, luxurious, noisy. Surface: grassy. ◻ 01/01-31/12
Distance: ⊾900m ⊿150m ☒900m ☖400m ☞on the spot.

⛟S Neustadt in Holstein ⛵ 7C1
P5, Am Binnenwasser. GPS: n54,11096 e10,81496.⬆➡.

10 ⌷Mo-Fr € 5/24h, Sa-Su free ⟋(2x)€0,50/kWh. ▣
Location: Urban, simple. Surface: metalled. ◻ 01/01-31/12
Distance: ⊾on the spot.

⛟S Niebüll 5C3
Parkplatz, Lornsenstrasse 19. GPS: n54,78901 e8,82546.⬆.

25 ⌷€5 ⟶€1 ▦€1 Ch ⟋(12x)€1. Location: Urban, simple, central, quiet. Surface: grassy. ◻ 01/01-31/12
Distance: ⊾on the spot ☒200m.
Remarks: Parking swimming pool, max. 24h.

⛟S Nordstrand ⛵ 5C3
Wohnmobilplatz Margarethenruh, Süderhafen 8.
GPS: n54,46944 e8,91000.⬆.

21 ⌷€ 14,80-17,50, 2 pers.incl. ⟶▦Ch ⟋€2,60 WC⌷▣€3 ▨.
▣ Location: Rural, comfortable, central, quiet. Surface: gravel.
◻ 01/01-31/12
Distance: ⊾3km ⊿300m ☖150m ☖3km.

⛟S Nordstrand ⛵ 5C3
Womoland, Norderquerweg 2. GPS: n54,51736 e8,93012.

38 ⌷€7 + € 3,50/pp ⟶▦Ch ⟋€2,50 WC⌷.
Surface: grassy/gravel. ◻ 01/01-31/12

⛟S Nordstrand ⛵ 5C3
Landgasthof Pohnshallig, Pohnshalligkoogstrasse 17.
GPS: n54,49772 e8,92906.⬆.

4 ⌷€ 5, guests free ⟶€2,50. ▣ Location: Rural, simple.
Surface: metalled.
◻ 01/07-31/10 ▣ Thu
Distance: ⊾3km ☒on the spot ⚲3km.
Remarks: Along through road.
Tourist information Nordstrand:
ℹ Former Wadden island.

ⒸS Norgaardholz ⛵⛵ 5D3
Campingplatz Nordstern, Nordstern 1. GPS: n54,78528 e9,79889.⬆.

10 ⌷€ 6, dog € 1 ⟶▦Ch ⟋€2/day WC⌷use sanitary €4/night ▣
free. ▣ Location: Rural, simple, quiet. Surface: gravel/metalled.
◻ 01/01-31/12
Distance: ⊿on the spot ☒on the spot.

▨S Ockholm 5C3
Wohnmobilstellplätze Altes Pastorat Ockholm, Baderstrasse 5/6.
GPS: n54,66517 e8,82940.⬆.

5 ⌷€ 8 ⟶▦Ch ⟋(5x)€1,60 WC⌷▣€5/5. ▣ Location: Rural,
simple, isolated, quiet. Surface: grassy. ◻ 01/01-31/12
Remarks: Along through road, bread-service.

⛟S Oeversee ♨ 5D3
Kranzbinderei Schnell, Frörupsand 2. GPS: n54,69134 e9,43602.⬆.

9 ⌷€6 ⟶▦Ch ⟋€1/night ▨free. ▣ Location: Rural, simple,
quiet. Surface: grassy. ◻ 01/01-31/12
Distance: ☒500m.

▨S Osterhever 5C3
Stellplatz Norderheverkoog, Norderheverkoogstraße 12, Norderheverkoog. GPS: n54,39656 e8,76163.⬆.

10 ⌷€6 ⟶▦€1 Ch ⟋(10x)€3 WC⌷€1. ▣ Location: Rural.
Surface: grassy. ◻ 01/04-31/10
Distance: ⊾1km ⊿2km ⚲1km ☖on the spot ☖on the spot.
Remarks: Bread-service.

⛟S Pahlen ⛵ 5C3
Fischerstrasse 17. GPS: n54,27101 e9,30015.⬆➡.

12 ⌷€ 6 + € 1/pp ⟶(12x)WC⌷included. ▣ Location: Rural,
comfortable, quiet. Surface: grassy. ◻ 01/01-31/12
Distance: ⊾200m ⊿50m ☞50m ☒200m ⚲200m.

⛟S Plön ♨ ⛵ 7B1
Wohnmobilhafen Plön, Ascheberger straße 76.
GPS: n54,14709 e10,39841.⬆➡.

14 ⌷€ 15 ⟶▦Ch ⟋ WC⌷▨included. Location: Comfortable,
noisy. Surface: grassy/gravel. ◻ 01/04-15/12
Distance: ⊾1,5km ☒on the spot.

⛟S Plön ♨ ⛵ 7B1
Womo-Stop Kleinen Plöner See, Hamburgerstrasse/Aschenberg
strasse, B430. GPS: n54,15278 e10,40417.⬆➡.

16 ⌷€ 5 ⟶€0,50 ⟋€0,50 Ch.▣ Location: Simple.
Surface: metalled. ◻ 01/01-31/12
Distance: ⊿on the spot.
Remarks: In front of passage to beach, max. 24h.

ⒸS Pommerby ⛵ 5D3
Campingplatz Seehof, Gammeldam 5. GPS: n54,76495 e9,96782.⬆.

5 ⌷€ 3,75 + € 4,50/pp, child € 2, dog € 2 ⟶▦Ch ⟋€2/day
WC⌷€0,50/5 ▣€2,50/time. ▣ Location: Rural, simple, quiet.
Surface: grassy/gravel. ◻ 01/04-31/10
Distance: ⊿on the spot ☞on the spot.

⛟S Preetz ♨♨ 5D3
Wohnmobilpark Kirchsee, Kahlbrook 25a.
GPS: n54,22811 e10,28616.⬆➡.

10 ⌷€ 5, 01/04-30/10 € 15 ⟶▦⟋included WC⌷▣. ▣
Surface: gravel. ◻ 01/01-31/12 ▣ service 01/11-31/03
Distance: ⊾10min ⊿on the spot ☒on the spot.
Remarks: Bread-service, canoe and bicycle rental.

DE

Puttgarden 5E3

Wohnmobilplatz Johannisberg, Johannisbergstrasse.
GPS: n54,50208 e11,18000.

50 € 6 + € 4/pp, dog € 2 €2,50 Ch €2,50 WC
Location: Rural, simple, quiet. **Surface:** grassy/metalled.
01/01-31/12
Distance: 2,5km 800m 800m on the spot.
Remarks: In nature reserve Am Grüner Brink, bread-service.

Puttgarden 5E3

Bade- und Surfstrand Grüner Brink, Krögenweg.
GPS: n54,51174 e11,18285.
30 € 8 €2,50 Ch. **Surface:** gravel. 01/01-31/12
Distance: on the spot.

Quickborn bei Burg 7A1

Am Helmschen-Bach, Hauptstraße 2. **GPS:** n54,01165 e9,21648.

6 € 5 **Location:** Rural, comfortable, quiet. **Surface:** grassy.
01/04-30/09
Distance: 300m on the spot.

Ratzeburg 7C1

Hallenbad Aqua Siwa, Fischerstrasse 43.
GPS: n53,69567 e10,77598.

12 € 7 €1/80liter Ch €0,50/kWh. **Location:** Urban,
simple, central, noisy. **Surface:** gravel.
01/01-31/12
Distance: 500m on the spot on the spot on the spot.

Reinfeld 7B1

Am Herrenteich, Klosterstraße. **GPS:** n53,83024 e10,48362.

5 free €0,50/70liter €0,50 Ch €0,50/kWh.
Location: Urban, simple, quiet. **Surface:** metalled.
01/01-31/12
Distance: 500m.

Rendsburg 5D3

Wohnmobil-Hafen Eiderblick, An der Untereider 9.
GPS: n54,30406 e9,65610.

45 € 13 €1/75liter Ch (45x)€0,50/kWh WC €0,50/
7minutes against payment. **Location:** Urban, luxurious,
central, quiet. **Surface:** gravel. 01/01-31/12
Distance: 800m on the spot 800m on the spot on the
spot on the spot.
Remarks: Bread-service, internetcafé.
Tourist information Rendsburg:
Eiserne Lady. Train-bridge North Sea-Baltic Canal, 42m high.
Blue Line. City walk 3 km.
Hausbrauerei Niewarker, Paradeplatz. Guided tour and tastery.

Reußenköge 5C3

Amsinck Haus, Sönke Nissenkoog 36a. **GPS:** n54,61666 e8,87027.

9 € 7 (6x)€2/day WC €3. **Location:** Rural, comfortable, isolated, quiet. **Surface:** asphalted. 01/01-31/12

Sankt Peter-Ording 5C3

Reisemobilhafen St.Peter-Ording, Am Ketelskoog.
GPS: n54,30881 e8,63522.

70 € 12 €1/50liter Ch (70x)€0,60/kWh WC€0,20 €1
1. **Location:** Rural, comfortable. **Surface:** gravel.
01/01-31/12
Distance: 300m 1km 300m 300m.
Remarks: Market Wednesday.
Tourist information Sankt Peter-Ording:
Westküstenpark, Wohldweg 6. Animal park. summer 9.30-19h,
winter 10.30h-sunset.

Schacht-Audorf 5D3

WohnmobilPark Schacht-Audorf, K76. **GPS:** n54,30611 e9,71250.

38 € 10 €0,50/100liter Ch (33x)€0,60/kWh WC€0,50/
time €1/time. **Location:** Rural, comfortable. **Surface:** gravel.
01/01-31/12
Distance: 700m A7 2km 800m 800m on the spot.
Remarks: Max. 3 nights.

Scharbeutz 7C1

Reisemobilplatz Hamburger Ring, Hamburgerring/Trelleborg Strasse.
GPS: n54,03028 e10,75222.

70 € 10/24h, 01/04-31/10 beach tax € 3,50 €1/100liter Ch
(2x)€1. **Location:** Rural. **Surface:** sand.
01/01-31/12
Distance: 300m 300m, dog friendly beach 1km 400m.

Schashagen 7C1

Wohnmobilpark Ostseeblick, Biesdorf.
GPS: n54,11934 e10,92108.

30 01/04-30/09 € 14,50-16,50 2 pers, incl., dog € 2,50-3,50
Ch €0,50/kWh WC. **Location:** Rural, comfortable, quiet.
Surface: grasstiles. 01/01-31/12 Service: winter
Distance: 300m.

Schleswig 5D3

Am Stadthafen, Am Hafen 5. **GPS:** n54,51167 e9,56917.

45 € 14 Ch WC €2,50/time included.
Location: Urban, comfortable, central.
Surface: gravel/metalled.
01/01-31/12
Distance: 150m 5km on the spot
50m 300m nearby
50m.
Remarks: Max. 48h, check in at harbourmaster.
Tourist information Schleswig:
Tourist Information Schleswig, Plessenstrasse 7. Historical city,
founded by the Vikings, Haithabu.
Schloß Gottorf. Regional museum, archeological museum and
museum for art and culture.
Museum am Danewerk, Ochsenweg 5, Dannewerk. Fortifications,
650-1200.
winter 10-16h, 01/04-31/10 Tue-Fri 9-17h, Sa-Su 10-18h.
Wikinger Museum Haithabu, Haddeby-Busdorf. All about the life of
the Vikings.
01/04-31/10 9-17h, 01/11-31/03 Tue-Su 10-16h.

Schönberg/Ostsee 5D3

Brasilien, Seesternweg. **GPS:** n54,42408 e10,39116.

40 € 9, 15/05-15/09 € 11 Ch included. **Location:** Rural,
simple. **Surface:** grassy. 01/01-31/12
Distance: 200m 200m.

DE

[S] Schönberg/Ostsee 5D3

Stellplatz Mittelstrand, Mittelstrand.
GPS: n54,42233 e10,39573.↑→.

50 🚐 € 9, 15/05-15/09 € 11 🚰 ♻ Ch ⚡ € 2 WC. 🐕 **Location:** Rural. **Surface:** grassy. ■ 01/01-31/12
Distance: ⛱ 200m 🚤 200m 🍴 on the spot.
Remarks: Bread-service in summer period.

Seestermühe 7A2

Achtern Diek. **GPS**: n53,70333 e9,56232.↑.
4 🚐 free. **Surface:** metalled. ■ 01/01-31/12
Distance: 🍴 200m.

[S] Sehestedt 5D3

Wohnmobilstellplatz Sehestedt, Fährstrasse 1.
GPS: n54,36466 e9,81973.↑→.

13 🚐 € 7/24h 🚰 € 0,50/80liter ♻ Ch. 🚌 **Surface:** gravel.
■ 01/01-31/12
Distance: 🏘 750m 🛣 A7 13km 🍴 on the spot 🛒 200m.
Remarks: Directly at North Sea-Baltic canal.

[S] Sierksdorf 7C1

Wohnmobilstellplatz Hof Sierksdorf, Altonaer Straße.
GPS: n54,06013 e10,75737.↑.
15 🚐 € 11 🚰 € 1 ♻ € 1 Ch ⚡ € 0,50/kWh WC 🚿 🧺. **Surface:** gravel.
■ 01/04-15/10
Distance: ⛱ beach 100m.

[S] Simonsberg 5C3

Nordsee Camping Zum Seehund, Lundenbergweg 4.
GPS: n54,45515 e8,96958.↑→.

30 🚐 € 15 🚰 ♻ Ch ⚡ WC 🚿 included 🧺 € 5. 🐕 **Location:** Rural, comfortable, isolated, quiet. **Surface:** gravel. ■ Easter-31/10
Distance: 🏘 2km ⛱ 500m 🚲 on the spot 🚶 on the spot.
Remarks: Use steam bath, sauna, fitness-studio incl.

[S] Sörup 5D3

Südensee, Seeblick. **GPS**: n54,71216 e9,66611.↑→.

5 🚐 € 4 🚰 ♻ Ch ⚡ € 2/night WC. 🐕 **Location:** Rural, simple, quiet.
Surface: grassy. ■ 01/01-31/12
Distance: ⛱ on the spot 🚤 on the spot 🍴 kiosk.
Remarks: Parking at small lake.

Süderlügum 5C3

Wohnmobilplatz Mehrzweckhalle, Jahnstrasse.
GPS: n54,87472 e8,90306.↑.

5 🚐 free. **Location:** Rural, central, quiet. **Surface:** metalled.
■ 01/01-31/12
Distance: 🏘 500m 🛒 300m.

[S] Timmendorfer Strand 7C1

Am Vogelpark, P4, Bäderrandstraße, B76.
GPS: n53,99136 e10,81439.↑→.

50 🚐 € 7,50 + tourist tax 🚰 € 0,50/120liter ♻ Ch ⚡. 🚌
Location: Rural. **Surface:** grassy/sand. ■ 01/01-31/12
Distance: 🍴 180m.
Remarks: Max. 1 night.

[S] Tönning 5C3

Wohnmobilplatz Eiderblick - Kapitänshaus, Am Strandweg.
GPS: n54,30920 e8,93684.↑.

33+15 🚐 € 11 2p incl., excl. tourist tax 🚰 € 1/100liter ♻ Ch ⚡ € 0,50/kWh 🚿 included 🧺 € 3,50/3. 🐕 **Location:** Rural, luxurious, isolated, quiet. **Surface:** grassy. ■ 01/01-31/12
Distance: 🏘 500m ⛱ on the spot 🚲 on the spot 🚶 on the spot.
Remarks: Along the Eider river.

[S] Travemünde 7C1

Wohnmobilparkplatz Kowitzberg, Kowitzberg.
GPS: n53,97598 e10,87830.↑→.

49 🚐 15/5-14/9 € 10, 15/9-14/5 € 6 🚰 € 1/100liter ♻ Ch ⚡ (48x) € 1/5kWh. **Location:** Urban. **Surface:** grassy. ■ 01/01-31/12
Distance: 🏘 2,5km ⛱ 800m 🚤 800m 🍴 300m 🛒 250m 🚌 50m.

[S] Travemünde 7C1

Parkplatz am Fischerreihafen, Auf dem Baggersand 15.
GPS: n53,95556 e10,86139.↑.

120 🚐 € 12-14 🚰 € 1/50liter ♻ Ch ⚡ (5x) € 3/kWh WC 🚿 € 2. 🐕
Location: Urban, simple. **Surface:** gravel. ■ 01/01-31/12
Distance: ⛱ beach 1,8km 🛒 max. 250m 🚌 express bus Altstadt Lubeck.
Remarks: Parking fishing port, no camping activities.

Uetersen 7A2

Am Stichhafen, Ziegelei. **GPS**: n53,67977 e9,66861.↑.
4 🚐 free. **Surface:** metalled. ■ 01/01-31/12
Distance: 🏘 400m 🛣 7,4km 🍴 300m.

[S] Wedel 7A2

Am Freibad. **GPS**: n53,57860 e9,69520.↑.

20 🚐 € 6 🚰 € 1/10minutes ♻ Ch ⚡ (14x) € 1/8h WC 🚿. 🐕
Location: Rural, simple, quiet. **Surface:** grassy/metalled.
■ 01/01-31/12 ◉ during event
Distance: 🏘 800m.
Remarks: Max. 3 days.

[S] Westerholz 5D3

Campingplatz Fördeblick, Kummle 1. **GPS**: n54,81998 e9,66686.↑.
45 🚐 € 7 🚰 € 1 ♻ Ch ⚡ € 2,50/night WC 🚿. 🐕 **Location:** Rural, simple, quiet. **Surface:** grassy. ■ 01/04-15/10
Distance: ⛱ 150m.
Remarks: At Flensborg Fjord, max. 24h.

DE

[S] Wilster 7A1

Colosseumplatz, Etatsrätin-doos-strasse 14-17.
GPS: n53,92419 e9,37449.↑→.

15 🚐 free 🚰 ♻ Ch ⚡ € 0,50.
Location: Urban, simple, central, quiet. **Surface:** grassy/gravel.
■ 01/01-31/12 ◉ fair
Distance: 🏘 200m 🛒 100m 🚲 on the spot.

[S] Wischhafen 7A1

Hafenstrasse 6. **GPS**: n53,77278 e9,32278.↑→.

15 🚐 € 3 ⚡ (6x) € 1/kWh. 🐕 **Location:** Rural, simple.
Surface: grassy/gravel. ■ 01/01-31/12
Distance: 🍴 500m 🛒 1km.

[S] Wischhafen 7A1

Ziegelstraße, Gewerbegebiet Wischhafen.
GPS: n53,76417 e9,32111.↑→.

8 ⚏ € 3 🚻 Ch free. ♨ **Location:** Rural, simple. **Surface:** gravel.
⬛ 01/01-31/12
Distance: 🚲 1km 🛒 200m.

Wischhafen 7A1

Süder-Elbe, Glückstädter Straße. **GPS:** n53,78678 e9,34017. ⬆️➡️

15 ⚏ € 3. ♨ **Location:** Rural, simple, isolated. **Surface:** sand.
⬛ 01/01-31/12
Distance: 🚲 3km ⊗150m.
Remarks: Parking at ferry-boat.

Wischhafen 7A1

Unterm Deich 7. **GPS:** n53,77528 e9,32111. ⬆️➡️

6 ⚏ € 3. ♨ **Location:** Rural, simple. **Surface:** grassy.
⬛ 01/01-31/12
Distance: 🚲 300m ⊗on the spot 🛒 1km.

Lower Saxony/Bremen

Adendorf 7C2

Freizeitzentrum, Scharnebecker Weg. **GPS:** n53,28925 e10,45398. ⬆️

30 ⚏ € 8 🔌 € 1/10minutes ⚡(4x)€0,50/kWh.
Location: Rural, simple, noisy. ⬛ 01/01-31/12
Distance: 🚲 500m.
Remarks: Parking sports centre, max. 3 days, swimming pool and sauna on site.

Aerzen 9A2

Restaurant Waldquelle, Waldquelle 1.
GPS: n52,05952 e9,26146. ⬆️➡️

4 ⚏ € 4,50 ⚡(1x)€1,50/day. **Location:** Rural, isolated.
Surface: gravel. ⬛ 01/01-31/12 🅿️ Tue
Distance: 🚲 2km 🛒 1km 🚌 500m ☂ on the spot.

Remarks: Check in at hotel.

Ahlerstedt 7A2

Ahlerstedt Ottendorf, Rickstücken 2. **GPS:** n53,38908 e9,41017. ⬆️➡️

25 ⚏ € 8 🚻 Ch 🔌 included. ♨ **Location:** Rural, simple.
Surface: metalled. ⬛ 01/01-31/12
Distance: 🚲 3km 🛒 3km.

Alfeld/Leine 9B2

Bornstrasse. **GPS:** n51,98586 e9,82769. ⬆️

4 ⚏ free. **Location:** Simple. **Surface:** metalled.
⬛ 01/01-31/12
Distance: 🚲 on the spot ⊗80m 🛒 200m.
Remarks: Parking in city centre behind the evangelical church.

Altenau ❄ 9C2

Alter Bahnhof Altenau, Rothenbergerstrasse 52.
GPS: n51,79879 e10,43320. ⬆️➡️

20 ⚏ € 13, tourist tax incl 🔌 € 1/50liter ⚡€1 Ch ⚡(10x)€2,50/day
WC. **Location:** Quiet. **Surface:** gravel. ⬛ 01/01-31/12
Distance: 🚲 1km ⊗2km 🛒 1km 🚌 on the spot ☂ on the spot 🚴 2km
☃ on the spot.

Altenau ❄ 9C2

Kristall-Saunatherme Heißer Brocken, Karl-Reinecke-Weg 35.
GPS: n51,79836 e10,44408. ⬆️

20 ⚏ € 10 + € 2/pp tourist tax 🔌 €0,50/40liter ⚡Ch ⚡€0,50/kWh.
Location: Rural, quiet. **Surface:** metalled.
⬛ 01/01-31/12
Distance: 🚲 1,5km ⊗on the spot 🛒 on the spot 🚌 on the spot.
Remarks: Pay at pay-desk of theTherme.

Amelinghausen 7B3

Lopausee, Auf der Kalten Hude. **GPS:** n53,13324 e10,23441. ⬆️➡️

---

50 ⚏ € 5, 1/9-1/7 € 3,50 🔌 ⚡Ch included. **Location:** Simple, isolated,
quiet. **Surface:** gravel/sand. ⬛ 01/01-31/12
Distance: 🚲 1km ⚓100m 🚣100m ⊗1km 🛒 1km 🚴 on the spot
☂ on the spot.
Remarks: Ticket available at petrol stations, kiosk Lopausee, pay-desk
Waldbad and tourist office.

Amelinghausen 7B3

Waldbad, Zum Lopautal. **GPS:** n53,12402 e10,23018. ⬆️

40 ⚏ € 8 🔌 ⚡Ch ⚡included. ♨ **Location:** Comfortable.
⬛ 01/01-31/12
Distance: 🚲 1km ⚓500m ⊗1km 🛒 1km 🚴 on the spot ☂ on the
spot.
Remarks: Bread-service, incl. access swimming pool.

Amelinghausen 7B3

Kronsbergheide, Hochseilgarten. **GPS:** n53,13500 e10,23389. ⬆️➡️

10 ⚏ € 5, 1/9-1/7 € 3,50. **Location:** Rural, simple, isolated, quiet.
⬛ 01/01-31/12
Distance: 🚲 1km ⚓500m 🚣on the spot ⊗1km 🛒 1km 🚴 on the
spot ☂ on the spot.
Remarks: Ticket available at petrol stations, kiosk Lopausee, pay-desk
Waldbad and tourist office.

Amelinghausen 7B3

Schwindbeckerheide, Steinbeckerstrasse, Soderstorf.
GPS: n53,12247 e10,09934. ⬆️

15 ⚏ € 5. **Location:** Rural, simple, isolated. **Surface:** metalled/sand.
⬛ 01/01-31/12
Distance: 🚲 6km 🚴 on the spot ☂ on the spot.
Remarks: Ticket available at petrol stations, kiosk Lopausee, pay-desk
Waldbad and tourist office.

Amelinghausen 7B3

Gasthaus Eichenkrug, Unter den Eichen 10, Dehnsen.
GPS: n53,12804 e10,16817.

4 ⚏ € 5 🔌 ⚡ included. ♨ **Location:** Simple, isolated.
Surface: metalled. ⬛ 01/01-31/12
Distance: 🚲 4km ⊗on the spot 🛒 4km 🚴 on the spot ☂ on the spot.
Remarks: Max. 3 nights.

Amelinghausen 7B3

Gasthaus Schenck, Lüneburgerstrasse 48.
GPS: n53,12568 e10,21426. ⬆️

15 ⛺ € 5 ⛽🚿 WC included. ♨️🧺 **Location:** Simple, central.
Surface: metalled.
Distance: 🛒on the spot ⊗on the spot 🍴on the spot 🚲on the spot
🚶on the spot.

Tourist information Amelinghausen:
👁 Oldendorfer Totenstatt. Hunnebed cineraria from the ice-age.
🕐 guided tour 01/05-30/09.

🏕 S   Ankum   8G1

Ferienhof Buse-Glass, Tütingen 5. **GPS:** n52,51431 e7,86842. ⬆️

5 ⛺ € 14 ⛽🚿 WC included 🔲. **Location:** Quiet. **Surface:** grassy.
🕐 01/01-31/12
Distance: 🛒2,5km ⊗500m 🚲2,5km.

🏕   Apen   6G3

Am Freibad, Hauptstraße, Hengstforde. **GPS:** n53,21795 e7,78706. ⬆️

10 ⛺free. **Location:** Rural, simple. **Surface:** metalled.
🕐 01/05-15/09
Distance: 🏊5,8km ⊗50 m
Remarks: Along railwayline, swimming pool Hengstforde.

🏕   Apen   6G3

Viehmarktplatz, Hauptstraße. **GPS:** n53,21820 e7,80221.

10 ⛺free. **Location:** Simple. **Surface:** metalled.
🕐 01/01-31/12
Distance: 🛒100m 🚲5km.

🏕 S   Artlenburg   〰️   7C2

Am Sportboothafen, Am Deich 9. **GPS:** n53,37680 e10,48550.

40 ⛺ € 10 ⛽🔲Ch 🚿 WC 🔲. **Location:** Comfortable, quiet.
Surface: grassy. 🕐 15/04-15/10
Distance: 🛒500m ⊗on the spot 🚤on the spot ⊗500m 🍴500m
🚂500m.

Remarks: Along the river Elbe.

🏕 S   Aurich   6G2

Familienbad De Baalje, Tannenbergstraße.
GPS: n53,46540 e7,47568. ⬆️
20 ⛺ € 9 ⛽€1/100liter 🔲Ch🚿(24x)€1/kWh 🔲€1.
Surface: metalled. 🕐 01/01-31/12
Distance: 🛒500m ⊗100m.
Remarks: Check in and pay at pay desk swimming pool.

🏕   Aurich   6G2

An den Kiesgruben, Tannenhausen. **GPS:** n53,52173 e7,47834. ⬆️

⛺free. **Surface:** unpaved.
Distance: 🏊10m ⊗on the spot.
Remarks: At the lake of Tannenhausen.

🍽 S   Aurich   6G2

Landgasthof Alte Post, Essenerstrasse. **GPS:** n53,54573 e7,60736.

6 ⛺ € 6, guests € 3 ⛽€1 🔲Ch🚿 WC. **Surface:** metalled.
🕐 01/01-31/12
Distance: ⊗on the spot.
Remarks: Caution key electricity € 10.

🏕 S   Bad Bentheim   🌿🌺🎠   8F2

Am Mühlenberg, Mühlenberg. **GPS:** n52,29360 e7,10095. ⬆️➡️

10 ⛺ € 7 ⛽€1/80liter 🔲Ch🚿€0,50/kWh WC. **Location:** Rural.
Surface: metalled. 🕐 01/01-31/12
Distance: 🛒200m ⊗50m 🚶on the spot.

🏕 S   Bad Bentheim   🌿🌺🎠   8F2

Am Schloßpark, Funkenstiege. **GPS:** n52,30328 e7,15448. ⬆️

30 ⛺ € 7 ⛽€1/80liter 🔲Ch🚿€0,50/kWh WC. 🔲
Surface: metalled. 🕐 01/01-31/12
Distance: 🛒200m ⊗100m.

🏕 S   Bad Bevensen   〰️   7C3

Reisemobilplatz, Am Waagekai. **GPS:** n53,07417 e10,60139. ⬆️➡️

30 ⛺ € 10, 2 pers.incl ⛽🔲Ch included 🚿€1. 🔲 **Location:** Rural,
simple, quiet. **Surface:** gravel/sand. 🕐 01/01-31/12
Distance: 🛒1km 🚤on the spot ⊗1km 🍴600m.

🏕 S   Bad Essen   8H1

Wohnmobilstellplatz Falkenburg, Falkenburg 3.
GPS: n52,32352 e8,36384. ⬆️

50 ⛺ € 7 ⛽€1/100liter 🔲Ch🚿€2/4kWh WC 🔲€0,50.♨️
Location: Rural, comfortable, quiet. **Surface:** grassy/metalled.
🕐 01/03-30/10
Distance: 🛒1,2km ⊗900m 🚲300m.
Remarks: At the Mittelland canal, near marina.

🏕 S   Bad Gandersheim   ⛲   9B2

Wohnmobil-Stellplatz Rio Gande, An der Wiek.
GPS: n51,87191 e10,01881. ⬆️➡️

24 ⛺ € 8/24h, tourist tax incl ⛽€1/100liter 🔲Ch🚿(14x)€0,50/kWh.
🔲 **Location:** Rural, simple. **Surface:** gravel.
🕐 01/01-31/12
Distance: 🛒400m ⊗100m 🍴200m 🚲on the spot 🚶on the spot.
Remarks: Max. 3 nights, bread-service only in summer.

🏕 S   Bad Lauterberg   9C3

Erlebnisbad Vitamar, Mast Tal 1. **GPS:** n51,63358 e10,48661. ⬆️

5 ⛺free ⛽€1 🔲€1 Ch🚿1. **Location:** Simple, quiet.
Surface: metalled. 🕐 01/01-31/12
Distance: 🛒1,5km ⊗30km 🍴1,5km 🚌on the spot.

🏕 S   Bad Lauterberg   🌺🎠   9C3

Wiesenbeker Teich, Wiesenbek 75. **GPS:** n51,61719 e10,49074. ⬆️➡️

4 ⛺ € 13 ⛽🔲Ch🚿 included. **Location:** Isolated, quiet.
Surface: gravel.
🕐 01/01-31/12

DE

Distance: 🚶2km 🏊30km ⛵on the spot ⛴on the spot ⊗on the spot 🚲2km 🚌2 km 🕴on the spot.
Remarks: Check in and pay at reception campsite, max. 1 night.

Bad Münder · 9A2

Rhomelbad, Lindenallee. **GPS**: n52,19305 e9,47111.⬆️.

5 🚐free. **Location:** Simple. **Surface:** metalled.
🅿️ 01/01-31/12
Distance: 🚶400m ⊗on the spot 🚌400m 🚐200m.

Bad Nenndorf · 9A1

Wohnmobilstellplatz am Schulzentrum, Bahnhofstrasse 77.
GPS: n52,34294 e9,37666.⬆️.

15 🚐free 🚰€2/45liter 🔌Ch 🚿(8x)€1/6h WC. **Location:** Simple.
Surface: grassy. 🅿️ 01/01-31/12
Distance: 🚶700m 🏊3,4km ⊗on the spot 🚌on the spot 🚐on the spot.

Bad Pyrmont · 9A2

Reisemobilhafen in den Emmerauen, Hauptmann Boelke-Weg.
GPS: n51,98092 e9,25108.⬆️➡️.
65 🚐€9 + € 2,30-3,20/pp tourist tax 🚰€0,10/10liter 🔌Ch (44x)€0,60/kWh WC free. **Location:** Urban, central.
Surface: grassy/gravel.
🅿️ 01/01-31/12
Distance: 🚶historical centre 400m ⊗200m 🚌400m 🚐100m.
Remarks: Bread-service, free swimming < 9AM, e-bike rental, free shuttle to spa resort.
Tourist information Bad Pyrmont:
ℹ️ Bad Pyrmont Tourismus GmbH, Europa-Platz 1, www.badpyrmont.de. Health resort.

Bad Sachsa · 9C3

Wohnmobilplatz auf dem Schützenplatz, Im Osteral.
GPS: n51,60470 e10,54949.⬆️.

72 🚐€7 🚰€0,50 🔌€0,50 🚿(10x)€0,50/kWh WC.
Location: Rural, simple, quiet. **Surface:** gravel.
🅿️ 01/01-31/12
Distance: 🚶on the spot ⊗500m 🚌800m 🚐500m.
Remarks: Service 200m, discount on access terme.

Bad Sachsa · 9C3

Harzer Schnitzelhaus & Waffelbäckerei, Schützenstrasse 13.
GPS: n51,59778 e10,55056.⬆️.

---

2 🚐guests free. **Location:** Rural, simple, central. **Surface:** asphalted.
🅿️ 01/01-31/12
Distance: 🚶on the spot ⊗on the spot 🚌100m.
Remarks: Max. 2 days.

Bad Salzdetfurth · 9B2

Am Solebad, Solebadstraße, Detfurth.
GPS: n52,07193 e10,01859.⬆️➡️.

10 🚐€ 5/24h 🚰€1/50liter 🔌Ch 🚿€1/6h. **Location:** Rural.
Surface: asphalted.
🅿️ 01/01-31/12
Distance: 🚶2km ⊗Bistro 50m 🚌100m 🚴on the spot 🕴on the spot.
Remarks: Market Friday-morning.

Bad Zwischenahn · 6G3

Wohnmobilstellplatz Am Badepark, Am Badepark.
GPS: n53,18722 e8,00021.⬆️➡️.

35 🚐€ 8,50 🚰€0,50/70liter 🔌Ch 🚿(35x)€1/2kWh WC €3,(spa resort). **Location:** Urban, simple. **Surface:** metalled.
🅿️ 01/01-31/12
Distance: 🚶on the spot 🏊6,8km ⛵on the spot 🚌on the spot ⊗100m 🚌500m 🚐on the spot.

Balge · 9A1

Blenhorster Bauernhof, Klünderberg 1. **GPS**: n52,71361 e9,13011.⬆️.

20 🚐€ 5 🚌included. **Surface:** grassy. 🅿️ 01/01-31/12
Distance: ⊗on the spot.

Balje · 7A1

Naturkundemuseum Niederelbe, Neuenhof, Neuhaus.
GPS: n53,81958 e9,03867.⬆️.

6 🚐free. **Location:** Rural, simple, isolated. 🅿️ 01/01-31/12
Distance: 🚶4km ⛵on the spot ⊗4km 🚌4km.

Barßel · 6G3

Am Bootshafen, Deichstrasse. **GPS**: n53,16754 e7,73441.⬆️➡️.

14 + 20 🚐€ 6 🚰🔌Ch 🚿(34x)€2/24h WC included 🚿€1. 🚿
Location: Urban, simple. **Surface:** grasstiles.
🅿️ 01/01-31/12
Distance: 🚶500m ⛵on the spot ⊗on the spot 🚌500m.

Barsinghausen · 9A1

Wohnmobilstellplatz am Besucherbergwerk Klosterstollen, Conrad-Bühreweg. **GPS**: n52,29858 e9,46943.⬆️➡️.

5 🚐€ 6,50 🚰🚿(5x)included. 🚿 **Location:** Rural, simple.
Surface: gravel. 🅿️ 01/01-31/12
Distance: 🚶300m ⊗nearby 🚌300m.
Remarks: Max. 3 days, visit coalmine possible.

Berge · 8G1

Stift Börstel, Börstel 5. **GPS**: n52,64957 e7,69438.
2 🚐€ 5, in envelope in mail box 🚰🚿on demand. **Surface:** metalled.
🅿️ 01/01-31/12
Remarks: Near abbey, max. 2 nights.

Berge · 8G1

Dorfteich Berge, Schienenweg 19. **GPS**: n52,62011 e7,75099.
2 🚐free. 🅿️ 01/01-31/12

Bergen · 7B3

Ziegeleiweg. **GPS**: n52,81273 e9,96457.⬆️.

6 🚐€ 3,50 🚰€1 🔌Ch 🚿. **Surface:** gravel.
🅿️ 01/01-31/12
Distance: 🚶nearby ⊗on the spot.
Remarks: Caution key € 20 at town hall.
Tourist information Bergen:
🐾 Wildpark Lüneburger Heide, Nindorf. Game preserve.
🅿️ 01/03-31/10 8-19h, 01/11-28/02 9-16.30h.

Berne · 6H3

Fähranleger Motzen, Motzener Strasse. **GPS**: n53,17972 e8,55778.⬆️.

4 🚐free 🚰€1/60liter 🔌Ch 🚿(4x)€1/6h. **Location:** Urban, simple, isolated, noisy. **Surface:** gravel/sand.
🅿️ 01/01-31/12
Distance: 🚶3,5km 🚌on the spot ⊗1km 🚌100m 🚴100m.
Remarks: Parking at ferry-boat at river Weser.

Bevern · 9A2

Schwimm- und Freizeitzentrum, Jahnstrasse.
GPS: n51,85750 e9,50805.➡️.

5 🛏free. **Location:** Rural, simple. **Surface:** asphalted.
⬛ 01/01-31/12
Distance: 🚶1,2km 🚊500m 🚌500m.

| 🚐S | Bienenbüttel 🛶 | 7C3 |

Wohnmobilstellplatz Ilmenauwiese, Niendorfer strasse, K42.
GPS: n53,14514 e10,49051.⬆.

12 🛏€ 6 🚰€1/8minutes 💧Ch💧(12x)€1/8h WC🚽€1.
🚿 **Location:** Rural, comfortable, quiet. **Surface:** metalled.
⬛ 01/01-31/12
Distance: 🚶500m ➤on the spot ⊗on the spot 🚊500m 🚌500m
🚶special sculpture route.

| 🚐S | Bippen 🛖🌳 | 8G1 |

Dorfteich, Hauptstrasse. **GPS:** n52,58209 e7,73887.
2 🛏free. ⬛ 01/01-31/12

| 🚐S | Bippen 🛖🌳 | 8G1 |

Ferienhof Neyenhuis, Hallweg. **GPS:** n52,59360 e7,73005.➤.

20 🛏€ 10 🚰💧WC🚽€2. 🚿 **Location:** Rural, simple, quiet.
Surface: grassy. ⬛ 01/01-31/12
Distance: 🚶1km.

| 🍴S | Bippen 🛖🌳 | 8G1 |

Gasthof Mol, Einigkeitsstraße 20, Lonnerbecke.
GPS: n52,54337 e7,67118.
10 🛏free 🚰💧Service€7/day.
Distance: ⊗on the spot.

| 🍴S | Bippen 🛖🌳 | 8G1 |

Hotel-Restaurant-Café Sülte Mühle, Ölmühle 1, Lonnerbecke.
GPS: n52,54972 e7,69594.
2 🛏free 🚰€2.

| 🚐S | Bispingen 🛖 | 7B3 |

Parkplatz Oberhaverbeck, Oberhaverbeck. **GPS:** n53,14281 e9,91998.

100 🛏€ 3/day, € 6/night 🚰€1/10minutes 💧Ch💧(8x)€1/10h.
🚐 **Location:** Rural, simple, isolated. **Surface:** grassy/gravel.
⬛ 01/01-31/12 ⬛ Service: winter
Distance: ⊗on the spot 🚴on the spot 🚶on the spot.
Remarks: In nature reserve the the Lüneburg Heide (heath).

| 🚐S | Bispingen 🛖 | 7B3 |

Parking Rathaus, Borsteler Straße 4-6. **GPS:** n53,08499 e9,99789.

5 🛏free. **Location:** Simple, central. **Surface:** metalled.
⬛ 01/01-31/12
Distance: 🚶on the spot 🎣1km ⊗100m 🚊100m 🚴on the spot 🚶on the spot.

| 🚐S | Bispingen 🛖 | 7B3 |

Reiter- und Ferienhof Cohrs, Volkwardingen 1, Moorweg.
GPS: n53,13409 e10,00047.

10 🛏€ 14 🚰💧Ch💧included WC🚽⬛€3. 🚿
Location: Comfortable, isolated, quiet. **Surface:** grassy.
⬛ 01/01-31/12
Distance: 🚶3km 🎣5,5km ⊗500m 🚊5km 🚴on the spot.
Remarks: Bread-service.

| 🚐S | Bissendorf | 8H2 |

Reisemobil-Center Veregge & Welz, Gewerbepark 14, A30 Abfahrt
Bissendorf. **GPS:** n52,24026 e8,13977.⬆.

5 🛏free 🚰€1/5minutes 💧Ch💧(4x)€1/6h. **Location:** Urban,
simple, quiet. **Surface:** metalled. ⬛ 01/01-31/12
Distance: 🚶1km 🎣650m ⊗800m 🚊800m.

| 🚐S | Bleckede 🛖 | 7C2 |

Campingpark Elbtalaue, Am Waldbad 23.
GPS: n53,25948 e10,80526.⬆➤.

15 🛏€ 14, 2 pers incl 🚰€1 💧Ch💧€3,50/night,or€0,50/0,8kWh
WC🚽included ⬛€3,50/3 📶€4/day,€ 9/3 days. **Location:** Rural,
luxurious, isolated, quiet. **Surface:** grassy. ⬛ 01/01-31/12
Distance: 🚶2km ➤300m ⊗800m 🚊6km 🚌50m.

| 🚐S | Blomberg | 6G2 |

Dorfplatz Blomberg, Hauptstrasse. **GPS:** n53,57718 e7,55815.⬆➤.

20 🛏free 🚰€1 💧Ch€1 🔌€0,50/kWh WC.
Surface: grassy/metalled. ⬛ 01/01-31/12

Distance: 🚶on the spot ⊗200m 🚊200m 🚌50m.

| 🚐S | Bockenem | 9B2 |

Am Freibad, In den Reesen. **GPS:** n52,00787 e10,13610.⬆.

5 🛏free. **Location:** Rural, simple, quiet. **Surface:** gravel.
⬛ 01/01-31/12
Distance: 🚶800m ⊗200m 🚊300m.

| 🍴S | Bockenem | 9B2 |

Hotel Sauer am Aral Autohof, Allensteiner strasse 7.
GPS: n52,00224 e10,13379.⬆.

20 🛏guests free 🚰€1,50 💧Ch💧(8x)€2,50 WC🚽€1,50.
Location: Rural, simple. **Surface:** metalled. ⬛ 01/01-31/12
Distance: 🚶300m ⊗on the spot 🚊500m.

| 🚐S | Bockhorn | 6G2 |

Reisemobilplatz Germer, Am Geeschendamm 1.
GPS: n53,38575 e8,00857.⬆.

30 🛏€ 6 🚰€1,50 💧Ch💧(30x)€1,50/24h WC🚽€2. 🚿 **Location:** Comfortable. ⬛ 01/01-31/12

| 🚐S | Bockhorn | 6G2 |

Erlebnisbad, Urwaldstrasse 35a. **GPS:** n53,39876 e7,99410.⬆.

5 🛏free. **Location:** Rural. **Surface:** metalled. ⬛ 01/01-31/12 🚶on
the spot.
Remarks: Parking swimming pool, max. 1 day.

| 🍴S | Bockhorn | 6G2 |

Gaststätte Altdeutsche Diele, Landesstrasse 11, Steinhausen.
GPS: n53,41539 e8,03622.⬆.

3 🛏free 💧(3x)against payment. **Location:** Simple.
Surface: metalled. ⬛ 01/01-31/12

DE

Bockhorn 6G2

Gaststätte Zum Sandkrug, Sandkrugsweg 21,Grabstede. **GPS:** n53,35893 e8,00186. ⬆.

4 free. **Location:** Rural, simple, quiet. **Surface:** grassy.
◻ 01/01-31/12
Distance: ⊗on the spot.

Bodenwerder 9A2

Wohnmobilstellplatz Bodenwerder, Am Mühlentor. **GPS:** n51,98037 e9,51795. ⬆→.

25 €6 + € 1/pp tourist tax ⚡€2/10minutes Ch €2,50/ day WC €1,50. **Location:** Urban, simple. **Surface:** grassy.
◻ 01/01-31/12
Distance: 200m Weser 200m ⊗200m 500m 200m.
Remarks: Check in and pay at pay desk swimming pool.

Bohmte 8H1

Golfclub Arenshorst, Arenshorster Kirchweg 2. **GPS:** n52,35651 e8,28450. →.

3 guests free. **Location:** Rural, simple. **Surface:** grassy/metalled.
◻ 01/01-31/12
Distance: 3km ⊗on the spot 3km.

Bohmte 8H1

Landgasthaus Gieseke-Asshorn, Bremer strasse 55. **GPS:** n52,36674 e8,31261.

4 guests free ⚡ free. **Location:** Urban, quiet.
Surface: metalled. ◻ 01/01-31/12
Distance: on the spot ⊗on the spot 200m.

Bohmte 8H1

VARIOmobil Fahrzeugbau GmbH, Bremer strasse. **GPS:** n52,38623 e8,30761. →.

---

2 free Chfree. **Location:** Rural, quiet. **Surface:** metalled.
◻ 01/01-31/12
Distance: 500m 1km 1km.
Remarks: Service only during opening hours.

Bomlitz 7A3

Am Weltvogelpark, Am Vogelpark. **GPS:** n52,88425 e9,59720. ⬆.

50 free. **Location:** Rural, simple, central. **Surface:** grassy.
◻ 01/01-31/12
Distance: 2,5km ⊗on the spot 2,5km.
Remarks: Max. 1 night.

Brake 6H2

City-Parkplatz, Breite Strasse. **GPS:** n53,32534 e8,47982. ⬆→.

2 free. **Location:** Urban, simple, central, noisy. **Surface:** metalled.
◻ 01/01-31/12
Distance: on the spot ⊗on the spot 200m 200m on the spot.

Brake 6H2

Am Binnenhafen, Hafenstrasse. **GPS:** n53,32802 e8,48296. ⬆.

4 free ⚡€1/10minutes Ch (4x)€0,50/6h. **Location:** Urban, simple, central, noisy. **Surface:** grasstiles.
◻ 01/01-31/12
Distance: on the spot 1km ⊗100m 200m 200m on the spot.

Bramsche 8G1

Wohnmobilstellplatz Waldwinkel, Zum Dreschhaus 4. **GPS:** n52,39591 e8,10244. ⬆→.

60 €6 ⚡€1,50/70liter Ch (80x)€2 WC €1. **Location:** Rural, comfortable, quiet. **Surface:** grassy.
◻ 01/01-31/12
Distance: 3,5km ⊗100m 3,5km on the spot on the spot.
Remarks: Next to campsite Waldwinkel.

Bramsche 8G1

Hasebad, Malgartener strasse 49. **GPS:** n52,41493 e7,99423. ⬆.

10 free. **Location:** Urban, simple, quiet. **Surface:** metalled.
◻ 01/01-31/12
Distance: 500m.

Bramsche 8G1

Reisemobile Lewandowsky, Am Kanal 1b. **GPS:** n52,38524 e7,92958. ⬆→.

2 free Chfree ⚡€2/day. **Location:** Rural, simple.
Surface: gravel. ◻ 01/01-31/12
Distance: 1km ⊗1km 1km.
Remarks: Also repairs possible, service during opening hours, walking and bicycle area.

Braunlage 9C3

Schützenplatz, Schützenstrasse 21. **GPS:** n51,71658 e10,60847. ⬆.

85 €9,50 + € 2,20/pp tourist tax Ch €0,50/kWh WCincluded €1 €3. **Location:** Rural, luxurious, quiet. **Surface:** gravel. ◻ 01/01-31/12
Distance: 400m ⊗Café Restaurant Hubertushöhe on the spot on the spot on the spot.

Braunschweig 9C1

Theodor-Heuss-Straße. **GPS:** n52,24964 e10,51835. ⬆→.

16 free ⚡€1/10minutes Ch (16x)€1/8h. **Location:** Urban, simple, noisy. **Surface:** asphalted.
◻ 01/01-31/12
Distance: 2km ⊗400m 200m on the spot.
Remarks: Max. 2 nights.

Bremen 6H3

Wohnmobil Oase Bremen, Schoster born, via Emil von Behringstrasse. **GPS:** n53,06778 e8,86333. ⬆.

8 €15 + tourist tax € 1/pp ⚡€2/time Ch WCincluded

🛁€1,50, use luxurious bathroom €5, sauna €5 🚿€6/time 🧹
🧺 **Location:** Urban, comfortable, central. **Surface:** gravel.
📅 01/01-31/12
Distance: 🚲4km ⊗on the spot 🛒50m 🚋Tram on the spot.
Remarks: Motorhome < 7m.

| 🅂 | Bremen 🏊⚓🍺🧺 | 6H3 |

Am Kuhhirten, Kurhirtenweg. **GPS:** n53,06500 e8,81871. ⬆️➡️.

70 🏠€ 13 ⛽€1/100liter 🗑Ch 🔌(70x)€0,50/kWh 🚾€1/24h
🛁€1. **Location:** Urban, comfortable, central. **Surface:** gravel.
📅 01/01-31/12
Distance: 🚲Old city centre 1,3km 🏊500m ⊗on the spot 🛒800m
🚋Tram 700m 🚲on the spot.

| 🅂 | Bremen 🏊⚓🍺🧺 | 6H3 |

Bremer Schweiz, Im Pohl, Lesum. **GPS:** n53,16765 e8,69560. ⬆️➡️.

7 🏠€ 5/24h ⛽€1/10minutes 🗑Ch 🔌(8x)€1/8h. 🚐
Location: Urban, comfortable, quiet. **Surface:** gravel.
📅 01/01-31/12
Distance: 🚲on the spot 🏊2,4km ⊗on the spot 🛒300m 🚋on the
spot 🚲on the spot.

| 🅂 | Bremen 🏊⚓🍺🧺 | 6H3 |

Maritime Meile, Schulkenstrasse. **GPS:** n53,17298 e8,60906. ⬆️➡️.

5 🏠€ 5 + tourist tax ⛽€1/80liter 🗑Ch 🔌(4x)€1/8h. 🧺
Location: Urban, comfortable, central, quiet. **Surface:** asphalted.
📅 01/01-31/12
Distance: 🚲Bremen 20km ⊗100m 🚋200m 🚲on the spot.

| 🅲🅂 | Bremen 🏊⚓🍺🧺 | 6H3 |

Camping Stadtwaldsee, Hochschulring 1.
GPS: n53,11381 e8,84389. ⬆️.

20 🏠€ 12-15 ⛽€1/80liter 🗑Ch 🔌(20x)€1/5h 🚾included. 🧺
Location: Rural, luxurious. **Surface:** grasstiles. 📅 01/01-31/12
Distance: 🚲5,5km 🏊3km 🏊on the spot 🚤on the spot ⊗on the
spot 🚋100m 🚲on the spot.

Tourist information Bremen:
ℹ️ Tourist Information, Obernstrasse en Hauptbahnhof, www.bremen-
tourism.de. Hanseatic city and second harbour of Germany.
👁 Böttcherstrasse. Pedestrian passage.
⛲ Weserpromenade Schlachte. Antiques and flea market. 📅 Sa
8-14h.

| 🅂 | Bremerhaven 🏊⚓🍺🧺 | 6H2 |

Reisemobil-Parkplatz Doppelschleuse, An der Neuen Schleuse.
GPS: n53,53230 e8,57607. ⬆️➡️.

63 🏠€ 10 ⛽€1/100liter 🗑Ch 🔌(40x)€0,50/kWh 🚾€0,50/time 🛁€
0,50/time. 🚐 **Location:** Urban, comfortable, luxurious, central, quiet.
Surface: asphalted. 📅 01/01-31/12
Distance: 🚲1km 🚤8km 🏊1km ⊗1,5km 🛒1,2km 🚲on the spot.
Remarks: Bread-service.

| 🅂 | Bremerhaven 🏊⚓🍺🧺 | 6H2 |

Reisemobil-Parkplatz Fischereihafen, Hoebelstrasse, Fischereihafen
1. **GPS:** n53,52634 e8,57610. ⬆️➡️.

47 🏠€ 10, tourist tax incl ⛽€1/100liter 🗑Ch 🔌(36x)€0,50/kWh
🚾included. 🚐 **Location:** Urban, luxurious, central, quiet.
Surface: asphalted/metalled. 📅 01/01-31/12
Distance: 🚲4km 🏊on the spot 🚤on the spot ⊗500m 🛒500m
🚋200m 🚲200m.
Remarks: At harbour, caution key sanitary € 5.

| 🅂 | Bremervörde 🧺 | 7A2 |

Wohnmobilstation Bremervörde, Kiebitzweg 1.
GPS: n53,49453 e9,15576. ⬆️➡️.
40 🏠€ 9,50, 01/11-28/02 € 6,50 ⛽🗑Ch 🔌(21x)€3/day,10Amp
🚾included 🛁€1. 🧺 **Location:** Rural, comfortable, quiet.
Surface: metalled. 📅 01/01-31/12
Distance: 🚲1,5km 🏊100m 🚤100m ⊗300m 🛒1km 🚋1,5km
🚲on the spot 🚶on the spot.

| 🅂 | Brietlingen 🧺🌿 | 7B2 |

Reihersee, Grosse strabe. **GPS:** n53,34344 e10,45844. ⬆️.

50 🏠€ 8. **Location:** Rural, simple, isolated. **Surface:** grassy.
📅 01/03-31/10
Distance: ⊗on the spot.

| 🍴 | Brietlingen 🧺🌿 | 7B2 |

Hotel Franck, Bundesstrasse 31b. **GPS:** n53,32951 e10,44491. ⬆️.

5 🏠free 🔌(1x)€2/night. **Location:** Rural, simple, quiet.
Distance: 🚲on the spot ⊗on the spot 🛒500m.

| 🅂 | Bruchhausen-Vilsen | 7A3 |

Reisemobilstellplatz Bruchhausen-Vilsen, Bollenstrasse.
GPS: n52,82671 e8,99536. ⬆️➡️.

20 🏠€ 6 ⛽€1/100liter 🗑Ch 🔌(6x)included 🚾. **Surface:** gravel.
📅 01/01-31/12
Distance: 🚲200m 🏊200m 🛒200m.

| 🅲🅂 | Buchholz/Nordheide 🌿🎣🧺 | 7B2 |

Buchholz/Nordheide, Weg zum Badeteich 20.
GPS: n53,28202 e9,87495. ⬆️.

12 🏠€ 12-15 ⛽🗑Ch 🔌(6x)€2 🚾included 🛁. 🧺 🧹
Location: Rural, comfortable. **Surface:** metalled/sand.
📅 01/01-31/12
Distance: 🚲200m 🏊on the spot ⊗on the spot 🛒200m.

| 🅂 | Bückeburg ⚓ | 9A2 |

Am Schloss, Georgstrasse/Liebesallee. **GPS:** n52,25777 e9,04583. ⬆️➡️.

20 🏠€ 5 ⛽€1 🗑Ch 🔌(24x)€1/12h 🧹🚐 **Location:** Urban, quiet.
Surface: gravel/metalled. 📅 01/01-31/12
Distance: 🚲500m 🏊500m 🛒500m 🚋200m 🚶on the spot.

| 🅂 | Bückeburg ⚓ | 9A2 |

Neumarktplatz, Unterwallweg 5c. **GPS:** n52,26326 e9,05040. ⬆️.

15 🏠free ⛽€1/80liter 🗑Ch 🔌(6x)€0,50/kWh. 🚐
Location: Urban, simple. **Surface:** gravel. 📅 01/01-31/12
Distance: 🚲250m 🏊250m 🛒250m.

DE

Büddenstedt 9C2

Am Sportplatz. **GPS:** n52,17567 e11,01843. ⬆️.

3 ⛺free. **Location:** Rural, simple, quiet. **Surface:** asphalted.
🅿️ 01/01-31/12
Distance: 🚶1km ⊗on the spot 🗑️2km.
Remarks: Parking swimming pool.

Büddenstedt 9C2

Parking K22, Barneberger Straße, Offleben.
GPS: n52,13738 e11,04409. ⬆️.

2 ⛺free. **Location:** Rural, simple. **Surface:** asphalted.
🅿️ 01/01-31/12
Distance: 🚶500m ⊗500m 🗑️500m.

Bühren 9B3

Alter Festplatz, Im Teich. **GPS:** n51,48378 e9,67451. ⬆️➡️.

20 ⛺2 🚰€2. **Location:** Rural, isolated. **Surface:** grassy.
🅿️ 01/01-31/12
Distance: 🚶700m 🗑️5km on the spot on the spot.

Bunde 6F3

Am Friedhofsweg. **GPS:** n53,18500 e7,26639. ⬆️➡️.

10 ⛺3 🚰€1 Ch€1/10h. **Surface:** grasstiles.
🅿️ 01/01-31/12
Distance: 🚶100m 2,3km ⊗350m 🗑️200m.
Remarks: At townhall, max. 3 days.

Bunde 6F3

Freizeitgelände, Denkmalstrasse 11, Ditzumerverlaat.
GPS: n53,26028 e7,26861. ⬆️➡️.

10 ⛺3/24h 🚰€0,50 Ch (8x)€1/8h. **Surface:** metalled.
🅿️ 01/01-31/12 🅾️ during event
Distance: 🚶250m on the spot ⊗350m 🗑️250m.

Remarks: Max. 3 days.

Bunde 6F3

Möhlenlandbad, Kellingwold 25. **GPS:** n53,18683 e7,27418.
10 ⛺3. **Surface:** metalled. 🅿️ 01/01-31/12
Distance: 🚶500m.

Butjadingen 6H2

Henken's Stellplatz, Am Hafen 6, Fedderwardersiel.
GPS: n53,59581 e8,35669. ⬆️➡️.

80 ⛺€5 + € 1,10-2,20/pp tourist tax 🚰€0,01/1liter Ch€1/24h
(48x)€2,50/day. **Location:** Rural, comfortable, central, quiet.
Surface: grassy. 🅿️ 01/01-31/12
Distance: 🚶500m on the spot on the spot ⊗on the spot 🗑️on the spot 500m on the spot on the spot.
Remarks: Bread-service.

Butjadingen 6H2

Jachthaven Fedderwardersiel. GPS: n53,59518 e8,35700. ⬆️.

30 ⛺€ 10 excl. tourist tax 🚰Ch€1,50/time (20x)€2,50/day
WC 4minutes €6/time. **Location:** Rural, comfortable, isolated,
quiet. **Surface:** grassy. 🅿️ 01/01-31/12
Distance: 🚶800m on the spot on the spot ⊗800m 🗑️800m on the spot on the spot on the spot.

Butjadingen 6H2

Hof Iggewarden, Iggewarden 1. **GPS:** n53,58622 e8,32653. ⬆️➡️.

20 ⛺€8 🚰€1/100liter Ch (2x)€2/day WC. **Location:** Rural,
comfortable, isolated, quiet. **Surface:** gravel.
🅿️ 01/01-31/12
Distance: 🚶2km 2km ⊗on the spot 🗑️on the spot 300m on the spot on the spot.

Butjadingen 6H2

Knaus Campingpark Burhave, Strand Allee, Burhave.
GPS: n53,58306 e8,37000. ⬆️➡️.

50 ⛺€ 9,80 + € 2,20/pp tourist tax 🚰€2,20 Ch€0,70/kWh
WC€3,30. **Surface:** grassy. 🅿️ 15/04-15/10
Distance: 🚶1km on the spot ⊗200m 🗑️1km.

Buxtehude 7A2

Pfingstmarktplatz, Cuxhavenerstrasse, Neukloster, B73.
GPS: n53,47974 e9,63528. ⬆️.

40 ⛺free 🚰€0,50/90liter Ch€2. **Location:** Rural, simple.
Surface: asphalted. 🅿️ 01/01-31/12 🅾️ week before/after
Whitsuntide
Distance: 🚶3km ⊗Imbiss bakery 200m.
Remarks: Key shower at Imbiss.

Buxtehude 7A2

Schützenplatz, Genslerweg. **GPS:** n53,47139 e9,69528. ⬆️➡️.

30 ⛺free 🚰€1/90liter Ch (36x)€1/kWh. **Location:** Urban,
central. **Surface:** gravel. 🅿️ 01/01-31/12
Distance: 🚶nearby Old city centre ⊗50m bakery 50m.
Tourist information Buxtehude:
Das Fleth. Old inland-port.

Cadenberge 7A1

Reisemobilvermietung Hennig, Alter Postweg 1.
GPS: n53,76686 e9,05681. ⬆️.

4 ⛺€5 🚰€0,50/100liter €1,50/24h. **Location:** Rural, simple.
Surface: grassy. 🅿️ 01/01-31/12
Distance: 🚶on the spot ⊗on the spot 🗑️50m.

Celle 9B1

Schützenplatz, Hafenstraße. **GPS:** n52,62794 e10,07348. ⬆️.

35 ⛺free 🚰€1 ChWC. **Surface:** grassy/metalled.
🅿️ 01/01-31/12
Distance: 🚶150m ⊗100m.

Celle 9B1

Langensalzaplatz. GPS: n52,61842 e10,08052. ➡️.

3 ⛺free. **Surface:** metalled. 🅿️ 01/01-31/12
Distance: 🚶on the spot.

Clausthal-Zellerfeld 🏕🏞 9C2

Busbahnhof, Bahnhofstraß 5. **GPS**: n51,81360 e10,33602.⬆.

4 🚐tourist tax € 1,50. **Location:** Rural, simple. **Surface:** metalled.
🅿 01/01-31/12
Distance: 🚶on the spot ⊗200m 🛒600m 🚗on the spot 🚲on the spot 🚶on the spot.

Clenze 🏞 7C3

Regenbogen-Hof, Mützen. **GPS**: n52,94079 e10,93899.⬆➡.

5 🚐€ 5/pp 🚰🛢Ch 🔌WC🚽included. **Location:** Rural, simple,
isolated, quiet. **Surface:** grassy. 🅿 01/01-31/12
Distance: 🚶3km ⊗on the spot 🛒3km 🚗on the spot.
Remarks: Arrival <22h.

Cloppenburg 6G3

Am Stadtpark, Hagenweg. **GPS**: n52,84649 e8,04687.⬆.

3 🚐free 🚰€0,50/80liter 🛢Ch. **Location:** Urban, simple.
Surface: metalled. 🅿 01/01-31/12
Distance: 🚶100m 🚲2km.
Remarks: Max. 3 days.

Cloppenburg 6G3

Museumsdorf Cloppenburg, Bether Straße.
GPS: n52,85197 e8,05335.⬆.

20 🚐free. **Location:** Rural, simple. **Surface:** metalled.
🅿 01/01-31/12
Distance: 🚶900m 🚲1km.
Remarks: Parking in front of museum village, max. 24h.

Coppenbrügge 🏞 9A2

Parkplatz am Frei- und Hallenbad, Felsenkellerweg.
GPS: n52,11613 e9,53676.⬆➡.

12 🚐€ 3,50 🚰€2,50 🛢Ch 🔌(12x)€1. **Location:** Rural, simple.

Surface: grassy/gravel. 🅿 01/01-31/12
Distance: 🚶1,5km ⊗500m 🛒500m 🚲on the spot 🚶on the spot.
Remarks: Check in at campsite.

Cuxhaven 🏖🏞 6H1

Duhner Allee, Duhnen. **GPS**: n53,88284 e8,64814.⬆.

60 🚐€ 10, 1/9-1/7 € 6 🚰🛢Ch 🔌€2/day WC€0,50 🚽€1. 🏪 **Location:** Simple. **Surface:** asphalted. 🅿 01/01-31/12
Remarks: Beach parking, in front of campsite am Bäderring.

Cuxhaven ⚓🏞 6H1

Elbe-Ferry, Am Fährhafen. **GPS**: n53,87508 e8,70315.⬆➡.

100 🚐€ 10-13, tourist tax incl 🚰🛢Ch. 🏪 **Location:** Urban, simple.
Surface: asphalted. 🅿 01/01-31/12
Distance: 🚶1km ⊗500m.
Remarks: Bread-service.

Cuxhaven ⚓🏞 6H1

Privatparkplatz Kugelbake Halle, Nordfeldstraße.
GPS: n53,89033 e8,67703.⬆.

80 🚐€ 8 🚰🛢ChWC. 🏪 **Location:** Urban, simple.
Surface: metalled. 🅿 01/01-31/12
Distance: 🏊200m ⊗100m.

Cuxhaven ⚓🏞 6H1

Campingplatz Finck, Am Sahlenburger Strand 25.
GPS: n53,86039 e8,59167.⬆➡.

12 🚐€ 15,00 🚰🛢Ch 🔌(12x) WC. 🚿🏞 **Location:** Comfortable.
🅿 01/01-31/12
Distance: 🚶3km 🏊on the spot ⊗on the spot 📺on camp site
🚗100m.

Damme 8H1

Am Flugplatz 8. **GPS**: n52,49055 e8,17925.⬆➡.

25 🚐€ 5 🚰€0,50/80liter 🛢Ch 🔌(12x)€0,50/kWh WC 🚽€1.
Location: Luxurious. **Surface:** grassy/gravel. 🅿 01/01-31/12
Distance: ⊗on the spot.
Remarks: Parking airport Damme.

Damme 8H1

Parkplatz Altes Amtsgericht, Große Straße.
GPS: n52,52381 e8,19486.⬆.
5 🚐free. **Surface:** metalled. 🅿 01/01-31/12
Distance: 🚶300m.

Damme 8H1

Olgahafen, Dümmerstrasse, Dümmerlohausen.
GPS: n52,52917 e8,31098.⬆.

12 🚐free 🚰€1 🛢Ch 🔌€1. **Location:** Rural, simple, quiet.
Surface: gravel. 🅿 01/01-31/12
Distance: 🏊100m 🚶100m ⊗on the spot 🛒bakery.
Remarks: At lake Dümmer, max. 3 days.

Dassel 9B2

Am Badesee in der Ortschaft, Lauenberg.
GPS: n51,75750 e9,76389.⬆➡.

8 🚐free, 01/05-01/10 € 5 🚰€1/80liter 🛢Ch 🔌€1/8h
🚽included,01/05-30/09. 🚿 **Location:** Rural, isolated, quiet.
Surface: asphalted. 🅿 01/01-31/12
Distance: 🚶8,5km 🏊on the spot ⊗300m 🛒300m 🚗300m 🚲on the spot 🚶on the spot.

Dassel 9B2

Am Sollingbad, An der Badeanstalt. **GPS**: n51,80722 e9,68917.⬆➡.

5 🚐free. **Location:** Rural, isolated. 🅿 01/01-31/12
Distance: 🚶Old city centre 500m 🛒1km 🚲on the spot 🚶on the spot.

Delmenhorst 🛒 6H3

Reisemobilhafen Delmenhorst, An den Graften.
GPS: n53,04722 e8,62278.⬆➡.

8 🚐free 🚰🛢Chfree 🔌€1/kWh.
Location: Urban, simple, central, quiet. **Surface:** gravel/sand.
🅿 01/01-31/12 📷 during event
Distance: 🚶on the spot 🚲2,8km ⊗on the spot 🛒200m.
Remarks: Max. 7 days.

Detern 6G3

Reisemobilhafen Detern, Alte Heerstrasse 6, Stickhausen.
GPS: n53,21560 e7,64743.⬆➡.

DE

40 Ⓢ€5 ⌐€1/100liter ⌷Ch ⚡(44x)€2/24h WC ⓢ€1 ⓢ€0,50.
♨ **Location:** Urban, luxurious. **Surface:** asphalted/gravel.
ⓘ 01/01-31/12
Distance: ⚓on the spot ⚑6km ⚓on the spot ⚓on the spot ⚓on the spot ♨ on the spot ⚓ on the spot.
Remarks: Behind tourist info, bread-service.

| ♿Ⓢ | **Diepenau** | 8H1 |

Am Bahnhof. **GPS:** n52,42470 e8,74106.⬆.

6 Ⓢfree ⌐€1 ⌷Ch ⚡€1/8h. **Surface:** metalled.
ⓘ 01/01-31/12
Distance: ⚓500m ⚓500m ⚓500m.

| ♿Ⓢ | **Diepholz** | 8H1 |

Parkplatz Am Heldenhain, Am Heldenhaim (B69).
GPS: n52,61250 e8,37056.⬆➡.

12 Ⓢfree ⌐€1 ⌷Ch ⚡(12x)€0,50/kWh. **Location:** Urban.
Surface: grassy. ⓘ 01/01-31/12
Distance: ⚓500m ⚓500m ⚓500m.

| ♿Ⓢ | **Ditzum** | 6F2 |

Nah und Gut Blank, Pogumer Straße. **GPS:** n53,31489 e7,27619.⬆.

14 Ⓢ€7/24h ⌐€1/100liter ⌷Ch ⚡(10x)€1/kWh.
Surface: metalled. ⓘ 01/01-31/12
Distance: ⚓100m ⚓300m ⚓300m ⚓100m ⚓on the spot.

| ♿Ⓢ | **Ditzum** | 6F2 |

Reisemobilstellplatz Ditzum, Am Deich.
GPS: n53,31555 e7,28666.⬆.

45 Ⓢ€7/night ⌐€1/100liter ⌷Ch ⚡(45x)€1/2kWh.
Surface: metalled.
ⓘ 01/01-31/12
Distance: ⚓100m ⚓100m ⚓100m ⚓100m ⚓300m.

Remarks: Bread-service, waste dump €1, shower €1.

| ♿Ⓢ | **Dornum** | 6G2 |

Wohnmobilplatz, Schöpfwerkstraße, Dornumersiel.
GPS: n53,67272 e7,48092.⬆.
30 Ⓢ€9, Nordsee-ServiceCard incl ⌐€1/8h. **Surface:** metalled.
ⓘ 01/01-31/12
Distance: ⚓500m ⚓100m ⚓100m.

| ♿Ⓢ | **Dornum** | 6G2 |

Wohnmobilplatz, Schützenplatz. **GPS:** n53,64850 e7,42365.⬆⬆.

30 Ⓢ€9, Nordsee-ServiceCard incl ⌐€1/65liter ⌷Ch ⚡€1/8h.
Surface: grassy. ⓘ 01/01-31/12
Distance: ⚓on the spot ⚓300m ⚓50m.
Remarks: Max. 1 night.

| Ⓒ Ⓢ | **Dornum** | 6G2 |

Am Nordseestrand, Hafenstraße 7. **GPS:** n53,68063 e7,48294.⬆.
13 Ⓢ€17 Nordsee-ServiceCard incl ⌐⌷Ch ⚡included.
ⓘ 01/04-30/09
Distance: ⚓on the spot ⚓300m ⚓500m.
Remarks: Bread-service.

| ♿Ⓢ | **Dörpen** ♨ | 6F3 |

Festplatz, Veeneweg. **GPS:** n52,97115 e7,33425.⬆➡.

10 Ⓢfree. **Location:** Simple. **Surface:** grassy/metalled.
ⓘ 01/01-31/12 ⬛ 1st week in June: fair
Distance: ⚓500m ⚓on the spot ⚓500m ⚓on the spot.

| ♿Ⓢ | **Dorum** ⚓ | 6H2 |

Wohnmobilhafen Am Deich, Am Neuen Deich 2a.
GPS: n53,73838 e8,51966.⬆➡.

24 Ⓢ€12,50 + €1,50/pp tourist tax ⌐⌷Ch ⚡included WC ⓢ€1
⚓ ♨ **Location:** Simple. **Surface:** metalled. ⓘ 01/01-31/12
Distance: ⚓on the spot ⚓on the spot ⚓on the spot.
Remarks: Check in at Deichhotel.

| ♿Ⓢ | **Dörverden** ♨⚓♨♨ | 7A3 |

In der Worth. **GPS:** n52,84529 e9,22568.⬆➡.

5 Ⓢfree ⌐€1/80liter ⚡(5x)€1/8h. **Location:** Urban, simple, quiet.
Surface: gravel. ⓘ 01/01-31/12
Distance: ⚓200m ⚓200m ⚓200m ⚓Bremen/Hanover ♨100m
♨1km.
Remarks: Behind town hall, max. 3 nights.

| ◔◔ | **Dörverden** ♨⚓♨♨ | 7A3 |

Wolfcenter, Kasernenstraße, Barme. **GPS:** n52,82635 e9,21417.
10 Ⓢfree. **Location:** Simple. **Surface:** concrete. ⓘ 01/01-31/12
Distance: ⚓Dörverden 3km ⚓on the spot ⚓Aldi 3km.
Remarks: Parking wolf park.

| ♿Ⓢ | **Drage/Elbe** ⚓ | 7B2 |

Reisemobilplatz Stover Strand, Stover Strand 10.
GPS: n53,42467 e10,29213.⬆.

100 Ⓢ€12 ⌐€1/80liter ⌷Ch ⚡(100x)€0,50/kWh WC ⓢ€0,50/
4minutes ⬛€4/4 ⚡€2/h. **Location:** Comfortable. **Surface:** grassy.
ⓘ 01/01-31/12
Distance: ⚓on the spot ⚓on the spot ⚓on the spot ⚓on the spot
⚓500m ♨ on the spot ♨ on the spot.
Remarks: Next to campsite.

| ♿Ⓢ | **Drochtersen** ⚓ | 7A2 |

Krautsand, Deichverteitigungsweg. **GPS:** n53,75167 e9,39028.⬆➡.

12 Ⓢ€10 ⚡(12x)included.⚓ **Location:** Rural, simple.
Surface: metalled. ⓘ 01/01-31/12
Distance: ⚓Elbestrand ⚓300m.

| ♿Ⓢ | **Drochtersen** ⚓ | 7A2 |

Hallenbad Drochtersen, Am Sportplatz. **GPS:** n53,70548 e9,38215.⬆.

6 Ⓢfree. **Location:** Simple. **Surface:** metalled.
ⓘ 01/01-31/12
Distance: ⚓1km ⚓1km.
Remarks: Parking at swimming pool.

| ♿Ⓢ | **Drochtersen** ⚓ | 7A2 |

Am Alten Hafen, Asseler Sand. **GPS:** n53,69418 e9,43928.⬆.

6 Ⓢfree. **Location:** Rural, simple. **Surface:** gravel.
ⓘ 01/01-31/12
Distance: ⚓500m ⚓1km.

| ♿Ⓢ | **Duderstadt** ♨⚓ | 9C3 |

P&R Parkplatz, Adenauerring. **GPS:** n51,51043 e10,27278.⬆➡.

50 ⅗free ⌇€1/120liter ⅗€1/time Ch€1/time ⚡(4x)€0,50/kWh.
Location: Rural, quiet. **Surface:** gravel. ☐ 01/01-31/12
Distance: 800m ⚓17km ⊗800m ⛽200m 🚋100m.

Duderstadt 9C3
Eichsfeldhalle, August Werner Allee. **GPS:** n51,50662 e10,25890.⬆️.

5 ⅗free. **Location:** Rural, simple.
Surface: gravel.
☐ 01/01-31/12
Distance: 900m ⚓17km ⊗900m ⛽900m 🚋700m.
Remarks: Max. 1 night.
Tourist information Duderstadt:
ℹ️ Gästeinformation der Stadt Duderstadt, Marktstrasse 66, www.duderstadt.de. Old part of town with half-timbered houses.

Edewecht 6G3
Rathhausstrasse. **GPS:** n53,12834 e7,98201.⬆️.

20 ⅗free ⌇€1/80liter ⅗Ch ⚡(8x)€1/6h. **Location:** Urban, simple.
Surface: grasstiles. ☐ 01/01-31/12
Distance: on the spot ⊗400m ⛽Aldi 50m.

Egestorf 7B3
Naturerlebnisbad Acquadies, Ahornweg 5.
GPS: n53,19796 e10,05455.⬆️➡️.

40 ⅗€7 ⌇€1 ⅗Ch ⚡(30x)€2/10h WC 🚽.
Location: Simple, quiet. **Surface:** gravel/metalled.
☐ 01/01-31/12
Distance: 1km ⚓2,2km ⊘on the spot ⊗700m ⛽1km.
Remarks: At swimming pool.

Eggermühlen 8G1
Reiterhotel Vox, OT Bockraden 1. **GPS:** n52,57278 e7,79553.⬆️➡️.

8 ⅗€25, clients €7,50 ⌇⅗Ch ⚡WC 🚽included. **Location:** Rural.

Surface: grassy. ☐ 01/01-31/12
Distance: 3km ⛽3km.

Eggestedt 6H3
Eggestedt, Betonstrasse/Habichthorsterweg.
GPS: n53,22819 e8,63902.⬆️➡️.

8 ⅗free. **Location:** Simple, isolated, noisy. **Surface:** metalled/sand.
☐ 01/01-31/12
Distance: 4km ⚓400m.

Einbeck 9B2
Am Schwimmbad, Ochsenhofweg. **GPS:** n51,82433 e9,86464.⬆️➡️.

30 ⅗free ⌇€1/60liter ⅗€1 Ch ⚡(18x)€0,50/kWh.
Location: Simple. **Surface:** gravel. ☐ 01/01-31/12
Distance: 800m ⊗500m ⛽500m ⚡on the spot ⚡on the spot.
Remarks: Parking at swimming pool.
Tourist information Einbeck:
⛪ Alte Marktplatz. ☐ Wed + Sa morning.

Elsfleth 6H3
Im Hafen, An der Kaje. **GPS:** n53,23771 e8,46545.⬆️➡️.

20 ⅗€8/24h ⌇€1/80liter ⅗Ch ⚡(16x)€2/8h WC 🚽€2/time.📷
Location: Urban, comfortable, central, noisy. **Surface:** concrete.
☐ 01/01-31/12
Distance: 150m ⚓900m ⊘on the spot ⊗100m ⛽500m ⚡on the spot ⚡on the spot.

Emden 6F2
Alter Binnenhafen, Am Eisenbahndock. **GPS:** n53,36306 e7,20778.⬆️.

45 ⅗€8 ⌇€0,50/100liter ⅗€0,50 Ch ⚡(36x)€0,50/kWh WC€0,50 🚽€3. **Surface:** metalled. ☐ 01/01-31/12
Distance: 500m ⊗500m ⛽500m.
Remarks: Pay at harbourmaster.

Emden 6F2
Wohnmobilstellplatz Knock, Jannes Ohling Strasse.
GPS: n53,35559 e7,00367.⬆️.

25 ⅗€4,50. **Surface:** metalled. ☐ 01/01-31/12
Distance: 13km ⚓500m ⊗on the spot ⛽13km.
Remarks: Beautiful view.

Emden 6F2
Außenhafen Emden, An der Nesserlanderschleuse.
GPS: n53,34571 e7,19132.⬆️.
10 ⅗€5. **Surface:** asphalted. ☐ 01/01-31/12
Distance: 3,5km ⚓on the spot ⛽on the spot.

Emden 6F2
Nordkai, Zum Nordkai 6. **GPS:** n53,35037 e7,21712.⬆️.
9 ⅗€8. **Surface:** metalled. ☐ 01/01-31/12
Distance: centre 2,5km ⊗Hafenbistro ⛽on the spot.

Emsbüren 8F1
Landgasthof Elberger Schlipse, Elbergen 1, Elbergen.
GPS: n52,46825 e7,30103.

40 ⅗€3 ⌇⅗Ch ⚡(15x)€2,50/24h WC 🚽. ⚡ **Location:** Rural,
quiet. **Surface:** grassy. ☐ 01/01-31/12
Distance: 2km ⛽100m ⛽2km ⚡on the spot ⚡on the spot.

Eschershausen 9B2
Reisemobil-Stellplatz am Angerplatz, Angerweg.
GPS: n51,92965 e9,62806.⬆️➡️.

10 ⅗free ⌇€1/100liter ⅗€1 Ch ⚡€0,50/kWh. **Surface:** metalled.
☐ 01/01-31/12
Distance: 1km.

Esens 6G2
Wohnmobil-Stellplatz Esens, Schützenplatz.
GPS: n53,63921 e7,61077.⬆️.

20 ⅗€2 + €2,80/pp tourist tax ⌇⅗Ch ⚡included. ⚡
Surface: grassy. ☐ 01/01-31/12
Distance: 500m ⚓50m ⛽200m.
Remarks: Max. 2 nights.

Essel 9B1
Hotel Heide-Kröpke, Esseler Damm 1. **GPS:** n52,73240 e9,69419.⬆️.

5 ⬛free 🔧✂🌊. **Surface:** grassy.
⬛ 01/01-31/12
Distance: ⊗on the spot 🚰9km.
Remarks: Use of a meal desired, bird reserve Ostenholzer-Moor.

🏕S **Esterwegen** 🏞 **6G3**
Am Erikasee. GPS: n52,99366 e7,66768.⬆.

6 ⬛free 🔧€1/100liter 🗑Ch ✂(6x)€1/2kWh WC⬛.
Location: Rural, simple, isolated. **Surface:** gravel/metalled.
⬛ 01/01-31/12
Distance: 🚶2km ⛵100m ⊗Imbiss 80m.
Remarks: Walking and bicycle area.

🏕 **Eystrup** **7A3**
Bahnhofstrasse 21. **GPS:** n52,78004 e9,21840.⬆➡.

5 ⬛free. **Surface:** grassy. ⬛ 01/01-31/12
Distance: 🚰100m.
Remarks: Max. 5 days.

🏕S **Faßberg** **7B3**
Am Schützenplatz, Moorweg. **GPS:** n52,90518 e10,16991.⬆.

50 ⬛€2 🔧€1 🗑Ch WC. **Surface:** grassy. ⬛ 01/01-31/12
Distance: 🚰700m.

🏕S **Faßberg** **7B3**
Parkplatz Heidesee, Unterlüßerstraße, L280, Müden.
GPS: n52,87889 e10,12472.⬆.

20 ⬛€2 🔧€1 🗑Ch ✂€1. **Surface:** grassy. ⬛ 01/01-31/12 ◉ end
Sep
Distance: ⊗500m 🚰1km.

🏕 **Faßberg** **7B3**
Parkplatz am Wildpark, Willinghäuser Kirchweg, Müden.
GPS: n52,87222 e10,10861.⬆.

---

20 ⬛€2. **Surface:** grassy. ⬛ 01/01-31/12
Distance: 🚶1km ⊗1km.

🏕S **Freiburg/Elbe** **7A1**
Am Bassin. **GPS:** n53,82285 e9,29305.⬆➡.

50 ⬛€8 🔧🗑Ch ✂WCincluded ⬛€1. 🦆 **Location:** Rural, simple.
Surface: metalled.
⬛ 01/01-31/12
Distance: 🚶200m 🚐50m ⊗300m 🚰400m.
Remarks: Find more possibilities on the city plan.

🏕S **Friedeburg** **6G2**
Schützenplatz. **GPS:** n53,45488 e7,83349.⬆.

20 ⬛free 🔧🗑Chfree ✂(6x)€1/1. **Location:** Rural, simple.
Surface: grassy. ⬛ 01/01-31/12
Distance: ⛵15/05-15/09 🚰400m.
Remarks: Max. 3 days.

🏕S **Fürstenau** **8G1**
Schlossinsel Fürstenau, Schlossplatz 1. **GPS:** n52,51638 e7,67333.⬆.

2 ⬛free 🔧€3 🗑Ch ✂€2/day. **Location:** Quiet. **Surface:** metalled.
⬛ 01/01-31/12
Distance: 🚶100m ⊗100m 🚰100m 🚲on the spot 🚶on the spot.
Remarks: Next to castle.

🏕S **Gartow** **7D3**
Imbiss am See, Springstraße 88. **GPS:** n53,02944 e11,44944.⬆.

20 ⬛€5 WC. **Surface:** gravel/metalled. ⬛ 01/04-30/10
Distance: 🚶1km ⛵on the spot 🚐on the spot ⊗on the spot.
Remarks: Imbiss 11-21h.

🏕S **Geeste** **8F1**
Am Speicherbecken, Biener Straße. **GPS:** n52,59407 e7,27417.⬆.

---

50 ⬛free. **Location:** Quiet. **Surface:** metalled. ⬛ 01/01-31/12
Distance: 🚶2km ⊗100m.
Remarks: Max. 1 night.

🏕S **Geeste** **8F1**
P Biotop/Ausblick, Osterbrocker Strasse. **GPS:** n52,59840 e7,29279.⬆.

4 ⬛free. **Surface:** metalled. ⬛ 01/01-31/12
Distance: 🚶1,5km 🚰1,5km 🚲on the spot 🚶on the spot.
Remarks: Max. 1 night, hiking area.

🏕S **Gehrden** **9B1**
An den Sporthallen, Lange Feldstraße 12.
GPS: n52,31197 e9,60971.⬆.

2 ⬛free ✂(2x)€0,50/kWh. **Location:** Simple. **Surface:** metalled.
⬛ 01/01-31/12
Distance: 🚶centre 700m ⊗200m.

🏕S **Gifhorn** 🌊 **9C1**
Frei- und Hallenbad Allerwelle, Konrad Adenauerstrasse.
GPS: n52,48437 e10,55407.⬆➡.
12 ⬛free 🔧€1/time 🗑Ch ✂(12x)€1/8h WC. **Location:** Rural,
comfortable, quiet. **Surface:** grasstiles. ⬛ 01/01-31/12
Distance: 🚶200m ⛵100m ⊗250m 🚰200m 🚐200m 🚲on the
spot 🚶on the spot.
Remarks: Max. 3 days.

🏕S **Gifhorn** 🌊 **9C1**
Fischer Camping + Gas, Schmiedeweg 4, Wische.
GPS: n52,50863 e10,48462. ⬆.

8 ⬛free 🔧€0,50/50liter 🗑Ch ✂(8x). **Location:** Rural, simple,
isolated. **Surface:** grassy. ⬛ 01/01-31/12
Distance: 🚶3km ⛵500m 🚰3km.
Remarks: Accessory shop.

🏕S **Gnarrenburg** **7A2**
Parkplatz Brillit, Alte Strasse, Brillit. **GPS:** n53,41390 e9,00007.⬆➡.

DE

15 🗓free 🚰Chfree. **Location:** Rural, simple. **Surface:** gravel.
⬛ 01/01-31/12
Distance: 🦽1km ⊗3km 🚰1km.
Remarks: At community centre.

⬛Ⓢ Gnarrenburg 7A2
Schulzentrum, Brilliterweg. **GPS:** n53,39000 e9,00028.⬆➡.

15 🗓free 🚰Chfree. **Surface:** metalled. ⬛ 01/01-31/12
Distance: ⊗1km 🚰500m.
Remarks: Sports centre.

⬛Ⓢ Gorleben 〰 7D3
Am Sportboothafen, Ringstraße. **GPS:** n53,04972 e11,35111.⬆.

5 🗓€ 5 🚰€1/10minutes 🔌(4x)€1/10h WC🗓.🚿
Location: Rural, comfortable, quiet. **Surface:** grasstiles.
⬛ 01/01-31/12
Distance: ≈on the spot ⊷on the spot ⊗500m.
Remarks: Bakery 500m.

🗓Ⓢ Göttingen 🎪🏺 9B3
Reisemobilhafen Eiswiese, Windausweg 6.
GPS: n51,52320 e9,92965.⬆➡.

28 🗓€ 9 🚰€1/100liter 🗓Ch🔌(24x)€0,50/kWh WC🔊€1/15h.
Location: Comfortable. **Surface:** gravel. ⬛ 01/01-31/12
Distance: 🦽500m 🚲5,2km ≈100m ⊷20-400m ⊗100m 🚰500m
🚋100m.
Remarks: Max. 3 nights.

🗓Ⓢ Grasberg 7A3
P&R, Wörpedorfer Straße. **GPS:** n53,18411 e8,98433.⬆.

10 🗓free 🚰€1 🗓Ch 🔌(8x)€1/6h. **Location:** Simple.
Surface: gravel. ⬛ 01/01-31/12
Distance: 🦽on the spot ⊗on the spot 🚰on the spot 🚋> Bremen.

🗓Ⓢ Gronau/Leine 9B2
Kuhmasch. GPS: n52,08265 e9,77034.⬆➡.

4 🗓€ 5 🚰€1,50 WCincluded. **Location:** Rural, simple.
Surface: grassy. ⬛ 01/01-31/12
Distance: 🦽200m ⊗300m 🚰300m 🚶on the spot.
Remarks: Check in at swimming pool, caution key electricity € 10.

🍴Ⓢ Großefehn 6G2
Ostfriesen-Bräu Bagband, Voerstad 8, Badband.
GPS: n53,35034 e7,61060.⬆.

4 🗓€ 5,70, after consumption € 7/pp free 🚰🔌16Amp WC.
Surface: metalled. ⬛ 01/01-31/12
Distance: 🦽10km ⊷4km ⊗on the spot 🚰600m.

🗓 Großenkneten 6H3
Dorfplatz, Bahnhofstrasse, Huntlosen. **GPS:** n52,99139 e8,28611.⬆.

6 🗓free. **Location:** Rural, simple. **Surface:** grasstiles.
⬛ 01/01-31/12
Distance: 🦽on the spot ⊗50m 🚰1km.

🗓 Großenkneten 6H3
Wilhelm-Wellman-Platz, Ahlhorner Strasse.
GPS: n52,94274 e8,25751.⬆.

15 🗓free. **Location:** Rural, simple. **Surface:** grasstiles.
⬛ 01/01-31/12
Distance: 🦽200m ⊗200m 🚰on the spot.

🗓 Großenwieden 〰 9A2
Am Steinbrink. GPS: n52,17191 e9,18982.⬆➡.

5 🗓free. **Location:** Rural. **Surface:** gravel.
Distance: 🦽on the spot ⊗Gasthaus/Biergarten 300m 🚲Weserrad-weg 🚶on the spot.

🗓 Großheide 6F2
Kirchweg, Berumerfehn. **GPS:** n53,56040 e7,34713.⬆.

6 🗓free. **Surface:** metalled. ⬛ 01/01-31/12
Distance: 🦽on the spot ⊗on the spot 🚰2km.
Remarks: Max. 2 nights.

🗓 Großheide 6F2
P Freizeitanlage Am Kiessee, Doornkaatsweg.
GPS: n53,58656 e7,35787.
🗓free.
Distance: ≈on the spot.

🗓Ⓢ Hage 6F2
Kurzentrum, Wichter Weg, Blandorf-Wichte.
GPS: n53,60373 e7,31998.⬆.
12 🗓€ 9 🚰€0,50/80liter 🗓Ch🔌€1/2kWh🔊included.
Surface: metalled. ⬛ 01/01-31/12

🗓Ⓢ Hagenburg 9A1
Grillplatz, Steinhuder-Meer-Straße. **GPS:** n52,43684 e9,32388.⬆.

8 🗓free 🔌(8x)€1/6h. **Location:** Rural, isolated. **Surface:** gravel.
⬛ 01/01-31/12
Distance: 🦽500m ≈Lake Steinhude 1,1km 🚰200m.
Remarks: At sports park.

🗓 Hahnenklee 🌺🏕🎪❄ 9C2
Am Bocksberg. GPS: n51,85757 e10,34176.⬆.
🗓free 🚰€2/60liter 🗓Ch. **Location:** Rural, comfortable, quiet.
Surface: concrete. ⬛ 01/01-31/12
Distance: 🦽500m ⊷1km ⊗500m ⊗on the spot 🚶on the spot
🎿on the spot.

🗓Ⓢ Hambergen 🎪 6H2
Festplatz, Kirchweg/Am Langenend. **GPS:** n53,31050 e8,82389.⬆➡.

20 🗓€ 3,50 🚰🗓Ch🚿. **Location:** Urban, simple.
Surface: gravel/sand. ⬛ 01/01-31/12
Distance: 🦽on the spot ⊗50m 🚋50m ⊷1km 🚴on the spot 🚶on the spot.
Remarks: Caution key service € 25.

🗓Ⓢ Hameln 🚢 9A2
Hannes Weserblick, Ruthenstrasse 14.
GPS: n52,09623 e9,35853.⬆➡.

27 🗓€ 8/24h 🚰€1/100liter 🗓Ch🔌(27x)€1/8h. **Location:** Urban,
simple. **Surface:** metalled. ⬛ 01/01-31/12

🟦 DE

Distance: 🚶1km ⊗600m 🛒600m 🚲800m Weser-Radweg.

🅢 **Hankensbüttel** 7C3

Parkplatz Am Boldhamm, Wiesenweg.
GPS: n52,73111 e10,61417. ⬆➡.

20 🚐€6 🚰🔌Ch included. ♨ **Location:** Rural. **Surface:** grassy.
📅 01/01-31/12
Distance: 🚶900m ⊗1km 🛒1km.
Remarks: Service: Mo/Fr 6-12h, Sa/Su 8-10h.
Tourist information Hankensbüttel:
😊 Otter-Zentrum. Zoo.
📅 15/03-31/10 9.30-18h, 01/11-14/03 9.30-17h
📅 15/12-15/01.

🅢 **Hannoversch Münden** 9B3

Am Weserstein, Tanzwerder. **GPS:** n51,42000 e9,64888. ⬆➡.

30 🚐€6/24h 🚰€1 Ch 🔌(16x)€1/8h. 🅿 **Location:** Central.
Surface: metalled. 📅 01/01-31/12 📅 Easter Market, service: 01/11-31/03
Distance: 🚶900m ⊗100m 🚲on the spot 🚶on the spot.
Remarks: 01/11/- 31/03 no service.

🅢 **Hannoversch Münden** 9B3

Am Hochbad, Rattwerder. **GPS:** n51,40595 e9,64643. ⬆.

15 🚐free. **Location:** Rural. **Surface:** asphalted. 📅 01/01-31/12
Distance: 🚶1,7km 🚲on the spot.

🅢 **Hannoversch Münden** 9B3

Am Werraweg, Werraweg. **GPS:** n51,41701 e9,66176. ➡.

10 🚐free. **Location:** Simple. **Surface:** gravel. 📅 01/01-31/12
Distance: 🚶700m 🚲on the spot.
Remarks: Along the Werra river.

🅖🅢 **Hannoversch Münden** 9B3

Grüne Insel Tanzwerder, Tanzwerder 1. **GPS:** n51,41694 e9,64751. ⬆.

20 🚐€6 + €1,50/pp 🚰€1/80 Ch 🔌(6x)€0,60/kWh,+€2 WC 🚿€3/h. **Location:** Simple.
Surface: grassy.
📅 01/01-31/12
Distance: 🚶100m ⊗150m 🛒150m on the spot 🚶on the spot.
Remarks: Max. 3t.
Tourist information Hannoversch Münden:
ℹ Touristik Naturpark Münden e.V, Rathaus, www.hann-muenden.net/spontan. Old city centre with 430 half-timbered houses.

🅢 **Hardegsen** 9B3

Wohnmobilhafen Steinbreite, Alte Uslarer Straße 1.
GPS: n51,65093 e9,82267. ⬆➡.

15 🚐€6 🚰€1/100 Ch 🔌(16x)€1/8h WC €2/day 🚿€2/day 🚿€2,50/day. ♨ **Location:** Comfortable. **Surface:** grasstiles.
📅 01/01-31/12
Distance: 🚶500m 🚲on the spot 🚲on the spot.

🅢 **Haren/Ems** 🏕🌳 8F1

Freizeitzentrum Schloss Danken, Rentmeisterstrasse.
GPS: n52,79724 e7,20530. ⬆.

17 🚐€10/24h 🚰🚰Ch 🔌(18x) WC 🚿€1. **Location:** Rural, simple.
Surface: grassy/gravel. 📅 21/03-25/10
Distance: 🚶1km 🚲2,8km 🔌on the spot ⊗on the spot 🛒on the spot 🚲on the spot.

🅢 **Haren/Ems** 🏕🌳 8F1

Schleusenstraße. **GPS:** n52,78873 e7,24705.
15 🚐free. **Surface:** grasstiles. 📅 01/01-31/12
Distance: 🚶500m 🚲550m.

🅢 **Harsefeld** 7A2

Klosterpark, Kirchenstrasse. **GPS:** n53,45384 e9,50344. ⬆➡.

5 🚐free. **Location:** Rural, simple. 📅 01/01-31/12
Distance: 🚶100m ⊗100m 🛒100m 🚲100m on the spot 🚶on the spot.
Remarks: Parking park of monastery, max. 5 days.

🅢 **Haselünne** 8G1

Plesseparkplatz, Plessestrasse. **GPS:** n52,67210 e7,48865. ⬆.

3 🚐free 🚰€2/10minutes Ch WC. **Location:** Urban, simple, noisy.
Surface: metalled. 📅 01/01-31/12
Distance: 🚶400m ⊗300m 🛒300m.
Remarks: Parking behind town hall.

🅢 **Haselünne** 8G1

Lingener Strasse. GPS: n52,66778 e7,48222. ⬆.

4 🚐free. **Location:** Simple, quiet. **Surface:** metalled.
📅 01/01-31/12
Distance: 🚶400m ⊗400m 🛒400m 🚲100m on the spot.
Remarks: Parking swimming pool.

🍴 **Haselünne** 8G1

Restaurant Esders-Ab der Hasebrücke, Lingenerstrasse 1.
GPS: n52,66992 e7,48638.

10 🚐€ 10, guests free. **Location:** Urban. **Surface:** metalled.
📅 Mo
Distance: 🚶200m ⊗on the spot.

🅢 **Helmstedt** 🌿🌳 9C1

Am Maschweg, Maschweg. **GPS:** n52,23535 e11,01128. ⬆➡.

25 🚐free. **Location:** Rural, simple. **Surface:** metalled.
📅 01/01-31/12
Distance: 🚶500m 🚲800m ⊗50m 🛒200m 🚲on the spot 🚶on the spot.
Remarks: Other parking in case of festivities.

🅢 **Helmstedt** 🌿🌳 9C1

Brunnentheater, Brunnenweg 6A, Bad Helmstedt.
GPS: n52,23676 e11,06411. ⬆➡.

5 🚐free. **Location:** Rural, simple, isolated, quiet. **Surface:** asphalted.
📅 01/01-31/12
Distance: 🚶3km ⊗500m 🛒4km 🚲on the spot 🚶on the spot.

DE

Hermannsburg 7B3

Parkplatz Waldschwimmbad, Lotharstrasse 66.
GPS: n52,82718 e10,10807.⬆️.

6 🏕free ⛽€1 🚰€1 Ch. **Surface:** metalled. ⬛ 01/01-31/12
Distance: 🚶500m.
Remarks: Parking at swimming pool.

Hermannsburg 7B3

Schützenplatz, Lotharstraße 75. **GPS:** n52,82787 e10,10963.⬆️.

40 🏕€2 ⛽🚰Ch. **Surface:** grassy. ⬛ 01/01-31/12
Distance: 🚶500m 🚿on the spot.
Remarks: Max. 1 night, service at Waldbad (50m).

Hermannsburg 7B3

Grillplatz Bonstorf, Schulstrasse. **GPS:** n52,86492 e10,05134.⬆️.

4🏕free. **Surface:** grassy. ⬛ 01/01-31/12
Distance: 🚿5km.
Remarks: Parking sports park.

Hermannsburg 7B3

Parkplatz am Feuerwehrhaus, Weesenerstrasse, Weesen.
GPS: n52,83645 e10,13692.⬆️.

3 🏕free. **Surface:** grassy. ⬛ 01/01-31/12
Distance: 🚶500m.
Remarks: Parking fire-station.

Hermannsburg 7B3

Parkplatz Örtzetal- Halle, Lutterweg. **GPS:** n52,83363 e10,09579.⬆️.

5🏕free. **Surface:** metalled. ⬛ 01/01-31/12
Distance: 🚿100m.

Hermannsburg 7B3

Lutter Hof, Waldstrasse, Lutter. **GPS:** n52,84188 e10,09894.⬆️.

5 🏕€5 ⛽🚿 included. **Surface:** grassy. ⬛ 01/01-31/12

Herzlake 8G1

Hasetal, Im Mersch. **GPS:** n52,68211 e7,60780.⬆️.

30 🏕free ⛽🚰Ch WC free. **Surface:** grassy. ⬛ 01/03-30/11
Remarks: Parking sports centre.

Hesel 6G2

Marktplatz, Kirchstrasse. **GPS:** n53,30497 e7,59174.⬆️➡️.

12 🏕€4 ⛽€1 🚰Ch 🚿€1/8h 🚰€1, at swimming pool Hesel.
Surface: metalled. ⬛ 01/01-31/12
Distance: 🚶on the spot 🚿1km.

Hessisch Oldendorf 9A2

Südwall P1, Weserstraße. **GPS:** n52,16693 e9,25049.⬆️➡️.

4 🏕free ⛽€0,50/5minutes 🚰€0,50 Ch€0,50. **Location:** Rural,
simple. **Surface:** grassy/gravel. ⬛ 01/01-31/12
Distance: 🚶400m 🚿500m 🚿500m 🚲 Weserradweg 1km.
Remarks: Max. 5 days.

Hitzacker 7C3

Bleichwiesen, K36, Elbufferstrasse. **GPS:** n53,15074 e11,04941.⬆️.

40 🏕free ⛽€1/70liter 🚰Ch 🚿(17x)€1/6h WC. **Location:** Rural,
comfortable. **Surface:** metalled.
⬛ 01/01-31/12
Distance: 🚶200m 🚿450m.
Remarks: Max. 2 nights.

Hohne 9C1

Am Waldbad, Am Schwimmbad 23. **GPS:** n52,59340 e10,37398.⬆️.

4 🏕€5 ⛽🚰Ch 🚿(4x)WC included.
Location: Rural, comfortable, quiet. **Surface:** gravel. ⬛ 01/01-31/12
Distance: 🚶1km 🚿50m 🚿200m.
Remarks: Max. 7 days, caution key € 50, use sanitary only during opening hours swimming pool.

Hohnstorf/Elbe 7C2

Wohnmobilstellplatz Hohnstorf, Schulstraße 1.
GPS: n53,36234 e10,56223.⬆️.

8 🏕€8 ⛽🚰Ch 🚿(3x)€1/10h. 🔌 **Location:** Comfortable.
Surface: metalled. ⬛ 01/01-31/12
Distance: 🚶on the spot 🚿500m 🚿500m.
Remarks: Along the river Elbe.

Holdorf 8H1

Erholungszentrum Heidesee, Zum Heidesee 53.
GPS: n52,57696 e8,11533.⬆️➡️.

60 🏕€ 4/pp ⛽🚰Ch 🚿€2.
Surface: grasstiles.
⬛ 01/03-15/10
Distance: 🚶1,5km 🏊3,4km 🏖Sandy beach 🚿on the spot 🚿1,5km.

Hollern 7A2

Am Deich, Twielenfleth. **GPS:** n53,60417 e9,55917.⬆️➡️.

15 🏕€ 5/0-24h. 🔌 **Location:** Rural, simple. **Surface:** metalled.
⬛ 01/01-31/12
Distance: 🚶200m 🚿Imbiss 300m.
Remarks: Along the river Elbe.

Holzminden 9A2

Mobilcamping Holzminden, Stahler Ufer 16.
GPS: n51,82681 e9,43909.⬆️➡️.

145 🏕€ 7,50 ⛽€1/100liter 🚰Ch 🚿€0,60/kWh WC 🚰€0,50 🚿.

DE

Location: Comfortable. **Surface:** grassy. ◻ 01/01-31/12
Distance: 🏊550m ⛽100m ⊗100m 🛒100m 🚲200m 🚴on the spot 🚶on the spot.
Remarks: Bread-service.

| 🍴S | **Hornburg** 🌿🌳 | 9C2 |

Iberg-Gaststätte, Schützenallee 1. **GPS:** n52,03133 e10,59677. ⬆️➡️.

20 🛏€2 ⛽(6x)€1/night. **Location:** Rural, simple, quiet.
Surface: grassy/metalled. ◻ 01/01-31/12
Distance: 🏊600m ✈5,6km 🛒on the spot 🚱1km 🚶on the spot.

| 🅿S | **Hoya/Weser** | 7A3 |

Reisemobilstellplatz Weserblick, Stettiner Straße.
GPS: n52,80106 e9,13987. ⬆️➡️.

10 🛏voluntary contribution ⛽€1/150liter 🗑Ch.
Surface: grassy/gravel. ◻ 01/01-31/12
Distance: 🏊500m ⛱100m ⊗500m.

| 🅿S | **Hude** 🌳🌿 | 6H3 |

Wohnmobilstellplatz Hude, Schützenstrasse.
GPS: n53,10758 e8,45867. ⬆️➡️.

10 🛏€5 ⛽€1/time 🗑Ch ✈(12x)€0,50/kWh. 🚐 **Location:** Urban,
quiet. **Surface:** gravel. ◻ 01/01-31/12
Distance: 🏊on the spot ⊗on the spot 🚱400m 🚲on the
spot 🚶1km.

| 🅿S | **Hüde (49448)** | 8H1 |

Freizeitarena Dümmer See, Rohrdommelweg 33.
GPS: n52,50176 e8,35425. ⬆️.

50 🛏€10 🗑Ch ✈€2,50 WC🚱. **Location:** Rural, quiet.
Surface: grassy. ◻ 15/04-15/10
Distance: ⛱150m ⊗on the spot.

| 🅿S | **Jade** 🌿🌳🌾 | 6H2 |

Quittenweg, Süderschweiburg. **GPS:** n53,39139 e8,26639. ⬆️.

8 🛏free ⛽€1 🗑Ch✈(8x)€1/8h. **Location:** Rural, comfortable,
isolated. **Surface:** gravel/metalled. ◻ 01/01-31/12
Distance: 🏊800m ⛱500m ⊗1km 🚱800m 🚲on the
spot.

| 🅿S | **Jade** 🌿🌳🌾 | 6H2 |

Drei Eichen, Kreuzmoorstrasse 28. **GPS:** n53,31531 e8,23084. ⬆️.

10 🛏€10 ⛽🗑Ch ✈(3x)WCincluded 🚱against payment. 🚐
Location: Rural, simple, quiet. **Surface:** grassy/gravel.
◻ 01/01-31/12
Distance: 🚱4km.
Remarks: At manege.

| 🅿S | **Jade** 🌿🌳🌾 | 6H2 |

Schützenhof, Am Schützenplatz, Vareler Strasse.
GPS: n53,34111 e8,18667. ⬆️.

10 🛏guests free ⛽on demand ✈(3x)€2/night. 🚐
Location: Simple. **Surface:** metalled. ◻ 01/01-31/12
Distance: 🏊on the spot ⊗on the spot 🚱on the spot.
Remarks: Parking of Shooting Club.

| 🅿S | **Jade** 🌿🌳🌾 | 6H2 |

Jaderberg, Tiergartenstrasse 69, Jaderberg.
GPS: n53,32679 e8,18521. ⬆️.

20 🛏free. **Location:** Simple. **Surface:** gravel. ◻ 01/01-31/12
Distance: 🏊on the spot ⊗on the spot.
Remarks: Parking Jarderpark, zoo and adventure park.

| 🅿S | **Jever** 🌿🌳🌾 | 6G2 |

Jahnstrasse. **GPS:** n53,57733 e7,89074. ⬆️➡️.

20 🛏€8 ⛽€2 🗑Ch ✈(20x)€2. **Surface:** metalled.
◻ 01/01-31/12
Distance: 🏊Old city centre 750m 🚱100m.

Remarks: Sports centre, max. 3 days, coins at petrol station Henn.
Tourist information Jever:
Ⓜ Schloßmuseum. Castle, English gardens and museum. ◻ Tue-
Su 10-18h, 01/07-31/08 Mo-Su 10-18h.
Ⓜ Frisiesches Brauhaus. Brewery with museum. Guided tour 2 hours, 2
drinks included. ◻ Mo-Fri 9.30-16.30h, Sa 9.30-12.30h.

| 🅿S | **Jork** ⚓ | 7A2 |

Festplatz, Schützenhofstrasse/Festplatzweg.
GPS: n53,53100 e9,68336. ⬆️➡️.

80 🛏free ⛽€1/100liter 🗑ChWC🚱€0,50. **Location:** Rural, simple.
Surface: metalled. ◻ 01/01-31/12
Distance: 🏊200m ⊗200m 🚱200m.
Remarks: Parking event ground, max. 24h.

| 🅿S | **Jork** ⚓ | 7A2 |

Stellplatz Lühe-Anleger, Fährstraße, Grünendeich.
GPS: n53,57271 e9,63129. ⬆️.
10 🛏€10/24h. **Surface:** gravel. ◻ 01/01-31/12

| ⚓S | **Jork** ⚓ | 7A2 |

Am Yachthafen, Neuenschleuse. **GPS:** n53,55375 e9,66858. ⬆️➡️.

18 🛏free ⛽€1/90liter 🗑Ch ✈(18x)€0,50/kWh WC🚱€2.
Location: Urban, simple. **Surface:** unpaved.
◻ 01/01-31/12
Distance: 🏊Jork 3km ⊗on the spot 🚲on the spot 🚶on the spot.
Remarks: Along the river Elbe.

| 🍴S | **Jork** ⚓ | 7A2 |

Stubbe's Gasthaus, Lühe 46. **GPS:** n53,56861 e9,63333. ⬆️.

7 🛏€8 ✈€2 🚐. **Location:** Rural, comfortable.
Surface: grasstiles. ◻ 01/01-31/12
Distance: ⊗on the spot.
Remarks: Bread-service, picnic area Am Gartenteich.

| 🅿S | **Kirchlinteln** 🌳 | 7A3 |

Auf dem Kleberhof, Scharnhorster Weg 1. **GPS:** n52,95562 e9,30651.

7 🛏€10 ⛽(4x)WCincluded 🚱€3. 🚐 **Location:** Rural,
comfortable, quiet. **Surface:** grassy. ◻ 01/01-31/12
Distance: 🏊3,5km ✈6km ⊗3,5km 🚱3,5km.
Remarks: Bread-service.

| 🅿S | **Königslutter am Elm** 🌿🌳 | 9C1 |

P1 Niedernhof, Amtsgarten. **GPS:** n52,25009 e10,81996. ⬆️➡️.

5 �free ⟋€1/5minutes ▦€1/time Ch€1/time ⚲(4x)€1/8h.
Location: Urban, comfortable, central, noisy. **Surface:** grasstiles.
◻ 01/01-31/12
Distance: ⚑on the spot ⊗on the spot ⚑on the spot.

⌗S Krummendeich 7A1

Stellplatz Krummendeich, Schulweg 107.
GPS: n53,83145 e9,20231. ⬆➡.

5 ⌐free WC€0,50 ⃞€0,50. **Location:** Rural, simple. **Surface:** gravel.
◻ 01/01-31/12
Distance: ⚑100m ⚑300m.

⌗S Krummhörn 🌿⚓🖼 6F2

Reisemobilhafen Greetsiel, Mühlenstrasse 3, Greetsiel.
GPS: n53,49711 e7,10181. ⬆.

55 ⌐€ 11 incl. 2 pers., tourist tax incl ⟋€2/90liter ▦Ch ⚲(40x)
€1/8h. 🚿 **Surface:** gravel. ◻ 01/01-31/12
Distance: ⚑250m.

Lamspringe 9B2

Am Bahnhof. **GPS:** n51,95404 e10,00656. ⬆➡.

3 ⌐free. **Location:** Rural, isolated. **Surface:** gravel.
◻ 01/01-31/12
Distance: ⚑750m ⊗1km ⚑400m 🚲250m 🚴 Radweg zur Kunst
🚶 on the spot.
Remarks: Max. 3 days.

⌗S Lauenau 9A1

Brauhaus Felsenkeller, Feggendorfer Straße 10.
GPS: n52,27914 e9,36906.

10 ⌐free ⟋🚿⚲free. **Location:** Rural, simple. **Surface:** gravel.
◻ 01/01-31/12
Distance: ⚑500m 🏊2,4km 🚌on the spot.

Remarks: Check in at restaurant.

⚓S Lauenförde ⚓ 9A3

Yachthafen Dreiländereck, Würgasser Straße.
GPS: n51,65045 e9,37983. ⬆➡.

50 ⌐€ 7 ⟋▦Chincluded ⚲(35x)€2,20/day WC⃞€0,50 ⊡€
2,50 📶€4,95. **Location:** Rural, comfortable. **Surface:** gravel.
◻ 01/04-01/11
Distance: ⚑3km ⊗on the spot ⚑3km 🚴on the spot 🚶on the spot.
Remarks: Bread-service.

⌗S Lautenthal 🏕🖼 9C2

Kaspar Bitter Strasse 7b. **GPS:** n51,87020 e10,28729. ⬆.

25 ⌐€ 4 + € 1/pp tourist tax ⟋€1/60liter ▦€2/time Ch€2/time
⚲(8x)€1/6h. **Location:** Rural, comfortable, quiet. **Surface:** gravel.
◻ 01/01-31/12
Distance: ⚑300m ⊗300m ⚑500m 🚌50m.

⌗S Leer 6G3

P9, Grosse Bleiche. **GPS:** n53,22577 e7,44686. ⬆.

6 ⌐free ⟋€1/100liter ▦€1 Ch ⚲(6x)€1/24h WC€0,50 ⃞€1.
Location: Urban, simple. **Surface:** metalled. ◻ 01/01-31/12
Distance: ⚑200m ⊗on the spot ⚑2km.
Remarks: Caution key sanitary € 30, sanitary at offices Bruchbrücke.

⌗S Leer 6G3

Hallen- und Freibad, Burfehnerweg 32. **GPS:** n53,23927 e7,44998. ⬆.

10 ⌐free. **Location:** Urban, simple. **Surface:** metalled.
◻ 01/01-31/12
Distance: ⚑on the spot ⊗on the spot ⚑1km.

⚓S Leer 6G3

Am Hafen, Nessestrasse. **GPS:** n53,22527 e7,45472. ⬆➡.

10 ⌐free WC€0,50 ⃞€1. **Location:** Urban, simple.

Surface: asphalted/gravel. ◻ 01/01-31/12
Distance: ⚑500m ⊗300m ⚑2km.
Remarks: Caution key sanitary € 30, sanitary at offices Bruchbrücke.

⌗S Leer 6G3

Windmühlenhof Eiklenborg, Logabirumer Straße, Logabirum.
GPS: n53,24745 e7,51582. ⬆.
5 ⌐€ 11 ⟋▦Ch ⚲WC⃞€2. **Surface:** grassy/metalled.
◻ 01/01-31/12
Remarks: Near old Dutch windmill.

Leese 9A1

Loccumer straße. **GPS:** n52,50272 e9,11733. ⬆.

4 ⌐free. **Surface:** metalled. ◻ 01/01-31/12
Distance: ⚑200m ⊗on the spot ⚑200m.

⌗S Leese 9A1

Rasthaus Leeser Tanger, Bahlweg. **GPS:** n52,49372 e9,12055. ⬆.

8 ⌐€ 15, discount for clients ⟋⚲⃞included. **Surface:** metalled.
◻ 01/01-31/12
Distance: ⚑800m ⊗on the spot.

Lembruch ⚓🖼 8H1

Stellplatz Dümmer-See Lembruch, Seestraße.
GPS: n52,52439 e8,36703. ⬆.

20 ⌐free. **Location:** Rural. **Surface:** grassy. ◻ 01/01-31/12
Distance: ⚑300m ⚑100m.

⌗S Lembruch ⚓🖼 8H1

Campingplatz Seeblick, Birkenallee. **GPS:** n52,52583 e8,36056. ⬆.

20 ⌐€ 9 ⟋▦Chon camp site. **Location:** Rural. **Surface:** grassy.
◻ 01/01-31/12
Distance: ⚑50m ⚑50m.
Remarks: Max. 1 night.

⌗S Lemwerder 🌿🖼 6H3

Reisemobilhafen Peter-Baxmann-Platz, Schulstrasse 44.
GPS: n53,15784 e8,61783. ⬆➡.

DE

50 🛏 € 3 🚰⊟ Ch included. 🚿(40x)€1/8h. **Location:** Urban, comfortable, isolated, quiet. **Surface:** gravel.
Distance: 🚶on the spot ⊗200m 🚲500m 🚏500m 🚌300m.
Remarks: Nearby swimming pool.

Lemwerder 6H3
Vulkanparkplatz, Uferweg. **GPS:** n53,17000 e8,60028. ⬆➡.

5 🛏 free. **Location:** Urban, simple, quiet. **Surface:** asphalted/metalled. 📅 01/01-31/12
Distance: 🚶2km 🚲on the spot ⊗2km 🚏2km 🚌on the spot.

Lingen/Ems 8F1
Linus Bad, Teichstrasse. **GPS:** n52,51863 e7,30606. ⬆➡.

30 🛏 € 5 🚰€1 Ch 🚿(16x)€0,50/kWh. **Location:** Rural.
Surface: gravel. 📅 01/01-31/12
Distance: 🚶1km 🚏on the spot 🚌on the spot.
Remarks: Max. 3 days.

Loxstedt 6H2
Stotel, Alte Schulstraße 75. **GPS:** n53,44067 e8,59356. ➡.

4 🛏 free. **Location:** Urban, simple, quiet. **Surface:** grassy. 📅 01/01-31/12
Distance: 🚶600m 🚲1km 🏊Stoteler See ⊗100m 🚌on the spot.

Loxstedt 6H2
Am Bootshafen, Fährstrasse. **GPS:** n53,44438 e8,49942. ⬆.

5 🛏 free. 🚿(6x)€0,50/kWh. **Location:** Rural, simple.
Surface: gravel/sand. 📅 01/04-15/10
Distance: 🚶300m 🏊on the spot ⊗on the spot 🚌on the spot.
Remarks: Along the Weser river.

Lüchow 7C3
Parkstraße. **GPS:** n52,96983 e11,14594. ⬆.

2 🛏 free. **Location:** Urban, simple. **Surface:** asphalted/metalled. 📅 01/01-31/12
Distance: 🚶900m ⊗900m 🚏1,7km.
Remarks: Max. 3 nights.

Lüdersfeld 9A1
Heinrichs'Reisemobil Stellplatz, Am Hülsebrink 10+11. **GPS:** n52,35972 e9,25512. ⬆.

30+15 🛏 € 6 🚰⊟Ch 🚿(8x)included. **Location:** Rural, simple.
Surface: gravel. 📅 01/01-31/12
Distance: 🚶500m ⊗on the spot.
Remarks: Check in at hotel, bread-service.

Lüneburg 7B2
Am Sülzwiesen, Pieperweg. **GPS:** n53,24556 e10,39694. ⬆.

50 🛏 € 8/24h 🚰€1/10minutes 🚟Ch 🚿(40x)€1/8h,30/09-01/05€2/8h. **Location:** Rural, comfortable, isolated, quiet.
Surface: metalled. 📅 01/01-31/12
Distance: 🚶1km 🚏300m.
Remarks: Max. 1 night.

Mardorf 9A1
Wohnmobilstellplatz Steinhuder Meer, Rote-Kreuz-Strasse 16. **GPS:** n52,48704 e9,30065. ⬆➡.

60 🛏 € 6 🚰€1/100liter 🚟Ch 🚿(60x)€3. **Surface:** grassy. 📅 01/01-31/12
Distance: 🚶1km 🏊300m ⊗1km.
Remarks: Bread-service.

Melle 8H2
Am Wellenbad 43. **GPS:** n52,20497 e8,32368. ⬆.

10 🛏 free. **Location:** Simple, quiet. **Surface:** metalled. 📅 01/01-31/12

Distance: 🚶on the spot 🚲1,2km ⊗nearby 🚏300m.
Remarks: Parking swimming pool.

Meppen 8F1
Reisemobilplatz am Hallenbad, An der Bleiche. **GPS:** n52,69107 e7,28399. ⬆.

10 🛏 € 6 2 pers, swimming pool incl 🚰€2/100liter 🚟Ch 🚿(4x) €1/12h. **Surface:** metalled. 📅 01/01-31/12
Distance: 🚶200m ⊗on the spot 🚏300m.
Remarks: Parking swimming pool, max. 2 nights.
Tourist information Meppen:
🛈 📅 Tue-Sa morning.

Moormerland 6G2
Am Rathaus, Theodor Heussstrasse 12, Warsingsfehn. **GPS:** n53,31062 e7,48618. ⬆➡.

4 🛏 free. **Surface:** metalled. 📅 01/01-31/12
Distance: 🚶50m ⊗250m 🚏50m 🚌50m.
Remarks: Parking townhall, max. 3 nights.

Moormerland 6G2
Bei Cassi, Deichlandstraße 10, Rorinchem. **GPS:** n53,32010 e7,35473. ⬆➡.

15 🛏 € 5, free with a meal 🚰€1 🚟Ch 🚿€2 🚟€1. **Surface:** gravel.
📅 01/04-31/10 🍽 Restaurant: Mo
Distance: ⊗on the spot.

Moringen 9B3
Domänenhof, Amtsfreiheit. **GPS:** n51,69833 e9,86861. ⬆➡.

3 🛏 free. **Location:** Rural, simple. **Surface:** gravel. 📅 01/01-31/12
Distance: 🚶on the spot 🚲5,5km ⊗300m.
Remarks: At city park.

Neuharlingersiel 6G2
Wohnmobilstellplatz am Ostanleger, Am Hafen Ost. **GPS:** n53,70173 e7,70741. ⬆.

DE

23 🛏️ € 12 🚐 € 1 🔌 Ch 🚰 included WC. 🚻 **Location:** Rural, comfortable, quiet. **Surface:** metalled. ⏲️ 01/01-31/12 **Distance:** 🚶 500m 🏖️ 800m 🛒 1km. **Remarks:** Max. 3 nights.

Neuharlingersiel 6G2
Neuharlingersiel, Alt Addenhausen 4. **GPS:** n53,69580 e7,69021.⬆️.

8 🛏️ € 12, tourist tax incl 🚐 € 1 🔌 Ch 🚰 included WC on campsite 🛁 on campsite. 🧺 **Location:** Rural, simple. **Surface:** metalled. ⏲️ 01/01-31/12 **Distance:** 🚶 800m 🏖️ sandy beach 1km. **Remarks:** Max. 1 night.

Nienburg 9A1
Reisemobilstellplatz Nienburg/Weser, Oyler Straße. **GPS:** n52,64094 e9,20137.⬆️➡️.

25 🛏️ € 5 🚐 € 1/120liter 🔌 Ch 🚰 (12x) € 1/8h. **Surface:** gravel. ⏲️ 01/01-31/12 **Distance:** 🚶 10 min walking 🏊 on the spot 🛒 on the spot ⊗ 300m 🛒 500m. **Remarks:** Along the river Weser.

Nienburg 9A1
Am Theaterparkplatz, Mühlenstraße. **GPS:** n52,63651 e9,20563. 🛏️. **Surface:** metalled. ⏲️ 01/01-31/12 **Distance:** 🚶 on the spot.

Norddeich 6F2
Wohnmobilhafen Norddeich, Itzendorferstrasse. **GPS:** n53,61073 e7,15649.⬆️➡️.

44 🛏️ € 10/24h, 2 pers. + tourist tax, incl. 50% discount Erlebnisbad Ocean Wave 🚐 🔌 Ch 🚰 (48x) € 1/2kWh WC 🛒 € 1. **Surface:** metalled. ⏲️ 01/01-31/12 **Distance:** 🚶 100m 🏖️ 100m ⊗ 100m 🛒 500m 🚲 100m.

Norddeich 6F2
Womo Park Norddeich, Deichstraße 24. **GPS:** n53,60166 e7,13527.⬆️.

44 🛏️ € 11, tourist tax excl., dog € 2 🚐 € 1/100liter 🔌 Ch 🚰 € 1/kWh WC 🛒 € 1 🚿 € 3/1,50 🚽. **Surface:** gravel. ⏲️ 01/01-31/12 **Distance:** 🚶 2km 🏖️ beach 1,5km, beach (dog allowed) 1km ⊗ on the spot 🛒 500m 🚲 100m. **Remarks:** Bread-service.

Nordenham 6H2
Freizeitbad Störtebeker, Atenser Allee. **GPS:** n53,49478 e8,47368.⬆️➡️.

15 🛏️ € 6 🚐 € 1/liter 🔌 Ch free 🚰 (16x) € 1/8h 🚽 € 2, at sauna. 🚻 **Location:** Urban, comfortable, noisy. **Surface:** grasstiles. ⏲️ 01/01-31/12 **Distance:** 🚶 1km 🚗 2km ⊗ on the spot 🛒 400m 🚲 on the spot. **Remarks:** Max. 3 days, bread-service.

Nordenham 6H2
Volkers, Deichstrasse 158. **GPS:** n53,54003 e8,50905.⬆️.

6 🛏️ € 5 🚐 € 1/100 🔌 Ch 🚰 (6x) € 2/day WC 🚽 on demand. 🧺 **Location:** Rural, comfortable, quiet. **Surface:** gravel. ⏲️ 01/01-31/12 **Distance:** 🚶 2km 🏊 100m 🛒 500m 🚲 on the spot.

Nordholz 6H1
Wuster Strasse 12, Spieka. **GPS:** n53,75772 e8,59409.⬆️.

5 🛏️ free 🚐 € 1/100liter 🔌 € 1 Ch 🚰 (5x) € 1/2kWh. **Location:** Rural, simple. **Surface:** metalled. **Distance:** 🚶 on the spot ⊗ 100m.

Nordhorn 8F1
Vechtesee, Heseperweg. **GPS:** n52,43683 e7,08190.⬆️.

35 🛏️ € 5 🚐 € 1/100liter 🔌 Ch 🚰 € 1/5h. 🚻 **Location:** Rural. **Surface:** grassy. ⏲️ 01/01-31/12

Distance: 🚶 400m ⊗ 300m 🛒 300m 🚲 on the spot 🧍 on the spot.

Northeim 9B3
Grosser Freizeitsee, Am Nordhafen. **GPS:** n51,72920 e9,96286.⬆️.

10 🛏️ € 6 🚐 € 0,50/50liter 🔌 Ch 🚰 (8x) € 1/kWh. 🚻 **Location:** Rural, simple, noisy. **Surface:** gravel. ⏲️ 01/01-31/12 **Distance:** 🚶 5km 🚗 3km ⊗ on the spot 🛒 2km.

Oberndorf/Oste 7A1
Wohnmobilplatz Bentwisch, Hoffmann-von-Fallersleben-Straße 10. **GPS:** n53,75398 e9,15054.⬆️➡️.

8 🛏️ € 5 🚐 € 2/100liter 🔌 Ch 🚰 (6x) € 2/8h WC € 0,50 🚽 € 0,50. 🧺 **Location:** Rural, comfortable. **Surface:** grassy/gravel. ⏲️ 01/01-31/12 **Distance:** 🚶 2km 🏊 100m 🛒 100m 🚲 on the spot.

Oldenburg 6H3
Am Küstenkanal, Westfalendamm. **GPS:** n53,12927 e8,21465.⬆️.

3 🛏️ free. **Location:** Rural, simple. **Surface:** gravel. ⏲️ 01/01-31/12 **Distance:** 🚶 on the spot 🚗 1km 🏊 on the spot ⊗ 100m 🛒 400m. **Remarks:** Alternative: in front of campsite Am Flötenteich, 53,166944 8,235, 2 pitches free.

Osnabrück 8G2
Schlosswallhalle, Heinrichstrasse. **GPS:** n52,27074 e8,03953.⬆️.

8 🛏️ € 5 🚐 € 1/100liter 🔌 Ch. 🚻 **Location:** Urban, simple. **Surface:** asphalted. ⏲️ 01/01-31/12 **Distance:** 🚶 on the spot ⊗ 300m 🛒 300m.

Osnabrück 8G2
Wohnmobilplatz Netebad, Im Haseesch 6. **GPS:** n52,30470 e8,05413.⬆️.

DE

5 ⛺€5 ⛽€1/100liter 🅒Ch ✈€1/6h. 🅟 **Location:** Urban, simple, quiet. **Surface:** grassy/metalled. 🔲 01/01-31/12
Distance: 🚌on the spot.
Remarks: Max. 48h.

Osnabrück 8G2
Natruper Straße / Nobbenburger Straße. **GPS:** n52,28116 e8,03651.
⛺€5. **Surface:** metalled. 🔲 01/01-31/12
Distance: 🚶1,5km.

Osten 7A2
Festhalle, Altendorf 13. **GPS:** n53,69602 e9,18813. ⬆➡.

5 ⛺€5 🅒Ch ✈(2x)included. 🚿 **Location:** Rural, simple.
Surface: metalled. 🔲 01/01-31/12
Distance: 🚶on the spot ⊗on the spot 🛒500m.
Remarks: Pay at Hotel Fährkrug.

Osterholz-Scharmbeck 6H3
August Schlüter Turnhalle, Lange Strasse.
GPS: n53,22562 e8,79000. ⬆➡.

4 ⛺free ⛽€1 🗑. **Location:** Urban, simple, central.
Surface: metalled. 🔲 01/01-31/12

Osterode 9C3
Aloha-Aqualand, Schwimmbadstraße.
GPS: n51,72263 e10,24998. ⬆➡.

7 ⛺€8-10 ⛽€1/75liter 🅒€1/time Ch ✈(7x)1,50/8h. 🅟
Location: Rural, noisy. **Surface:** metalled. 🔲 01/01-31/12
Distance: 🚶1km ⊗200m 🛒500m.
Remarks: Max. 2 nights.

Osterode 9C3
Campingplatz Eulenburg, Scheerenberger Straße 100.
GPS: n51,72766 e10,28347. ⬆➡.

13 ⛺€8, 2 pers.incl ⛽€1/100liter 🅒Ch ✈(12x)€1/kWh WC €
0,70/4minutes 📶€4/day. **Location:** Rural, comfortable, quiet.
Surface: gravel. 🔲 01/01-31/12
Distance: 🚶2km ⊗on the spot 🛒2,5km 🚶on the spot.
Remarks: Bread-service, swimming pool incl.

Ostrhauderfehn 6G3
Reisemobilhafen Ostrhauderfehn, Hauptstrasse 115.
GPS: n53,13872 e7,62318. ⬆.

20 ⛺€5 🅒Ch ✈(12x)€1/2kWh WC €0,50 ▣. 🚿
Surface: asphalted.
🔲 01/01-31/12 ▣ during fair in June
Distance: 🚶100m ⊗100m 🛒100m.
Remarks: Caution key € 10, sanitary at bar.

Otterndorf 6H1
Parking Mitte, Jahnstrasse. **GPS:** n53,80861 e8,89444. ⬆➡.

8 ⛺free. **Location:** Rural, simple. **Surface:** metalled.
🔲 01/01-31/12
Distance: 🚶on the spot ⊗200m.

Otterndorf 6H1
Seglertreff, Schleuse 5. **GPS:** n53,82250 e8,89472. ⬆.

12 ⛺free, 01/04-31/10 € 7,00 ⛽🅒Ch ✈€2,50/24h WC 🚿 🚿
Location: Rural, comfortable. **Surface:** metalled.
🔲 01/01-31/12
Distance: 🚶2km ⊘50m on the spot ⊗on the spot 🛒2km 🚲on the spot 🚶on the spot.

Ottersberg 7A3
Am Sportzentrum, Fährwisch. **GPS:** n53,10721 e9,13558. ⬆.

8 ⛺free ⛽€1 🅒Ch ✈€1/8h. **Location:** Simple.
Surface: gravel/sand. 🔲 01/01-31/12
Distance: 🚶500m ⊗200m.

Ovelgönne 6H2
Burgdorf Ovelgönne, Am Sportplatz. **GPS:** n53,34333 e8,42750. ⬆➡.

5 ⛺free ⛽€1/100liter 🅒Ch ✈free. **Location:** Urban, simple, isolated, quiet. **Surface:** grassy. 🔲 01/01-31/12
Distance: 🚶700m ⊗700m 🛒700m 🚲on the spot.

Oyten 7A3
KNAUS Reisemobilpark, Oyter See 1. **GPS:** n53,04645 e9,00396.

20 ⛺€ 12-15 ⛽€2,20 🅒Ch ✈€0,70/kWh WC included ▣ 📶€1
🚿 🚿 **Location:** Rural, comfortable. **Surface:** metalled.
🔲 01/04-01/11
Distance: 🚶2,5km ⊘3km ⊘Oyter See 150m.
Remarks: Caution key € 5.

Papenburg 6G3
Roten Kreuz, Rathausstraße. **GPS:** n53,07646 e7,39266.
30 ⛺free. **Surface:** gravel. 🔲 01/01-31/12
Distance: 🚶on the spot ⊗300m.

Papenburg 6G3
Poggenpoel, Zum Poggenpoel. **GPS:** n53,06526 e7,42630. ⬆➡.

20 ⛺€8 ⛽€3/100liter 🅒€3 Ch ✈(8x)€2/24h WC €2 🚿 🚿
Location: Rural, simple. **Surface:** gravel. 🔲 01/01-31/12
Distance: 🚶3,5km ⊘Badesee.
Remarks: At lake, max. 3 nights.

Polle 9A2
Weserpromenade, Mühlenweg 2. **GPS:** n51,89871 e9,40830. ⬆.

15 ⛺€8 + € 1/pp tourist tax, 01/10-31/05 free ⛽🅒Ch included ✈
Location: Rural, simple. **Surface:** grassy. 🔲 01/01-31/12
Distance: 🚶100m ⊘on the spot on the spot ⊗100m 🛒100m
🚲 Weser-Radweg.
Remarks: Along the Weser river, check in at campsite.

Rastede 6H3
Mühlenstraße. **GPS:** n53,24806 e8,20944. ⬆.

4 ⛺free. **Location:** Urban, simple. **Surface:** metalled.
🔲 01/01-31/12
Distance: 🚶1km ⊘2,7km ⊗1km 🛒2km.

Rehburg-Loccum 9A1
Wohnmobilstellplatz Rehburg, Auf der Bleiche.
GPS: n52,47370 e9,23227. ⬆➡.

8 🛌 €5 ⚡€1/12h. **Surface:** gravel. 🅾 01/01-31/12
Distance: 🚻400m.
Tourist information Rehburg-Loccum:
🌐 Dinosaurierpark Münchehagen. Attractions park around the dinosaur. 🅾 28/02-30/11 10h, summers 9h.

| 🅂 | **Rhauderfehn** 🚣 | 6G3 |

Paddel- und Pedalstation, Am Siel 8. **GPS:** n53,13878 e7,58689. ⬆➡.

16 🛌 €5 ⛽€1/100liter 🔋Ch⚡(16x)€1/8h WC🔋€2. 🚽
Location: Rural, luxurious, quiet. **Surface:** grassy. 🅾 01/01-31/12
Distance: 🚻500m 🏊on the spot ⚓on the spot ⊗50m.
Remarks: Caution key sanitary € 10, canoe and bicycle rental.

| 🅂 | **Rhede/Ems** | 6F3 |

Emspark, Am Sportplatz 6. **GPS:** n53,05853 e7,27621. ⬆.

5 🛌 free. **Location:** Simple. **Surface:** metalled.
🅾 01/01-31/12
Distance: 🚻500m ⊗500m 🛒500m.
Remarks: Parking in front of sports park.

| 🅂 | **Rinteln** 🏛 | 9A2 |

Reisemobilplatz am Weseranger, Dankerser strasse.
GPS: n52,19226 e9,07842. ⬆➡.

40 🛌 free ⛽€2/100liter 🔋€2 Ch€2 ⚡(36x)€0,50/kWh.
Location: Rural, simple. **Surface:** grassy/gravel.
🅾 01/01-31/12
Distance: 🚻600m 🏊on the spot ⚓on the spot ⊗100m 🛒400m 🚲400m 🚲Weserradweg 🚶on the spot.
Remarks: Max. 3 days.

| 🅂 | **Rodewald** | 9A1 |

Am Freibad, Im Zentrum. **GPS:** n52,66369 e9,48020. ⬆.

10 🛌 free ⚡(10x)€0,50/kWh. **Surface:** grasstiles.

🅾 01/01-31/12
Distance: 🛒200m 🚲on the spot.

| 🅂🅂 | **Rotenburg (Wümme)** 🏛🚣 | 7A3 |

Am Weichelsee, Bremer Straße. **GPS:** n53,11960 e9,38230. ⬆➡.

20 🛌 €5 ⛽€2 Ch ⚡(20x)€2. 🚽 🧺 **Location:** Rural, simple.
Surface: metalled.
🅾 01/01-31/12
Distance: 🚻2km 🏊on the spot ⊗Strandhaus 🚲2km 🚲on the spot.
Remarks: Check in at StrandHouse.

| 🅂🅂 | **Salzgitter** 🌿🚣 | 9B2 |

Reisemobilstellplatz am Salzgittersee, Zum Salzgittersee.
GPS: n52,15222 e10,31306. ⬆➡.

18 🛌 free ⛽€2/100liter 🔋Ch⚡(14x)€1/6h. **Location:** Rural, comfortable. **Surface:** grassy/metalled. 🅾 01/01-31/12
Distance: 🚻1km 🏊on the spot ⊗500m 🛒1km 🚲on the spot 🚶on the spot.
Remarks: Max. 4 days, boat rental.

| 🛑 | **Salzgitter** 🌿🚣 | 9B2 |

Thermalsolebad, Parkallee 3, Salzgitter-Bad.
GPS: n52,03724 e10,38351. ⬆➡.

6 🛌 free. **Location:** Rural, simple, quiet. **Surface:** metalled.
🅾 01/01-31/12
Distance: 🚻1,5km ⊗on the spot 🛒1,5km 🚲on the spot 🚲on the spot 🚶on the spot.
Remarks: Max. 4 days, no camping activities.

| 🅂🅂 | **Salzhausen** | 7B2 |

Am Waldbad, Schwienbrink. **GPS:** n53,22199 e10,17841. ⬆.

6 🛌 free ⛽€1/10minutes 🔋Chfree ⚡(4x)€1/8h. **Location:** Rural, simple. **Surface:** gravel. 🅾 01/01-31/12
Distance: 🚻1km 🛒500m.

| 🛑🅂 | **Salzhemmendorf** ♨ | 9B2 |

Ith-Sole-Therme, In der Saale-Aue. **GPS:** n52,07093 e9,58564. ⬆.

20 🛌 €7,50 ⛽€0,20/20liter ⚡€1 Ch ⚡(20x)€1/kWh.
Location: Rural, quiet. **Surface:** grassy/gravel. 🅾 01/01-31/12
Distance: 🚻400m 🚲on the spot.
Remarks: Check in at pay-desk of the Therme.

| 🅂 | **Salzhemmendorf** ♨ | 9B2 |

Rasti-land, Quanthofer strasse 9. **GPS:** n52,09706 e9,66451. ⬆.

5 🛌 free. **Location:** Isolated. **Surface:** gravel/sand.
Distance: 🚻1km.
Remarks: Bus parking amusement park.
Tourist information Salzhemmendorf:
🌐 Rasti-Land, Quanthofer strasse 9. Amusement park. 🅾 01/04-31/10 10-17/18h, Apr, Sep: Mo, Sa, Su.

| 🅂 | **Sande (Nieder-Sachsen)** | 6G2 |

Am Markt. GPS: n53,50251 e8,01113. ⬆.

4 🛌 free. **Location:** Urban, simple. **Surface:** metalled.
🅾 01/01-31/12
Distance: 🚻100m ⊗100m 🛒100m.

| 🅂 | **Sande (Nieder-Sachsen)** | 6G2 |

Paddel- und Pedalstation, Altmarienhausen.
GPS: n53,51174 e8,01076. ⬆.
4 🛌 free. **Surface:** gravel. 🅾 01/01-31/12
Distance: 🚻1km 🏊Sander See 50m.

| 🅂 | **Sande (Nieder-Sachsen)** | 6G2 |

Sander See, Loppelter Weg. **GPS:** n53,51162 e8,00206. ⬆.

4 🛌 free. **Surface:** metalled. 🅾 01/01-31/12
Distance: 🚻2km 🏊on the spot.

| 🅂 | **Sande (Nieder-Sachsen)** | 6G2 |

Freizeitmobile von der Kammer, Huntestraße 1.
GPS: n53,49076 e8,02292. ⬆.

⚓ ⊟Ch ✎ on demand. ◉ winter

⚓S Sandstedt 🌿⚓🌊 6H2

Wohnmobilstellplatz Sandstedt Sandstedt

- ■ **Beautiful view**
- ■ **Paved and flat motorhome pitches**
- ■ **Located near marina**

www.hagen-cux.de
info@hagen-cux.de

Wohnmobilstellplatz Sandstedt, Am Radarturm 5.
GPS: n53,36317 e8,51231.⬆➡.
9 🚐 free 🚰€1/100liter 🔌€1 Ch€1 ✎(9x)€1 WC 🚽150m on campsite.
Location: Rural, comfortable, isolated, quiet. **Surface**: grassy/gravel.
◉ 01/04–30/09
Distance: 🚶500m 🚴3km ⛵100m 🎣950m ⊗3km 🚆500m 🍴 on the spot 🛒 on the spot.

⚓S Sankt Andreasberg 🏔❄✳ 9C3

Silbererzgrube Samson, Am Samson 4. **GPS**: n51,71398 e10,51625.⬆.

20 🚐€11 ✎(20x)included. 📶 **Location**: Rural, simple, quiet.
Surface: gravel. ◉ 01/01–31/12
Distance: 🚶1km ⊗400m 🍴1km 🛒 on the spot.
Remarks: At Historical Mine of Sllver Ores.

⚓S Saterland 🏔🌊 6G3

Reisemobilhafen am Maiglöckchensee, Am Sportplatz, Scharrel.
GPS: n53,07060 e7,70116.⬆➡.

28+7 🚐€4 🚰€1/100liter 🔌€1 Ch€1 ✎(28x)€2/24h WC 🚽€0,50. ◉€2. 📶 **Location**: Rural, luxurious, quiet. **Surface**: grassy.
◉ 01/01–31/12
Distance: 🚶300m ⛵50m 🎣50m ⊗1km 🍴500m 🚆500m.

⚓S Saterland 🏔🌊 6G3

Reisemobilplatz Am Bootshafen, Hauptstrasse 640, Strücklingen.
GPS: n53,12819 e7,66762.⬆.

15 🚐€3 🚰€1/100liter 🔌€1 Ch ✎€1,50/24h WC€1 🚽€0,50. 📶
Location: Rural, simple. **Surface**: grassy/gravel.
◉ 01/01–31/12
Distance: 🚶100m ⛵on the spot 🎣on the spot ⊗on the spot 🍴on the spot 🚆100m.

⚓S Scharnebeck 🌿🌊 7C2

Wohnmobilstellplatz Am Schiffshebewerk, Adendorfer Straße 40.
GPS: n53,29196 e10,49320.⬆.

15 🚐€6/24h, park €2 🚰€1/10minutes 🔌Ch ✎(8x)€1/8h. 🚽
Location: Rural, comfortable, isolated, quiet. **Surface**: metalled.
◉ 01/01–31/12
Distance: 🚶1km ⊗200m 🛒Aldi 400m.
Remarks: Climbing wall 100m, boat lift Scharnebeck.

⚓S Schneverdingen 🏔👥🌊 7B3

Wohnmobil-Park Lüneburger Heide Schneverdingen

Comfortable motorhome stopover
Located in nature reserve
Restaurant with regional specialties

www.wohnmobilhafen-lueneburger-heide.de
info@camping-LH.de

Wohnmobil-Park Lüneburger Heide, Badeweg 3, Heber.
GPS: n53,07104 e9,86481.⬆.
44 🚐€12 🚰€1/80liter 🔌Ch ✎(40x)included,10Amp WC€2/day 🚽use sanitary €2/pp 📶. 📶 **Location**: Rural, comfortable.
Surface: grassy/metalled. ◉ 01/04–31/10
Distance: 🚶7km 🚴5km ⛵on the spot ⊗on the spot 🍴on camp site 🛒on the spot 🚶on the spot.
Remarks: Use sanitary facilities at campsite, car rental, shuttle bus.

⚓S Schneverdingen 🏔👥🌊 7B3

Am Quellenbad, Inseler Straße. **GPS**: n53,13110 e9,77280.⬆➡.

20 🚐 free 🚰€2 🔌ChWC 🚽€1. **Location**: Urban, simple.
Surface: grassy. ◉ 01/01–31/12
Distance: 🚶2km ⛵on the spot 🛒on the spot 🚶on the spot.
Remarks: Use sanitary only during opening hours swimming pool.

⚓S Schneverdingen 🏔👥🌊 7B3

Parkplatz Festhalle, Im Osterwald. **GPS**: n53,11893 e9,80681.⬆.

---

4 🚐 free. **Location**: Simple. **Surface**: metalled.
◉ 01/01–31/12
Distance: 🚶2km 🚆2km.
Remarks: Entrance via Festhalle.

⚓S Schneverdingen 🏔👥🌊 7B3

Mariechens Hoff, Voßbarg 15, Reinsehlen.
GPS: n53,17122 e9,83316.⬆➡.

8 🚐€8 🚰🔌Ch included ✎(8x)€0,40/kWh. 📶 **Location**: Rural, simple, isolated, quiet. **Surface**: grassy. ◉ 01/01–31/12
Distance: 🚶7km 🚴15km ⛵3km 🍴4 km 🛒on the spot 🚶on the spot.

⚓S Schneverdingen 🏔👥🌊 7B3

Reisemobilhafen Lüneburgerheide, Badeweg 3, Heber.
GPS: n53,07108 e9,86464.⬆.

5 🚐€12 🚰🔌Ch ✎(5x)included WC 🚽€2,50. 🚽 📶
Location: Rural, luxurious, quiet. **Surface**: grasstiles/metalled.
◉ 01/04–31/10
Distance: 🚶5km 🍴on camp site 🛒on the spot 🚶on the spot.
Remarks: Sanitary at campsite.

⚓S Schöppenstedt 9C2

Elm-Asse-Platz, Schützenplatz am Berge.
GPS: n52,14756 e10,77737.⬆.

15 🚐 free. **Location**: Rural, simple, noisy. **Surface**: asphalted.
◉ 01/01–31/12
Distance: 🚶600m ⊗1km 🚆km.
Remarks: Next to sports fields.

Tourist information Schöppenstedt:
ℹ The region of Till Eulenspiegel. Tills-Tauf-Tour: cycle and hiking routes in the country of Jester Till, start at the Till Eulenspiegel museum.
◉ Tue-Fri 14-17h, Sa-Su 11-17h.
Ⓜ Till Eulenspiegelmuseum, Nordstrasse 4a. ◉ Tue-Fri 14-17h, Sa-Su 11-17h ◉ Mo.

⚓S Schortens 6G2

Aqua-toll, Beethovenstrasse. **GPS**: n53,53961 e7,93780.

2 🛏free. **Surface:** metalled. 🅾 01/01-31/12
Distance: 🛒200m 🚰25m.
Remarks: Parking swimming pool, max. 6,5m.

Schortens   6G2

Reisemobilstellplatz Fair-Cafe, Birkenstraße.
GPS: n53,55281 e7,97650.

6 🛏guests free. **Surface:** unpaved. 🅾 01/01-31/12
Distance: 🚶3km 🏊100m.

Schulenberg 🌿🌼❄   9C2

Wiesenbergstrasse. **GPS:** n51,83535 e10,43464. ⬆

20 🛏€ 5 + € 1,50/pp tourist tax 🚰€1/80liter 🗑Ch 🔌(6x)€0,60/
kWh WC. 🚿 **Location:** Rural, comfortable, quiet. **Surface:** gravel.
🅾 01/01-31/12
Distance: 🚶on the spot ⊗on the spot 🛒6km 🚌on the spot 🏃on
the spot.
Remarks: Check in at tourist office, view at Okerstausee.

Schüttorf   8F2

Am Kuhmplatz, Graf-Egbert-Straße. **GPS:** n52,32123 e7,22642. ⬆

10 🛏free. 🚰🗑Chfree. **Location:** Rural, simple. **Surface:** gravel.
🅾 01/01-31/12
Distance: 🚲2,4km 🛒100m.
Remarks: Parking swimming pool.

Schwanewede   6H3

Am Markt, Am Markt. **GPS:** n53,22412 e8,59644. ⬆

3 🛏free. **Location:** Simple, central. **Surface:** metalled.
🅾 01/01-31/12
Distance: 🚶on the spot ⊗on the spot 🛒on the spot.

Schwanewede   6H3

Brücke zu Harriersand, Inselstraße. **GPS:** n53,26489 e8,49762. ⬆

5 🛏free. **Location:** Rural, simple, isolated. **Surface:** grassy.
🅾 01/01-31/12
Distance: 🚶7km.

Schwanewede   6H3

Löhnhorst, Hammersbeckerweg/Am Fosshall.
GPS: n53,20355 e8,62453. ⬆

2 🛏free. **Location:** Rural, simple, isolated, quiet. **Surface:** metalled.
🅾 01/01-31/12
Distance: 🚶6km ⊗6km 🛒6km.

Schwanewede   6H3

Wohnmobilstellplatz, Klint, Neuenkirchen.
GPS: n53,23670 e8,50919. ⬆

5 🛏free. **Location:** Rural, simple, quiet. **Surface:** unpaved.
🅾 01/01-31/12
Distance: 🚶500m.
Remarks: Dead end street.

Seelze   9A1

Marina Rasche Werft, Werftstraße 10. **GPS:** n52,39560 e9,56435. ⬆

13 🛏€ 6,50 🚰🗑Chincluded 🔌(13x)€3 WC🚿€2 🗑
🅾 01/04-15/10
Distance: 🚶2km 🚲4,5km ⊗on the spot. **Remarks:** Bread-service.

Selsingen   7A2

Wohnmobilstation, Im Sick. **GPS:** n53,37573 e9,20681. ⬆➡

25 🛏free. 🚰🗑Chfree. **Location:** Rural, simple. **Surface:** metalled.
🅾 01/01-31/12
Distance: 🚶500m 🛒100m.

Sittensen 🌿🎡🍰   7A2

Parkplatz, Mühlenstrasse. **GPS:** n53,27652 e9,50750. ⬆

---

5 🛏free 🚰🗑ChWCfree. **Location:** Simple, central.
Surface: metalled. 🅾 01/01-31/12
Distance: 🚶centre ⊗200m 🚴on the spot 🏃on the spot.

Soltau 🌿🎡🍰🎭   7B3

Soltau Therme, Stubbendorffweg. **GPS:** n52,99301 e9,84443.

10 🛏free. **Location:** Simple, central, quiet. **Surface:** metalled.
🅾 01/01-31/12
Distance: 🚶1km ⊗on the spot 🚴on the spot 🏃on the spot.
Remarks: Max. 1 night.

Soltau 🌿🎡🍰🎭   7B3

Heidepark. **GPS:** n53,02166 e9,87370.

100 🛏€ 5. 🚿 **Location:** Rural, simple, isolated.
Surface: grasstiles.
🅾 01/01-31/12
Remarks: Parking amusement park.
Tourist information Soltau
🅱 Heidepark. Amusement park.
🅾 01/04-31/10 9-18h, 01/07-15/08 Sa 9-21h.

Spieka-Neufeld   6H1

Wohnmobilhafen, Deichweg. **GPS:** n53,78899 e8,55060. ⬆

40 🛏€ 8 🚰€1/100liter 🗑Ch 🔌(18x)€1/2kWh. **Location:** Rural,
simple. **Surface:** gravel/metalled. 🅾 01/01-31/12
Distance: 🚶300m 🛒on the spot 🚴on the spot ⊗200m.
Remarks: Bread-service.

Springe   9A2

Auf dem Burghof. **GPS:** n52,20765 e9,55717. ⬆

5 🛏free. **Location:** Simple. **Surface:** asphalted. 🅾 01/01-31/12
Distance: 🚶Old city centre 200m ⊗300m.

DE

🏕️S Stade 🚤🛒 7A2

Wohnmobilstellplatz Am Schiffertor, Schiffertorsstrasse 21.
GPS: n53,60278 e9,46667.⬆️➡️.

79 🅿️€ 8,50/24h 🚰€1/80liter 🚽Ch 🔌€0,50/kWh.🚮
Location: Urban, central. **Surface**: gravel.
📅 01/01-31/12
Distance: 🛒500m ⊗700m.

🏕️S Stadland 🏕️🌳🚲 6H2

Am Sportplatz, Hauptstrasse, Seefeld. **GPS**: n53,45639 e8,35778.⬆️

5 🅿️free 🚰€1/10minutes 🔌(4x)€1/8h. **Location**: Urban, simple,
quiet. **Surface**: asphalted. 📅 01/01-31/12
Distance: 🛒on the spot ⊗on the spot 🚰on the spot 🚆on the spot
🚲on the spot.
Remarks: Next to sports fields.

🏕️S Stadland 🏕️🌳🚲 6H2

Deichparkplatz, Fährstrasse, Kleinensiel. **GPS**: n53,44250 e8,47833.⬆️

5 🅿️free 🚰€1/100liter 🔌(4x)€1. **Location**: Rural, simple, isolated,
quiet. **Surface**: gravel. 📅 01/01-31/12
Distance: 🛒500m ⛱️200m Weserstrand 🚲300m on the spot.

🏕️S Stadland 🏕️🌳🚲 6H2

Rathausplatz, Am Markt, Rodenkirchen. **GPS**: n53,39944 e8,45444.⬆️

10 🅿️free 🚰€1/10minutes 🚽Ch 🔌(4x)€1/8h. **Location**: Urban,
simple, central, quiet. **Surface**: grasstiles/metalled.
📅 01/01-31/12
🔲 Thu 5-13h market
Distance: 🛒on the spot ⊗500m 🚰500m 🚆on the spot 🚲on the
spot.

S Stadland 🏕️🌳🚲 6H2

Birkenweg, Kleinensiel. **GPS**: n53,44194 e8,47444.

🚮Chfree. **Location**: Urban. 📅 01/01-31/12

🏕️S Stadthagen 9A1

Reisemobilplatz am Tropicana, Jahnstraße 2.
GPS: n52,32236 e9,18896.⬆️

15 🅿️free 🚰€1/100liter 🚽Ch 🔌(4x)€1/2kWh WC🍽️📶.🚮
Location: Rural, quiet. **Surface**: gravel. 📅 01/01-31/12
Distance: 🛒2km ⊗1km 🚰1km 🚶on the spot 🏊on the spot.
Remarks: Max. 3 days, service at Tropicana.

🏕️S Stadtoldendorf 9B2

Mobilcamping unter den Homburg, Linnenkämper Strasse 33.
GPS: n51,87777 e9,63500.⬆️➡️.

30 🅿️€ 5/day 🚰€1 🚽Ch 🔌(25x)€2/day. 🚲 **Location**: Simple.
Surface: grassy. 📅 01/01-31/12
Distance: 🛒1km 🚰1km.
Remarks: Check in at restaurant.

🏕️S Steinfeld 8H1

Zur Schemder Bergmark, Dammer Strasse.
GPS: n52,58308 e8,21476.⬆️➡️.

20 🅿️free 🚰€1/100liter 🚽€0,50 Ch€0,50. **Location**: Rural, quiet.
Surface: metalled. 📅 01/01-31/12
Distance: 🛒500m 🚰500m.
Remarks: Parking swimming pool.

🏕️S Steinhude 9A1

Wohnmobilstellplatz Steinhude, Am Bruchdamm.
GPS: n52,44874 e9,35478.⬆️

180 🅿️€ 7,50 🚰🚽€1 Ch 🔌(60x)€3/day WC🚽€1 🔲€2,50/2,50.
Surface: grassy.
📅 01/01-31/12
Distance: 🛒500m ⛱️500m ⊗500m 🚰500m.
Remarks: Max. 3 nights, bread-service.

Tourist information Steinhude:
ℹ️ Marina on lake of the same name.

🏕️S Steyerberg 9A1

Waldferienpark Steyerberg, Zum Ferienpark 37.
GPS: n52,57395 e9,01096.⬆️

40 🅿️€ 5 🚰€1 🚽Ch 🔌€2 WC🚽€2. **Surface**: metalled.
📅 01/01-31/12
Distance: 🛒1km ⊗1km 🚰1km.

🏕️S Steyerberg 9A1

Wohnmobilstellplatz Steyerberg, Kleine Straße 7.
GPS: n52,56655 e9,02505.⬆️
4 🅿️free 🚰€1/100liter 🚽€1 Ch€1 🔌(8x)€1/8h. **Surface**: gravel.
📅 01/01-31/12
Distance: 🛒on the spot.

🍴S Steyerberg 9A1

Gasthaus Zur Eiche, Sarninghausen 2. **GPS**: n52,56944 e8,99444.⬆️.

15 🅿️guests free 🚰. **Surface**: grassy. 📅 01/01-31/12

🏕️S Stolzenau 9A1

Reisemobilstellplatz Stolzenau, Weserstrasse.
GPS: n52,51021 e9,08104.⬆️➡️.

33 🅿️€ 4 🚰€1/60liter 🚽Ch 🔌(24x)€2/12h. **Surface**: grasstiles.
📅 01/01-31/12 🔧 service 01/11-31/03
Distance: 🛒250m ⛱️on the spot 🚰on the spot ⊗300m 🚰300m.
Remarks: Along the Weser river.

🏕️S Sulingen 8H1

Am Stadtsee, Kornstraße. **GPS**: n52,67653 e8,80127.⬆️

10 🅿️free 🚰€1/5minutes 🚽€1 Ch€1. **Surface**: metalled.
📅 01/01-31/12
Distance: 🛒600m ⛱️300m.

🏕️S Surwold 6G3

Erholungsgebiet Surwolds Wald, Waldstrasse.
GPS: n52,96743 e7,51535.⬆️

20 🅿️€ 5 🚰€1/100liter 🚽Ch 🔌€2 WC🚽€0,50. **Surface**: grassy.
📅 01/01-31/12

DE

Distance: 🚶800m 🚏250m.

🅂 **Surwold** 6G3

Privatplatz Klapper, Papenburgerstrasse 57.
GPS: n53,01774 e7,48470. ⬆️.

10 🚐 € 10 ⛽ 🗑️Ch 🚿(4x)€1/24h WC 💧€2. **Location:** Rural, simple. **Surface:** grassy. 🅾️ 01/01-31/12
Distance: 🚶1km 🏊1,5km 🛒1km 🚉1km.
Remarks: Swimming pool and picnic area available.

🅂 **Tarmstedt** 7A3

Landtechniek Grabau, Bahnhofstraße.
GPS: n53,22421 e9,08728. ⬆️➡️.

15 🚐 € 6 ⛽🗑️Ch 🚿included. 🚲 **Location:** Simple.
Surface: metalled. 🅾️ 01/01-31/12
Distance: 🚶on the spot 🚏500m 🚉on the spot.

🅂 **Thedinghausen** 7A3

Reisemobilstellplatz Erbhof, Braunschweiger Straße.
GPS: n52,96188 e9,03020. ⬆️.

8 🚐 € 5 ⛽€1/10minutes 🗑️Ch 🚿€1/6h WC. **Surface:** grasstiles.
🅾️ 01/01-31/12
Distance: 🚶500m 🚲on the spot 🚶on the spot.

🅂 **Twist** 8F1

Am Hallenbad. **GPS**: n52,64719 e7,08918. ⬆️.

6 🚐free ⛽€1/100liter 🗑️Ch 🚿(8x)€1/2kWh. **Surface:** metalled.
🅾️ 01/01-31/12
Distance: 🚶on the spot 🏊on the spot.
Remarks: Barefoot path.

🅂 **Uchte** 9A1

Balkenkamp. **GPS**: n52,49761 e8,90618. ⬆️.

3 🚐free ⛽€1 🗑️Ch. **Surface:** metalled. 🅾️ 01/01-31/12

Distance: 🚶100m 🚏500m 🚉100m.

🅂 **Uelsen** 8F1

Festplatz, Hardinghauserstrasse. **GPS**: n52,49575 e6,88840. ⬆️➡️.

10 🚐free ⛽€2 🗑️ChWC. **Surface:** asphalted. 🅾️ 01/01-31/12

🅂 **Uelzen** 7C3

Im Sportboothafen, Riedweg 7. **GPS**: n52,95722 e10,59444. ⬆️.

8 🚐€ 8 + € 1/pp ⛽€1/70liter 🗑️€1 Ch 🚿(8x)€1/6h WC included 💧€2,50/2,50. **Location:** Rural, simple, quiet. **Surface:** metalled.
🅾️ 01/01-31/12
Distance: 🏊on the spot 🚏on the spot 🚏on the spot 🚉1,9km on the spot 🚶on the spot.
Remarks: Max. 3 nights, free bicycles available, playground.

🅂 **Undeloh** 7B3

Am Naturschutzpark, Wilseder Straße. **GPS**: n53,19253 e9,97709.

30 🚐€ 3/day, € 6/night. 🚘 **Location:** Rural, simple.
Surface: unpaved. 🅾️ 01/01-31/12
Distance: 🚶500m 🚏100m 🚶on the spot.
Remarks: In nature reserve the the Lüneburg Heide (heath).

🅂 **Uplengen** 6G2

Remelser Paddel- & Pedalstation, Uferstrasse.
GPS: n53,30123 e7,75151. ⬆️.

5 🚐€ 5 ⛽🗑️Ch 🚿(4x)€2. **Surface:** metalled. 🅾️ 01/01-31/12
Distance: 🚶500m 🏊50m 🚉500m.
Remarks: Max. 3 days, canoe and bicycle rental.

🅂 **Uplengen** 6G2

Schützenplatz, Schützenstraße. **GPS**: n53,30719 e7,74708. ⬆️➡️.

10 🚐€ 5 ⛽🗑️Ch 🚿€1/12h. **Surface:** grasstiles. 🅾️ 01/01-31/12
🅾️ 10/06-15/06
Distance: 🚶500m.

Remarks: Max. 3 nights.

🅂 **Uslar** 9B3

Reisemobilpark am Badeland, Zur Schwarzen Erde.
GPS: n51,66753 e9,62831. ⬆️➡️.

20 🚐€ 6 + reduction swimming pool ⛽€1/10minutes 🗑️Ch 🚿€1/8h WC€0,50. **Location:** Quiet. **Surface:** grasstiles.
🅾️ 01/01-31/12
Distance: 🚶1km 🚏on the spot 🚉500m 🚐on the spot.

🅂 **Uslar** 9B3

Am Lindenhof, Lindenhof 1. **GPS**: n51,67213 e9,62952. ⬆️➡️.

5 🚐first night € 8, € 2 each additional night ⛽🗑️Chincluded 🚿€0,40/kWh. 🚲 **Location:** Rural, simple. **Surface:** grassy/gravel.
🅾️ 01/01-31/12
Distance: 🚶2,5km 🏊2,5km 🚉2,5km 🚐on the spot.

Tourist information Uslar:
⛪ Market, city centre. 🅾️ Fri 9-13h.
🦋 Alaris Schmetterlingspark. Butterfly park in tropical rain forest.
🅾️ 01/04-31/10 Tue-Su 9.30-17.30h.
🏊 Uslarer Badeland. Swimming pool complex. 🅾️ Sa/Su 10-18h, Tue-Fri 10-20h, Mo 10-13h.

🅂 **Vechta** 8H1

Am Hallenwellen- und Freibad, Dornbusch.
GPS: n52,74000 e8,29639. ⬆️.

10 🚐free. **Location:** Urban, simple. **Surface:** grassy/metalled.
🅾️ 01/01-31/12
Distance: 🚶1km 🚏1km 🚉1km.
Remarks: Parking swimming pool, max. 3 days, service Bokenerddamm 40.

🅂 **Vechta** 8H1

Oldenburgerstraße. **GPS**: n52,73245 e8,28833. ⬆️.

5 🚐free. **Location:** Urban, simple. **Surface:** metalled.
🅾️ 01/01-31/12
Distance: 🚶on the spot 🚏on the spot 🚉on the spot.

🅂 **Verden** 7A3

Conrad-Wode-Straße. **GPS**: n52,92572 e9,22738. ⬆️➡️.
14 🚐€ 6/24h ⛽€1/90liter 🗑️Ch 🚿€1/8h. 🚘
Location: Urban, comfortable, central. **Surface:** grassy.
🅾️ 01/01-31/12 🅾️ 26/05-05/06
Distance: 🚶350m 🚏300m 🚉300m 🚐300m.

DE

Tourist information Verden:

ℹ️ Reiterstadt, horse city of international reputation.

Ⓜ️ Deutsches Pferdemuseum, Holzmarkt 9 . Horse museum.

🕐 Tue-Su 10-17h.

✠ Verdener Bauernmarkt.

🕐 Sa 8-13h.

Vienenburg 🌳 ⚓ 9C2

Schacht I. **GPS**: n51,95705 e10,56772. ⬆️➡️.

4 🅿️free. **Location**: Rural, simple, quiet. **Surface**: metalled.
🕐 01/01-31/12
Distance: 🚶700m ⊗700m 🏊600m 🚲 on the spot 🚶 on the spot.
Remarks: At Vienenburg Lake, max. 24h.

Visselhövede 7A3

Zu den Visselwiesen, Wüstenhof 1. **GPS**: n52,98530 e9,57772. ⬆️➡️.

8 🅿️free. **Location**: Urban, simple. **Surface**: metalled.
🕐 01/01-31/12
Distance: ⊗100m 🛒200m.

Walchum 🌳 6F3

Marinapark Emstal, Steinbilder Straße. **GPS**: n52,92680 e7,29624.

10 🅿️€ 10 🚰🔌Ch🚿(6x) WC🚽€1,50.♨️ **Location**: Rural.
Surface: grassy. 🕐 01/01-31/12
Distance: 🎣fishing permit obligatory ⊗300m 🛒on the spot 🚲on the spot 🚶on the spot.

Walsrode 7A3

Forellenhof, Hünzingen 3. **GPS**: n52,89855 e9,59122.

10 🅿️€ 10 🚰🔌🚿(2x). ♨️ **Location**: Rural, simple, isolated, quiet. **Surface**: grasstiles/grassy.
Distance: 🚶3km on the spot 🛒3km.
Remarks: Free with a meal.

Tourist information Walsrode:

🦜 Vogelpark Walsrode. Bird park and botanical garden. 🕐 01/03-31/10 8-19h.

Wangerland 6G2

An der Ostdüne, Bäderstrasse, Hooksiel.
GPS: n53,64103 e8,03514. ⬆️➡️.

75 🅿️€ 12 + € 2,90/pp tourist tax, dog € 3,10 🚰🔌
Ch🚿WC🚽📶included. **Surface**: gravel. 🕐 01/04-30/10
Distance: 🚶1,7km 🏊beach ±250m.

Wangerland 6G2

Nordsee-Camping-Schillig, Jadestraße, Schillig.
GPS: n53,69986 e8,02338. ⬆️➡️.

80 🅿️€ 12 + € 2,90/pp tourist tax, dog € 3,10 🚰🔌Ch🚿
(80x)WC🚽📶included. **Surface**: grassy. 🕐 01/04-31/10
Distance: 🚶200m.

⚓S Wangerland 6G2

Am Yachthafen, Zum Hafen, Horumersiel.
GPS: n53,68293 e8,02091. ⬆️➡️.

22 🅿️€ 15,80 🚰🔌Ch🚿WC🚽included. **Surface**: concrete.
🕐 01/04-30/10
Distance: 🚶600m 🏊on the spot.

S Wardenburg 6H3

Keilstrasse, Astrup. **GPS**: n53,04770 e8,21197. ⬆️.

5 🅿️free 🚿(3x). **Location**: Urban, simple. **Surface**: gravel.
🕐 01/01-31/12
Distance: 🚲2,5km.

S Wardenburg 6H3

Marktplatz, Huntestraße. **GPS**: n53,06401 e8,19832. ⬆️➡️.

3 🅿️free. **Location**: Urban, simple. **Surface**: metalled.
🕐 01/01-31/12
Distance: 🚶on the spot 🚲3,6km.

⚓S Weener 🏰 ⚓ 6F3

Am Alten Hafen, Panneborgstrasse. **GPS**: n53,16953 e7,36167. ⬆️.

45 🅿️€ 7,50/24h 🚰€1/100liter 🔌Ch🚿(45x)€2,50/24h WC🚽€1.🚽
Location: Urban, comfortable. **Surface**: asphalted. 🕐 01/01-31/12
🕐 during harbor festival 3rd week of June
Distance: 🚶on the spot ⊗on the spot 🛒on the spot.
Remarks: Max. 3 days.

⚓S Weener 🏰 ⚓ 6F3

Am Yachthafen, Am Marina-Park. **GPS**: n53,16570 e7,36480. ⬆️➡️.
24 🅿️€ 7,50 🚿€2,50 🔌€2. **Surface**: metalled. 🕐 01/04-30/09
Distance: 🚶centre 1,2km 🛒50m.

S Werlte 6G3

Kreutzmanns Mühle, Kirchstraße. **GPS**: n52,85463 e7,68155. ⬆️.

6 🅿️free 🚰€1/100liter 🔌Ch🚿(8x)€1/2kWh. **Location**: Urban,
comfortable. **Surface**: metalled. 🕐 01/01-31/12
Distance: 🚶200m ⊗200m 🛒200m.

Westergellersen 7B2

Turniergelände Luhmühlen, Westergellerser Heide.
GPS: n53,23306 e10,21623. ⬆️➡️.

35 🅿️€ 8 🚰€1 🔌Ch🚿(35x)€ 1/8h WC🚽. ♨️ **Location**: Rural,
comfortable, isolated, quiet. **Surface**: grassy. 🕐 01/01-31/12
Distance: 🚶4km 🏊1,5km ⊗4km 🛒4km 🚌2km.

S Westerholt 6G2

Am Schul- und Sportzentrum, Ewigsweg. **GPS**: n53,59089 e7,44907.
5 🅿️free 🚰🔌Chfree. **Surface**: metalled. 🕐 01/01-31/12
Distance: 🚶500m 🛒600m.

Westerstede ⚓ 6G3

Albert-Post-Platz, Auf der Lohe. **GPS**: n53,25883 e7,92685. ⬆️.

5 🅿️free. **Location**: Urban, simple. **Surface**: metalled.
🕐 01/01-31/12
Distance: 🚶100m 🚲2km ⊗250m.

Westerstede ⚓ 6G3

Badesee Karlshof, Bekassinenweg. **GPS**: n53,18811 e7,86954. ⬆️.

DE

5 ⛟free. **Location:** Rural, simple, isolated. **Surface:** gravel.
☐ 01/01-31/12
Distance: ⚓Badesee.
Remarks: Max. 3 days.

Ⓒ Ⓢ Westerstede 🏖 6G3

Wohnmobilhafen Westerstede, Süderstraße 2.
GPS: n53,24968 e7,93438.⬆.

50 ⛟€5 🚰🔌Ch🔌€2/24h WC€2/pppd use sanitary €2,50. 🚗
🏖**Location:** Urban, comfortable, quiet. **Surface:** grassy/gravel.
☐ 01/01-31/12
Distance: 🚶800m 🚲1,4km ⊗McDonalds 200m.

Ⓢ Westoverledingen 6G3

Rathausplatz, Bahnhofstrasse 18, Ihrhove.
GPS: n53,16634 e7,45173.⬆➡.

3 ⛟free 🚰€1/100liter 🔌Ch. **Location:** Urban, simple.
Surface: grassy. ☐ 01/01-31/12 ◉ last week Jun
Distance: 🚶on the spot ⊗50m.
Remarks: At townhall.

🍴Ⓢ Westoverledingen 6G3

Reisemobilhafen zur Mühle, Mühlenstrasse 214, Steenfelderfehn.
GPS: n53,12944 e7,44051.⬆➡.

30 ⛟€5 🚰🔌Ch🔌(18x)included. **Location:** Rural, simple.
Surface: grassy/metalled. ☐ 01/01-31/12
Distance: ⊗on the spot 🚊1km.

🍴Ⓢ Westoverledingen 6G3

Schützenplatz Flachsmeer, Papenburger strasse 74, Flachsmeer.
GPS: n53,12700 e7,46367.⬆➡.

10 ⛟€5 🚰🔌🔌(10x)included. **Location:** Rural, simple.
Surface: grassy. ☐ 01/01-31/12

Distance: ⊗on the spot 🚐100m.

Ⓢ Wiefelstede 6G3

Wohnmobilstellplatz am Bernsteinsee, Dorfstrasse 11, Conneforde.
GPS: n53,32657 e8,06362.⬆➡.

25 ⛟€6 🚰€0,50 🔌€2 Ch🔌(25x)€0,50/kWh WC€0,50 ◉
on campsite. **Location:** Rural, comfortable. **Surface:** grassy.
☐ 01/01-31/12
Distance: ⚓on the spot ⊗on the spot.
Remarks: In front of campsite, caution sepkey € 5.

Ⓢ Wiefelstede 6G3

Freibad Wiefelstede, Alter Damm 11. **GPS:** n53,26146 e8,10713.⬆.

10 ⛟free. **Location:** Rural, simple, quiet. **Surface:** metalled.
☐ 01/01-31/12
Distance: 🚶500m ⊗on the spot 🚊1,5km.

⚓Ⓢ Wiesmoor 6G2

Bootshafen Ottermeer, Am Stadion. **GPS:** n53,40951 e7,71841.⬆➡.

14 ⛟€5,50 🚰🔌Ch🔌included. **Surface:** grassy/metalled.
☐ 01/01-31/12
Distance: 🚶1,5km.
Remarks: Key service at Gaststätte (12-19h).

🏖Ⓢ Wietzendorf 7B3

Übernachtungsoase Südsee Camp, Südsee camp 1, K41.
GPS: n52,93120 e9,96474.⬆.

40 ⛟€14 🚰€1/100liter 🔌🔌€0,50/kWh WC🔌.
Location: Comfortable. **Surface:** metalled.
Distance: 🚶2km 🚲100m 🚊on the spot.
Remarks: Caution key service € 3.

Ⓢ Wildeshausen 6H3

Am Krandel, Krandelstrasse. **GPS:** n52,90042 e8,42728.⬆➡.

16 ⛟€5 🚰€1/80liter 🔌Ch🔌(15x)included. **Location:** Rural,
simple. **Surface:** grassy/metalled. ☐ 01/01-31/12
Distance: 🚶500m 🚲4,4km ⊗400m 🚊700m.
Remarks: Parking at swimming pool.

Ⓢ Wilhelmshaven 🌼⛵🏖 6G2

Wohnmobilhafen Nautimo, Friedenstrasse 99.
GPS: n53,53546 e8,10104.⬆➡.

26 ⛟€8 🚰€1/100liter 🔌Ch🔌(26x)€1/6h,10Amp WCincluded 🔌€1
📶€2/h. **Surface:** metalled. ☐ 01/01-31/12
Distance: 🚶2km 🚲3km 🏊4km 🚶1,5km ⊗on the spot 🚊200m
◉1,5km 🚐100m 🚌on the spot 🛝on the spot.
Remarks: Max. 7 days.

Ⓢ Wilhelmshaven 🌼⛵🏖 6G2

Wohnmobilstellplatz Schleuseninsel, Schleussenstrasse 37.
GPS: n53,51478 e8,15218.⬆.

30 ⛟€9, trailer €5 🚰€0,50/50liter 🔌Ch🔌(28x)€3/24h WC🔌.
Surface: gravel. ☐ 01/01-31/12
Distance: ⊗250m ⚓Jadebus.

Ⓢ Wilhelmshaven 🌼⛵🏖 6G2

Am Freibad Nord, Möwenstraße 30. **GPS:** n53,57032 e8,10368.⬆➡.

6 ⛟€3,50, free with use of swimming pool 🚰🔌Ch🔌€1/6h WC🔌.
Surface: gravel. ☐ 01/05-31/08
Distance: 🚶1,5km.
Remarks: Use sanitary only during opening hours swimming pool.

Ⓢ Wilhelmshaven 🌼⛵🏖 6G2

Reisemobilstellplatz Wilhelmshaven Südstadt, Banterweg 12.
GPS: n53,51559 e8,09072.⬆.

20 ⛟€8 🚰🔌Ch🔌(16x)included 📶. **Surface:** gravel.
☐ 01/01-31/12

Ⓢ Wilhelmshaven 🌼⛵🏖 6G2

Fliegerdeich West, Fliegerdeich. **GPS:** n53,50996 e8,12718.⬆.

DE

40 🛏 € 0,75/h, € 12/day. 🏠 **Location:** Rural. **Surface:** metalled.
☀ 01/01-31/12
Distance: 🚲 2,5km ⛵ sea ✕ nearby.
Remarks: No camping activities.

| ⛰ S | Wilhelmshaven 🌊🏖🌊 | 6G2 |

Wohnmobilstellplatz Jade, Bunsenstraße 10.
GPS: n53,51110 e8,08153. ⬆.

10 🛏 € 10 💧 included. **Surface:** asphalted. ☀ 01/01-31/12
🚿 water: 01/11-31/03
Tourist information Wilhelmshaven:
👁 Aquarium Wilhelmshaven, Südstrand. Sea aquarium. ☀ 10-18h.

| 🏞 | Winsen/Luhe | 7B2 |

Festplatz Bleiche, Tönnhäuserweg. **GPS:** n53,36452 e10,21228. ⬆.

10 🛏 free. **Location:** Simple, central. **Surface:** asphalted.
☀ 01/01-31/12
Distance: 🚲 100m ✕ 100m 🛒 100m.

| 🏞 | Winsen/Luhe | 7B2 |

GreenEagle Golf, Radbrucher Straße 200. **GPS:** n53,32278 e10,22778.
15 🛏 free, playing golf obligatory. **Location:** Simple. **Surface:** gravel.
☀ 01/01-31/12
Distance: 🚲 6km ⛵ 2,2km ✕ on the spot.

| 🏞 S | Winsen/Luhe | 7B2 |

Freizeit Center Albrecht, Porchestrasse 15, Gewerbegebiet Lühdorf.
GPS: n53,33750 e10,21947. ⬆.

11 🛏 free 🚰 € 2 🛢 Ch 💧 (11x) WC. **Location:** Rural, simple.
Surface: metalled. ☀ 01/01-31/12
Distance: 🚲 4,5km ✕ on the spot.

| ⛰ S | Wittingen 🌊🌊 | 7C3 |

Wittinger Sporthafen, Am Sporthafen 1.
GPS: n52,72706 e10,66187. ⬆➡.

20 🛏 € 9 + € 0,50 pp 🚰 🛢 Ch 💧 (20x) WC 🚽 included 🚿 € 2,50/2,50.
Location: Rural, comfortable. **Surface:** grassy. ☀ 01/04-01/10
Distance: 🚲 4km ⛵ on the spot ⛵ on the spot ✕ on the spot 🛒 4km
🚌 200m 🚲 on the spot.
Remarks: Near marina.

| 🏞 | Wittmund | 6G2 |

Schützenplatz, Auricherstrasse. **GPS:** n53,55763 e7,69156. ⬆.
30 🛏 free. **Surface:** grassy. ☀ 01/01-31/12
Distance: 🚲 800m 🛒 bakery 200m.

| ⛴ S | Wittmund | 6G2 |

Hafen Harlesiel, Am Harlesiel. **GPS:** n53,70853 e7,80888. ⬆➡.

54 🛏 € 10-13 + € 2 tourist tax 🚰 🛢 Ch 💧 € 3 WC 🚽.
Surface: metalled. ☀ 15/03-31/10
Distance: ⛵ on the spot.
Remarks: Caution key electricity € 10.

| 🏞 S | Wolfenbüttel 🌊🏖 | 9C2 |

Alte Spinnerei, Am Seeligerpark. **GPS:** n52,16228 e10,52632.
10 🛏 free 🚰 € 1 💧 (3x) € 1. **Surface:** metalled. ☀ 01/01-31/12
Distance: 🚲 800m ✕ 300m.
Remarks: Max. 3 days, quiet at night, crowdy during the day.

| 🏞 S | Wolfenbüttel 🌊🏖 | 9C2 |

Sporthalleninsel, Vor dem Wehre. **GPS:** n52,16168 e10,52646. ⬆➡.

2 🛏 free 🚰 € 1/80liter 💧 (4x) € 1/8h. **Location:** Urban, central, noisy.
Surface: metalled. ☀ 01/01-31/12
Distance: 🚲 250m ✕ 500m 🛒 500m 🚌 200m.
Remarks: Along railwayline.

| 🏞 S | Wolfsburg 🌊 | 9C1 |

Autostadt, Berliner Brücke. **GPS:** n52,43485 e10,79716. ⬆.
9 🛏 € 3/day, € 10/24h 🚰 💧 included. 🏠 **Location:** Urban, noisy.
Surface: asphalted. ☀ 01/01-31/12
Distance: 🚲 2km ✕ on the spot 🛒 2km.
Tourist information Wolfsburg:
😊 Autostadt. Of the Volkswagen-concern; with pavilion of several car
makes, car tower of 20 floors, test driving. ☀ 9-20h.

| 🏞 S | Zetel 🏖🌳 | 6G2 |

Johann Quathamer, Fuhrenkampstrasse 60.
GPS: n53,40084 e7,91893. ⬆.

15 🛏 € 7 🚰 € 1/100liter 🛢 Ch 💧 (15x) WC included 🚽 € 0,50. 🚲
Location: Rural, comfortable, quiet. **Surface:** grassy.
☀ 01/01-31/12
Distance: 🚲 4km.

| 🏞 S | Zetel 🏖🌳 | 6G2 |

Markthamm, Neuenburger Strasse. **GPS:** n53,41706 e7,97000. ⬆.

40 🛏 free 🚰 🛢 Ch free 💧 (6x) € 1/kWh. **Location:** Urban, simple,
central. **Surface:** grasstiles. ☀ 01/01-31/12
Distance: 🚲 on the spot ✕ Imbiss.
Remarks: Parking centre, max. 2 days, service Kläranlage open: Mo/Tue
11-23h, Thu/Sa 11-23h, Su 16-23h.

| 🏞 | Zetel 🏖🌳 | 6G2 |

Driefeler Esch. **GPS:** n53,41835 e7,98445. ⬆.

10 🛏 free. **Location:** Simple. **Surface:** gravel. ☀ 01/01-31/12
Remarks: Parking swimming pool, max. 48h.

| 🏞 | Zetel 🏖🌳 | 6G2 |

Schulmuseum Bohlenbergerfeld, Wehdestrasse.
GPS: n53,41322 e7,92143. ⬆.

25 🛏 free. **Location:** Rural, simple, isolated. **Surface:** grassy/gravel.
☀ 01/01-31/12
Distance: 🚲 2,5 km.

| 🏞 | Zetel 🏖🌳 | 6G2 |

Urwald, Urwaldstrasse, Neuenburg. **GPS:** n53,39293 e7,96547. ⬆.

20 🛏 free. **Location:** Rural, simple, quiet. ☀ 01/01-31/12
Remarks: Max. 1 day.

| S | Zetel 🏖🌳 | 6G2 |

Kläranlage, Mohrstrasse. **GPS:** n53,42302 e7,97937.
🚰 🛢 Ch free. ☀ 01/01-31/12
Remarks: Mo/Thu 7-16h, Fri 7-13h, Sa/Su 9-9.30h.

Zeven 7A2

Viehmarkt, Meyerstrasse/Godenstedterstrasse.
GPS: n53,29764 e9,27514. ⬆️➡️.

4 🚐 free. **Location:** Simple. **Surface:** metalled.
⬛ 01/01-31/12
Distance: 🚶500m.

Zorge 9C3

Campingplatz im Waldwinkel, Kunzental 2.
GPS: n51,64188 e10,64881. ⬆️➡️.

30 🚐 € 9,50, 2 pers.incl 🚰€0,20/10liter ♻️Ch ⚡(15x)€2/day
WC🚽€1/pp. **Location:** Rural, simple, quiet. **Surface:** grassy/gravel.
⬛ 01/01-31/12
Distance: 🚶1,5km ⊗on the spot 🔌6km 🚆300m 🚲on the spot
🚶on the spot.
Remarks: Max. 2 nights.

Mecklenburg-Western Pomerania

Ahlbeck 7G1

Caravanplatz Am Wiesenrand, Gothenweg 5a.
GPS: n53,94100 e14,17600. ⬆️➡️.

24 🚐 € 10, peak season € 12,50 🚰 ♻️Ch ⚡2 WC🚽€1 🚿€3/3.
Surface: grassy. ⬛ 01/03-31/10
Distance: 🚶10min ⊘10min ⊗500m 🔌200m.
Remarks: Bread-service.

Ahlbeck 7G1

Wohnmobilstellplatz Rauthe, Waldstrasse 7.
GPS: n53,93660 e14,18660. ⬆️➡️.

30 🚐 € 15 🚰 ♻️Ch ⚡ WC🚽€2 🚿€4. **Surface:** grassy.
⬛ 01/01-31/12
Distance: 🚶on the spot ⊘5 min ⊗200m 🔌200m.

Ahlbeck 7G1

Parkplatz an der Grenze, Swinemüdestrasse.
GPS: n53,92380 e14,21280. ⬆️.

30 🚐 € 5. **Surface:** metalled. ⬛ 01/01-31/12
Distance: 🚶3km.
Remarks: Max. 24h.

Ahrenshoop 5F3

Dorfstraße. GPS: n54,39155 e12,43914. ⬆️.

10 🚐 € 6/day, € 25/night. 🏠 **Location:** Rural, simple, isolated, noisy.
Surface: gravel. ⬛ 01/01-31/12
Distance: 🚶2km ⊿beach 50m.

Alt Schwerin 7E2

Insel Camping Werder, Wendorf 8. **GPS:** n53,48696 e12,31833. ➡️.

13 🚐 € 9,80 🚰 ♻️Ch ⚡2 🚿€3/3. **Surface:** grassy.
⬛ 01/01-31/12
Distance: 🚶4km ⊿on the spot 🔌on the spot 🔌on the spot.

Altwarp 7G1

Hafen, Seestrasse. **GPS:** n53,73905 e14,27147. ⬆️.

40 🚐 € 11 🚰 ♻️Ch ⚡ WC🚽included 🚿. ⬛ 01/01-31/12
Distance: 🚶on the spot ⊿300m 🔌on the spot ⊗300m 🔌400m.

Anklam 7G1

Wasserwanderrastplatz, Demminer strasse.
GPS: n53,85610 e13,67870. ⬆️.

5 🚐 € 9,50, dog € 1 🚰 ♻️Ch ⚡€0,40/kWh WC🚽€0,50.
Surface: metalled. ⬛ 01/01-31/12
Distance: 🚶500m ⊗on the spot.

Bansin 5H3

Waldparkplatz Bansin. GPS: n53,99800 e14,11260. ➡️.

80 🚐 € 4-5 + € 2,50-3/pp, dog € 1,50 🚰 ♻️Ch ⚡€2,50 WC🚽€1.
Surface: metalled. ⬛ 01/05-30/09
Distance: 🚶3km ⊿400m ⊗300m 🔌on the spot.

Barth 5F3

Segelverein, Am Westhafen. **GPS:** n54,37130 e12,72510.

20 🚐 € 10 🚰 ♻️Ch ⚡€2 WC🚽€1. **Surface:** grassy.
⬛ 01/05-01/10
Distance: 🚶on the spot ⊿on the spot 🔌on the spot.
Remarks: Caution key sanitary € 20.

Barth 5F3

Wohnmobilparkplatz Barth, Am Osthafen.
GPS: n54,36965 e12,73251. ⬆️.

10 🚐 € 7 ⚡(8x)€0,50/kWh. 🏠 **Location:** Urban, simple, noisy.
Surface: metalled. ⬛ 01/01-31/12
Distance: 🚶300m ⊿300m 🔌300m 🚲on the spot 🚶on the spot.

Beckerwitz 7D1

Ostseecamping Beckerwitzer Strand, Ostseestrasse 10.
GPS: n53,94137 e11,31682. ⬆️➡️.

12 🚐 € 6-8 🚰€1 ♻️Ch ⚡€2,60/night WC🚽€0,50 🚿€3,50/3,50.
Location: Rural, comfortable. **Surface:** grassy. ⬛ 01/04-10/10
Distance: ⊿on the spot 🔌on the spot ⊗on the spot 🔌4km 🚲on
the spot 🚶on the spot.

Bergen/Rügen — 5G3

Wohnmobilstellplatz Rügen
Bergen auf Rügen

- Open all year
- Located in a quiet area
- Convenient for longer stays

www.wohnmobil-stellplatz-ruegen.de
info@wohnmobil-stellplatz-ruegen.de

Wohnmobilstellplatz Rügen, Tilzower Weg 32A.
GPS: n54,40757 e13,42949. ⬆️➡️.
16 € 12 €1/60liter Ch (16x)€2/day,25Amp WC included €2/6minutes €4/4 €2. **Surface**: metalled. 01/01-31/12
Distance: 1km 400m 500m 100m on the spot.
Remarks: Bread-service, car rental.

Binz — 5G3

Wohnmobil-Oase Rügen, Proraer Chaussee 60.
GPS: n54,44819 e13,56181. ⬆️➡️.

150 € 11, Jul/Aug € 14 €1 €1 Ch €1/kWh WC €0,50 €0,50 €4/4. **Location**: Luxurious, isolated, quiet. **Surface**: grassy/gravel. 01/04-31/10
Distance: Binz 5km 1,5km 700m on the spot.
Remarks: Bread-service.

Binz — 5G3

Parkplatz Zentrum, Proraer Chaussee 5.
GPS: n54,40278 e13,60194. 🏕.

60 € 14/24h, € 3/2h €1/50liter Ch included WC €1.
Surface: grassy/metalled. 01/01-31/12
Distance: on the spot 50m on the spot.
Remarks: Next to petrol station.

Boiensdorf — 7D1

Am Strand, Bungalowsiedlung. **GPS**: n54,02412 e11,54744. ⬆️➡️.

35 € 8/24h €0,20/10liter €2 Ch €2/day WC €0,50.
Location: Rural, comfortable, quiet. **Surface**: grassy. 01/01-31/12
Distance: on the spot on the spot 50m on the spot on the spot.

Boltenhagen — 7C1

Krämer's Wohnmobilhafen, Ostsee-allee 58b.
GPS: n53,98122 e11,21908. 🏕.

45 € 10-14, 2 pers.incl €0,20/20liter Ch €2,50/day WC €0,50. **Location**: Urban, comfortable, central, noisy.
Surface: grassy/gravel. 01/01-31/12
Distance: 800m 200m 200m 100m 700m on the spot on the spot on the spot.
Remarks: Bread-service in summer period, bicycle rental.

Boltenhagen — 7C1

Wohnmobilpark Boltenhagen, Ostsee-allee 58.
GPS: n53,98133 e11,21854. 🏕.

50 € 9-13 + € 2,10/pp tourist tax €2,50 Ch €2,50/day WC €1/time €5/time. **Location**: Urban, simple, noisy.
Surface: grassy. 01/01-31/12
Distance: 700m 200m 200m on the spot 700m on the spot on the spot.

Boltenhagen — 7C1

Swin Golf Boltenhagen, Ausbau 15, Redewisch.
GPS: n54,00851 e11,17180. 🏕.

10 € 13-15 €2/day. **Location**: Rural, comfortable, quiet. **Surface**: grassy. 01/04-31/10
Distance: on the spot on the spot on the spot.
Remarks: At golf court.

Boltenhagen — 7C1

Regenbogen Boltenhagen, Ostseeallee 54.
GPS: n53,98196 e11,21714. 🏕.

20 € 20 WC included €4/3 €1/h. **Location**: Urban, comfortable, central, noisy. **Surface**: grassy/metalled.
01/01-31/12
Distance: 600m 200m 200m on the spot 100m on the spot on the spot on the spot.
Remarks: Max. 1 night, check in at reception.

Brenz — 7D2

Landhaus Böttcher, Parchimer strasse 11.
GPS: n53,38688 e11,67103. 🏕.

5 € 10, guests free €1,50 (4x)€2/day WC included.
Location: Rural, simple. **Surface**: grassy/metalled.
01/01-31/12
Distance: on the spot 3km on the spot 5km 200m.

Broock — 7E2

Hotel-Restaurant Am Worns-Berg, Am Worns-Berg 1.
GPS: n53,46734 e12,10698. 🏕.

6 € 5, free with a meal Ch €2 WC €1,50. **Surface**: gravel.
01/01-31/12
Distance: 5km 1,5km 1,5km on the spot 5km 500m.

Carpin — 7F2

Landgasthof Am Schlersersee, Hauptstrasse 25.
GPS: n53,35424 e13,24028. 🏕.

10 € 5, guests free WC included. **Surface**: metalled.
01/01-31/12
Distance: 500m on the spot on the spot on the spot 4km.

Dabitz — 5F3

Hafen Dabitz, Boddenstraße. **GPS**: n54,36217 e12,80610. ⬆️➡️.

5 € 6/night. **Location**: Rural, simple, quiet. **Surface**: concrete.
01/01-31/12
Distance: 500m on the spot on the spot on the spot on the spot.

Dalwitz — 7E1

Ferien Gut Dalwitz, Dalwitz 46. **GPS**: n53,93484 e12,53830. 🏕.

2 € 10 €1 WC €3/3. **Surface**: grassy.
01/01-31/12
Distance: 15km on the spot on the spot.

DE

Remarks: Parking estate.

Dassow 🍴S 7C1

Reisemobilplatz Ostseestrand, Straße des Friedens 14, Rosenhagen.
GPS: n53,96195 e10,93944. ↑.

5 🎫 € 10 ⛽🗑Ch ✦€3 WC €3. 🚐 **Location:** Rural, comfortable, quiet. **Surface:** grassy. ◻ 01/01-31/12
Distance: 🏊500m ⊗on the spot.
Remarks: At Café Strandgut.

Dobbertin Ⓒ S 7E1

Campingplatz Am Dobbertiner See, Am Zeltplatz 1.
GPS: n53,61868 e12,06440. ↑.

10 🎫 € 10, 2 pers.incl ⛽🗑Ch ✦€0,50/kWh. **Surface:** grassy.
◻ 01/04-31/10
Distance: 🏊500m 🏊on the spot ►on the spot ⊗500m 🛒500m
🚆500m.

Dömitz 🚐S Ⓦ 7D3

Campingpark Marina Dömitz, An der Schleuse 1.
GPS: n53,14078 e11,25908. ↑.

26 🎫 € 10 ⛽🗑Ch ✦ WC 🗑 included. **Location:** Rural, comfortable, quiet. **Surface:** grassy. ◻ 01/01-31/12
Distance: 🏊400m 🏊20m ►20m ⊗100m 🛒800m.

Dömitz 🚢S Ⓦ 7D3

Dömitzer Hafen, Hafenplatz 3. **GPS**: n53,13724 e11,26034. ↑.

22 🎫 € 8 ⛽€1/50liter 🗑Ch ✦(10x)€2/day WC 🗑. **Location:** Rural, comfortable, quiet. **Surface:** grassy.
◻ 01/01-31/12
Distance: 🏊1km 🏊10m ►10m ⊗200m 🛒800m 🚆600m.

Dranske/Bakenberg Ⓒ S 5G3

Küstencamp, Nonnevitz 23. **GPS**: n54,66288 e13,26929. →.

---

18 🎫 € 15 ⛽🗑Ch ✦ WC 🗑 ⊡.
Distance: 🏊400m ►400m ⊗100m 🛒800m.
Remarks: Bread-service.

Eldena 🚐S 🌳🏕🚤 7D2

Bootshafen und Campingplatz Eldena, Am Bootshafen 1.
GPS: n53,23163 e11,42422.

12 🎫 € 10,50 ⛽🗑Ch ✦ WC included 🗑€1,10 ⊡€3,50/3,50.
Location: Rural, comfortable, quiet. **Surface:** grassy.
◻ 01/04-31/10
Distance: 🏊400m 🏊10m ►10m ⊗50m 🛒400m 🚲on the spot.

Feldberg 🚐 7F2

Weidendamm 1. GPS: n53,33583 e13,44176.

10 🎫 € 10. **Surface:** grassy/metalled. ◻ 01/01-31/12
Distance: 🏊on the spot 🛒150m 🚆400m.

Fresenbrügge 🚐S 7D2

Womo & Caravan Stelplatz Eldekrug, Eldeufer 1.
GPS: n53,26355 e11,54243. ↑.

20 🎫 € 10 ⛽€1/100liter 🗑Ch ✦€0,50/kWh WC included 🗑€1/pp.
🚐 **Location:** Rural, comfortable, isolated, quiet. **Surface:** grassy.
◻ 01/01-31/12
Distance: 🏊on the spot ►on the spot ⊗2km 🛒2km 🚲on the spot
🚶on the spot.

Graal-Müritz 🚐 🍴 5F3

Strandmitte, Buchenkampweg. **GPS**: n54,25663 e12,25005. ↑→.

20 🎫 € 15/24h, tourist tax € 2/pp ⛽€1/100liter 🗑. 🏠
Location: Rural, simple, quiet. **Surface:** grassy/metalled.
◻ 01/01-31/12
Distance: 🏊500m 🏊on the spot ►on the spot ⊗500m 🛒500m
🚲on the spot 🚶on the spot.
Remarks: Max. 3 days.

Grabow 🚢S 7D2

Stadthafen, Canalstrasse. **GPS**: n53,27738 e11,55949. ↑.

18 🎫 free ⛽€0,50/time 🗑Ch€0,50 ✦ WC€0,50 🗑€1. 🚐
Surface: metalled. ◻ 01/01-31/12, service: 8-9.30h and 18.30-20h
Distance: 🏊200m 🏊10m ►10m 🛒50m.

Greifswald 🚢S 5G3

Am Museumhafen, Marienstraße 10. **GPS**: n54,09887 e13,38945. ↑.

20 🎫 € 11 ⛽€2 🗑Ch€2 ✦€1 WC 🗑.
Surface: metalled.
◻ 01/04-30/11
Distance: 🏊8 min walking ⊗300m.

Tourist information Greifswald:
👁 Fischerdorf Greifswald-Wieck. Fishermen's village worth seeing.

Güstrow 🚐 7E1

Gleviner Platz. GPS: n53,79117 e12,18054. ↑.

3 🎫 free. **Surface:** asphalted. ◻ 01/01-31/12
Distance: 🏊400m 🏊5km ►5km ⊗100m 🛒100m.

Güstrow 🍴S 7E1

Hotel Am Tierpark, Verbindungschaussee 7.
GPS: n53,79159 e12,21577. ↑.
30 🎫 € 10, 2 pers.incl ⛽🗑Ch ✦€2,50 WC 🗑use sanitary €2,50/pp.
Surface: grassy. ◻ 01/01-31/12
Distance: 🏊5km ⊗on the spot 🛒5km.

Gützkow 🚐S 7F1

Rittergut Schloss Pentin, Zum Bollwerk 11.
GPS: n53,91824 e13,46763. →.

40+10 🎫 € 8 ⛽€0,50/80liter 🗑Ch ✦€0,50/kWh WC 🗑€1.
Surface: grassy/gravel. ◻ 01/01-31/12
Distance: 🏊1km 🚆400m.
Remarks: Bread-service.

Heringsdorf 🚐S Ⓦ 5H3

Blasendorff, Labahnstrasse 10. **GPS**: n53,95940 e14,15680. ↑.

3 🛏️ € 10 excl. tourist tax ⛽ €0,50/40liter 🚿 €1,50. 🚽 €1,80.
Surface: grassy. ☀️ 01/01-31/12
Distance: 🚶10min 🏖️300m ⊗300m 🚰300m.

🚐S Heringsdorf 🌿🏖️ 5H3
P An der Kirche, Rudolf-Breitscheid-Straße. **GPS:** n53,95762 e14,16219.
30 🛏️ € 10,50, 2,50 pers.incl. tourist tax € 2,50/pp ⛽ Ch🚿 €1,50
🚽€1. **Surface:** grassy/sand. ☀️ 01/01-31/12
Distance: 🚶on the spot 🏖️beach 500m ⊗250m.

🚐S Heringsdorf 🌿🏖️ 5H3
Pension Ariane, Bülowstrasse 13. **GPS:** n53,95240 e14,16600. ⬆️

6 🛏️ € 12 ⛽€1/40liter 🚿 Ch🚿€2 WC🚽€2. **Surface:** grassy.
☀️ 01/04-30/09
Distance: 🚶on the spot 🏖️300m ⊗on the spot 🚰on the spot.

🚐S Hinrichshagen 5G3
Reisemobilstellplatz Wöller, Chausseestraße 12.
GPS: n54,07450 e13,35230. ⬆️

50 🛏️ € 10 ⛽🚿Ch🚿included WC🚽use sanitary €5/day.
Surface: metalled. ☀️ 01/01-31/12
Distance: 🚶1km ⊗800m 🚰1km.

🚐S Hornstorf 7D1
Gartencenter Offermann, Dorfstraße 1. **GPS:** n53,89473 e11,54159. ⬆️

20 🛏️ € 10 ⛽🚿Ch🚿included. **Location:** Rural, simple, noisy.
Surface: concrete. ☀️ 01/01-31/12

🚐S Insel Poel 🏖️🚤 7D1
Strandparkplatz Timmendorf, Tau n Lüchttorm.
GPS: n53,99287 e11,38058. ⬆️

60 🛏️ € 5/day, € 4/night + € 2/pp tourist tax ⛽€0,50/80liter 🚿
Ch🚿(64x)€2/2kWh 🚽€1/time. 🚐 **Location:** Rural, simple, quiet.
Surface: grassy. ☀️ 01/01-31/12

Distance: 🚶150m 🏖️500m ⊗200m 🚰300m 🚲on the spot 🚶on the spot.
Remarks: Check in at kosk, caution key sanitary € 10.

🍴S Insel Poel 🏖️🚤 7D1
Poeler Forellenhof, Niendorf 13. **GPS:** n53,99454 e11,44714. ⬆️➡️

16 🛏️ € 13, 2 pers.incl ⛽€2/100liter 🚿🚿WC🚽included 🚽€2,60/
2,60. 🚐 **Location:** Rural, simple.
Surface: concrete. ☀️ 01/01-31/12 **Distance:** 🚶1,5km 🏖️on the spot
🚤on the spot ⊗on the spot 🚰1,5km 🚲on the spot 🚶on the spot.
Remarks: Check in at restaurant, steam bath and sauna, fish smoke-house.

⚓ Kamminke 7G1
Ortstraße. **GPS:** n53,86750 e14,20480. ⬆️

15 🛏️ € 8. **Surface:** grassy. ☀️ 01/01-31/12
Distance: 🚶on the spot ⊗on the spot.

🚐S Karenz 👫 7D2
Reiterhof am Steinberg, Grebserstrasse 1. **GPS:** n53,23638 e11,34836.

3 🛏️ € 10 ⛽€1 🚿 Ch🚿€1,50 WC🚽. **Location:** Rural, simple,
isolated. **Surface:** grassy. ☀️ 01/01-31/12
Distance: 🚶1km 🚤1km ⊗300m.
Remarks: Parking at manege.

🚐S Kargow 7F2
Reisemobilstellplatz Ziegenwiese, Schwarzenhof 7.
GPS: n53,46433 e12,79925. ⬆️

10 🛏️ € 7,50 ⛽€3 🚿 Ch🚿€3. **Surface:** grassy. ☀️ 01/01-31/12
Distance: 🏖️1km 🚤1km ⊗200m 🚰4km.

⚓ Karnin 7G1
Hafen, Karnin 14a. **GPS:** n53,84450 e13,85860. ⬆️

3 🛏️ € 10 ⛽€0,50/100liter 🚿 Ch€1 🚿€0,50/kWh WC🚽€1 🚽.

Surface: metalled. ☀️ 01/01-31/12
Distance: ⊗500m.

🚐S Kühlungsborn 🌿🏖️🍽️ 5F3
Hafenstrasse. **GPS:** n54,15051 e11,76329. ⬆️➡️

20 🛏️ € 8/24h. 🚐 **Location:** Urban, simple, noisy. **Surface:** concrete.
☀️ 01/01-31/12
Distance: 🏖️500m ⊗on the spot 🚲on the spot 🚶on the spot.

🍴S Langen Brütz 👫 7D1
Landhaus Bondzio, Hauptstrasse 21a. **GPS:** n53,65722 e11,55737. ⬆️

4 🛏️ € 12 🚿🚿WCincluded 🚽€2. 🚿 **Location:** Rural, simple.
Surface: asphalted/grassy. ☀️ 01/01-31/12 🍽️ Restaurant: Mo
Distance: 🚶150m ⊗on the spot 🚗50m.

⚓S Lenz über Malchow 7E2
Lenzer Hafen, Zum Hafen 1. **GPS:** n53,46793 e12,34929. ⬆️

25 🛏️ € 8,30- €12,40 ⛽🚿Ch🚿WC🚽€1,30 🚽€2.
Surface: grassy.
☀️ 01/03-31/10
Distance: 🚶6km 🏖️on the spot 🚤on the spot ⊗on the spot 🚰6km.
Remarks: Parking eastern bank Plauersee.

🚐S Lohme 🏖️🚤 5G3
Knöpfle Dorfladen, Arkonastrasse 4. **GPS:** n54,58300 e13,61150.

35 🛏️ € 12 ⛽€1/50liter 🚿 Ch🚿€1/8h WC🚽€0,50 🚽€2 🚽.
Surface: grassy/metalled. ☀️ 01/01-31/12
Distance: 🚶on the spot 🏖️200m ⊗on the spot 🚰on the spot
🚗on the spot.

🚐S Lohme 🏖️🚤 5G3
Zum Königsstuhl, Stubbenkammerstraße 57, Hagen.
GPS: n54,56220 e13,62590. ⬆️

40 🛏️ € 10,50 ⛽€2/100liter 🚿 Ch€2 🚿€2,50/24h WC🚽€1 📶.

Surface: metalled. ◻ 01/01-31/12
Distance: ⊗on the spot ⚑600m ⇌on the spot.

Ludwigslust 7D2
Am Schloss, Friedrich-Naumann-Allee. **GPS:** n53,32735 e11,49080. ➡

20◻free ⚑€1 ▣€1 Ch€1 ✦. **Location:** Rural, simple, quiet.
Surface: gravel/sand. ◻ 01/01-31/12
Distance: ⚓600m ⊗500m ⚑600m.

Lütow 5G3
Yachtlieger Achterwasser, Netzelkow. **GPS:** n54,02690 e13,90950. ➡

22◻€1/m + € 1/pp ⚑▣Ch✦(20x)€0,25/kWh WC▯€2.
Surface: grassy. ◻ 01/01-31/12
Distance: ⚓on the spot ⇢on the spot ⊗on the spot.
Remarks: Bread-service, bike/car rental.

Malchin 7E1
Malchiner Kanu-club, Am Kanal 2. **GPS:** n53,74417 e12,76611.

7◻€9 ▣ ✦WC▯€0,50 ▣€1/1. **Surface:** grassy.
◻ 01/01-31/12
Distance: ⚓500m ⚓on the spot ⇢on the spot ⊗500m ⚑500m.

Malchow 7E2
Marina Malchow, Ziegeleiweg 5. **GPS:** n53,46432 e12,42417. ⬆

20◻€ 10-20 excl. tourist tax ⚑▣Ch✦€2,50 WC▯€2,50 ✦.
Surface: grassy. ◻ 01/01-31/12
Distance: ⚓2km ⚓on the spot ⇢on the spot ⊗100m ⚑4km
⇌250m.
Remarks: Bread-service.

Malchow 7E2
Wohnmobilstellplatz Am Plauer See, Zum Plauer See 1.
GPS: n53,49192 e12,37268. ⬆

6◻€ 8-10, 2 pers.incl ⚑included ▣Ch€1,50 ✦(5x)€3,30 WC▯€1 ▯€

1/5minutes ▦ ✦. **Surface:** gravel. ◻ 01/01-31/12
Distance: ⚓4km ⚓on the spot ⇢on the spot ⊗on the spot ⚑on
the spot.

Mirow 7F2
Schloßstraße 1A. **GPS:** n53,27623 e12,81348.

8◻free ⚑€1 ▣€1 ✦(8x)€0,50 WC€0,50.
Surface: grasstiles/metalled. ◻ 01/01-31/12
Distance: ⚓400m ⊗200m ⚑400m.

Mistorf 7E1
Wohnmobilpark Mistorf, Dorfstraße 50.
GPS: n53,88152 e12,14325. ⬆
10◻€8 ⚑Ch ✦€2,50 WC▯€2,50.
Surface: grassy.
◻ 01/01-31/10
Remarks: Check in at Imbiss, bread-service, grill and picknic area.

Mönkebude 7G1
Stettinger Haff, Am Hafen. **GPS:** n53,77174 e13,96868. ⬆

25+15◻€ 8,50-10 + € 1/pp tourist tax, dog € 2 ⚑€0,50/100liter
▣Ch✦€2/24h WC▯€1 ▣€3,50/3 ✦1,50/h. **Surface:** grassy.
◻ 01/01-31/12
Distance: ⚓50m ⊗nearby ⚑50m.
Remarks: Peak season: sanitary installation, nov/apr service only on demand.

Mönkebude 7G1
Gastätte Kregelin's Bistro, Hauptstrasse.
GPS: n53,76663 e13,97614. ⬆

4◻guests free. **Surface:** metalled.

Muess 7D2
Feriendorf Muess, Alte Crivitzer Landstrasse 6.
GPS: n53,59995 e11,47940. ⬆

15◻€ 10, 01/03-30/09 € 20, dog € 1 ⚑▣
Ch✦WC▯included, winter fee no shower ▣€2/1,70. ✦
Location: Rural, comfortable. **Surface:** grassy. ◻ 01/01-31/12
Distance: ⚓100m ⊗100m ⚓100m ⇌100m ⚲ 100m Åon the spot.
Remarks: At open air museum, check in at reception, bicycle rental.

Neu Kaliss 7D2
Find's Hier, An der Elde 2. **GPS:** n53,17810 e11,29720. ⬆

13◻€8 ⚑€1 Chincluded ✦€2/night WC▯€1. ✦
Location: Rural, simple, isolated, quiet. **Surface:** grassy.
◻ 01/01-31/12
Distance: ⚓on the spot ⇢on the spot ⊗on the spot ⚑400m
⇌400m.

Neubrandenburg 7F1
Wassersportzentrum Tollensee, Augustastrasse 7.
GPS: n53,53861 e13,25665. ➡

30◻€ 10 ⚑€1 Ch✦€0,50/kWh WC▯€1 ✦€2/day.
Surface: grassy/metalled.
◻ 15/03-31/10
Distance: ⚓2km ⚓on the spot ⇢on the spot ⊗on the spot ⚑1km.
Remarks: Water sports centre.

Neuendorf 5F3
Wohnmobilstellplatz Saal Neuendorf, Am Hafen.
GPS: n54,33516 e12,52812. ⬆

36◻€ 10 ⚑✦included WC€0,20/time ▯€1/time ✦on demand. ✦
Location: Rural, simple, quiet. **Surface:** grassy.
◻ 01/04-31/10
Distance: ⚓100m ⚓on the spot ⇢on the spot ⊗Imbiss ⚑kiosk
⇌400m ⚲on the spot Åon the spot.

Neuenkirchen 5G3
Marktkauf, Dorfstrasse. **GPS:** n54,11810 e13,36390.

10◻free ⚑€1 Ch✦(5x)€1. **Surface:** metalled.
◻ 01/01-31/12
Distance: ⊗on the spot ⚑on the spot.

Neukloster 7D1
Wohnmobilpark Neuklostersee, Alte Gärtnerei 3.
GPS: n53,86121 e11,69536. ⬆

DE

69 ⬛€ 9,50 €1,50 Ch €1/2kWh WC €2 €4/2.
Location: Rural, comfortable, luxurious, quiet. **Surface:** gravel.
16/03-31/10
Distance: 500m on the spot 50m 500m 1,2km 500m
on the spot on the spot.

Neustrelitz 7F2

Parkplatz Am Stadthafen, Zierker Nebenstrasse 6.
GPS: n53,36568 e13,05551.

25 ⬛€ 8 €0,50/80liter €1 Ch €1 (25x)€0,50/kWh WC €0,20 €0,50 €2/2.
Location: Comfortable, quiet. **Surface:** metalled.
Distance: on the spot 100m, swimming 1km 200m 100m 200m 200m on the spot on the spot.
Remarks: Coins at harbourmaster (200m), historical centre.

Nossentin 7E2

Am Fleesensee, Am Park 33. **GPS:** n53,51866 e12,46766.

4 ⬛€ 8 WC included. **Surface:** grassy. 01/04-31/10
Distance: 5km 100m 100m on the spot 5km.

Ostseebad Sellin/Rügen 5G3

Reisemobilhafen Sellin, Kiefernweg 4b. **GPS:** n54,37170 e13,70165.

50 ⬛€ 12 + € 1,40-2,80/pp tourist tax €0,50/50liter Ch €1 (50x)€0,50/kWh WC €0,50 €2/day. **Surface:** grassy/metalled.
15/03-15/11
Distance: 300m 1km 1km 200m 300m 300m.

Ostseebad Sellin/Rügen 5G3

Hafen Seedorf, Seedorf 8. **GPS:** n54,35410 e13,65359.
5 ⬛€ 10 €1/100liter €0,50/kWh. 01/05-15/10
Distance: 250m, Sellin 5km 250m 250m.

Ostseebad Wustrow 5F3

Surfcenter Wustrow, An der Nebelstation 2.
GPS: n54,34080 e12,38040.

30 ⬛€ 16-29, dog € 2,50-5 Ch €2,50/day WC €0,50 €1/2minutes included. **Location:** Rural, simple, quiet.
Surface: asphalted. 01/04-31/10
Distance: 1km 50m on the spot on the spot on the spot.

Ostseebad Wustrow 5F3

Hafenstraße. **GPS:** n54,34363 e12,40053.

30 ⬛€ 4/day, € 10/night. **Location:** Rural, simple, quiet.
Surface: grassy/sand. 01/01-31/12
Distance: 400m 1,5km on the spot on the spot on the spot on the spot.
Remarks: Max. 1 night.

Parchim 7D2

Yachthafen, Am Fischerdamm. **GPS:** n53,42594 e11,84494.

8 ⬛€ 5 €0,50 Ch WC. **Surface:** asphalted.
01/01-31/12
Distance: 100m on the spot on the spot 100m 100m.

Pepelow 7D1

Wohnmobilpark Am Salzhaff, Seeweg 1.
GPS: n54,03805 e11,58441.

39 ⬛€ 8-12, 2 pers.incl Ch €3,30/night WC €2,50/pp €
3/3 included. **Location:** Rural, comfortable, luxurious, quiet.
Surface: grassy. 01/01-31/12
Distance: 700m on the spot on the spot on the spot on the spot on the spot on the spot.

Petersdorf 7E2

Hotel Haus Waldesruh, Lenzerstrasse 19.
GPS: n53,45892 e12,36060.

10 ⬛€ 7,50 €1 Ch €2 WC €1,50 €1,50/1,50.
Surface: grassy. 01/01-31/12
Distance: 7km 600m 600m on the spot 7km.

Priepert 7F2

Wohnmobilpark Am Großen Priepertsee, An der Freiheit 8.
GPS: n53,22043 e13,04201.

22 ⬛€ 7 Ch €2 WC €3/day €1 €5/5. **Surface:** grassy.
01/01-31/12
Distance: 70m 70m.

Putbus 5G3

Im-Jaich Wasserferienwelt, Am Yachthafen 1, Lauterbach.
GPS: n54,34278 e13,50167.

20 ⬛€ 13, peak season € 15 + € 1,20/pp tourist tax
WC included €1 €4/3. **Surface:** gravel.
01/01-31/12
Distance: 500m on the spot on the spot on the spot 800m.
Remarks: Bread kiosk, seaview.

Putgarten 5G3

Kap Arkona, Varnkevitzer Weg. **GPS:** n54,67190 e13,40800.

30 🚐 € 5, ^3,10m € 15. **Surface:** asphalted. ▢ 01/01-31/12
Distance: 🚰100m ⊗Imbiss 🛒6km.

Rerik 🌿⛲🍽🌊 **5E3**

Ostsee Wohnmobilpark Rerik, Straße am Zeltplatz 8.
GPS: n54,11332 e11,63037. ⬆➡.

35 🚐 € 13, Jul/Aug € 23 🔌Ch✂ WC🚽€0,30 🚿€3/3 📶included.
🅿 **Location:** Rural, comfortable, quiet. **Surface:** grassy.
▢ 01/01-31/12
Distance: 🏖sandy beach 500m 🛒on the spot ⊗on the spot 🛒on
the spot 🚲 on the spot 🚶on the spot.
Remarks: Check in at reception.

⚓ **Ribnitz-Damgarten** 🌿⛲🍽🌊 **5F3**

Gänsewiese, Am See 50. **GPS:** n54,24513 e12,42265. ⬆➡.

25 🚐free, night € 8 🚰€0,50/100liter 🔌Ch✂€0,50/12h WC.
🅿 **Location:** Rural, simple, quiet. **Surface:** grasstiles/grassy.
▢ 01/01-31/12
Distance: 🚰500m 🛒on the spot 🛒on the spot ⊗500m 🛒500m
🚲 on the spot 🚶on the spot.

⚓ **Ribnitz-Damgarten** 🌿⛲🍽🌊 **5F3**

Hafen Ribnitz, Am See 44. **GPS:** n54,24536 e12,42921. ⬆.

10 🚐free, night € 10 WC🚽€1/3minutes. 🅿 **Location:** Urban, simple,
quiet. **Surface:** concrete.
▢ 01/01-31/12
Distance: 🚰100m 🛒on the spot 🛒on the spot ⊗on the spot
🛒200m 🚲 on the spot 🚶on the spot.

⚓ S **Röbel** 🌊 **7E2**

Am Seglerhafen, Müritzpromenade 20. **GPS:** n53,38734 e12,61755.

45 🚐 € 12 🚰🔌Ch✂€1 WC🚽. **Surface:** grasstiles/metalled.
▢ 01/04-31/10

Distance: 🛒on the spot ⊗300m.

Rüterberg **7C3**

Wohnmobilparkplatz Dorfrepublik Rüterberg, Ringstraße 2.
GPS: n53,15294 e11,18511. ⬆.

10 🚐 € 5/24h+ € 0,50/pp 🚰€1/50liter 🔌€1 Ch🔌1 ✂€1/kWh
WC🚽€1. **Location:** Rural, simple, central, quiet. **Surface:** grassy.
▢ 01/01-31/12
Distance: 🚰10m ⊗50m.
Remarks: Bread-service.

Schwerin **7D1**

Am Hauptbahnhof, Wismarsche Straße. **GPS:** n53,63692 e11,40893. ⬆.

4 🚐 € 8/24h 🚰€1/80liter 🔌Ch✂(4x)€1/2kWh. 🚐
Location: Urban, simple, central, noisy. **Surface:** metalled.
▢ 01/01-31/12
Distance: 🚰on the spot ⊗on the spot 🛒on the spot 🛒on the spot.

Schwerin **7D1**

Am Stadthafen, Schliemannstraße. **GPS:** n53,62977 e11,41966. ⬆.

10 🚐 € 16/24h 🚰(8x)€0,50/kWh. 🅿 **Location:** Urban, simple,
central, noisy. **Surface:** metalled.
▢ 01/01-31/12
Distance: 🚰on the spot 🚲8km ⊗on the spot 🛒on the spot 🛒on
the spot 🚲 on the spot 🚶on the spot.
Remarks: No camping activities.

Schwerin **7D1**

Marina-Nord Schwerin, Buchenweg 19.
GPS: n53,64584 e11,43264. ⬆➡.

16 🚐 € 10 + € 1/pp 🚰🔌Ch✂(14x)€0,50/kWh WC🚽€1,50 📶€
1/24h. 🅿 **Location:** Rural, comfortable, quiet. **Surface:** grassy.
▢ 15/04-15/10
Distance: 🚰4km 🚲5km 🛒on the spot 🛒on the spot ⊗on the spot
🛒1km 🚲100m 🚲 on the spot 🚶on the spot.
Remarks: Check in at reception, bread-service.

Schwerin **7D1**

Sportbootzentrum Ziegelsee, Güstrower Straße 88.
GPS: n53,64823 e11,43004. ⬆.

10 🚐 € 12/24h 🚰€0,50/70liter 🔌Ch✂€1/24h WC🚽€1/6minutes
🔌€5/5. 🅿 **Location:** Rural, comfortable, quiet. **Surface:** concrete.
▢ 01/04-30/10
Distance: 🚰2km 🚲8km 🛒on the spot 🛒on the spot ⊗2km
🛒300m 🛒on the spot 🚲 on the spot 🚶on the spot.

Seehof 🍽🌊 **7D1**

Campingplatz Seehof, Am Zeltplatz 1. **GPS:** n53,69676 e11,43658. ⬆.

10 🚐 € 15-24, 2 pers.incl 🚰🔌Ch✂WC included 🚽€1/time
🔌€3,50/3,50. 🅿 **Location:** Rural, comfortable. **Surface:** grassy.
▢ 01/01-31/10
Distance: 🚰1,2km 🛒on the spot 🛒on the spot ⊗on the spot
🛒on the spot 🚲 on the spot 🚶on the spot.
Remarks: Bike/boat rental.

Sembzin **7E2**

An der Müritz, Dorfstrasse 2. **GPS:** n53,46445 e12,60386.

14 🚐 € 8 🚰🔌Ch✂included WC🚽€1 🚽€2 📶€2/24h.
Surface: grassy/gravel. ▢ 01/01-31/12
Distance: 🚰5km ⊗on the spot.
Remarks: Swimming pool.

Sievershagen **5F3**

Ferienhof Dubberke, Alt Sievershagen 16.
GPS: n54,11480 e12,03481. ⬆.

7 🚐 € 10 🚰🔌Ch✂WC included 🚽€1. 🅿 **Location:** Rural,
comfortable, quiet. **Surface:** grassy. ▢ 01/01-31/10
Distance: 🚰500m, Rostock 5km 🚲2km ⊗800m 🛒800m 🚲 on the
spot 🚶on the spot.

Sommersdorf **7F1**

Wohnmobilpark Sommersdorf, Am Kummerower See.
GPS: n53,79824 e12,87576.

23 🛏 € 8-12, 2 pers.incl ⚡€3 🍴Ch ⚡€3/night WC€2 🚿€1/5minutes 📶. **Surface:** grassy. ⭕ 01/01-31/12
Distance: 🏊on the spot 🛒on the spot 🍽on the spot.

Sternberg · 7D1

Sternberger, Maikamp 11. **GPS:** n53,71318 e11,81236. ⬆➡.

15 🛏 € 14-18 ⚡🍴Ch ⚡€2,70/day WC included 📶.
Surface: grasstiles. ⭕ 01/04-31/10
Distance: 🚶1km 🏊on the spot 🛒on the spot ✗on the spot 🍽500m 🚌500m.

Stralsund · 5G3

An der Rügenbrücke, Werftstrasse 16.
GPS: n54,30190 e13,10110. ⬆➡.

40 🛏 € 15, 2 pers.incl ⚡€1/5minutes 🚿€1 Ch€1 💡(40x)€0,50/kWh 🚽€1 📷. **Surface:** grassy/gravel. ⭕ 01/01-31/12
Distance: 🚶1,5km 🚌on the spot.
Remarks: Bread-service.

Ueckermünde · 7G1

An der Uecker, Ueckerstrasse 125. **GPS:** n53,73470 e14,04930. ⬆.

13 🛏 € 8 + € 1/pp tourist tax ⚡🍴Ch ⚡included.
Surface: grassy/metalled. ⭕ 01/01-31/12
Distance: 🚶Old city centre 200m ✗200m 🍽100m.

Usedom · 7G1

Am Hafen Usedom, Peenestraße. **GPS:** n53,87099 e13,92679. ⬆.

20 🛏 € 5 ⚡🍴Ch ⚡€5 WC€0,50 🚽€2. **Surface:** metalled.
⭕ 01/01-31/12
Distance: 🚶600m 🏊on the spot ✗on the spot.
Remarks: At former fishing-port.

Usedom · 7G1

Gaststätte Haffschänke, Dorfstraße 19, Karnin.
GPS: n53,84348 e13,86537. ⬆.

---

20 🛏 € 7 ⚡🍴Ch ⚡€3 WC€2,50. **Surface:** grassy.
⭕ 01/01-31/12
Distance: 🏊on the spot 🛒on the spot ✗on the spot.

Vielank · 7C2

Vielanker Brauhaus, Lindenplatz 1. **GPS:** n53,23443 e11,14023. ⬆.

12 🛏free ⚡€3 WC. **Location:** Rural, simple, quiet. **Surface:** grassy.
⭕ 01/01-31/12
Distance: 🚶20m ✗20m.
Remarks: Check in at reception.

Waren · 7E2

Blumen und Parken, Mecklenburgerstrasse.
GPS: n53,51363 e12,69431. ⬆.

40 🛏 € 9 + € 1-1,50/pp tourist tax ⚡🍴Ch ⚡€0,50/kWh WC included 🚿€1/5minutes. **Surface:** grassy/gravel. ⭕ 01/01-31/12
Distance: 🚶100m 🏊1km 🛒1km ✗1km 🍽1km 🚌on the spot.

Waren · 7E2

Wohnmobilpark Kamerun, Zur stillen Bucht 3, Müritz.
GPS: n53,51175 e12,65174. ⬆.

49 🛏 € 8-14, tourist tax excl ⚡🍴Ch ⚡€3,25 WC sanitary €2/pp 📷📶. **Surface:** grassy. ⭕ 01/01-31/12
Distance: 🚶3km 🏊on the spot 🛒on the spot ✗on the spot 🍽on the spot 🚌500m.

Waren · 7E2

Wohnmobilpark Müritz, Teterower Straße 35, Waren-Müritz.
GPS: n53,52611 e12,67194. ⬆➡.

22 🛏 € 8/24h, tourist tax € 1,50/pp ⚡🍴Ch ⚡€0,40/kWh WC 🚽€1,50. **Surface:** grasstiles/grassy. ⭕ 01/01-31/12
Distance: 🚶4km 🏊4km 🛒4km ✗4km 🍽Edeka 10m.

Waren · 7E2

Parkplatz Am Hafen, Strandstrasse 3b. **GPS:** n53,51194 e12,68583. ⬆.

20 🛏 € 10 ⚡🍴Ch ⚡📶. **Surface:** metalled.
⭕ 01/01-31/12, holidays 16.30-11h
Distance: 🚶on the spot 🏊on the spot 🛒on the spot ✗on the spot 🍽on the spot.

Waren · 7E2

Campingplatz Ecktannen, Fontanestraße 66.
GPS: n53,49944 e12,66361. ⬆➡.

16 🛏 € 16 ⚡🍴Ch ⚡WC included 📷€2,60/2,60 📶.
Surface: grasstiles/metalled.
⭕ 01/01-31/12
Distance: 🚶3,5km 🏊500m 🍽500m ✗Bistro 🍽3km 🚌on the spot.

Warnemünde · 5F3

Am Bahnhof. GPS: n54,17762 e12,09002. ⬆.

100 🛏 € 6/3h, € 12/12h, € 16/24h ⚡€0,50/100liter. 🚐
Location: Urban, simple, central, noisy. **Surface:** grassy/metalled.
⭕ 01/01-31/12
Distance: 🚶on the spot 🏊on the spot 🛒on the spot ✗on the spot 🍽on the spot 🚴on the spot 🚶on the spot.

Warnemünde · 5F3

Parkplatz Strand-Mitte, Parkstrasse 46. **GPS:** n54,17643 e12,05765. ⬆.

100 🛏 € 10/24h. 🚐 **Location:** Urban, simple, noisy.
Surface: metalled. ⭕ 01/01-31/12
Distance: 🚶2,5km 🏊100m ✗400m 🍽2km 🚌on the spot 🚴on the spot 🚶on the spot.

Wesenberg · 7F2

Wohnmobilstellplatz Wesenberg, Ahrensberger weg 11.
GPS: n53,27666 e12,98694. ⬆.

DE

34 € 14, 2 pers.incl € 1/80liter € 1 Ch € 1 WC included.
Surface: grassy/gravel. 01/01-31/12
Distance: 1km on the spot on the spot on the spot 2,5km 1km.

S Wismar 7D1

Wohnmobilpark Westhafen Wismar, Schiffbauerdamm 12.
GPS: n53,89430 e11,45151.

65 € 7/12h, € 10/24h € 1/100liter Ch € 1/8h WC € 1.
Location: Urban, simple, central, noisy. **Surface:** asphalted/gravel.
01/01-31/12
Distance: 800m 500m 300m, Burger King 400m 300m 800m 100m.
Remarks: Caution key sanitary € 10.

S Wittenbeck 5F3

Sanddornstrand, Bäderweg. **GPS:** n54,14513 e11,79277.

120 € 12-14 Ch (30x)€2/night WC € 0,50/time included.
Location: Rural, simple, quiet. **Surface:** grassy/metalled.
01/01-31/12
Distance: 1,5km on the spot on the spot on the spot on the spot.
Remarks: Bread-service.

S Zingst 5F3

Strandübergang 6, Straminke. **GPS:** n54,44070 e12,70750.

40 € 10/15 + € 2/pp tourist tax € 1/100liter € 3 WC included € 1. **Location:** Rural, simple, quiet. **Surface:** grassy.
01/01-31/12
Distance: 500m on the spot 500m 500m 1km 1km on the spot on the spot.

S Zingst 5F3

Wohnmobilhafen Am Freesenbruch, Am Bahndamm 1.
GPS: n54,44060 e12,66058.

40 € 12 + € 9/pp, dog € 4 Ch € 2,30/day WC included € 3/3. **Location:** Rural, comfortable, noisy. **Surface:** grassy.
01/01-31/12
Distance: 1,5km 50m on the spot on the spot on the spot on the spot.
Remarks: Bread-service.

S Zurow 7D1

Urlaub am Schloss, Kastanienallee 56, Krassow.
GPS: n53,87379 e11,56618.

10 € 5 € 1 Ch € 2/day WC € 2. **Location:** Rural, simple, quiet. **Surface:** grassy/metalled. 01/01-31/12
Distance: 1,5km 1km 3km 100m on the spot on the spot.
Remarks: Caution key sanitary € 10.

Saxony Anhalt

S Ahlum 7C3

Fischreihütte Ahlumer See, Am Mühlenberg 63.
GPS: n52,69541 e11,00583.

100 € 8 Ch € 0,50/kWh WC included. 01/01-31/12
Distance: on the spot on the spot.
Remarks: Bread-service.

S Allrode 9C3

Hotel Harzer Land, Teichstraße 28. **GPS:** n51,67774 e10,96478.

25 € 15,50 Ch WC included. **Surface:** grassy.
01/01-31/12
Distance: on the spot on the spot.

Altenbrak 9C2

Bodewiese, Am Bielstein. **GPS:** n51,72569 e10,94196.

8 € 5, overnight stay free. **Location:** Rural, simple.
Surface: metalled. 01/01-31/12
Distance: 100m on the spot 100m 200m on the spot.

S Altenbrak 9C2

Hotel Zur Talsperre, Oberbecken 1, Wendefurth.
GPS: n51,73434 e10,90690.

20 € 10 excl. tourist tax (20x)€0,50/kWh WC included.
Location: Rural, simple, isolated. **Surface:** asphalted/grassy.
01/01-31/12
Distance: on the spot.

S Arendsee 7D3

Im kleinen Elsebusch, Lüchower strasse 6a.
GPS: n52,87656 e11,46121.

20 € 10 € 1 € 1 Ch. **Surface:** grassy. 01/01-31/12
Distance: 2,5km on the spot 2,5km.

S Aschersleben 9D2

Sport- und Freizeitzentrum Ballhaus, Seegraben.
GPS: n51,76101 e11,45760.

8 free € 1/15minutes € 2/time Ch € 2/time (12x)€ 1/6h.
Location: Urban, comfortable, central, quiet. **Surface:** asphalted.
01/01-31/12
Distance: 1km 200m 200m on the spot on the spot on the spot.
Remarks: Caution key € 15, key at reception desk BallHaus.

Bad Bibra 11D1

Parkplatz am Schwimmbad. **GPS:** n51,21214 e11,60002.

20 € 3. **Location:** Rural, simple, isolated, quiet.
Surface: gravel/metalled. 01/01-31/12
Distance: 1,5km 200m 1,5km.
Remarks: At swimming pool.

Bad Bibra 11D1

Parkplatz Bürgergarten, Haus des Gastes.
GPS: n51,20526 e11,57929.

10 € 3. **Location:** Urban, simple, central, quiet.
Surface: gravel/metalled. 01/01-31/12
Distance: 200m 500m.

S Bad Kösen 11E1

Am Saalebogen, Stendorf 14. **GPS:** n51,11356 e11,69609.

DE

15 ⬛🅂€ 8 🔌🚰(15x)€2/day WCincluded 🚽€1/time. 🛁
Location: Rural, comfortable, quiet. **Surface:** grasstiles/metalled.
🗓 01/01-31/12
Distance: 🛒3km ⊗200m 🥖bakery 200m 🚌on the spot 🚲on the spot.

🍴🅂 Bad Suderode ❀🐚 9D2
Restaurant Am Kurpark, Jägerstrasse 7. **GPS:** n51,72685 e11,12078.⬆

4 ⬛🅂€ 10, € 13 service incl 🔌🚰Ch🚰€5/day. 🛁 **Location:** Urban,
comfortable, central, quiet. **Surface:** grasstiles/grassy.
🗓 01/01-31/12
Distance: 🛒100m ⊗on the spot 🚰200m 🚌200m 🚲on the spot
🚶on the spot.

🅂 Ballenstedt ❀ 9D2
Verkehrslandeplatz Ballenstedt/Quedlinburg, Asmusstedt 13.
GPS: n51,74190 e11,23427.⬆

32 ⬛🅂€ 4,50/pppn 🔌🚰Ch🚰(16x)WC🚽included. 🛁
Location: Rural, simple, quiet. **Surface:** grasstiles/metalled.
🗓 01/01-31/12
Distance: 🛒2km ⊗on the spot 🚰2km 🚌200m.

🅂 Bergwitz 🏖 9F2
Camping Bergwitzsee, Strandweg. **GPS:** n51,79439 e12,57773.⬆

20 ⬛🅂€ 6 🔌€3 Ch. 🛁 **Location:** Rural, simple, isolated, quiet.
Surface: grassy/sand. 🗓 01/01-31/12
Distance: 🛒1km 🚰50m 🚌50m ⊗300m 🚰1,5km.
Remarks: Check in at reception campsite, service on campsite.

🍴 Berssel 9C2
Gasthof Zum Schloß, Am Schloß 1. **GPS:** n51,95266 e10,76027.⬆

5 ⬛free 🔌on demand. **Location:** Rural, simple, quiet.
Surface: metalled. 🗓 01/01-31/12

Distance: 🛒200m ⊗on the spot 🚲on the spot 🚶on the spot.

🅂 Bertingen 9D1
Hotel La Porte, Im Wald 2. **GPS:** n52,35994 e11,82264.⬆➡

30 ⬛🅂€ 7,50 🔌🚰Ch🚰included. **Surface:** grassy. 🗓 01/01-31/12
Distance: ⊗on the spot 🚰5km.
Remarks: Bread-service.

🅂 Bitterfeld 9E2
Spaßbad Woliday, Reudener Straße, Bitterfeld-Wolfen.
GPS: n51,67102 e12,24842.⬆.

10 ⬛🅂€ 13 🔌🚰WC🚽included. 🛁 **Surface:** grasstiles.
🗓 01/01-31/12
Distance: 🛒1,2km ⊗on the spot 🚰900m.
Remarks: Incl. access swimming pool.

🅂 Blankenburg ❀ 9C2
Am Schnappelberg, Schnappelberg 2. **GPS:** n51,78862 e10,96036.⬆

4 ⬛🅂€ 6 🚽€1/time 🚰€2/night WC. 🛁 **Location:** Urban, simple,
central, quiet. **Surface:** asphalted.
🗓 01/01-31/12
Distance: 🛒500m ⊗300m 🚰on the spot.

🅂 Blankenburg ❀ 9C2
Busparkplatz, Am Schnappelberg. **GPS:** n51,78884 e10,96076.⬆

6 ⬛🅂€ 4/24h 🔌(6x)€1/kWh. 🏧 **Location:** Urban, simple, quiet.
Surface: metalled. 🗓 01/01-31/12
Distance: 🛒400m ⊗300m 🚰200m 🚌on the spot 🚶on the spot.

🅂 Blankenburg ❀ 9C2
Teichwirtschaft, Harzstraße 31a, Timmerode.
GPS: n51,76874 e10,99134.⬆

10 ⬛🅂€ 9 🔌€1 🚰Ch🚰€1 🚽€1. 🛁 **Location:** Rural, simple, quiet.
Surface: grassy/metalled. 🗓 01/01-31/12

Distance: 🛒Blankenburg 5km 🚰on the spot ⊗on the spot.
Remarks: Fishpond.

⚓🅂 Brachwitz 🏖 9E3
Marina Saale-Ufer, An der Fähre. **GPS:** n51,53270 e11,87059.⬆➡

30 ⬛🅂€ 5 🚰(4x)€0,50/kWh WC. 🛁 **Location:** Rural, comfortable,
quiet. **Surface:** grassy. 🗓 01/01-31/12
Distance: 🛒500m 🚰on the spot ⊗500m.

🍴🅂 Braunsbedra 9E3
Mobilpark am Geiseltalsee, Schortauer Weg.
GPS: n51,29421 e11,85346.⬆

25 ⬛🅂€ 10 🔌🚰Ch🚰WCincluded 🚽€2/time 🔌against payment.
🛁 **Location:** Urban, comfortable, quiet. **Surface:** grassy/metalled.
🗓 01/01-31/12
Distance: ⛱700m 🚰500m.

🅂 Breitenstein ⛪ 9C3
Hauptstrasse, L236. **GPS:** n51,61756 e10,94957.⬆

8 ⬛free 🔌stay 🚰(4x)€1/8h. **Location:** Rural, simple, quiet.
Surface: gravel. 🗓 01/01-31/12
Distance: 🛒400m ⊗Sportgaststätte.

⚓🅂 Burg bei Magdeburg ❀ 9E1
Wassersportfreunde Burg, Am Kanal 20a.
GPS: n52,28329 e11,84808.⬆

6 ⬛🅂€ 18 🔌€1/100liter 🚰WC🚽included. **Surface:** grassy.
🗓 01/05-30/09
Distance: 🛒1km 🚰on the spot.

🍴🅂 Burg bei Magdeburg ❀ 9E1
Eschenhof, Parchauer Chaussee 5. **GPS:** n52,28718 e11,86583.⬆➡

15 ⬛🅂€ 12 2 pers.incl, dog € 1 🔌🚰Ch🚰WC🚽included.
Surface: grassy. 🗓 01/01-31/12

Distance: 🚶2km ⊗on the spot 🚉1km.

| 🏕️S | **Coswig/Anhalt** | 9E2 |

Marina Coswig, Post Elbstrasse 22. **GPS:** n51,88071 e12,43552. ⬆️➡️.

40 🚐€ 7,50 2 pers.incl. dog € 1 🔌€1/100liter 🅲Ch🚰€0,50/kWh WC🚿€1,50/time. **Location:** Comfortable, quiet. **Surface:** gravel.
📅 01/01-31/12
Distance: 🚶750m 🏊on the spot ⊗on the-spot 🚉150m 🚌on the spot.

| 🏕️S | **Coswig/Anhalt** | 9E2 |

Hotel Zur Fichtenbreite, Fichtenbreite 5.
GPS: n51,88723 e12,40749. ⬆️➡️.

15 🚐€ 5 🔌🅲Ch included 🚰(4x)€2,50/day 🚿€3,50/time 🧺♻️. **Location:** Rural, simple, noisy. **Surface:** grassy.
📅 01/01-31/12
Distance: 🚶2km 🚲500m ⊗on the spot 🚉2km.
Remarks: Bread-service, bicycle rental.

| 🏕️S | **Dankerode** 🌳 | 9D3 |

Campingplatz Panoramablick, Hinterdorf 79.
GPS: n51,58832 e11,14189. ⬆️➡️.

12 🚐€ 10 excl. tourist tax 🔌€1 🅲€1 Ch€1 🚰(6x)€2,50 WC♻️🛰️.
📅 **Location:** Rural, simple, isolated, quiet. **Surface:** grassy.
📅 01/04-30/10
Distance: 🚶500m ⊗on the spot 🚉500m 🚴on the spot 🧍on the spot.

| 🏕️S | **Darlingerode** ⚓ | 9C2 |

Wohnmobilpark Harzblick, Hinter den Gärten 11.
GPS: n51,85278 e10,73667. ⬆️➡️.

25 🚐€ 8 🔌€1/80liter 🅲Ch🚰(12x)€0,60/kWh 🛰️€1/day.♻️
Location: Rural, comfortable, quiet. **Surface:** grassy/gravel.
📅 01/01-31/12
Distance: 🚶600m ⊗500m 🚉500m 🚌500m 🚴on the spot 🧍on the spot.

| 🏕️S | **Dessau-Roßlau** | 9E2 |

Flugplatz Hugo Junkers, Alte Landesbahn 27.
GPS: n51,83447 e12,18289. ⬆️.

8 🚐€ 9 🔌🅲Ch🚰WC included. ♻️ **Location:** Rural, comfortable, isolated, quiet. **Surface:** grassy/metalled.
📅 01/01-31/12
Distance: 🚶5km.
Remarks: Arrival < 19h, max. 8M.

| 🏕️S | **Drübeck/Harz** 🌳 | 9C2 |

Zur Waldschänke, Tänntalstraße 6. **GPS:** n51,84564 e10,71415. ⬆️.

8 🚐first day € 10, then € 5 🔌🅲Ch🚰included. ♻️ **Location:** Rural, simple, quiet. **Surface:** grassy/gravel. 📅 01/01-31/12 🍽️ Restaurant: Mo-Tue
Distance: 🚶1,5km ⊗on the spot.

| 🏕️S | **Elend** 🏔️🌳❄️ | 9C2 |

Waldbad Schenke, Am Waldbad 1. **GPS:** n51,74612 e10,69531. ⬆️.

10 🚐€ 5 + € 1,50/pp tourist tax 🚰(5x). ♻️ **Location:** Rural, simple, quiet. **Surface:** grassy/metalled.
📅 01/01-31/12
Distance: 🚶600m ⊗on the spot 🚉500m 🚴on the spot 🧍on the spot.

| 🏕️S | **Freyburg/Unstrut** 🏔️🍇 | 9E3 |

Stellplatz Schleusenblick, Wasserstraße 22.
GPS: n51,21049 e11,76979. ⬆️.

8 🚐€ 10 + € 1/pp tourist tax 🔌🅲Ch🚰WC included 🚿€2/day.♻️
Location: Urban, comfortable, central, quiet. **Surface:** metalled.
📅 01/01-31/12
Distance: 🚶100m ⊗50m 🚉300m.
Remarks: Along the Unstrut river.

| 🏕️S | **Gernrode** 🏔️🌳 | 9D2 |

Osterteich, Osterallee. **GPS:** n51,72449 e11,16007. ⬆️.

20 🚐free. **Location:** Rural, simple, isolated, quiet. **Surface:** metalled.

📅 01/01-31/12
Distance: 🚶1,5km ⊗300m 🚉1,5km 🧍on the spot.
Remarks: Next to train stop Selketalbahn.

| 🏕️S | **Haldensleben** | 9D1 |

Am Stendaler Turm, Bornsche Strasse. **GPS:** n52,29291 e11,41342. ⬆️.

10 🚐free. **Surface:** concrete. 📅 01/01-31/12
Distance: 🚶200m 🚉250m 🚉150m Aldi.

| ⚓S | **Haldensleben** | 9D1 |

Am Sportboothafen, Kronesruhe. **GPS:** n52,27933 e11,40240. ⬆️.

15 🚐€ 10 🔌🅲Ch included 🚰€0,50/kWh WC🚿€1. **Location:** Rural.
Surface: grassy. 📅 15/04-31/10
Distance: 🚶2km 🚲14km 🏊on the spot ⊗on the spot 🚉200m.
Remarks: Bread-service.

| 🏕️S | **Halle/Saale** 🌿 | 9E3 |

Parkplatz, Fährstraße. **GPS:** n51,50210 e11,95397. ⬆️.

3 🚐€ 5 🔌€1/80liter 🅲Ch🚰stay WC against payment. 🚌
Location: Urban, simple, central, noisy. **Surface:** metalled.
📅 01/01-31/12
Distance: 🚶2km 🚲7km ⊗200m 🚉500m 🚌on the spot.
Remarks: Max. 5 days, green zone: environmental badge obligatory.

| 🏕️S | **Halle/Saale** 🌿 | 9E3 |

P25, An der Stadtschleuse. **GPS:** n51,48065 e11,96183. ⬆️.

10 🚐free. **Location:** Urban, simple, central, noisy. **Surface:** metalled.
📅 01/01-31/12 **Distance:** 🚶Old city centre 500m 🚌on the spot.
Remarks: Along railwayline, green zone: environmental badge obligatory.

| 🏕️S | **Harzgerode** | 9D3 |

Parkplatz Wallgarten, Wallstrasse. **GPS:** n51,64210 e11,13983. ⬆️.

5 🚐free. **Location:** Urban, simple, quiet. **Surface:** metalled.

DE

🅿 01/01-31/12
Distance: 🚶100m ⛵1km 🚲3km ⊗100m 🍴100m 🚌100m
🏊1km.

Hasselfelde 🚿   9C3
P Pullman City/Westernstadt, Im Rosentale.
GPS: n51,70179 e10,86604. ⬆.

10 🛏free. **Location:** Rural, simple, quiet. **Surface:** gravel.
🅿 15/04-31/10

Havelberg   7E3
Campinginsel. GPS: n52,82830 e12,06853.

🛏€6 🚰€1 🛢€3 Ch ⚡(24x)€1/kWh. **Surface:** metalled.

Kelbra 🌊   9D3
Seecamping Südharz, L1040. **GPS:** n51,42583 e11,00287. ⬆.

15 🛏€ 10-12 🚰🛢Ch⚡ included 📶against payment.
Location: Rural. **Surface:** gravel. 🅿 01/01-31/12
Distance: 🚶2,5km 🍴on the spot ⊗on the spot 🛒on the spot.

P Lutherstadt Wittenberg 🌿🏛   9F2
Platz der Jugend. **GPS:** n51,86712 e12,63120. ⬆.

5 🛏free. **Location:** Urban, simple, noisy. **Surface:** metalled.
🅿 01/01-31/12
Distance: 🚶centre 500m ⊗150m 🛒150m.
Remarks: Max. 8h, overnight stay allowed.

Magdeburg   9D2
Stellplatz Petriförde, Petriförder 1. **GPS:** n52,13289 e11,64714.

50 🛏€8 🚰€1 🛢€1 Ch€1. **Surface:** metalled. 🅿 01/01-31/12
Distance: 🚶on the spot.
Remarks: Along the river Elbe.

Merseburg 🛫   9E3
Am Saaleufer, Brühl. **GPS:** n51,35491 e12,00234. ⬆➡.

3 🛏free. **Location:** Urban, simple. **Surface:** metalled.
🅿 01/01-31/12
Distance: 🚶500m.

Merseburg 🛫   9E3
Luftfahrt und Technik-museum Merseburg, Kastanienpromenade
50. **GPS:** n51,36004 e11,97044. ⬆.

6 🛏€ 3, guests free. 🚿 **Location:** Rural, simple, quiet.
Surface: gravel/metalled. 🅿 01/01-31/12
Distance: 🚶1km 🛒1,5km.

Naumburg/Saale   11E1
Altstadtparkplatz Vogelwiese, Luisenstraße.
GPS: n51,14861 e11,81391. ⬆.

15 🛏€ 5/night 🚰€0,50/80liter 🛢Ch⚡(6x)€0,50/kWh WC.
Surface: gravel. 🅿 01/01-31/12
Distance: 🚶500m ⊗50m 🛒500m 🚌50m.
Remarks: Max. 3 days.

Oranienbaum-Wörlitz   9E2
Jugendverkehrsschule Oranienbaum, Dessauer Strasse 47.
GPS: n51,80279 e12,39023. ⬆➡.

6 🛏€ 7,50 🚰🛢Ch⚡(6x)WC included 🍴€1/day. 🚿
Location: Rural, comfortable, quiet. **Surface:** gravel/metalled.
🅿 01/01-31/12
Distance: 🚶1km.

Oranienbaum-Wörlitz   9E2
Seespitze 25. **GPS:** n51,84729 e12,41301.
24 🛏€ 10 🚰(24x)€2. **Surface:** metalled. 🅿 01/01-31/12
Distance: 🚶600m 🚲7,5km 🍴on the spot ⊗600m.

Prettin   9F2
Bade- und Angelsee, Hinterfährstraße. **GPS:** n51,66485 e12,90551. ⬆.

5 🛏€ 6 + € 2,80/pp 🛢Ch included ⚡€0,30/kWh.
Surface: gravel. 🅿 01/04-31/10
Distance: 🚶1,2km.

Quedlinburg 🌿🏛   9D2
An den Fischteichen. GPS: n51,79308 e11,14863. ⬆➡.

20 🛏€ 10 + € 5/pp tourist tax 🚰€1/80liter 🛢⚡
(8x)€1/6h. **Location:** Urban, comfortable, central, quiet.
Surface: grasstiles/metalled. 🅿 01/01-31/12
Distance: 🚶350m ⊗300m 🛒250m 🚌150m.

Quedlinburg 🌿🏛   9D2
Marschlinger Hof. GPS: n51,79138 e11,13965. ⬆➡.

6 🛏€ 10/24h 🚰€1/80liter 🛢Ch⚡(4x)€1/6h WC. 🚽
Location: Urban, comfortable, central, quiet. **Surface:** metalled.
🅿 01/01-31/12
Distance: 🚶100m ⊗50m 🛒400m 🚌200m.
Remarks: Max. 7m.

Quedlinburg 🌿🏛   9D2
Schloßparkplatz, Schenkgasse. **GPS:** n51,78755 e11,13507. ⬆➡.

6 🛏€ 6/24h 🚰€1/80liter 🛢Ch⚡(4x)€1/6h. 🚽
Location: Urban, comfortable, quiet. **Surface:** metalled.
🅿 01/01-31/12
Distance: 🚶on the spot ⊗100m.

Quedlinburg 🌿🏛   9D2
Wohnmobilparkplatz Familie Jahnke, Feldmark links der Bode 17.
GPS: n51,80373 e11,17548. ⬆➡.

10 🛏€ 10 🚰⚡€2/day WC included 🍴. 🚿 **Location:** Rural, simple,
quiet. **Surface:** concrete. 🅿 01/01-31/12
Distance: 🚶2,5km.

DE

Salzwedel 7C3

Stellplatz der Hansestadt Salzwedel, Dämmchenweg 41. **GPS**: n52,85049 e11,13911.⬆.

6 €3 🚰🚽Ch✦€2 WC sanitary€2. **Surface**: metalled. 🗓 01/01-31/12
Distance: historical centre 1km ✗100m.

Sangerhausen 9D3

An der Walkmühle, Taubenberg. **GPS**: n51,49056 e11,31127.⬆.

50 free. **Surface**: sand. 🗓 01/01-31/12
Distance: 2km ✗on the spot.

Sangerhausen 9D3

P7, An der Probstmühle. **GPS**: n51,47707 e11,30798.⬆.

20 free. **Surface**: unpaved. 🗓 01/01-31/12
Distance: 500m ✗200m 🚐100m.

Sangerhausen 9D3

Rosarium, Sotterhäuser Weg. **GPS**: n51,47245 e11,31798.⬆.
🚰€2 🚽Ch. 🗓 15/04-15/10
Remarks: Check in at shop.

Schierke 9C2

Campingplatz Am Schierker Stern, Hagenstrasse. **GPS**: n51,75696 e10,68398.⬆.

6 € 10 excl. tourist tax 🚰🚽Ch included ✦(6x)against payment. 🏠 **Location**: Rural, simple, quiet. **Surface**: gravel/metalled. 🗓 01/01-31/12
Distance: 1km ✗on the spot 🖥on the spot 🚐on the spot 🏕on the spot 🛶on the spot.

Seehausen 7D3

Stellplatz Seehausen, Schulstrasse 6. **GPS**: n52,89068 e11,75119.⬆.

12 €5 🚰€2 🚽Ch✦(3x)€2. **Surface**: metalled.
Distance: 100m 🚐200m.
Remarks: Check in at tourist office.

Stassfurt 9D2

Neumarkt, Lehrter Straße. **GPS**: n51,85424 e11,58284.⬆.

6 free. **Location**: Urban, simple, central, quiet. **Surface**: gravel. 🗓 01/01-31/12
Distance: 500m 🚐100m.
Remarks: Along the Bode river.

Stendal 9D1

Nordwall-Schützenplatz. **GPS**: n52,61116 e11,86121.⬆.

20 free 🚰€1/80liter 🚽€1 Ch. **Surface**: grassy/metalled. 🗓 01/01-31/12
Distance: on the spot 🚐bakery 50m.

Stolberg/Harz 9C3

Am Bahnhof. **GPS**: n51,56727 e10,95696.⬆.

5 free. **Location**: Rural, simple, quiet. **Surface**: asphalted. 🗓 01/01-31/12
Distance: centre 800m.
Remarks: Max. 2 days.

Stolberg/Harz 9C3

Am Rittertor, Rittergasse. **GPS**: n51,57655 e10,94539.⬆.

5 free. **Location**: Rural, simple, quiet. **Surface**: asphalted. 🗓 01/01-31/12
Distance: 1km.
Remarks: Max. 2 days.

Stolberg/Harz 9C3

Freizeitbad Thyragrotte, Thyratal 5. **GPS**: n51,56378 e10,95796.⬆.

3 free. **Location**: Rural, simple. **Surface**: asphalted. 🗓 01/01-31/12
Distance: city centre 1km 🏕1km on the spot.

Tangermünde 9E1

Tangerplatz, Klosterberg. **GPS**: n52,53774 e11,96803.⬆➡.

30 €5 🚰🚽Ch✦ included. **Surface**: metalled. 🗓 01/01-31/12
Distance: 700m ✗150m.

Wahrenberg 7D3

Stellplatz Storchenwiese, Eichenwinkel 34. **GPS**: n52,98342 e11,67362.⬆.

8 €5 🚰€1/100liter 🚽Ch€2 ✦(6x)€3. **Surface**: grassy. 🗓 01/01-31/12

Weissenfels 9E3

Caravan- und Freizeitmarkt Gerth, Drei Wege. **GPS**: n51,19822 e11,99875.⬆.

7 free 🚰€1/80liter 🚽Ch✦(4x)€1/stay. **Location**: Urban, simple, noisy. **Surface**: asphalted. 🗓 01/01-31/12
Distance: 4km ✗on the spot 🚐on the spot.

Wernigerode 9C2

Am Katzenteich. **GPS**: n51,83882 e10,78168.⬆➡.

20 € 5/stay 🚰€1/40liter 🚽Ch✦(20x)€1/kWh WC€0,50/time. **Location**: Comfortable, quiet. **Surface**: metalled. 🗓 01/01-31/12
Distance: 500m ✗200m 🚐500m 🚐on the spot 🚲on the spot 🏕on the spot.

Wernigerode 9C2

Schlossparkplatz am Anger, Halberstädter strasse 1. **GPS**: n51,83807 e10,79535.⬆.

24 € 5, overnight stay free 🚰€2/time 🚽Ch WC€0,50/time.

DE

Location: Urban, simple, central, quiet. **Surface:** metalled.
01/01-31/12, service 9-18h
Distance: 300m 200m 600m on the spot on the spot.

| | | Wernigerode | 9C2 |

Harzpension Familie Mann, Mühlental 76, B244.
GPS: n51,81902 e10,81430.

6 € 10 excl. tourist tax €0,50/time Ch included €0,50/kWh WC €0,50/time. **Location:** Rural, simple, quiet. **Surface:** gravel.
01/04-10/11
Distance: 4km on the spot.
Remarks: Arrival <21h, check in at restaurant.

| | | Wörlitz | 9E2 |

Seeparke, Seespitze, K2376. **GPS:** n51,84899 e12,41296.

24 € 5 day/€ 5 night free (24x)€2 WC €0,50/time €0,50/time. **Location:** Rural, comfortable, quiet. **Surface:** metalled.
01/01-31/12
Distance: 800m 500m 800m 800m on the spot on the spot.
Remarks: Parking at the edge the Wörlitzer park, max. 24h, caution key sanitary € 15.

| | | Wörlitz | 9E2 |

Hotel Coswiger Elbterrasse, Elbterrasse 1.
GPS: n51,87750 e12,45097.

10 € 5, guests free. **Location:** Simple, quiet. **Surface:** grassy.
01/01-31/12
Distance: 1,5km on the spot 4km.
Remarks: Check in at hotel, guests free.

| | | Zeitz | 11E1 |

Obsthof Martin, Kloster Posa 1. **GPS:** n51,05836 e12,15797.

20 € 5 Ch (4x)€3/day. **Location:** Rural, comfortable, quiet. **Surface:** grassy. 01/01-31/12
Distance: 1,5km 200m 1km.

Brandenburg/Berlin

| | | Abbendorf | 7D3 |

Gasthaus Dörpkrog an Diek, Am Deich 7.
GPS: n52,89663 e11,90975.

6 € 5, guests free Ch WC included. 01/01-31/12
Remarks: Bread-service.

| | | Alt-Zeschdorf | 9H1 |

Reiterhof Blumrich, Falkenhagerweg 11.
GPS: n52,42649 e14,42328.

30 € 10 Ch included. **Surface:** grassy. 01/01-31/12
winter Mo
Distance: 1,5km.
Remarks: At manege, bread-service.

| | | Altdöbern | 9H2 |

Q1 Rasthof Altdöbern, Senftenberger strasse 11.
GPS: n51,64523 e14,03544.

20 € 10 WC included. **Surface:** metalled.
01/01-31/12
Distance: 500m on the spot 500m.

| | | Angermünde | 7G2 |

Parkplatz Am Oberwall, Oberwall 5. **GPS:** n53,01501 e14,00371.

5 free €1/100liter €1/2kWh. **Location:** Urban, simple, central.
Surface: metalled. 01/04-31/10
Distance: on the spot on the spot on the spot Historische Stadtkerne Märkischer Landweg.
Remarks: Near city wall.

| | | Angermünde | 7G2 |

NABU-Erlebniszentrum Blumberger Mühle, Blumberger Mühle 2.
GPS: n53,03572 e13,96806.

10 free. **Location:** Rural, simple, isolated, quiet.
Surface: grassy/metalled. 01/01-31/12
Distance: 4km near fish pond on the spot on the spot on the spot.

Remarks: At biosphere reserve.

| | | Bad Saarow | 9G1 |

Parkplatz Strolin, Silberbergerstrasse. **GPS:** n52,28726 e14,03895.

4 free. **Surface:** metalled. 01/01-31/12
Distance: 100m 100m.

| | | Bad Saarow | 9G1 |

Saarow-Therme, Ringstrasse. **GPS:** n52,29399 e14,06243.

6 free. **Surface:** metalled. 01/01-31/12
Distance: on the spot 300m 400m.

| | | Bad Wilsnack | 7E3 |

Kur- und Gradier-Therme Bad Wilsnack, Am Kähling.
GPS: n52,96316 e11,95007.

43 € 13,50 + € 1/pp tourist tax Ch (43x) WC included.
Surface: sand. 01/01-31/12
Distance: 500m 200m 500m.
Remarks: Check in at pay-desk of the Therme, bread-service.

| | | Berlin | 9F1 |

Historisches Fährhaus Berlin, Muggelbergallee 1, Berlin-Köpenick.
GPS: n52,41851 e13,58734.

15 01/03-01/11 € 18, 02/11-28/02 € 14 Ch (15x)€2/24h WC included €1/time €5/stay. **Location:** Urban, luxurious, quiet. **Surface:** grassy/gravel. 01/01-31/12
Distance: on the spot 8km on the spot on the spot on the spot 100m, supermarket 750m 1km tram 100m.
Remarks: Sauna € 5.

| | | Berlin | 9F1 |

WohnmobilPark Berlin, Waidmannsluster Damm 12-14.
GPS: n52,59559 e13,28910.

90 € 10-22, 2 pers.incl, tourist tax € 1/pp, dog € 2 €1/100liter

DE

Ch ♨€3,50/24h WC ⬛€1, ▣€4/4 ⬛. ⚙ **Location:** Urban, central.
Surface: grassy/metalled.
⬛ 01/01-31/12
Distance: ⬛centre Berlin 16km ⬛ 600m ⊗on the spot ⬛on the spot ⬛metro 1km.
Remarks: Key sanitary building € 4/day, hotline-Nr.: 0176 – 99 55 25 00.

⬛S Berlin ⬛⬛⬛⬛ 9F1
Reisemobilhafen Berlin Spandau, Askanierring 70.
GPS: n52,55309 e13,20050.⬆.

180 ⬛€ 15, 2 pers.incl, tourist tax € 1/pp ⬛€0,10/10liter ⬛Ch ♨
WCincluded ⬛€1/5minutes ⬛€2/24h. ⚙ **Location:** Urban, simple,
central, noisy. **Surface:** grassy/gravel.
⬛ 01/01-31/12
Distance: ⬛on the spot ⊗100m ⬛on the spot ⬛300m.
Remarks: Near approach route of airport, 23-5h quiet, check in at kosk,
outside environmental zone. In area of the former English barracks 'Alexander Barracks', A10 exit Berlin-Spandau, follow road till cross roads
Heerstraße/Gatowerstraße,here to the left, at Flakenseerplatz straight
on, Neuendorferstraße, before Hohenzollernring to the left.

⬛S Berlin ⬛⬛⬛⬛ 9F1
Int. Reisemobilstation Berlin-Mitte, Chausseestrase 82.
GPS: n52,53817 e13,37304.⬆.

50 ⬛€ 20-22, 2 pers.incl ⬛⬛Ch ♨WC⬛included.
⚙ **Location:** Urban, comfortable, central, noisy.
Surface: grassy/metalled. ⬛ 01/01-31/12
Distance: ⬛on the spot ⊗500m ⬛500m ⬛200m.
Remarks: Check in at reception.

⬛S Berlin ⬛⬛⬛⬛ 9F1
Köpenicker Hof, Stellingdamm 15, Berlin-Köpenick.
GPS: n52,45929 e13,58532.⬆➡.

40 ⬛€ 10-14, 2 pers.incl ⬛stay ⬛Ch ♨€0,50/kWh
WC⬛⬛included12h. ⚙ **Location:** Simple, quiet.
Surface: grassy/metalled. ⬛ 01/01-31/12
Distance: ⬛on the spot ⊗on the spot ⬛Tram (centre 300m).
Remarks: Caution key sanitary building € 20, bread-service.

⬛S Berlin ⬛⬛⬛⬛ 9F1
Marina Lanke Berlin, Scharfe Lanke 109-131.
GPS: n52,50344 e13,18801.⬆.

20 ⬛€ 1,50/m + € 3,50/pp, dog €2 ⬛⬛Ch ♨WC⬛included ▣€3/2

⬛. **Location:** Urban. **Surface:** asphalted.
⬛ 01/05-15/10
Distance: ⬛centre Berlin 16km ⬛on the spot ⊗on the spot ⬛1km.
Remarks: Check in at harbourmaster.

⬛S Berlin ⬛⬛⬛⬛ 9F1
Marina Wendenschloss, Wendenschlossstrasse 350-354.
GPS: n52,42558 e13,58384.⬆.

10 ⬛€ 15 ⬛⬛Ch ♨WCincluded ⬛€1/time. ⚙ **Location:** Simple,
quiet. **Surface:** grassy/metalled. ⬛ 01/04-31/10
Distance: ⬛18km city centre ⬛on the spot ⬛100m ⬛Tram 200m.
Remarks: Outside environmental zone.

Tourist information Berlin:
ℹ Tourist Info, Europacenter, Eingang Budapester strasse 3; Brandenburgertor, Südflügel; Fernsehturm, Alexanderplatz, www.btm.de.
Documentation available, via Internet.
◉Ⓜ Zeughaus. German historical museum.
◉ Alexanderplatz. The old historical centre of Berlin.
◉ Brandenburger Tor. Built in 1791 as a triumphal arch after the
construction of the Berlin Wall the arch remained as a symbol of the
German separation. Ⓣ free.
◉ Haus am Checkpoint Charly, Friedrichstrasse 44. At the former
border crossing. History of the Wall is told with photographs. ⬛ 9-22h.
✖ Schloß Charlottenburg, Luisenplatz. Summer residence of the
Prussian kings.
⬛ Tue-Fri 9-17h, Sa-Su 10-17h.
⛪ Arkonaplatz. Flea market.
⬛ Su 10-16h.
⛪ Ostbahnhof. Antiques and flea market.
⬛ Su 9-17h.
⛪ Strasse des 17. Juni. Arts and fleamarket.
⬛ Sa-Su 10-17h.
☺ Zoologischer Garten, Hardenbergplatz 8. City-zoo.
⬛ 01/04-30/09 9-18.30h, 01/10-31/10 9-18h, 01/11-28/02 9-17h.

⬛S Brandenburg ⬛⬛⬛⬛ 9E1
Am Brandenburger Dom, Grillendamm.
GPS: n52,41724 e12,56576.⬆.

60 ⬛€ 10 ⬛€1/100liter ⬛Ch ♨(26x)€1/kWh WC ⬛€
1/4minutes. ⬛ **Location:** Urban, simple, noisy. **Surface:** asphalted.
⬛ 01/01-31/12
Distance: ⬛Neustadt 15min, Altstadt 15min ⬛on the spot ⊗Imbiss
⬛on the spot ⬛on the spot ⬛on the spot.

⬛S Brandenburg ⬛⬛⬛⬛ 9E1
Wassersportzentrum Alte Feuerwache, Franz Zieglerstrasse 27.
GPS: n52,40485 e12,54868.⬆➡.

30 ⬛€ 12 ⬛⬛Ch ♨€1/day WC⬛€1/time ⬛included. ⚙
Location: Urban, simple, central, noisy. **Surface:** grassy/metalled.
⬛ 01/01-31/12
Distance: ⬛500m ⬛on the spot ⊗500m ⬛on the spot ⬛on the
spot ⬛on the spot.
Remarks: Bread-service, boat rental, bike and e-bike rental.

⬛S Brieske 9H3
Reimann, Brieske Dorf 27. **GPS:** n51,49203 e13,94743.➡.

20 ⬛€ 6 ⬛⬛Ch ♨(12x)€2 WCincluded. **Surface:** grassy.
⬛ 01/01-31/12
Distance: ⬛200m ⬛9,3km ⬛2km.

⬛S Burg/Spreewald 9H2
Hagens Insel - Wasserwanderrastplatz, Weidenweg 4.
GPS: n51,86138 e14,11527.

10 ⬛€ 10 ⬛⬛Ch ♨WC ⬛included. **Surface:** grassy.

⬛S Burg/Spreewald 9H2
Landgasthof zur Wildbahn, Wildbahnweg 20.
GPS: n51,85104 e14,09384.

9 ⬛€ 13, 2 pers.incl, tourist tax € 1,50/pp, dog € 2 ⬛⬛ ♨WCincluded. **Surface:** metalled. ⬛ 01/03-30/10

⬛S Dollenchen 9G2
Gasthaus Stuckatz, Hauptstrasse 29. **GPS:** n51,60745 e13,86226.➡.

20 ⬛€ 8 ⬛⬛Ch ♨WC ⬛included. **Surface:** grassy.
⬛ 01/01-31/12
Distance: ⬛on the spot ⊗on the spot ⬛3km.

⬛S Dreetz 7E3
Reiterhof Müller, Schulstrasse 61. **GPS:** n52,79796 e12,46874.⬆.

10 ⬛€ 12 ⬛⬛Ch ♨included WC. ⚙ **Location:** Rural, simple,
isolated, quiet. **Surface:** grassy. ⬛ 01/01-31/12
Distance: ⬛800m ⊗300m ⬛500m ⬛500m.

⬛S Fehrbellin 7F3
FF Freizeitmobile, Gewerbepark 29. **GPS:** n52,79770 e12,78624.⬆➡.

DE

10 🛏 € 7,50 🔌 Ch included. 🚿 € 2,50/day 📶 free.
Location: Urban, simple, quiet.
Surface: grassy.
📅 01/01-31/12
Distance: 🚉 1km 🚲 2km 🛒 1km 🛒 1km 🛒 on the spot 🚶 on the spot.
Remarks: Accessory shop.

⚓ S Fürstenberg/Havel 7F2
Marina Fürstenberg, Ravensbrücker Dorfstrasse 26.
GPS: n53,19489 e13,14895. ⬆➡.

50 🛏 € 9 🔌 Ch included. 🚿 € 2,50/day WC € 1,50/time 📶 free.
Location: Rural, comfortable, quiet. **Surface:** grassy.
📅 01/01-31/12
Distance: 🚉 1km 🏊 on the spot 🛒 on the spot 🛒 on the spot 🛒 1km 🚲 on the spot 🚶 on the spot.
Remarks: Wifi code at harbour master, boat rental, near the former women's concentration camp Ravensbrück.

S Höhenland 7G3
Das Forsthaus, Bahnhofstraße 13. **GPS:** n52,68433 e13,88171. ⬆➡.

8 🛏 € 10,50 🔌 Ch 🚿 WC included 📶 € 5/day.
Location: Rural, comfortable, quiet. **Surface:** grasstiles.
📅 01/01-31/12
Distance: 🚉 3km 🚲 on the spot 🚶 on the spot.
Remarks: Bread-service.

S Kienitz 7H3
Ferienhaus Marth, Kienitzeroderstrasse 20.
GPS: n52,67616 e14,39890. ⬆.

8 🛏 € 6 🔌 Ch 🚿 € 1,50 WC € 1,50. **Surface:** grassy.
📅 01/04-30/09
Distance: 🚉 3km 🛒 3km.

S Klein-Ossnig 9H2
Caravan-Krokor, Haupstrasse 12/a, B169.
GPS: n51,69962 e14,27917. ➡.

15 🛏 € 7 🔌 Ch 🚿 included. **Surface:** grassy.
📅 01/01-31/12
Distance: 🚉 on the spot 🏊 3km 🛒 50m 🛒 2km 🚲 on the spot 🚶 on the spot.
Remarks: Arrival only during opening hours: Mo-Fr 8-19, Sa 8-13h.

S Kloster Lehnin 9F1
Hotel Seehof, Am See 51. **GPS:** n52,34924 e12,70374. ⬆.

15 🛏 € 10, guests free 🚿 € 2/day WC € 2/time.
Location: Rural, simple, comfortable. **Surface:** grassy.
📅 01/01-31/12
Distance: 🚲 1,8km 🏊 on the spot 🛒 on the spot 🚲 on the spot 🚶 on the spot.
Remarks: Check in at hotel.

S Kolkwitz 9H2
Bauernhof Korreng, Papitzerstrasse 48. **GPS:** n51,76676 e14,22410. ⬆.

3 🛏 € 10 🔌 Ch 🚿 WC included. **Surface:** grassy.
📅 01/03-31/10
Distance: 🚉 2,5km.

S Kyritz 7E3
Parkplatz Wässering, Graf-von-der-Schulenburg-Straße.
GPS: n52,94044 e12,40053. ⬆.

15 🛏 free 🔌 € 1/100liter 🔌 Ch 🚿 € 1/8h WC € 0,50/time € 1/time. **Location:** Urban, comfortable, noisy. **Surface:** grasstiles.
📅 01/01-31/12
Distance: 🚉 city centre 100m 🏊 on the spot 🛒 250m 🛒 250m.

S Lindow/Mark 7F3
Am Wutzsee. **GPS:** n52,97205 e12,98924. ⬆.

3 🛏 free, tourist tax € 0,50/pp. **Location:** Urban, simple, noisy.
Surface: metalled. 📅 01/01-31/12

Distance: 🚉 on the spot 🏊 on the spot 🛒 150m 🛒 150m 🚲 on the spot 🚶 on the spot.
Remarks: Max. 1 night, pay at tourist office.

S Lübbenau 9G2
Autocamping im Spreewald, Chausseestrasse 17a, Lübbenau-Zerkwitz.
GPS: n51,86559 e13,93324. ⬆➡.

6 🛏 € 14/24h, tourist tax € 1,50/pp, dog € 1 🔌 € 1,50 Ch 🚿 WC included. **Surface:** grasstiles. 📅 Easter-31/10
Distance: 🚲 2,5km 🛒 500m.

S Lübbenau 9G2
Am Bahnhof, Bahnhofstraße (B115). **GPS:** n51,86139 e13,96361.

10 🛏 € 8 🔌 € 1/80liter Ch 🚿 € 0,50/kWh. **Surface:** asphalted.
📅 01/01-31/12
Distance: 🚉 800m 🚲 3,3km 🛒 350m 🛒 50m.
Remarks: Along railwayline, max. 2 days.

⚓ Lübbenau 9G2
Kahnfährhafen Leipe, Dorfstrasse 34, Leipe.
GPS: n51,85301 e14,05023. ⬆.

4 🛏 € 5. **Surface:** metalled. 📅 01/01-31/12
Distance: 🚲 11,6km.

S Luckenwalde 9F2
Restaurant Elsthal, Teichwiesenweg, Elsthal.
GPS: n52,07428 e13,16744. ⬆.
10 🛏 € 10 🔌 🚿 WC included. **Surface:** sand.
📅 01/01-31/12
Distance: 🛒 on the spot.
Remarks: Max. <>2.35m.

⚓ S Lychen 7F2
Marina-Yachthafen Lychensee, Schlüssstrasse 7.
GPS: n53,21187 e13,29686. ⬆.

6 🛏 € 10 🔌 Ch 🚿 € 2,50/day WC € 1/time. **Location:** Rural, simple, quiet. **Surface:** grassy. 📅 15/04-15/10
Distance: 🚉 700m 🛒 650m.
Remarks: Check in at harbourmaster, boat rental.

S Nackel 7E3
Gaststätte Birkenhof, Segeletzerstrasse 2.
GPS: n52,82503 e12,56528. ⬆.

3 ⬛ € 3 ⌁🔌 Ch included. ⚡€3/day WC. 🚿
Location: Rural, simple, isolated, quiet. **Surface:** metalled.
📅 01/01-31/12 ⬛ Tue
Distance: 🚶5km ⊗on the spot 🚲on the spot 🏊on the spot.

Neuruppin 7F3

Sportcenter Neuruppin, Trenckmannstraße 14.
GPS: n52,91573 e12,80365.⬆

30 ⬛ € 6 WC ⚡€2,50/time 📶. 🚿 **Location:** Urban, simple, quiet.
Surface: grasstiles. 📅 01/01-31/12
Distance: 🚶on the spot ⌁Neuruppiner See 500m ⊗on the spot
🚲200m, bakery 400m 🏊on the spot 🏃on the spot.
Remarks: Check in at sport centre.

Oberkrämer 7F3

Bäckerei Plentz, Dorfstraße 43. **GPS:** n52,73643 e13,08540.⬆➡

4 ⬛ € 8 ⌁🔌 Ch ⚡ WC included. 🚿 **Location:** Rural, simple, quiet.
Surface: metalled. 📅 01/01-31/12
Distance: 🚶on the spot 🚌1km 🚲500m 🚆train 500m 🏊on the spot
🏃on the spot.
Remarks: Along railwayline, in front of bakery.

Oranienburg 7F3

Am Schlosshafen, Rungestrasse 47. **GPS:** n52,75760 e13,23879.⬆

26 ⬛ € 10 ⌁€1/80liter 🔌Ch ⚡(16x)€1/kWh WC€0,50/time ⊡€
1/5minutes ⊡€5/time. 🚐 **Location:** Rural, comfortable, central,
quiet. **Surface:** metalled.
📅 01/01-31/12
Distance: 🚶600m ⌁on the spot ⊗600m 🚲600m 🏊on the spot
🏃on the spot.
Remarks: Tallycard: service, electricity, sanitary building, caution € 10.

Oranienburg 7F3

Motel Havelidyll, Havelhausener Brücke 1, Havelhausen.
GPS: n52,72161 e13,25047.⬆

10 ⬛ € 15 ⌁🔌Ch ⚡ WC 📶included. 🚿 **Location:** Rural,
simple, isolated, quiet. **Surface:** grassy. 📅 01/04-15/11
Distance: 🚶10km 🚲4km ⌁on the spot ⊗on the spot.

Potsdam 9F1

Am Krongut, Potsdamer Straße 196. **GPS:** n52,41332 e13,02905.⬆

11 ⬛ € 10/24h. 🚐 **Location:** Urban, simple. **Surface:** concrete.
📅 01/01-31/12
Distance: 🚶city centre 2km ⊗100m 🚊Tram 300m.

Potsdam 9F1

P historische Mühle, Zur Historischen Mühlen.
GPS: n52,40562 e13,03453.⬆

5 ⬛ € 2/h, max. € 20/24h. 🚐 **Location:** Urban, simple.
Surface: metalled. 📅 01/01-31/12
Distance: 🚶2km ⊗on the spot.
Tourist information Potsdam:
🎡 Filmpark Babelsberg, August-Bebel-Str. 26-53. Attractions park
concerning the film. 📅 23/03-31/10 10-18h.

Rehfelde 7G3

Campershof, Alt Werder 8. **GPS:** n52,52093 e13,94080.⬆➡

10 ⬛ € 7,50 ⌁🔌Ch included. ⚡€1,50/day WC ⊡. 🚿
Location: Rural, comfortable, quiet. **Surface:** grassy.
📅 01/01-31/12
Distance: 🚶2km ⌁2km 🚲2km 🏊on the spot 🏃on the spot.
Remarks: Bread-service.

Schmergow 9F1

Zum fröhlichen Landmann, Ziegeleiweg 17.
GPS: n52,45416 e12,80553.⬆➡

30 ⬛ € 7,50 ⌁🔌Ch ⚡€1/2kWh 📶included. 🚿 **Location:** Rural,
simple, isolated. **Surface:** grassy. 📅 01/04-31/10

Distance: 🚶500m ⊗on the spot 🚲500m 🏊400m.

Schwedt/Oder 7H2

Wassersportzentrum Schwedt, Wasserplatz 4.
GPS: n53,05759 e14,29861.⬆

30 ⬛ € 10 ⌁🔌Ch ⚡ WC included. **Surface:** grassy.
📅 01/01-31/12
Distance: 🚶1km ⌁on the spot ⊗on the spot 🚲500m.
Remarks: Check in at harbourmaster or bar.

Senftenberg 9H3

Wohnmobilstellplatz Buchwalde, Buchwalder Straße 52.
GPS: n51,51256 e14,02278.
12 ⬛ € 11-14 ⌁🔌Ch included. ⚡€2 WC ⊡0,50. **Surface:** grasstiles.
📅 01/04-01/11
Distance: 🚶2km ⌁Senftenberger See ⊗on the spot 🏊on the spot.
Remarks: Max. 4 nights, caution key sanitary € 20.

Stolzenhagen 7G3

Am Kietz, Kietz 9. **GPS:** n52,94916 e14,10833.⬆➡

20 ⬛ € 7,50 ⌁🔌Ch ⚡(10x)€2,50/day WC included ⊡€2,50/pp.
🚿 **Location:** Rural, comfortable, quiet. **Surface:** grassy/metalled.
📅 01/01-31/12
Distance: ⌁on the spot ⊗Imbiss 🏊Oder-Neiße-Radweg 🏃on the
spot.
Remarks: Directly on the canal, check in at Imbiss, bread-service.

Storkow/Mark 9G1

An der Schleuse, Kirchstrasse. **GPS:** n52,25792 e13,93178.⬆➡
5 ⬛ € 10 ⌁⚡included. **Surface:** grasstiles. 📅 01/01-31/12
Distance: 🚶200m ⊗300m 🚲500m.
Remarks: At the Storkower Canal, max. 36h.

Templin 7F2

Alter Knehdenerstrasse. GPS: n53,12359 e13,49423.⬆➡

40 ⬛ free ⌁€1/60liter 🔌Ch. **Location:** Urban, simple, quiet.
Surface: asphalted/metalled. 📅 01/01-31/12
Distance: 🚶300m ⊗300m 🚲300m 🏊on the spot 🏃on the spot.

Tiefensee 7G3

Reisemobilplatz, Country Camping Tiefensee, Schmiedeweg 1.
GPS: n52,68302 e13,84292.⬆⬆

64 ⬛ € 14, dog € 1,50 ⌁🔌Ch ⚡(51x)WC included ⊡0,50/time ⊡€
2,50/h. 🚿 **Location:** Rural, comfortable, quiet. **Surface:** grassy.
📅 01/01-31/12

DE

Distance: 🚶on the spot 🏊on the spot 🛒on the spot ⊗on the spot ☕on the spot 🚰on the spot 🅿️on the spot 🚶on the spot.
Remarks: Check in at reception campsite.

Weisen 7D3

Wohnmobilstellplatz Am Biotop, Heinrich-Heine-Strasse 4.
GPS: n53,02062 e11,78086.⬆️➡️.

8 🚐€ 5 🚰🔌Ch included. **Surface:** gravel. ☀️ 01/01-31/12
Distance: 🚶300m ⊗200m ☕300m.

Werder/Havel 9F1

An der Föhse. **GPS:** n52,37807 e12,93704.⬆️.

25 🚐€ 6,50 + € 1,50/pp tourist tax 🚰€0,50/80liter 🔌Ch 🔌(8x)€
0,50/kWh,(8x) €0,50/kWh WC€0,50/time. 🚿 **Location:** Urban, simple.
Surface: gravel. ☀️ 01/01-31/12
Distance: 🚶on the spot 🏊on the spot ⊗on the spot ☕on the spot
🚌100m 🚶on the spot.
Remarks: Check in at harbourmaster.

Wusterhausen/Dosse 7E3

Dossehalle, Zur Dossehalle 6. **GPS:** n52,89337 e12,46537.⬆️.

3 🚐free 🚰🔌Ch free 🔌€1/8h. **Location:** Urban, simple, quiet.
Surface: asphalted. ☀️ 01/01-31/12
Distance: 🚶centre 500m ☕450m.

Saxony

Adorf 11E2

Waldbad, Waldbadstrasse 5. **GPS:** n50,30778 e12,25056.

3 🚐free. **Surface:** metalled. ☀️ 01/03-30/11
Distance: 🚶1km ☕500m.
Remarks: Max. 24h.

Tourist information Adorf:
ℹ️ TouristInfo, Freiberger Str. 8.

Amtsberg 11F1

Waldcamping Erzgebirge, B174, An der Dittersdorfer Höhe, Dittersdorf.
GPS: n50,76583 e13,01444.

60 🚐€ 13-15 🚰🔌Ch 🔌€2 WC included.
Surface: grassy/metalled. ☀️ 01/01-31/12

Bad Düben 9F3

Im Kurgebiet, Parkstraße 1. **GPS:** n51,60139 e12,58247.⬆️.

4 🚐free, tourist tax € 1,20-1,50/pp 🚰€1/80liter 🔌€1/time Ch€
1/time WC. **Location:** Rural, simple, isolated. **Surface:** metalled.
☀️ 01/01-31/12
Distance: 🚶750m ⊗1,4km ☕1,4km.

Bad Elster 11E2

Albertbad, Austus-Klingner Straße. **GPS:** n50,28545 e12,24034.⬆️.
5 🚐€ 8 + € 2,20/pp tourist tax 🚰€1/100liter 🔌 included.
Surface: asphalted. ☀️ 01/01-31/12
Distance: 🚶1km ⊗250m.
Remarks: Check in at pay desk swimming pool, caution € 20.

Bad Lausick 11F1

Freizetbad Am Riff, Am Riff 3. **GPS:** n51,14321 e12,65383.⬆️.

10 🚐free. **Location:** Rural, simple, central, quiet. **Surface:** grasstiles.
☀️ 01/01-31/12
Distance: ⊗100m ☕100m 🚶on the spot 🚶on the spot.
Remarks: At swimming pool.

Bad Muskau 35A1

Am Fürst-Pückler-Park, Bautzener Straße 39.
GPS: n51,53382 e14,71838.⬆️.

25 🚐€ 8, € 12 service incl. + € 1,25/pp tourist tax 🚰€1/time 🔌
Ch 🔌(25x)day WC. 🚿 **Location:** Urban, comfortable, central,
quiet. **Surface:** grasstiles/metalled. ☀️ 01/01-28/12
Distance: 🚶400m ⊗4km ☕2km 🚌on the spot 🚶on the spot.

Breitenbrunn 11F2

Sportpark Rabenberg, Rabenbergweg. **GPS:** n50,45556 e12,74417.

---

15 🚐€ 5 + € 5/pp 🚰🔌Ch 🔌€2/day WC €0,50. **Surface:** metalled.
☀️ 01/01-31/12
Distance: 🚶5km ⊗5km ☕5km.
Remarks: Arrival <22h, dog € 2/day.

Dennheritz 11F1

Caravan Service Bressler, Zwickauerstrasse 78.
GPS: n50,80889 e12,48667.

6 🚐€ 4/night 🚰€1 🔌Ch 🔌€2. **Surface:** metalled. ☀️ 01/01-31/12
Distance: 🚶2,1km.

Diera-Zehren 9G3

Zum Zuessenhaus, Elbstraße 10. **GPS:** n51,19500 e13,41917.⬆️.

10 🚐€ 5. **Location:** Rural, simple. **Surface:** grassy/metalled.
☀️ 01/01-31/12

Diesbar-Seusslitz 9G3

Parkplatz Am Schloss, An der Weinstraße.
GPS: n51,24111 e13,41575.⬆️.

6 🚐€ 4 (9-19h), overnight stay free 🔌(6x)€ 1/6h. 🚐
Location: Rural, simple, quiet. **Surface:** metalled.
☀️ 01/01-31/12
Distance: 🏊100 m ⊗200 m 🚶on the spot 🚶on the spot.

Dresden 11G1

Parkplatz Grosse Meissner, Wiesentor Strasse.
GPS: n51,05639 e13,74306.⬆️.

60 🚐€ 18/24h 🚰€2/100liter 🔌Ch €2 🔌(14x)€4/day WC. 🚿
Location: Urban, simple, central. **Surface:** asphalted.
☀️ 01/01-31/12
Distance: 🚶100m ⊗on the spot 🚌on the spot 🚶on the spot.

Dresden 11G1

Sachsenplatz Dresden, Käthe-Kollwitz-Ufer 4.
GPS: n51,05700 e13,75990.⬆️.
150 🚐€ 10 🔌(25x)€3/24h. **Location:** Urban, central.
☀️ 01/01-31/12
Distance: 🚶Old city centre 2,2km ⊗300m ☕Aldi 700m 🚌500m.

Dresden 11G1

Werner Knopf, B6, Meissner Landstrasse.
GPS: n51,08131 e13,65563.⬆️.

DE

7 🚐€ 5/6m + € 1/m 🚰€2/time 💧(8x)€2/night ⚡1,50/time. 🔧
Location: Urban, simple, quiet. **Surface:** grasstiles.
📅 01/03-30/10
Distance: 🚶6km 🚌500m 🚲on the spot.
Remarks: Gate closes at 22h.

🏕️S   Dresden 🌲♨️🍺🏊   11G1
Wohnmobilstellplatz am Blüherpark, Zinzendorfstraße 7.
GPS: n51,04426 e13,74371.⬆️

50 🚐€ 14 🚰€1/time 🗑️€1/time 💧€3/night,16Amp ⚡€2/day. 🔧
Location: Urban, comfortable, central. **Surface:** grassy/metalled.
📅 01/01-31/12
Distance: 🚶1km 🚲5km 🛒500m 🚉450m.
Remarks: Check in at Cityherberge, Lingnerallee 3, 24/24.

🏕️S   Dresden 🌲♨️🍺🏊   11G1
Wohnmobilstellplatz Dresden, Kesselsdorfer Straße 153.
GPS: n51,03988 e13,66949.⬆️

5 🚐€ 12 🚰Ch💧(5x)€2,50/night ⚡€2/pppd. 🔧
Location: Urban, comfortable, central. **Surface:** gravel/metalled.
📅 01/01-31/12
Distance: 🚶centre Dresden 4km 🚲4km 🛒on the spot 🚉200m
🚌800m.
Remarks: At Wellnesshotel Landlust.

🏕️S   Dresden 🌲♨️🍺🏊   11G1
CaravaningPark Schaffer, Kötzschenbroderstrasse 125.
GPS: n51,08639 e13,68222.⬆️

100 🚐€ 11 🚰€0,50/60liter 🗑️€0,50 Ch€0,50 💧€0,50/kWh WC
⚡€0,50 📶.
Location: Urban, comfortable.
Surface: grassy. 📅 01/01-31/12
Distance: 🚶Dresden 5km 🚊2km 🚲200m 🛒500m 🚌200m
🚲500m.
Remarks: Bread-service, repair possibilities motorhome,
access <19h.

Tourist information Dresden:
ℹ️ Dresden-City-Card. Card gives among other things for free public
transport, entrance to many museums, discounts on boat trips,
restaurants etc.
📅 01/01-31/12. 🅣 € 18/48h.
ℹ️ Tourist Information, Prager strasse; Schinkelwache/Theaterplatz,
www.dresden.de. Former residence city with many curiosities.

🌟 Striezelmarkt, Altstadt. Christmas fair.
🎪 advent season.

🏕️S   Ebersbach/Sachsen 🌲   35A1
Fest- und Parkplatz am Freibad, Kottmarsdorfer Strasse 1.
GPS: n51,00972 e14,59806.⬆️

7 🚐€ 5, € 10 service incl 🚰🗑️Ch💧WC⚡. **Location:** Rural, simple,
isolated, quiet. **Surface:** metalled. 📅 01/01-31/12
Distance: 🚶1km 🚲500m 🚉1km 🚲on the spot.

🏕️S   Elsterheide   9H3
Wohnmobilstellplatz Lothar Meusel, Am Hochwald 27, Tätzschwitz.
GPS: n51,48304 e14,10750.⬆️➡️

14 🚐€ 8,50 🚰€1/time 🗑️Ch💧included WC€2,50/
day ⚡. 🔧 **Location:** Rural, comfortable, isolated, quiet.
Surface: grasstiles/grassy. 📅 Easter-31/10
Distance: 🚲3km 🚉8-10km 🚲on the spot.

🏕️S   Freiberg ♨️   11G1
Am Johannisbad, Lessingstraße. **GPS:** n50,91461 e13,33368.⬆️

10 🚐first night € 10, € 7,50 second night 🚰€1/80liter 🗑️€1/time
Ch€1/time 💧(10x)€0,50/kWh WC⚡. 🔧 **Location:** Urban, simple,
central, quiet. **Surface:** metalled.
📅 01/01-31/12
Distance: 🚶Altstadt 900m 🚲150m 🚉Kaufland 500m 🚲on the spot.

🏕️S   Geierswalde 🍺   9H3
Ferien- und Freizeitpark Geierswalde See, Promenadeweg 1-3.
GPS: n51,49372 e14,13481.⬆️

100+ 🚐€ 6 🚰€2/day 🗑️Ch💧€3 WC⚡. 🔧 **Location:** Rural, simple,
isolated, quiet. **Surface:** grassy. 📅 01/01-01/12
Distance: 🚶500m 🚊Geierswaldesee 300m 🚲1km 🛒5km 🚲on
the spot.

🏕️S   Großenhain   9G3
Carl-Maria-von-Weber-Allee. **GPS:** n51,29032 e13,53584.⬆️
5 🚐€ 5, 15/09-15/05 free 🚰€1/70liter 🗑️€1/time 💧€1/4h.
Surface: metalled. 📅 01/01-31/12
Distance: 🚶500m 🚲100m.
Remarks: To pay at swimming pool.

🏕️S   Grünhain   11F2
Freizeitpark, Auer Strasse 82, Haus des Gastes, Grünhain-Beierfeld.
GPS: n50,58139 e12,79167.

---

6 🚐€ 5 🚰€1 🗑️€1,customers free Ch💧€1,50/day WC⚡€1.
Surface: metalled. 📅 01/01-31/12
Distance: 🚶1km 🚲on the spot 🚉3km.

🏨S   Hermsdorf 🏔️❄️   11G1
Ski- & Sporthotel SWF, Bahnhofstraße 7.
GPS: n50,73241 e13,66400.⬆️

8 🚐€ 5, tourist tax € 0,50/pp 🚰€2 🗑️€2 Ch💧€0,50/kWh. 🔧
Location: Rural, simple, isolated, quiet. **Surface:** gravel/metalled.
📅 01/01-31/12
Distance: 🚲on the spot 🚲on the spot 🚶on the spot 🚲on the spot.

△S   Königsfeld-Stollsdorf   11F1
Spreer's Ferienhaus, Hauptstrasse 28. **GPS:** n51,04861 e12,74500.

4 🚐€ 8 🗑️Ch💧€2. 📅 01/01-31/12
Distance: 🚶4km 🚉4km.

🏨S   Königstein ♨️   11H1
Panoramhotel Lilienstein, Ebenheit 7. **GPS:** n50,92505 e14,07546.⬆️

10 🚐€ 22 🚰🗑️💧included ⚡€5. 🔧 **Location:** Rural, simple,
isolated, quiet. **Surface:** grassy/gravel. 📅 Easter-15/11
Distance: 🚲on the spot 🚶on the spot.
Remarks: Bread-service and breakfast buffet.

🏕️S   Leipzig 🌲♨️🍺   9E3
Reisemobilhafen Leipzig, Im Dölitzer Holz 20.
GPS: n51,28525 e12,38352.⬆️➡️

30 🚐€ 7,50 🚰€1/time 🗑️€1/time Ch€1/time 💧(12x)€
2,50/day 📶free. ⚡ **Location:** Rural, comfortable, quiet.
Surface: gravel/metalled. 📅 01/01-31/12
Distance: 🚶5,5km 🚊2,5km 🚲100m 🚌Tram 850m.
Remarks: Can be reached without environmental: from the direction
Goethesteig.

Leipzig 🌿⛺🍴 9E3

Stellplatz Melinenburg, Störrerstraße 3.
GPS: n51,36648 e12,42717.⬆️

20 🛏️€ 10, 2 pers.incl, extra pers € 1, dog € 1 💧€1/time ⚡€1/time Ch€1/time 💧(8x)€2/day. ♿ **Location:** Urban, comfortable, central, quiet. **Surface:** concrete. 🅿️ 01/01-31/12
Distance: 🚶4,5km 🛒1,2km 🚉200m.
Remarks: Bread-service, outside environmental zone.

Löbau ⛺ 35A1

Am Löbauer Berg, Beethovenstraße. **GPS:** n51,09508 e14,68088.⬆️

3 🛏️free 💧(3x)against paymentkWh. **Location:** Rural, simple, isolated, quiet. **Surface:** grasstiles/metalled. 🅿️ 01/01-31/12
Distance: 🚶1km.

Lohsa ⛵ 9H3

Dreiweibern See, Am strand Weißkollm 1.
GPS: n51,40782 e14,40008.⬆️➡️

14 🛏️€ 10 💧€1/80liter 🔵Ch 💧(14x)stay WCincluded. ♿
Location: Rural, comfortable, isolated, quiet.
Surface: grasstiles/grassy. 🅿️ 01/01-31/12
Distance: 🚶1,5km 🛒on the spot ⊗Imbiss 🚲on the spot.

Marienberg 🎭❄️ 11G2

Rätzteich, Gelobtland 27c. **GPS:** n50,62417 e13,17861.

3 🛏️€ 3 💧€1 ⚡€1 Ch€1 💧€1. **Surface:** metalled.
🅿️ 01/01-31/12
Distance: 🚶5km 🛒on the spot ⊗500m 🛒5km 🚲3km 🏊on the spot.
Remarks: Recreation area.

Meissen 9G3

Wellenspiel, Berghausstraße 2. **GPS:** n51,17444 e13,49861.⬆️➡️
19 🛏️€ 5 💧€2/day. ♿ **Location:** Rural, simple, quiet.
Surface: grassy/metalled. 🅿️ 01/01-31/12
Distance: 🚶900m.
Remarks: At swimming pool, caution key € 20.

Meissen 9G3

An der Elbe, Hochuferstraße. **GPS:** n51,16806 e13,47361.⬆️

20 🛏️€ 5. 🚩 **Location:** Urban, simple, central. **Surface:** metalled.
🅿️ 01/01-31/12
Distance: 🚶800m 🛒on the spot ⊗800m 🚉300m 🚲on the spot.

Oberwiesenthal ⛺🏔️❄️ 11F2

OTG Tennishalle, Vieren Strasse 1a. **GPS:** n50,42722 e12,96944.

20 🛏️€ 18, 01/11-31/03 € 25, tourist tax excl 💧🔵Ch 💧WCincluded ⚡€1. **Surface:** metalled.
🅿️ 01/01-31/12
Distance: ⊗on the spot 🚲250m.
Remarks: Check in at reception tennishall < 22h, bread-service.

Oderwitz ⛺ 35A1

Rodelpark Oberoderwitz, Spitzbergstraße 4a.
GPS: n50,96528 e14,70111.⬆️

5 🛏️free. **Location:** Rural, simple, isolated, quiet.
Surface: gravel/metalled. 🅿️ 01/01-31/12
Distance: 🚶600m ⊗on the spot.

Pirna 11H1

Schloßpark Pirna, Schloßpark 13a. **GPS:** n50,95998 e13,95232.⬆️

8 🛏️€ 12 💧🔵Chincluded 💧€1/kWh. **Location:** Quiet.
Surface: metalled. 🅿️ 01/01-31/12
Distance: 🚶2,5km 🚉500m.

Pirna 11H1

Elbeparkplatz, Hauptplatz 14. **GPS:** n50,96654 e13,93775.⬆️

15 🛏️free. **Surface:** asphalted. 🅿️ 01/01-31/12
Distance: 🚶650m 🚏on the spot ⊗350m 🚲on the spot.
Remarks: Along the river Elbe, max. 24h.

Seiffen 11G1

Berghof, Kurhausstrasse 36. **GPS:** n50,64605 e13,48114.

20 🛏️guests free 💧💧. 🅿️ 01/01-31/12
Distance: 🚶2,5km ⊗on the spot 🚉300m.

Struppen 11H1

Camping-Stellplatz Struppen, Kirchberg 20.
GPS: n50,93814 e14,01307.⬆️

30 🛏️€ 10, 25/03-05/11 € 13 + € 0,75/pp tourist tax 💧€1/100liter Ch 💧(30x)€0,60/kWh ⚡€1 🔵€3/3. **Location:** Luxurious.
Surface: grassy/metalled. 🅿️ 01/01-31/12
Distance: 🚶500m 🚉500m.

Weißwasser 9H2

Am Tierpark, Teichstraße 56. **GPS:** n51,51205 e14,63665.⬆️

10 🛏️free. **Location:** Urban, simple, central. **Surface:** metalled.
🅿️ 01/01-31/12
Distance: 🚶500m 🛒on the spot ⊗500m 🚉500m 🚲on the spot.

Wermsdorf 🌿 9F3

Zum Goldnen Hirsch, Hirschplatz 2. **GPS:** n51,28300 e12,94065.⬆️

4 🛏️€ 5 💧€1 ⚡(4x) WC 🔵. **Location:** Urban, simple.
Surface: metalled. 🅿️ 01/01-31/12
Distance: 🚶on the spot ⊗on the spot 🚉on the spot.

Zittau ⛺🍴 35A1

Zittau Am Dreiländereck, Brückenstrasse 23.
GPS: n50,89457 e14,82143.⬆️➡️

100 🛏️€ 7 💧€1/10minutes 🔵Ch 💧(32x)€1/6h WC. 🚩
Location: Urban, comfortable, central, quiet. **Surface:** grassy.
🅿️ 01/01-31/12
Distance: 🚶1,5km 🚉200m 🚏🚉100m 🚲on the spot.
Remarks: Three Countries' Corner Germany-Czech Republic-Poland.

DE

Zwota 11F2

Natur Camping Platz, Merkneukirchner Strasse 79.
GPS: n50,35111 e12,38111.⬆.

40 🛏€ 10 ⌐€1,50 ⬛€1 Ch ✎(16x)WC included. **Surface:** gravel.
⬛ 01/01-31/12
Distance: ⚓Klingenthal 6km ⚓6km.

North Rhine Westphalia

Aachen 10E2

Aachen-Camping, Branderhofer Weg 11.
GPS: n50,76111 e6,10306.⬆➡.

46 🛏€ 15/night ⌐⬛Ch✎WC included ⬛€1.🚿 **Location:** Urban,
luxurious, central, quiet. **Surface:** metalled.
⬛ 01/01-31/12
Distance: ⚓1,7km ⚓700m ⚓700m ⚓300m.
Remarks: Baker 8.30-09.00.

Ahaus 8F2

Am Aquahaus, Vredener Dyk. **GPS:** n52,07778 e6,98361.⬆➡.

8 🛏 ⌐€0,50/40liter ⬛Ch✎(8x)€0,50/kWh,16Amp WC⬛.
Location: Rural, simple, isolated. **Surface:** metalled.
⬛ 01/01-31/12
Distance: ⚓2km ⚓on the spot ⚓1,5km ⚓on the spot.
Remarks: Max. 3 days.

Ahaus 8F2

Krimesplatz, Schlossstrasse. **GPS:** n52,07450 e7,00299.⬆➡.

8 🛏free ⌐€0,50/80liter ⬛Ch✎(6x)€0,50/stay,16Amp WC⬛.
Location: Rural, simple, isolated. **Surface:** metalled. ⬛ 01/01-31/12
⬛ during event
Distance: ⚓on the spot ⚓on the spot ⚓600m ⚓600m.
Remarks: Parking centre, max. 3 nights.

Ahlen 8G3

Parkbad Ahlen, Dolbergerstrasse 66. **GPS:** n51,75559 e7,89694.⬆.

4 🛏 €8/24h ⌐⬛Ch✎included. **Location:** Rural, comfortable,
quiet. **Surface:** metalled. ⬛ 01/01-31/12
Distance: ⚓centre 300m ⚓100m ⚓300m ⚓on the spot ⚓on the
spot.
Remarks: Max. 3 nights, caution key service € 10, 50% discount at
swimming pool.

Alpen 8E3

An der Motte, Burgstrasse 66. **GPS:** n51,57985 e6,51846.⬆.

11 🛏€ 7,50 ⌐⬛Ch✎included. 🚐 **Location:** Rural, comfortable.
Surface: gravel. ⬛ 01/01-31/12
Distance: ⚓500m ⚓2,5km ⚓500m.

Altena 10G1

Sauerlandhalle Pragpaul, Hermann Vossstrasse 14.
GPS: n51,30861 e7,66056.⬆➡.

12 🛏free ⌐€0,50 ⬛€0,50 Ch✎(6x)€0,50/kWh. **Location:** Rural,
simple, quiet. **Surface:** asphalted/gravel.
⬛ 01/01-31/12
Distance: ⚓2km ⚓10km ⚓nearby ⚓2km ⚓on the spot ⚓on the
spot.

Altenbeken 9A3

Landhaus Friedenstal, Hüttenstrasse 42. **GPS:** n51,75992 e8,95111.⬆.

5 🛏€ 5 ✎(5x)€2,50/24h WC on demand, at restaurant. 🚿🚲
Location: Simple, central. **Surface:** grassy/gravel.
⬛ 01/01-31/12
Distance: ⚓200m ⚓on the spot ⚓200m.

Altenberge 8G2

Sportpark Grosseberg, Sportzentrum. **GPS:** n52,05528 e7,47056.⬆.

15 🛏free ⌐€0,50/60liter ⬛Ch. **Location:** Rural, isolated, quiet.
Surface: metalled. ⬛ 01/01-31/12 ⬛ water disconnected in winter

Distance: ⚓1,6km ⚓nearby ⚓1,5km.
Remarks: Parking sports centre.

Arnsberg 8H3

An der Schlacht/Ruhrstrasse. **GPS:** n51,40127 e8,06468.⬆.
4 🛏free. **Location:** Simple. **Surface:** gravel.
Distance: ⚓3,3km ⚓Lidl 50m.

Ascheberg 8G3

Appelhof, Appelhofstraße. **GPS:** n51,79003 e7,61902.⬆➡.

4 🛏free. **Location:** Rural, simple, central, quiet. **Surface:** metalled.
⬛ 01/01-31/12
Distance: ⚓on the spot ⚓on the spot ⚓on the spot.

Ascheberg 8G3

Gasthaus Eickholt, Frieport 22, Davensberg. **GPS:** n51,82619 e7,59391.

6 🛏€ 5, free with a meal ⌐✎€3/24h WC 📶free. **Location:** Simple.
Surface: grassy. ⬛ 01/01-31/12 ⬛ Mo
Distance: ⚓800m ⚓1km ⚓on the spot ⚓1km ⚓800m ⚓on the
spot.
Remarks: Swingolf.

Attendorn 10G1

Land-Hotel-Struck, Repetalstrasse 245, Niederhelden.
GPS: n51,12073 e7,97284.

6 🛏guests free ✎€3,50 WC. ⬛ 01/01-31/12
Distance: ⚓on the spot ⚓on the spot ⚓2km ⚓on the spot ⚓on
the spot.

Attendorn 10G1

Atta Höhle, Finnentroper Straße 39. **GPS:** n51,12489 e7,91421.⬆.
8 🛏€ 7,50 ⌐⬛Ch✎included. **Surface:** metalled.
⬛ 01/01-31/12
Distance: ⚓500m ⚓Lidl 400m.

Bad Berleburg 10H1

Bismarckstraße. **GPS:** n51,04986 e8,39406.⬆.
3 🛏free ⌐€2/100liter ⬛Ch✎€1/8h. **Surface:** metalled.
⬛ 01/01-31/12
Distance: ⚓500m ⚓500m.

Bad Berleburg 10H1

Pension-Bauernladen Schmelzhütte, K52 Hoheleye.
GPS: n51,13874 e8,45742.

6 🛏€ 10 ⌐⬛Ch✎€2. **Surface:** asphalted.
⬛ 01/01-31/12 ⬛ Mo

DE

Distance: 🚰1km ⊗on the spot 🍽1km.
Remarks: Bread-service.

| 🍴 | **Bad Berleburg** 🌲❄ | 10H1 |

Hotel-Restaurant Erholung - Laibach, Auf dem Laibach 1.
GPS: n51,06776 e8,44527.

5 🅿free with a meal 🚰💧(1x)€5/day WC. **Surface:** asphalted.
📅 01/01-31/12
Distance: 🚰5km ⊗on the spot 🍽5km 🛵on the spot 🚶on the spot ⛵1,5km.

| ⛲S | **Bad Driburg** 🌲🎡 | 9A3 |

P Driburg Therme, Georg-Nave-Strasse 24.
GPS: n51,74194 e9,02542.⬆

10 🅿€ 5 + tourist tax 💧(10x)€3/24h WC.🚿
Location: Rural, simple, quiet. **Surface:** asphalted.
📅 01/01-31/12
Distance: 🚰1km ⊗on the spot 🍽1km 🛵on the spot 🚶on the spot.
Remarks: Max. 7m, caution € 10, key electricity at pay-desk.

| 🍴S | **Bad Laasphe** 🌲 | 10H1 |

Mühlenstrasse. **GPS:** n50,92412 e8,41146.⬆➡

7 🅿€ 6/day 🚰€0,50/80liter 💧Ch 💧€0,50/kWh.
Surface: asphalted. 📅 01/01-31/12
Distance: 🚰500m ⊗500m 🍽500m.
Remarks: Parking at town hall.

| 🍴S | **Bad Laasphe** 🌲 | 10H1 |

Hotel Jagdhof Glashütte, Glashütterstrasse 20, Volkholz.
GPS: n50,92008 e8,28070.

6 🅿€ 13,80, free with a meal 💧WC 🔊.🚿 **Location:** Rural.
Surface: grassy. 📅 01/01-31/12 🔒23-24/12
Distance: 🚰4km ⊗on the spot ⊗on the spot 🍽4km 🛵1,5km.

| ⛲S | **Bad Lippspringe** | 9A3 |

Arminiuspark, Burgstraße 10. **GPS:** n51,78124 e8,82447.

11 🅿€ 2,80/1p +1p € 2/pp 🚰💧Ch 💧. **Location:** Urban, quiet.
Surface: metalled. 📅 01/01-31/12
Distance: 🚰300m ⊗350m on the spot 🚶on the spot.
Remarks: Pay at tourist office.

| ⛲S | **Bad Münstereifel** | 10F2 |

Wohnmobilpark Eifel, Dr.Grevestraße 16.
GPS: n50,54600 e6,76514.⬆➡

30 🅿€ 7 + € 1/pp tourist tax 🚰€1/100 💧€1 Ch 💧(30x)
included WC 💧1,80. 🚿 **Location:** Rural, comfortable, quiet.
Surface: grassy/metalled.
📅 01/01-31/12
Distance: 🚰350m ⊗on the spot 🍽100m.
Remarks: Pay and coins at swimming pool, 20% discount pool.

| ⛲ | **Bad Oeynhausen** 🎡 | 8H2 |

Südbahnstraße/Detmolder Straße. **GPS:** n52,19680 e8,80038.⬆
3 🅿free. **Surface:** asphalted. 📅 01/01-31/12
Remarks: Max. 2 days.

| 🍴 | **Bad Oeynhausen** 🎡 | 8H2 |

Siekmeiers Hof, Volmerdingser strasse 111.
GPS: n52,24679 e8,78394.

10 🅿guests free. **Location:** Urban, quiet. **Surface:** gravel.
📅 01/01-31/12 🔒 Mon, Tue
Distance: 🚰on the spot ⊗on the spot 🍽1km.

| ⛲S | **Bad Salzuflen** | 8H2 |

Wohnmobil-Park Flachsheide, Forsthausweg.
GPS: n52,09868 e8,74569.⬆

25 🅿€ 7, tourist tax € 2,90/pp 🚰💧Ch 💧WC 💧included.
Location: Rural, quiet. 📅 01/01-31/12
Distance: 🚰1,5km 🚴5,5km ⛱on the spot ⊗500m 🍽1,5km 🛵free.

| ⛲S | **Bad Sassendorf** 🎡 | 8H3 |

Kurcamping Rumkerhof, Weslarnerstrasse 30.
GPS: n51,59581 e8,17909.⬆➡

93 🅿€ 8,50 🚰💧Ch 💧(93x)included. **Surface:** gravel.
📅 01/01-31/12
Distance: 🚰1,3km ⊗1,3km.
Remarks: Waste dump € 0,50, bread-service.

| ⛲S | **Bad Waldliesborn** | 8H3 |

Wohnmobilstellplatz, Quellenstraße. **GPS:** n51,71759 e8,33587.⬆

10 🅿€ 4,40 + € 7/pp 🚰€2/100liter 💧Ch 💧(8x)€2/24h.
Location: Rural, quiet. **Surface:** gravel. 📅 01/01-31/12
Distance: 🚰400m ⊗200m 🍽400m 🛵400m.
Remarks: Discount on access terme.

| ⛲S | **Bad Westernkotten** | 8H3 |

Wohnmobilplatz An den Sole-Thermen, Mühlenweg 1.
GPS: n51,63126 e8,35195.⬆

46 🅿€ 7, tourist tax € 2/pp 🚰€1/100liter 💧Ch 💧€0,50/kWh.🔌
Surface: grassy. 📅 01/01-31/12
Distance: 🍽bakery 300m.
Remarks: Bread-service.

| ⛲S | **Bad Wünnenberg** 🌲 | 8H3 |

Wohnmobilhafen, In den Erlen. **GPS:** n51,52058 e8,70133.⬆➡

12 🅿€ 4 🚰€1/100liter 💧Ch 💧(12x)€1/24h.🚿 **Location:** Urban,
central. **Surface:** gravel.
📅 01/01-31/12
Distance: 🚰100m 🛒400m ⊗100m 🍽400m 🛵on the spot 🚶on the spot.

| ⛲S | **Balve** 🔔🌲 | 10G1 |

Am Hallenbad, In der Murmke 9. **GPS:** n51,32729 e7,86920.⬆➡

3 🅿free 🚰€1/100liter 💧💧€1/kWh. **Location:** Urban, simple.
Surface: metalled. 📅 01/01-31/12
Distance: 🚰600m ⊗600m 🍽600m 🛵on the spot 🚶on the spot.

Barntrup 9A2

Badeanstaltsweg. **GPS:** n51,98790 e9,10990.

4 € 6 €1/100liter Ch €0,50/kWh. **Location:** Rural, simple. **Surface:** asphalted. 01/01-31/12
Distance: 450m 450m 450m 450m.
Remarks: To be paid at campsite Teutoburger Wald.

Barntrup 9A2

Ferienpark Teutoburger Wald, Badeanstaltsweg 4.
GPS: n51,98768 e9,11027.

9 € 20,50 Ch €5/5 included. **Location:** Rural, luxurious, quiet. **Surface:** grassy/metalled. 01/04-31/10
Distance: 450m 450m 450m 450m on the spot on the spot.

Beckum 8G3

Am Hallenbad, Paterweg 4. **GPS:** n51,75129 e8,03585.

3 free €0,50/100liter Ch (2x)€0,50/kWh.
Location: Urban, simple, noisy. **Surface:** metalled. 01/01-31/12
Distance: 1km 4km 1km 1km.

Bedburg-Hau 8E3

Womo-Moyland, Moyländer Allee 3a, Moyland.
GPS: n51,75562 e6,24381.

50 € 6 €0,50/100liter Ch €2,50/24h.
Location: Rural, comfortable. **Surface:** grasstiles. 01/01-31/12
Distance: Kleve-zentrum 8km 2,5km 300m.
Remarks: Golf court 500m, Schloss Moyland 300m.

Bedburg-Hau 8E3

Landgasthaus Schwanenhof, Mühlenstraße 71, Ortsteil Schneppenbaum. **GPS:** n51,76096 e6,20404.

25 € 5 Ch (18x). **Location:** Rural, comfortable.
Surface: grassy. 01/01-31/12
Distance: 500m on the spot 1km.
Remarks: Bread-service.

Tourist information Bedburg-Hau:
Schloß Moyland, Am Schloss 4. Castle. Tue-Fri 11-18h, sa-su 10-18h, 1/4-31/3 tue-so 11-17h Mon.

Bergheim 10F1

Stellplatz Paffendorf, Königsstrasse/Kastanienallee.
GPS: n50,96389 e6,61194.

8 free. **Location:** Rural, simple, quiet. **Surface:** asphalted. 01/01-31/12
Distance: Bergheim 2km 2,3km 300m 500m.
Remarks: Max. 2 days, castle Paffendorf 100m.

Bergkamen 8G3

Wohnmobilhafen Marina Rünthe, Hafenweg, Rünthe.
GPS: n51,64106 e7,64309.

18 € 7/24h €1/80liter Ch (12x)€0,50/kWh.
Surface: grassy/gravel. 01/01-31/12
Distance: 500m 3,8km.
Remarks: Max. 3 days, only exact change.

Bergkamen 8G3

Freizeitzentrum Im Häupen, Häupenweg 29.
GPS: n51,61300 e7,63075.

5 free. **Surface:** metalled. 01/01-31/12
Distance: 500m 3,4km 500m 500m.
Remarks: Max. 72h.

Bestwig 8H3

Besucherbergwerk, Ziegelwiese, Ramsbeck.
GPS: n51,31821 e8,40318.

6 free. **Location:** Simple. **Surface:** metalled. 01/01-31/12
Distance: 800m.

Bestwig 8H3

Ludwigstrasse. **GPS:** n51,36064 e8,40165.

4 free. **Location:** Simple, simple. **Surface:** metalled. 01/01-31/12
Distance: on the spot 300m 200m.

Beverungen 9A3

Wohnmobilhafen Weser, Am Hakel. **GPS:** n51,66167 e9,37639.

12 free €1/100liter Ch €1 (12x)€1/6h.
Location: Urban, simple. **Surface:** grassy/metalled. 01/01-31/12
Distance: on the spot on the spot on the spot on the spot on the spot.
Remarks: Next to Festplatz.

Bielefeld 8H2

Am Johannisberg, Dornbergerstrasse. **GPS:** n52,02270 e8,51155.

10 01/03-01/12 € 5/24h €1/8 Ch (10x)€0,50/kWh.
Location: Rural, comfortable, quiet. **Surface:** metalled. 01/01-31/12
Distance: 2km Imbiss 2km 2km.

Billerbeck 8F2

Am Freibad, Osterwickerstrasse. **GPS:** n51,97928 e7,28190.

11 € 5 €1/100liter Ch (8x)€1/2kWh,16Amp.
Location: Urban, simple. **Surface:** gravel. 01/01-31/12
Distance: 500m 500m.
Remarks: At swimming pool.

DE

S **Billerbeck** 8F2

Am Konzert Theater, Osterwicker Straße 39.
GPS: n51,95322 e7,17390.⬆.

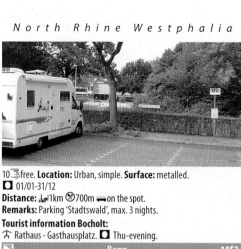

12 free €1/100liter Chfree (12x)€1/2kWh €1.
Location: Rural, simple. **Surface:** gravel/metalled.
01/01-31/12
Distance: 800m 800m 100m.

S **Blankenheim** 10F2

Weiherhalle, Koblenzerstrasse. **GPS:** n50,43499 e6,65439.⬆.

15 €5/24h €1/80liter Ch (12x)€2/10h.
Location: Rural, simple. **Surface:** metalled. 01/01-31/12
Distance: 150m.

S **Bocholt** 8F3

WoMo Park am Aasee, Uhlandstraße 39.
GPS: n51,83496 e6,63146.⬆.

50 €6 €0,50/50liter Ch€0,50 (44x)€0,50/kWh WC€0,50
€1 €3,50/2,50 €1/24h. **Location:** Rural, simple, noisy.
Surface: asphalted. 01/01-31/12
Distance: 800m 300m 300m 300m 300m 200m
on the spot on the spot.

S **Bocholt** 8F3

Inselbad Bahia, Hemdenerweg 169. **GPS:** n51,86265 e6,61002.⬆➡.

10 free Ch. **Location:** Rural, simple.
Surface: grasstiles.
01/01-31/12
Distance: 2,5km 450m 1km on the spot.
Remarks: Max. 48h, coins at swimming pool, first coin € 3, next € 0,50.

Bocholt 8F3

Euregio-Gymnasium, Unter den Eichen, Blücherstrasse.
GPS: n51,84884 e6,63700.⬆.

10 free. **Location:** Urban, simple. **Surface:** metalled.
01/01-31/12
Distance: 1km 700m on the spot.
Remarks: Parking 'Stadtswald', max. 3 nights.
Tourist information Bocholt:
Rathaus - Gasthausplatz. Thu-evening.

S **Bonn** 10F2

An der Rheinaue, Ludwig-Erhard-Allee. **GPS:** n50,70981 e7,13904.⬆.
18 free. **Surface:** asphalted.
01/01-31/12
Distance: centre 4km A565 4,6km 300m line 66 > Bonn centre.

S **Borken** 8F3

Reisemobilstellplatz am Aquarius-Freizeitbad, Parkstraße.
GPS: n51,83618 e6,86074.⬆➡.

15 €6 Ch . **Location:** Rural, simple. **Surface:** grasstiles.
01/01-31/12
Distance: 1km 1km 800m 500m on the spot on the
spot.
Remarks: Parking swimming pool, max. 72h.

Borken 8F3

Festplatz Weseke, Borkenwirther strasse, Weseke.
GPS: n51,90529 e6,85210.⬆.

5 free. **Location:** Rural, simple. **Surface:** metalled.
01/01-31/12
Distance: 500m 500m 500m.
Remarks: Max. 3 nights.

Borken 8F3

Schlossklinik Pröbsting, Pröbstinger Allee.
GPS: n51,83861 e6,80556.⬆.

10 free. **Location:** Rural, noisy. **Surface:** metalled.
01/01-31/12
Distance: Badesee 150m 300m on the spot on the spot.

Borken 8F3

Wasserburg Gemen, Coesfelderstrasse, Gemen.
GPS: n51,86172 e6,86909.⬆➡.

5 free. **Location:** Rural, simple. **Surface:** metalled.
01/01-31/12
Distance: 1km 500m 500m 1km 1km.
Remarks: Parking sports park, max. 3 nights.

S **Borken** 8F3

Gestüt Forellenhof Wolter, Zum Homborn 9.
GPS: n51,86245 e6,89797.⬆.

15 € 10 Ch (7x)included. **Location:** Rural. **Surface:** gravel.
01/01-31/12
Distance: Borken 3,5km fish pond on the spot.
Remarks: Check in at Gaststätte, € 5 euro discount coupon.

S **Borken** 8F3

Camping Pröbstingersee, Dirkshof 11, Hoxfeld.
GPS: n51,83237 e6,78764.

10 free Ch. **Surface:** metalled.
01/01-31/12
Distance: 6,5km 100m 100m.
Remarks: Max. 3 nights, service against payment on campsite.

Bottrop 8F3

Movie Park, Kirchhellen, Warner Allee 1. **GPS:** n51,62400 e6,97096.⬆.

100 € 5. **Surface:** metalled. 01/04-31/10
Distance: 2,7km 100m 2,7km.
Tourist information Bottrop:
Alpincenter, Prosperstrasse. Indoor ski centre. 9-24h. T day
ticket € 25, <18h € 18.

S **Brakel/Bellersen** 9A3

Wohnmobilhafen Mühlengrund, Meinolfussstrasse 6.
GPS: n51,77217 e9,18804.⬆.

23 € 8,50 €0,50 Ch (23x)included. **Location:** Rural,

DE

comfortable, isolated. **Surface:** grasstiles. ▣ 01/01-31/12
Distance: 🚶800m ⊗400m 🍴800m 🚰800m ⚑ on the spot.

Bruchhausen 9A3

Bruchhäuserstrasse. **GPS:** n51,70714 e9,29192. ⬆.

4 🛌free. **Location:** Rural, simple. **Surface:** grassy/gravel.
▣ 01/01-31/12
Distance: 🚶200m ⊗200m 🚰200m.

Brüggen 10E1

Wohnmobilhafen Brüggen, Bornerstraße 48.
GPS: n51,24264 e6,18955. ⬆ ➡.

30 🛌€ 4 🚰🍴Chincluded ⚡€2. **Surface:** gravel.
▣ 01/01-31/12
Distance: 🚶500m ⊗100m 🚰50m ⚑50m.
Remarks: Behind Aldi-süd.

Brüggen 10E1

Freizeitplatz Brachter Wald, St.-Barbara-Straße 40–42, Bracht.
GPS: n51,25713 e6,17022.

14 🛌€ 9, 2 pers.incl 🚰🍴Ch ⚡€2/day WC 🚰€1. **Surface:** grasstiles.
▣ 01/01-31/12
Distance: 🚶2km ⊗on the spot 🚰on the spot.

Brühl 10F2

Phantasialand P1, Berggeiststrasse 31-41.
GPS: n50,79919 e6,87875. ⬆.

10 🛌€ 12,50/night 🚰⚡ WC 🚰. **Location:** Comfortable, quiet.
Surface: metalled.
▣ 04/04-31/10
Distance: ⊗100m.

Tourist information Brühl:
🎡 Phantasialand. Large amusement park.
▣ 01/04-31/10 9-18h, winter changing visiting hours.

Bünde 8H2

Stadtgarten, Steinmeisterstrasse/Viktoriastrasse.
GPS: n52,19869 e8,58986. ⬆.

5 🛌free. **Location:** Urban, simple. **Surface:** metalled.
▣ 01/01-31/12
Distance: 🚶50m ⊗50m 🚰50m.
Remarks: Max. 72h.

Büren 8H3

Parkplatz an der Afte, Fürstenberger Strasse.
GPS: n51,54897 e8,56381.

8 🛌free 🚰🍴Ch ⚡. **Location:** Urban, simple.
▣ 01/01-31/12
Distance: 🚶on the spot ⊗500m 🚰200m.
Remarks: Parking nearby swimming pool.

Coesfeld 8F2

Brauhaus Stephanus, Overhagenweg 1. **GPS:** n51,93719 e7,15617. ⬆.

4 🛌guests free 🚰. **Location:** Urban, simple, noisy. **Surface:** metalled.
▣ 01/01-31/12
Distance: ⊗on the spot 🚰100m ⚑on the spot.

Dahlem 10E3

Flugplatz Dahlemer Binz, Dahlemer Binz.
GPS: n50,40663 e6,53700. ⬆.

3 🛌free 🚰€1 🍴Ch. **Location:** Rural, simple. **Surface:** asphalted.
▣ 01/01-31/12
Distance: ⊗on the spot.
Remarks: Airport Dahlemer Binz.

Dahlem 10E3

Wohnmobilstellplatz Kronenburger See, Seeuferstrasse 6.
GPS: n50,35785 e6,46989. ⬆ ➡.

16 🛌€ 8/24h 🚰€1/120liter 🍴Ch ⚡(12x)included. **Location:** Rural,
simple, quiet. **Surface:** grassy. ▣ 01/01-31/12
Remarks: At artificial lake.

Delbrück 8H3

Landgasthaus Roseneck, Haselhorster Strasse 3.
GPS: n51,75770 e8,43441.

10 🛌€ 5, free with a meal ⚡(10x)included. **Location:** Rural, simple.
Surface: metalled. ▣ 01/01-31/12
Distance: 🚶2km ⊗on the spot 🚰2km.

Detmold 9A2

Detmolder City Camp, Bahnhofstrasse 8.
GPS: n51,94055 e8,87123. ⬆ ➡.

14 🛌€ 8 🚰€1/100liter 🍴Ch ⚡(14x)€2,16Amp WC 🚰.
Location: Urban. **Surface:** asphalted. ▣ 01/01-31/12
Distance: 🚶500m ⊗500m 🚰200m kiosk ⚑50m.

Dinslaken 8F3

Am Rotbachsee, Am Freibad. **GPS:** n51,56707 e6,77807. ⬆ ➡.

10 🛌free. **Surface:** sand. ▣ 01/01-31/12
Distance: 🚶100m ⊗100m 🚰100m.

Dormagen 10F1

Parkplatz Flügeldeich, Herrenweg, Feste Zons.
GPS: n51,12553 e6,85001. ⬆.

3 🛌€ 5. **Surface:** metalled. ▣ 01/01-31/12
Distance: 🚶400m ⚡on the spot 🚰on the spot ⊗100m 🚰500m.
Remarks: Near the Rhine river, max. 3 days.

Dorsten 8F3

Reisemobilhafen An der Lippe, Zur Lippe.
GPS: n51,66550 e6,96744. ⬆ ➡.

38 🛌€ 5 🚰🍴Ch ⚡(34x)€1/8h. **Surface:** metalled/sand.
▣ 01/01-31/12
Distance: 🚶300m ⊗300m 🚰300m.

Tourist information Dorsten:

⛺ Marler Str.. Flea market. ☐ 2nd Su of the month, 11-18h.

Dortmund 8G3

Mobil-Camp Wischlingen, Wischlinger Weg 50-61, Wischlingen. **GPS:** n51,52001 e7,39868. ⬆️➡️.

50 ⬆️€ 8, 2 pers.incl ⬆️€1/80liter ⬆️Ch⬆️(30x)€0,50/kWh WC⬆️1. **Surface:** asphalted. ☐ 01/01-31/12 **Distance:** 🚶1km 🛒Rewe 1km 🚌200m. **Remarks:** Former tennis-court in recreation area.

Drensteinfurt 8G3

Am Erlbad, Im Erlfeld 2. **GPS:** n51,78972 e7,74778. ⬆️.

3 ⬆️€ 3/pp ⬆️Ch⬆️€3/24h WCincluded ⬆️€3. **Location:** Rural, simple, noisy. **Surface:** asphalted/metalled. ☐ 01/05-15/09 **Distance:** 🚶800m 🚲9km 🛒800m. **Remarks:** Max. 3 nights, max. 8M, check in at swimming pool, swimming pool incl.

Duisburg 8F3

Landschaftspark Duisburg-Nord, Emscherstraße 71, Meiderich. **GPS:** n51,48413 e6,78077. ⬆️free ⬆️Ch. **Surface:** asphalted. ☐ 01/01-31/12 **Distance:** 🚲1,6km.

Dülmen 8F3

Reisemobilstellplatz Hüttendyk, Ecke Halterner Strasse. **GPS:** n51,82606 e7,27228. ⬆️➡️.

8 ⬆️free ⬆️€1/80liter ⬆️Ch(8x)€2/8h. **Location:** Rural, simple. **Surface:** metalled. ☐ 01/01-31/12 **Distance:** 🚶500m 🛒200m 🚌100m. **Remarks:** Max. 72h.

Dülmen 8F3

Reisemobilstellplatz Kapellenweg, Kapellenweg. **GPS:** n51,82331 e7,27945. ⬆️.

7 ⬆️free ⬆️Ch. **Location:** Rural, simple. **Surface:** metalled. ☐ 01/01-31/12 **Distance:** 🚶500m 🛒600m on the spot on the spot. **Remarks:** Max. 72h.

Dülmen 8F3

Reisemobilstellplatz Düb, Nordlandwehr 99. **GPS:** n51,84408 e7,27300. ⬆️➡️.

7 ⬆️free. **Location:** Rural, simple. **Surface:** grasstiles/metalled. ☐ 01/01-31/12 **Distance:** 🚶2km 🛒1km. **Remarks:** Max. 72h.

Dülmen 8F3

Reisemobilstellplatz Hausdulmen, Sandstrasse. **GPS:** n51,80707 e7,24746. ⬆️➡️.

20 ⬆️free. **Location:** Rural, simple, quiet. **Surface:** grassy. ☐ 01/01-31/12 **Distance:** 🚶2,5km ⊗500m 🛒400m on the spot. **Remarks:** Max. 72h.

Düren 10E2

IG Reisemobilhafen Düren, Rurstrasse 188. **GPS:** n50,80861 e6,46556.

20 ⬆️€7 ⬆️Chincluded ⬆️(18x)€2. **Location:** Rural, simple, quiet. **Surface:** gravel. **Distance:** 🚶900m ⊗Bistro 100m 🛒Lidl 500m. **Remarks:** Service passerby € 2.

Düsseldorf 10F1

P Rheinterasse/Tonhalle, Robert-Lehr-Ufer. **GPS:** n51,23710 e6,77029. ⬆️.

30 ⬆️€ 2/h, max. € 12/24h. **Surface:** metalled. ☐ 01/01-31/12 **Distance:** 🚶Old city centre 1km ⊗50m 🛒1,3km.

Düsseldorf 10F1

Wohnmobilstellplatz Düsseldorf/Erkrath, Heinrich-Hertz-Straße 18, Unterfeldhaus, Düsseldorf/Erkrath. **GPS:** n51,19825 e6,91679. ⬆️.

6 ⬆️€ 6 ⬆️€1/100liter ⬆️Ch included. **Location:** Urban, simple, quiet. **Surface:** metalled. ☐ 01/01-31/12 **Distance:** 🚶500m 🚲5,5km ⊗300m 🚌50m. **Tourist information Düsseldorf:**

ℹ️ Tourist Info, Immermannstrasse, Gegenüber Station; Kö-Galerie/Finanzhaus, Berliner Alee; Burgplatz, Berliner Allee, www.duesseldorf-tourismus.de. Historical centre, important city of fashion, all large marks established in the Königsallee, Umweltzone: the green environmental badge is required. During the Caravan Salon (by the end of August/beginning September) there is a large area for motorhomes available. Free shuttlebus to the exhibition and Old city centre. Also several events on the exhibition grounds.

Eckenhagen 10G1

Rodener Festplatz, Rodener Platz. **GPS:** n50,98667 e7,69361. ⬆️.

20 ⬆️free ⬆️Chfree. **Location:** Urban, simple, quiet. **Surface:** asphalted/gravel. ☐ 01/01-31/12 **Distance:** 🚶200m 🚲4km ⊗300m 🛒300m on the spot 🧍on the spot.

Emmerich 8E3

Auf dem Eltenberg, Luitgardisstraße. **GPS:** n51,86559 e6,17265. ⬆️➡️.

25 ⬆️free. **Location:** Rural, simple. **Surface:** grasstiles. ☐ 01/01-31/12 **Distance:** 🚶1km ⊗1km 🛒on the spot.

Emmerich 8E3

P6, Kleiner Wall, Rheinpromenade. **GPS:** n51,83229 e6,23594. ⬆️.

6 ⬆️free. **Location:** Urban, simple, noisy. **Surface:** unpaved. ☐ 01/01-31/12 **Distance:** 🚶on the spot.

Emmerich 8E3

Yachthafen, Fackeldeystrasse 15-65. **GPS:** n51,83693 e6,21948. ⬆️.

75 ⬆️€ 8,50 ⬆️Ch(80x) WC⬆️€0,50 ⬆️1. **Location:** Rural, comfortable. **Surface:** grassy/metalled. ☐ 01/01-31/12 **Distance:** 🚶2,5km on the spot ⊗on the spot 🛒on the spot on the spot 🧍on the spot.

Ennepetal 10G1

Am Platsch, Mittelstraße 108. **GPS:** n51,29295 e7,37668. ⬆️.

DE

4 ⛺ € 3 ⚡ included. 🚿 **Surface:** gravel. 📅 01/01-31/12
Distance: 🚲 10,8km ⊗5km 🚰5km 🚮on the spot ♻️on the spot
🚶routes for nordic walking.
Remarks: Check in at pay-desk of swimming pool, on the spot: bistro, pool, sauna and golf court.

Ennepetal 🌿🌳 10G1

Firma Möller-Elektronic, Königstrasse 17, Oelkinghausen.
GPS: n51,29086 e7,32050.

5 ⛺ free 🔌€3 🚰Ch 🚿. **Location:** Urban, simple, quiet.
Surface: metalled. 📅 01/01-31/12
Distance: 🚶2km 🚲11km ⊗1km 🚰200m 🚮on the spot 🚶on the spot.

Ennigerloh 8G3

Am Freibad 3. **GPS:** n51,83304 e8,01629. ⬆️➡️

2 ⛺ free 🔌€0,50/50liter 🚰Ch 🚿€0,50/kWh. **Location:** Rural, simple, noisy. **Surface:** metalled. 📅 01/01-31/12
Distance: 🚶600m 🚮600m 🚰600m ♻️on the spot 🚶on the spot.

Erftstadt 10F2

Mobilcamp am Ville-Express, Carl-Schurz-strasse 1a, Liblar.
GPS: n50,81781 e6,81986. ⬆️➡️

11 ⛺ € 6 🔌€1/80liter 🚰Ch 🚿(11x)€0,50/kWh. 🚌
Location: Urban, comfortable. **Surface:** metalled.
📅 01/01-31/12
Distance: 🚶1km 🚲4,4km 🚰500m ⊗200m 🚰1km.

Erndtebrück 10H1

Pension Hofius, Hilchenbachterweg 2, Zinse.
GPS: n51,00599 e8,21224. ➡️

3 ⛺ € 7/24h 🔌 🚰Ch 🚿WC 🚮 📅 01/01-31/12
Distance: 🚶5km ♻️on the spot 🚶on the spot.

Everswinkel 8G2

Vitus-Bad, Alverkirchenerstrasse 29. **GPS:** n51,92309 e7,83776. ⬆️.

3 ⛺ free 🔌€0,50/50liter 🚰Ch 🚿€0,50/kWh. **Location:** Rural, simple, noisy. **Surface:** metalled. 📅 01/01-31/12
Distance: 🚶500m 🚮on the spot 🚰100m 🚮on the spot
♻️100-Schlösser-Route 🚶on the spot.
Remarks: Parking swimming pool.

Freudenberg (NRW) 10G1

Lohmühle, P5. **GPS:** n50,89625 e7,87636. ⬆️.

5 ⛺ free. **Surface:** metalled. 📅 01/01-31/12
Distance: 🚶on the spot ⊗100m 🚰200m.
Remarks: Max. 3 days.

Gangelt 10E1

Rodebachtal, Am Freibad 13. **GPS:** n50,98583 e5,99806. ⬆️➡️.

40 ⛺ € 7, weekend € 10 🔌 🚰Ch 🚿WC 🔌€0,50/4minutes.
Location: Rural, luxurious, quiet. **Surface:** metalled. 📅 01/01-31/12
Distance: 🚶on the spot ⊗on the spot 🚰1,5km.
Remarks: Caution key € 10.

Geldern 8E3

Am Holländer See, Am Holländer See 19.
GPS: n51,51131 e6,32867. ⬆️➡️.

50 ⛺ € 7/24h, 3 days € 17 🔌€1/80liter 🚰Ch 🚿€0,50/kWh.
Surface: grassy/metalled. 📅 01/01-31/12
Distance: 🚶1km ⊗1km 🚰1km.
Remarks: Parking centre.

Geldern 8E3

Reisemobilhafen Am Freibad, Am Freibad 6, Walbeck.
GPS: n51,49461 e6,22666. ⬆️➡️.

50 ⛺ € 7/24h 🔌€1/80liter 🚰Ch 🚿(36x)€0,50/kWh.

Surface: grassy/sand. 📅 01/01-31/12
Distance: 🚶city centre Walbeck 1km, city centre Geldern 6km ⊗1km
🚰1km.
Remarks: At swimming pool.

Geldern 8E3

Reisemobilstellplatz Am Sportplatz, Hülspassweg 20, Veert.
GPS: n51,52960 e6,30347. ⬆️➡️.

30 ⛺ free. **Surface:** gravel. 📅 01/01-31/12
Distance: 🚶city centre Veert 200m, city centre Geldern 2km 🚰500m.
Remarks: Parking at sports park.

Geldern 8E3

Freizeit-Store Diepers, Liebligstrasse 33. **GPS:** n51,52971 e6,35456.
🔌€1 🚰€1 Ch. 📅 01/01-31/12, during opening hours

Tourist information Geldern:

🎪 Internationaler Wettbewerb der strassenmaler und strassenmusikanten und -theatergruppen, Centrum. International street painting competition, street musicians and theater groups. 📅 beginning Sep.
🎪 Internationales Reisemobilfest. International festival for motorcaravanners with vast tourist program. Not necessary to book in advance,.
📅 last weekend April. 🎫 free.

Gelsenkirchen 8F3

Revierpark Nienhausen, Feldmarkstraße 201.
GPS: n51,50167 e7,06333. ⬆️.

20 ⛺ € 7, 2 pers.incl. 🔌€1/80liter 🚰Ch 🚿€1/2kWh.
Surface: metalled. 📅 01/01-31/12
Distance: 🚶2,8km 🚲3,2km ⊗100m 🚰2km 🚊Tram 700m.
Remarks: Bread-service.

Gladbeck 8F3

Freizeitstätte Wittringer Wald, Bohmertstrasse 277.
GPS: n51,55912 e6,98403. ⬆️➡️.

20 ⛺ free 🔌 🚰Ch. **Surface:** grasstiles/grassy. 📅 01/01-31/12
Distance: 🚶2km 🚲1km ⊗200m 🚰1km.
Remarks: Green zone: environmental badge obligatory, Wasserschloß Wittringen 450m.

Goch 8E3

Friedensplatz, Thielenstrasse. **GPS:** n51,67556 e6,16639. ⬆️➡️.

70 ⛺ € 4/24h 🔌€1/100liter 🚰Ch 🚿(60x)€0,50/kWh.
Surface: grassy. 📅 01/01-31/12
Distance: 🚶700m 🚮on the spot ⊗700m 🚰700m 🚊100m.

DE

Remarks: Along the Niers river.

| 🏕 | **Goch** | 8E3 |

Reisemobilstellplatz GochNess, Kranenburger Strasse 20, Kessel.
GPS: n51,70291 e6,08915.⬆️.

6 🛏free. **Surface:** grassy.
📅 01/01-31/12
Distance: 🚶1km ⊗1km 🍺1km.
Tourist information Goch:
🏛 Pilgrimage for motorhomes.
☀ last weekend Jun.
☀ Museumscafé Edison, Museum Goch. Collection of gramophones.
📅 Su 15-17h.
🚲 Herrensitz-Route. Cycle route along the Meuse and the Niers, available at Kultourbühne Goch. 🎫 € 5.

| 🏕 | **Grefrath** | 10E1 |

Eissportzentrum Grefrath, Stadionstrasse. **GPS:** n51,34889 e6,33972.
50 🛏free.
Surface: grasstiles.
Distance: 🚶2km 🚊500m ⊗300m 🍺2km.
Remarks: Niederrheinisches Freilichtmuseum, Open air museum 650m.

| 🏕 S | **Greven** | 8G2 |

Reisemobilhafen Camp Marina, Fuestruperstrasse 37, Fuestrup.
GPS: n52,04449 e7,68328.⬆️➡️.

90 🛏€ 11 ⛽€0,50/50liter 🚽Ch🚿€2,50 WC🚻€1 💧€3/2,50.
Location: Comfortable. **Surface:** grassy.
📅 01/01-31/12
Distance: 🏊on the spot ⊗Restaurant/Biergarten 🍺3km 🚴on the spot 🚶on the spot.
Remarks: Marina at canal, bread-service, shopping service.

| 🏕 S | **Gronau** 〰 | 8F2 |

Erholungsgebiet Dreiländersee, Brechter Weg.
GPS: n52,23716 e7,08006.⬆️➡️.

80 🛏€ 8/24, only exact change ⛽€0,50/130liter 🚽Ch🚿(32x)€1/4h
WC🚻 🏠 **Location:** Rural, simple, isolated. **Surface:** grassy/metalled.
📅 01/01-31/12
Distance: 🚶3km 🚊100m 🚴on the spot ⊗200m 🍺50m (camping) 🚐on the spot.
Remarks: Near the lake, max. 48h.

| 🏕 S | **Haltern am See** | 8F3 |

Wohnmobilpark Haltern am See, Hullerner Straße 45-49.
GPS: n51,74186 e7,20179.⬆️.
20 🛏€ 10 ⛽€1/100liter 🚽Ch🚿(20x)€0,50/kWh WC🚻🚻.
Surface: grasstiles.
Distance: 🚶1km 🚊300m ⊗on the spot.
Remarks: At swimming pool.

| 🏕 | **Haltern am See** | 8F3 |

RMS ReisemobileSpezialist, Hellweg 252.
GPS: n51,75589 e7,20127.⬆️.

4 🛏€ 7 ⛽€1/70liter 🚽Ch🚿€3,50. 🏠 **Location:** Rural, simple, isolated. **Surface:** grassy/gravel. 📅 01/01-31/12
Distance: 🚶Old city centre 1km ⊗800m 🍺800m.

| 🏕 | **Hamm** | 8G3 |

Freizeitpark Maximilian Park, Alter Grenzweg 2.
GPS: n51,68392 e7,88395.⬆️.

10 🛏free. **Location:** Rural, simple. **Surface:** grassy.
📅 01/01-31/12
Distance: 🚶300m ⊗300m 🍺300m 🚊200m 🚴on the spot 🚶on the spot.

| 🏕 | **Harsewinkel** | 8H2 |

Frei- und Hallenbad, Prozessionsweg 8. **GPS:** n51,96556 e8,21935.

6 🛏free. **Location:** Rural, simple, quiet. **Surface:** grassy.
📅 01/01-31/12
Distance: 🚶200m ⊗100m 🍺200m 🚊200m 🚴on the spot.
Remarks: Parking next to swimming pool, max. 48h.

| 🏕 S | **Hattingen** 🍴 💧 | 8F3 |

Wohnmobilstellplatz Ruhrtal, Ruhrdeich 24.
GPS: n51,40839 e7,18091.⬆️➡️.

15 🛏€ 7 ⛽€1/80liter 🚽Ch🚿(12x)€1/2kWh 📶free.
Location: Rural, comfortable, quiet. **Surface:** gravel.
📅 01/01-31/12
Distance: 🚶2,5km 🚊5km 🏊on the spot 🚴on the spot ⊗500m 🍺1km.
Remarks: Along the Ruhr river, next to midget golf, bread-service.

| 🏕 | **Hattingen** 🍴 💧 | 8F3 |

August-Bebel strasse. **GPS:** n51,39833 e7,18028.

2 🛏€ 3. 🏠 **Location:** Urban, simple, central, noisy. **Surface:** metalled.
📅 01/01-31/12

Distance: 🚶on the spot 🚊5km ⊗on the spot 🍺on the spot 🚐on the spot.
Remarks: At shopping centre Carré.

| 🏕 | **Hattingen** 🍴 💧 | 8F3 |

Roonstrasse. **GPS:** n51,40167 e7,18389.⬆️➡️.

2 🛏free. **Location:** Urban, simple, quiet. **Surface:** asphalted/metalled.
📅 01/01-31/12
Distance: 🚶300m 🚊5km ⊗300m 🍺300m.

| 🏕 | **Hattingen** 💧 | 8F3 |

Ruhrgasse, Bahnhofstrasse. **GPS:** n51,40127 e7,17700.➡️.

3 🛏free. **Location:** Urban, simple, quiet. **Surface:** gravel.
📅 01/01-31/12
Distance: 🚶500m 🚊5km ⊗500m 🍺500m.
Remarks: Parking behind the Amtshäusern, only on Sa and Su.

| 🏕 | **Hattingen** 🍴 💧 | 8F3 |

Wanderparkplatz, Isenbergstrasse. **GPS:** n51,38969 e7,15340.⬆️.

3 🛏free. **Location:** Rural, simple. **Surface:** gravel.
📅 Mo-Fri, 01/01-31/12
Distance: 🚶2km 🚊5km ⊗300m 🍺1km 🚐on the spot 🚴on the spot 🚶on the spot.
Remarks: Parking along the Ruhr, max. 2 days.

| 🏕 S | **Havixbeck** 🌿 | 8G2 |

Freibad, Kardinal von Hartmann strasse.
GPS: n51,97507 e7,42092.⬆️➡️.

8 🛏free ⛽€1/80liter 🚽Ch🚿against payment WC🚻.
Location: Simple, quiet. **Surface:** metalled. 📅 01/01-31/12
Distance: 🚶1km 🚊1km ⊗800m 🍺800m.
Remarks: Parking at swimming pool, small pitches.

| 🏕 | **Havixbeck** 🌿 | 8G2 |

Blickallee 44. **GPS:** n51,97480 e7,41168.⬆️.

4 free. **Location:** Urban, simple, noisy. **Surface:** metalled. 01/01-31/12
Distance: 100m 100m on the spot 100m.
Remarks: At supermarket, small pitches.

Havixbeck 8G2
Klute's Historischem Brauhaus, Poppenbeck 28.
GPS: n51,98938 e7,39291.

15 free. **Location:** Rural, simple. **Surface:** grasstiles. 01/01-31/12
Distance: 500m 200m.
Remarks: Service on campsite.

Hellenthal 10E3
Wohnmobilhafen Weißer Stein, Am Weissen Stein, Udenbreth, B265.
GPS: n50,40896 e6,37220.

22 €5 Ch **Location:** Rural, comfortable.
Surface: metalled. 01/01-31/12
Distance: on the spot 2km 200m.
Remarks: At swimming pool.

Herford 8H2
Am Stadion, Dennewitzstrasse 15. **GPS:** n52,10474 e8,68931.

15 guests free (8x)€5 . **Location:** Rural, simple, isolated. **Surface:** metalled. 01/01-31/12
Distance: 2km on the spot 2km.

Heiligenhaus 10F1
Westfalenstrasse. **GPS:** n51,32853 e6,97327.
3 free. **Location:** Simple. **Surface:** metalled. 01/01-31/12
Distance: 200m 200m 200m.

Heimbach 10E2
Womohafen Heimbach, An der Laag 4. **GPS:** n50,63683 e6,47265.

28 €9 €2 Ch (28x).
Location: Rural, simple. **Surface:** metalled. 01/01-31/12
Distance: on the spot on the spot.
Remarks: Service on campsite, winter sports area Hellenthal am Wald.

Hellenthal 10E3
Breuerhof, Zum Wilsamtal 39, Udenbreth.
GPS: n50,41081 e6,38992.

3 free. **Location:** Rural, simple. 01/01-31/12
Distance: 2,5km 1,8km 100m 100m 2,5km 2,5km.

Herscheid 10G1
Am Warmwasserfreibad, Unterdorfstraße.
GPS: n51,17567 e7,74368.

19 €7,50/24h, €0,45/pp tourist tax €1/100liter Ch (20x)€0,50/kWh. **Location:** Rural, simple, noisy. **Surface:** gravel. 01/01-31/12
Distance: 200m 100m on the spot.
Remarks: Nearby Regioshuttle Rurtallbahn.

Heinsberg 10E1
Heinsberg am Lago, Fritz-Bauer-Strasse 3.
GPS: n51,07333 e6,09278.

2 €10 Ch (2x). **Location:** Rural, comfortable, quiet.
Surface: metalled.
Distance: 2km on the spot.
Remarks: Check in at nr. 35.

Tourist information Hellenthal:
Greifvogelstation. Predatory bird station. 01/11-31/03 9-17h, 01/04-31/10 9-18h.

Hemer 8G3
Wohnmobilstellplatz Hemer, Hönnetalstraße.
GPS: n51,37841 e7,77151.

3 free. €1/10minutes Ch (4x)€1/8h.
Location: Rural, comfortable, quiet. **Surface:** gravel. 01/01-31/12
Distance: 1,2km 10km 400m 650m on the spot.

Hilchenbach 10H1
Hallenbad Dahlbruch, Bernhard-Weiss-Platz, Dahlbruch.
GPS: n50,97792 e8,05343.

44 P1 €10/day, P2 €10/2 days €1/100liter Ch (31x)€0,50/kWh. **Location:** Rural, luxurious, quiet.
Surface: grasstiles.
Distance: 1km Bagger See on the spot 800m.

Hellenthal 10E3
Grenzlandhalle Hellenthal, Aachenerstrasse.
GPS: n50,49251 e6,43651.

20 €2/8-20h €1/100liter Ch €1 (12x)€0,50/kWh.
Location: Urban, comfortable, quiet. **Surface:** asphalted/grassy. 01/01-31/12
Distance: 1km 6km 300m bakery 500m on the spot.

Herford 8H2
H2O, Wiessenstrasse 90. **GPS:** n52,10750 e8,68534.

3 free. €1/10minutes . **Surface:** asphalted/metalled. 01/01-31/12
Distance: 400m 400m.
Remarks: Parking behind swimming pool, max. 48h.

Hilchenbach 10H1
Bürgerhaus, Merklinghäuser weg, Müsen.
GPS: n50,99267 e8,04497.

3 free. **Surface:** asphalted. 01/01-31/12
Remarks: Max. 48h.

DE

Hilchenbach 10H1

Parkplatz P4, Rothenberger strasse, L728.
GPS: n50,99702 e8,11103.

3 free. **Surface**: metalled.
01/01-31/12
Distance: 100m 200m 100m.
Remarks: Parking in front of shopping centre Gerberpark, max. 48h.

Hilchenbach 10H1

Landhotel Steubers Siebelnhof, Siebelnhoferstrasse, Vormwald.
GPS: n50,98658 e8,13173.
6 € 20,50, use sanitary facilities/swimming pool sauna incl
WC included. 01/01-31/12
Distance: on the spot.

Hille 8H1

Am Marktplatz, Sportplatzweg 31. **GPS**: n52,34205 e8,73017.

8 free €1 Ch €1. **Location**: Rural, quiet. **Surface**: gravel.
01/01-31/12
Distance: 1km 500m.

Hopsten 8G1

Dreifachturnhalle, Rüschendorfer strasse 4.
GPS: n52,38544 e7,60490.

6 free Chfree. **Location**: Rural, simple.
Surface: grassy/metalled. 01/01-31/12
Distance: 100m 100m 100m on the spot on the spot.
Remarks: Parking at gymnasium, max. 3 days.

Horn 9A2

Wohnmobilhafen Mein Bad, Wällenweg, Bad Meinberg.
GPS: n51,89818 e8,99249.

35 € 5 + € 2,60/pp tourist tax €1/100liter Ch €0,50/kWh.
Location: Rural, quiet. **Surface**: grassy/metalled.
01/01-31/12
Distance: 200m on the spot 200m 100m.
Remarks: Behind spa, discount at swimming pool.

Hörstel 8G2

Wohnmobilhafen Riesenbeck, Postdamm-Lazarusbrücke.
GPS: n52,25574 e7,63387.

20 free €1/2kWh. **Location**: Rural, comfortable, central, noisy.
Surface: grassy/gravel. 01/01-31/12
Distance: 700m on the spot on the spot 300m on the
spot 100-Schlösser-Route on the spot.
Remarks: Max. 3 nights.

Hövelhof 8H2

P Bahnhof, Westfalenstrasse. **GPS**: n51,82417 e8,66099.

6 free free (6x)€1/kWh. **Location**: Urban. **Surface**: gravel.
01/01-31/12
Distance: 500m 4,2km 500m 500m 50m on the spot
on the spot.

Höxter 9A3

Freizeitanlage Godelheimer See, Godelheimer Strasse, Höxter-
Godelheim. **GPS**: n51,75787 e9,37557.

50 € 6 ChWC included. **Location**: Comfortable.
Surface: grasstiles. 01/01-31/12 service: 01/10-01/04
Distance: 2km on the spot river 500m on the spot 2km
on the spot on the spot.
Remarks: Bread-service, recreation area.

Höxter 9A3

Wohnmobilhafen Flossplatz, Milchweg.
GPS: n51,77325 e9,38781.

50 € 6, only overnight stay € 4 €1/100liter Ch (18x)€
0,50/kWh. **Location**: Rural, comfortable, central, quiet.
Surface: grassy/gravel. 01/01-31/12
Distance: 300m on the spot fishing permit available 100m
300m 500m on camp site 50m.
Remarks: Parking beside river Weser.

Hückelhoven 10E1

Hückelhovener Ruraue, Rheinstraße 4b. **GPS**: n51,05111 e6,21306.

6 € 4,50 €0,50/100liter Ch €0,50/kWh.
Location: Rural, simple, isolated, quiet. **Surface**: metalled.
01/01-31/12 With snow
Distance: 1,5km.

Hürtgenwald 10E2

Einmünding Kall-Rur, Zerkall. **GPS**: n50,69156 e6,45212.

10 free. **Location**: Rural, simple. **Surface**: gravel.
01/01-31/12
Distance: 100m on the spot on the spot 200m.
Remarks: Along the river Kall/Rur.

Hürtgenwald 10E2

Parkplatz Burgstrasse, Burgstrasse, Bergstein.
GPS: n50,69582 e6,43848.

5 free. **Location**: Simple. **Surface**: metalled.
01/01-31/12

Hürtgenwald 10E2

Soldatenfriedhof, Höhenstrasse, Hürtgen.
GPS: n50,70552 e6,36063.

9 free. **Location**: Rural, simple, noisy. **Surface**: asphalted.
01/01-31/12

Hürtgenwald 10E2

Simonskall 20, Kallweg. **GPS**: n50,66716 e6,35395.

5 free. **Location**: Rural, comfortable, quiet. **Surface**: metalled.
01/01-31/12
Distance: 200m on the spot.

Hüsten 8G3

Parkplatz Große Wiese. **GPS**: n51,43151 e8,00475.
4 free. **Surface**: asphalted.
Distance: 2km.

DE

Remarks: Next to the Sole-Bad.

Ibbenbüren 8G2
Aseebad, An der Umfluth 99. **GPS:** n52,26181 e7,73171.

30 €3. **Location:** Comfortable, central, quiet.
Surface: grassy.
Distance: 2,3km.
Remarks: Parking next to swimming pool, max. 4 nights.

Iserlohn 8G3
Parkplatz Seilerblick, Friesenstraße. **GPS:** n51,38456 e7,71128.

5 free €1 Ch€1 (4x)€0,50. **Location:** Urban, simple, noisy.
Surface: asphalted. 01/01-31/12
Distance: 2km 2,5km on the spot on the spot.
Remarks: Next to tennis-court.

Isselburg 8E3
Hotel Restaurant Brüggenhütte, Hahnerfeld 23, Anholt.
GPS: n51,85301 e6,47187.

5 free. **Location:** Rural, simple. **Surface:** grassy.
01/01-31/12
Distance: 200m on the spot.
Remarks: Along through road, behind restaurant.

Isselburg 8E3
Parkplatz Zentrum, Münsterdeich. **GPS:** n51,83452 e6,46477.

5 free. **Location:** Simple. **Surface:** grassy. 01/01-31/12
Distance: on the spot on the spot 300m 100m.
Remarks: At the Issel, parking centre, max. 72h.

Isselburg 8E3
Spargelhof Mäteling, Buchenallee 4, Anholt.
GPS: n51,84120 e6,41597.

5 free. **Location:** Rural, simple. **Surface:** asphalted.

01/01-31/12
Distance: on the spot.
Remarks: Max. 72h.

Isselburg 8E3
Bürgerhaus, Anholter strasse, Vehlingen. **GPS:** n51,83089 e6,42297.

3 free. **Location:** Rural, simple. **Surface:** gravel. 01/01-31/12
May
Distance: on the spot.
Remarks: Max. 2 nights.

Isselburg 8E3
Ponyhof Leiting, Alte Bundesstrasse 3, Werth.
GPS: n51,81332 e6,49258.

10 free. **Location:** Simple. **Surface:** grassy. 01/01-31/12
Distance: on the spot.
Remarks: Max. 72h.

Issum-Sevelen 8E3
Wohnmobilpark Hexenland-Sevelen, Koetherdyck 18.
GPS: n51,49926 e6,43676.

20 €9 Ch €3/24h WC.
Surface: gravel. 01/01-31/12
Distance: Sevelen 1km 200m 100m 1km.

Jülich 10E1
Brückenkopf-Park, Rurauenstrasse 11. **GPS:** n50,92345 e6,34029.

22 €8,50 €1/100liter Ch WC. **Location:** Simple, noisy. **Surface:** grassy. 01/01-31/12 sanitary building: 1/11-31/3
Remarks: Parking at the Rur.

Tourist information Jülich:
Old fortress city.

Kalkar 8E3
Reisemobilstellplatz Kalkar, Waysche strasse.
GPS: n51,74008 e6,30101.

35 €4/24h €1/100liter Ch €1/5kWh.
Location: Rural, comfortable. **Surface:** grassy/gravel.
01/01-31/12
Distance: 500m 400m 700m.
Remarks: Max. 3 nights.

Tourist information Kalkar:
KernWasser Wunderland. Amusement park.

Kall 10F2
Im Kallbachtal, Kapellenstrasse 25, Golbach.
GPS: n50,52784 e6,53681.

6 €6 €1 Ch (8x)€0,50/kWh. **Location:** Rural, simple,
quiet. **Surface:** gravel. 01/01-31/12

Kamp-Lintfort 8E3
Pappelsee, Berthastraße 74. **GPS:** n51,50026 e6,53861.

20 free. **Surface:** asphalted. 01/01-31/12
Distance: 1,5km 1km 1,5km.
Remarks: Caution € 2,50 to pay-desk of the park.

Tourist information Kamp-Lintfort:
Marktplatz, Eberstrasse. Thu, Sa.
Rathausplatz. Tue 7.30-13h.
Mittelalterlicher Markt, Abteiplatz. Medieval market. 3rd
weekend Sep.

Kempen 10E1
Reisemobilpark Kempen am Aqua-sol, Berliner Allee.
GPS: n51,36719 e6,40910.

29 €7 €1/100liter Ch €0,50/kWh. **Surface:** metalled.
01/01-31/12
Distance: 1,5km on the spot 1,5km.

Kerken 8E3
Wohnmobilpark Aldekerker Platte, Kempener Straße 9, Aldekerk.
GPS: n51,43551 e6,41902.

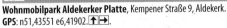

30 ⌰€9 ⌁—⌁Ch⌁€3. **Surface:** grassy/gravel. ⌂ 01/01-31/12
Distance: 600m ⊗600m 600m.

Kevelaer 8E3

Den Heyberg, Im Auwelt 45, Twisteden. **GPS**: n51,56345 e6,19418.⬆

150 ⌰€ 8,50 ⌁—Ch⌁(150x)included.
Surface: asphalted/metalled. ⌂ 01/01-31/12
Distance: 2km ⊗100m 2km 100m.
Remarks: Bread-service (weekend), barbecue place.

Kevelaer 8E3

Sporthotel Schravelsche Heide, Grotendonkerstrasse 54-58.
GPS: n51,59556 e6,25306.⬆⮕

80 ⌰€7 ⌁—Ch⌁WC⌁included. **Surface:** grassy.
⌂ 01/01-31/12
Distance: 1,5km ⊗100m 1km.
Remarks: To pay at sanitary building tennis-courts.

Kevelaer 8E3

Europaplatz, Bahnhof/Geldernstrasse, B9.
GPS: n51,57904 e6,25192.⬆

3 ⌰free. **Surface:** asphalted.
Distance: 500m ⊗500m on the spot.

Tourist information Kevelaer:
⌂ Fr 14-18h.

Kirchhundem 10H1

Restaurant Rhein-Wester-Turm, Alfons Kleffmann, Rhein-Weser-Turm. **GPS**: n51,07109 e8,19791.

10 ⌰€ 10 ⌁—Ch⌁included. ⌂ 01/01-31/12
Distance: ⊗on the spot.

Kirchhundem 10H1

Panorama-Park, Rinsecker Straße 100. **GPS**: n51,06972 e8,17417.⬆
10 ⌰free. ⌂ 01/01-31/12

Kleve 8E3

Van-den-Bergh-Straße. GPS: n51,78917 e6,14836.⬆

60 ⌰€ 4 ⌁—Ch⌁(30x)€0,50/kWh. ⌁ **Location:** Urban, simple.
Surface: metalled. ⌂ 01/01-31/12
Distance: 500m.

Kleve 8E3

Reisemobilpark Kleve, Landwehr/Spyckstraße.
GPS: n51,80083 e6,13222.⬆

75 ⌰€ 6,50, 2 pers.incl ⌁—€1 ⌁Ch⌁(45x)€2,50 WC€0,50 ⌁€1 ⌁.
⌁ **Location:** Comfortable. **Surface:** grassy/metalled. ⌂ 01/01-31/12
Distance: Kleve-zentrum 1,5km ⊗300m 400m.

Kleve 8E3

Am Willisee, Zyfflicherstrasse 33, Keeken.
GPS: n51,84013 e6,08307.⬆

25 ⌰€ 9 ⌁—Ch⌁(25x)€2/day ⌁⌁. **Surface:** grassy/gravel.
⌂ 01/01-31/12
Distance: 900m, Kleve city centre 7km on the spot 200m
⊗400m.
Remarks: Fishing permit available.

Kleve 8E3

Parkplatz Bürgerhaus, Drususdeich, Rindern.
GPS: n51,81212 e6,12884.⬆

5 ⌰free. **Location:** Simple. **Surface:** asphalted. ⌂ 01/01-31/12
Distance: Kleve-zentrum 2,3km ⊗450m 400m.
Remarks: Behind church.

Kleve 8E3

Parkplatz Sporthalle Kleve-Kellen, Postdeich, Kellen.
GPS: n51,80463 e6,16378.⬆

20 ⌰free. **Location:** Rural, simple. **Surface:** metalled.
Distance: 2,5km ⊗Steakhaus 350m on the spot.

Kleve 8E3

Parkplatz Sportplatz Reichswalde, Dorfanger, Reichswalde.
GPS: n51,75985 e6,10243.⬆

10 ⌰free. **Location:** Urban, simple. **Surface:** metalled.
Distance: 5km 500m.

Kleve 8E3

Schenkenschanz. **GPS**: n51,83526 e6,11205.⬆

5 ⌰free. **Location:** Simple. **Surface:** metalled.
⌂ 01/01-31/12
Distance: 2,5km.

Kleve 8E3

Tiergarten, Tiergartenstrasse, B9 dir Nijmegen.
GPS: n51,79784 e6,12059.⬆

5 ⌰free. **Location:** Highway, simple. **Surface:** metalled.
⌂ 01/01-31/12
Distance: 800m ⊗250m.

Kleve 8E3

Wehrpöhl, Griethausen. **GPS**: n51,82476 e6,16448.⬆

5 ⌰free. **Location:** Rural, simple. **Surface:** asphalted.
⌂ 01/01-31/12
Distance: 2,5km ⊗300m 300m.
Remarks: Access via Brienen.

Tourist information Kleve:
⌁ Lichterfest. City celebration. ⌂ 2nd Sa of the month.
⌁ Tiergarten Kleve, Tiergartenstrasse. Animal park.

Köln 10F1

Reisemobilhafen Köln, An der Schanz, Cologne (Köln).
GPS: n50,96265 e6,98254. ⬆➡.

65 🚐€ 10/24h 🚰€1 Ch 🔌(30x)€0,50/kWh. 🚽📷
Location: Urban, comfortable, quiet. **Surface:** asphalted.
Distance: 🚶on the spot 🚲5km 🚇 metro 10 min walking.
Remarks: Along the Rhine river.

Königswinter 10F2

Hauptstrasse, Niederdollendorf. **GPS:** n50,69697 e7,17641. ⬆.

30 🚐free. **Location:** Urban, simple. **Surface:** asphalted/metalled.
🗓 01/01-31/12
Distance: 🚶400m 🚲9km 🚌800m on the spot 🚶 on the spot.

Kranenburg 8E3

Am Sportzentrum, Großen Haag. **GPS:** n51,79242 e6,01033. ⬆➡.

30 🚐€ 4 🚰€0,20/liter Ch 🔌(12x)€0,50/kWh. 🚽
Location: Rural, simple. **Surface:** grassy. 🗓 01/01-31/12
Distance: 🚶500m 🏊1km 🚲1km ⊗500m 🚰500m.
Remarks: Service 500m.

Kreuztal 10G1

Heugraben. **GPS:** n50,95778 e7,99167. ⬆.

2 🚐free 🚰€1/100liter Ch 🔌€1/2kWh. **Surface:** metalled.
Distance: 🚶300m 🚲7,5km ⊗300m 🚰300m 🚌 station 100m.
Remarks: Max. 3 days.

Kürten 10G1

Wohnmobil Park - Kürten, Broch 8. **GPS:** n51,05586 e7,28943. ⬆.

20 🚐€ 8 🚰€2 Chincluded 🔌€3. **Location:** Rural, simple, quiet.
Surface: gravel.
🗓 01/01-31/12
Distance: 🚶2km 🚲17km ⊗on the spot on the spot 🚶 on the spot.

Ladbergen 8G2

Rathauspark, Jahnstrasse. **GPS:** n52,13652 e7,74009.

8 🚐free. **Location:** Rural, simple, quiet. **Surface:** grassy.
🗓 01/01-31/12
Distance: 🚶200m ⊗200m 🚰300m 🚌200m 🚶 on the spot.
Remarks: Parking behind town hall.

Lennestadt 10H1

Parkplatz P4, An der Sauerlandhalle. **GPS:** n51,10557 e8,08017. ⬆.

4 🚐free 🔌(4x)€0,50/4h. **Surface:** asphalted. 🗓 01/01-31/12
Distance: 🚶700m ⊗700m 🚰100m.

Leverkusen 10F1

Camping-Caravaning Meier, Adolf-Kaschny-Straße 9, Küppersteg.
GPS: n51,05211 e7,00003. ⬆.

10 🚐free 🚰€0,50 Ch€0,50. **Location:** Urban. **Surface:** gravel.
🗓 01/01-31/12
Distance: 🚲3,2km.
Remarks: Motorhome dealer, accessory shop, repairs.

Lienen 8G2

Hallenfreibad, Holperdorperstrasse 37/39.
GPS: n52,15575 e7,97392. ⬆➡.

3 🚐free 🚰€5 Ch 🔌 WC €3. **Location:** Simple, quiet.
Surface: metalled. 🗓 01/01-31/12
Distance: 🚶1km ⊗100m 🚰2km 🚶 on the spot 🚶 on the spot.
Remarks: Parking in front of swimming pool, max. 3 nights, service to be paid at swimming pool.

Lindlar 10G1

Am Freizeitpark, Brionner Straße. **GPS:** n51,01550 e7,36645. ⬆➡.

2 🚐free 🚰€1 Ch 🔌(4x)€1/6h. **Location:** Urban, simple.

Surface: metalled. 🗓 01/01-31/12
Distance: 🚶1km 🚲16km ⊗1km 🚰1km 🚶 on the spot 🚶 on the spot.

Lippstadt 8H3

Campingoase Lange, Dorfstraße 47, Benninghausen.
GPS: n51,66103 e8,24435.

15 🚐€ 10, 2 pers.incl 🚰 Ch 🔌 included. **Location:** Rural, simple.
Surface: metalled. 🗓 01/01-31/12
Distance: 🚶300m 🚰 on the spot.

Löhne 8H2

Reisemobilstellplatz, Albert-Schweitzer-strasse 12.
GPS: n52,20399 e8,71892. ⬆➡.

18 🚐€ 8 🚰 Chincluded 🔌(18x)€1/2kWh. **Location:** Rural, quiet.
Surface: metalled. 🗓 01/01-31/12
Distance: 🚶500m 🚲1km 🚌100m ⊗500m 🚰500m.

Lotte 8G2

Fam. Arendröwer, Am Nordberg 4. **GPS:** n52,26306 e7,89833. ⬆.

4 🚐€ 4 🚰 🔌€2/24 📶included. **Location:** Simple, isolated, noisy.
Surface: grassy/metalled. 🗓 01/03-01/10
Distance: 🚶3km 🚲500m 🚰3km.

Lotte 8G2

Tennishalle Lotte, Kornweg 3. **GPS:** n52,27192 e7,92275. ⬆.

10 🚐free. **Location:** Simple, quiet. **Surface:** gravel/metalled.
🗓 01/01-31/12
Distance: 🚶900m 🚲3,5km 🚌1km 🚌300m.

Lübbecke 8H1

Stellplatz Lübbecke, Rahdener Straße. **GPS:** n52,31019 e8,61839.

4 🚐€ 6 🚰€3 Ch 🔌€3. ⬆ **Location:** Urban, central.
Surface: metalled. 🗓 01/01-31/12

DE

Distance: 🛏600m 🚽500m.
Remarks: Max. 3 days.

| 🖼S | Lüdenscheid 🚻 | 10G1 |

Familienbad Nattenberg, Talstraße 59.
GPS: n51,21042 e7,61803. ⬆➡.

4 🚐free 🚰€1 🔧Ch 💧€1/6h. **Location:** Urban, simple.
Surface: metalled. 📅 01/01-31/12
Distance: 🚶city centre 1,6km 🚲4km ⊗Burger King 450m 🚽Aldi 900m 🚰on the spot.

| 🖼 | Lüdinghausen 🚻 | 8G3 |

Parkplatz Aqua-See, Rohrkamp 23. **GPS:** n51,77229 e7,42731. ⬆.

10 🚐free. **Location:** Rural, simple, quiet. **Surface:** metalled.
📅 01/01-31/12
Distance: 🚶1,5km ⊗1km 🚰on the spot.
Remarks: Parking swimming pool.

| 🖼 | Lüdinghausen 🚻 | 8G3 |

Parkplatz Rosengarten, Am Rosengarten, Seppenrade.
GPS: n51,76407 e7,39728. ⬆.

2 🚐free. **Location:** Simple, quiet. **Surface:** asphalted.
📅 01/01-31/12
Distance: 🚶200m ⊗200m 🚽800m.

| 🖼S | Marsberg 🚻 | 9A3 |

Wohnmobilhafen, Am Sportplatz. **GPS:** n51,45974 e8,84864. ⬆➡.

4 🚐€5 🚰🔧Ch 💧(4x)included. 🧺 **Location:** Urban.
Surface: asphalted.
📅 01/01-31/12
Distance: 🚶100m ⊗200m 🚽200m.
Remarks: Max. 5 days, caution key € 20 (pay-desk of theTherme).

| 🖼S | Mechernich | 10F2 |

Parkplatz Essensgasse, Am Kirchberg, Kommern.
GPS: n50,61376 e6,64479.

8 🚐free. **Location:** Rural, simple, noisy. **Surface:** metalled.
📅 01/01-31/12
Distance: 🚶historical centre 200m.
Remarks: Via B266.

| 🖼 | Mechernich | 10F2 |

Mühlental, Elisabethhütte, B477. **GPS:** n50,59686 e6,63207. ⬆.

40 🚐free. **Location:** Rural, simple, noisy. **Surface:** asphalted.
📅 01/01-31/12
Distance: 🚶500m.

| 🖼S | Meinerzhagen | 10G1 |

An der Musikschule, Schulplatz. **GPS:** n51,10865 e7,64329. ⬆.

3 🚐free 💧(4x)€0,50/kWh. **Location:** Urban, simple, quiet.
Surface: asphalted. 📅 01/01-31/12
Distance: 🚶400m 🚲3km ⊗400m 🚽400m 🚴on the spot 🚶on the spot.

| 🖼S | Meschede 🍽🚻♨ | 10H1 |

Am Wofibad, Im Ohl 13, Freienohl. **GPS:** n51,37574 e8,17664. ⬆.

3 🚐free 🚰against payment. **Location:** Simple. **Surface:** metalled.
📅 01/01-31/12

| 🖼S | Meschede 🍽🚻♨ | 10H1 |

P Hallenbad, Arnsberger Strasse. **GPS:** n51,34897 e8,27356. ⬆➡.

3 🚐free. **Location:** Simple. **Surface:** metalled.
📅 18.30-9.30h
Distance: 🚶500m ⊗on the spot 🚴on the spot ⊗500m 🚽500m.

| 🖼S | Meschede 🍽🚻♨ | 10H1 |

Knaus Campingpark Hennesee, Mielinghausen 7.
GPS: n51,29846 e8,26366. ⬆.

16 🚐€ 8-10 🚰€1/60liter 🔧€0,50 Ch€0,50 💧(16x)€0,70/kWh WC sanitary€2,30-3,50 📍. **Surface:** grassy/metalled.
📅 01/01-31/12
Distance: 🚶5km ⛱100m 🚤100m ⊗on the spot 🚽on the spot 🚴on the spot 🚶on the spot.

| 🖼S | Mettingen | 8G2 |

Hallenbad, Bahnhofstrasse 18-20. **GPS:** n52,31738 e7,78312. ⬆.

2 🚐free 🚰🔧 💧WC. **Location:** Simple. **Surface:** metalled.
📅 01/01-31/12
Distance: 🚶on the spot ⊗200m 🚽200m 🚴on the spot 🚴on the spot 🚶on the spot.
Remarks: Parking swimming pool, service: Kläranlage, Neuenkirchen-erstrasse 208, bicycle rental.

| 🖼S | Minden | 9A2 |

Reisemobilstellplatz Kanzlers Weide, Hausbergerstrasse.
GPS: n52,28750 e8,92551. ⬆.

100 🚐free 🚰€1/120liter 🔧€0,50 Ch 💧(18x)€0,50/kWh,6Amp.
Location: Urban, simple, quiet. **Surface:** metalled.
📅 01/01-31/12
Distance: 🚶200m ⛱50m 🚤50m ⊗200m 🚽200m 🚴200m.
Remarks: Max. 3 nights, not during big events.

| 🖼S | Moers | 8F3 |

Freizeitpark Schoßpark, Krefelder straße.
GPS: n51,44659 e6,61642. ⬆➡.

4 🚐free. **Surface:** grasstiles. 📅 01/01-31/12
Distance: 🚶700m ⊗700m 🚽500m.

| 🖼S | Möhnesee 🚻♨ | 8H3 |

Freizeitanlage Möhnesee-Körbecke, Börnigeweg.
GPS: n51,49160 e8,12555. ⬆.

DE

20 🛏€6/24h ⚡(8x)€2/24h. 🚽 **Location:** Simple.
Surface: metalled. ☐ 01/01-31/12
Distance: 🚰1km ⚓on the spot ⊗on the spot 🍴1km ♻on the spot
🏃on the spot.
Remarks: Max. 24h.

〼Ⓢ **Möhnesee** 🌳🏊 **8H3**
Strandbad, Linkstraße 20, Delecke. **GPS:** n51,49177 e8,08255.⬆.
50 🛏€12 🚰Ch 🔌(16x)WC 🚽included. 🚽🏊 **Location:** Rural,
comfortable, quiet. **Surface:** gravel. ☐ 01/03-01/11
Distance: 🚰Möhnesee 3,5km ⛵7,3km A44 ⚓Möhnesee

Möhnesee 🌳🏊 **8H3**
Völlinghausen, Kettelbötel. **GPS:** n51,47360 e8,19831.⬆➡.

10 🛏free. **Surface:** grassy/gravel. ☐ 01/01-31/12
Distance: ⚓1,5km ⊗on the spot 🏃on the spot.

〼 **Mönchengladbach** **10E1**
Schloß Wickrath, Neukircherweg, Wickrath.
GPS: n51,12889 e6,42258.⬆.

10 🛏free. **Surface:** asphalted. ☐ 01/01-31/12
Distance: 🚰2km ⊗2km 🍴500m.
Remarks: Parking behind castle (500m), max. 2 days.

〼Ⓢ **Mönchengladbach** **10E1**
Camping-Center Krings, Monschauerstrasse 10/32.
GPS: n51,19454 e6,40884.⬆➡.

15 🛏free 🚰Ch free. **Surface:** metalled. ☐ 01/01-31/12
Distance: 🚰3km ⚓1km 🍴500m.
Remarks: Max. 2 nights, service during opening hours.

〼Ⓢ **Monschau** 🌿🏊🌳🍷 **10E2**
Biesweg, B258. **GPS:** n50,55389 e6,23194.⬆➡.

4 🛏€5/19-10h ⚡€5/7minutes 🏊Ch 🔌(4x)€5/10h.🚽
Location: Simple, noisy. **Surface:** asphalted. ☐ 01/01-31/12
Distance: 🚰600m ⊗600m 🍴600m.
Remarks: Max. 1 night.

🍴 **Monschau** 🌿🏊🌳🍷 **10E2**
Haus Vennblick, Hauptstrasse 24, Höfen. **GPS:** n50,53934 e6,25292.⬆.

6 🛏guests free. **Location:** Rural, simple, noisy. **Surface:** gravel.
⦿ Wed
Distance: 🚰300m ⊗on the spot 🍴4km 🏃on the spot ⚓4km.

〼 **Mülheim/Ruhr** 🏃🏊 **8F3**
Mintarder Straße 4. **GPS:** n51,41462 e6,86934.⬆.

6 🛏free. **Surface:** metalled. ☐ 01/01-31/12
Distance: 🚰2,7km ⊗50m 🍴100m ♻on the spot 🏃on the spot.
Remarks: Max. 72h.

Ⓢ **Mülheim/Ruhr** 🏃🏊 **8F3**
Hymer Zentrum, Kölner Strasse 35-37. **GPS:** n51,39985 e6,87700.
🚰€0,50/80liter 🚽Ch.

〼 **Münster** 🌿🌳🍴 **8G2**
Am Ostbad, Mauritz-Lindenweg. **GPS:** n51,95922 e7,65879.⬆.

6 🛏free. **Location:** Urban, simple. **Surface:** metalled.
☐ 01/01-31/12
Distance: 🚰2,5km 🚃100m ⊗300m 🍴300m ⚓on the spot.
Remarks: At swimming pool, max. 8M.

〼 **Münster** 🌿🌳🍴 **8G2**
Hafenstraße/Albersloher Weg. **GPS:** n51,95199 e7,63600.

6 🛏€2/h, overnight stay free. **Location:** Urban, simple, central, noisy.
Surface: asphalted. ☐ 01/01-31/12
Distance: 🚰Old city centre 1km ⊗on the spot 🍴on the spot 🚃on
the spot.
Remarks: Along railwayline.

〼Ⓢ **Münster** 🌿🌳🍴 **8G2**
Campingplatz Münster, Laerer Werseufer.
GPS: n51,94583 e7,69082.⬆.

24 🛏€15 2 pers.incl, dog €3,50 🚰€0,50 🚽€0,50/time Ch€0,50/
time 🔌WC included 🛢€0,50/3 ⚡€3/day. **Location:** Rural, simple.

Surface: gravel. ☐ 01/01-31/12
Distance: 🚰Münster 4,5km ⊗100m 🍴on the spot 🚃100m ♻on
the spot 🏃on the spot.
Remarks: Pay at reception campsite.

〼Ⓢ **Netphen** **10H1**
Freizeitpark Netphen, P3, Brauersdorferstrasse.
GPS: n50,91250 e8,12567.➡.

3 🛏€3,50/day 🚰€1/70liter 🚽Ch. **Surface:** metalled.
☐ 01/01-31/12
Distance: 🚰2km 🍴2km.
Remarks: Max. 48h, coins at swimming pool.

〼Ⓢ **Nettersheim** **10F2**
Wohnmobilhafen Nettersheim, Urftstraße.
GPS: n50,48591 e6,62597.⬆➡.

30 🛏€8/24h 🚰€1 🚽Ch 🔌included. 🚽
Location: Rural, simple, quiet. **Surface:** metalled.
☐ 01/01-31/12 ♻on the spot 🏃on the spot.
Remarks: Bread-service.

〼 **Nettetal** **10E1**
Am Nettebruch, Flothender straße/Flothend.
GPS: n51,30188 e6,26715.⬆➡.

5 🛏free. **Surface:** grassy/gravel. ☐ 01/01-31/12
Distance: 🚰1km ⚓on the spot ⊗on the spot 🍴1km.

🍴 **Nettetal** **10E1**
Am Krickenbeck See, Krickenbecker Allee 38. **GPS:** n51,34460 e6,25793.

50 🛏Free, use of a meal desired. **Surface:** asphalted. ☐ 01/01-31/12
Distance: 🚰2km ⊗on the spot 🍴2km.

〼 **Neuss** **10F1**
Allrounder Winterworld/Skihalle, An der Skihalle 1.
GPS: n51,17316 e6,64862.

30 🛏free. **Surface:** metalled. ☐ 01/01-31/12
Distance: ⊗on the spot 🎿indoor ski.

| 🛏 | **Nideggen** 👥 | 10E2 |

Parkplatz Danzley, Bahnhofstrasse. **GPS:** n50,69247 e6,47952. ⬆.

14 🛏free. **Location:** Rural, simple. **Surface:** metalled.
☐ 01/01-31/12
Distance: 🚰500m 🍴500m.

| 🍴 | **Nordkirchen** | 8G3 |

Hotel Plettenberger Hof, Schlossstrasse 28.
GPS: n51,73659 e7,52819. ⬆.

2 🛏guests free. **Surface:** asphalted. ☐ 01/01-31/12
Distance: 🚰200m ⊗on the spot.

| 🛏S | **Nottuln** 👥 | 8G2 |

Wellenfreibad/Hallenbad, Rudolf-Harbigstrasse.
GPS: n51,92410 e7,34514. ⬆.

5 🛏free. **Location:** Rural, simple. **Surface:** metalled.
☐ 01/01-31/12
Distance: 🚰1,5km 🍴bakery 800m 🚐on the spot.
Remarks: Parking swimming pool, service during opening hours.

| 🛏S | **Oberhausen** | 8F3 |

Am Kaisergarten. **GPS:** n51,48690 e6,85551. ⬆➡.

60 🛏€ 7 🚰€1 🗑Ch 🧹€0,50/3h. **Surface:** grassy.
☐ 01/01-31/12
Distance: 🚶Oberhausen City 30 min walking 🚲1,6km ⊗1,7km
🍴1,7km.

| 🛏 | **Oberhausen** | 8F3 |

Parking 10 - CentrO, Arenastraße. **GPS:** n51,48930 e6,87063. ⬆➡.

---

40 🛏free. **Surface:** metalled. ☐ 01/01-31/12
Distance: 🚰100m ⊗on the spot 🍴on the spot.
Remarks: At CentrO.

Tourist information Oberhausen:
☺ CentrO Park, Promenade 10. Amusement park. ☐ 01/04-31/10 11-18/19h.
🧺 CentrO. Large shopping centre, 300 shops, 100 restaurants/bars and a market. ☐ Mo-Thu 10-20h restaurant 10-22h, Fri-Sa 10-22h restaurant 10-24h.

| 🛏 | **Oedt** 👥 | 10E1 |

Wohnmobile-Stellplatz Niers-Perle-Oedt, Mühlengasse.
GPS: n51,32327 e6,37650. ⬆.

7 🛏free. **Surface:** asphalted. ☐ 01/01-31/12
Distance: 🚰800m ⊗500m 🍴500m.

| 🍴S | **Oelde** 🧺 | 8H3 |

Pott's Brau und Backhaus, In der Geist 120.
GPS: n51,81192 e8,13103. ⬆➡.

6 🛏€ 5 🚰€1/60liter 🗑Ch 🧹included. **Location:** Simple, noisy.
Surface: grassy/metalled. ☐ 02/01-23/12
Distance: 🚲500m 🍴on the spot.
Remarks: Caution key € 35.

| 🛏S | **Olpe** | 10G1 |

Freizeitbad Olpe, Seeweg 5. **GPS:** n51,03242 e7,84163. ⬆➡.

10 🛏€ 5 🚰€0,20/liter 🗑Ch 🧹(4x)€1/2kWh WC☐included, at swimming pool 7-22h. **Location:** Urban. **Surface:** asphalted.
☐ 01/01-31/12
Distance: 🚰500m 🚲2km ⊗250m.
Remarks: On the banks of the Biggesee, max. 3 days.

| 🛏S | **Ostbevern** | 8G2 |

Bever Bad, Am Hanfgarten 22. **GPS:** n52,03673 e7,84392. ⬆.

6+10 🛏€ 10, overnight stay only 20-9h free 🚰🗑Ch 🧹 WCincluded.
Location: Luxurious, quiet. **Surface:** grassy.
☐ 01/01-31/12
Distance: 🚰400m ⊗300m 🍴300m 🚐300m.
Remarks: Parking swimming pool, caution key service € 10, incl. access swimming pool.

| 🛏S | **Overhetfeld** | 10E1 |

Camp Graskamp, Graskamp 19. **GPS:** n51,22259 e6,13977. ⬆.

5 🛏€ 8 🚰🗑Ch 🧹 WC☐included. **Surface:** grassy.
☐ 01/01-31/12
Distance: 🚰200m ⊗200m 🍴on the spot.

| 🛏S | **Paderborn** 🌱🧺👥 | 8H3 |

Maspernplatz, P4, Hathumarstrasse. **GPS:** n51,72278 e8,75417. ⬆➡.

8 🛏€ 5/24h 🧹(4x)€0,50/h. **Location:** Urban, central, noisy.
Surface: metalled. ☐ 01/01-31/12
Distance: 🚰on the spot 🚲4km ⊗100m 🍴500m 🚐on the spot.

| 🛏S | **Paderborn** 🌱🧺👥 | 8H3 |

Wilhelm-Kaufmann-Allee/Fürstenweg. **GPS:** n51,72825 e8,74509.

16 🛏€ 5/24h 🚰€0,50/60liter 🗑Chfree 🧹(16x)€0,50/kWh.
Surface: asphalted. ☐ 01/01-31/12
Distance: 🚰1,5km ⊗on the spot.
Remarks: Max. 72h.

| 🛏 | **Paderborn** 🌱🧺👥 | 8H3 |

Liboriberg, Liboriberg. **GPS:** n51,71543 e8,75529. ⬆➡.

4 🛏€ 3,50/24h. **Location:** Urban, noisy. ☐ 01/01-31/12
Distance: 🚰on the spot ⊗on the spot 🍴on the spot 🚐on the spot.
Remarks: Small pitches.

Paderborn 🌼🍴🎶 8H3

Lippesee-Nordufer, Sennelagerstraße 58, Sande.
GPS: n51,76087 e8,67756. ⬆.

20 🅿free. **Location**: Rural, simple. **Surface**: grassy.
🗓 01/01-31/12
Distance: 🚶1km 🏊150m 🚣150m ⊗1km 🍺500m 🚲on the spot
🚶on the spot.

Petershagen 9A1

Stellplatz Petershagen, Hohoffstrasse.
GPS: n52,37532 e8,96875. ⬆➡.

10 🅿free 🚰€1/90liter 🔌(8x)€1/kWh. **Location**: Urban, quiet.
Surface: metalled. 🗓 01/01-31/12
Distance: 🚶100m ⊗100m 🍺100m.
Remarks: Nearby football ground, max. 3 days.

Plettenberg 🎶 10G1

Aqua Magis, Albert Schweizerstrasse, Böddinghausen.
GPS: n51,23220 e7,85308. ⬆➡.

10 🅿free 🚰€1/40liter 🍽Ch 🔌(8x)€0,50. **Location**: Rural,
comfortable, quiet. **Surface**: metalled. 🗓 01/01-31/12
Distance: 🚶on the spot 🚲11km ⊗on the spot 🍺200m 🚲on the
spot 🚶on the spot.
Remarks: At paradise pool, max. 48h.

Raesfeld 🌼 8F3

Wohnmobilstellplatz Graf Alexander, Südring.
GPS: n51,76523 e6,83035. ⬆➡.

8 🅿€8 🚰€1/8minutes 🍽Ch 🔌(8x)€1/12h WC 🖥. 🖥
Location: Rural, simple, quiet. **Surface**: gravel.
🗓 01/01-31/12
Distance: 🚶1km ⊗150m 🚲on the spot 🚶on the spot.
Remarks: At historic moated castle, max. 2 nights.

Recke 8G1

Yackthafen Marina Recke, Auf der Haar 23.
GPS: n52,35082 e7,71174. ⬆.

40 🅿€6,50 🚰🍽Ch 🔌(10x)€1,50 WC 🖥€1,50 🖥.
Surface: grassy/metalled. 🖥 01/01-31/12
Distance: 🚶1km, Recke 3,5km 🏊on the spot 🚣on the spot ⊗on the
spot 🍺900m 🛒400m 🚲on the spot 🚶on the spot.
Remarks: At the Mittelland canal, check in at harbourmaster.

Rees 8E3

Wohnmobilstellplatz, Ebentalstrasse. **GPS**: n51,76428 e6,38829. ⬆.

31 🅿€6/day 🚰🍽Ch 🔌included 🖥€1. 🖥 **Location**: Urban,
comfortable. **Surface**: grassy. 🗓 01/01-31/12
Distance: 🚶400m.
Remarks: Behind swimming pool.

Reken 🎶 8F3

Wohnmobilstellplatz Reken, Bergen 2a.
GPS: n51,82864 e7,05895. ⬆➡.

20 🅿€6 🚰€1/200liter 🍽Ch 🔌(20x)€0,50/kWh. 🖥
Location: Rural, comfortable, quiet. **Surface**: grassy.
🗓 01/01-31/12
Distance: 🚶1km ⊗1km 🍺1km 🚲on the spot.
Remarks: Max. 2 days, friday market.

Remscheid 10F1

Brückenpark Müngsten, Mügstener Brückenweg.
GPS: n51,16833 e7,13750. ⬆.

4 🅿free. **Location**: Rural, simple, quiet. **Surface**: gravel.
🗓 01/01-31/12
Distance: 🚶5km 🚲4km 🏊100m 🚣100m 🚶on the spot.

Remscheid 10F1

Dörperhöhe, Bei Haus nr. 15, Lennep. **GPS**: n51,17986 e7,30205.
4 🅿free. **Surface**: asphalted.

Remscheid 10F1

Jahnplatz, Am Stadion, Lennep. **GPS**: n51,19052 e7,26110.
4 🅿free. **Surface**: asphalted. 🗓 01/01-31/12
Distance: 🚶historical centre of Lennep 300m.

Remscheid 10F1

Garage Pauli GmbH, Lenneperstrasse 152 (Bundesstrasse 229).
GPS: n51,18020 e7,22591.
🚰🍽Chfree. 🗓 01/01-31/12

Rheda-Wiedenbrück 8H2

Am Werl, Gütersloherstrasse. **GPS**: n51,85456 e8,29768.

4 🅿free 🚰🍽Ch 🚲WCfree. **Location**: Urban. **Surface**: metalled.
🗓 01/01-31/12
Distance: 🚶300m 🍺300m.
Remarks: Max. 3 days.

Rheda-Wiedenbrück 8H2

P Hallenbad, Ostring/Am Hallenbad, Wiederbrück.
GPS: n51,83188 e8,32350. ⬆➡.

4 🅿free. **Location**: Urban, quiet. **Surface**: metalled.
🗓 01/01-31/12
Distance: 🚶1km ⊗200m 🍺bakery 200m 🚲on the spot 🚶on the
spot.
Remarks: Parking swimming pool.

Rhede 8F3

Reisemobilstellplatz Kettelerplatz, Kettelerstrasse 9.
GPS: n51,83677 e6,69346. ⬆.

15 🅿free 🚰€1/75liter 🍽Ch 🔌(6x)€1/2kWh. **Location**: Urban,
simple. **Surface**: grassy. 🗓 01/01-31/12
Distance: 🚶750m ⊗750m 🍺500m.

Rhede 8F3

Hallen- und Freibad, Heideweg 59. **GPS**: n51,83164 e6,68635. ⬆.

2 🅿free. **Location**: Urban, simple. **Surface**: metalled.
🗓 01/01-31/12
Distance: 🚶1,5km.
Remarks: Parking swimming pool, max. 3 days.

Rheinbach 10F2

Parkplatz Freizeitpark/Erlebnisbad Monte Mare, Münstereifeler-
straße 69. **GPS**: n50,61883 e6,93262. ⬆➡.

4 🅿free. **Location**: Rural, simple. **Surface**: metalled.
🗓 01/01-31/12

DE

Distance: 1,5km 1,5km.
Remarks: Max. 3 days.

🅂 Rheine 8G2

Im Stadtpark, Kopernikusstrasse. **GPS:** n52,28137 e7,45478. ⬆

2 free. **Location:** Urban, simple. **Surface:** metalled.
◻ 01/01-31/12
Distance: 500m ⊗on the spot ⚊500m 300m on the spot
on the spot.

🅂 Rheine 8G2

Am Naturzoo, Weihbishof-Dalhaus-strasse.
GPS: n52,29526 e7,41645. ⬆

10 free. **Location:** Rural, simple. **Surface:** grasstiles.
◻ 01/01-31/12
Distance: 1,5km 5km on the spot 100m.

🅂 Rheurdt 8E3

Wohnmobilhafen Ökodorf, St. Nikolausweg 15.
GPS: n51,46382 e6,46780. ⬆➡

21 €9 Ch €3/24h WC.
Surface: metalled. ◻ 01/01-31/12
Distance: 500m ⚊500m 500m.

🅂 Rietberg 8H3

Jakobistrasse, Mastholte. **GPS:** n51,75667 e8,39111. ⬆

4 free €0,50/80liter Ch. **Location:** Rural, central.
Surface: asphalted. ◻ 01/01-31/12
Distance: 100m ⊗100m 100m.

🅂 Rietberg 8H3

Am Heimathaus, Langenberger Strasse, Mastholte.
GPS: n51,75765 e8,38945. ⬆

2 free. **Location:** Urban. **Surface:** asphalted. ◻ 01/01-31/12

🅂 Rietberg 8H3

Schulzentrum, Torfweg. **GPS:** n51,80724 e8,43295. ⬆

2 free. **Location:** Urban, simple. **Surface:** metalled.
◻ 01/01-31/12
Distance: 200m 100m ⊗200m 200m on the spot.

🅂 Roetgen 10E2

Am Bahnhof, Bahnhofstrasse. **GPS:** n50,64868 e6,18506.

10 free. **Location:** Rural, simple, noisy. **Surface:** gravel/metalled.
◻ 01/01-31/12
Distance: 300m 300m.

🅂 Rosendahl 8F2

Wohnmobilplatz Darfeld, Sudetenstrasse, Darfeld.
GPS: n52,02696 e7,26501. ⬆➡

20 free €1/100liter Ch (12x)€1/6h. **Location:** Rural,
simple. **Surface:** grassy/metalled. ◻ 01/01-31/12
Distance: 500m on the spot 500m 1km.

🅂 Rüthen 8H3

Am Hachtor, Hachtorstrasse. **GPS:** n51,49405 e8,43119. ⬆➡

4 free. **Surface:** metalled. ◻ 01/01-31/12
Distance: 50m ⊗50m 50m, Aldi 200m.

🅂 Sassenberg 8H2

Parkplatz Feldmark, Feldmark. **GPS:** n52,00370 e8,06528. ⬆

3 free €1/80liter Ch. **Location:** Rural, simple.
Surface: metalled.
Distance: 2,5km 100m ⊗on the spot on the spot on the
spot on the spot.

🅂 Schieder 9A2

Freizeitzentrum Schiedersee, Kronenbruch.
GPS: n51,92073 e9,16471. ⬆➡

300 €10 €1/100liter Ch €0,50/kWh WC €0,50 €2
Location: Rural, comfortable, quiet. **Surface:** grassy/metalled.
◻ 01/01-31/12
Distance: 1,3km 50m 50m ⊗on the spot on the spot
on the spot on the spot.

🅂 Schleiden 10E2

Wohnmobilhafen am Nationalpark-Eifel, Pfarrer-Kneipp-strasse,
Gemünd. **GPS:** n50,57855 e6,49107. ⬆➡

40 €7 + € 1/pp tourist tax €0,50/50liter Ch €0,50/kWh
100m. **Location:** Rural, comfortable, quiet.
Surface: gravel/metalled. ◻ 01/01-31/12
Distance: within walking distance ⊗500m 500m.
Remarks: Bread-service.

🅂 Schleiden 10E2

Am Freibad, Im Wiesengrund. **GPS:** n50,52993 e6,47022. ⬆

8 free. **Location:** Rural, simple, quiet. **Surface:** asphalted.

🅂 Schloss Holte/Stukenbrock 8H2

Reisemobilstellplatz Am Sennebach, Liemkerstrasse 27, Liemke.
GPS: n51,86979 e8,61531. ⬆

20 €5 €2 Ch (18x)included. **Location:** Rural, isolated,
quiet. **Surface:** grasstiles. ◻ 01/01-31/12 service: sa/su
Distance: ⊗1km 1km.
Remarks: Behind Froli Kunstoffwerk Fromme.

🅂 Schmallenberg 10H1

Im Sorpetal, Winkhausen 21. **GPS:** n51,16083 e8,34056. ➡

12 €9 €0,50/80liter Ch (12x)€0,50/kWh. ◻ 01/01-31/12

DE

Distance: ⊶on the spot ⊗100m ⚡2km ⟷500m ♨1km Ⰱon the spot.
Remarks: Trout pond, golf court 500m, playground.

| 🏕S | **Schöppingen** 🌿🌳 | 8F2 |

Schulze Althoff, Heven 48. **GPS:** n52,07361 e7,22361.⬆.

30 🅿€ 14/night, 3 pers. Incl, 4th pers. € 4 ⟷⚡Ch⚡(12x) included,6Amp WC⟀sanitary€2/pp ⦿€5. 🌊 **Location:** Rural, simple.
Surface: grassy.
Distance: ⚓2,5km ⊿on the spot ⊶on the spot ⚡2,5km ⟷on the spot.
Remarks: Swimming pool available.

| 🏕S | **Senden** | 8G2 |

Sportpark Senden, Buldenerstrasse 13b. **GPS:** n51,85419 e7,47433.⬆.

10 🅿free. **Location:** Simple, noisy. **Surface:** grasstiles.
⭕ 01/01-31/12
Distance: ⚓on the spot ⊗200m ⚡300m ⟷on the spot.
Remarks: Parking at sports park.

| 🏕S | **Senden** | 8G2 |

Wohnmobilstellplatz Steinhoff, Gettrup 37.
GPS: n51,83305 e7,46878.⬆.

10 🅿€ 6 ⟷⚡Ch⚡(6x)€0,50/kWh. **Location:** Rural, isolated.
Surface: grassy/metalled. ⭕ 01/01-31/12
Distance: ⚓Senden 4km ⊗2,5km ⚡2,5km.

| 🏕S | **Sendenhorst** 🌿🏖 | 8G2 |

Westor 31. **GPS:** n51,84286 e7,81849.⬆➡.

3 🅿free ⟷€0,50/40liter ⚡Ch⚡€0,50. **Location:** Urban, simple, central, noisy. **Surface:** metalled.
⭕ 01/01-31/12
Distance: ⚓on the spot ⊗300m ⚡1km ⟷on the spot.
Remarks: Max. 3 nights.

| 🏕S | **Siegen** | 10H1 |

Am Hallenbad, Poststraße. **GPS:** n50,89463 e8,02405.➡.

3 🅿free ⟷€1/10minutes ⚡Ch⚡(2x)€1/8h. **Location:** Urban.
Surface: metalled. ⭕ 01/01-31/12
Distance: ⚓200m ⊗200m ⚡200m ⟷250m ♨on the spot Ⰱon the spot.
Remarks: Max. 3 days.

| 🏕S | **Siegen** | 10H1 |

An der Alche, Freudenbergerstraße 67. **GPS:** n50,88073 e8,00764.⬆.
4 🅿free ⟷€0,50/50liter ⚡Ch⚡€0,50/kWh. ⭕ 01/01-31/12
Distance: ⚓1km ⊿5km ⊗200m ⚡1km.
Remarks: Max. 3 days.

| 🏕S | **Simmerath** ≋ | 10E2 |

Wohnmobilhafen Rurseezentrum, Seeufer 1, Rurberg.
GPS: n50,60658 e6,38177.⬆.

10 🅿€ 8/24h ⟷€2 ⚡Ch.🚿 **Location:** Rural, comfortable.
Surface: grasstiles. ⭕ 01/01-31/12
Distance: ⛱100m ⊗50m.

| 🏕S | **Soest** | 8H3 |

City Motel, Altes Stellwerk 9. **GPS:** n51,57503 e8,11478.⬆.

14 🅿€ 8 ⟷⚡Ch⚡(14x)WC⟀€2 ⦿€3 📶included.
Location: Urban, comfortable, central, quiet. **Surface:** gravel.
⭕ 01/01-31/12
Distance: ⚓200m ⊗200m ⚡200m ⟷200m ♨on the spot Ⰱon the spot.

| 🏕S | **Solingen** 🍷 | 10F1 |

Am Brandteich, Gräfrath. **GPS:** n51,21151 e7,07217.⬆.

10 🅿free. **Location:** Urban, simple, quiet. **Surface:** concrete.
⭕ 01/01-31/12
Distance: ⚓on the spot ⊿2,7km ⊗on the spot ⚡300m.
Remarks: Parking fire-station.

| 🏕S | **Stadtlohn** 🍷 | 8F2 |

Freizeit- und Hallenbad, Uferstrasse 29.
GPS: n51,99792 e6,93019.⬆➡.

4 🅿free ⟷€0,50/100liter ⚡Ch⚡(4x)€1/kWh WC⟀.
Location: Rural, simple, isolated. **Surface:** metalled.
⭕ 01/01-31/12 ⦿ water disconnected in winter
Distance: ⚓800m ⊿1km ⚡800m.
Remarks: Parking swimming pool.

| 🏕S | **Steinfurt** 🏖 | 8G2 |

Wohnmobilstellplatz Steinfurt, Liedekerkerstrasse 70, Burgsteinfurt.
GPS: n52,14738 e7,34746.⬆➡.

20 🅿free ⟷€1/100liter ⚡Ch⚡€1/2kWh. **Location:** Rural, simple.
Surface: gravel. ⭕ 01/01-31/12
Distance: ⚓1km ⊗500m ⚡200m.
Remarks: Parking behind police station, max. 3 nights, voluntary contribution.

| 🏕 | **Steinfurt** 🏖 | 8G2 |

Am Rathaus, Emsdettener Strasse 40. **GPS:** n52,12822 e7,39356.

6 🅿free. **Location:** Urban, simple. **Surface:** asphalted.
⭕ 01/01-31/12
Distance: ⚓400m ⊿200m ⊗400m ⚡400m ⟷200m.

| 🏕 | **Steinhagen** | 8H2 |

Am Cronsbach. **GPS:** n51,99998 e8,42351.⬆➡.

2 🅿free. **Location:** Urban, simple. **Surface:** metalled.
⭕ 01/01-31/12
Distance: ⚓100m ⊗100m ⚡100m.

| 🏕 | **Stemwede** 🍷 | 8H1 |

Fest- und Schiesshalle, Schrottinghauserstrasse, Levern.
GPS: n52,37217 e8,44552.⬆➡.

2 🅿free. **Location:** Rural, simple, isolated. **Surface:** metalled.
⭕ 01/01-31/12
Distance: ⚓1,5km ⊗1,5km ⚡1,4km.

DE

Stemwede 8H1

Park Stemwederberg, Stemwederbergstrasse/Freudeneck, Westrup.
GPS: n52,43246 e8,43973. ⬆➡.

8 🚐free. **Location**: Rural, comfortable. **Surface**: grassy.
🅾 01/01-31/12
Distance: 🚶2km ⊗2km 🍴2km 🚶 on the spot.

Stemwede 8H1

Hotel-Gasthof Moorhof, Wagenfelderstrasse 34, Oppenwehe.
GPS: n52,49979 e8,53507. ⬆.

20 🚐€ 7, free with a meal 🔌🚰included 🔋€2,16Amp.
Location: Rural, quiet. **Surface**: grassy. 🅾 01/01-31/12 ⚪ Thu
Distance: ⊗on the spot.

Stemwede 8H1

Rila Feinkost-Importe, Schröttinghauser Strasse/Hinterm Teich 3,
Levern. **GPS**: n52,36783 e8,43833.

50 🚐€ 15 🔌🚽Ch 🔋 WC 🖥included. **Location**: Rural,
comfortable. **Surface**: grassy/gravel. 🅾 01/01-31/12
Distance: ⊗on the spot.
Remarks: Voucher incl. € 6 for 'Rila erleben': restaurant, Tapas bar,
food, garden, playground.

Straelen 8E3

Fitnessbad Wasserstraelen, Lingsforterstraße 100.
GPS: n51,45201 e6,25708. ⬆.

27 🚐€ 7 🔌€1/80liter 🚽Ch 🔋(8x)€0,50/8kWh. **Surface**: asphalted.
🅾 01/01-31/12
Distance: 🚶1,2km ⊗1km 🍴1km.
Remarks: Max. 3 days.

Tecklenburg 8G2

Parkplatz Bismarckturm, Am Weingarten.
GPS: n52,22129 e7,79905. ⬆➡.

5 🚐€ 4. 🚽 **Location**: Simple, quiet. **Surface**: asphalted.
🅾 01/01-31/12
Distance: 🚶800m 🚐200m.

Tecklenburg 8G2

Regenbogen-Camp, Grafenstraße. **GPS**: n52,22941 e7,89052. ⬆.
4 🚐€ 10 > 17h < 13h 🔌🚽Ch 🔋included. **Location**: Urban, simple,
noisy. **Surface**: asphalted. 🅾 01/01-31/12
Distance: 🚶Tecklenburg 7km.

Telgte 8G2

Am Dümmert, Emstor. **GPS**: n51,98497 e7,79151. ⬆➡.
3 🚐free 🔌€1/100liter 🚽Ch 🔋€1/kWh. **Location**: Simple.
Surface: gravel. 🅾 01/01-31/12
Distance: 🚶600m ⊗600m 🍴600m 🚐on the spot.

Telgte 8G2

Waldschwimmbad Klatenberge, Waldweg.
GPS: n51,99459 e7,78328. ⬆.

20 🚐free. **Location**: Rural, simple. **Surface**: asphalted.
🅾 01/01-31/12
Distance: 🚶1km ⊗300m 🍴900m 🚶 on the spot.
Remarks: Parking swimming pool, recreation area.

Telgte 8G2

Altes Gasthus Lauheide, Lauheide 3, K17.
GPS: n51,99862 e7,75319. ⬆.

80 🚐€ 10 🔌🚽Ch 🔋included. **Location**: Quiet. **Surface**: grassy.
🅾 01/01-31/12 ⚪ Restaurant: Wed
Distance: 🚶4km ⊗on the spot 🚌Bus 300m 🚲on the spot 🚶on the
spot.

Uedem 8E3

Reisemobilstellplatz Uedem, Bergstraße 99.
GPS: n51,66173 e6,28734. ⬆.

26 🚐€ 9 🔌🚽Ch 🔋 WC 📶included. **Surface**: grassy.
🅾 01/01-31/12
Distance: 🚶1,5km 🚲on the spot 🚶on the spot.

Velbert 10F1

Unter der Saubrücke, Parkstraße, Velbert-Mitte.
GPS: n51,34097 e7,03050. ⬆➡.

8 🚐€ 3 🔌€1/100liter 🚽Ch 🔋€0,50/kWh. **Location**: Urban, simple,
quiet. **Surface**: gravel. 🅾 01/01-31/12
Distance: 🚶800m 🚲1,6km ⊗250m 🚶on the spot.

Velbert 10F1

Panoramabad Velbert-Neviges, Wiesenweg.
GPS: n51,30582 e7,08546. ⬆.

5 🚐free 🔌€1/80liter 🚽Ch. **Location**: Urban, simple, quiet.
Surface: concrete. 🅾 01/01-31/12
Distance: 🚶800m ⊗nearby 🍴500m.
Remarks: Parking swimming pool, max. 3 nights.

Velbert 10F1

Domparkplatz, Bernsaustrasse Schloss Hardenberg.
GPS: n51,31565 e7,08724. ⬆.

5 🚐€ 2. 🚲🔋 **Location**: Urban. **Surface**: gravel.
🅾 01/01-31/12
Distance: 🚶600m ⊗on the spot.

Velbert 10F1

Nizzabad, Kalversiepen, Langenberg. **GPS**: n51,34362 e7,13766. ⬆➡.

4 🚐free. **Location**: Simple, quiet. **Surface**: gravel.
🅾 01/01-31/12
Distance: 🚶Langenberg 2,5km ⊗on the spot.

Velen 8F2

Erholungsgebiet Waldvelen, ven der Buss, Klyer Damm 8-10.
GPS: n51,90167 e7,01167. ⬆➡.

30 🚐€ 15, 2 pers.incl 🔌🚽Ch 🔋(50x). **Location**: Rural, luxurious.
Surface: gravel. 🅾 01/01-31/12
Distance: 🚶2km 🚲8,5km.

Velen 🏕 8F2

Freibad Ramsdorf, Velener Straße, Ramsdorf.
GPS: n51,88955 e6,92503. ⬆.

5 🛏free. **Location:** Rural, simple, noisy. **Surface:** asphalted.
⬛ 01/01-31/12
Distance: 🚂Ramsdorf 300m 🛒200m 🚲on the spot 🚶on the spot.
Remarks: At swimming pool.

S Viersen 10E1

Am Familienbad Ransberg, Heesstraße 80, Viersen-Dülken.
GPS: n51,25083 e6,35291. ⬆.

9 🛏free 🚰€0,50/100liter 🔧Ch ⚡(6x)€1/2kWh. **Surface:** metalled.
⬛ 01/01-31/12
Distance: 🚂Dülken 400m, Viersen 3km ⊗400m 🛒2km 🚌100m.
Remarks: Max. 3 days.

🍴S Vreden 🏕 8F2

Hotel Zum Möwenparadies, Zwillbrockerstrasse 39.
GPS: n52,05305 e6,70733. ⬆.

10 🛏€ 10 🚰🔧Ch ⚡WC included. 🧺
Location: Simple, isolated. **Surface:** grassy. ⬛ 01/01-31/12
Distance: 🚂4km ⌇on the spot 🎣on the spot ⊗on the spot
🚌200m.
Remarks: Trout pond.

🍴S Vreden 🏕 8F2

Wohnmobilpark Vreden, Ottensteiner Strasse 59.
GPS: n52,03962 e6,84136. ⬆.

50 🛏€ 8, 4 pers.incl 🚰🔧Ch ⚡(14x)included WC €2 📶€3/h 🧺
Location: Rural, simple, quiet. **Surface:** grassy.
⬛ 01/01-31/12
Distance: 🚂500m ⊗on the spot.
Remarks: Breakfast-service, swimming pool € 2/pp.

🛁S Wachtendonk 8E3

Bleiche P4, Achter de Stadt. **GPS**: n51,40601 e6,33170. ⬆➡.

24 🛏€ 5 🚰€0,50/80liter 🔧€0,50 Ch ⚡(12x)€0,50/kWh.
Surface: gravel. ⬛ 01/01-31/12
Distance: 🚂400m ⊗100m 🛒400m.

🛁S Wadersloh 8H3

Im Klostergarten 18, Liesborn. **GPS**: n51,71414 e8,25960. ⬆➡.

4 🛏free 🚰€0,50/80liter 🔧Ch ⚡(4x)€0,50/12h. **Location:** Rural.
Surface: metalled. ⬛ 01/01-31/12
Distance: 🚂400m ⊗100m 🛒400m 🚲on the spot 🚶on the spot.
Remarks: Behind gymnasium.

🛁S Waldbröl 🎠 10G2

Am Hallenbad, Vennstrassse. **GPS**: n50,87511 e7,60987. ⬆.

5 🛏free. **Location:** Rural, simple, quiet. **Surface:** metalled.
⬛ 01/01-31/12
Distance: 🚂on the spot 🚣18km 🚲on the spot 🚶on the spot.
Remarks: Max. 2 days.

🛁S Waldfeucht-Brüggelchen 10E1

Reisemobilstellplatz Tilder Weg, Tilderweg.
GPS: n51,07076 e5,99454. ⬆.

18 🛏€ 4 🚰€0,50/80liter 🔧Ch ⚡(8x)€0,50/kWh. 🧺
Location: Rural, simple, quiet. **Surface:** metalled.
⬛ 01/01-31/12
Distance: 🚂1km ⊗on the spot 🛒500m 🚲100m.
Remarks: Max. 4 nights.

🍴S Waltrop 🎠 8G3

Restaurant Zur Lohburg, Lohburgerstrass 105, A2 Ausfahrt henreichen-
burg, Schiffshebewerk. **GPS**: n51,60613 e7,34882.

10 🛏€ 5 🚰⚡€3. **Surface:** grassy. ⬛ 01/01-31/12
Distance: 🚂1km ⊗on the spot 🛒1km.

🛁S Warburg 9A3

Schützenplatz, Paderborner Tor. **GPS**: n51,48993 e9,13810.
5 🛏€ 5 🚰🔧Ch ⚡included. **Surface:** metalled. ⬛ 15/09-15/10
Distance: 🚂500m.

🛁S Warendorf 🌿🚲⛲🌳🧺 8G2

Parkplatz Emssee, Sassenberger Strasse 26.
GPS: n51,95447 e7,99904. ⬆.

15 🛏free 🚰€1/50liter 🔧Ch ⚡€1/kWh.
Location: Rural, simple, central, quiet. **Surface:** metalled.
⬛ 01/01-31/12
Distance: 🚂1km 🚣on the spot ⊗on the spot 🛒500m 🚌100m
🚲on the spot 🚶on the spot.
Remarks: Max. 3 days.

🛁S Warendorf 🌿🚲⛲🌳🧺 8G2

Parkplatz Zwischen den Emsbrücken, Am Emswehr.
GPS: n51,95426 e7,99164. ⬆.

2 🛏free. ⬛ 01/01-31/12
Distance: 🚂100m.

🛁S Warstein 🌿⛲🌳 8H3

Camperpark zum Bayernstadl, Enkerbruch 12a.
GPS: n51,43041 e8,37432. ⬆➡.

18+22 🛏€ 8 🚰€1/100liter 🔧Ch ⚡(18x)€2/16,€1summer,€2winter
Surface: gravel. ⬛ 01/01-31/12
Distance: 🚂1,5km ⊗on the spot 🛒1,5km 🚌1,5km.
Remarks: Bread-service.

🛁S Warstein 🌿⛲🌳 8H3

Vans in Paradise, Zu Hause im Waldpark. **GPS**: n51,42615 e8,35525. ⬆.

60 🛏€ 15 🚰🔧Ch ⚡(76x),16Amp WC included 🔌€2/2.
Location: Isolated, quiet. **Surface:** grassy/gravel. ⬛ 01/01-31/12
Distance: 🚂2km ⊗small menu 🛒2km 🚌2km.
Remarks: At Warstein brewery, bread-service + breakfast-service.

🛁S Warstein 🌿⛲🌳 8H3

Wohnmobilstellplatz, Dammweg. **GPS**: n51,45103 e8,34750. ⬆➡.

DE

5 ⌷free. **Location:** Simple. **Surface:** gravel/metalled.
◻ 01/01-31/12
Distance: 2km 500m 1km 1km.
Remarks: At sports park.
Tourist information Warstein:
👁 Warsteiner Brauerei, Zu Hause im Waldpark. Guided tour 1.45h, 2 drinks included.
◻ daily 12-17, Su 13-15h.

| S | **Wassenberg** | **10E1** |

Parkbad Wassenberg, Auf dem Taubenkamp 2.
GPS: n51,09833 e6,14364. ↑ →

11 ⌷€ 5/day, € 20/week €1/100 €1 Ch €0,50/
kWh. **Location:** Rural, comfortable, quiet. **Surface:** metalled.
◻ 01/01-31/12
Distance: 1,5km.
Remarks: To be paid at swimming pool.

| S | **Weeze** | **8E3** |

Tierpark Fährsteg, L5 Fährsteg. **GPS:** n51,63074 e6,20086. ↑

13 ⌷€ 5 €0,50/kWh. ◻ 01/01-31/12
Distance: 500m 500m.

| S | **Weeze** | **8E3** |

Aral, Industriestraße. **GPS:** n51,62029 e6,20972. ↑
€1 Ch.

| S | **Wegberg** | **10E1** |

Wegberger Reisemobilstellplatz, Schul- und Sportzentrum,
Maaseiker Strasse 67. **GPS:** n51,13389 e6,28266. ↑ →

10 ⌷€ 8 Ch included. **Surface:** gravel/sand.
◻ 01/01-31/12
Distance: 400m 400m 400m on the spot.
Remarks: Caution key € 20.

| S | **Werne** | **8G3** |

Natur Solebad, Am Hagen. **GPS:** n51,65910 e7,63414. ↑ →

12 ⌷€ 5/24h €1/80liter Ch €0,50/kWh. **Surface:** metalled.
◻ 01/01-31/12
Distance: 400m 200m 400m.
Remarks: Tuesday and Friday market.

| S | **Wesel** | **8F3** |

Reisemobilstellplatz Römerwardt, Rheinpromenade.
GPS: n51,66116 e6,59256. ↑ →

48 ⌷€ 6-8 €1/80liter Ch €1/kWh. **Surface:** grassy/metalled.
◻ 01/01-31/12
Distance: 1,5km 100m on the spot on the spot.

| S | **Westerkappeln** | **8G2** |

Am Freibad, Bullerteichstraße 12. **GPS:** n52,31556 e7,88070. ↑

2 ⌷free. **Location:** Urban, simple. **Surface:** grasstiles.
◻ 01/01-31/12
Distance: 600m 400m 50m.

| S | **Wiehl** | **10G1** |

Freizeitpark Wiehl, Brüchnerstrasse. **GPS:** n50,94716 e7,54585. ↑ →

3 ⌷free €1/80liter Ch.
Location: Simple, central.
Surface: metalled.
Distance: 300m 5,4km 400m.
Remarks: Parking next to recreation park and disco, max. 2 days.
Tourist information Wiehl:
ℹ www.wiehl.de. Small town in the green hills. 180 kilometres marked hiking routes.
👁 Wiehler Dahlienschau. 400 varieties of dahlias.
◻ 15/08-15/10 daily 8-18h. 🎫 free.
👁 Wiehler Trofsteinhöhle. Caves Temperature is approx. 8°C.
◻ 15/03-31/10 9-17h, 01/11-14/03 Sa-Su 11-16h.
🚐 Bergische Postkutsche, Nümrecht Post. Ride by mail-coach between Wiehl and Nümbrecht.
◻ 01/05-30/09 Fri-Su 10-16h.

| S | **Wilnsdorf** | **10H2** |

Wielandshof, Bauhofstraße 5. **GPS:** n50,80692 e8,10896. ↑

5 ⌷€ 5 €0,50/60liter Ch (4x)€1/12h. **Surface:** gravel.
◻ 01/01-31/12
Distance: 900m 900m.
Remarks: Check in at farm.

| S | **Windeck** | **10G2** |

Am Sportplatz, Im Bungert, Herchen. **GPS:** n50,78025 e7,51308. →

8 ⌷free (10x)€0,50/kWh. **Location:** Rural, simple, quiet.
Surface: gravel. ◻ 01/01-31/12
Distance: 200m 8,5km 200m 200m on the spot on the spot.
Remarks: Parking sports park.

| S | **Windeck** | **10G2** |

Hallenbad, Bergische strasse 21, Dattenfeld.
GPS: n50,80754 e7,56105. ↑ →

4 ⌷free €1,50 €1,50 Ch€1,50. **Location:** Rural, simple, quiet.
Surface: metalled. ◻ 01/01-31/12
Distance: 8,5km on the spot on the spot.

| S | **Windeck** | **10G2** |

Museumsdorf Altwindeck, Im Thal Windeck 17, Alt-Windeck.
GPS: n50,81276 e7,57554. ↑

4 ⌷free. **Location:** Rural, simple, quiet. **Surface:** gravel.
◻ 01/01-31/12
Distance: 2km 8,5km on the spot 2km on the spot on the spot.
Remarks: Parking museum, max. 3 days.

| S | **Windeck** | **10G2** |

Auf dem Greent, Dattenfeld. **GPS:** n50,80697 e7,55495. ↑

50 ⌷free. **Location:** Rural, simple, quiet. **Surface:** asphalted/grassy.
◻ 01/01-31/12

Distance: ⚓500m ⚓8,5km ⊗500m ☕500m.
Remarks: Fair ground.

Windeck ⚑ 10G2

Brunnenweg, Dattenfeld. **GPS:** n50,80486 e7,56087. ⬆➡

5 ⌇free. **Location:** Simple, quiet. **Surface:** grassy/gravel.
◯ 01/01-31/12
Distance: ⚓200m ⚓8km ⊗200m ☕150m 🚲on the spot 🚶on the spot.
Remarks: Recreation park.

Winterberg ⛰⚑❄ 10H1

Wohnmobilpark Winterberg, Neuastenberger Straße 4a, OT Neuastenberg. **GPS:** n51,15974 e8,48383. ⬆
70 ⌇€ 11,50 + tourist tax € 1,75/pp ⛽€1/100liter 🔌Ch ⚡€0,50/kWh ⛲€1 🚿€2,50/2,50 ⚑. **Surface:** gravel. ◯ 01/01-31/12 🚲on the spot 🚶on the spot.
Remarks: Bread-service.

Winterberg ⛰⚑❄ 10H1

Parkplatz Stadthalle, Schulstrasse. **GPS:** n51,19163 e8,53810. ⬆

20 ⌇€ 8/24h ⛽€0,50/50liter 🔌Ch ⚡(10x)€0,50/3h.
Surface: metalled. ◯ 01/01-31/12
Distance: ⚓1km ☕1km.

Winterberg 🍴⚑❄ 10H1

Kirchmeier Sporthotel, Renauweg 54, Altastenberg.
GPS: n51,19391 e8,46844.

10 ⌇€ 26 + € 1,75/pp tourist tax ⛽🚿⚡(10x) ⛲🚿📶⚑📷
Surface: asphalted. ◯ 01/01-31/12
Distance: ⚓Winterberg 5km 🚲on the spot 🚶on the spot 🚡800m on the spot.
Remarks: Free entrance swimming pool, Dampfbad, sauna, shuttle-bus, cross-country skiing piste.

Winterberg ⛰⚑❄ 10H1

Bergrestaurant Bobhaus, Auf der Kappe 1. **GPS:** n51,18493 e8,50559.

8 ⌇€ 12, free with a meal. ⚑ **Location:** Rural.
Surface: asphalted.
Distance: ⚓2km ⊗on the spot 🚲on the spot 🚶on the spot 🚡on the spot 🎿on the spot.
Remarks: Parking ski-lift, check in at restaurant.

Winterberg ⛰⚑❄ 10H1

Campingplatz Winterberg. GPS: n51,18632 e8,50445. ⬆

⌇€ 7,50-8 + € 5,50-6/pp, dog € 2 ⛽🔌Ch ⚡(25x)€0,55/kWh ⛲🚿€1 🚻€0,50. ⚑ **Location:** Rural, luxurious. **Surface:** metalled.
Distance: ⚓2km ⊗on the spot ☕2km 🚐20m 🚲on the spot 🚶on the spot 🎿on the spot.
Remarks: Parking at skipistes.

Witten 8G3

Reisemobil-Center, Pferdebachstrasse 150.
GPS: n51,45411 e7,35246. ⬆

8 ⌇free ⛽€1/80liter 🔌Ch. **Surface:** gravel. ◯ 01/01-31/12
Distance: ⚓3km ⊗3km ☕3km.

Wülfrath ⚑ 10F1

Parkplatz, Mettmanner strasse 42. **GPS:** n51,28188 e7,02741. ⬆

10 ⌇free. **Location:** Urban, simple, quiet.
Surface: concrete. ◯ 01/01-31/12
Distance: ⚓on the spot ⊗500m ☕800m.

Xanten 8E3

Womopark Xanten, Fürstenberg 6. **GPS:** n51,65413 e6,46389. ⬆➡

60+20 ⛽🔌Chincluded ⚡€3 ⛲€1. **Surface:** grassy.
◯ 01/01-31/12
Distance: ⚓1,7km ⊗300m ☕200m.
Remarks: Check in on arrival.

Zülpich 10F2

Wohnmobilpark Seepark, Eichenallee.
GPS: n50,67660 e6,65867. ⬆➡

40 ⌇€ 9 ⛽€1 🔌Ch ⚡included. 🚌 **Location:** Rural, simple, isolated. **S**grassy.
◯ 01/01-31/12 **Distance:** ⛵100m.
Remarks: Service nearby tenniscourt 100m.

Rhineland-Palatinate/Saarland

Alf ⚑🌊 10F3

Freizeitbad Arrastal, Mühlenstraße. **GPS:** n50,05273 e7,11326. ⬆➡

100 ⌇€ 6 ⛽🔌Chincluded ⚡€2,50/day 🚿 ⚑ **Location:** Rural, simple. **Surface:** asphalted/grassy. ◯ 01/01-31/12
Distance: ⚓800m.

Alken 🌊 10G3

P2, Moselstraße. **GPS:** n50,24525 e7,44573.

6 ⌇free. **Surface:** metalled. ◯ 01/01-31/12
Distance: ⚓500m ⊗on the spot 🚐200m 🚲on the spot 🚶on the spot.

Alsheim 15H1

Weingut Elisabethenhof, In den Weingärten 10.
GPS: n49,76563 e8,34748. ⬆

4 ⌇€ 10 ⛽🔌included ⚡€2/24h. ⚑ **Location:** Rural, simple, quiet.
Surface: concrete. ◯ 01/01-31/12
Distance: ⚓300m ☕500m.

Altdorf 15H2

Schulstraße. **GPS:** n49,28426 e8,22035.
⌇free. **Surface:** metalled.
Distance: ⚓300m ⊗300m.

Altdorf 15H2

Spelzenhof, Hauptstrasse 77. **GPS:** n49,28869 e8,22028. ⬆

6 ⌇€ 7,50 ⛽⚡included. **Location:** Simple. **Surface:** grassy.
◯ 01/01-31/12 ⛔ Mon, Tue
Distance: ⚓nearby ⚓7km ⊗150m ☕400m 🚐nearby.

Altendiez 🍴⚑ 10H3

Restaurant Bimbes-Stubb, Lahnblick 4.
GPS: n50,36612 e7,98041. ⬆➡

DE

6 ⌇ € 8 ⊓ ⌁ €2. **Location:** Simple. **Surface:** gravel.
⬤ 01/01-31/12 ⬤ Mo
Distance: ⬥on the spot ⊗on the spot ⬤500m.

Altenglan 15G1

Draisine, Austrasse. **GPS:** n49,55001 e7,46465. ⬆.

3 ⌇free ⊓ €1/80liter ⬤Ch ⬤ (4x). **Surface:** gravel.
⬤ 01/04-31/10
Distance: ⊗100m ⬤100m.

Andernach 10G2

Wohnmobilstellplatz Andernach, Scheidsgasse/Uferstrasse.
GPS: n50,44176 e7,40796. ⬆.

70 ⌇€ 7 ⊓ €1/100liter ⬤Ch ⬤(40x)€1/2kWh WC €0,50/time. ⬤
Surface: metalled. ⬤ 01/01-31/12
Distance: ⬥on the spot ⬤Rhine river ⊗200m ⬤400m.
Remarks: Max. 3 nights.

Andernach 10G2

Wohnmobilstellplatz Monte Mare, Klingelswiese 1.
GPS: n50,42633 e7,38492. ⬆.

12 ⌇€ 3 ⊓ €1/100liter ⬤Ch ⬤(12x)€0,50/kWh WC ⬤ ⬤
Surface: concrete. ⬤ 01/01-31/12
Distance: ⬥2km.
Remarks: Bread-service.

Annweiler 15H2

Am Kurpark, Bindersbacherstrasse. **GPS:** n49,19624 e7,96817. ⬆ ➡.

10 ⌇free ⊓ €1/80liter ⬤Chfree. **Location:** Rural, quiet.
Surface: asphalted. ⬤ 01/01-31/12.
Distance: ⬥1km ⬤600m.
Remarks: Max. 3 days.

Bacharach 10G3

Reisemobilplatz Sonnenstrand, B9 Leinpfad.
GPS: n50,05487 e7,77123. ⬆ ➡.

30 ⌇€ 8 ⊓ €1 ⬤Ch ⬤(12x)€2,50/24h ⬤€1 ⬤€3/3 ⬤.
Location: Comfortable, central, quiet. **Surface:** gravel.
⬤ 01/01-31/12 ⬤ high water
Distance: ⬥on the spot ⬤Rhine river ⊗300m ⬤300m.
Remarks: Bread-service.

Bad Bergzabern 15H2

Schloßgärten, Weinbergstrasse. **GPS:** n49,10322 e7,99737. ⬆ ➡.

7 ⌇€ 4 ⊓ €1/80liter ⬤€1 Ch ⬤€1. ⬤ **Location:** Urban, simple,
central, noisy. **Surface:** metalled. ⬤ 01/01-31/12 ⬤ water
disconnected in winter
Distance: ⬥on the spot ⊗on the spot ⬤200m.

Bad Bergzabern 15H2

Weingut Hitziger, Liebrauenbergweg 3. **GPS:** n49,10667 e7,99611. ⬆.

8 ⌇€ 5 ⊓ ⬤Chincluded ⬤€1/kWh. ⬤ **Location:** Rural, simple,
quiet. **Surface:** grassy. ⬤ 01/01-31/12
Distance: ⬥1km ⊗2km ⬤2km.

Bad Dürkheim 15H1

In der Silz, Leistadterstrasse. **GPS:** n49,46944 e8,16722. ⬆ ➡.

170 ⌇€ 6 ⊓ €1/80liter ⬤Ch ⬤€1/kWh. ⬤ **Location:** Urban,
simple. **Surface:** grassy/gravel. ⬤ 01/01-31/12
Distance: ⬥300m ⬤100m ⬤300m ⬤200m.
Remarks: Servicepoint at Knaus Park.

Bad Dürkheim 15H1

Katharinenhof, In den Kornwiesen 1. **GPS:** n49,46633 e8,20144.
10 ⌇€ 10 ⊓ ⬤Ch. **Surface:** grassy. ⬤ 01/01-31/12
Remarks: Bread-service.

Bad Dürkheim 15H1

Knaus park, In den Almen 3. **GPS:** n49,47472 e8,19167. ⬆.

16 ⌇€ 9,50 ⊓ €1/70liter ⬤Ch ⬤€0,70/kWh ⬤€3,30/pp ⬤.
Surface: gravel/metalled. ⬤ 01/01-31/12

Bad Ems 10G3

Yachthafen Kutscher's Marina, Nievernerstrasse 20.
GPS: n50,33278 e7,70167. ⬆ ➡.

16 ⌇€ 10 ⊓ ⬤Ch ⬤€1/kWh WC ⬤€1. ⬤ **Location:** Comfortable,
quiet. **Surface:** gravel. ⬤ 01/03-15/11
Distance: ⬥on the spot ⬤on the spot ⬤1km ⬤300m.

Bad Kreuznach 15G1

Wohnmobilstellplatz Salinental, Karlshalle 11, Saline.
GPS: n49,82778 e7,85001. ⬆ ➡.

35 ⌇€ 12 ⊓ €0,50/60liter ⬤Ch ⬤€2,50/night WC ⬤€1.
Surface: gravel. ⬤ 01/01-31/12
Distance: ⬥2km ⬤on the spot ⬤on the spot ⊗200m ⬤2km
⬤on the spot.

Bad Kreuznach 15G1

Weingut Desoi, Am Darmstädter Hof. **GPS:** n49,82803 e7,88934. ⬆.

3 ⌇€ 5 ⊓ ⬤included. ⬤ **Location:** Rural, simple, quiet.
Surface: concrete. ⬤ 01/01-31/12
Distance: ⬥1,5km ⬤10km ⬤500m.

Bad Kreuznach 15G1

Weingut Gut Neuhof, Gut Neuhof. **GPS:** n49,86923 e7,85924. ⬆.

4 ⌇€ 10 ⊓ ⬤included. ⬤ **Location:** Rural, simple, quiet.
Surface: grassy. ⬤ 01/01-31/12
Distance: ⬥3km ⬤2,5km.

Bad Marienberg 10G2

Marienbad, Bismarckstrasse 65. **GPS:** n50,64321 e7,93515. ➡.

DE

40 ⛺ € 10 🚰 €1/80liter ♨Ch 🔌(40x)€0,50/kWh 🗑included.
Location: Luxurious, quiet. **Surface:** metalled. 🕐 01/01-31/12
Distance: 🚆2km ⊗Bistro.
Remarks: 10 days € 78, bread-service, free use of sun beds and beach chairs.

Bad Münster am Stein-Ebernburg 15G1

Reisemobilstellplatz Weingut Rapp, Schlossgartenstrasse 74.
GPS: n49,80800 e7,83208.⬆.

3 ⛺ € 9,50 🚰 €1/100liter 🔌.🛁 **Location:** Rural, simple, quiet.
Surface: gravel. 🕐 01/01-31/12
Distance: 🚲15km.

Bad Neuenahr ♨ 10F2

Am Schwimmbad. **GPS:** n50,53806 e7,10139.⬆.

25 ⛺ € 7 🚰€0,50 ♨Ch 🔌€1/2kWh 🗑€0,50.🛁 **Location:** Urban, central. **Surface:** metalled. 🕐 01/01-31/12
Distance: 🚆400m ⊗300m 🛒bakery 500m.
Remarks: Along the Ahr river, max. 24h.

Bad Neuenahr ♨ 10F2

Apolinaris-Stadion, Kreuzstrasse. **GPS:** n50,54456 e7,15132.➡.

50 ⛺ € 5/24h 🚰 €1/80liter ♨Ch.🏠 **Surface:** asphalted.
🕐 01/01-31/12
Distance: 🚲3km.

Bad Neuenahr ♨ 10F2

St Piusstrasse. **GPS:** n50,53962 e7,10775.

20 ⛺ € 5/24h.🏠 **Location:** Urban, simple. **Surface:** asphalted.
🕐 01/01-31/12
Distance: 🚆700m ⊗700m.
Remarks: Parking at the Ahr.

Bad Sobernheim ⚓ ♨ 15G1

Reisemobilstellplatz am Nohfels Bad Sobernheim

**Nearby things of interest
Located in a quiet area
Ideal base for walking and cycling**

**www.amnohfels.de
Am_Nohfels@web.de**

Reisemobilstellplatz am Nohfels, Hömigweg 1.
GPS: n49,77993 e7,65702.⬆.
39 ⛺ € 9 🚰€0,10/10liter ♨Ch 🔌(48x)€2,50/day,16Amp WC 📶.🛁
Location: Rural, comfortable, quiet. **Surface:** metalled.
🕐 01/01-31/12
Distance: 🚆500m 🏊100m 🚤100m ⊗200m 🍺500m 🚌300m
🛁 on the spot 🚶 on the spot.
Remarks: Bread-service.

Battweiler 🌿 15G2

Flugplatz Pottschütthöhe, Pottschütthöhe.
GPS: n49,26761 e7,49096.⬆.

10 ⛺ € 15 🚰♨Ch 🔌(10x)included. **Location:** Simple, isolated,
quiet. **Surface:** grassy/gravel. 🕐 01/01-31/12 ⊙ Mo
Distance: 🚆2km 🚲10km ⊗on the spot.
Remarks: At airfield.

Baumholder 15G1

Freizeitzentrum Am Weiher, Ringstrasse.
GPS: n49,61111 e7,33917.➡.

3 ⛺free 🔌. **Surface:** asphalted. 🕐 01/03-31/10
Distance: 🚆2km 🏊on the spot ⊗on the spot 🍺250m.

Becheln 🌳 10G3

Restaurant Zum Wolfsbusch, Emser strasse 1.
GPS: n50,29609 e7,71503.⬆.

5 ⛺ € 2, guests free 🚰€2. **Location:** Simple, quiet.
Surface: gravel/metalled.
Distance: 🚆on the spot ⊗on the spot 🍺300m.

Beckingen 15F2

Wohnmobilstellplatz Düppenweiler, Brunnenstrasse 11, Düppenweiler. **GPS:** n49,41414 e6,76973.

30 ⛺ € 4 🚰 €1/100liter ♨Ch 🔌€1/8h. **Surface:** metalled.
🕐 01/03-31/10
Distance: 🚆on the spot.

Beckingen 15F2

Landgasthaus Wilscheider Hof, Zum Wilscheider Hof, Düppenweiler.
GPS: n49,42585 e6,76431.

15 ⛺ € 5 🚰♨Ch 🔌€1 WC 🗑1,50 🚿. **Surface:** grassy.
🕐 01/01-31/12
Distance: 🚆1,5km ⊗on the spot 🍺1,5km.

Bellheim 15H2

Wohnmobilstellplatz Bellheim, Auchtweide.
GPS: n49,19552 e8,27466.⬆.

8 ⛺ € 5 🚰 WCincluded 🗑€1/pp.🛁 **Location:** Simple, isolated, quiet.
Surface: grassy/gravel. 🕐 01/05-31/10
Distance: 🚆700m 🚲3km ⊗750m 🍺1km 🚌200m.
Remarks: At tennis-courts, max. 24h.

Bendorf 10G2

Wohnmobilstellplatz Bendorf, Koblenz Olper Strasse.
GPS: n50,43998 e7,57486.
6 ⛺free. 🕐 01/01-31/12
Distance: 🚲4km.

Bernkastel 🌿🍰🍷 10F3

Weingut Studert-Prüm im Maximin Hof, Hauptstrasse 150, Wehlen.
GPS: n49,93771 e7,04811.⬆.

43 ⛺ € 10 🚰♨Ch 🔌 WCincluded.🛁 **Location:** Rural, comfortable,
quiet. **Surface:** grassy. 🕐 01/04-31/10
Distance: 🚆on the spot 🏊on the spot 🚤on the spot ⊗on the spot
🍺2km, bakery 300m 🚲on the spot 🚶on the spot.

Bernkastel 🌿🍰🍷 10F3

Nikolausufer. **GPS:** n49,91119 e7,06721.⬆.

40 ⌧10-18h ⬛Ch. 🚐 **Location:** Urban. **Surface:** grasstiles.
⬛ 01/01-31/12
Remarks: Max. 6h.

Betzdorf 10G2

Friedrichstrasse. **GPS:** n50,78636 e7,87781.⬆.

1 ⌧free. **Location:** Urban, simple, noisy. **Surface:** asphalted.
⬛ 01/01-31/12
Distance: 🚶500m.
Remarks: Max. 24h.

Betzdorf 10G2

Schützenplatz, Martin-Luther-Strasse. **GPS:** n50,79323 e7,86793.⬆.

1 ⌧free. **Location:** Urban, simple. **Surface:** gravel.
⬛ 01/01-31/12
Distance: ⊗on the spot 🍴 on the spot.
Remarks: Max. 1 night.

Betzdorf 10G2

Vor dem Stadion, Eberhardystrasse. **GPS:** n50,78524 e7,86507.⬆.

1 ⌧free. **Location:** Urban, simple, central. **Surface:** gravel.
⬛ 01/01-31/12
Distance: 🚶1km ⊗50m 🚌on the spot 🚲on the spot.
Remarks: Max. 1 night.

Bexbach 15G2

Bexbacher Reisemobilhafen, Im Blumengarten.
GPS: n49,34161 e7,25698.⬆→.

35 ⌧€ 7 ⬛€1/80liter ⬛Ch ⚡(36x)€2,50/night WC.
Surface: grassy. ⬛ 01/01-31/12
Distance: 🚶900m ⊘5km ⊗on the spot 🍴500m 🚌200m.
Remarks: Bread-service.

Wohnmobilpark am Petersberg, Flonheimer Strasse 34.
GPS: n49,79432 e8,16236.

20 ⌧€ 5 ⬛€2 ⬛Ch ⚡€2. **Surface:** metalled. ⬛ 01/01-31/12
Distance: 🚶1km ⊘1,5km ⊗Bistro Am Petersberg 🍴1km.
Remarks: Max. 2 nights.

Biebernheim 10G3

Reiterhof Pabst, Auf dem Flürchen. **GPS:** n50,14127 e7,70828.⬆→.

20 ⌧€ 6, 2 pers.incl ⬛⬛Ch ⚡(6x)€2. 🐴 **Location:** Rural, simple,
isolated, quiet. **Surface:** grassy. ⬛ 01/01-31/12
Distance: ⊘10km.
Remarks: Bread-service.

Bingen/Rhein 10H3

Wohnmobilpark Bingen, Mainzer Straße, Bingen/Kempten.
GPS: n49,96860 e7,94417.⬆→.

39 ⌧€ 6,50/night ⬛⬛Ch ⚡€2,50/24h ⬛€3/3 🚿includedstay.
Location: Comfortable, quiet. **Surface:** grassy/metalled.
⬛ 01/01-31/12
Distance: 🚶2,5km ⊘1,5km ⊗800m 🍴2,7km.
Remarks: Bread-service.

Birgel 10F3

Historische Wassermühle, Bahnhofstrasse 16.
GPS: n50,32033 e6,61764.⬆.

10 ⌧€ 15, free with a meal > € 15 ⬛⬛Ch ⚡(2x)included.
Location: Simple, quiet. **Surface:** gravel. ⬛ 01/01-31/12
Distance: 🚶500m ⊘25km ⊗on the spot 🍴1km.

Freizeitanlage Würzbacher Weiher, Marxstraße, Niederwürzbach.
GPS: n49,24674 e7,19226.⬆→.

10 ⌧€ 4,50 ⬛€1/10minutes ⬛€1 Ch ⚡€1/4h.
Surface: grassy/gravel. ⬛ 01/01-31/12
Distance: 🚶500m ⊘on the spot 🚐on the spot ⊗100m 🍴600m
🚌600m.
Remarks: At lake, Würzbacher Weiher.

Blieskastel 15G2

Hotel Restaurant Hubertushof, Kirschendell 32.
GPS: n49,24456 e7,21573.⬆⬆.

8 ⌧€ 5, free with a meal ⬛ ⚡. **Surface:** asphalted.
⬛ 01/01-31/12
Distance: 🚶on the spot ⊗on the spot 🍴1km.
Remarks: Arrival < 19h, max. 2 nights, bread-service.

Blieskastel 15G2

Freizeitzentrum Blieskastel, Bliesaue 1, Webenheim.
GPS: n49,23527 e7,26946.⬆.

3 ⌧free. **Location:** Urban, simple, noisy. **Surface:** metalled.
⬛ 01/01-31/12
Distance: 🚶on the spot ⊘5km 🍴on the spot.

Bobenthal/Bornich 15H2

Hotel-Restaurant St. Germanshof, Hauptstrasse 10.
GPS: n49,04749 e7,89985.

4 ⌧guests free. **Surface:** metalled. ⬛ 01/01-31/12 ⬛ Mo
Distance: 🚶5km ⊗on the spot 🍴7km.

Bockenheim 15H1

Weingut Benss, Am Spiegelpfad 10. **GPS:** n49,59959 e8,17823.⬆.

6 ⌧free ⬛free ⚡(6x)€2,50/24h WC . **Location:** Rural, simple,
quiet. **Surface:** grassy. ⬛ 01/01-31/12
Distance: ⊘7km ⊗500m 🍴3km.

Bockenheim 15H1

Weingut W. Kohl, Am Sonnenberg 3. **GPS:** n49,59902 e8,17925.⬆.

6 ⌧ € 8/night ⛽ WC included. **Surface:** metalled.
⬛ 01/01-31/12
Distance: 🚊 500m ⊗ 500m 🍺 3km.

Braubach 10G3

Braubacher Rheintreff, Rheinuferstrasse, B42.
GPS: n50,26972 e7,64750.⬆

30 ⌧ € 8 ⛽ €1/80liter 🗑 €1 Ch €1 ⚡€0,50/kWh WC included 🔲€3.
Location: Comfortable, quiet. **Surface:** asphalted. ⬛ 01/01-31/12
Distance: 🚊 300m ⊘ on the spot ⚓ on the spot ⊗ 300m 🍺 300m 🚌 300m.
Remarks: Bread-service.

Brauneberg 15F1

Wohnmobilplatz Juffer, Moselweinstrasse.
GPS: n49,90518 e6,97760.➡

25 ⌧ € 8 ⛽🗑 Ch ⚡ **Surface:** metalled. ⬛ 01/01-31/12
Distance: 🚊 100m ⊘ on the spot ⊗ 300m 🍺 300m 🚌 100m.

Bremm 10F3

Weingut Oster-Franzen, Calmontstrasse 96.
GPS: n50,09593 e7,12383.⬆➡

16 ⌧ € 14, 2 pers incl ⛽ €0,50/60liter 🗑 Ch ⚡€0,60/kWh WC €2/6minutes 🔲€3,50 🚿. **Location:** Rural, comfortable.
Surface: gravel. ⬛ 01/03-30/11
Distance: 🚊 on the spot ⊗ 800m ⚓ on the spot ⚶ on the spot.

Briedern 10F3

Wohnmobilstellplatz Briedern, Birkenweg.
GPS: n50,11165 e7,20867.➡

15 ⌧ € 4,50. ⚡ **Location:** Rural, simple.
Surface: grassy/gravel.
Distance: 🚊 on the spot ⊗ 300m 🍺 200m ⚓ on the spot.

Brodenbach 10G3

Historische Mühle Vogelsang, Rhein-Mosel-strasse 63.
GPS: n50,22142 e7,44573.
⌧ € 4,80 + € 5/pp ⛽€2 WC €1,30/6minutes 🔲€3. ⬛ 01/01-31/12
Distance: ⊘ on the spot.

Brodenbach 10G3

Moselufer. GPS: n50,22471 e7,43930.⬆

2 ⌧ free. **Location:** Urban, simple. **Surface:** metalled.
⬛ 01/01-31/12
Distance: 🚊 500m ⊗ 500m ⚓ on the spot.

Brodenbach 10G3

Salzwiese 9. GPS: n50,22519 e7,44291.⬆➡

4 ⌧ free. **Location:** Urban. **Surface:** concrete. ⬛ 01/01-31/12
Distance: 🚊 400m ⚓ Moselle river 200m ⊗ 400m.

Burgen 10G3

Hotel Schmause Mühle, Baybachstrasse 50.
GPS: n50,20859 e7,39365.⬆

20 ⌧ € 8 ⛽🗑 Ch ⚡€2,50/day WC €1. **Location:** Quiet.
⬛ 01/01-31/12
Distance: 🚊 on the spot ⊗ on the spot 🍺 300m.

Burgen bei Bernkastel-Kues 15F1

Weingut Bohn-Leimbrock, Lindenstrasse 6.
GPS: n49,87986 e6,99967.⬆

4 ⌧ € 8 ⛽ ⚡ WC. ⚡ **Surface:** grassy. ⬛ 01/01-31/12
Distance: 🚊 150m ⊗ 50m 🍺 2km 🚌 50m ⚓ on the spot ⚶ on the spot.

Burrweiler 15H2

Wein- und Sektgut Hermann-Bruno Eberle, Böchingerstrasse 1a.
GPS: n49,24649 e8,07989.⬆

3 ⌧ € 6 ⛽⚡ WC included. ⚡ **Location:** Rural, quiet.
Surface: metalled. ⬛ 01/01-31/12
Distance: 🚊 100m 🍺 200m.
Remarks: Arrival <21h.

Burrweiler 15H2

Weingut Diether Bauer, Weinstrasse 52. **GPS:** n49,21982 e8,03059.⬆

3 ⌧ € 5 ⛽⚡ WC included. ⚡ **Location:** Rural, quiet.
Surface: metalled. ⬛ 01/01-31/12
Distance: 🚊 on the spot 🍺 300m.

Burrweiler 15H2

Weingut Hertel, Raiffeisenstrasse 2. **GPS:** n49,24861 e8,07705.⬆

3 ⌧ € 5 ⛽ free ⚡ WC on demand. **Location:** Rural, simple, quiet.
Surface: metalled. ⬛ 01/04-31/10

Burrweiler 15H2

Weingut Winzerhof, Am Schlossberg 3. **GPS:** n49,25147 e8,07902.⬆

4 ⌧ € 8 ⛽⚡ WC included. ⚡ **Location:** Rural, quiet.
Surface: metalled. ⬛ 01/01-31/12
Distance: 🚊 1km 🍺 300m.

Busenberg 15G2

Weißensteiner Hof, An der B427. **GPS:** n49,12152 e7,83943.⬆

3 ⌧ guests free ⛽ on demand. **Location:** Rural, simple.
Surface: asphalted. ⬛ 01/01-31/12 🔲 Mon + Fri

Cochem 10F3

Bergstrasse, K59. **GPS:** n50,15028 e7,17083.

DE

4 ⌆ € 2,50 9-19h, overnight stay free.
Surface: grasstiles/metalled.
Distance: 300m 300m.

🅰 Cochem ⚓ 🖼 10F3

Moselpromenade, B49. **GPS:** n50,14108 e7,16936. ⬆.

4 ⌆ € 1/h 8-19h, overnight stay free. **Surface:** metalled.
01/01-31/12

🅰 Cochem ⚓ 🖼 10F3

Wohnmobil-Stellplatz an der Nordbrücke, Moselstrasse, B49.
GPS: n50,15329 e7,16828. ⬆.

16 ⌆ € 1/h 8-19h, overnight stay free. **Location:** Urban, simple.
Surface: metalled. 01/01-31/12
Distance: 700m 200m 200m on the spot.

🅲 🅂 Cochem ⚓ 🖼 10F3

Wohnmobil-Stellplatz am Freizeitzentrum, Stadionstrasse.
GPS: n50,16051 e7,17956. ⬆.

50 ⌆ € 0,50/h 🖼. **Surface:** gravel/sand. 01/01-31/12
Distance: 2,5km 400m on the spot.
Remarks: Along ther Moselle river, max. 24h.

🅳 🅂 Dahn/Reichenbach 15G2

Altes Bahnhöf'l, An der Reichenbahn 6. **GPS:** n49,13890 e7,79908. ⬆.

10 ⌆ free. **Location:** Rural, simple, quiet. **Surface:** gravel.
01/01-31/12 Mo
Distance: on the spot on the spot 100m.

🅸 🅂 Darscheid/Vulkaneifel 10F3

Kucher's Landhotel, Karl-Kaufmann-Strasse 2.
GPS: n50,21060 e6,88270.
3 ⌆ guests free . 01/01-31/12 Tue

🅂 Deidesheim 15H2

Weinhaus Villa Giessen, Weinstrasse 3. **GPS:** n49,41210 e8,19105.
3 ⌆ € 7,50 🖼. 01/01-31/12
Distance: 5km.

🅂 Deudesfeld 10F3

Meisburgerstrasse. **GPS:** n50,10084 e6,72932.
8 ⌆ free €1/120liter €1 Ch €0,50/kWh. **Location:** Rural.
01/01-31/12
Distance: 13km.

Deudesfeld 10F3

Leyendecker Platz, Mandertscheider Strasse. **GPS:** n50,10164 e6,73217.
4 ⌆ free. 01/01-31/12
Distance: 13km.

🅂 Deuselbach 15F1

Wohnmobilstellplatz Erbeskopf, K130. **GPS:** n49,73589 e7,08327.
50 ⌆ € 4,00 Ch (5x)€3/day WC . **Surface:** metalled.
01/01-31/12
Distance: 10km.

🅳 Dexheim 15H1

Weingut Bacchushof, Wörrstädter Strasse 14.
GPS: n49,84812 e8,31144. ⬆.

5 ⌆ free. **Location:** Rural, simple. **Surface:** concrete.
01/01-31/12
Distance: 12km.

🅂 Dierbach 15H2

Jahnstrasse. **GPS:** n49,08177 e8,06201. ⬆.

10 ⌆ € 5 Ch (5x)free. 🚌 **Location:** Simple, quiet.
Surface: asphalted. 01/01-31/12
Distance: 700m 12km 1km 3km 50m.
Remarks: At sports centre.

🅳 🅂 Dierbach 15H2

Weingut Geiger, Hauptstrasse 21. **GPS:** n49,08344 e8,06673. ⬆ ➡.

30 ⌆ € 10 Ch WCincluded €2/day. **Location:** Rural,
comfortable, luxurious, quiet. **Surface:** grassy. 01/03-31/12
Distance: on the spot 12km 500m.
Remarks: Bread-service.

🅳 🅂 Dohm 10F3

Am Heidberghof, Heidberghof 1, Dohm-Lammersdorf.
GPS: n50,26696 e6,67366.

6 ⌆ € 10 Ch (6x)€2 WC 🖼€3,50.
Surface: grassy/gravel.
Ascension-31/09
Distance: 15km.
Remarks: Bread-service, incl. swimming pool (summer).

🅳 🅂 Dolgesheim 15H1

Weingut Seck, Weinolsheimer Strasse 12. **GPS:** n49,79752 e8,26154. ⬆.

3 ⌆ € 5 🖼 📶included. **Location:** Rural, simple, quiet.
Surface: grassy. 01/01-31/12
Distance: 200m 13km 300m 2km.

🅳 🅂 Dörrenbach 15H2

Übergasse. **GPS:** n49,08840 e7,96921. ⬆.

10 ⌆ € 6 Ch included. **Location:** Rural, quiet.
Surface: gravel/sand. 01/01-31/12
Distance: 500m 700m.
Remarks: Next to sports fields.

🅳 Eckersweiler 15G1

Am Sportplatz. GPS: n49,55646 e7,30577. ⬆.

4 ⌆ free. **Location:** Rural, simple, isolated. **Surface:** grassy.
01/01-31/12
Distance: 1,3km on the spot on the spot.

🅳 🅂 Edenkoben 15H2

Wohnmobilstellplatz Kirchbergplatz, Bahnhofstraße.
GPS: n49,28234 e8,13116. ⬆.

40 ⌆ € 5/24h €1/100liter Ch (8x)€1/kWh.
Surface: asphalted. 01/01-31/12
Distance: on the spot 2km 300m Aldi 800m.
Remarks: Max. 3 nights.

Edenkoben 15H2

Obstgut & Brennerei Göring, Blücherstrasse 45.
GPS: n49,27792 e8,13487.

5 🗓 € 10 🚰 🍽️ Ch 🚿 included WC 🗑️. **Surface:** grassy.
⏲ 01/01-31/12
Distance: 🚲 3km.

Edenkoben 15H2

Weingut Bernd und Herbert Schäfer, Rhodter Strasse 24.
GPS: n49,27844 e8,12572.
3 🗓 free 🚰 🚿 €5. ⏲ 01/01-31/12
Distance: 🚲 3,5km.

Edenkoben 15H2

Weingut Edel Brauch, St.-Martiner-Strasse 30.
GPS: n49,28901 e8,12236.
4 🗓 free 🚰 €2 Ch 🚿 €2. ⏲ 01/01-31/12
Distance: 🚲 3km.

Edenkoben 15H2

Gasthof Ziegelhütte, Luitpoldstrasse 75-79. **GPS:** n49,28539 e8,13872.

3 🗓 € 5/night 🚿. **Surface:** metalled. ⏲ 01/01-31/12
Distance: 🚰 on the spot 🚲 1km 🛒 on the spot 🍺 on the spot.

Edesheim 15H2

Weingut Boos, Ludwigstrasse 150. **GPS:** n49,25785 e8,11673.⬆️.

3 🗓 € 6 🚰 🍽️ Ch 🚿 (3x)included. **Location:** Rural, simple, quiet.
Surface: grassy. ⏲ 01/01-31/12
Distance: 🚰 500m ⊗ 300m 🍺 1km.

Edesheim 15H2

Weingut Braun & Sohn, Ludwigsstrasse 151.
GPS: n49,25761 e8,11587.⬆️.

3 🗓 € 5 🚰 🍽️ Ch 🚿 included. 🚻 **Location:** Rural, simple, quiet.
Surface: grassy. ⏲ 01/01-31/12
Distance: 🚰 300m ⊗ 300m.

Edesheim 15H2

Weingut Rehm, Ludwigsstrasse 36. **GPS:** n49,26015 e8,12734.⬆️.

Remarks: Arrival <23h.

6 🗓 € 5 🚰 included 🚿(6x)€2,50/day WC 🗑️ €2,50. 🚻 **Location:** Rural,
simple, quiet. **Surface:** grassy. ⏲ 01/01-31/12

Edesheim 15H2

Weingut Erlenmühle, Erlenmühle 1. **GPS:** n49,25865 e8,11417.⬆️.

5 🗓 € 5 🚰 🍽️ Ch 🚿 included 🗑️ on demand. 🚻 **Location:** Rural,
simple, quiet. **Surface:** gravel. ⏲ 01/01-31/12
Distance: 🚰 500m ⊗ on the spot 🍺 1km.
Remarks: Arrival <22h.

Ediger/Eller 10F3

Stellplatz Ediger, Moselweinstrasse. **GPS:** n50,09320 e7,15942.⬆️.

18 🗓 € 5 🚰 🍽️ Ch included. **Location:** Rural, simple.
Surface: gravel/metalled. ⏲ 01/04-30/11
Distance: 🚰 100m 🛁 on the spot 🍴 on the spot ⊗ on the spot 🛒
the spot 🍺 on the spot.
Remarks: Along the Moselle river in Ediger.

Ediger/Eller 10F3

Stellplatz Moselufer, Eller. **GPS:** n50,09915 e7,14370.⬆️.

10 🗓 € 5. 🚻 **Location:** Rural, simple. **Surface:** metalled.
⏲ 01/04-30/11
Distance: 🛁 on the spot 🍴 on the spot ⊗ on the spot 🍺 200m
🛒 on the spot.
Remarks: Along the Moselle river in Eller.

Eisenschmitt 10F3

Hotel-Restaurant Molitors Mühle, Eichelhütte.
GPS: n50,03681 e6,73766.⬆️.

5 🗓 guests free 🚰 🚿 WC included. **Location:** Rural, simple.
Surface: gravel. ⏲ 01/01-31/12
Distance: 🚰 1km 🚲 6km 🛁 on the spot 🍴 on the spot ⊗ on the spot
🍺 1km 🚌 300m 🛒 on the spot.

Ellenz/Poltersdorf 10G3

Weingut Loosen, Im Goldbäumchen 4. **GPS:** n50,11389 e7,23528.⬆️➡️.

12 🗓 € 9 🚿 WC included. **Location:** Rural, comfortable, quiet.
Surface: gravel. ⏲ 01/01-31/12
Distance: 🚰 on the spot 🛁 150m ⊗ 500m 🍺 1km 🛒 on the spot.
Tourist information Ellenz/Poltersdorf:
🍷 Strassenweinfest. Wine-growers and -houses open their doors,
wine-tastery. ⏲ end Sep.
🍷 Wein- und Heimatfeste. Traditional wine celebration. ⏲ last
weekend Jul, 1st weekend Aug.

Elmstein 15H2

NaturFreundeHaus Elmstein, Esthaler Strasse 63.
GPS: n49,36133 e7,95123.⬆️.

12 🗓 € 3 🚰 €1 🚿 €2 🗑️ €1/pp. 🚻 **Location:** Rural, simple, central,
quiet. **Surface:** gravel. ⏲ 01/01-31/12
Remarks: Bread-service.

Elmstein 15H2

Stellplatz Elmstein, Bahnhofstrasse 88. **GPS:** n49,34803 e7,94337. ⬆️➡️.

4 🗓 free 🚿(4x)€0,50/kWh. **Location:** Rural. **Surface:** gravel.
⏲ 01/01-31/12
Distance: 🚰 500m ⊗ 100m 🍺 500m.

Elmstein 15H2

Wohnmobilplatz Waldesruhe, Schwarzbach 36.
GPS: n49,34037 e7,83397.⬆️.

10 🗓 € 5, free with a meal. **Location:** Rural, simple, isolated, quiet.
Surface: grassy. ⏲ 01/01-31/12
Remarks: To be paid at restaurant.

Elzweiler 15G1

Stellplatz Elzweiler, Hauptstraße 7. **GPS:** n49,58036 e7,51393.⬆️➡️.

DE

2 🚐free ⛽€1 🚰Ch 🚿€1. **Location:** Rural. **Surface:** metalled.
🅿 01/01-31/12
Distance: 🛒on the spot 🚰on the spot 🚲on the spot 🏊on the spot.
Remarks: Small pitches.

📷S **Enkirch** 🌿 **10F3**
Wohnmobilplatz an der Mosel, Moselvorgelände, B53.
GPS: n49,98396 e7,12157. ⬆️➡️.

200 🚐7 ⛽€1/80liter 🚰Ch 🔌(90x)€1/2kWh WC🚿€1🅿🚿€
1,50/30minutes 🧺🛒 **Location:** Rural, comfortable, quiet.
Surface: grassy. 🅿 Easter-31/10
Distance: 🛒on the spot 🚰on the spot.
Remarks: Along ther Moselle river.

📷S **Ensch** **15F1**
Reisemobilplatz An den 2 Pappeln, Am Moselufer/ B53.
GPS: n49,82760 e6,83549. ⬆️➡️.

45 🚐5 ⛽🚰Ch 🔌(45x)€2. 🛒 **Surface:** grassy.
🅿 01/04-31/10
Distance: 🛒200m ⊗300m 🚿500m 🛒100m.
Remarks: Bread-service.

📷S **Eppelborn** **15F2**
Wohnmobilstellplatz Finkenrech, L303. **GPS:** n49,43285 e6,99986.
🚐5 🚿€0,50. 🅿 01/01-31/12
Distance: 🚲3km.

📷 **Eppenbrunn** **15G2**
Im Sportzentrum. **GPS:** n49,11179 e7,56512. ⬆️.

6 🚐free. **Location:** Rural, simple, quiet. **Surface:** metalled.
🅿 01/01-31/12
Distance: 🛒500m ⊗on the spot 🚿1km.
Remarks: Parking sports centre in nature reserve Pfälzer Wald.

📷 **Eppenbrunn** **15G2**
Neudorfstrasse. **GPS:** n49,11531 e7,55360. ⬆️.

5 🚐free. **Location:** Rural, simple, noisy. **Surface:** metalled.
🅿 01/01-31/12
Distance: 🛒on the spot 🚣on the spot 🚲on the spot ⊗on the spot.

📷S **Erden** **10F3**
Wohnmobilstellplatz Erden, An Moselufer 1.
GPS: n49,97989 e7,02120.
21 🚐8 ⛽🚰Ch 🔌(21x)€2,50 🅿€0,30/minutes 📶.
🅿 01/04-31/10
Distance: 🚲15km 🚿300m.

📷S **Ernst** 🌿🍇 **10G3**
Wohnmobilstellplatz im Weinberg, Weingartenstrasse 106.
GPS: n50,14339 e7,23237. ⬆️➡️.

30 🚐9 ⛽🚰Ch 🔌included 📶€5/10h. **Location:** Rural,
comfortable. **Surface:** gravel. 🅿 01/01-31/12
Distance: 🛒300m 🚰on the spot 🚿200m 🛒100m.

📷S **Ernst** 🌿🍇 **10G3**
Mosella Schinkenstube, Weingatenstrasse 97.
GPS: n50,14382 e7,23071. ⬆️.

18 🚐8 ⛽🚰Ch 🔌📶included. **Surface:** grassy.
Distance: ⊗on the spot.

📷S **Eschbach** **15H2**
Weingut Wind, Weinstrasse 3-5. **GPS:** n49,17594 e8,02171. ⬆️.

3 🚐€5, discount for clients ⛽€1/100liter 🔌€3 WCincluded. 🛒
Location: Rural, simple, quiet. **Surface:** gravel.
🅿 01/01-31/12
Distance: 🛒on the spot ⊗on the spot 🚿250m.
Remarks: Check in on arrival.

📷S **Essingen** **15H2**
Weingut Schweikart Dalberghof, Kirchstrasse 16.
GPS: n49,23478 e8,17524. ⬆️.

3 🚐€5 ⛽€1/100liter 🔌(3x)€1/night WC€1. **Location:** Simple,
quiet. **Surface:** grassy. 🅿 01/01-31/12
Distance: 🛒on the spot 🚲3km ⊗1km 🚿3km 🖥7km 🛒30m.
Remarks: Sale of wines.

📷S **Fell** **15F1**
Besucherbergwerk, Auf den Schiefergruben, K82.
GPS: n49,75440 e6,79731. ⬆️.

30 🚐4 🚿€2. **Location:** Isolated, quiet. **Surface:** concrete.
🅿 01/01-31/12

👥S **Fischbach** 🎏🍇 **15G1**
Wohnmobilpark, Marktstraße 1. **GPS:** n49,74046 e7,40444. ⬆️➡️.

40 🚐€ 6,50/night ⛽🚰Chincluded 🔌(40x)€2,. 🛒
Location: Rural, simple, central. **Surface:** grassy.
🅿 01/01-31/12
Distance: 🛒800m 🚰on the spot ⊗300m 🚿1,5km.
Remarks: Bread-service.

📷S **Fischbach** 🎏🍇 **15G1**
Historisches Kupferbergwerk, Hosenbachstraße.
GPS: n49,75398 e7,38287. ⬆️.

10 🚐free. **Location:** Rural, simple, isolated, quiet. **Surface:** gravel.
🅿 01/01-31/12
Distance: 🛒1,7km ⊗on the spot.
Remarks: Visitors' center former copper mine.

👥S **Flemlingen** **15H2**
Weingut Eichhorn, Maxstrasse 21. **GPS:** n49,24122 e8,09341. ⬆️.

10 🚐€5 ⛽🔌(10x)€2 WCincluded 🅿€2/pp. 🛒 **Location:** Rural,
simple, quiet. **Surface:** grassy. 🅿 01/01-31/12
Distance: 🚲6km 🚿400m.

Flonheim — 15H1

Weingut Meyerhof, Aussiedlerhof. **GPS:** n49,78836 e8,04531.

4 🚐 € 8 ⚡ (4x)included. **Location:** Rural, simple, quiet. **Surface:** concrete. 🅾 01/01-31/12 **Distance:** 🚶700m 🚲4km 🛒100m 💧100m. **Remarks:** Bread-service.

Föckelberg — 15G1

Wildpark Potzberg, Auf dem Potzberg. **GPS:** n49,52240 e7,48079.

4 🚐 free. **Location:** Rural, simple, quiet. **Surface:** asphalted/sand. 🅾 01/01-31/12 **Distance:** 🚶1km.

Forst an der Weinstrasse — 15H1

Weingut Margarethenhof, Wiesenweg 4. **GPS:** n49,42814 e8,19219. 3 🚐 € 8 ⚡ WC. 🅾 01/01-31/12 **Distance:** 🚶1km 🚲7km 💧1km.

Freisen — 15G1

Weiselbergbad, Zum Schwimmbad. **GPS:** n49,53324 e7,26048.

3 🚐 € 5 ⚡ €2/day. **Location:** Rural, simple, noisy. **Surface:** metalled. 🅾 01/01-31/12 **Distance:** 🚶1km 🚲3km. **Remarks:** Check in at swimming pool.

Gau-Algesheim — 10H3

Reimo Gau-Algesheim, Bingerstrasse 8. **GPS:** n49,96331 e8,01213.

40 🚐 € 4/night ⚡ Chincluded ⚡(40x)€2. **Location:** Comfortable, quiet. **Surface:** metalled. 🅾 01/01-31/12 **Distance:** 🚶800m 🚲2,5km 🛒500m 💧200m.

Gau-Bickelheim — 15H1

Winzerhof Schnabel, Bahnhofstrasse 31. **GPS:** n49,83941 e8,02116.

15 🚐 € 5 ⚡included ⚡(8x)€3/day. **Location:** Rural. **Surface:** grassy. 🅾 01/01-31/12 **Distance:** 🚲3km 🛒5km 💧1km.

Gau-Bickelheim — 15H1

Am Autohof, B50. **GPS:** n49,83461 e7,99664.

15 🚐 free. **Location:** Rural, simple, noisy. **Surface:** asphalted. 🅾 01/01-31/12 **Distance:** 🚲 on the spot.

Gau-Heppenheim — 15H1

Weingut Gustavshof, Hauptstrasse 53. **GPS:** n49,74138 e8,17082.

3 🚐 € 8 ⚡(3x)included. **Location:** Rural, simple, quiet. **Surface:** concrete. 🅾 01/04-31/10 **Distance:** 🚲4km 🛒2km 💧3km.

Gau-Odernheim — 15H1

Petersberghalle, Mühlstraße. **GPS:** n49,78528 e8,19575.

3 🚐 free. **Surface:** metalled. 🅾 01/01-31/12 **Distance:** 🚶200m 💧200m.

Gebhardshain — 10G2

Festwiese, Steinebacherstrasse. **GPS:** n50,74412 e7,82079.

5 🚐 free. **Location:** Urban, simple, central, quiet. **Surface:** asphalted 🅾 01/01-31/12 **Distance:** 🚶500m 🛒500m 💧500m.

Geiselberg — 15G2

Grillplatz Geiselberg, Hauptstrasse, K31. **GPS:** n49,32381 e7,70957.

10 🚐 free. **Location:** Rural, simple, quiet. **Surface:** gravel. 🅾 01/01-31/12 **Remarks:** Max. 2 days.

Germersheim — 15H2

Carnot'sche Mauer, Rüdolf von Habsburgstrasse. **GPS:** n49,22004 e8,37906.

8 🚐 € 3/24h ⚡€1/100liter Ch ⚡(8x)€1/5kWh. **Location:** Simple, central. **Surface:** grassy. 🅾 01/01-31/12 **Distance:** 🚶300m 🚲2km 🛒500m 💧300m 🚌100m 🚶 on the spot.

Gerolstein — 10F3

Wohnmobilplatz Gerolstein, Raderstrasse 22. **GPS:** n50,22096 e6,65387.

20 🚐 € 10/24h ⚡€1/100liter Ch ⚡(12x)€1/day. **Location:** Urban, simple. **Surface:** grassy/metalled. 🅾 15/03-15/11 **Distance:** 🚶nearby 🚲25km 🛒500m 💧1km. **Remarks:** At swimming pool.

Gevenich — 10F3

Am Sportplatz. GPS: n50,14727 e7,08385. 7 🚐 free. 🅾 01/01-31/12 **Distance:** 🚶1km 🛒on the spot.

Gillenfeld — 10F3

Wohnmobilhafen Pulvermaar, K14. **GPS:** n50,13294 e6,93218.

30 🚐 € 7 ⚡€1/100liter Ch ⚡€0,50/kWh WC €2/time. **Location:** Simple. **Surface:** gravel. 🅾 01/01-31/12 **Distance:** 🚶3km 🏊on the spot 🎣on the spot 🛒200m 💧200m 🚌300m.

Gillenfeld — 10F3

Feriendorf Pulvermaar, Vulkanstrasse. **GPS:** n50,13000 e6,93194.

12 🛏€ 7, 2 pers.incl ⛽€1/100liter 🚿Chincluded ⚡€0,50/kWh WC ⬛€1/7minutes. **Surface:** grassy. 🔵 01/03-30/11
Distance: 🛒3km 🚂7km 🏊on the spot 🚤on the spot ⊗150m 🍽150m 🚌200m.

Schwimbadstrasse. **GPS:** n49,77806 e8,38278.

8 🛏€ 4/night. **Surface:** asphalted/grassy. 🔵 15/05-15/09
Distance: 🛒500m 🍽300m.

Weingut Falger-Baier, Alsheimerstrasse 25. **GPS:** n49,77733 e8,36959.
3 🛏€ 5 ⛽🚿Ch⚡. 🔵 01/01-31/12
Distance: 🛒3km 🍕Pizzeria 50m 🍽500m.

Am Bahnhof, Bahnhofstraße. **GPS:** n49,46935 e7,44420. ⬆

3 🛏free ⛽€1 🚿Ch⚡(4x)€1/2h. **Location:** Urban, simple, central, noisy. **Surface:** metalled. 🔵 01/01-31/12
Distance: 🏊750m 🍽150m 🚤on the spot.

Weingut Kost, Hainbachtalstrasse 3. **GPS:** n49,23862 e8,06737. ⬆

3 🛏free ⛽free. **Location:** Rural, quiet. **Surface:** grassy.
🔵 01/01-31/12
Distance: 🏊8km ⊗on the spot.

Weingut Schoenlaub, Bergstrasse 14. **GPS:** n49,13131 e8,00465. ⬆

2 🛏free ⛽free. **Location:** Rural, simple, quiet. **Surface:** grassy.
🔵 01/01-31/12
Distance: 🏊15km ⊗500m.
Remarks: Check in at Weingut.

Wohnmobilpark Sun-Park, Gestade 16a. **GPS:** n49,93322 e7,06249. ⬆

140 🛏€ 10/day ⛽liter 🚿Ch⚡(132x)€3/day WCincluded ⬛€1,50/pp 📷€2,50. **Location:** Rural, simple. **Surface:** grassy.
🔵 27/03-03/11
Distance: 🛒200m 🚤on the spot ⊗200m 🚂2km 🚌on the spot 🏊on the spot 🎣on the spot.
Remarks: Bread-service.

Panorama Sauna, Panoramaweg 2. **GPS:** n50,56029 e7,05368. ⬆

20 🛏free. **Surface:** gravel. 🔵 01/01-31/12
Distance: 🏊5km ⊗300m 🚌300m.

Seestube am Ohmbachsee, Bahnhofstrasse 17b.
GPS: n49,41664 e7,40377. ⬆

12 🛏€ 6 ⛽€1/80liter 🚿Ch⚡(12x)€0,60/kWh. 🚿
Location: Rural, simple, quiet. **Surface:** grassy.
🔵 01/01-31/12
Distance: 🏊6km 🏊on the spot 🚤on the spot.
Remarks: Bread-service.

Huppert's Wohnmobile Wingert, Untere Grabenstraße 21.
GPS: n49,69499 e8,20465. ⬆➡

12 🛏€ 5 ⛽€3. **Surface:** gravel/sand. 🔵 01/01-31/12
Distance: 🏊1km ⊗on the spot 🍽300m.
Remarks: Max. 3 nights.

Am Sportanlage, Alsheimerstrasse 85. **GPS:** n49,78974 e8,34373. ⬆

16 🛏€ 5 ⛽€1/80liter 🚿Ch⚡(12x)€0,50/kWh. **Location:** Rural.

Surface: gravel. 🔵 01/01-31/12
Distance: 🛒500m ⊗500m 🍽500m.

Weingut Katharinenhof, Alsheimerstrasse 95.
GPS: n49,78667 e8,34324. ⬆

10 🛏€ 5 ⛽included ⚡(7x)€2/24h. 🚿 **Location:** Rural, simple, quiet. **Surface:** grassy. 🔵 01/01-31/12
Distance: 🛒1km ⊗1km 🍽1km.

P4 - Burggarten, Alexanderring. **GPS:** n50,66250 e7,82694. ⬆

8 🛏free ⛽€1/70liter 🚿Ch⚡€1/6h WC. **Location:** Urban, simple, quiet. **Surface:** grasstiles. 🔵 01/01-31/12
Distance: 🛒300m ⊗300m 🍽300m 🚌on the spot 🏊on the spot.
Remarks: June 2014 during inspection service out of order, just electricity, historical centre.

Stadtbrauhaus Hagenbach, Stixwörthstrasse 2-4.
GPS: n49,00884 e8,25902.

10 🛏free. 🔵 01/01-31/12 ⬤ Mon, Tue
Distance: 🏊5km ⊗on the spot.

Modenbach. **GPS:** n49,25730 e8,10328.

20 🛏free. **Location:** Simple, quiet. **Surface:** gravel.
Distance: 🛒150m 🚂3km ⊗250m 🍽1km 🏊on the spot.

Weingut Edgar und Andreas Lutz, Weinstrasse 57.
GPS: n49,25696 e8,09882.
4 🛏€ 6, € 8 service incl ⚡WC⬛. **Location:** Simple.
Surface: metalled.
Distance: 🛒on the spot ⊗100m.

Hotel Sägmühle, Sägmühlweg 140. **GPS:** n49,34674 e8,25491.

DE

2 ☒€ 12, guests free ✐(2x)WC included. Location: Simple, isolated, quiet. ▣ 01/01-31/12
Distance: ⬥ 10km.
Remarks: Bicycle rental.

| Hassloch | 15H2 |

Badepark Hassloch, Lachener Weg 175. GPS: n49,34804 e8,24677.⬆.

9 ☒free ⚡free. Location: Simple, quiet. ▣ 01/01-31/12
Distance: ⬥2km ⬥10km ⊗50m ⬛200m ⬜100m.

| S | Hassloch | 15H2 |

Magin Reisemobile, Hans-Böckler-Strasse 52.
GPS: n49,34968 e8,23935.⬆➡.

8 ☒€ 12,50, 2 pers.incl ⚡☒Ch ✐(8x)included.
Location: Urban, simple, quiet.
Surface: gravel/metalled.
▣ 01/01-31/12
Distance: ⬥2km ⬥7km ⊗50m ⬛200m.

Tourist information Hassloch:
😊 Holiday Park. Attractions park with shows.
▣ 01/04-30/09 10h, summer 9h, Oct weekend. ⊤ € 21.

| S | Hauenstein | 15G2 |

Stellplatz am Deutschen Schumuseum Hauenstein, Turnstrasse.
GPS: n49,18896 e7,85669.⬆.

12 ☒€ 7 ⚡80liter ☒Chfree ✐€0,55/kWh. Location: Rural, simple, quiet. Surface: gravel. ▣ 01/01-31/12
Distance: ⬥on the spot ⬛200m ⬜300m.
Remarks: Check in on arrival, pay at pay-desk of the museum.

| S | Heimborn | 10G2 |

Gasthaus zum Nisterstrand, Vor der Hardt.
GPS: n50,71609 e7,75322.⬆.

6 ☒guests free ⚡☒Ch ✐. Location: Rural, simple, quiet.
Surface: asphalted. ▣ 01/01-31/12
Distance: ⬥on the spot ⬥on the spot ⊗on the spot.

| Heltersberg | 15G2 |

Am Bergbad, Bergstrasse. GPS: n49,31654 e7,70380.⬆.

5 ☒free. Location: Rural, simple, quiet. Surface: grassy.
▣ 01/01-31/12
Distance: ⬥900m.
Remarks: Parking swimming pool.

| Hemmelzen | 10G2 |

Hotel Im Heisterholz, Heisterholzstrasse 10.
GPS: n50,69579 e7,58456.⬆.

4 ☒€ 12 ✐included. Location: Rural, quiet. Surface: gravel.
▣ 01/01-31/12 ▣ Mo
Distance: ⬥200m ⊗on the spot ⬜100m ⬥on the spot ⬥on the spot.
Remarks: € 2 reduction in restaurant.

| S | Herrstein | 15G1 |

Wohnmobilstellplatz Herrstein, Brühlstrasse.
GPS: n49,77963 e7,33569.⬆.

3 ☒free ⚡€1/80liter ☒✐€0,50/kWh WC. Surface: metalled.
▣ 01/01-31/12
Distance: ⬥300m ⊗on the spot.
Remarks: Max. 48h.

Tourist information Herrstein:
ℹ Touristinformation Deutsche Edelsteinstraße, Brühlstrasse 16. Renovated mall half-timbered city.
▣ 01/05-01/10.

| S | Herxheim | 15H2 |

Festhalle, Bonifatiusstraße. GPS: n49,14463 e8,21656.⬆➡.

8 ☒free ⚡☒Chfree. Location: Simple, central. Surface: grasstiles.
▣ 01/01-31/12
Distance: ⬥on the spot ⬥4km ⊗150m ⬛200m ⬜75m.

| S | Heuchelheim-Klingen | 15H2 |

Gästehaus am Fürstweg, Hauptstrasse 2. GPS: n49,14511 e8,05788.
3 ☒€ 5 ⚡☒Ch. ▣ 01/01-31/12
Distance: ⬥14km.

| S | Heuchelheim-Klingen | 15H2 |

Weingut Junghof, Hauptstrasse 21. GPS: n49,14572 e8,05580.

4 ☒€ 5, free with a meal ⚡€2/100liter ✐€2/night.
Location: Simple. Surface: grassy/metalled. ▣ 01/01-31/12
Distance: ⬥on the spot ⬥14km ⊗500m ⬛2km ⬜500m.

| S | Hillesheim | 10F3 |

Markt- und Messeplatz, Am Viehmarkt.
GPS: n50,28895 e6,67239.⬆➡.

6 ☒€ 4 ⚡☒Ch ✐(6x)WC included. Location: Urban, simple, central. Surface: gravel. ▣ 01/01-31/12
Distance: ⬥on the spot ⊗on the spot ⬛200m.

| S | Hillesheim | 10F3 |

Wohnmobilstellplatz Birkenhof, Birkenhof 1.
GPS: n50,28639 e6,69083.⬆.

8 ☒€ 10 ⚡(4x)included ⬙free. Location: Rural, simple, quiet.
Surface: gravel. ▣ 01/01-31/12
Distance: ⬥1,5km ⬥1,5km.
Remarks: Bread-service.

| S | Hillesheim | 10F3 |

Wohnmobile Theres, Prümer Straße 20. GPS: n50,28957 e6,66310.

15 ☒€ 5 ⚡☒Ch ✐included. Surface: asphalted. ▣ 01/01/31/12
Distance: ⬥750m ⬥750m ⬛750m.
Remarks: Motorhome dealer, accessory shop, repairs.

| S | Hochspeyer | 15G1 |

Am Schwimmbad, Mühlhofstraße. GPS: n49,44108 e7,89333.⬆.

6 ☒€ 5 ⚡€1/80liter ☒Ch ✐(12x)€0,50/kWh.
Location: Simple, central, quiet. Surface: asphalted.
▣ 01/01-31/12 ▣ 01/08-15/08
Distance: ⬥400m ⬥5km ⬛400m bakery.
Remarks: Max. 3 days.

DE

Höheinöd — 15G2

Am Haus des Bürgers, Hauptstrasse 24. **GPS:** n49,28691 e7,60468. ⬆️.

3 🚐 free. **Location:** Rural, simple, quiet. **Surface:** metalled.
☐ 01/01-31/12
Distance: 🚰 on the spot 🚲 8km.
Remarks: Max. 2 nights.

Höhr-Grenzhausen — 10G2

Ferbachstraße. **GPS:** n50,43330 e7,66833. ⬆️.

8 🚐 free. ☐ 01/01-31/12
Distance: 🚰 on the spot 🚲 2km 🛒 100m.

Holzappel — 10G3

Stellplatz am Herthasee, Am Herthasee. **GPS:** n50,36135 e7,90274. ➡️.

12 🚐 € 6/24h, € 11/48h, € 15/72h 🚰 € 1/90liter Ch ⚡(12x)€
1/2kWh. 🔌 **Location:** Rural, comfortable, quiet. **Surface:** grassy.
☐ 01/01-31/12
Distance: 🚰 1km 🏊 on the spot 🍴 on the spot 🛒 on the spot.

Hornbach — 15G2

Wohnmobilpark Hornbach, Bahnhofstraße.
GPS: n49,18382 e7,36560. ⬆️.

26 🚐 € 6 🚰 € 1/60liter Ch ⚡(30x)€1/2kWh. **Surface:** gravel.
☐ 01/01-31/12
Distance: 🚰 on the spot 🚲 8km 🛒 on the spot.

Hörschhausen — 10F3

Mechels Hof, Dauner Straße 24. **GPS:** n50,24248 e6,92770.
3 🚐 € 5 🚰 Ch ⚡ water and electricity € 2. **Location:** Rural.
☐ 01/01-31/12
Distance: 🚲 9km.
Remarks: Bread-service.

Idar/Oberstein — 15G1

Edelsteinbörse, Hauptstrasse 100. **GPS:** n49,71932 e7,30313. ⬆️.

12 🚐 € 6/day, first 24h free 🚰 € 1/100liter Ch WC.
Surface: asphalted. ☐ 01/01-31/12
Distance: 🚰 on the spot 🛒 on the spot 🚉 300m.
Tourist information Idar/Oberstein:
👁 Edelsteinminen des Steinkaulenberges. Gem mine. ☐ 15/03-15/11
9-17h.
Ⓜ Deutsches Edelsteinmuseum. Gem museum. ☐ 01/05-31/10 9-18h,
01/11-30/04 9-17h.

Impflingen — 15H2

Weingut Junker, Sonnenberghof 1. **GPS:** n49,16242 e8,10728. ⬆️➡️.

3 🚐 € 5 🚰 ⚡(4x)€2 WC. 🔌 **Location:** Simple, quiet.
Surface: gravel. ☐ 01/01-31/12
Distance: 🚰 1km 🚲 7km 🍴 on the spot 🚉 3km 🛒 200m 🚲 on the
spot 🚶 on the spot.

Ingelheim am Rhein — 10H3

Weingut Menk, Außenliegend 143. **GPS:** n49,97190 e8,09295. ⬆️.

6 🚐 € 10 🚰 Ch ⚡ WC included. **Location:** Rural, comfortable,
quiet. **Surface:** grassy. ☐ 01/01-31/12
Distance: 🚰 2km 🚲 9km 🚲 on the spot.

Jettenbach — 15G1

Freizeitgelände Schwimmbad, Austrasse.
GPS: n49,52919 e7,56453. ⬆️➡️.

6 🚐 free 🚰 Ch ⚡. **Surface:** asphalted. ☐ 01/01-31/12
Distance: 🚰 500m 🚉 800m.

Kaisersesch — 10F3

Am Markt. **GPS:** n50,23223 e7,14044.
4 🚐 free. ☐ 01/01-31/12
Distance: 🚲 1km.

Kaiserslautern — 15G1

Daennerplatz. **GPS:** n49,44300 e7,80230. ⬆️➡️.

11 🚐 € 10/24h 🚰 € 1/100liter Ch ⚡ € 2/2kWh. 🔌
Location: Urban. **Surface:** metalled.
Distance: 🚰 2,5km 🛒 on the spot 🚌 on the spot.
Remarks: Free bus to centre.

Kaiserslautern — 15G1

Gasthaus Licht Luft, Entersweilerstraße 51.
GPS: n49,43828 e7,80338. ⬆️.

14 🚐 free 🚰 Ch on demand. **Location:** Urban, central, quiet.
Surface: gravel. ☐ 01/01-31/12
Distance: 🚲 5km 🛒 on the spot 🍴 on the spot 🚲 on the spot
🚶 on the spot.

Kaiserslautern — 15G1

Am Monte Mare, Mailänder Straße 6. **GPS:** n49,45387 e7,81203. ⬆️.

10 🚐 free. **Location:** Rural, simple, quiet. **Surface:** metalled.
☐ 01/01-31/12
Distance: 🚲 1km.

Kamp-Bornhofen — 10G3

Bistro Rheinufer, Rheinuferstrasse 66 A.
GPS: n50,22305 e7,61888. ⬆️➡️.
7 🚐 € 7,50 🚰 € 1 ⚡ € 2,50 WC. **Surface:** metalled.
☐ 01/01-31/12
Distance: 🚰 on the spot 🛒 on the spot 🚉 300m 🚌 on the spot.
Remarks: Along the Rhine river, toilets only during opening hours
restaurant.

Kandel — 15H2

Adams Hof, Rheinzaberner Strasse 1. **GPS:** n49,08902 e8,22194. ⬆️.

30 🚐 € 10/night 🚰 € 2,50 ⚡(20x)€2,50/12h WC.
Location: Simple, quiet. **Surface:** grassy. ☐ 01/01-31/12
Distance: 🚰 1,5km 🍴 on the spot 🛒 on the spot 🚉 1,5km 🚲 1,5km.
Remarks: € 5 voucher Biergarten.

Kapellen-Drusweiler — 15H2

Weingut Manderschied, Dorfstrasse 4. **GPS:** n49,10482 e8,03723. ⬆️.

DE

10 ⌷free 🚰⚡(3x)free. **Location:** Rural, simple, quiet.
Surface: grassy. ☐ 01/01-31/12
Distance: 🚶500m ⛲500m 🍴2km.

| 🅿️S | **Kelberg** | 10F3 |

Maß-Schneider, Schulstrasse 14. **GPS:** n50,28453 e6,91594.
7 ⌷free 🚰Ch⚡. ☐ 01/01-31/12
Remarks: Producer of cushions and upholstery for motorhomes.

| 🅲S | **Kell am See** | 15F1 |

Am Camping Hochwald, L 143. **GPS:** n49,63800 e6,80140.
10 ⌷€ 6 + € 6/pp 🚰Ch⚡€0,50/kWh. ☐ 01/05-31/08

| 🛎️ | **Kempenich** | 10F2 |

Eifel-Gasthof Kleefuß, In der Hardt 1. **GPS:** n50,42209 e7,10951.

4 ⌷guests free. **Location:** Rural. **Surface:** gravel. ☐ 01/01-31/12
🔘 Mon, Tue
Distance: 🚶500m.

| | **Kempfeld** 🌿🍃 | 15G1 |

An der Wildenburg, Wildenburgstraße.
GPS: n49,77588 e7,25423.⬆️➡️

3 ⌷free. **Surface:** metalled. ☐ 01/01-31/12
Distance: ⊗2km ⛲2km.

| 🅿️S | **Kesten** 🏕️🍃🌊 | 15F1 |

Wohnmobilpark Kesten/Mosel
Kesten

■ **Flat motorhome pitches**
■ **Located directly at the river**
■ **Located in a quiet area**

www.wohnmobilpark-kesten.de
info@wohnmobilpark-kesten.de

Wohnmobilpark Kesten/Mosel, Urmetzgasse/K134.
GPS: n49,90306 e6,96232.➡️
100 ⌷€ 6/24h 🚰€0,50/50liter 🔲Chincluded ⚡(100x)€
2/24h,6Amp.
Surface: grassy/metalled. ☐ 01/04-31/10
Distance: 🚶300m ⛲10m 🚽10m ⊗300m ⛲1km 🚌300m
🐾 on the spot 🚶 on the spot.
Remarks: Parking at the Moselle River, bread-service.

| 🅿️S | **Kinheim** 🌊 | 10F3 |

Am Moselufer, Moselweinstraße, B53. **GPS:** n49,97218 e7,05706.⬆️➡️

50 ⌷€ 7 🚰🔲Chincluded ⚡€2/day. 🐾 **Location:** Rural, simple,
quiet. **Surface:** grassy. ☐ 01/01-31/12
Distance: 🚶100m ⛲on the spot ⊗on the spot 🍴150m 🐾on the
spot 🚶on the spot.
Remarks: Parking at the Moselle River.

Tourist information Kinheim:
🍷 Tag den offenen Weinkeller. Open wine-cellars. ☐ 2nd Thu after
Whitsuntide.
🍷 Wein- und Frülingsfest. Wine and spring celebration. ☐ Whitsun-
tide.
🍷 Winzerfest. Wine festival. ☐ 2nd weekend Sep.

| 🚐S | **Kirchberg** | 10G3 |

AMB-Reisemobile, Herbert-Kühn-Straße 10. **GPS:** n49,95349 e7,40759.
15 ⌷€ 6 🚰Ch⚡included. ☐ 01/01-31/12

| 🅿️S | **Kirchheimbolanden** 🚂 | 15H1 |

Festplatz Herrengarten, Hitzfeldstrasse. **GPS:** n49,66667 e8,01501.⬆️

20 ⌷free 🚰€1/70liter 🔲Ch⚡€0,50. **Surface:** metalled.
☐ 01/01-31/12 🔘 2nd weekend May-Aug-Oct
Distance: 🚶300m ⛲300m ⛲on the spot.

| 🅿️ | **Kirn** 🍃🌊 | 15G1 |

Wohnmobilstellplatz Auf der Kiesel, Fontaine-les-Dijon-Strasse.
GPS: n49,78406 e7,45798.

3 ⌷€ 1,25/day. 🚌 **Location:** Urban, comfortable, quiet, noisy.
Surface: concrete. ☐ 01/01-31/12
Distance: 🚶300m ⊗on the spot ⛲on the spot.
Remarks: Monday market.

| 🛎️ | **Klausen** | 15F1 |

Zentralparkplatz, Eberhardstrasse/ K51. **GPS:** n49,90550 e6,88104.➡️

5 ⌷free. ☐ 01/01-31/12
Distance: 🚤2km.

| 🛎️🅿️S | **Kleinbundenbach** 🍃 | 15G2 |

Auf der Stampermühle, Stampermühle 1.
GPS: n49,31778 e7,45694.⬆️

10 ⌷€ 7 🚰⚡🔲included. **Location:** Rural, simple, isolated.
Surface: gravel.
Distance: ⊗on the spot.

| 🅿️S | **Klüsserath** 🌊 | 15F1 |

Reisemobilpark Klüsserath, B53. **GPS:** n49,84170 e6,85475.⬆️

400 ⌷€ 6,50 🚰€1/90liter 🔲Ch⚡€1,50/24h. 🐾 **Surface:** grassy.
☐ Easter-31/10
Remarks: Along ther Moselle river, bread-service.

| 🅿️S | **Kobern** 🌊 | 10G3 |

Am Kalkofen B416, Kobern-Gondorf. **GPS:** n50,30524 e7,46064.⬆️

50 ⌷€ 5 🚰€1/80liter 🔲€0,10/time Ch€0,10/time. 🚌
Surface: metalled. ☐ 01/01-31/12
Distance: 🚶300m 🚤8km ⛲on the spot 🚽on the spot ⊗300m
🍴300m.

| 🅿️ | **Koblenz** 🌿🍰🌊 | 10G3 |

Busparkplatz, Pastor-Klein-Straße. **GPS:** n50,36557 e7,57417.⬆️

50 ⌷free. **Location:** Simple. **Surface:** gravel. ☐ 01/01-31/12
Distance: 🚶Old city centre 2km ⛲600m 🛒Aldi 500m.

| 🚽S | **Konz** | 15F1 |

An der Saarmündung, Am Moselufer 1. **GPS:** n49,70550 e6,57597.➡️
3 ⌷€ 8 🚰ChWC🔲against payment 🚿. **Surface:** grassy.
☐ 01/03-31/10
Distance: ⛲on the spot 🚽on the spot ⊗100m 🍴1km 🐾on the
spot 🚶on the spot.
Remarks: Service 100m.

| 🍷S | **Köwerich** 🌊 | 15F1 |

Weingut Hans Klären-Maringer 'Off'm Herrach', Beethovenstrasse
40. **GPS:** n49,84123 e6,86287.⬆️➡️

20 ⌷€ 7 🚰🔲Ch⚡€0,50/kWh WC🔲€1 🔘€4/time. 🐾

DE

Surface: grassy.
🔆 01/01-31/12
Distance: 🚶500m ⛱500m ⚓500m ⊗on the spot 🍺2km 🚌100m.
Remarks: Check in at restaurant, bread-service.

| 🅻🆂 | **Kusel** 🛬🍴 | 15G1 |

Parkplatz der Tuchfabriken, Trierer Straße 61.
GPS: n49,54016 e7,39626. ⬆➡.

3 🛏free 🚰🔌. **Surface:** asphalted.
🔆 01/04-31/10
Distance: 🚶500m 🍺300m.
Remarks: Max. 3 days, key service at Touristinformation (300m).

| 🅻 | **Lahnstein** | 10G3 |

Wohnmobilstellplatz Kränchen, Johannesstraße 44.
GPS: n50,30939 e7,59833. ➡.

60 🛏€ 9,50 🚰€1/100liter 🗑Ch 🔌€0,50/kWh WC🚻€1.
Location: Simple. **Surface:** gravel. 🔆 01/01-31/12
Distance: 🚶1km ⊗600m 🍺600m.

| 🅻 | **Lahnstein** | 10G3 |

Wohnmobilstellplatz Blücherstraße, Blücherstraße 20.
GPS: n50,31335 e7,59331. ➡.

10 🛏free. **Location:** Urban, simple, central. **Surface:** gravel.
🔆 01/01-31/12
Distance: 🚶2km ⛱on the spot ⛵on the spot ⊗on the spot.
Remarks: Max. 3 days.

| 🅻🆂 | **Lambrecht** | 15H2 |

Blainviller-Straße 1. **GPS:** n49,37030 e8,07448. ⬆➡.
7 🛏free 🚰€1 🗑Ch 🔌€1/8h. **Surface:** gravel.
🔆 01/01-31/12
Distance: 🚶on the spot ⊗on the spot.
Remarks: Near sports fields.

| 🅻🆂 | **Landau** 🍴 | 15H2 |

Wellnessoase La Ola, Horstring 2. **GPS:** n49,20230 e8,14270. ⬆➡.

5 🛏€ 10/24h 🚰€4 🗑Ch 🔌🐕. **Location:** Simple, quiet.
Surface: metalled. 🔆 01/01-31/12
Distance: 🚶3km ⛱1km ⊗500m 🚌100m.

| 🅻🆂 | **Landstuhl** | 15G2 |

Bahnstraße. **GPS:** n49,41595 e7,57092. ⬆➡.

2 🛏free 🚰🗑Ch 🔌free. **Location:** Urban, simple, noisy.
Surface: metalled. 🔆 01/01-31/12
Distance: 🚶on the spot ⛱1,3km ⊗350m 🍺Aldi 100m.
Remarks: Max. 3 days.

| 🅻🆂 | **Langenlonsheim** | 15G1 |

Weingut Im Zwölberich, Schützenstrasse 14.
GPS: n49,89672 e7,89466. ⬆.

5 🛏€ 10 🚰🔌 included. 🐕 **Location:** Rural, simple, central, quiet.
Surface: asphalted/grassy. 🔆 01/01-31/12
Distance: 🚲7km.

| 🅻🆂 | **Lauterecken** 🛬🍴 | 15G1 |

Wohnmobilstellplatz Villa Toskana, Friedhofweg 3a.
GPS: n49,65056 e7,58806. ⬆➡.

30 🛏€ 8 🚰€1/80liter 🗑Ch 🔌(18x)€1/8h WC🚻€1/5minutes.
Surface: grassy/gravel. 🔆 01/01-31/12
Distance: 🚶300m ⊗on the spot 🍺100m.
Remarks: Bread-service.

| 🅻 | **Leimersheim** 🎭🍴 | 15H2 |

Sport- und Freizeithalle, Rheinstraße 42.
GPS: n49,12534 e8,35457. ⬆.

5 🛏free. **Location:** Rural, simple, quiet.
Surface: gravel.
🔆 01/01-31/12
Distance: 🚶500m 🚲4km ⛱100m ⛵100m ⊗on the spot 🍺1km.
Remarks: At tennis-courts.

| 🅻🆂 | **Leinsweiler** | 15H2 |

Weingut Erlenswein, Wacholderhof. **GPS:** n49,18747 e8,03323. ⬆.

8 🛏€ 10 🚰🗑Ch 🔌included. 🐕 **Location:** Rural, simple, quiet.
Surface: grassy. 🔆 01/03-31/11

Distance: 🚶1km.
Remarks: Check in at Weingut.

| 🅻🆂 | **Leiwen** 🛬🍴 | 15F1 |

Weingut Heinz Spieles, Schulstrasse 20. **GPS:** n49,82331 e6,87524. ⬆.

4 🛏€ 8 🚰€1 🗑Ch 🔌🐕€1 📶included. 🐕 **Surface:** grassy/gravel.
🔆 01/01-31/12
Distance: ⛱400m ⚓400m.

| 🍴🆂 | **Leiwen** 🛬🍴 | 15F1 |

Moselblick, Flurgartenstrasse 2/ Weinallee.
GPS: n49,82611 e6,88057. ⬆.

12 🛏€ 8 🚰🗑Ch 🔌WC🚻€1 🐕. **Surface:** grassy/gravel.
🔆 01/01-31/12
Distance: 🚶500m ⛱on the spot ⛵on the spot ⊗on the spot
🍺300m 🚌500m.

| 🅻 | **Lemberg** | 15G2 |

Lemberger Weiher, Weiherstraße. **GPS:** n49,17284 e7,64731. ⬆.

5 🛏free, service/electricity incl. € 7 🔌🐕. **Location:** Rural.
Surface: grasstiles. 🔆 01/01-31/12
Distance: 🚶400m ⊗600m ⛵on the spot 🏃on the spot.
Remarks: Max. 3 days.

| 🅻 | **Linz am Rhein** 🌊🛬🍴 | 10G2 |

B42 Linzhausenstrasse. **GPS:** n50,56291 e7,27982. ⬆.

6 🛏free. **Surface:** asphalted. 🔆 01/01-31/12
Distance: 🚶500m ⛱on the spot ⊗50m.
Remarks: Along the Rhine river, max. 3 days.

| 🍴🆂 | **Löf** | 10G3 |

SOG Dahmann, In der Mark 2. **GPS:** n50,23194 e7,43750. ⬆.

9 🛏free 🚰🗑Ch 🔌(4x)€0,50/kWh WC. **Location:** Rural.
Surface: metalled. 🔆 01/01-31/12

Distance: 🚲13km ⊗1km.

Longuich/Mosel 15F1
Feiten, Rioler weg 2. **GPS:** n49,80417 e6,77899. ⬆️➡️.

40 🅿️€5 🚰€0,50/70liter 🅲h 🚿€3 WC 🗑️€1. Surface: grassy.
📅 01/01-31/12
Distance: 🚶300m 🏊2km ⚓on the spot 🚣on the spot ⊗on the spot 🚰1km.
Remarks: Playground.

Longuich/Mosel 15F1
WeinKulturgut Longen Schlöder, Kirchenweg 9.
GPS: n49,81023 e6,76427. ⬆️.

8 🅿️€7 🚰€2 🚿(3x)€2,50 WC 🗑️€3. Surface: gravel/metalled.
📅 01/01-31/12 🅿️ Tue
Distance: 🚲1km 🏊150m 🚣150m ⊗on the spot 🚰500m.

Losheim am See 15F1
Reisemobilplatz am Stausee, Zum Stausee.
GPS: n49,51999 e6,74123. ➡️.

20 🅿️€6 🚰🅲h 🚿WC 🗑️included. Surface: asphalted/grassy.
📅 01/01-31/12
Distance: 🚶1km 🏊200m 🚣200m ⊗100m 🚰1km.
Remarks: Parking at lake, in front of tourist office, incl. use sanitary and service on campsite 1km.

Lösnich 10F3
Stellplatz am Moselufer, Gestade. **GPS:** n49,97560 e7,04276. ⬆️.

96 🅿️€6 🚰🅲h included 🚿€2/day. Location: Rural, simple, quiet. Surface: grassy. 📅 01/03-01/11
Distance: 🚶on the spot 🏊on the spot 🚣on the spot ⊗on the spot 🚰3km 🚲on the spot 🚶on the spot.
Remarks: Along ther Moselle river, baker every morning.

Lutzerath 10F3
Trierer Strasse. **GPS:** n50,13015 e7,01002. ⬆️.

10 🅿️€5/day 🚰€0,50 🅲h 🚿(6x)€0,50/kWh. **Location:** Urban, simple. **Surface:** asphalted. 📅 01/01-31/12
Distance: 🚶on the spot ⊗on the spot 🚰on the spot.
Remarks: Check in at Hotel Restaurant Maas, Trierer Str. 30.

Maikammer 15H2
Sporthalle Kalmit, Johannes Dammstrasse.
GPS: n49,30307 e8,13219. ⬆️➡️.

🅿️€4/day 🚰🚿included. **Surface:** asphalted. 📅 01/01-31/12
Distance: 🚶100m ⊗nearby 🚰nearby.

Maikammer 15H2
Weingut Hubert Müller, Raiffeisenstrasse 59.
GPS: n49,30737 e8,13646.
3 🅿️€13 🚰🚿WC 🗑️included. **Surface:** gravel.
📅 01/01-31/12
Distance: 🚶on the spot 🚲7km.

Maikammer 15H2
Weingut Schädler, Dieterwiesenstraße. **GPS:** n49,30848 e8,12530.
3 🅿️€7 🚿WC included. 📅 01/01-31/12
Distance: 🚶500m 🏊1km ⚓on the spot 🚶on the spot.

Maikammer 15H2
Weingut Ziegler-Ullrich, Weinstraße Nord 46.
GPS: n49,30659 e8,13369.
2 🅿️€5 🚰🚿included. 📅 01/01-31/12
Distance: 🚲4km.

Mainz 10H3
Wohnmobilstellplatz Mainz, Dr.-Martin-Luther-King-Weg 21.
GPS: n49,99849 e8,24638.

56 🅿️€10 🚰€1/90liter 🅲h 🚿€0,50/kWh. 📅 01/01-31/12
Distance: 🚶Old city centre 1,7km ⊗150m 🚰Aldi 200m 🚌Bus 160m.

Mandelbachtal 15F2
Ommersheimer Weiher, L107. **GPS:** n49,21899 e7,16766. ⬆️.

2 🅿️free 🚰🚿(2x)€1/12h. **Location:** Rural, simple, isolated, quiet. **Surface:** asphalted. 📅 01/01-31/12
Distance: 🏊on the spot 🚣on the spot.

Mandelbachtal 15F2
Kloster Gräfinthal, Gräfinthal. **GPS:** n49,15975 e7,11924. ⬆️.

2 🅿️free. **Location:** Rural, simple, noisy. **Surface:** metalled.
📅 01/01-31/12
Distance: 🚲100m.

Manderscheid 10F3
Hotel Heidsmühle, Mosenbergstrasse 22.
GPS: n50,08504 e6,80021. ⬆️.

20 🅿️free 🚰🚿(4x)€2,50/day. **Location:** Rural, simple, isolated, quiet. **Surface:** grassy/gravel. 📅 01/01-31/12
Distance: 🚶2km 🚲6km 🚣on the spot ⊗on the spot 🚴on the spot 🚶on the spot.

Manderscheid 10F3
Campingplatz Vulkaneifel, Herbstwiese.
GPS: n50,09713 e6,79969. ➡️.

8 🅿️€6/pp, dog €1,50 🚰€0,50/100liter 🅲h 🚿€2,50 WC included 🚿. **Location:** Rural, simple, quiet. **Surface:** metalled.
📅 15/03-31/10
Distance: 🚶800m 🏊800m 🚰800m 🅿️on camp site 🚴on the spot 🚶on the spot.
Remarks: Bread-service.

Mayen 10F3
Wohnmobilstellplatz am Viehmarkt, Polcherstrasse.
GPS: n50,32194 e7,22806. ⬆️.

6 🅿️free 🚰€1/80liter 🅲hWC. **Location:** Simple. **Surface:** gravel.
📅 01/01-31/12
Distance: 🚶100m 🚲4km 🚣100m 🚰100m.
Remarks: Next to event ground.

Mayschoss 10F2
Ahruferplatz, Ahr-Rotweinstraße 46. **GPS:** n50,51736 e7,01948. ⬆️.

60 🅿️€6 🚰€1/100liter 🅲h 🚿(15x)€2,50/day WC. 🚿

Location: Rural, central. **Surface:** asphalted/gravel.
☐ 01/01-31/12
Distance: on the spot ⊗100m 🍞250m bakery 🚌50m.
Remarks: Along the Ahr river, parking at station.

Meckenheim 15H2
Sporthalle Meckenheim, Rödersheimerstraße.
GPS: n49,41167 e8,24056.⬆️
10 free €0,50/kWh. **Surface:** gravel. ☐ 01/01-31/12
Distance: 1km.

Meddersheim 15G1
Winzergenossenschaft, Naheweinstrasse 63. **GPS:** n49,77988 e7,61347.
10 free free €3/day. **Location:** Rural, simple, quiet.
Surface: gravel. ☐ 01/01-31/12
Distance: 800m.
Remarks: Max. 2 nights, gate can be opened manually.

Mehring 15F1
Weingut Zellerhof, Zellerhof 1. **GPS:** n49,79369 e6,81944.⬆️➡️

43 €6 €0,50/70liter Ch (43x)€0,50/kWh WC €1.
Surface: grassy/metalled. ☐ 01/01-31/12
Distance: 100m on the spot on the spot ⊗on the spot
100m.

Mehring 15F1
Wohnmobilstellplatz del Mosel, Moselweinstrasse 2.
GPS: n49,79423 e6,81726.⬆️

72 €6 + €1,50/pp €1,50/100liter Ch (60x)€2 WC €1,50.
Surface: grassy. ☐ 01/01-31/12
Distance: 100m ⊗on the spot 200m.
Remarks: Bread-service.

Meisenheim 15G1
Schwimmbad Meisenheim, In der Heimbach.
GPS: n49,71472 e7,65750.⬆️

12 €5 €1/100liter €1 Ch (12x)€1/kWh. **Surface:** gravel.
☐ 01/01-31/12 ☐ 01/07-09/07
Distance: 1,6km ⊗on the spot 500m.

Mendig 10G3
Brauerstraße. **GPS:** n50,37678 e7,28404.⬆️

20 free €1/50liter Ch (12x)€0,50/kWh. **Location:** Rural,
quiet. **Surface:** gravel. ☐ 01/01-31/12
Distance: 200m ⊗Vulkanbrauhaus&Felsenkeller 400m.

Remarks: In front of football ground, Vulkanmuseum Lava-Dome
100m.

Merzig 15F2
Das Bad, Saarwiesenring 3. **GPS:** n49,44541 e6,62418.⬆️➡️

12 €7,50 €1/100liter Ch included. **Location:** Rural,
simple, quiet. **Surface:** grasstiles. ☐ 01/01-31/12
Distance: 2km ⊗on the spot 2km.
Remarks: Check in at swimming pool, caution key € 50.

Mettlach 15F1
Cloef-Atrium, Alfred-Backer-strasse, Mettlach-Orscholz.
GPS: n49,50394 e6,53225.⬆️➡️

10 €5 WC. **Surface:** gravel. on the spot.
Remarks: Pay with SMS, max. 24h.

Mettlach 15F1
Mettlacher Abtei-Bräu, P6, Bahnhofstrasse 32.
GPS: n49,49847 e6,59612.⬆️

10 €5 Ch free. **Surface:** gravel. ☐ 01/01-31/12
Distance: 500m 7km on the spot on the spot ⊗on the
spot.
Remarks: Along the Saar River, pay with SMS.

Mettlach 15F1
Restaurant zum Kaltenborn, Zur Großwies 21, Orscholz.
GPS: n49,50916 e6,53030.⬆️

10 €5. ☐ 01/01-31/12 ☐ Thu
Distance: ⊗on the spot.

Tourist information Mettlach:
Ⓜ Erlebniszentrum Villeroy&Boch. Mo-Fr: 9.30-19h, Sa 9.30-
18h.
Villeroy&Boch Outletcenter, Freiherr-vom-Stein-Strasse 4-6.
☐ Mo-Fr: 9.30-19h, Sa 9.30-18h.

Minheim 15F1
Reisemobilpark Sonneninsel, K53. **GPS:** n49,86500 e6,94111.⬆️➡️

90 €6,50 €1/100liter Ch €1/2kWh.
Surface: grassy/gravel. ☐ 01/01-31/12
Distance: 10km ⊗400m 3km.
Remarks: Along the Moselle river, next to football ground.

Minheim 15F1
Weinhaus Moselblick, In der Olk 9. **GPS:** n49,86428 e6,93294.⬆️

10 €9 Ch €1,50/day. **Surface:** grassy/gravel.
☐ 01/01-31/12
Distance: 200m 200m.

Monzernheim 15H1
Weingut Helmut Geil, Am Römer 26. **GPS:** n49,72376 e8,22715.⬆️

3 €6 (3x)included. **Location:** Rural, simple, quiet.
Surface: grassy. ☐ 01/01-31/12
Distance: 8km 4km 4km.
Remarks: Check in at Weingut.

Monzingen 15G1
Parkplatz Festhalle, Rosengartenstrasse 11.
GPS: n49,79438 e7,59075.⬆️

3 free. **Location:** Rural, simple, noisy. **Surface:** asphalted.
☐ 01/01-31/12
Distance: ⊗on the spot 1km.

Monzingen 15G1
Weingut Axel Schramm, Soonwaldstrasse 49.
GPS: n49,81088 e7,48058.⬆️

3 free free. **Location:** Rural, simple, isolated, quiet.
Surface: concrete. ☐ 01/01-31/12
Distance: 1,2km.

Monzingen 15G1
Weingut Holger Alt, Hauptstrasse 67. **GPS:** n49,00000 e7,59144.

5 🛏 free. **Location:** Rural, simple, isolated, quiet. **Surface:** grassy.
◻ 01/01-31/12
Distance: 🏪800m.

| 📷S | **Morbach** 🏕 👫 | 15F1 |

Reisemobilhafen Morbach, Zum Camping 15, Hoxel.
GPS: n49,77855 e7,10695. ⬆➡.

40 🛏 € 5/night 🚰 €1/80liter 🗑Ch 💧(40x)€2/night. **Surface:** grassy.
◻ 16/03-15/11
Distance: ⊗300m 🏪300m.

| 📷S | **Neef** 🌿🍇 | 10F3 |

Wohnmobilstellplatz Zum Frauenberg.
GPS: n50,09455 e7,13730. ⬆➡.

100 🛏 € 6 🚰🗑Ch included 💧(42x)€2/24h,4Amp. 🚿
Location: Rural, simple. **Surface:** grassy. ◻ 01/04-01/11
Distance: 🚶on the spot 🏖on the spot ⊗200m.
Remarks: Along ther Moselle river, nearby sports fields, bread-service.

| 📷S | **Neuhäusel** | 10G3 |

Wohnmobilstellplatz Efferz, Im Feldchen. **GPS:** n50,38271 e7,70331.

20 🛏 € 8 🚰€1/80liter 🗑Ch 💧(12x)€1/2kWh WC🗑🚿.
Surface: metalled. ◻ 01/01-31/12
Distance: 🚶250m ⊗250m 🏪250m 🚆100m > Koblenz.
Remarks: Bread-service.

| 📷S | **Neumagen-Dhron** | 15F1 |

Gaststatte Beim Ketsch, In der Zeil. **GPS:** n49,86449 e6,90321. ⬆➡.

100 🛏 € 6 🚰🗑Ch included 💧€1,50/day WC🗑 ⊡€3 🚿against
payment. 🚿 **Surface:** grassy/gravel. ◻ 01/01-31/12
Distance: 🚶200m ⊗on the spot 🏪500m.
Remarks: Bread-service.

| ⚓S | **Neumagen-Dhron** | 15F1 |

Yachthafen Neumagen, Moselstrasse 21.
GPS: n49,85188 e6,89232. ⬆➡.

40 🛏 <9m € 6, >9m € 8 + € 2,50/pp 🚰€0,50/40liter 🗑Ch 💧€0,60/
kWh WC included ⊡ 🚿€3/24h. 🚿 **Surface:** gravel.
◻ 01/01-31/12
Distance: 🚶100m ⊗on the spot 🏖on the spot ⊗on the spot
🏪1,3km.
Remarks: Check in at harbourmaster.

| ⚓S | **Neunkirchen/Saar** 🍇 | 15F2 |

Prießnitz, Zweibrücker Straße 148. **GPS:** n49,32766 e7,19375. ⬆.

20 🛏 € 14 🚰🗑€2,50 Ch 💧 WC🗑🚿included. **Surface:** grassy.
◻ 01/03-31/10
Distance: 🚶3km 🏊1,7km ⊗1,4km.
Remarks: Next to campsite.

| 📷S | **Neustadt/Weinstrasse** | 15H2 |

Dammstrasse-Ost, Hambach. **GPS:** n49,33083 e8,13150. ⬆➡.

10 🛏 free 🚰€1/100liter 🗑€1 Ch. **Surface:** grassy.
◻ 01/01-31/12
Distance: 🚶nearby ⊗nearby 🏪nearby.
Remarks: Next to swimming pool, service 500m.

| 📷S | **Neustadt/Weinstrasse** | 15H2 |

Reisemobilstellpatz Martin-Luther-Kirche, Martin-Luther-Strasse.
GPS: n49,35485 e8,15255. ⬆.

30 🛏 € 4/24h 🚰🗑Ch included 💧(24x)€1/kWh. **Surface:** metalled.
◻ 01/01-31/12
Distance: 🚶300m ⊗250m 🏖on the spot.

| 📷 | **Neustadt/Weinstrasse** | 15H2 |

Festplatz Neustadt-Haardt, Am Mandelring, Haardt.
GPS: n49,36731 e8,13917.
2 🛏 free. ◻ 01/01-31/12
Distance: 🏊5km.

| 📷 | **Neustadt/Weinstrasse** | 15H2 |

Parkplatz am Rebenmeer, Am Falltor, Duttweiler.
GPS: n49,30148 e8,21192. ⬆.

10 🛏 free. **Location:** Rural, simple, quiet. **Surface:** gravel/metalled.
◻ 01/01-31/12
Distance: 🏊5km ⊗300m 🏪250m bakery.

| 📷S | **Neustadt/Weinstrasse** | 15H2 |

Wohnmobilstellplatz Gimmeldingen, Peter-Koch-Strasse.
GPS: n49,37771 e8,15448.
2 🛏 free. ◻ 01/01-31/12
Distance: 🚶500m 🏊5km ⊗on the spot 🏖on the spot.

| 📷S | **Neustadt/Weinstrasse** | 15H2 |

Altes Weingut Steigelmann, Lauterbachstrasse 33, Mussbach.
GPS: n49,37285 e8,17230.
5 🛏 € 5 🚰🗑Ch 💧€1,50. ◻ 01/01-31/12
Distance: 🏊3km.

| 📷S | **Neustadt/Weinstrasse** | 15H2 |

Rebenhof Wein- und Sektgut, Andergasse 93, Hambach.
GPS: n49,32157 e8,12241. ⬆.

5 🛏 € 8 🚰🗑included. **Surface:** grassy. ◻ 01/01-31/12
Distance: 🏊5km.

| 📷S | **Neustadt/Weinstrasse** | 15H2 |

Weingut & Weinschenke Hans Abel, Weinstrasse 103, Hambach.
GPS: n49,33784 e8,13157.
3 🛏 free 💧€2,50. ◻ 01/01-31/12 ⊡ Thu
Distance: 🏊4,5km.

| 📷S | **Neustadt/Weinstrasse** | 15H2 |

Weingut Andres, Langensteinstrasse 22, Lachen-Speyersdorf.
GPS: n49,33631 e8,20579.
3 🛏 free 💧. ◻ 01/01-31/12

| 📷S | **Neustadt/Weinstrasse** | 15H2 |

Weingut Carl Disson, Andergasse 96, Hambach.
GPS: n49,32123 e8,12220. ⬆.

4 🛏 € 7 WC🗑. **Surface:** grassy. ◻ 01/01-31/12
Distance: 🏊5km.
Remarks: Bread-service, wine tasting.

| 📷S | **Neustadt/Weinstrasse** | 15H2 |

Weingut Hammer, Zum Klausental 29. **GPS:** n49,32109 e8,13251.
3 🛏 € 5 🚰💧. ◻ 01/01-31/12
Distance: 🏊5km.

| 📷S | **Neustadt/Weinstrasse** | 15H2 |

Weingut Klohr, An der Eselshaut 67, Mussbach.
GPS: n49,36931 e8,17414.
2 🛏 🚰💧🗑. ◻ 01/01-31/12
Distance: 🏊2km.

| 📷S | **Neustadt/Weinstrasse** | 15H2 |

Weingut Kreiselmaier, Goethestrasse 77, Lachen.
GPS: n49,32215 e8,20071. ⬆.

DE

DE

3 ⬛€5 🚰€2/100liter ✐€2/night. **Location:** Simple, quiet.
Surface: grassy. ⬛ 01/03-31/10
Distance: ⛲on the spot ✐4,5km ⊗250m 🚰3km 🚌150m.
Remarks: Sale of wines.

🍇S Neustadt/Weinstrasse 15H2
Weingut Müller-Kern, Andergasse 38, Hambach.
GPS: n49,32266 e8,12681.⬆️

3 ⬛€6 + €3/pp ✐ WC 🚿. **Surface:** grassy. ⬛ 01/01-31/12
Distance: ✐4,5km ⊗300m on the spot 🚶on the spot.
Remarks: Adjacent walking and bicycle area.

🍇S Neustadt/Weinstrasse 15H2
Weingut Rumsauer, Von-Dalheim-Strasse 11, Diedesfeld.
GPS: n49,31978 e8,14028.
2 ⬛free 🚰✐. ⬛ 01/01-31/12
Distance: ✐5km.

🍇S Neustadt/Weinstrasse 15H2
Weingut Schäfer, Schiessmauer 56, Mussbach.
GPS: n49,36335 e8,17111.

5 ⬛€15 🚰🍽Ch✐ WC included 📶free. ⬛ 01/03-31/10
Distance: ✐2km.

🍇S Neustadt/Weinstrasse 15H2
Weingut Völcker, An der Eselshaut 15, Mussbach.
GPS: n49,36825 e8,16805.
3 ⬛€5 🚰✐. **Surface:** grassy. ⬛ 01/01-31/12
Distance: ✐3km.

🍇S Neustadt/Weinstrasse 15H2
Weinhaus Am Herzog, Mandelring 195, Haardt.
GPS: n49,36889 e8,14583.
2 ⬛€15 ✐WC included. ⬛ 01/01-31/12
Distance: ✐4km.

🍇S Neustadt/Weinstrasse 15H2
Weinland Königsbach-Neustadt, Deidesheimer Strasse 12, Königsbach. **GPS:** n49,38712 e8,16239.
5 ⬛🚰✐. ⬛ 01/01-31/12
Distance: ✐6,5km.

🍇S Neustadt/Weinstrasse 15H2
Weinland Meckenheim, An der Eselshaut 76, Mussbach.
GPS: n49,37037 e8,17479.
3 ⬛€5 ✐€2,50. ⬛ 01/01-31/12
Distance: ✐2,3km.

🍇 Neustadt/Weinstrasse 15H2
Weingut Helbighof, Andergasse 40, Hambach.
GPS: n49,32256 e8,12657.
3 ⬛. ⬛ 01/01-31/12
Distance: ✐4,5km.

⛲ Neustadt/Weinstrasse 15H2
Hambacher Schloss, Weinstrasse 110, Hambach.
GPS: n49,33706 e8,13155.
2 ⬛free. ⬛ 01/01-31/12 ⬛ 01/10-31/10

Distance: ✐4,5km.

⚓S Neuwied 10G2
Yachthafen Neuwied, Rheinstrasse 180. **GPS:** n50,41413 e7,47946.⬆️

40 ⬛€7, 2 pers.incl. 🚰🍽Ch✐€0,50/kWh WC included.
Surface: metalled. ⬛ 01/01-31/12
Distance: ⛲2km ⊗on the spot 🚰2km.
Remarks: Cash payment.

©S Niederbreitbach 10G2
Campingplatz Neuerburg, Im Freizeitparkt 1.
GPS: n50,52969 e7,41414.➡️

8 ⬛€6 🚰80liter 🍽Ch✐€1,50/day 🍽€1 🔌€3,50. 💧
Location: Rural, comfortable. **Surface:** gravel. ⬛ 01/01-31/12
Distance: ⛲250m 🚶13km 🏊on the spot ⊗on the spot 🚰on the spot 🚶on the spot.
Remarks: Bread-service.

🍇S Niederkirchen bei Deidesheim 15H2
Wohnmobilstellplatz Niederkirchen, An de Sportanlage 1.
GPS: n49,40891 e8,22141.
6 ⬛free ✐€1. **Surface:** gravel. ⬛ 01/01-31/12
Distance: ⛲1km ✐4,5km.

🍇S Nierstein 15H1
Mobilstellplatz auf dem Weingut Gehring, Ausserhalb 17.
GPS: n49,85621 e8,32520.⬆️

30 ⬛€8 🚰🍽Chincluded ✐(25x)€3/day 🍽€5/time. 💧
⬛ 01/01-31/12
Distance: ⛲2km 🚶on the spot 🚶on the spot.
Remarks: Bread-service.

©S Nohfelden 15F1
Campingplatz Bostalsee, P6, L325, Bosen.
GPS: n49,56039 e7,06113.⬆️➡️

10 ⬛€8/24h 🚰€0,50/50liter 🍽Ch✐€1/2kWh. **Surface:** metalled.
⬛ 01/01-31/12
Distance: ⛲500m ✐6km 🏊200m ⊗on the spot 🚰800m.

⚓S Nonnweiler 15F1
Stellplatz Am Hallenbad, Triererstrasse 2.
GPS: n49,60686 e6,97216.⬆️

5 ⬛free. **Surface:** grassy/metalled. ⬛ 01/01-31/12
Distance: ⛲on the spot ✐1km ⊗on the spot 🚰800m.
Remarks: Parking swimming pool, max. 48h.

🍇S Nürburg 10F3
Wohnmobilpark Motorsporthotel, Hauptstrasse 34.
GPS: n50,33982 e6,95131.
12 ⬛€10 🚰✐📶. ⬛ 01/01-31/12
Distance: ⊗on the spot.
Remarks: At racing circuit.

🍇S Ober-Hilbersheim 15H1
Napoleonshöhe, Sprendlingers Straße. **GPS:** n49,89785 e8,02421.⬆️

40 ⬛free 🚰🍽Ch. **Surface:** grassy. ⬛ 01/01-31/12
Distance: ⛲500m 🚰300m.

🍇S Oberbrombach 15G1
Wohnmobilstellplatz Höhenblick, Sonnenberger Strasse.
GPS: n49,69481 e7,25960.
75 ⬛€7 🚰🍽Ch✐(45x)€2/4kWh. **Surface:** grassy/gravel.
⬛ 01/01-31/12
Distance: ⛲400m ⊗600m.

⚓ Oberwesel/Rhein 10G3
Stellplatz am Schiffsanleger, B9. **GPS:** n50,10816 e7,72758.⬆️
10 ⬛€8/24h. 🚌 **Surface:** metalled. ⬛ 01/01-31/12
Distance: ✐10km 🏊on the spot 🚶on the spot.

©S Oberwesel/Rhein 10G3
Camping Schönburgblick, Am Hafendamm / B9.
GPS: n50,10294 e7,73663.⬆️

20 ⬛€8,50/24h 🍽Chincluded ✐€0,60/kWh WC €2,50 🔌
📶€2. **Location:** Comfortable, quiet. **Surface:** grassy.
⬛ 15/03-31/10
Distance: ⛲800m 🏊on the spot 🚶on the spot ⊗on the spot
🚰200m 🚌400m.

🍇 Offenbach an der Queich 15H2
Am Queichtalzentrum, Konrad-Lerch-Ring.
GPS: n49,20056 e8,19478.⬆️➡️

2 ⬛free. **Location:** Simple. **Surface:** metalled. ⬛ 01/01-31/12
Distance: ⛲100m ✐6km ⊗500m 🚰1km 🚌400m.
Remarks: Max. 3 days.

Oppenheim 15H1

Womoland Oppenheim, An der Festwiese.
GPS: n49,85673 e8,36502.

20 €7 €1/50liter Ch €3/24h. **Surface**: grassy.
01/01-31/12 week before/after Whitsuntide
Distance: 500m 500m 500m.

Osann-Monzel 15F1

Wohnmobilstellplatz Panorama, Moselstrasse 16.
GPS: n49,90904 e6,95624.

8 €5 €2 against payment. **Surface**: gravel.
01/06-31/10
Distance: 9km 50m.
Remarks: Key at aparthotel Panorama (50m).

Osthofen 15H1

Festplatz Wonnegauhalle, Herrnsheimer Strasse.
GPS: n49,69913 e8,32691.

50 free Ch free. **Surface**: gravel. 01/01-31/12
Distance: 500m 7km 500m.
Remarks: Max. 48h.

Osthofen 15H1

Sommerried Stadion, L439. **GPS**: n49,69222 e8,32805.

10 free. **Surface**: grassy/sand. 01/01-31/12
Distance: 6km 800m.
Remarks: Max. 48h.

Osthofen 15H1

Weingut Borntaler Hof, Alter Westhofer Weg.
GPS: n49,69985 e8,29860.

4 €5 WC included. **Surface**: metalled. 01/01-31/12
Distance: 9km.

Ottweiler 15F2

Stellplatz Wingertsweiher, Am Wingertsweiher.
GPS: n49,41134 e7,18076.

12 €5/24h €1/150liter €1 Ch (6x)€3/8h.
Surface: grassy/metalled. 01/01-31/12
Distance: 1,5km on the spot on the spot on the spot
1,5km 1km.
Remarks: Max. 7 days.

Palzem 15E1

Weingut E. Pauly, Obermoselstrasse 5.
GPS: n49,56402 e6,37581.

3 €7 WC. **Surface**: gravel/metalled. 01/01-31/12
Distance: 50m 4km.
Remarks: Not suitable for big motorhomes, beautiful view.

Perl 15E1

Am Perlbach, Auf dem Sabel 4. **GPS**: n49,47900 e6,38493.

6 € 8, winter € 5 €1/6minutes Ch €1/8h.
Surface: metalled. 01/01-31/12
Distance: 500m 3,5km 500m 500m.

Pfaffen-Schwabenheim 15H1

Pferdepension am Sonnenhof, Brühlstraße.
GPS: n49,85224 e7,95951.
10 €10 WC included. **Location**: Rural, simple,
isolated, quiet. **Surface**: concrete. 01/01-31/12
Distance: 7km.

Piesport 15F1

Piesporter Goldtröpfchen, Moselstrasse.
GPS: n49,87199 e6,92703.

30 €6 €1/80liter Ch €2. **Surface**: gravel.
01/01-31/12
Distance: 100m 11km on the spot on the spot on the
spot 500m.
Remarks: Bread-service mo-sa.

Piesport 15F1

Altes Kelterhaus, St. Martinstrasse 33. **GPS**: n49,87872 e6,92590.

6 €7,50, guests free €2,50 Ch €2,50.
Surface: gravel. 01/01-31/12
Distance: 10km on the spot on the spot.

Piesport 15F1

Weingut Heinz Kirsten, In der Noo. **GPS**: n49,88017 e6,92597.

6 €6 €1. **Surface**: gravel. 01/01-31/12
Distance: 7,5km on the spot on the spot.
Remarks: Check in at Bahnhofstrasse 28.

Piesport 15F1

Weingut Spang, Reisemobilplatz Rebengarten, In den Dur 11.
GPS: n49,88287 e6,92781.

3 €8 €0,70/kWh WC €2,50. **Surface**: gravel.
01/01-31/12
Distance: on the spot 8km 100m 100m 500m
500m.
Remarks: Bread-service.

Piesport 15F1

Wohnmobilstellplatz Loreleyblick, Loreleyblick 20.
GPS: n49,87323 e6,92535.

5 €8 Ch (10x) €1. **Surface**: gravel.
01/01-31/12
Distance: on the spot 11km 1km 300m.
Remarks: Bread-service.

Pirmasens 15G2

Am Messegelände, Zeppelinstraße. **GPS**: n49,20446 e7,60885.

8 €5/24h €1/100liter Ch €1/6h. **Location**: Urban,
simple, noisy. **Surface**: gravel. 01/01-31/12
Distance: 450m 6km 450m 450m.

DE

Pirmasens — 15G2

Forsthaus Beckenhof, Beckenhofer Strasse.
GPS: n49,19604 e7,65635.

10 guests free. **Location:** Rural, simple, quiet. **Surface:** gravel.
01/01-31/12

Plaidt — 10G3

Wohnmobilstellplatz am Vulkanpark, Rauschermühle 6.
GPS: n50,38790 e7,40444.

10 free. **Location:** Rural. **Surface:** metalled.
01/01-31/12
Distance: 5km.

Plein — 10F3

Hotel-Restaurant Waldschlößchen Plein, Zum Waldschlößchen 3.
GPS: n50,03223 e6,88074.
3 guests free. 01/01-31/12
Distance: 4km on the spot.

Polch — 10G3

Niesmann&Bisschof, Clou-strasse 1. **GPS:** n50,30680 e7,30684.

25 free €0,50/80liter Ch (12x)€0,50/kWh.
Surface: metalled. 01/01-31/12
Distance: on the spot on the spot.

Pronsfeld — 10E3

Am Alten Bahnhof, Bahnhofstrasse. **GPS:** n50,16343 e6,33669.

50 5 €0,50/60liter Ch (12x)€0,50/kWh. **Location:** Rural,
comfortable, quiet. **Surface:** grassy/gravel.
01/01-31/12
Distance: 600m 7,5km 600m 700m 500m on the
spot on the spot.

Prüm — 10E3

Wohnmobilstellplatz Prüm, Monthermeerstrasse.
GPS: n50,20956 e6,42715.

4 free. **Surface:** gravel. 01/01-31/12
Distance: 600m

Pünderich — 10F3

Wohnmobilstellplatz Pünderich, Moselallee.
GPS: n50,04355 e7,12548.

80 6 Chincluded (12x)€2/24h. **Location:** Rural,
simple, quiet. **Surface:** grassy. 01/04-31/10
Distance: on the spot on the spot on the spot 300m
500m.

Ramstein-Miesenbach — 15G1

City Parkplatz, Talstrasse. **GPS:** n49,45103 e7,55557.

3 free. **Location:** Urban, simple, noisy. **Surface:** gravel.
01/01-31/12
Distance: 3,7km.

Ramstein-Miesenbach — 15G1

Freizeitbad Azur, Schernauer Strasse 5. **GPS:** n49,44578 e7,56971.

30 free. **Location:** Rural, simple, noisy. **Surface:** metalled.
01/01-31/12
Distance: 5,5km.

Rech — 10F2

Wohnmobilstellpark Alt Bodendorf, Rotweinstraße 13.
GPS: n50,51458 e7,03738.

15 € 4. 01/01-31/12
Distance: 11km.

Rech — 10F2

Im Bungert. **GPS:** n50,51343 e7,03865.

10 € 4. **Location:** Rural, simple. **Surface:** gravel. 01/01-31/12
Distance: on the spot on the spot on the spot on the spot.

Reil/Mosel — 10F3

Am Moselufer, Moselstrasse. **GPS:** n50,02566 e7,11493.

70 6 Ch (48x)€2 WCincluded. **Location:** Rural,
comfortable, quiet. **Surface:** grassy. 01/03-31/10
Distance: 500m on the spot 450m.
Remarks: Along ther Moselle river.

Reipoltskirchen — 15G1

Wasserburg, Kegelbahnstrasse. **GPS:** n49,63448 e7,66373.

7 free €1/4minutes Ch €1/12h. **Surface:** metalled.
01/01-31/12
Distance: 150m on the spot bakery 100m.

Reipoltskirchen — 15G1

Stellplatz Ausbacherhof, K42, Ausbacherhof.
GPS: n49,61210 e7,65630.

4 free. **Surface:** gravel. 01/01-31/12

Remagen — 10F2

Wohnmobilhafen Goldene Meile, Simrockweg 9–13.
GPS: n50,57667 e7,24750.

30 € 12 €1/90liter Ch (18x)€1/6h. **Surface:** grassy.
01/04-31/10
Distance: 10km on the spot on the spot.

Rengsdorf — 10G2

Monte Mare, Monte-Mare-Weg 1. **GPS:** n50,50803 e7,48388.

4 free. **Location:** Rural. **Surface:** gravel. 01/01-31/12
Distance: 600m 600m.

Rheinbreitbach — 10F2

Wohnmobilstellplatz Siebengebirgsblick, Rolandsecker Weg 8.
GPS: n50,62193 e7,22812.

14 🛏 € 8 🔌 €1/90liter 🗑Ch 💧(12x)€1/2kWh. **Location:** Simple.
Surface: grassy/gravel. 📅 01/01-31/12
Distance: ⊗500m.
Remarks: To be paid at Rolandsecker Weg 8.

| 🔲 | **Rhodt unter Rietburg** | 15H2 |

Theresienstraße. **GPS:** n49,27464 e8,09917.⬆️.

20 🛏 € 4. 🚿 **Location:** Rural, simple. **Surface:** gravel.
📅 01/01-31/12
Distance: 🚰100m 🏊5km.

| 🔲 S | **Rhodt unter Rietburg** | 15H2 |

Meyer Karl Herman, Edesheimerstrasse 17.
GPS: n49,26883 e8,10868.⬆️.

6 🛏 € 9 💧(6x)included. 🚿 **Location:** Rural, simple, quiet.
Surface: gravel. 📅 01/01-31/12
Distance: 🚰200m ⊗200m 🏊200m.

| 🔲 S | **Rhodt unter Rietburg** | 15H2 |

Weingut Fader, Traminerweg 1. **GPS:** n49,26972 e8,11057.⬆️➡️.

12 🛏 € 10 🔌 🗑Ch 💧(12x)included. 🚿 **Location:** Rural, simple,
quiet. **Surface:** gravel. 📅 01/04-31/10
Distance: 🚰300m ⊗200m 🏊200m.

| 🔲 S | **Rhodt unter Rietburg** | 15H2 |

Weingut Krieger, Edesheimerstrasse 7. **GPS:** n49,26961 e8,10803.⬆️.

2 🛏 € 5 🔌free 💧on demand. 🚿 **Location:** Rural, simple, quiet.
Surface: grassy. 📅 01/01-31/12
Distance: 🚰100m 🏊6km ⊗200m 🏊200m.

| 🔲 S | **Rhodt unter Rietburg** | 15H2 |

Weingut Nichterlein, Mühlgasse 15. **GPS:** n49,27349 e8,10802.⬆️.

3 🛏 € 6 🔌 on demand WCfree. 🚿 **Location:** Quiet.
Surface: metalled. 📅 01/01-31/12
Distance: 🚰300m 🏊5km.

| 🔲 | **Rhodt unter Rietburg** | 15H2 |

Weingut Jürgen Heußler, Weyherer Strasse 34/35.
GPS: n49,27052 e8,10386.⬆️.

3 🛏 € 3. 🚿 **Location:** Simple. 📅 01/01-31/12
Distance: 🚰300m 🏊6km ⊗100m.

| 🔲 S | **Rockenhausen** | 15G1 |

Reisemobilhafen Rockenhausen, Obermühle.
GPS: n49,62136 e7,82146.⬆️.

5 🛏free 🔌 €1/80liter 🗑Ch 💧(6x)€1/6h. **Location:** Rural, simple.
Surface: gravel. 📅 01/01-31/12
Distance: 🚰800m 🏊on the spot.
Remarks: At swimming pool.

| 🔲 S | **Roschbach** | 15H2 |

Weingut Koch, Am Rosenkränzel 13. **GPS:** n49,24736 e8,11532.➡️.

3 🛏 € 5 🔌included 💧€2/night. 🚿 **Location:** Rural, quiet.
Surface: grassy. 📅 01/01-31/12
Distance: 🏊5km.

| 🔲 S | **Ruppertsberg** | 15H2 |

Winzerhaus Im Linsenbusch, Hauptstrasse 70.
GPS: n49,39944 e8,20044.
2 🛏 € 8 💧included WC €7/day. 📅 01/01-31/12
Distance: 🏊3km.

| 🔲 S | **Saarbrücken** 🌿 ⛲ | 15F2 |

Reisemobilhafen Calypso, Deutschmühlental 7.
GPS: n49,23027 e6,96222.⬆️.

20 🛏 € 6 + reduction swimming pool 🔌 🗑Ch 💧(4x)€1/24h.

Surface: metalled. 📅 01/01-31/12
Distance: 🚰on the spot ⊗on the spot 🏊500m.
Remarks: To pay at swimming pool.

| 🔲 S | **Saarburg** 🚣 | 15F1 |

Reisemobilpark Saarburg, Am Saarufer.
GPS: n49,60158 e6,55442.⬆️➡️.

70 🛏 € 8, winter € 5 🔌 €1 🗑Ch 💧(70x)€0,50/kWh WC 🚿€4/day.
🚿 **Surface:** grassy/metalled. 📅 01/01-31/12 🔲 Service: winter
Distance: 🚰850m 🏊on the spot 🏊on the spot 🏊200m.
Remarks: Bread-service.

| 🔲 S | **Saarburg** 🚣 | 15F1 |

Reisemobilstellplatz Leukbachtal, Leukbachtal 1.
GPS: n49,59921 e6,54130.⬆️➡️.

20 🛏 € 15 🔌 🗑Ch WC 🚿 included. **Location:** Comfortable,
quiet. **Surface:** grassy. 📅 01/03-31/10
Distance: 🚰1km 🏊150m.

| 🔲 S | **Saarlouis** | 15F2 |

In den Fliesen, Sankt Nazairer Allee. **GPS:** n49,32146 e6,74267.⬆️.

30 🛏free 🔌 €1/80liter 🗑Ch. **Location:** Urban, simple, quiet.
Surface: metalled. 📅 01/01-31/12
Distance: 🚰500m 🏊1,5km 🏊on the spot 🏊on the spot.
Remarks: At sports centre, bread-service.

| 🍴 | **Saarlouis** | 15F2 |

Hotellerie Waldesruh, Siersburger Strasse 8, Wallerfangen.
GPS: n49,34440 e6,67614.⬆️.

2 🛏 € 10, guests free. 🚿 **Location:** Rural, simple, noisy.
Surface: metalled. 📅 01/01-31/12
Distance: 🏊10km ⊗on the spot.

| 🔲 S | **Sankt Aldegund** 🚣 | 10F3 |

Am Moselstausee. **GPS:** n50,07899 e7,13119.⬆️.

DE

40 🛏€6 🚰⚡Ch included 🔌(28x)€2/day. **Location:** Rural, simple.
Surface: grassy/metalled. ◻ 01/04-01/12
Distance: 🚶250m ⊗on the spot ⊗250m.
Remarks: Bread-service.

Sankt Goarshausen — 10G3

Loreley Besucherzentrum, Auf der Loreley 7.
GPS: n50,14191 e7,73303.

25 🛏€8. **Location:** Simple, isolated.
Distance: ⛰600m ⚓600m.

Sankt Ingbert — 15F2

Reisemobilplatz 'Das Blau', Spieser Landstraße.
GPS: n49,28652 e7,13194. ⬆➡

8 🛏free 🚰€1/80liter ⚡Ch. **Surface:** grassy. ◻ 01/01-31/12
Distance: 🚶1,5km ⚓3,5km ⊗100m 🍺1,7km.
Remarks: Next to parking swimming pool.

Sankt Julian — 15G1

An der Ölmühle, An der Lenschbach. **GPS:** n49,60758 e7,51480. ⬆

10 🛏€5 🚰€1 ⚡Ch 🔌€1/kWh. **Location:** Rural, simple, quiet.
Surface: grassy. ◻ 01/04-31/10
Distance: 🚶on the spot 🍺300m.

Sankt Martin — 15H2

Edenkoperstrasse. **GPS:** n49,29702 e8,10838. ⬆

14 🛏€6/day. **Surface:** asphalted. ◻ 01/01-31/12
Distance: ⚓5km.
Remarks: Max. 1 night.

Sankt Martin — 15H2

Weingut Schreieck, Friedhofstrasse 8. **GPS:** n49,30113 e8,10560.
17 🛏€12 🚰⚡Ch ⚡WC included. ◻ 01/01-31/12
Distance: ⚓5km.

Sankt Martin — 15H2

Weinkellerei Ziegler, Mühlstrasse 26. **GPS:** n49,29921 e8,10028.
3 🛏€10 🚰⚡🔌 ◻ 01/01-31/12
Distance: ⚓5km.

Sankt Martin — 15H2

Consulat des Weines, Maikammerer strasse 44.
GPS: n49,29934 e8,10826.
10 🛏€1 pp. ◻ 01/01-31/12
Distance: ⚓4,5km.

Sankt Martin — 15H2

Winzer Holger Schneider, Riedweg. **GPS:** n49,29814 e8,10824. ⬆

🛏free for clients. **Surface:** gravel.
Distance: ⊗on the spot.

Sankt Martin — 15H2

Riedweg. **GPS:** n49,29814 e8,10824. ⬆
🚰€1 ⚡Ch.

Sankt Wendel — 15F1

Am Wendelinuspark, Tholeyer Straße. **GPS:** n49,46907 e7,14267. ⬆

12 🛏€5 🚰⚡Ch 🔌free. **Surface:** metalled. ◻ 01/01-31/12
Distance: 🚶1km ⊗on the spot 🍺100m ⚓20m.
Remarks: Tickets Wendelinusbad.

Schiersfeld — 15G1

Sulzbachtal, Bismarkstraße. **GPS:** n49,69274 e7,76895. ⬆

8-12 🛏free 🚰€1 🔌(8x)€1/4kWh. **Location:** Rural, simple, quiet.
Surface: gravel. ◻ 01/01-31/12
Distance: 🚶500m 🍺bakery 500m 🚴Moscheltalradweg 🚶on the spot.

Schleich — 15F1

Zum Moselufer, Am Moselufer. **GPS:** n49,81335 e6,84228. ⬆➡

6 🛏€5 🚰⚡Ch 🔌€2 WC. **Surface:** grassy. ◻ 01/01-31/12
Distance: ⛰on the spot 🚗on the spot ⊗on the spot 🍺200m.

Schwabenheim/Selz — 10H3

Reisemobilstellplatz Schwabenheim, Ingelheimer Straße.
GPS: n49,93284 e8,09430. ⬆➡

10 🛏free 🔌(12x)free. **Location:** Rural, comfortable, quiet.
Surface: grasstiles. ◻ 01/01-31/12
Distance: 🚶200m ⚓8,5km 🍺200m 🚴on the spot 🚶on the spot.
Remarks: Max. 96h free, then € 3/24h.

Schwabenheim/Selz — 10H3

Weingut Schuck Sonnenhof, Ausserhalb 6.
GPS: n49,93130 e8,09117. ⬆

3 🛏€5 🚰 🔌(3x)included WC. **Location:** Rural, comfortable, quiet.
Surface: grassy/gravel. ◻ 01/01-31/12
Distance: 🚶500m ⚓9km.

Schweich/Mosel bei Trier — 15F1

Wohnmobilpark zum Fahrturm, Am Yachthafen.
GPS: n49,81455 e6,75038. ➡

40 🛏< 6m € 11 incl. 2 pers, + € 1/m, dog € 2,10 🚰⚡Ch 🔌€0,60/
kWh,+ € 1 🚿€0,50 ⊗€3 🚽against payment. 🚿 **Surface:** grassy.
◻ 01/04-31/10
Distance: ⛰on the spot 🚗on the spot ⊗on the spot 🍺on the spot
🚗50m 🚴on the spot 🚶on the spot.
Remarks: Boat rental.

Selzen — 15H1

Weingut Kapellenhof, Kapellenstrasse 18.
GPS: n49,86484 e8,25528. ⬆

4 🛏€5 🚰 🔌(4x)included. 🚿 **Location:** Rural, simple, quiet.
Surface: grasstiles. ◻ 01/01-31/12
Distance: 🚶on the spot ⊗100m 🍺2km.

Siefersheim — 15H1

Weingut Sommer, Mühlweg 19. **GPS:** n49,79850 e7,95245. ⬆

6 🛏€5 🔌(6x)included. 🚿 **Location:** Rural, simple.
Surface: grassy. ◻ 01/04-31/10

DE

Distance: 🚲8km ⊗2km 🚰2km.

⬚S Sinzig ⛲🍽 **10F2**

Wohnmobilhafen am Sportplatz, Bäderstrasse.
GPS: n50,55128 e7,21731.⬆

10🛏€5/24h ⛽€1 Ch🚿(12x)€0,50/kWh WC🚽€1/1time,at
Freibad. 🏪 **Location:** Rural, simple. **Surface:** gravel.
◼ 01/01-31/12
Distance: 🚲7km ⊗800m 🚴on the spot 🚶on the spot.

⬚S Sinzig ⛲🍽 **10F2**

Sinziger Schloß, Jahnstrasse. **GPS:** n50,54684 e7,24844.⬆

20🛏free. **Location:** Urban, simple. **Surface:** metalled.
◼ 01/01-31/12
Distance: 🚶100m 🚌on the spot.

⬚S Sinzig ⛲🍽 **10F2**

Wohnmobilhafen am Thermalfreibad, Bäderstrasse.
GPS: n50,54912 e7,21749.⬆

50🛏€5/24h, electricity incl ⛽€1 🍽Ch🚿(18x)€0,50/kWh 🚽€1/pp.
🏪 **Location:** Rural, simple. **Surface:** metalled.
◼ 01/01-31/12
Distance: ⊗50m 🚴on the spot 🚶on the spot.

⬚S Speyer 🌸🍽 **15H2**

Techniek Museum Speyer, Geibstrasse. **GPS:** n49,31222 e8,45009.⬆

90🛏€22 ⛽🍽Ch🚿WC🚽included. 🚮 **Location:** Comfortable,
central, noisy. **Surface:** grassy. ◼ 01/01-31/12
Distance: 🚲8,5km 🚶150m 🚰200m 🚌on the spot 🚴on the spot
🚶on the spot.
Remarks: Bread-service, discount museum and theater.

⬚S Speyer 🌸🍽 **15H2**

An den Stadtwerken, Industriestraße 21. **GPS:** n49,30329 e8,44817.⬆

10🛏€5 ⛽€1 🍽€1 Ch€1 🚿included. 🚮 **Location:** Simple.
Surface: asphalted.
Distance: 🚶1,5km 🚲6km ⊗1,5km 🚰1,6km 🚌500m 🚴on the
spot.
Remarks: Check in at Stadwerke.

Tourist information Speyer:
Ⓜ Technik Museum Speyer/Imax Filmtheater, Geibstrasse. ◻ Mo-Fr
9-18h, Sa-Su 9-17h.

⬚S Spirkelbach 👥 **15G2**

Grillplatz Spirkelbach. **GPS:** n49,19454 e7,88208.⬆

4🛏€7 ⛽🍽Ch🚿WCincluded. 🚮 **Location:** Rural, simple, quiet.
Surface: gravel. ◼ 01/01-31/12
Distance: 🚶500m 🚰500m 🚴on the spot 🚶on the spot.
Remarks: Check in on arrival, tel: 0171 3355971, nature reserve Pfalzer
Wald.

⬚S Sprendlingen **15H1**

Wiesbach, Bachgasse/Bleichstrasse. **GPS:** n49,85424 e7,98538.⬆➡

24🛏€4 ⛽€2/10minutes 🍽Ch🚿(24x)€2/day. 🚮
Location: Rural, comfortable, quiet. **Surface:** asphalted.
◼ 01/01-31/12
Distance: 🚶700m 🚲3,4km ⊗500m 🚰900m 🚶on the spot.
Remarks: Parking at swimming pool, bread-service, entrance swim-
ming pool € 2/day.

⬚S Sprendlingen **15H1**

Weingut Annenhof, Außerhalb 13. **GPS:** n49,85778 e7,99278.⬆

4🛏free ⛽🚿WC🚽free. **Location:** Rural, simple. **Surface:** concrete.
◼ 01/01-31/12
Distance: 🚲3km ⊗500m 🚰800m.

⬚S Sprendlingen **15H1**

Weingut Hembd, Karlstrasse 24a. **GPS:** n49,86422 e7,98811.⬆

10🛏€10 ⛽🚿included. 🚮 **Location:** Rural, simple.
Surface: grassy. ◼ 01/01-31/12
Distance: 🚲4km ⊗500m 🚰500m.

⬚S Sprendlingen **15H1**

Eura Mobil Stellplatz, Graf-von-Sponheimstrasse.
GPS: n49,86297 e7,97612.⬆

38🛏free ⛽€1 Ch🚿(38x)free. **Location:** Rural, simple, quiet.
Surface: asphalted/metalled. ◼ 01/01-31/12
Distance: 🚶600m 🚲4,4km 🚰300m.
Remarks: Workdays from 9h guided tours (free).

⬚S Stadecken-Elsheim **10H3**

Weingut Mengel-Eppelmann, Mühlstrasse 16.
GPS: n49,91575 e8,12107.⬆

5🛏€5, free for clients ⛽🚿included. **Location:** Comfortable, quiet.
Surface: asphalted. ◼ 01/01-31/12
Distance: 🚶on the spot 🚲6km ⊗on the spot.

⬚S Stromberg **10G3**

Reisemobilplatz Michels Land, Königsberger Straße.
GPS: n49,94709 e7,78818.⬆➡

6🛏€5 ⛽🍽Chincluded 🚿(6x)€0,50/kWh. 🚮
Location: Comfortable, quiet. **Surface:** grassy. ◼ 01/01-31/12
Distance: 🚶500m 🚰500m 🚰50m Lidl.

⬚S Thalfang ⛲❄ **15F1**

Festplatz Thalfang, Talstrasse 2. **GPS:** n49,75103 e6,99902.⬆

40🛏€5 ⛽🍽Ch🚿(6x)free. **Surface:** gravel.
◼ 01/01-31/12 ◉ 21/09-30/09
Distance: 🚶200m 🚲on the spot 🚌on the spot ⊗on the spot
🚰200m.
Remarks: Max. 4 nights, check in at swimming pool.

⬚S Thalfang ⛲❄ **15F1**

Ferienpark Himmelberg, Birkenweg 73. **GPS:** n49,74835 e6,98721.
2🛏free. ◼ 01/01-31/12

⬚S Thallichtenberg 🌸 **15G1**

Burg Lichtenberg, K23. **GPS:** n49,55716 e7,35975.⬆➡

4🛏free. **Surface:** asphalted. ◼ 01/01-31/12

Distance: 7km 300m 1km.
Remarks: Max. 3 days.

Tholey 15F1
Parkplatz Am Schaumburg, Am Schaumberg.
GPS: n49,48965 e7,03804. ↑ →

±20 free. **Surface:** metalled. 01/01-31/12
Distance: 100m.

Traben-Trarbach 10F3

Wohnmobilstellplatz am Mosel Traben/Trabach

■ **Located directly at the river**
■ **Ideal base for walking and cycling**
■ **Restaurant with regional specialties**

www.moselstellplatz.de
info@moselcampingplatz.de

Wohnmobilstellplatz am Mosel, Rissbacherstraße 155.
GPS: n49,96583 e7,10583. ↑
45 €10 Ch (45x),6Amp WC included.
Location: Comfortable. **Surface:** grassy/gravel. 01/04-31/12
Distance: 500m on the spot on the spot 500m 200m 100m on the spot on the spot.
Remarks: Along the Moselle river.

Trechtinghausen 10G3
Camping Marienort, Mainzer Straße. **GPS:** n50,00426 e7,85516. ↑ →

20 €7 Ch included €2/24h WC 1.
Location: Comfortable, quiet. **Surface:** grassy.
01/01-31/12
Distance: on the spot on the spot on the spot.
Remarks: Bread-service, sanitary at campsite, narrow entrance.

Trier 15F1
Reisemobilpark Treviris, In den Moselauen.
GPS: n49,74092 e6,62502. ↑ →

110 € 0,20/h 10-18h, € 8/18-10h €1/100liter Ch (62x)€ 0,70/kWh WC €1/3minutes. **Surface:** grasstiles. 01/01-31/12
Distance: 3km 6km 400m McDonald's on the spot.
Remarks: Along ther Moselle river, bread-service.

Trier 15F1
Weingut Vonnell, Im Tiergarten 12. **GPS:** n49,73840 e6,65914. ↑ →

15 € 10 included. **Surface:** grassy/gravel.
01/01-31/12
Distance: 3km 7km.

Tourist information Trier:
ℹ Tourist Information, An der Porta Nigra, www.trier.de. Old Roman city with the best kept and also largest Roman gate in Europe: Porta Nigra.
ℹ Triercard. Free city bus and discount at museums, boat trips, swimming pool etc. T € 9,90, family card € 21, 3 days.

Trittenheim 15F1
Moselpromenade Reisemobilplatz Trittenheim, Moselstrasse.
GPS: n49,82436 e6,90295. ↑ →

50 € 6,50 €0,50/100liter Ch (30x)€3/24h.
Surface: grassy/metalled. 01/01-31/12
Distance: 500m on the spot on the spot 300m 400m.
Remarks: Bread-service.

Unkel 10F2
P3, Parkplatz Hallenbad, Kamenerstrasse.
GPS: n50,59776 e7,21962. ↑

6 free €1/80liter Ch WC. **Location:** Urban.
Surface: asphalted. 01/01-31/12
Distance: 100m 100m 150m on the spot.

Urmitz/Rhein 10G2
Wohnmobilhafen am Rhein, Kaltenengerser Straße 3.
GPS: n50,41849 e7,52448. ↑

24 € 5 €1/4minutes Ch €1/8h. **Surface:** metalled.
01/01-31/12
Distance: on the spot 5km on the spot on the spot 350m 300m.
Remarks: Along the Rhine river, bread-service.

Ürzig 10F3
Panorama-Mobilstellplatz Ürzig, Moselufer B53.
GPS: n49,97837 e7,00700. ↑

25 € 9,50 Ch included €1,50/day. **Location:** Rural, comfortable, quiet. **Surface:** grassy. 01/04-31/10
Distance: 9km on the spot on the spot bakery 150m on the spot on the spot.
Remarks: Along ther Moselle river.

Vallendar 10G3
Rheinufer. **GPS:** n50,39749 e7,61277. ↑

3 free . **Location:** Urban, simple.
Surface: asphalted/metalled. 01/01-31/12
Distance: centre 500m 3km on the spot 200m Aldi 200m.
Remarks: Along railwayline.

Valwig 10F3
Moselweinstrasse. **GPS:** n50,14271 e7,21292. ↑

40 € 5. **Surface:** grassy. 01/01-31/12
Distance: 100m on the spot 100m.

Veldenz 15F1
Wohnmobilpark Veldenz, Hauptstrasse, K88.
GPS: n49,89222 e7,01944. →

40 € 6 Ch (24x)included €2. **Surface:** grassy.
01/01-31/12
Distance: 300m 300m 300m 200m.

Völklingen 15F2
Weltkulturerbe Völklinger Hütte, Rathausstraße.
GPS: n49,24730 e6,84492. →

10 free €1/80liter Ch (6x)€0,25/h. **Location:** Urban, simple, central, noisy. **Surface:** asphalted.
01/01-31/12

DE

Distance: 500m 1,1km 400m 850m on the spot on the spot. **Remarks:** Visitors centre Industrial Heritage.

Wachenheim 15H1

Weingut Rudolf Hein, Hauptstrasse 38. **GPS:** n49,63860 e8,16832.

8 € 6 included (6x)€2/24h. **Location:** Rural, simple, quiet. **Surface:** grassy. 01/01-31/12
Distance: 10km 1km 3km.

Wadern 15F1

An der Stadthalle. GPS: n49,54188 e6,89232.

10 free €1,50/day. **Surface:** metalled. 01/01-31/12
Distance: on the spot 3km on the spot 100m.
Remarks: Parking in centre.

Wadern 15F1

Noswendeler See, Seestrasse. **GPS:** n49,52021 e6,86387.

5 free. 01/01-31/12
Distance: on the spot on the spot on the spot on the spot 3km.

Wadern 15F1

Zum Wiesental, Nunkirchen. **GPS:** n49,48905 e6,83679.

5 free. 01/01-31/12
Distance: on the spot on the spot on the spot.

Wadern 15F1

Hotel Pension Steil, Schlossstrasse 2, Lockweiler. **GPS:** n49,52765 e6,90158.

4 guests free. **Surface:** metalled. 01/01-31/12
Distance: 1km on the spot 500m.

Wadern 15F1

Hotel Restaurant Reidelbacher Hof, Reidelbach 5, Reidelbach. **GPS:** n49,57706 e6,86808.
5 € 5, guests free. 01/01-31/12
Distance: 3km 9km on the spot 3km.

Tourist information Wadern:
Tourist Information, Marktplatz 13, www.wadern.de. Nature reserve Saar Hunsrück, many signposted cycle and hiking routes.

Waldalgesheim 10G3

An der Keltenhalle, Niedergasse. **GPS:** n49,95371 e7,83614.

8 free €1/100liter Ch (8x)€1/6h. **Location:** Simple, quiet. **Surface:** metalled. 01/01-31/12
Distance: 400m 4km 200m 500m.

Waldfischbach-Burgalben 15G2

In den Bruchwiesen, Carentaner Platz. **GPS:** n49,28155 e7,64772.

6 free €1/80liter Ch €1/8h. **Surface:** asphalted. 01/01-31/12
Distance: 600m 100m.

Waxweiler 10E3

Wohnmobilplatz Waxweiler, Bahnhofstrasse. **GPS:** n50,09401 e6,35669.

30 € 5 €1 Ch €2. **Location:** Rural, simple, quiet. **Surface:** metalled. 01/01-31/12
Distance: on the spot 1km 500m.

Weiskirchen 15F1

Am Kurpark, Burgstrasse. **GPS:** n49,55868 e6,81810.

6 € 1,40/pp €0,50 €0,50 Ch €0,50. **Surface:** metalled. 01/01-31/12
Distance: on the spot 500m 300m. **Remarks:** Parking at the health resort, max. 2-3 days, pay at tourist office.

Westerburg 10H2

Am Segelhafen, Seestrasse, Pottum. **GPS:** n50,59526 e7,99860.

10 free. **Location:** Rural, simple, quiet. **Surface:** metalled. 01/01-31/12
Distance: 250m on the spot on the spot 250m.

Westhofen 15H1

Parkplatz Nickelgarten, Am Nickelgarten. **GPS:** n49,70559 e8,24672.

15 free (12x)€1/8h. **Surface:** metalled. 01/01-31/12
Distance: 100m 4km 100m.
Remarks: Max. 3 days.

Westhofen 15H1

Weingut Dreihornmühle, An der Brennerei. **GPS:** n49,70375 e8,25288.

3 € 5, guests free €1/day. **Surface:** grassy. 01/01-31/12
Distance: 600m 600m 150m.
Remarks: Max. 24h.

Westhofen 15H1

Tankstelle Raiffeisen. GPS: n49,70039 e8,24699.
Ch. 01/01-31/12
Remarks: Coins at petrol station.

Weyher 15H2

Weingut Möwes, Hübühl 10. **GPS:** n49,26982 e8,08663.

2 € 8 included. **Location:** Rural, quiet. **Surface:** metalled. 01/01-31/12
Distance: 200m 7km.

Weyher 15H2

Weingut Valentin Ziegler Sohn, Hübühl 9. **GPS:** n49,26937 e8,08609.

2 € 5 included on demand. **Location:** Rural, quiet. **Surface:** grassy. 01/01-31/12

DE

Distance: 📍200m ⛟7km.

🅂 Willroth 10G2

Steiger-Mühle, Steinstrasse. **GPS:** n50,57176 e7,52995. ⬆.

15 🍴€6 ⚡€2,50. **Location:** Rural. ◻ 01/01-31/12
Distance: ⛟2km ⊗on the spot.
Remarks: To be paid at Biergarten.

🅂 Wintrich 15F1

Mosel Stellplatz Wintrich
Wintrich

Located directly at the river
Located in a quiet area
Restaurant with regional specialties

www.moselstellplatz.de
info@moselcampingplatz.de

Mosel Stellplatz Wintrich, Moselstrasse.
GPS: n49,88417 e6,94833. ⬆➡.
90 🍴€9 ⚡€1/100liter Ch ⚡(90x)WC€0,50 ◻€1 included. **Surface:** grassy/gravel. ◻ 01/04-31/10
Distance: 📍on the spot ⚓on the spot ⊗100m
🍺200m 🚤200m 🚣on the spot 🧍on the spot.
Remarks: Along the Moselle river.

🅂 Wintrich 15F1

Weingut Clemens, Kurtfürstenstrasse 11.
GPS: n49,89000 e6,95416. ⬆➡.

20 🍴€5 ⚡€2 Ch ⚡€2 WC. **Surface:** gravel/metalled.
◻ 01/01-31/12
Distance: 📍on the spot ⊗on the spot 🍺1km.

🅂 Wissen 10G2

Hahnhof, Nistertalstraße. **GPS:** n50,76106 e7,72083. ⬆.

25 🍴€5 ⚡Ch ⚡€1/kWh WC ◻€1,50. **Location:** Rural, isolated, quiet. **Surface:** gravel. ◻ 01/01-31/12
Distance: 📍2,5km ⊗on the spot 🚣on the spot.

🅂 Wittlich 10F3

Zweibächen, Hasenmühlenweg. **GPS:** n49,99470 e6,87595. ⬆➡.

---

30 🍴€5/24h ⚡€1/80liter Ch. **Location:** Rural, simple.
Surface: grassy. ◻ 01/01-31/12
Distance: 📍1km ⛟4km ⊗1km 🍺1km.
Remarks: Max. 3 days, to be paid at swimming pool, service 50m.

🅂 Worms 15H1

Wohnmobilhafen, Kastanienallee. **GPS:** n49,63458 e8,37513. ⬆➡.

30 🍴€5/24h ⚡€1 Ch ⚡(12x)€1/8h. 🚐 **Surface:** gravel.
◻ 01/01-31/12
Distance: 📍15 min walking ⛟7km ⚓Rhine promenade ⊗300m 🍺500m ⊗on the spot.
Remarks: Along river, service at Gaststätte Hagenbräu 300m from the parking.

🅂 Wörrstadt 15H1

Spargelhof Weinmann, Rommersheimer Strasse 105.
GPS: n49,83446 e8,10673. ⬆.

3 🍴€6 ⚡(6x)included. **Location:** Rural, simple, central, quiet.
Surface: gravel. ◻ 01/01-31/12
Distance: ⛟4km ⊗300m 🍺300m.

🅂 Zell/Mosel 10F3

Wohnmobilstellplatz Römerquelle, Am Freizeitzentrum, Kaimt.
GPS: n50,01632 e7,17662. ⬆➡.

70 🍴€6 ⚡€1/100liter Ch ⚡€1/2kWh. **Location:** Rural, comfortable. **Surface:** grassy/metalled. ◻ 01/01-31/12
Distance: 📍1km ⚓on the spot ⚓on the spot ⊗500m 🍺1km.
Remarks: Along ther Moselle river, bread-service.

🅂 Zell/Mosel 10F3

Am Fussgängerbrücke. GPS: n50,02991 e7,17754. ⬆.

23 🍴€6 ⚡€0,50/90liter Ch ◻€2,at camp site.
Location: Simple, quiet. **Surface:** asphalted. ◻ Easter-31/10

Distance: 📍300m ⚓on the spot ⚓on the spot ⊗200m 🍺300m.

🅂 Zeltingen-Rachtig 10F3

An der Brücke, Uferallee. **GPS:** n49,95478 e7,00942. ⬆.
🍴8 ⚡Ch ⚡included. **Surface:** grassy. ◻ 01/03-31/11
◻ high water
Distance: 📍200m ⊗200m ⚓on the spot 🧍on the spot.

🅂 Zweibrücken 15G2

Eitel's Wohnmobil-Stellplatz, Californiastraße.
GPS: n49,26477 e7,36112. ➡.

2 🍴€7 ⚡€0,50/3minutes Ch ⚡included. **Location:** Rural, simple, noisy. **Surface:** asphalted. ◻ 01/01-31/12
Distance: 📍2 km ⛟3 km 🚌100m.
Remarks: Check in on arrival.

Hesse

🅂 Aarbergen 10H3

Im Brühl, Hauptstraße 58, Michelbach.
GPS: n50,23099 e8,05988. ⬆➡.

10 🍴€5 Ch ⚡included. **Location:** Rural. **Surface:** metalled.
◻ 01/01-31/12

🅂 Alsfeld 11A2

Erlenstadion, Fulder Weg. **GPS:** n50,74844 e9,27947. ⬆➡.

20 🍴€5 ⚡€1 Ch €1 Ch ⚡€0,50/kWh. **Location:** Simple.
Surface: metalled. ◻ 01/01-31/12
Distance: 📍200m ⛟1,8km.

🅂 Alsfeld 11A2

Hotel zum Schäferhof, A20 dir Eudorf. **GPS:** n50,76742 e9,29048. ⬆.

20 🍴free ⚡€6. **Location:** Urban, simple, quiet. **Surface:** metalled.
◻ 01/01-31/12
Distance: 📍2km ⊗on the spot 🍺500m.
Remarks: Check in at hotel, use of a meal desired.

🅂 Amöneburg 11A2

In den Lückeäckern. GPS: n50,79554 e8,93135. ⬆.

4 free. **Location:** Rural, simple. 01/01-31/12
Distance: Old city centre 1km 500m 500m.
Remarks: Parking tennishall.

| S | Bad Arolsen | 9A3 |

Reisemobilhafen Twistesee Bad Arolsen

- Located directely at lake
- Located in a quiet area
- Dogs beach

www.reisemobilhafen-twistesee.de
info@reisemobilhafen-twistesee.de

Reisemobilhafen Twistesee, Bericher Seeweg 1, Wetterburg.
GPS: n51,38396 e9,06546.
130 € 10, tourist tax incl €1/100liter Ch (120x)€0,50/kWh,16Amp WC included €1/time. **Location:** Rural, comfortable, isolated. **Surface:** grassy/gravel. 01/01-31/12
Distance: 500m 50m 50m 800m 800m on the spot on the spot.
Remarks: Directly at lake, bread-service, dogs beach.

| S | Bad Camberg | 10H3 |

Jahnstraße. **GPS:** n50,29650 e8,26660.

8 free €1 €1 Ch €1/2kWh. **Location:** Urban.
Surface: gravel. 01/01-31/12 water: 01/12-31/03
Distance: 350m 2,5km 250m.

| S | Bad Emstal | 11A1 |

Am Mineral-Thermalbad, Karlsbader Straße 4, Sand.
GPS: n51,24858 e9,24952.

8 € 7, tourist tax incl €1/100liter Ch (12x)€1/8h.
Location: Rural, comfortable. **Surface:** gravel/metalled.
01/01-31/12
Distance: 1km on the spot on the spot on the spot.

| S | Bad Emstal | 11A1 |

Erzeberg, Birkenstraße, Balhorn 21. **GPS:** n51,26927 e9,25147.

20 € 10, 2 pers.incl Ch WC €1 included.
Location: Rural, simple. **Surface:** metalled. 01/01-31/12
Distance: 100m.
Remarks: Check in at campsite (100m), use pool incl.

| S | Bad Endbach | 10H2 |

Kultur-, Sport- und Freizeitzentrum, Am Bewegungsbad 4.
GPS: n50,75669 e8,47875.

18 € 5 + tourist tax Ch WC included,sanitary at
spa resort. **Location:** Rural, simple, quiet. **Surface:** grasstiles.
01/01-31/12
Distance: 1km on the spot 100m.
Remarks: Check in at Lahn-Dill-Bergland-Therme 200m.

| S | Bad Hersfeld | 11B1 |

Geistalbad, Am Schwimmbad. **GPS:** n50,87485 e9,70025.

6 € 5 €0,50/80liter Ch (6x)€0,50/kWh. **Location:** Urban,
simple. **Surface:** asphalted/metalled. 01/01-31/12 Lullusfest
(Oct)
Distance: 50m 3,9km 1km.

| | Bad Hersfeld | 11B1 |

Acqua-fit, Kolpingstraße 6. **GPS:** n50,86771 e9,72951.
5 free. **Surface:** asphalted. 01/01-31/12
Distance: 2km.
Remarks: At swimming pool.

| | Bad Hersfeld | 11B1 |

Auf der Unteraue. GPS: n50,85764 e9,69786.

3 free. **Surface:** metalled. 01/01-31/12
Remarks: At tennis-court.

| | Bad Hersfeld | 11B1 |

Seilerweg. GPS: n50,87092 e9,71179.
free. 01/01-31/12
Distance: 500m 500m.

| S | Bad Hersfeld | 11B1 |

Waldhotel Glimmesmühle, Hombergerstraße.
GPS: n50,88420 e9,66984.

5 free with a meal included against payment. **Location:** Rural,
simple. **Surface:** metalled. 01/01-31/12
Distance: on the spot 2km.

Tourist information Bad Hersfeld:
Lullusfest. Traditional folk festival for the honour of the founder of
the city. week 16/10.

| S | Bad Karlshafen | 9A3 |

Am Rechten Weserufer, Am rechten Weserufer 2.
GPS: n51,64508 e9,44953.

24 € 11 Ch (12x)€1/2kWh. **Location:** Central.
Surface: grasstiles/grassy. 01/01-31/12
Distance: on the spot on the spot on the spot on the spot
on the spot on the spot.
Remarks: Max. 4 days.

| S | Bad König | 16A1 |

P3, Am Bahndamm. **GPS:** n49,74312 e9,00320.

9 € 5 (9x)included. **Location:** Urban, simple, central, noisy.
Surface: metalled. 01/01-31/12
Distance: 100m 100m 400m on the spot on the spot
on the spot.

| | Bad Nauheim | 11A3 |

Usa-Wellenbad, Friedberger Strasse 16-20.
GPS: n50,35352 e8,74305.

40 € 5. **Location:** Rural, simple, isolated. **Surface:** metalled.
01/01-31/12
Distance: 1km on the spot 300m on the spot.
Remarks: Check in at Wellenbad, 8-20h.

| S | Bad Orb | 11A3 |

Am Busbahnhof, Austraße. **GPS:** n50,23014 e9,34659.

DE

4 � € 7, tourist tax incl ⚡🔧 Ch 🔌(4x)WCincluded. 🏪
Location: Urban, simple, central, noisy. **Surface:** metalled.
⭕ 01/01-31/12
Distance: 🚶400m ⊗450m 🛒300m.
Remarks: Historical centre.

| ⛺S | Bad Orb ⚓🌲 | 11A3 |

Am Kurpark, Spessartstraße. **GPS:** n50,21700 e9,35477. ⬆➡.

9 ⌂ € 7 + tourist tax € 2,50/pp ⚡€1/90liter 🔧Ch 🔌€1/8h. 🏪
Location: Rural, simple, quiet. **Surface:** gravel.
⭕ 01/01-31/12
Distance: 🚶1,1km 🚲6km ⊗200m 🛒on the spot.

| ⛺S | Bad Salzschlirf ♨ | 11B2 |

Riedstraße. **GPS:** n50,62090 e9,50304. ⬆.

10 ⌂free ⚡€1 🔧Ch 🔌€1. **Location:** Simple. **Surface:** asphalted.
⭕ 01/01-31/12
Distance: 🚶100m ⊗100m.

| ⛺S | Bad Schwalbach | 10H3 |

Am Kurpark, Reitallee 21. **GPS:** n50,13988 e8,06362. ⬆➡.

4 ⌂free ⚡€0,50/50liter 🔧Ch 🔌€0,50/kWh. **Location:** Rural,
simple. **Surface:** metalled. ⭕ 01/01-31/12
Distance: 🚶500m ⊗400m.

| ⛺S | Bad Soden-Salmünster ♨♨ | 11A3 |

Spessart Therme, Parkstraße 12, Bad Soden.
GPS: n50,28544 e9,35917. ⬆➡.

33 ⌂ € 6, tourist tax incl ⚡€1/100liter 🔧Ch 🔌(33x)€1/2kWh.
Location: Rural, luxurious, quiet. **Surface:** metalled.
⭕ 01/01-31/12
Distance: 🚶1km ⊗300m 🛒850m.
Remarks: Pay and coins at Spessart Therme.

| ⛺S | Bad Sooden-Allendorf ♨ | 11B1 |

Reisemobilhafen Franzrasen, Am Alten Festplatz, Allendorf.
GPS: n51,27149 e9,97209. ⬆➡.

100 ⌂ € 8 ⚡€1/5minutes 🔧€0,50 Ch 🔌(40x)€0,50/kWh,16Amp
🚰€2,50/30minutes. 🏪**Location:** Rural, simple, isolated, quiet.
Surface: grassy/metalled. ⭕ 01/01-31/12
Distance: 🚶200m 🚲on the spot 🏃on the spot.
Remarks: Price including tourist taxes and public transport.

| ⛺S | Bad Wildungen ♨ | 11A1 |

Wohnmobilstellplatz Bad Wildungen, Bahnhofstrasse.
GPS: n51,12008 e9,13631. ⬆➡.

16 ⌂ € 5 ⚡€1/45liter 🔧Ch 🔌(15x)€1/2kWh. **Location:** Urban,
comfortable. **Surface:** grasstiles. ⭕ 01/01-31/12
Distance: 🚶1,5km 🛒on the spot 🚲on the spot.
Remarks: Max. 3 days.

| ⛺S | Bad Wildungen ♨ | 11A1 |

Wohnmobilstellplatz Frekot, Wiesenweg 23.
GPS: n51,11134 e9,06677.

15 ⌂ € 6 ⚡🔧Ch 🔌€0,33/kWh WC⌐included 🚿€2. 🚮
Location: Rural, simple. **Surface:** grassy. ⭕ 01/01-31/12
Distance: 🛒300m.
Remarks: Bread-service.

| ♨ | Bad Zwesten ♨ | 11A1 |

Reisemobilstellplatz, Hardtstr./Kasseler Straße.
GPS: n51,05849 e9,17613. ⬆.

10 ⌂ € 6 ⚡€1/100liter 🔧Ch 🔌(8x)€1/kWh. 🚮 🚿
Location: Urban, comfortable. **Surface:** gravel/metalled.
⭕ 01/01-31/12
Distance: 🚶400m ⊗on the spot 🛒300m.

| ⛺S | Battenberg ❄ | 10H1 |

Festhalle Battenberg, Festplatzweg. **GPS:** n51,00915 e8,63643. ⬆➡.

5 ⌂free ⚡🔧Ch. **Location:** Rural, simple. **Surface:** gravel/metalled.

⭕ 01/01-31/12
Distance: 🚶1km ⊗1km 🛒1km. **Remarks:** At community centre,
service: Esso-station, Battenfelderstr. 6.

| ⛺S | Battenberg ❄ | 10H1 |

Hallen- und Freibad, Senonchesstraße. **GPS:** n51,01233 e8,63532. ⬆.

3 ⌂free ⚡🔧Ch. **Location:** Rural, simple. **Surface:** asphalted.
⭕ 01/01-31/12
Distance: 🚶300m 🏊100m🛒on the spot 🛒on the spot 🚲on the
spot.
Remarks: Parking swimming pool, service: Esso-station, Battenfelderstr. 6. **Tourist information Battenberg:**
👁 Besucherbergwerk Burgbergstollen. 150 years old mine shaft, can
be reached from Marktplatz. ⭕ 01/05-30/09 1st Su of the month
14-17h.

| ⛺S | Baunatal ♨ | 11A1 |

Parkstadion. GPS: n51,25769 e9,39851. ⬆➡.

16 ⌂ € 5/24h ⚡€1/100liter 🔧Ch 🔌(16x)€0,50/kWh. 🏪
Location: Rural, simple, simple, quiet. **Surface:** grassy/gravel.
⭕ 01/01-31/12
Distance: 🚶500m 🚲4km 🚲on the spot 🏃on the spot.
Remarks: Max. 3 days.

| ⛺S | Bebra ⚓🚤 | 11B1 |

Natur- und Freizeitpark Fuldaaue Breitenbachen Seen, Hersfelder
Straße. **GPS:** n50,95899 e9,78764. ⬆.

30 ⌂ € 3, € 18/week ⚡€1/100liter 🔧Ch 🔌(18x)€0,50/kWh.
Location: Comfortable. **Surface:** grassy. ⭕ 01/01-31/12
Distance: 🚶1km 🏊on the spot 🚤on the spot 🛒1km 🚲on the spot
🏃on the spot.

| ♨ | Bebra ⚓🚤 | 11B1 |

Am Schwimmbad, Annastrasse 17. **GPS:** n50,97464 e9,79836. ⬆➡.

4 ⌂free. **Location:** Rural, simple. **Surface:** asphalted.
⭕ 01/01-31/12
Distance: 🚶400m.
Remarks: Parking swimming pool.

| ♨ | Bebra ⚓🚤 | 11B1 |

Mehrzweckparkplatz, Bei der Laupfütze/Rathausstrasse.
GPS: n50,97000 e9,79000. ⬆.

10 free. **Location:** Rural, simple. **Surface:** metalled.
01/01-31/12
Distance: on the spot.

Beerfelden 16A1

Parkplatz NordicCenter, Seeweg. **GPS**: n49,56034 e8,97557.

4 free €0,50/50liter Ch (4x)€0,50/kWh. **Location:** Rural, simple, quiet. **Surface:** asphalted.
01/01-31/12
Distance: 1km on the spot on the spot.

Berkatal 11B1

Am Sportplatz. **GPS**: n51,23763 e9,91504.

3 free. **Location:** Rural, simple, isolated, quiet. **Surface:** asphalted.
01/01-31/12
Distance: 800m 500m on the spot.

Biedenkopf 10H1

Freizeitzentrum Sackpfeife, An der Berggaststätte.
GPS: n50,94735 e8,53317.

6 € 5/24h. **Location:** Rural. **Surface:** concrete.
01/01-31/12
Distance: on the spot on the spot on the spot.
Remarks: Max. 3 days.

Biedenkopf 10H1

Parkplatz Stadtwerke, Mühlweg. **GPS**: n50,90925 e8,52687.

4 € 5/24h €1/12h. **Location:** Urban. **Surface:** asphalted.
01/01-31/12
Distance: 200m.
Remarks: Max. 3 days.

Biedenkopf 10H1

Parkhotel Bürgerhaus, Auf dem Radeköppel 2.
GPS: n50,91183 e8,53515.

5 free with a meal. **Location:** Urban. 01/01-31/12
Distance: on the spot on the spot 500m 12km 12km.

Bischoffen 10H2

P Aartalsee, Am See. **GPS**: n50,70172 e8,46726.

10 € 3/day, € 5,50/night. **Surface:** grassy/gravel. 01/01-31/12
Distance: 1,5km.

Borken 11A1

Borkener See, Westrandstrasse. **GPS**: n51,04447 e9,27392.

2 free. **Location:** Rural, simple. **Surface:** asphalted.
01/01-31/12
Distance: 500m 4,5km 100m 1km 500m.
Remarks: At swimming pool.

Braunfels 10H2

Wohnmobilstation Schloss Braunfels, Jahnplatz.
GPS: n50,51478 e8,38609.

4 € 5, € 7,50 service incl Ch. **Location:** Rural, simple, quiet. **Surface:** metalled. 01/01-31/12
Distance: on the spot 350m on the spot.
Remarks: Pay and key service: Gasthof am Turm, Marktplatz 11, caution € 15.

Breuberg 16A1

Bahnhofstraße 4, Neustadt. **GPS**: n49,81576 e9,04063.

4 free €1/5minutes Ch €1/time (4x)€0,50/kWh.
Location: Urban, simple, simple, central. **Surface:** asphalted
01/01-31/12
Distance: on the spot 300m 550m on the spot.

Breuna 9A3

Märchenlandtherme, Schulstraße. **GPS**: n51,41875 e9,18612.
3 free €3. **Surface:** gravel. 01/01-31/12
Distance: 500m 50m.

Büdingen 11A3

Hinter der Meisterei 20. **GPS**: n50,29094 e9,12587.

8 free. **Location:** Rural, simple, quiet. **Surface:** metalled.
01/01-31/12
Distance: Old city centre 750m 500m.
Remarks: At swimming pool.

Büdingen 11A3

Mühltorbrücke. **GPS**: n50,29051 e9,11581.

2 € 5/5h. **Surface:** metalled. 01/01-31/12
Distance: Old city centre 50m.

Burghaun 11B2

Oberste Straße. **GPS**: n50,69179 e9,73203.

3 free €1/100liter Ch (4x)€1/6h. **Location:** Urban, simple.
Surface: asphalted. 01/01-31/12
Distance: 800m on the spot on the spot.

Calden 9A3

Waldschwimmbad Calden, Zum Lindenrondell.
GPS: n51,39420 e9,40064.

3 free. **Location:** Rural, simple, isolated. **Surface:** grassy.
01/01-31/12
Distance: 1km 1,5km 2km.

Diemelsee 8H3

Terrassenparkplatz Hohes Rad, Hohes Rad 1.
GPS: n51,36470 e8,71935.

DE

30 🛏 € 5 WC ⬚. 🚿 **Location:** Rural, simple. **Surface:** grassy/gravel.
◯ 01/01-31/12
Distance: ⤢Diemelsee ⤙on the spot ⊗500m.

| 🅲🆂 | Diemelsee | 8H3 |

Campingpark Hohes Rad, Hohes Rad 1. **GPS:** n51,36355 e8,71830. ⬆.

5 🛏 € 5/pp ⛽Ch 🔌€0,53/kWh WC⬚included 📶€1/day. 🚻
Location: Rural, simple. **Surface:** grassy/gravel.
◯ 01/01-31/12
Distance: ⤢on the spot ⤙on the spot 🛒6km.

| 🅲🆂 | Diemelstadt | 9A3 |

Autohof, Kupferkuhle. **GPS:** n51,49034 e9,00885. ⬆.
10 🛏 free ⛽€1 🔌€1 Ch 🔌€1. **Location:** Highway.
Surface: asphalted. ◯ 01/01-31/12
Distance: ⤢500m ⊗250m McDonalds.

| 🅲🆂 | Dillenburg | 10H2 |

Aquarena-Bad, Stadionstrasse. **GPS:** n50,73994 e8,27815. ⬆➡.

8 🛏 free ⛽€1/90liter 🔌Ch 🔌(6x)€1/8h. **Location:** Urban, simple.
Surface: asphalted. ◯ 01/01-31/12
Distance: ⤢300m.

| 🅲🆂 | Edermünde | 11A1 |

Aueweg, Grifte. **GPS:** n51,21252 e9,44905. ⬆.

12 🛏 € 5 ⛽€1/100liter 🔌Ch 🔌(6x)included15h,then€1/3h. 🚐
Location: Rural, simple. **Surface:** asphalted.
◯ 01/01-31/12
Distance: ⤢300m 🚲1,7km ⊗300m 🛒100m 🚴Premium-Radweg
R1 🚶on the spot.

| 🅲🆂 | Edertal | 11A1 |

Wohnmobilstellplatz Hemfurth/Edersee, Kraftwerkstrasse.
GPS: n51,17022 e9,05096. ⬆➡.

30 🛏 < 8m € 6, >8m € 10 ⛽€1/100liter 🔌Ch€1. 🚻 **Location:** Rural,
simple. **Surface:** metalled. ◯ 01/01-31/12
Distance: ⤢500m ⤢on the spot ⊗100m 🛒500m.

| 🅲🆂 | Edertal | 11A1 |

Wohnmobilstellplatz Rehbach, Am Eschelberg.
GPS: n51,18394 e9,02618. ⬆.

20 🛏 < 8m € 6, >8m € 10. 🚐 **Location:** Rural, simple. **Surface:** gravel.
◯ 01/01-31/12
Distance: ⤢beach 200m.

| 🅲🆂 | Eltville am Rhein | 10H3 |

Parkplatz Weinhohle, Weinhohle. **GPS:** n50,02832 e8,12406. ⬆.

+20 🛏 € 5 ⛽€1/60liter 🔌€1 Ch. 🚐 **Location:** Urban, simple,
central. **Surface:** metalled.
Distance: ⤢200m ⊗400m 🛒50m.

| 🅲🆂 | Erbach | 16A1 |

Alexanderbad, In der Stadtwiese. **GPS:** n49,66349 e8,98863. ⬆.

10 🛏 free ⛽€1/70liter 🔌Ch 🔌(6x)€0,50/kWh. **Location:** Urban,
simple, quiet. **Surface:** metalled. ◯ 01/01-31/12
Distance: ⤢800m ⊗500m 🛒100m 🚐100m 🚶on the spot.
Remarks: Max. 72h.

| 🅲🆂 | Eschwege ❄ | 11B1 |

Reisemobilhafen Werratalsee, Am werratalsee 2.
GPS: n51,19196 e10,06728. ⬆➡.

20 🛏 € 9-15 ⛽€1/80liter 🔌Ch 🔌(18x)€2/5kWh WC⬚usesanitary
€3,30/pp. 🚻 **Location:** Rural, simple, central, noisy.
Surface: metalled. ◯ 01/01-31/12
Distance: ⤢2km 🚴on the spot 🚶on the spot.
Remarks: Pay at bistro.

Tourist information Eschwege:
👁 Besuchergwerk Grube Gustav, Höllethal, Meissner, Abterode. Slate
mine. ◯ 15/03-31/10 Tue -Su 13-16h.

| 🅲🆂 | Flörsbachtal-Lohrhaupten 👥 | 11B3 |

Am Schwimbad. **GPS:** n50,12178 e9,47258. ⬆➡.

10 🛏 € 9 ⛽🔌Ch 🔌€1,50/24h WCincluded ⬚against payment.
🚻 **Location:** Rural, comfortable, quiet. **Surface:** grassy/gravel.

◯ 01/01-31/12 ◯ Service: winter
Distance: ⤢1km ⊗100m 🛒1km 🚴on the spot 🚶on the spot.
Remarks: Check in at Gartenstrasse 10a.

| 🅲🆂 | Frankenberg/Eder 🚣 | 11A1 |

Ederberglandhalle, Teichweg 3. **GPS:** n51,05613 e8,80195. ⬆➡.

10 🛏 free ⛽€1/25liter 🔌Ch 🔌(4x)€1/kWh WC⬚.
Location: Urban, central. **Surface:** grassy/gravel.
◯ 01/01-31/12 ◯ water disconnected in winter
Distance: ⤢500m ⊗200m 🛒100m.
Remarks: Use sanitary only during opening hours swimming pool.

| 🅲🆂 | Friedberg 🌿 | 11A3 |

Engel Caravaning, Dieselstraße 4. **GPS:** n50,34646 e8,75685. ⬆.

2 🛏voluntary contribution is appreciated ⛽€0,50/time 🔌Ch 🔌(2x)
Location: Urban, simple, central. **Surface:** metalled.
◯ 01/01-31/12
Distance: ⤢800m ⊗100m 🛒800m.
Remarks: Motorhome dealer, accessory shop, closed at night.

| 🅲🆂 | Frielendorf | 11A1 |

Wohnmobilpark Silbersee, Zum Silbersee.
GPS: n50,98389 e9,34667. ⬆➡.

50 🛏 € 10 ⛽🔌Chincluded 🔌€2/stay. 🚻 **Location:** Rural, simple,
quiet. **Surface:** grassy/metalled. ◯ 01/04-01/11
Distance: ⤢1km ⤢250m.

| 🅲🆂 | Fritzlar 🌿🏛 | 11A1 |

Grauen Turm. **GPS:** n51,13221 e9,26974. ⬆➡.

6 🛏 € 7 ⛽€1/90liter 🔌Ch 🔌€1/2kWh. 🚐
Location: Urban, central. **Surface:** metalled.
◯ 01/01-31/12
Distance: ⤢100m ⊗100m.

Tourist information Fritzlar:
⚔ Stadtführingen. Guided tour around the historic city center.
◯ 01/04-31/10 Tue-Sa 10.30h, Su 11h. 🎫 € 2,50.

| 🅲🆂 | Fulda 🏛 | 11B2 |

Weimarerstrasse. **GPS:** n50,55685 e9,66663. ⬆.

30 🛏 € 0,10/1h, € 5/24h 🚰 €1 ⛽ Ch 🚿 € 1/6h 🗑.🚐
Location: Urban, simple, central. **Surface:** asphalted.
🅿 01/01-31/12
Distance: 🛒400m 🛏 50m.

Gelnhausen 🔝 11A3
Am Hallenbad. **GPS:** n50,20125 e9,17795.🔼.

4 🛏 free. **Location:** Urban, simple, noisy. **Surface:** asphalted.
🅿 01/01-31/12
Distance: 🛒1000m 🔲100m 🛏 100m 🚆on the spot.
Remarks: Parking at swimming pool.

Gießen 10H2
Badezentrum Ringallee, Gutfleischstraße.
GPS: n50,58947 e8,68406.🔼.

6 🛏 € 3 🚿 (6x)€0,50/kWh.🚐 **Location:** Urban, simple.
Surface: metalled. 🅿 01/01-31/12
Distance: 🛒600m 🚲 1,5km.

Gilserberg 11A1
Landgasthof Steller, Marburgerstrasse 3.
GPS: n50,59047 e9,06220.🔼.

4 🛏€ 5, guests € 2,50 🚰€2,50 🚿€2,50 WC. 🚿 **Location:** Urban,
simple. **Surface:** asphalted. 🅿 01/01-31/12 🔴 Wed
Distance: 🛏 250m 🚆on the spot 🏃on the spot.

Gladenbach 10H2
Restaurant Rosengarten, Hoherainstrasse 45.
GPS: n50,77462 e8,57952.🔼➡️.

3 🛏€ 5,50 🚰 🗑 🚿. **Location:** Urban, simple. **Surface:** grassy.
🅿 01/01-31/12
Distance: 🛒600m 🔲on the spot 🛏 1km.
Remarks: Pay and key at restaurant.

Grebenau 11B2
Borngasse 20. **GPS:** n50,74134 e9,47212.🔼➡️.

4 🛏free 🚰🗑free. **Location:** Rural, simple. **Surface:** grassy.
🅿 01/01-31/12
Distance: 🛒on the spot 🔲200m 🛏 200m.
Remarks: At fire-station.

Grebenhain 11A2
Reisemobilstellplatz am Kurpark, Hindenburgstraße, Hochwaldhausen. **GPS:** n50,51910 e9,31756.🔼.

30 🛏€ 6 🚰🗑 Ch 🚿 WC included. **Location:** Rural, simple, central.
Surface: gravel. 🅿 01/01-31/12
Distance: 🛒500m 🔲500m 🚲bike-bus 200m 🚴Vulkanradweg 200m
🏃on the spot.
Remarks: Pay in at kiosk.

Grebenhain 11A2
Gasthof Zum Felsenmeer, Jean-Berlit-Straße 1.
GPS: n50,51926 e9,31424.🔼.

10 🛏€ 5 + € 1/pp tourist tax 🚿(2x)€0,50/kWh,+ € 1. **Location:** Rural.
Surface: grassy. 🅿 01/01-31/12
Distance: 🔲on the spot.

Großalmerode 11B1
Am Mühlgraben, Oststraße. **GPS:** n51,25841 e9,79349.🔼.
20 🛏free 🚰🗑Ch 🚿. **Location:** Rural. **Surface:** grassy.
🅿 01/01-31/12
Distance: 🛒700m 🔲150m.

Grünberg 🌼🌳 11A2
Gallusplatz, Gerichtsstraße. **GPS:** n50,59517 e8,95593.🔼➡️.

10 🛏free 🚰€0,50 🗑Ch 🚿(10x)0,50/10h. **Location:** Urban,
simple, central. **Surface:** gravel. 🅿 01/01-31/12
Distance: 🛒Old city centre 300m 🔲100m 🛏 Aldi 400m 🚴on the spot
🏃on the spot.

Habichtswald 9A3
Am Kressenborn, Bergweg, Dörnberg. **GPS:** n51,34361 e9,34389.🔼.

---

4 🛏free 🚿(2x)€2/24h WC. **Location:** Simple, quiet. **Surface:** gravel.
🅿 01/01-31/12
Distance: 🛒200m 🚲5,5km 🔲200m.
Remarks: Caution € 20, key electricity/toilet at petrol station.

Habichtswald 9A3
Hasenbreite, Ehlen. **GPS:** n51,32291 e9,31961.🔼➡️.

6 🛏free 🚿€2/24h WC. **Location:** Rural, simple, isolated, quiet.
Surface: grassy/metalled. 🅿 01/01-31/12
Distance: 🛒400m 🚲2,5km 🔲400m 🛏 400m.
Remarks: Caution € 20, key electricity/toilet at swimming pool.

Hatzfeld 🚣 10H1
Parking Edertal strasse. **GPS:** n50,99144 e8,54817.🔼.

5 🛏. **Location:** Urban, simple, quiet. **Surface:** grassy/gravel.
🅿 01/01-31/12
Distance: 🛒on the spot 🚆on the spot 🛏 200m 🚴on the spot.
Remarks: Behind fire-station.

Helsa 11B1
Sportplatzweg. **GPS:** n51,25444 e9,68638.🔼➡️.

4 🛏free. **Surface:** metalled. 🅿 01/01-31/12
Distance: 🛒800m 🔲800m 🛏 700m 🚆400m.

Herborn 🚣 10H2
Herborner Schießplatz, Sinner Landstraße.
GPS: n50,67950 e8,30672.🔼➡️.

6 🛏free 🚰€1/90liter 🗑Ch 🛏stay 🚿(6x)€1/kWh.
Location: Simple. **Surface:** metalled. 🅿 01/01-31/12
Distance: 🛒200m 🚲1,8km.

Herbstein 🌼🌿 11A2
VulkanTherme Herbstein, Zum Thermalbad 1.
GPS: n50,56883 e9,34647.🔼➡️.

DE

11 ⛺ € 6 + € 1,50/pp tourist tax ⛽€1/100liter 🔲Ch ⚡(11x)€1/2kWh WC 🚿1,50. **Location:** Rural, comfortable, quiet. **Surface:** metalled. 🔲 01/01-31/12
Distance: 🚂1,1km ⊗800m 🛒300m 🚲on the spot. 🚶on the spot.
Remarks: Coins available at pay-desk of theTherme.

🅂 Hessisch Lichtenau 🌊♨🏕👪 11B1
Sportcenter Fürstenhagen, Breslauer strasse 18.
GPS: n51,20672 e9,69443. ⬆➡.

10 ⛺€ 5/24h ⛽€1/80liter 🔲Ch ⚡€0,50/kWh 🔧. **Location:** Rural, simple, quiet. **Surface:** metalled.
🔲 01/01-31/12
Distance: 🚂3km ⊗1km 🛒2km.
Remarks: Check in at sport centre.

🅂 Hessisch Lichtenau 🌊♨🏕👪 11B1
Alter Bahnhof/Western Rail Station, Bahnhofstrasse 5, Warlburg.
GPS: n51,20055 e9,77833. ⬆➡.

10 ⛺€ 10. 🔧 **Location:** Rural, isolated, quiet. **Surface:** asphalted.
🔲 01/01-31/12
Distance: 🚂5km ⊗700m 🚃1km 🚶on the spot.

🅂 Hessisch Lichtenau 🌊♨🏕👪 11B1
Hopfelderstrasse. **GPS:** n51,19417 e9,72389. ⬆➡.

14 ⛺free. **Location:** Urban, simple, isolated, quiet. **Surface:** metalled.
🔲 01/01-31/12
Distance: 🚂500m ⊗400m 🛒500m.

🅂 Hessisch Lichtenau 🌊♨🏕👪 11B1
Wohnmobilstellplatz am Hallenbad, Freiherr vom Stein strasse 12.
GPS: n51,20445 e9,72655. ⬆.

6 ⛺free. **Location:** Rural, simple, isolated, quiet. **Surface:** metalled.
🔲 01/01-31/12

Distance: 🚂600m.
Remarks: Parking swimming pool.

🍴🅂 Hessisch Lichtenau 🌊♨🏕👪 11B1
Berggasthof Hohe Meissner, Hoher Meissner 1.
GPS: n51,20376 e9,84852. ⬆.

10 ⛺free ⛽ ⚡ WC. **Location:** Rural, simple, isolated, quiet.
Surface: metalled. 🔲 01/01-31/12
Distance: 🚂10km ⊗on the spot 🚃on the spot 🎿on the spot 🏊 on the spot.

🍴 Hilders 11B2
Ulsterwelle, Heideweg 19. **GPS:** n50,56909 e9,99351. ⬆.

5 ⛺free. **Location:** Rural. **Surface:** gravel. 🔲 01/01-31/12
Distance: 🚂750m ⊗50m 🛒800m.

🅂 Hirschhorn 🏞 16A1
Beim Ätsche, Jahnstraße 2. **GPS:** n49,44214 e8,89804. ⬆.

25 ⛺€ 7 ⛽€0,50/40liter 🔲Ch ⚡€2,50/day. **Location:** Rural, comfortable, quiet. **Surface:** grassy.
🔲 01/01-31/12 ⚫ high water
Distance: 🚂500m ⊗on the spot 🚃train 400m 🚲on the spot.
Remarks: Along the Neckar river.

🍴 Hirzenhain 11A2
Festplatz Hirzenhain, Robert-Eichenauerweg.
GPS: n50,39259 e9,13593. ⬆➡.

6 ⛺free. **Location:** Urban, simple, central. **Surface:** metalled.
🔲 01/01-31/12
Distance: 🚂100m ⊗100m 🛒on the spot 🚲on the spot.

🅂 Hirzenhain 11A2
Müller-Mobil, Junkernwiese 2. **GPS:** n50,40004 e9,14744. ⬆.

6 ⛺free ⛽€1/130liter 🔲Ch ⚡(6x). **Location:** Rural, simple, quiet.

Surface: metalled. 🔲 01/01-31/12
Distance: 🚂1,5km on the spot 🚲on the spot 🚶on the spot.

🅂 Hofgeismar ☕ 9A3
Am Sälber Tor. **GPS:** n51,49521 e9,37547. ⬆.

100 ⛺free ⛽€1/80liter 🔲Ch ⚡(18x)€1/2kWh. **Location:** Rural, comfortable, central, quiet. **Surface:** gravel.
Distance: 🚂on the spot 🛒300m 🚲on the spot 🚶on the spot.

🅂 Homberg/Efze ⚓ 11A1
Wassmuthshäuserstrasse, Dresdener Alee.
GPS: n51,02757 e9,41470. ⬆➡.

7 ⛺free ⛽€1/80liter 🔲Ch ⚡free. **Location:** Urban, simple.
Surface: gravel. 🔲 01/01-31/12
Distance: 🚂on the spot ⊗1km 🛒500m.

🅂 Homberg/Ohm 11A2
An der Stadthalle, Stadthallenweg. **GPS:** n50,72626 e8,99439. ⬆➡.

4 ⛺free ⛽€1/80liter 🔲Ch ⚡(4x)€0,50. **Location:** Rural, simple.
Surface: metalled. 🔲 01/01-31/12
Distance: 🚂400m ⊗350m 🛒1km 🚶on the spot.

🅂 Hünfeld ⚓👪❄ 11B2
Hessisches Kegelspiel, Zu den Unaben.
GPS: n50,67626 e9,77622. ⬆➡.

12 ⛺€ 5 ⛽€1/120liter 🔲Ch ⚡(12x)€1/2kWh. **Location:** Urban, simple. 🔲 01/01-31/12
Distance: 🚂500m ⊗250m 🛒500m.

🅂 Hungen 🏞 11A2
Inheiden, Am Köstgraben. **GPS:** n50,45509 e8,90049. ⬆➡.

6 ⛺free ⛽€1/100liter 🔲Ch ⚡€2/8h WC. **Location:** Rural, comfortable, quiet. **Surface:** grasstiles. 🔲 01/01-31/12 ⚫ water:

01/11-31/03
Distance: ⚓Trais-Horloffer See ⊗3km 🛒500m 🚌bike-bus 1km.

Idstein � 10H3

Wohnmobilhafen Idstein, Himmelsbornweg.
GPS: n50,21775 e8,27923.⬆➡.

12 🚐€10 ⛽€1/80liter 🗑Ch ⚡€1/8h. 🚲 **Location:** Rural.
Surface: gravel/metalled. 📅 01/01-31/12 💧 water disconnected in winter **Distance:** 🚶500m Altstadt 🚴3,3km.

Kassel 🏺 11A1

Wohnmobilplatz Kassel, Am Sportzentrum/Giessenallee, Kassel-süd.
GPS: n51,29250 e9,48750.⬆➡.

12 🚐€12,50/day ⛽€1/100liter 🗑€0,50 Ch€0,50 ⚡(8x)€0,50/kWh.
Location: Rural, simple, isolated, quiet.
📅 01/01-31/12
Distance: 🚴1,4km ⊗500m 🚌50m 🎪 on the spot 🚶 on the spot.
Remarks: With parking ticket free public transport, max. 3 nights.

Tourist information Kassel:
👁🏛 Treppenstrasse, shopping promenade, modern architecture.

Kaufungen 👫 11B1

Festplatz, Am Steckkopf. **GPS:** n51,28525 e9,61956.⬆➡.

4 🚐free ⛽€2 🗑Ch. **Location:** Rural, simple, quiet.
Surface: metalled. 📅 01/01-31/12
Distance: ⚓800m Steinersee ⊗300m 🛒500m.
Remarks: 2013: during inspection service out of order.

Kirchheim 11B2

Campingplatz Seepark, Brunnenstrasse 20.
GPS: n50,81400 e9,52000.⬆➡.

50 🚐€13, dog €2 ⛽€1 🗑Ch ⚡(30x)€3/day 💧€1,50.
Location: Rural, simple. **Surface:** metalled. 📅 01/01-31/12
Distance: 🚶5km 🚴4,9km ⚓20m 🛒on the spot ⊗20m.

Korbach 🌿 11A1

Westring. **GPS:** n51,27260 e8,85509.➡.

5 🚐free. **Location:** Urban, quiet. **Surface:** grasstiles/metalled.
📅 01/01-31/12
Distance: 🚶1km 🛒Lidl 200m.
Remarks: Max. 3 nights.

Laubach 🌿🏖 11A2

Quick Camp Caravanpark Laubach, Kurze Hohl.
GPS: n50,55021 e9,00806.⬆.

30 🚐€6, 2 pers.incl ⛽€2/time 🗑€2/time Ch WC 💧€2/time ⚡.
Location: Rural, simple, isolated, quiet. **Surface:** grasstiles/grassy.
📅 01/01-31/12
Distance: 🚶1,5km ⊗1,5km 🛒1,5km.

Lauterbach 11A2

Auf der Bleiche, Bleichstrasse. **GPS:** n50,63849 e9,40444.⬆➡.

5 🚐free. **Location:** Rural, simple. **Surface:** metalled.
📅 01/01-31/12
Distance: 🚶100m ⊗150m 🛒on the spot.

Lauterbach 11A2

Freizeitzentrum, Am Sportfeld. **GPS:** n50,62758 e9,39288.⬆➡.

8 🚐free. **Location:** Urban. **Surface:** metalled. 📅 01/01-31/12
Distance: 🚶800m ⊗50m 🛒on the spot 🚶on the spot.

Lauterbach 11A2

David-Eifertstrasse. **GPS:** n50,64288 e9,39393.⬆.
⛽€1/80 🗑Ch 🧽. **Location:** Urban. 📅 01/01-31/12

Leun 🏊 10H2

Lahnwiese, Limburger Straße. **GPS:** n50,55089 e8,35346.⬆➡.

5 🚐€6 ⚡€2 WC. **Location:** Rural, simple. **Surface:** grassy.
📅 01/01-31/12
Distance: 🚶400m ⊗400m 🛒400m.
Remarks: Along the Lahn river, max. 4 days.

Lich 🌿 11A2

P6, Ringstraße. **GPS:** n50,51816 e8,82257.⬆➡.

3 🚐free. **Location:** Rural, simple, central, quiet.
Surface: grassy/metalled. 📅 01/01-31/12
Distance: 🚶300m ⊗400m 🛒Lidl 50m 🚌100m.
Remarks: Max. 3 days.

Limburg 10H2

Freizeitfalzeuge Singhof, Hoenbergstraße 2.
GPS: n50,40312 e8,07148.

3 🚐free ⚡€3 💧free. **Location:** Rural, simple. **Surface:** metalled.
📅 01/01-31/12

Limburg 10H2

Lahn Camping, Schleusenweg 16. **GPS:** n50,38902 e8,07387.⬆➡.

8 🚐max. €12-15/24h ⛽€0,50/50liter 🗑Ch ⚡€0,50/kWh 💧€2/day. **Location:** Rural, simple, quiet. **Surface:** gravel.
📅 01/01-31/12
Distance: 🚶900m 🚴1,5km ⊗Gaststätte.
Remarks: Along the Lahn river, summer: bread-service, biergarten.

Lindenfels 🌿 16A1

Kappstraße. **GPS:** n49,68077 e8,78304.⬆➡.

10 🚐€5 ⛽€1/80liter 🗑Ch ⚡(4x)€0,50/6h WC. 🍞
Location: Rural, comfortable, quiet. **Surface:** grassy.
📅 01/01-31/12
Distance: 🚶on the spot ⊗on the spot 🛒on the spot.
Remarks: Max. 3 days.

Lorsch 🏺 15H1

Odenwaldallee. **GPS:** n49,65206 e8,57855.⬆.

16 🚐€10 ⛽€1/80liter 🗑Ch ⚡(16x)€1/2kWh. 🍞🧽
Location: Rural, comfortable, quiet. **Surface:** metalled.

DE

⊙ 01/01-31/12
Distance: 🚰800m 🛒4,5km ⊗800m 🗑800m 🚲on the spot.

| **Maintal** 🏞 | 11A3 |

Wohmobilstellplatz Maintal, Uferpromenade, Dörnigheim.
GPS: n50,13067 e8,83920. ⬆➡.

2 🏕free. **Location:** Rural, simple, central. **Surface:** grasstiles.
⊙ 01/01-31/12
Distance: 🚰on the spot ⊗on the spot 🗑1km 🚲on the spot
🚶on the spot.
Remarks: Along Main river.

| 🏕S **Marburg** 🌿⛺🧺 | 11A2 |

Jahnstraße. **GPS**: n50,80354 e8,77544. ⬆➡.

8 🏕€ 10/24h 🚰€1/100liter Ch ⚡(4x)€1/4h. 🏠 **Location:** Urban,
simple. **Surface:** gravel. ⊙ 01/01-31/12
Distance: 🚰300m 🗑500m.

| 🏕S **Meineringhausen** | 11A1 |

Hobbywiese, Walmenstrasse 25. **GPS**: n51,25945 e8,93807. ⬆➡.

17 🏕€ 7 🚰 Chincluded ⚡€0,50/kWh,or€3/day WC 🚿€1. 🔧
Location: Rural, comfortable. **Surface:** grassy/gravel.
⊙ 01/01-31/12
Distance: 🚰2km Korbach ⊗800m 🗑2km 🚲on the spot 🚶on the
spot.

| 🏕 **Melsungen** | 11B1 |

Am Sand, Sandstraße. **GPS**: n51,13280 e9,54502. ⬆.

🏕€ 0,30/h, overnight stay free. 🏠 **Location:** Urban, central.
Surface: metalled. ⊙ 01/01-31/12
Distance: 🚰200m 🛒5km 🚲on the spot 🚶on the spot.
Remarks: Along the Fulda river.

| 🏕 **Melsungen** | 11B1 |

Waldparkplatz, Dreuxallee. **GPS**: n51,12352 e9,55169. ⬆.

5 🏕free. **Location:** Urban, simple. **Surface:** grassy/gravel.
⊙ 01/01-31/12
Distance: 🚰centre 1,1km 🛒5km.

| 🏕S **Mernes** 🏘 | 11B3 |

Wohnmobilstellplatz Mernes, Jossastraße, Mernes.
GPS: n50,24109 e9,47700. ➡.

6 🏕€ 5 🚰€0,50/80liter Ch ⚡€0,50/kWh. **Location:** Rural,
comfortable, quiet. **Surface:** grasstiles.
⊙ 01/01-31/12
Distance: 🚰200m ⊗250m 🗑200m 🚲on the spot.
Remarks: To be paid at Gasthaus Zum Jossatal, Salmünsterer Straße 15.

| 🏕S **Michelstadt** 🌿 | 16A1 |

Parkplatz Altstadt, Wiesenweg. **GPS**: n49,68038 e9,00143. ⬆➡.

9 🏕free 🚰€1/90liter Ch ⚡€1/2kWh WC. **Location:** Urban,
simple, central, noisy. **Surface:** gravel/metalled.
⊙ 01/01-31/12
Distance: 🚰200m ⊗200m 🗑50m 🚲on the spot 🚶on the spot.

| 🏕 **Münzenberg** | 11A2 |

Sporthallenparkplatz, Am Viehtrieb. **GPS**: n50,45712 e8,77171. ⬆➡.

5 🏕free. **Location:** Rural, simple, quiet. **Surface:** gravel.
⊙ 01/01-31/12
Distance: 🚰800m 🛒2,6km ⊗500m.
Remarks: Max. 3 days.

| 🏕 **Münzenberg** | 11A2 |

Sportplatz, Butzbacher Straße, Gambach. **GPS**: n50,45770 e8,73412. ⬆.

15 🏕free. **Location:** Rural, simple, noisy. **Surface:** asphalted.
⊙ 01/01-31/12
Distance: 🛒2,4km ⊗400m.
Remarks: Max. 3 days.

| ℂS **Neuental** 🏞 | 11A1 |

Neuenhainer See, Seeblick 14, Neuenhain.
GPS: n50,99533 e9,26652. ➡.

12 🏕€ 4 🚰€1 Ch ⚡€1/12h WC 🚿€0,50 ⚡. **Location:** Rural,
simple. **Surface:** asphalted. ⊙ 01/01-31/12
Distance: 🚰Neuental 6km ⚓on the spot ⊗250m.
Remarks: Use sanitary facilities at campsite.

| 🏕S **Neukirchen** | 11A1 |

Reisemobilpark Urbachtal, Urbachweg 1.
GPS: n50,87139 e9,34861. ⬆➡.

49 🏕€ 10 + € 1/pp tourist tax 🚰€1/100liter Ch ⚡€0,60/
kWh WC 🚿€2,80 ⚡€1,30min ⚡. **Location:** Rural, luxurious.
Surface: grassy/metalled. ⊙ 01/01-31/12
Distance: 🚰500m ⊗500m 🗑200m Rewe.

| 🏕S **Neukirchen** | 11A1 |

Birkenallee, Knüllgebirge. **GPS**: n50,86567 e9,34478.

5 🏕free ⚡free. **Surface:** asphalted. ⊙ 01/01-31/12
Distance: 🚰500m ⊗200m.

| 🏕 **Niedenstein** | 11A1 |

Am Hallenbad, Schulstraße. **GPS**: n51,22739 e9,31657. ⬆➡.

2 🏕free. **Location:** Rural, simple. **Surface:** gravel.
⊙ 01/01-31/12
Distance: 🚰300m 🗑300m.

| 🏕S **Niestetal** | 9B3 |

Spiekershäuser Straße/Fuldablick. **GPS**: n51,32686 e9,55490. ⬆.
3 🏕free 🚰€1/100liter Ch ⚡€1/2kWh. **Surface:** asphalted.
⊙ 01/01-31/12
Distance: 🚰1,1km 🚲on the spot 🚶on the spot.
Remarks: Along the Fulda river, Kassel centre 6km.

| 🏕S **Oberaula** 🏘 | 11B1 |

Sportplatz, Schwimbadstraße. **GPS**: n50,85421 e9,45908. ⬆➡.

DE

5 🛏free 🚿🗑Chfree. **Location:** Rural, simple. **Surface:** asphalted.
🅿 01/01-31/12
Distance: 🚶800m 🛒Rewe 100m 🚐on the spot.

| 🏕 | **Oberaula** 👥 | 11B1 |

Golfplatz, Am Golfplatz 1. **GPS:** n50,83590 e9,46211.⬆️➡️

3 🛏free. **Location:** Rural, simple, isolated, quiet.
Surface: grassy.
🅿 01/01-31/12 🏊
Distance: 🚶2,5km 🏊11km.
Remarks: Max. 4 days, follow the signs 'Golfplatz', 18-holes golf course.

| 🏕 | **Oberaula** 👥 | 11B1 |

Teichstrasse. GPS: n50,86116 e9,47353.⬆️➡️

10 🛏free. **Location:** Rural, simple, isolated, quiet. **Surface:** metalled.
🅿 01/01-31/12
Distance: 🚶500m ⊗500m 🛒Edeka 500m.
Remarks: Parking tennis-court, max. 4 days.

| 🏕 S | **Oberaula** | 11B1 |

Reiterhof Aumühle, Aumühle 1. **GPS:** n50,85235 e9,47794.⬆️
3 🛏€ 10 🚿🗑Ch included. **Location:** Rural, comfortable.
Surface: grassy/gravel. 🅿 01/01-31/12
Distance: 🚶1km ⊗1km 🛒1,5km.
Remarks: Use of sauna against payment.

| 🏕 S | **Oberursel** | 10H3 |

Wanderparkplatz Taunus, Alfred-Lechler-Straße.
GPS: n50,21533 e8,53606.⬆️

5 🛏€ 7.🏭 **Location:** Simple, quiet. **Surface:** metalled.
🅿 01/01-31/12
Distance: 🚶4km ⊗100m 🚈metro 100m 🚲on the spot 🚶on the spot.

| 🏕 | **Oestrich-Winkel** | 10H3 |

Am Sportzentrum, Kirchstraße 125. **GPS:** n50,00470 e7,99904.⬆️➡️

12 🛏free. **Location:** Rural, simple, central. **Surface:** metalled.
🅿 01/01-31/12
Distance: 🚶1km.
Remarks: Max. 2 days.

| 🏕 S | **Ottrau** | 11A2 |

Am Schwimmbad 10. **GPS:** n50,80400 e9,38500.⬆️

4 🛏€ 6 🚿🗑💧WC🚽. **Location:** Rural, simple. **Surface:** asphalted.
🅿 01/01-31/12
Distance: 🚶on the spot.

| 🏕 S | **Poppenhausen** 👥 | 11B2 |

Sport- und Freizeitgelände Lüttergrund, Sebastian-Kneippweg,
Wasserkuppe. **GPS:** n50,49012 e9,87689.⬆️➡️

10 🛏€ 6 🚿€1 🗑Ch 💧€1/6h. **Location:** Rural, simple.
Surface: metalled. 🅿 01/01-31/12
Distance: 🚶300m ⊗300m 🚲300m 🚲on the spot 🚶on the spot.

| 🏕 S | **Rasdorf** | 11B2 |

Sport- und Freizeitgelände, Setzelbacher Straße.
GPS: n50,71422 e9,90306.⬆️➡️

4 🛏€ 4 🚿€1/120liter 🗑Ch 💧€1/10h. **Location:** Rural, simple.
Surface: metalled. 🅿 01/01-31/12
Distance: 🚶850m 🛒500m.
Remarks: Max. 3 days.

| 🏕 S | **Reichelsheim/Odenwald** 🌾 | 16A1 |

Reichenbergschule, Beerfurhterstrasse.
GPS: n49,71507 e8,84234.⬆️➡️

20 🛏free 🚿€1 🗑Ch 💧(8x)€0,50/kWh. **Location:** Urban, simple,
central. **Surface:** asphalted. 🅿 01/01-31/12
Distance: ⊗100m 🚶on the spot.

| 🏕 | **Reinhardshagen** 👥 | 9B3 |

Freibad, Klinkersweg. **GPS:** n51,48694 e9,59194.⬆️

4 🛏free. **Location:** Rural, simple, isolated. **Surface:** asphalted.
🅿 01/01-31/12
Distance: 🚶2km 🏊on the spot ⊗2km 🛒2km 🚐on the spot
🚲on the spot 🚶on the spot.
Remarks: Parking swimming pool, OT Veckerhagen.

| 🏕 S | **Ringgau** | 11B1 |

Am Festplatz, In der Röste, Gandenborn. **GPS:** n51,08139 e10,04239.⬆️

20 🛏free, service/electricity incl. € 7 🚿🗑Ch 💧. **Location:** Rural,
simple, quiet. **Surface:** gravel. 🅿 01/01-31/12
Distance: 🚶100m ⊗200m.

| 🏕 S | **Rosenthal** | 11A1 |

Fischewosse, Willershäuser Straße 2. **GPS:** n50,97561 e8,86884.⬆️

6 🛏free 🚿🗑 💧€2/day. **Location:** Urban, comfortable.
Surface: metalled. 🅿 01/01-31/12 🔘 first 2 weeks of July
Distance: 🚶400m ⊗on the spot 🛒800m.
Remarks: Max. 48h.

| 🏕 S | **Rotenburg a/d Fulda** 🌾 | 11B1 |

Wohnmobilpark Am Wittlich, Braacher Straße 14.
GPS: n51,00049 e9,72074.

50 🛏€ 6,50 🚿€1 🗑Ch 💧€0,50/kWh. 🏭 **Location:** Simple, quiet.
Surface: grassy. 🅿 01/01-31/12
Distance: 🚶Old city centre 650m 🛒200m 🚲on the spot 🚶on the
spot. **Remarks:** Along the Fulda river.

| 🏕 S | **Rotenburg a/d Fulda** 🌾 | 11B1 |

Am Kuckucksmarktgelände, Braach. **GPS:** n51,00583 e9,69361.➡️

15 🛏free 🚿€1/50liter 🗑Ch. **Location:** Rural. **Surface:** unpaved.
🅿 01/01-31/12

Distance: 🛒200m 🏊on the spot ⛽on the spot ⊗200m.
Remarks: Max. 72h.

Rotenburg a/d Fulda 🌿 | 11B1
Im Heienbach. **GPS:** n51,00223 e9,74141. ⬆️➡️.

5 🅿free. **Location:** Simple. ⏰ 01/01-31/12
Remarks: Parking swimming pool.

Rotenburg a/d Fulda 🌿 | 11B1
Biergarten Hof Hafermas, Rotenburgerstrasse 13, Braach.
GPS: n51,00316 e9,69085.

3 🅿free ⚡€1. 🚰Ch. **Surface:** gravel. ⏰ 01/01-31/12
Distance: 🛒on the spot ⊗on the spot.

Tourist information Rotenburg a/d Fulda:
🎪 Kuckucksmarkt, Braach. Farmers market. ⏰ 01/05-30/09 last
weekend of the month10-18h.

Schlitz | 11B2
Damenweg. **GPS:** n50,66909 e9,56908. ➡️.

3 🅿free ⚡€1. **Location:** Rural, simple. **Surface:** gravel.
⏰ 01/01-31/12
Distance: 🛒2,3km.
Remarks: At swimming pool.

Schlüchtern | 11B2
Ludovica-von-Stumm-Straße. **GPS:** n50,34935 e9,53023. ⬆️.

5 🅿free. **Location:** Urban, simple, noisy. **Surface:** asphalted.
⏰ 01/01-31/12
Distance: 🛒300m 🚲4,3km ⊗on the spot.

Schwalmstadt | 11A1
Altstad Schwalmstadt-Treysa, Zwalmstraße. **GPS:** n50,91447 e9,19327.

10 🅿free ⚡🚰Ch. ⏰ 01/01-31/12

Distance: 🛒100m.
Remarks: Service nearby, indicated.

Schwalmstadt | 11A1
Fünftenweg, Ziegenhain. **GPS:** n50,91753 e9,24633. ⬆️➡️.

10 🅿free ⚡🚰Ch. **Location:** Rural, simple. **Surface:** metalled.
⏰ 01/01-31/12
Distance: 🛒on the spot.
Remarks: Parking swimming pool, service nearby, indicated.

Schwalmtal | 11A2
Reisemobilplatz, Friedenstrasse, Storndorf.
GPS: n50,65579 e9,26935. ⬆️➡️.

15 🅿€3 ⚡€1/80liter 🚰Ch. ⚡(6x)€0,50/kWh. 🚿 **Location:** Rural,
simple. **Surface:** asphalted. ⏰ 01/01-31/12
Distance: 🛒300m 🚲on the spot 🚶on the spot.
Remarks: Nearby sports park.

Sinntal | 11B3
Am Naturbad, Aspenweg, Altengronau.
GPS: n50,25453 e9,63316. ⬆️➡️.

7 🅿free ⚡€0,50/50liter 🚰Ch. ⚡(7x)€3/24h. **Location:** Rural,
simple, quiet. **Surface:** metalled.
⏰ 01/01-31/12
Distance: 🛒1,5km ⊗1,5km 🍺1,5km 🚶on the spot.

Sontra | 11B1
Langhelle/Jahnstrasse. **GPS:** n51,07227 e9,94673.

5 🅿free ⚡€0,50/80liter 🚰Ch. ⚡€1/12h WC. **Location:** Rural,
simple, isolated, quiet. **Surface:** asphalted/metalled.
⏰ 01/01-31/12
Distance: 🛒600m 🚐on the spot.
Remarks: Parking behind swimming pool.

Sontra | 11B1
Vimoutiersstrasse. **GPS:** n51,07139 e9,93306. ⬆️.
8 🅿free. **Location:** Urban, simple. **Surface:** gravel/metalled.
⏰ 01/01-31/12
Distance: 🛒400m ⊗300m 🍺50m.

Steinau/Strasse 🏰 | 11B3
Am Steines. **GPS:** n50,31605 e9,46029. ⬆️.

5 🅿free ⚡€1 🚰Ch€1 ⚡(4x)€1/kWh. **Location:** Rural, simple,
quiet. **Surface:** asphalted. ⏰ 01/01-31/12
Distance: 🛒1km ⊗350m.
Remarks: Parking near sports centre, max. 2 days.

Tann/Rhön | 11B2
Festplatz Tann, Am Unsbach. **GPS:** n50,64195 e10,01802. ⬆️➡️.

8 🅿€5 ⚡€1/120liter 🚰Ch. ⚡(8x)€1/6h. **Location:** Rural, simple,
isolated. **Surface:** gravel. ⏰ 01/01-31/12
Distance: 🛒1km ⊗1km 🍺1km.
Remarks: Max. 3 days, tickets available at tourist office, petrol station
or Schreib- und Spielwaren Krenzer.

Ulrichstein 🌲🐄 | 11A2
Reisemobilstellplatz Panoramablick, Erlenweg.
GPS: n50,57588 e9,20619. ⬆️➡️.

12 🅿€5 ⚡€1/80liter 🚰Ch. ⚡(6x)€0,50/kWh. 🚿
Location: Rural, comfortable, quiet. **Surface:** asphalted.
⏰ 01/01-31/12
Distance: 🛒1km ⊗1km 🍺1km 🚲on the spot 🚶on the spot
🚴on the spot.
Remarks: Beautiful view.

Villmar | 10H2
P3, König-Konrad-Straße. **GPS:** n50,39102 e8,18625. ⬆️➡️.

10 🅿free. **Location:** Rural, simple. **Surface:** metalled.
⏰ 01/01-31/12
Distance: ⊗on the spot.
Remarks: Parking at the river.

Vöhl | 11A1
Camping-und Ferienpark Teichmann, Herzhausen.
GPS: n51,17472 e8,89103. ⬆️.

10 ⌇€ 10-14 ⛽, ⚡, Ch ✒ WC ⌇included ◨€3/time ⌇€4,50. ♨
♨ **Location:** Rural, comfortable. **Surface:** metalled.
◘ 01/01-31/12
Distance: ⌷1km ⌇on the spot ⌇fishing permit € 8/day ⊗on the spot.
Remarks: Max. 1 night.

Volkmarsen 9A3
Schulstraße. **GPS:** n51,41249 e9,11058. ↑
4 ⌇free. **Surface:** asphalted. ◘ 01/01-31/12
Distance: ⌷200m ⛵7,8km ⍟Aldi 650m.

Wahlsburg 9B3
Landhotel "Zum Anker", Weserstrasse 14.
GPS: n51,62447 e9,55212. ↑→.

60 ⌇€7 ⛽€0,50/50liter ⚡Ch ✒(60x)€0,50/kWh WC ⌇. ♨
Location: Rural, comfortable, quiet. **Surface:** grassy.
◘ 01/01-31/12
Distance: ⌷200m ⌇on the spot ⊗on the spot ⍟500m ⌇on the spot ⌇on the spot.
Remarks: Along the Weser river, bread-service.

Waldeck 11A1
Edersee Alm, Am Bettenhagen 2. **GPS:** n51,18861 e9,00944. ↑→.

85 ⌇€12 ⛽€1/100liter ⚡Chincluded ✒€0,50/kWh WC ⌇€1/stay.
Location: Rural, luxurious. **Surface:** gravel. ◘ 01/01-31/12
Distance: ⌇on the spot ⌇fishing permit obligatory ⊗on the spot.
Remarks: Bread-service.

Waldeck 11A1
Seeblick Wohnmobil, Güldener Ort 12. **GPS:** n51,20309 e9,05004. ↑.

⌇€ 11 2 pers.incl, dog € 1 ⛽⚡Ch ✒€3 WC ⌇included. ♨
Location: Rural, simple. **Surface:** grasstiles.
◘ 01/01-31/12
Distance: ⌇50m ⊗on the spot.
Remarks: At Edersee, waste dump € 2.

Waldkappel 11B1
Am Sportplatz. **GPS:** n51,14177 e9,87278. ↑→.

4 ⌇free ⛽€1/100liter. **Location:** Rural, simple, isolated, quiet.
Surface: gravel. ◘ 01/03-31/10
Distance: ⌷400m ⛵400m ⍟400m bakery ⌇Waldpark 500m.
Remarks: At sports park.

Wanfried 11B1
In der Werraaue, Eschweger Straße. **GPS:** n51,18722 e10,16528. ↑→.

12 ⌇€ 5 ⛽€2/100liter ⚡Ch ✒(12x)€1/24h. ♨ **Location:** Rural,
simple, quiet. **Surface:** metalled.
◘ 01/01-31/12
Distance: ⌷50m ⍟50m ⌇on the spot ⌇on the spot.

Weilburg 10H2
Wohnmobilstation, Hainallee. **GPS:** n50,48385 e8,25848. ↑→.

80 ⌇€ 6 ⛽⚡included ✒€2 WC 10-17h. ♨ **Location:** Urban,
simple. **Surface:** metalled. ◘ 01/01-31/12 ◉ events
Distance: ⌇on the spot ⊗on the spot.
Remarks: Caution key € 15.

Weilmünster 10H2
In der Au, Am Froschgraben, L3054. **GPS:** n50,43345 e8,37343. ↑→.

12 ⌇voluntary contribution ⛽⚡Chfree ✒€2/16h.
Location: Rural, simple. **Surface:** metalled. ◘ 01/01-31/12
Distance: ⌇on the spot ⊗100m ⍟100m.

Weilrod 10H3
Taunus Mobilcamp, Hochtaunusstrasse. **GPS:** n50,31138 e8,42581. ↑.

30 ⌇€7 + € 1,50/pp, dog € 1 ⛽€1/80liter ⚡Ch ✒€0,50/
kWh WC ⌇included. **Location:** Rural, simple, isolated, noisy.
Surface: metalled. ◘ 01/01-31/12
Distance: ⌷500m ⍟6km.

Weilrod 10H3
Golfclub Taunus, Merzhäuser Straße 29. **GPS:** n50,32082 e8,42694. ↑.
2 ⌇free, only guest players. **Location:** Noisy. **Surface:** asphalted.
◘ 01/05-30/09
Distance: ⊗on the spot.

Wetzlar 10H2
An der Dill, Falkenstrasse. **GPS:** n50,55667 e8,49111. ↑→.

16 ⌇€ 8 ⛽⚡Ch ✒(16x)included. **Location:** Urban, simple.
Surface: gravel. ◘ 01/01-31/12
Distance: ⌷800m ⛵3km ⍟500m ⌇on the spot.

Wetzlar 10H2
Parkplatz Lahninsel, Lahninsel. **GPS:** n50,55488 e8,49756. ↑.

4 ⌇€ 8 (8-19h), overnight stay free ⛽⚡Ch ✒included WC. ⌇
Location: Urban. **Surface:** asphalted. ◘ 01/01-31/12
Distance: ⌷300m ⛵1,5km ⍟250m.

Wiesbaden 10H3
Reisemobilhafen Wiesbaden, Wörther-See-Strasse/Saarstrasse.
GPS: n50,05583 e8,20972. ↑.

+40 ⌇€ 7, overnight stay 21-9h € 3,50 ⛽€1/60liter ⚡Ch ✒(40x)
€0,50/kWh WC ⌇€1. ♨ **Location:** Urban, comfortable.
Surface: gravel. ◘ 01/01-31/12
Distance: ⌷150m ⊗800m ⍟800m ⌇150m.
Remarks: Can be reached without environmental: A643 exit Wiesbaden Dotzheim.

Willingen 10H1
Wohnmobilpark Willingen, Am Hagen.
GPS: n51,29050 e8,61278. ↑→.

55 ⌇€ 12, 2 pers.incl ⛽€1/10minutes ⚡Ch ✒€1/2kWh WC ⌇
€1,50/30minutes, at swimming pool ⌇. ♨ **Location:** Rural,
comfortable. **Surface:** metalled. ◘ 01/01-31/12 **Distance:** ⌷1km
⊗100m ⍟1km ⌇300m ⌇300m **Remarks:** Discount at subtropical
swimming pool and indoor skating rink.

Witzenhausen 9B3
Reisemobilplatz Diebesturm, Oberburgstrasse.
GPS: n51,34110 e9,85435. ↑→.

4 ⌇€ 2,50 ⛽€0,50/100liter ⚡Ch ✒(4x)€0,50. ⌇ **Location:** Urban,

DE

simple, central, noisy. **Surface:** gravel.
⬜ 01/01-31/12
Distance: 🚶500m ⊗on the spot 🗑500m.

| 🖼S | Witzenhausen 🏕🏖👥 | 9B3 |

Reisemobilplatz Josef-Pott-Platz, Laubenweg.
GPS: n51,34477 e9,85503.⬆

10 🛏€5 ⛽€1/100liter 🚰Ch🚿(10x)€0,50/6h.🛒 **Location:** Rural, simple, quiet. **Surface:** metalled.
⬜ 01/01-31/12
Distance: 🚶800m 🚲9km ⊗800m 🗑Aldi 100m 🚴on the spot 🚶on the spot.

| 🖼S | Witzenhausen 🏕🏖👥 | 9B3 |

Haus des Gastes, Ringkopfstrasse, Dohrenbach.
GPS: n51,31061 e9,83372.⬆⬆➡

8 🛏€4 ⛽🚰Chfree 🚿€2/24h WC. 🛒 **Location:** Rural, simple, isolated, quiet. **Surface:** metalled.
⬜ 01/01-31/12
Distance: 🚶on the spot ⊗on the spot 🗑300m 🚶on the spot.
Tourist information Witzenhausen:
🏖 Kesperkirmes. Village fair. 🗓 beginning Jul.

| 🖼S | Wolfhagen | 9A3 |

Freizeitanlange Bruchwiesen, Siemensstrasse.
GPS: n51,32944 e9,17083.⬆➡

35 🛏€3/24h ⛽€1/80liter 🚰Ch🚿(12x)€1/8h.🛒 **Location:** Rural, simple, isolated, quiet. **Surface:** grassy/gravel.
⬜ 01/01-31/12
Distance: 🚶on the spot ⊗500m 🗑200m 🚴on the spot 🚶on the spot.

| 🖼S | Ziegenhagen 🌿 | 9B3 |

Erlebnispark Ziegenhagen, Ziegenberg 3.
GPS: n51,37191 e9,76472.➡

30 🛏€5 ⛽€1 🚰Ch.🛒 **Location:** Simple, isolated, quiet.
⬜ 01/03-31/10
Distance: 🚶6km.

Thuringia

| 🖼S | Asbach/Sickenberg | 11B1 |

Grenzmuseum Schifflersgrund, Sickenberger Straße 1.
GPS: n51,28667 e10,01052.

---

6 🛏€3 ⛽🚰Ch🚿. **Surface:** gravel.

| 🖼S | Bad Berka 🦯 | 11D1 |

P2, Bleichstrasse. **GPS:** n50,89969 e11,28528.⬆➡

3 🛏free ⛽€1/3minutes 🚰€1 Ch 🚿(3x)€1/3h. **Surface:** asphalted.
⬜ 01/01-31/12
Distance: 🚶200m ⚓on the spot 🗑200m 🚶200m.
Remarks: 10/7/10 during inspection service out of order.

| 🖼S | Bad Colberg/Heldburg | 11C3 |

Rainbrünnlein. **GPS:** n50,27967 e10,73063.⬆

5 🛏free ⛽€1/60liter 🚰Ch🚿€1/8h. **Location:** Simple.
Surface: grasstiles. ⬜ 01/01-31/12
Distance: 🚶100m ⊗200m 🗑200m.
Remarks: At sports park.

| 🖼S | Bad Frankenhausen/Kyffhäuser 🦯 | 9D3 |

Bornstraße, B85. GPS: n51,35550 e11,10333.⬆➡

15 🛏€14 ⛽🚿included. **Location:** Rural. **Surface:** metalled.
⬜ 01/01-31/12
Distance: 🚶500m ⊗200m 🗑300m.
Remarks: Check in at pay-desk of the Therme.

| 🖼S | Bad Klosterlausnitz | 11E1 |

Kristall Sauna-Wellnesspark/Soletherme, Köstritzerstrasse 16.
GPS: n50,91190 e11,87242.⬆➡

15 🛏€10 + € 1,30/pp tourist tax ⛽€1/80liter 🚰Ch🚿€1/2kWh WC🛒. **Surface:** gravel. ⬜ 01/01-31/12
Distance: 🚶800m ⚓2,8km ⊗on the spot.

| 🖼S | Bad Langensalza 🦯 | 11C1 |

Friederiken Therme, Böhmenstrasse.
GPS: n51,11535 e10,64440.⬆➡

40 🛏€4, tourist tax € 1,20/pp ⛽€1 🚰Ch🚿(8x)€1/10h.

Surface: metalled. ⬜ 01/01-31/12
Distance: 🚶1km ⊗on the spot 🗑200m.
Remarks: Parking spa resort, pay at pay-desk of theTherme.

| 🖼S | Bad Liebenstein 🌿🏖 | 11C1 |

Villa Georg, Friedensallee 12. **GPS:** n50,81876 e10,35517.⬆

6 🛏€8 ⛽€1/100liter 🚰Ch🚿€2 WC. **Location:** Comfortable, quiet.
Surface: gravel. ⬜ 01/01-31/12 🗓 Tuesday
Distance: 🚶500m ⊗on the spot 🗑800m 🚶on the spot.

| 🖼S | Bad Lobenstein | 11E2 |

Ardesia Therme, Parkstrasse 8. **GPS:** n50,44981 e11,64294.⬆➡

11 🛏€ 2,50 + € 1/pp tourist tax, free with use of spa ⛽€2 🚰Ch🚿 0,50/kWh WC€3. **Surface:** metalled. ⬜ 01/01-31/12
Distance: 🚶200m ⊗on the spot 🗑200m ⛽on the spot.

| 🖼S | Bad Salzungen 🌿🏖🧁🦯 | 11C1 |

ErlebnisINSEL Flößrasen, Flössrasen 1. **GPS:** n50,81541 e10,23748.⬆

88 🛏€ 7,50 + € 1,50/pp tourist tax ⛽€1/60liter 🚿(88x)€ 1/2kWh 🔌against payment. **Location:** Urban, comfortable.
Surface: metalled. ⬜ 01/01-31/12
Distance: 🚶500m ⊗400m 🗑400m ⛽on the spot 🚶on the spot.

| 🖼S | Bad Tennstedt | 11C1 |

Am Swimmbad, Zweifeldersporthalle. **GPS:** n51,15994 e10,83952.
5 🛏free. **Location:** Urban, simple. **Surface:** metalled.
⬜ 01/01-31/12
Distance: 🚶500m ⊗500m 🗑500m.

| 🖼S | Breitungen | 11C2 |

Hotel Jagdhaus Seeblick, Seeblick. **GPS:** n50,74250 e10,32306.⬆➡

15 🛏€5 ⛽voluntary contribution 🚿€2/day WC.🛒 **Location:** Rural, simple, quiet. **Surface:** grassy. ⬜ 01/01-31/12 🗓 Mon
Distance: 🚶2km ⚓1km ⊗2km 🚶on the spot.

| 🖼S | Brotterode | 11C1 |

Inselbergbad, Am Bad 1. **GPS:** n50,82290 e10,45302.⬆

10 ⌂ € 5. ⚿ **Location:** Rural, simple. **Surface:** gravel.
⏱ 01/01-31/12
Distance: 🚲500m ⊗on the spot 🛒Edeka 250m 🚌50m.
Remarks: To be paid at swimming pool.

⌖S **Dorndorf** 11B1

Kultur- und Freizeitzentrum, Hardtstraße 3a.
GPS: n50,83453 e10,09087.⬆.

8 ⌂ € 4 ⛽€1/90liter ⬜€1 Ch ⚡€0,50/kWh. ⚿ **Location:** Urban, simple. **Surface:** grasstiles. ⏱ 01/01-31/12
Distance: 🚲1km ⊗50m.
Remarks: Next to Fahrradherberge.

⌖ **Eisenach** 🌿⚓ 11C1

Automobilmuseum, Heinrich-Erhardt-Platz.
GPS: n50,98122 e10,32342.⬆.

3 ⌂free. **Location:** Simple. **Surface:** metalled.
⏱ 01/01-31/12
Distance: 🚲1km ⊗400m 🛒100m.

⌖ **Eisenach** 🌿⚓ 11C1

Burg Wartburg, Auf der Wartburg. **GPS:** n50,96775 e10,30989.⬆.

5 ⌂ € 5. ⚿ **Location:** Urban. **Surface:** metalled. ⏱ 01/01-31/12
Distance: 🚲on the spot.
Remarks: Nearby castle Wartburg.

⌖ **Eisenach** 🌿⚓ 11C1

Karl Marxstrasse. **GPS:** n50,97861 e10,32083.⬆.

3 ⌂9-17h max. € 6, free overnight stay. **Surface:** gravel.
⏱ 01/01-31/12
Distance: 🚲500m ⊗100m 🛒100m.

⌖S **Eisenach** 🌿⚓ 11C1

Wohnmobile A. Waldhelm, Ringstrasse 27.
GPS: n51,00194 e10,32667.⬆.

20 ⌂ € 10 ⛽Chincluded ⚡€3/day WC ⬜€0,50. ⚿
Location: Urban, simple. **Surface:** grasstiles.
⏱ 01/01-31/12
Distance: 🚲1km ⊗1km 🛒1km 🚌Shuttle bus.
Remarks: Motorhome dealer, accessory shop, check in on arrival, bread-service.

Eisfeld 11D2

Festplatz, Am Volkshaus. **GPS:** n50,42615 e10,90992.➡.

5 ⌂free. **Location:** Simple. **Surface:** grasstiles. ⏱ 01/01-31/12
⦿ Whitsuntide
Distance: 🚲200m ⊗200m 🛒300m 🚶on the spot.

⌖S **Eisfeld** 11D2

Waldhotel Hubertus, Coburgerstrasse 501.
GPS: n50,39680 e10,92269.⬆.

20 ⌂free, use of a meal desired ⛽€2 ⚡€2. **Location:** Rural, simple.
Surface: asphalted/grassy. ⏱ 01/01-31/12
Distance: 🚲3km ⊗on the spot 🛒2km 🚌on the spot.

⌖S **Erfurt** 🌿⚓🍞 11D1

Wohnmobilpark Trautmann, Rottenbacherweg 11, Melchendorf.
GPS: n50,95404 e11,06654.
15 ⌂ € 7,50 ⛽€1,50/150liter ⬜€1,50 Ch€1,50 ⚡(15x)€1,50/5kWh,16Amp WC ⬜€1,50 ⬛€3,50/1,50 📶included.
Surface: gravel. ⏱ 01/01-31/12
Distance: 🚲on the spot 🚴1,2km 🛒300m ⊗200m 🚌300m.
Remarks: Discount on access sauna/wellness.

⌖S **Erfurt** 🌿⚓🍞 11D1

P&R, Am Urbicher Kreuz. **GPS:** n50,94992 e11,09456.➡.

15 ⌂free ⛽⬜Ch. **Surface:** asphalted.
⏱ 01/01-31/12
Distance: 🚲7km 🛒Total-shop 🚌Tram till 24am.
Remarks: Service at petrol station.

⌖ **Erfurt** 🌿⚓🍞 11D1

Am kleinen Ring, Juri-Gagarin-Ring. **GPS:** n50,98111 e11,03472.⬆.

4 ⌂free. **Surface:** asphalted. ⏱ 01/01-31/12
Distance: 🚲Old city centre 1km ⊗500m 🛒500m.
Remarks: Max. 48h.

⌖ **Erfurt** 🌿⚓🍞 11D1

Eichenstrasse. **GPS:** n50,97327 e11,02737.⬆➡.

4 ⌂ € 12. 🅿 **Surface:** asphalted. ⏱ 01/01-31/12
Distance: 🚲200m ⊗200m 🛒300m 🚌on the spot.
Remarks: Max. 48h.

⌖ **Erfurt** 🌿⚓🍞 11D1

P&R Parkplatz Messe, Gothaerstrasse. **GPS:** n50,95818 e10,98296.⬆.

4 ⌂free. **Surface:** asphalted. ⏱ 01/01-31/12
Distance: 🚲centre 4km 🚌Bus <23.00h.
Remarks: Parking exhibition ground.

⌖ **Erfurt** 🌿⚓🍞 11D1

P&R Parkplatz Thüringerhalle, Werner-Seelenbinderstrasse.
GPS: n50,95771 e11,03605.⬆.

7 ⌂free. **Surface:** gravel. ⏱ 01/01-31/12
Distance: 🚲2,6km 🚌Tram till 23am.
Remarks: Nearby B4, south edge of the city.

Tourist information Erfurt:
ℹ Erfurt-Card. Card gives for free entrance on among other things public transport and city museums, and discount on a lot of curiosities, guided tours, swimming pools, theater, souvenirs. Ⓣ € 14,90.

⚓ Stadtführung, Tourist Information, Benediktsplatz 1. Guided tour around the historic city center. ⬛ 01/04-31/12 Mo-Fri 13h, Sa-Su 11h, 13h, 01/01-31/03 Sa-Su 11h, 13h. 🎫 € 5,50.

Gotha — 11C1
Parkallee 1. GPS: n50,94402 e10,70948. ⬆.
3 🅿 free. **Location:** Urban, simple. **Surface:** metalled.
Distance: 🚶800m ⊗800m.

Heiligenstadt — 9B3
Stadthalle, Aegidienstrasse 20. GPS: n51,37407 e10,13715. ⬆.

6 🅿 free 🚰€0,50/time 🚽Ch 🔌€1/3kWh WC.
Location: Comfortable. **Surface:** asphalted. ⬛ 01/01-31/12
Distance: 🚶150m ⊗200m.
Remarks: At swimming pool, in front of town hall.
Tourist information Heiligenstadt:
ℹ City of churches, health resort.
Ⓜ Literaturmuseum Theodor Storm. Museum of important German writer. ⬛ Tue-Fri 9-12h, 13-16h, Sa-Su 14-16h.

Ichtershausen — 11D1
Autohof, Thöreyerstrasse. GPS: n50,88824 e10,93478. ⬆.

20 🅿 € 6,50/24h, first hour free 🚰€0,50 🚽Ch€0,50 WC.
Location: Highway. **Surface:** asphalted. ⬛ 01/01-31/12
Distance: 🚶4km ⊗on the spot 🔋Esso-shop.

Ichtershausen — 11D1
Freizeitfahrzeuge Mobilease, Feldstrasse 1.
GPS: n50,86907 e10,96563. ⬆.

5 🅿 € 7,50 🚰🚽Ch 🔌(4x)included WC during opening hours.
Surface: gravel. ⬛ 01/01-31/12
Distance: 🚶3km ⊗500m 🔋bakery 500m.

Ilfeld — 9C3
Gasthof Brauner Hirsch, Dorfstrasse 42, Sophienhof.
GPS: n51,63467 e10,79223. ⬆.

15 🅿 € 5 🚰🚽Ch 🔌(3x)€0,35/kWh WC 🚿€2 **Location:** Rural.
Surface: metalled. ⬛ 01/01-31/12
Distance: ⊗on the spot 🚌3km ⚡on the spot ⚓on the spot.

Ilmenau — 11D2
Festhalle, Naumannstraße. GPS: n50,68139 e10,90472. ⬆.

4 🅿 free 🚰€2/80liter 🚽Ch. **Surface:** asphalted. ⬛ 01/01-31/12
Distance: 🚶1km ⊗100m 🔋500m.
Remarks: Max. 24h.

Kühndorf — 11C2
Flugschule Dolmar, Am Flugplatz 1. GPS: n50,61198 e10,47079. ➡.

20 🅿 € 6 🚰€1 🚽Ch€1,50/time 🔌€2/day WC 🚽€1,50/time. 🚿
Location: Rural, isolated. **Surface:** grassy/gravel.
⬛ 01/01-31/12
Distance: 🚶2km ⊗on the spot ⚓on the spot.
Remarks: Bread-service, parking behind the hangar.

Lauscha ❄ — 11D2
Parkplatz Obermühle. GPS: n50,48026 e11,16795. ⬆.

10 🅿 free. **Location:** Simple. **Surface:** asphalted. ⬛ 01/01-31/12
Distance: 🚶300m ⊗100m 🔋1km ⚓on the spot ⚡on the spot.

Lauscha ❄ — 11D2
Sommerrodelbahn, Lauschaer Straße, Ernstthal.
GPS: n50,48726 e11,17243. ⬆.

10 🅿 free. **Location:** Simple. **Surface:** asphalted. ⬛ 01/01-31/12
Distance: 🚶650m 🚌50m ⚡50m.

Linda — 11E2
Knappmühle, Ortsstraße. GPS: n50,68473 e11,78324. ⬆.

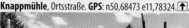

10 🅿 € 6 🚰🚽Ch 🔌(6x)€1/kWh. **Surface:** grassy/gravel.
⬛ 01/03-31/10
Distance: 🚶300m 🚌5km ⊗3km 🔋5km.

Meiningen — 11C2
Rohrer Stirn, Frankental. GPS: n50,56976 e10,43477. ⬆.

10 🅿 free 🔌(6x)€0,50/kWh. **Location:** Urban, simple, quiet.
Surface: asphalted. ⬛ 01/01-31/12
Distance: 🚶2km.
Remarks: Parking at swimming pool.

Meiningen — 11C2
Grossmutterwiesen, Werrastrasse. GPS: n50,56172 e10,41266. ⬆➡.

5 🅿 free. **Location:** Simple. **Surface:** concrete. ⬛ 01/01-31/12
Distance: 🚶on the spot ⊗200m 🔋100m.
Remarks: Service possible at Kläranlage.

Meiningen — 11C2
Volkshausplatz, Landsbergerstrasse. GPS: n50,57427 e10,41369. ⬆➡.

5 🅿 free. **Location:** Urban, simple. **Surface:** metalled.
⬛ 01/01-31/12
Distance: 🚶200m ⚓on the spot ⊗200m 🔋200m.
Remarks: Service possible at Kläranlage.

Mihla — 11C1
Graues Schloss, Thomas-Müntzer-Straße 4.
GPS: n51,07854 e10,33166. ⬆➡.

15 🅿 € 8, guests free. **Location:** Rural, simple, quiet.
Surface: unpaved. ⬛ 01/01-31/12 ⬤ Whitsuntide
Distance: 🚶on the spot 🎣fishing permit obligatory ⊗on the spot
🔋500 m 🚲on the spot ⚓on the spot.

Neustadt/Orla — 11E1
Gaststätte & Pension Heinrichs-Ruhe, Heinrichsruhe 1, Rodaer Strasse. GPS: n50,75545 e11,75595. ⬆.

10 🅿 guests free 🔌(6x)€0,50/kWh. **Surface:** grassy/gravel.
⬛ 01/01-31/12 ⬤ Restaurant: Mo
Distance: 🚶2,6km ⊗12,2km ⊗on the spot 🔋2,6km.

Nimritz 11E2

Wohnmobilstellplatz Nimritz, Ortsstrasse 29.
GPS: n50,70079 e11,64858.⬆➡.

10 ⬛voluntary contribution ⛽€0,50 ⬛Ch ⚡(7x)€0,50/kWh.
Surface: grasstiles.
Distance: 🚶300m ⊗300m.

Nordhausen 9C3

Am Badehaus, Grimmelallee 40. **GPS:** n51,50450 e10,78508.⬆➡.

2 ⬛€ 5, € 10 service and swimming pool incl ⛽€2 ⬛€1 Ch€1 ⚡€1
⬛3. **Location:** Simple. **Surface:** metalled.
Distance: 🚶800m ⊗500m 🍺300m.

Nordhausen 9C3

Am Kuhberg, Parkallee. **GPS:** n51,51502 e10,78492.⬆.

10 ⬛free. **Location:** Rural, isolated. **Surface:** asphalted.
◻ 01/01-31/12
Distance: 🚶2km ⊗on the spot 🍺500m.

Oberhof 11C2

Wohnmobilstellplatz Oberhof, Jahnstrasse 7.
GPS: n50,70278 e10,72694.⬆➡.

+60 ⬛€ 10 + € 2/pp tourist tax ⛽€1/80liter ⬛Ch ⚡(50x)€
0,50/kWh. **Location:** Urban, simple. **Surface:** asphalted.
◻ 01/01-31/12
Distance: 🚶400m ⊗200m 🍺500m ⛵on the spot.
Remarks: Bread-service.

Tourist information Oberhof:
👁 Rennsteiggarten Oberhof. Botanical garden. ◻ 01/05-30/09 9-18,
01/10-31/10 9-17h.
Ⓜ Thüringer Wintersportausstellung, Crawinkler strasse 1 / Oberer
Hof. Winter sport museum. ◻ 10-13h, 14-17h.
🅰 Rennsteig Thermen. Swimming pool complex.
◻ daily 10-22h.

Reichenbach 11E1

Holzland Freizeitcenter, Rodaer Landstrasse.
GPS: n50,86118 e11,87607.⬆.

---

50 ⬛€ 8, guests free ⛽€1 ⬛Ch ⚡(15x)€2/day WC ⬛€2/pp.
Surface: concrete. ◻ 01/01-31/12
Distance: 🚶2km ⊗on the spot 🍞bakery 500m.

Rudolstadt 11D2

Freizeit- und Erlebnisbad Saalemaxx, Hugo-Trinckler-Straße 6.
GPS: n50,70635 e11,31659.

9 ⬛€ 7/24h ⛽€1/80liter ⬛Ch ⚡€0,50/kWh. **Surface:** gravel.
◻ 01/01-31/12
Distance: 🚶2km 🚗100m.
Remarks: Discount at swimming pool.

Saalfeld 11D2

Reschwitzerstrasse, B281. **GPS:** n50,63720 e11,36751.⬆➡.

10 ⬛free. **Surface:** gravel. ◻ 01/01-31/12
Distance: 🚶2,8km.
Remarks: Parking at swimming pool.

Saalfeld 11D2

Saalfelder Feengrotten, Feengrottenweg 2.
GPS: n50,63468 e11,33982.⬆➡.

30 ⬛free ⛽€3/5minutes ⬛€3 Ch ⚡(6x)€0,50/kWh WC ⬛.
Surface: grassy. ◻ 01/01-31/12
Distance: 🚶2,3km ⊗on the spot 🍞bakery 500m 🚌500m.

Schleiz 11E2

Spitzbergs Zollhaus, Burgkerstrasse 25.
GPS: n50,55507 e11,73438.⬆➡.

5 ⬛€ 5, free with a meal ⛽€⬛Ch ⚡(7x)€2/24h.
Surface: gravel/metalled.
◻ 01/01-31/12 ◉ Mo
Distance: 🚶7km ✈5,4km ⊗on the spot 🍺7km.

Schleiz 11E2

HEM-Großtankstelle, Saalburgerstrasse.
GPS: n50,55004 e11,78788.⬆.

8 ⬛€ 2 ⛽€1 ⬛€1 ChWC. **Location:** Highway. **Surface:** asphalted.
◻ 01/01-31/12
Distance: 🚶5km ⊗on the spot 🍺shop.
Remarks: Industrial area, max. 24h.

Schmiedefeld 11C2

Sportplatz, Sportplatzstraße. **GPS:** n50,60324 e10,81491.⬆.

20 ⬛€ 3 + € 1/pp tourist tax. **Location:** Rural, simple, quiet.
Surface: grasstiles/metalled. ◻ 01/01-31/12
Distance: 🚶500m 🚗400m ⊗on the spot 🚲on the spot.
Remarks: Pay at tourist office or Gasthaus Thüringer Hof.

Sitzendorf 11D2

Sitzendorfer Porzellanmanufaktur, Hauptstrasse 26.
GPS: n50,63174 e11,16788.⬆.

5 ⬛free. **Surface:** asphalted. ◻ 01/01-31/12
Distance: 🚶on the spot ⊗200m 🍺200m.

Sondershausen 9C3

P7 zur Windleite, Hospitalstrasse. **GPS:** n51,37824 e10,86234.⬆➡.

5 ⬛free ⛽€1 ⬛Ch ⚡(4x)€1/2h. **Surface:** metalled.
◻ 01/01-31/12
Distance: 🚶2,5km ⊗500m 🍺100m.

Sondershausen 9C3

Freizeitpark Possen, Possen 1. **GPS:** n51,33800 e10,86265.

10 ⬛€ 4/stay. **Surface:** metalled. ◻ 01/01-31/12
Distance: 🚶5km ⊗on the spot.

DE

Stadtlengsfeld 11B2

Am Schwimmbad, Eisenacher Straße. **GPS**: n50,79065 e10,11373.

6 free €1/80liter against payment. **Location:** Rural, simple.
Surface: asphalted. 01/01-31/12
Distance: 1,5km.

Steinheid 11D2

Am Rennsteig, Eisfelder Straße, Limbach.
GPS: n50,47568 e11,06937.

4 free. **Location:** Rural, simple, noisy. **Surface:** gravel.
01/01-31/12
Distance: 150m 10km on the spot.

Steinheid 11D2

Thüringer Baumschmuck, Neuhäuser Strasse 8-10.
GPS: n50,47302 e11,08672.

8 € 5, free for clients €2/90liter included.
Location: Simple. **Surface:** unpaved. 01/01-31/12
Distance: 3km, bakery 50m on the spot on the spot on the spot.
Remarks: At Christmas Balls manufacturer.

Tabarz 11C1

Karl-Kornhaß-Straße. **GPS**: n50,87782 e10,52038.

8 free, tourist tax € 1,50/pp. **Location:** Rural, simple, quiet.
Surface: metalled. 01/01-31/12
Distance: 200m Rewe 400m.
Remarks: To be paid at TABBS sports centre.

Tambach-Dietharz 11C1

Festplatz, Burgstallstraße. **GPS**: n50,78902 e10,60897.

4 free, tourist tax € 1/pp Ch. service €6.
Location: Urban, simple. **Surface:** gravel. 01/01-31/12

Distance: on the spot on the spot.
Remarks: Key service at town hall.

Tambach-Dietharz 11C1

Freigelande Lohmühle, Lohmühle 1-5. **GPS**: n50,81056 e10,62778.

30 € 6 + € 4/pp Ch. €2 WC €1 €1.
Location: Rural, simple, quiet. **Surface:** grassy.
01/02 -31/12 Mon
Distance: on the spot 3km on the spot
on the spot.
Remarks: Check in on arrival, barefoot park, museum.

Themar 11C2

Am Hexenturm, Mauerstrasse. **GPS**: n50,50512 e10,61194.

5 free €1/50liter Ch. €1/kWh. **Location:** Urban, simple,
quiet. **Surface:** grasstiles. 01/01-31/12
Distance: 100m 300m 400m on the spot on the spot.
Remarks: Along the Werra river, 01/11-31/03 water disconnected.

Tiefenort 11B1

Freizeitanlage Heerstatt, Auf der Heerstatt.
GPS: n50,83444 e10,16306.

6 free €2/day. **Location:** Rural, simple. **Surface:** concrete.
01/03-31/10
Distance: on the spot 50m bakery 900m on the spot.
Remarks: On island in the Werra river.

Treffurt 11C1

Unter den Linden. **GPS**: n51,13398 e10,23659.

20 free €0,50/80liter Ch. (8x)€0,50/kWh.
Location: Rural, simple, quiet. **Surface:** grasstiles/grassy.
01/01-31/12 15/07-31/07
Distance: 300m on the spot 50m 500m on the spot
on the spot.
Remarks: Along river, water closed during wintertime.

Tourist information Treffurt:
Small town with half-timbered houses and medival castle
Normannstein.

Vacha 11B1

Frankfurter Strasse. **GPS**: n50,81856 e10,01327.
5 free. **Location:** Simple.
Distance: 1km 1km.
Remarks: At swimming pool.

Weimar 11D1

Hermann Brill-Platz. **GPS**: n50,98501 e11,31701.

20 €10/24h €1 Ch. (6x)€1/6h. **Surface:** metalled.
01/01-31/12
Distance: Weimar centre 1,2km on the spot 500m.

Zella-Mehlis 11C2

Toschis Station, An der Quelle 5. **GPS**: n50,64375 e10,68436.

10 € 5 Ch. (20x). **Location:** Simple, central.
Surface: grassy/gravel. 01/01-31/12
Distance: on the spot 300m.
Remarks: Check in at reception.

Zeulenroda 11E2

Badewelt Waikiki, Am Birkenwege 1. **GPS**: n50,66543 e11,99355.

6 €10 Ch. included, water and electricity € 10/day.
Surface: metalled. 01/01-31/12

Baden Württemberg

Aalen 16C3

Hirschbach, Hirschbachstrasse 68. **GPS**: n48,84524 e10,10712.

10 free €1/80liter Ch. **Location:** Rural. **Surface:** asphalted.
01/01-31/12
Distance: 800m 100m 200m.
Remarks: At swimming pool, max. 3 days.

Aalen 16C3

Limes-Thermen, P1, Osterbucher Steige.
GPS: n48,82047 e10,07918.

12 free. **Location:** Rural. **Surface:** grasstiles. 01/01-31/12
Distance: 100m.

⬛S | Achern ♨🧁 | 15H3

Wohnmobilstellplatz Achern, Kapellenstrasse/Badstrasse.
GPS: n48,62436 e8,07359.⬆.

12 🛏€ 4 ⛽€1/100liter 🔲Ch.🚿(12x)€1/16h.🚮
Location: Urban, simple, quiet. **Surface**: gravel/metalled.
🕒 01/01-31/12
Distance: 🚶500m 🚲4,8km 🍴650m 🚂 on the spot 🚶 on the spot.

©S | Albstadt 🌿🌳❄ | 19A1

Sonnencamping, Beibruck 54. **GPS**: n48,21438 e8,97879.⬆.
16 🛏€ 8 🚿€0,57/kWh 🔲€2 ⬛. **Surface**: grassy.
🕒 01/01-31/12

🍴 | Allensbach | 19A2

Landgasthaus Mindelsee, Gemeinmärk 7.
GPS: n47,74279 e9,04411.⬆.

15 🛏€ 8, guests free. **Surface**: metalled. 🕒 01/01-31/12 🔘 Tue
Distance: 🚶5km ⊗ on the spot.
Remarks: Max. 1 night, max 3,5t.

🍴S | Amtzell | 19B2

Wohnmobilanlage Büchelweisen, Haus 3.
GPS: n47,70871 e9,76684.⬆➡.

25 🛏€ 9 ⛽🔲Ch.🚿(24x)€0,50/kWh 🔲€3/day.
Surface: grasstiles. 🕒 01/01-31/12
Distance: 🚶1,5km 🏊1km 🚣1km ⊗ on the spot 🚂1,5km.
Remarks: Bread-service.

⬛ | Aspach 🌳 | 16B2

Wanderparkplatz Fautenhau, Im Fautenhau, Hohrot.
GPS: n48,97823 e9,39483.⬆.

5 🛏free. **Location**: Rural. **Surface**: metalled. 🕒 01/01-31/12
Remarks: Max. 1 night, parking P0.

⬛ | Aspach 🌳 | 16B2

Wanderparkplatz Heiligental, Heiligentalstrasse, Rietenau.
GPS: n48,99158 e9,40519.⬆.

4 🛏free ⛽€1/90liter 🔲Ch. **Location**: Rural, simple.
Surface: gravel. 🕒 01/01-31/12

5 🛏free. **Location**: Rural, quiet. **Surface**: asphalted/grassy.
🕒 01/01-31/12 🚶 on the spot.
Remarks: Max. 1 night.

⬛ | Aspach 🌳 | 16B2

Wanderparkplatz Kelter, Kelterstrasse, Allmersbach.
GPS: n48,99543 e9,39006.⬆.

5 🛏free. **Location**: Rural, isolated. **Surface**: asphalted.
🕒 01/01-31/12 🚶 on the spot.
Remarks: Max. 1 night.

⬛ | Aspach 🌳 | 16B2

Wanderparkplatz Lapidarium, Ortsstrasse, Kleinaspach.
GPS: n48,99738 e9,35711.⬆.

2 🛏free. **Location**: Simple. 🕒 01/01-31/12
Distance: 🚶 on the spot ⊗1km 🚂1,5km 🚶 on the spot.
Remarks: Max. 1 night.

⬆ | Aulendorf | 19B1

Schwaben-Therme, Ebisweilerstrasse 5. **GPS**: n47,95797 e9,63728.➡.

20 (P3) 🛏free. **Location**: Rural. **Surface**: metalled.
🕒 01/01-31/12
Distance: 🚶500m ⊗ on the spot 🚂500m.
Remarks: Parking swimming pool, max. 2 nights.

⬛S | Aulendorf | 19B1

Carthago City, Carthago ring 1. **GPS**: n47,93156 e9,65429.
6 🛏free ⛽€0,50 🔲Ch.🚿€0,50/kWh. **Surface**: metalled.
🕒 01/01-31/12
Distance: 🚶2,5km.
Remarks: At motohome manufacturer.

⬛S | Backnang 🌳 | 16B2

Gartenstrasse. **GPS**: n48,95041 e9,45281.⬆.

⬛S | Bad Bellingen ♨ | 18G2

Balinea Thermen, Badstrasse 14. **GPS**: n47,72963 e7,55233.⬆.

31 🛏€ 10 + € 1,45-2,25 tourist tax ⛽€1/80liter 🔲Ch.🚿
(24x)€1/kWh 🔲€1,50. 🚽 **Location**: Urban, noisy.
Surface: asphalted/metalled. 🕒 01/01-31/12
Distance: 🚶500m 🚲5,5km ⊗ on the spot 🚂 on the spot.

⬛S | Bad Buchau | 19B1

Adelindis Therme, Am Kurpark. **GPS**: n48,06865 e9,60653.⬆.

21 🛏€ 9,50 XL-pitch € 11 ⛽€1/80liter 🔲Ch.🚿€0,50/kWh 🔲€1.🚮
🚽 **Surface**: metalled. 🕒 01/01-31/12
Distance: 🚶500m.

⬛S | Bad Buchau | 19B1

Seegasse. **GPS**: n48,06801 e9,60977.

17 🛏€ 9,50 ⛽€1/80liter 🔲Ch.🚿(17x)€0,50/kWh.🚮
Surface: metalled. 🕒 01/01-31/12
Distance: 🚶500m.
Remarks: Adelindis Therme 300m.

⬛S | Bad Buchau | 19B1

Federseemuseum, Wellerstraße. **GPS**: n48,07051 e9,60949.➡.

12 🛏€ 9 🚿(12x)€0,50/kWh 🔲.🚮 **Location**: Rural.
Surface: asphalted. 🕒 01/01-31/12
Distance: 🚶800m.
Remarks: Adelindis Therme 500m.

⬛ | Bad Buchau | 19B1

Am Freibad, Friedhofstrasse. **GPS**: n48,06292 e9,61714.⬆.

10 🛏€ 9. **Surface**: asphalted. 🕒 01/01-31/12

DE

Distance: ⬆️700m.

🅢 Bad Ditzenbach 16B3

Vinzenz Therme, Badstraße 20. **GPS**: n48,59003 e9,70553.⬆️

10 ⬛€ 5, winter € 6 🚰⬛Ch⬛🚿 **Surface:** asphalted.
⭕ 01/01-31/12

🅢 Bad Dürrheim 19A1

Reisemobilhafen Bad Dürrheim, Huberstraße 34/2.
GPS: n48,01204 e8,53506.⬆️➡️

300 ⬛€ 9 🚰€1/100liter ⬛Ch🚿€2,50/night WC€2⬛.
Location: Rural, comfortable. **Surface:** gravel. ⭕ 01/01-31/12
Distance: ⊗on the spot.
Remarks: Pay at reception, bread-service, special health arrangement possible.

🅢 Bad Herrenalb 15H3

Therme Siebentäler, Schweizer Wiese. **GPS**: n48,80334 e8,44067.⬆️

10 ⬛€ 4,10 + € 2,50/pp 🚰€1⬛€1 Ch€1⬛ (4x)€1.
Location: Rural, simple. **Surface:** asphalted. ⭕ 01/01-31/12
Distance: ⬆️500m ⊗100m 🍺200m 🚌200m on the spot 🚶on the spot.
Remarks: Max. 2 nights, discount on access terme.

Tourist information Bad Herrenalb:
🖋 Quellenerlebnispfad, Kurpark Herrenalb. Hiking trails past 60 fountains.

🅢 Bad Krozingen 18G2

Wohnmobilstellplatz Vita Classica Bad Krozingen

■ **Reservations possible**
■ **Rural location**
■ **Open all year**

www.bad-krozingen.info
tourist.info@bad-krozingen.info

Wohnmobilstellplatz Vita Classica, Thürachstraße.
GPS: n47,91763 e7,68821.⬆️➡️
80 ⬛⬛Ch🚿€3,50/day,16Amp WC⬛€3⬛ included.
Location: Rural, comfortable.
Surface: asphalted/metalled.
⭕ 01/01-31/12

Distance: ⬆️600m 🚲3km ⊗50m 🍺600m 🛒800m 🚌on the spot 🚴on the spot 🚶on the spot.
Remarks: Bread-service, trailer € 2,50/night, bike and e-bike rental.

🅒🅢 Bad Liebenzell 16A3

Campingpark Bad Liebenzell, Pforzheimer strasse 34.
GPS: n48,77850 e8,73120.⬆️

16 ⬛€ 8, tourist tax € 2/pp 🚰⬛Ch🚿(16x)WC⬛included ⬛€3 📶
📷🍴 **Location:** Rural, simple, noisy. **Surface:** metalled/sand.
⭕ 01/01-31/12
Distance: ⬆️on the spot 🚲17km ⊗500m 🍺100m 🚌on the spot 🚴on the spot 🚶on the spot.

🅢 Bad Mergentheim 16B1

Festplatz beim Freibad, Erlenbachweg.
GPS: n49,49194 e9,79167.⬆️➡️

20 ⬛€ 5 🚰€1/80liter ⬛Chfree 🚿(16x)€1/8h. **Location:** Rural, simple. **Surface:** gravel. ⭕ 01/01-31/12
Distance: ⬆️Old city centre 1km ⊗200m 🛒Lidl 800m 🚌100m.
Remarks: Max. 3 nights, check in at restaurant tennispark.

🅢 Bad Niedernau 16A3

Wohnmobilparkplatz Bad Niedernau, Blaue Brücke.
GPS: n48,45931 e8,89959.⬆️➡️

5 ⬛free. **Location:** Rural, simple. **Surface:** gravel.
⭕ 01/01-31/12
Distance: ⬆️500m 🚲3km 🚶on the spot.
Remarks: Along the Neckar river, max. 3 nights.

🅢 Bad Rappenau 16A2

Weinbrennerstrasse. **GPS**: n49,23517 e9,11396.⬆️➡️

30 ⬛€ 3/pp, child € 2 🚰€1/80liter ⬛Ch🚿(16x)€1/4h.
Location: Comfortable. **Surface:** metalled. ⭕ 01/01-31/12
Distance: ⬆️1km ⊗50m 🍺1km.
Remarks: Therme 400m.

🅢 Bad Rappenau 16A2

Autohof Bad Rappenau, A6, Wilhelm-Hauff-Straße 43, Fürfeld.
GPS: n49,21043 e9,06927.⬆️
15 ⬛€ 10, free for clients 🚰⬛Ch⬛. **Location:** Highway, simple.
Surface: metalled. ⭕ 01/01-31/12
Distance: 🚲300m ⊗on the spot 🍺on the spot.
Remarks: Breakfest-service.

🅢 Bad Säckingen 18H2

Reisemobilplatz Am Rheinufer, Ausstrasse.
GPS: n47,54903 e7,94765.⬆️➡️

30 ⬛€ 10/24h 🚰€0,50/100liter ⬛€0,20 Ch🚿(39x) WC⬛.
Location: Urban, comfortable, quiet. **Surface:** gravel.
⭕ 01/01-31/12 ⬤ beginning Mar, end Oct
Distance: ⬆️300m 🚲6km ⊗50m 🚌on the spot 🚴on the spot.
Remarks: Several offers, i.e. free public transport.

Tourist information Bad Säckingen:
🖋 Nachtwächterführungen. Evening tour guided by night watch in historical cloths and with lantern. Information and booking: Kurverwaltung. 🎫 € 2.

🅢 Bad Saulgau 19B1

GolfPark Bad Saulgau, Koppelweg 103. **GPS**: n47,97928 e9,48623.⬆️

30 ⬛€ 10, golfers free 🚰€1/100liter ⬛Ch🚿€1/6h 🚴📷
Location: Rural, quiet. **Surface:** metalled. ⭕ 01/03-31/10
Distance: ⬆️4km ⊗on the spot 🍺4km.

🅢 Bad Saulgau 19B1

Wohnmobilstellplatz Sonnenhof-Therme, Am Schönen Moos.
GPS: n48,01703 e9,48838.⬆️

53 ⬛€ 11 + € 1,50/pp tourist tax 🚰stay ⬛Ch🚿(69x)included ⬛.
🍴 **Location:** Rural. **Surface:** metalled.
⭕ 01/01-31/12
Distance: ⬆️on the spot ⊗on the spot 🍺on the spot.
Remarks: Bread-service, discount on access terme.

🅢 Bad Schönborn 16A2

Reisemobilhafen WellMobilPark, Kraichgaustraße 16.
GPS: n49,21839 e8,67144.⬆️➡️

86 ⬛€ 9, >10m € 13 🚰€1/100liter ⬛Ch🚿(112x)€0,50/kWh
⬛1,50 📶. **Location:** Rural, luxurious. **Surface:** metalled.
⭕ 01/01-31/12
Distance: ⬆️500m ⊗on the spot 🍺1km 🚌200m.
Remarks: Bread-service, swimming pool available.

🅢 Bad Schussenried 19B1

Am Zellersee, Zellerseeweg. **GPS**: n48,00160 e9,64724.⬆️

DE

12 🛏 € 5 + € 1,20/pp tourist tax 🚰🗑Ch 🔧 Surface: asphalted.
⏱ 01/01-31/12
Distance: 900m on the spot on the spot.

| 🅿️ S | Bad Schussenried | 19B1 |

Bierkrugmuseum, Wilhelm Schussenstrasse 12.
GPS: n48,00325 e9,65902.

30 🛏 free 🚰🗑Ch 🔧€5, reduction for guests WC. **Location:** Quiet.
Surface: metalled. ⏱ 01/01-31/12
Distance: on the spot 150m 250m.
Remarks: Brewery and brewery museum.

Tourist information Bad Schussenried:
Ⓜ Kloster Schussenried. History of the monastry. ⏱ Easter-Oct 13.30-17.30h.

| Bad Teinach | 16A3 |

Zavelsteiner strasse. **GPS:** n48,68890 e8,69440.

20 🛏 free. **Location:** Rural, simple. **Surface:** asphalted.
⏱ 01/01-31/12
Distance: 50m 100m 100m on the spot on the spot
on the spot.
Remarks: Parking swimming pool, max. 24h.

| 🅿️ S | Bad Urach | 16B3 |

Wohnmobilstellplatz Bad Urach, Bäderstraße.
GPS: n48,50060 e9,37713.

26 🛏 € 8 🚰€0,50/60liter 🗑€0,50 Ch 🔧 included.
Location: Urban, simple. **Surface:** asphalted. ⏱ 01/01-31/12
Distance: on the spot 5km 200m 800m 200m 10km
10km.

| 🅿️ S | Bad Waldsee | 19B1 |

Bauernhof Lott, Mattenhaus 4. **GPS:** n47,95113 e9,75838.

---

10 🛏 € 10, 2 pers.incl, tourist tax € 2/pp 🚰🗑Ch 🔧(10x)€0,50/kWh
WC 🗑€4. ⏱ 01/03-30/11
Distance: 3,5km 3km 3km 200m 3km.
Remarks: Bread-service.

| 🅿️ S | Bad Waldsee | 19B1 |

Waldsee-Therme, Unterurbacher weg. **GPS:** n47,91441 e9,76047.

40 🛏 € 5 + € 2/pp tourist tax 🚰€1 🗑€1 Ch 🔧€0,50/kWh.
Surface: metalled. ⏱ 01/01-31/12
Distance: 1km 1km 1km 500m 1km 500m.
Remarks: Bread-service.

| 🅿️ S | Bad Wildbad | 15H3 |

Kernerstrasse. **GPS:** n48,74132 e8,54740.

16 🛏 € 5, tourist tax € 2,90/pp 🚰€1/60liter Ch 🔧(16x)€2/8h.
Location: Rural, simple, noisy. **Surface:** asphalted.
⏱ 01/01-31/12
Distance: 500m 500m 300m on the spot on the spot
on the spot.
Remarks: Max. 3 days.

| 🅿️ S | Bad Wimpfen | 16A2 |

Am alter Bahnhof, Carl Ulrichstrasse 1. **GPS:** n49,22942 e9,16745.

10 🛏 € 2, overnight stay free. **Location:** Urban, simple.
Surface: gravel. ⏱ 01/01-31/12
Distance: 400m 400m 50m on the spot.

| 🅿️ S | Bad Wimpfen | 16A2 |

An der Alten Saline 2. **GPS:** n49,23604 e9,15630.

8 🛏 € 8, tourist tax excl 🚰€1/70liter 🗑Ch 🔧(8x)€1/12h
WC. **Location:** Rural, comfortable, quiet. **Surface:** asphalted.
⏱ 01/01-31/12
Distance: 800m.
Remarks: Parking at health resort.

| 🅿️ S | Bad Wurzach | 19C2 |

Wohnmobilstellplatz Vitalium, Riedhalde.
GPS: n47,91437 e9,90363.

17 🛏 € 5,50 + € 1,50/pp tourist tax 🚰€0,50 🗑€0,50 Ch 🔧 WC.
Location: Rural, quiet. **Surface:** asphalted.
⏱ 01/01-31/12
Distance: 500m 300m 500m.
Remarks: Check in at pay-desk of Vitalum.

| 🅿️ S | Baden-Baden | 15H3 |

Wohnmobilparkplatz, Hubertusstraße 2, Badenscheunern.
GPS: n48,78193 e8,20388.

28 🛏 € 12 🚰€1/100liter 🗑Ch 🔧(28x)€0,50/kWh.
Location: Urban, comfortable, noisy. **Surface:** metalled.
⏱ 01/01-31/12
Distance: Baden-Baden 4km 1km 100m 150m on the spot on the spot on the spot.
Remarks: Max. 4 days, video surveillance.

| 🅿️ S | Baiersbronn | 15H3 |

Schelklewiesen, Neumühleweg/Lochweg.
GPS: n48,51016 e8,37272.

15 🛏 € 6 🚰€1/80liter 🗑Ch 🔧(12x)€0,50/kWh. **Location:** Rural,
simple, quiet. **Surface:** metalled.
⏱ 01/01-31/12
Distance: 300m on the spot 100m 200m on the spot
on the spot.

| 🅿️ S | Balingen | 19A1 |

Wohnmobilstellplatz an der Eyach, Heinzlerstrasse.
GPS: n48,27024 e8,85300.

10 🛏 free 🚰€1/time 🗑Ch 🔧(8x)€0,50/kWh. **Location:** Urban,
simple. **Surface:** asphalted. ⏱ 01/01-31/12
Distance: on the spot 500m 300m 300m.
Remarks: Max. 4 days.

| Benningen am Neckar | 16A2 |

Parkplatz Gemeindehalle, Max-Eyth Strasse.
GPS: n48,94574 e9,23363.

4 ⌐free. **Location:** Rural, simple. **Surface:** metalled.
⬤ 01/01-31/12
Distance: ⛽on the spot ⊗50m 🚊1km.

⚊S Bernau im Schwarzwald ⛰❄ 18H2
Sportzentrum Spitzenberg, Sportplatzstraße.
GPS: n47,80614 e8,02803.⬆➡.

15 ⌐16/04-30/09 free, 01/10-15/04 € 3,50 + € 2,20/pp tourist tax
⛽€1/100liter 🔧Ch ⚡€1/8h 🚽. **Location:** Rural, simple, quiet.
Surface: grassy/gravel. ⬤ 01/01-31/12
Distance: ⛽500m 🚊1km 🚗500m.
Remarks: Pay at tourist office.

⚊S Besigheim ⚇⛲🍴≈ 16A2
Wohnmobilstellplatz bei der Minigolfanlage, Auf dem Kies 32.
GPS: n48,99771 e9,14863.⬆➡.

6 ⌐€5 ⛽€1/80liter 🔧Ch ⚡(6x)€0,50/kWh. **Location:** Rural,
comfortable, quiet. **Surface:** metalled. ⬤ 01/01-31/12
Distance: ⛽500m 🏊500m ⊗200m 🚊500m 🚗200m on the
spot 🚶on the spot.
Remarks: After 2 nights € 20/night.

⚊S S Beuren ⚓ 16B3
Panorama Therme, Goethestraße. **GPS:** n48,56621 e9,39944.⬆.

4 ⌐€6 ⚡€1/3kWh. **Location:** Urban, simple. **Surface:** metalled.
⬤ 01/01-31/12
Distance: ⛽500m ⊗on the spot 🚊500m 🚗100m.

⚊S Beuron 19A1
Kloster Beuron, Abteistraße. **GPS:** n48,05306 e8,96704.⬆.

±4 ⌐free. **Location:** Urban, simple. **Surface:** gravel.
⬤ 01/01-31/12
Distance: 🚗on the spot.

Remarks: Parking monastery.

⚊S Beuron 19A1
Besi-Kanu-Sport, Bahnhofstrasse 29. **GPS:** n48,08597 e9,09559.⬆.

10 ⌐€5 ⛽🔧Ch ⚡WCincluded. 🚿 **Location:** Rural, simple.
Surface: gravel. ⬤ 01/01-31/12
Distance: ⛽1km ⊗200m 🚊5km.
Remarks: Canoe rental.

⚊S Biberach/Riss 19B1
Rissstrasse. **GPS:** n48,10401 e9,79582.⬆.

10 ⌐free, voluntary contribution ⛽🔧Chfree. **Surface:** gravel.
⬤ 01/01-31/12 ⬤ service: 01/11-28/02
Distance: ⛽700m.
Remarks: Max. 3 days.

⚊S Bietigheim-Bissingen 16A2
Wohnmobilstellplatz an der Enz, Mühlwiesenstrasse.
GPS: n48,96110 e9,13329.⬆.

9 ⌐€5 ⛽€0,50/80liter 🔧Ch ⚡(8x)€0,50/kWh. **Location:** Urban.
Surface: metalled.
⬤ 01/01-31/12
Distance: ⛽200m 🏊1km ⚡1km ⊗100m 🚊100m 🚗100m.
Remarks: Max. 4 days, check in at Lama Bar.

⚊S Blaubeuren 16B3
Parkplatz P6, Dodelweg. **GPS:** n48,41351 e9,79102.➡.

20 ⌐€5 ⛽€1/5minutes 🔧Ch€1. **Surface:** metalled.
⬤ 01/01-31/12
Distance: ⛽1km ⊗1km 🚊1km 🚗800m.
Remarks: Parking at swimming pool, max. 2 days.

⚊S Blaustein 16B3
Freizeitbad Bad Blau, Boschstraße. **GPS:** n48,41757 e9,91630.⬆.
3 ⌐free. **Location:** Simple. **Surface:** gravel.
Distance: ⚡6,5km ⊗200m 🚊500m.

⚊S Blumberg 18H2
P1, Festplatz, Oberes Ried. **GPS:** n47,83943 e8,54226.⬆➡.

48 ⌐€ 6,50-7,50 ⛽€1/50liter 🔧Ch ⚡(36x)€1/24h.🚿
Location: Comfortable, quiet. **Surface:** gravel/metalled.
⬤ 01/01-31/12
Distance: ⛽800m ⊗100m 🚊80m.
Remarks: With payment: KONUS guest card with many advantages.

⚊S Blumberg 18H2
P2, Parkplatz Bahnhof Zollhaus, Achdorf.
GPS: n47,83767 e8,55777.⬆.

10 ⌐€ 6,50-7,50 ⛽. **Location:** Urban, noisy. **Surface:** gravel.
⬤ 01/01-31/12
Distance: ⛽1,5km.

⚊S Blumberg 18H2
P3, Achdorfer Tal. **GPS:** n47,83528 e8,49833.⬆.

10 ⌐€ 6,50-7,50 ⛽€1 🔧Ch ⚡(12x)€1/night,winter€1,50.
🚿 **Location:** Rural, simple, isolated, quiet. **Surface:** gravel.
⬤ 01/01-31/12
Distance: ⛽4km.
Remarks: With payment: KONUS guest card with many advantages,
caution key € 10 (connection electricity), service at Kläranlage 800m.

⚊S Böblingen ⛲🍴 16A3
Im Zimmerschlag. **GPS:** n48,67000 e9,03272.⬆➡.

4 ⌐free ⛽🔧Chfree. **Location:** Urban, simple.
Surface: grasstiles/metalled. ⬤ 01/01-31/12
Distance: ⛽3km ⊗100m 🚊1,5km 🚶on the spot.

⚊S Bodman-Ludwigshafen ⚓ 19A2
Am Sportplatz. **GPS:** n47,82369 e9,05153.⬆.

20 ⌐€ 8 ⛽🔧Ch ⚡(4x)€2. **Location:** Simple.
Surface: grassy/metalled. ⬤ 01/01-31/12
Distance: ⛽1km ⚡3,2km 🏊1,4km.

DE

Bonndorf 18H2

Wohnmobilstellplatz Holzschlag, Schulstrasse/Bonndorfer Strasse, Bonndorf-Holzschlag. **GPS**: n47,84970 e8,26784.

€5 Ch included. **Location:** Simple, noisy.
Distance: 100m.

Bönnigheim 16A2

Mineralfreibad Bönnigheim, Bachstrasse 40.
GPS: n49,03910 e9,08439.

4 free. **Location:** Rural, simple. **Surface:** grasstiles/metalled.
01/01-31/12
Distance: 500m 500m 1km.
Remarks: Caution key € 10 (water).

Bopfingen 16C3

Gasthof zum Bären, Nördlinger strasse 3.
GPS: n48,85715 e10,35508.

€6 €1 €1 Ch €1. **Surface:** asphalted. 01/01-31/12
Distance: on the spot 16km on the spot 100m.

Boxberg 16B1

Gasthof Hagenmühle, Uiffinger strasse 74.
GPS: n49,48710 e9,61299.

12 €5 (12x)€2,50. **Location:** Rural, simple.
Surface: grassy/gravel. 01/01-31/12 Restaurant: Mo
Distance: 2km trout pond on the spot 1km 200m.

Brackenheim 16A2

Weingut und Besenwirtschaft 'Zum Alten Pflug', Seebergweg.
GPS: n49,10261 e9,04994.

3 €6, free for clients Ch (3x)€2 WC €2.
Surface: metalled. 01/01-31/12
Distance: 3km 3km.

Remarks: Sunday on demand.

Brackenheim 16A2

Weingut Winkler, Stockheimer strasse 13.
GPS: n49,08001 e9,06270.

5 €5 included. **Location:** Rural, simple.
Surface: grassy/metalled.
01/01-31/12
Distance: on the spot 10km 10km 300m 1km 300m.

Breisach/Rhein 18G1

Wohnmobil-Parkplatz, Josef-Buebstrasse.
GPS: n48,02944 e7,57576.

80 free 8-20h, € 6/night, 2 nights € 10, 3 nights € 13, winter
free €1/100liter €1 Ch €1. **Location:** Urban, simple.
Surface: asphalted. 01/01-31/12 Other parking in case of
festivities
Distance: 300m on the spot on the spot 300m 1,5km.
Remarks: Ground of wine festival, bread-service.

Breisach/Rhein 18G1

Restaurant Am Rhein, Hafenstrasse 11. **GPS**: n48,04292 e7,57378.

5 free. **Location:** Simple. **Surface:** metalled.
01/01-31/12
Distance: 2km on the spot 500m.
Remarks: Along the Rhine river, guests only.
Tourist information Breisach/Rhein:
Weinfest Kaiserstuhl Tuniberg. Wine festivals. end Aug.

Bretten 16A2

Reisemobil-Stellplatz Bretten, Willi-Hesselbacher-Weg.
GPS: n49,02980 e8,71914.
4 free €1/100liter €1/10h. **Surface:** metalled.
Distance: city centre 1,5km.
Remarks: Max. 2 days.

Bruchsal 16A2

Giesgrabenweg. **GPS**: n49,13227 e8,58981.

2 free. **Location:** Urban, simple, central. **Surface:** metalled.
01/01-31/12
Distance: 1km 4km 100m 1km on the spot.
Remarks: At sports centre, max. 48h.

Bruchsal 16A2

Autohaus Konrad, Murgstrasse 9-13, Gewerbegebiet Stegwiesen.
GPS: n49,13700 e8,59437.

3 free €1/80liter Ch (4x) WC. **Location:** Urban.
Surface: metalled. 01/01-31/12
Distance: 2km 3km 2km 200m 300m.
Remarks: Max. 3 nights, service during opening hours.

Buchen/Odenwald 16A1

Wohnmobilhafen Morretal, Mühltalstraße. **GPS**: n49,52888 e9,31020.

12 € 5/24h, 3 days € 20 €1/100liter Ch included
(12x)€0,50/kWh WC €0,20/time €3/day. **Location:** Rural,
comfortable, quiet. **Surface:** grassy. 01/01-31/12
Distance: 800m on the spot. **Remarks:** Parking Waldbad, use
sanitary only during opening hours swimming pool.

Buchenbach 18H2

Wanglerhof, Vogtweg 1. **GPS**: n47,96820 e7,99269.

10 € 10 + € 1,20/pp tourist tax Ch included €2/day.
Location: Rural, simple. **Surface:** grassy.
01/01-31/12
Distance: 1km 100m 1km.

Bühl 15H3

Wohnmobilstellplatz am Schwarzwaldbad, Ludwig-Jahn-strasse 8.
GPS: n48,68862 e8,12995.

50 € 5 €2/100liter €2 Ch. **Location:** Urban, simple,
noisy. **Surface:** metalled. 01/01-31/12
Distance: 1km 6km 500m 1km on the spot on the
spot.
Remarks: Bread-service.

Calw 16A3

Wohnmobilstellplatz Am Alten Bahnhof, Bahnhofstrasse.
GPS: n48,70592 e8,73808.

6 🚐free ⛽€1/80liter 🚰€1 Ch€1 ⚡(4x)€0,50/kWh.
Location: Rural, simple, noisy. **Surface:** asphalted.
🕐 01/01-31/12
Distance: 🚲1km 🏪100m 🚌200m 🚴on the spot 🧍on the spot.

Cleebronn/Tripsdrill 🐚 16A2
Erlebnispark Tripsdrill. GPS: n49,03102 e9,05096.⬆➡.

100 🚐free.
Location: Rural, isolated, quiet.
Surface: grassy. 🕐 28/03/2015-08/11/2015
Distance: 🚲1km 🚴on the spot 🏊3km 🚌400m.
Remarks: Max. 3 days.

Tourist information Cleebronn/Tripsdrill:
😊 Erlebnispark Tripsdrill. Amusement park.
🕐 01/04-31/10 9-18h.

Crailsheim 16C2
Autohof Euro Rastpark, Marco-Polo-Straße 1, Satteldorf.
GPS: n49,18146 e10,06889.
10 🚐€5, free with a meal ⛽🍴🛒. **Surface:** metalled.
🕐 01/01-31/12
Distance: 🍴600m 🚴on the spot.

Dettenheim 15H2
Kartbahn Liedolsheim, Kartbahnring 1. **GPS:** n49,14326 e8,43118.

20 🚐free ⛽🚰Ch ⚡(8x)€3 WC🚽€2,50. **Location:** Rural, simple,
isolated. **Surface:** grassy/metalled. 🕐 01/01-31/12
Distance: 🚲2km 🏊2km 🚴2km 🚴on the spot 🏊5km.
Remarks: Parking at Karting.

Donaueschingen 🐚 19A2
Prinz Fritz Allee. **GPS:** n47,94746 e8,51183.⬆➡.

10 🚐free ⚡(14x)€1. **Location:** Rural, simple, quiet. **Surface:** grassy.
🕐 01/01-31/12
Distance: 🚲1,5km 🚴Danube Bike Trail.
Remarks: Max. 2 days, service 300m.

Donaueschingen 🐚 19A2
Kläranlage, Haberfeld. **GPS:** n47,94931 e8,52209.⬆➡.
⛽€1/50liter 🚰Ch.
🕐 01/01-31/12

Tourist information Donaueschingen:
ℹ Tourismus- und Sportamt, Karlstrasse 58, www.donaueschingen.de.
Horse city, named after the source of the River danube.

🚴 Der Donau Radweg. Signposted cycle route along the Donau.

Durbach 15H3
Grol/Festplatz, Almstrasse. **GPS:** n48,49407 e8,01105.⬆➡.

15 🚐€6 ⚡(8x)€1/8h. 📶 **Location:** Simple. **Surface:** gravel.
🕐 01/01-31/12 💡 festivities
Distance: 🚲500m 🚴10km 🚌50m.

Durbach 15H3
Halle am Durbach, Wiesenstraße, Ebersweier.
GPS: n48,50122 e7,98940.⬆➡.

6 🚐€6 ⛽€1/80liter 🚰Ch ⚡(6x)4h. 📶 **Location:** Rural, simple.
Surface: grasstiles. 🕐 01/01-31/12
Distance: 🚲500m 🚴10km 🏊750m 🚌200m.

Eberbach 🐚 16A1
Wohnmobilstellplatz In der Au, In der Au.
GPS: n49,46162 e8,97812.⬆.

7 🚐free ⚡(6x)€1/2kWh WC. **Location:** Simple, isolated.
Surface: gravel. 🕐 01/01-31/12 💡 16/08-31/08
Distance: 🚲1km 🏊on the spot.
Remarks: Max. 2 nights.

Eberbach 🐚 16A1
Wohnmobilstellplatz Neckarlauer, B37, Uferstrasse.
GPS: n49,46012 e8,98652.⬆.

7 🚐free. **Location:** Central. **Surface:** metalled.
🕐 01/01-31/12 💡 high water
Distance: 🚲300m 🚴300m 🚌500m.

Eberbach 🐚 16A1
In der Au. **GPS:** n49,46217 e8,97351.⬆.
⛽€1/80liter 🚰Ch.

Ebringen 18G2
An der Schönberghalle, Schulstraße 8.
GPS: n47,95639 e7,77667.⬆➡.

3 🚐free. **Location:** Simple. **Surface:** grasstiles.
🕐 01/01-31/12
Distance: 🚴7,6km 🚴on the spot.
Remarks: Max. 2 days, max. 6,5m.

Ehingen 🐚 19B1
Wohnmobilstellplatz, Am Stadion. **GPS:** n48,28053 e9,73571.⬆.

10 🚐free ⛽€1/100liter 🚰Ch ⚡(4x)€1/4h. **Surface:** metalled.
🕐 01/01-31/12
Distance: 🚲1km 🚴1km 🚴on the spot 🏊500m 🚌10m 🚴Danube
Bike Trail.

Eichstetten 18G1
Weingut Köbelin, Altweg 131. **GPS:** n48,09472 e7,72083.

5 🚐€13 ⛽🚰Ch ⚡included. 🍷 **Location:** Rural, comfortable,
isolated, quiet. **Surface:** gravel/sand.

Eigeltingen 19A2
Landgasthof Mönchhof, Mönchhof. **GPS:** n47,88094 e8,95278.

4 🚐guests free ⛽🚰Ch ⚡. **Surface:** metalled.
🕐 01/01-31/12
Distance: 🚲6km 🚴on the spot 🚴4km 🚌on the spot.

Eisenbach 18H2
Reisemobilpark Höchstberg. GPS: n47,94938 e8,25441.⬆.

20 🚐€8, tourist tax €1,60/pp ⛽€1/100liter 🚰Ch ⚡
(20x)⚡included,only in summer. 🍷 **Location:** Rural, comfortable,
quiet. **Surface:** grassy/gravel. 🕐 01/01-31/12
Distance: 🚴on the spot 🧍on the spot.
Remarks: Altitude 1033m, at sports park.

Ellwangen 16C2
Maxi-Autohof Ellwangen, Max-Eyth-Strasse 1.
GPS: n48,95628 e10,18319.⬆.

15 🛏 €5/night 🚰 🔌 ChWC ⬛ 📶 against payment.
Location: Highway. **Surface:** asphalted. ⬛ 01/01-31/12
Distance: 🚶3km ⊗on the spot 🛒1km.

Emmendingen 18H1

Wohnmobilstellplatz am Sportfeld, Am Sportfeld.
GPS: n48,11869 e7,84154.⬆.

20 🛏 free 🚰 €1/80liter Ch. **Location:** Urban, simple.
Surface: asphalted. ⬛ 01/01-31/12
Distance: 🚶1km ⊗400m 🛒600m.
Remarks: In front of swimmingpool, max. 3 days.

Endingen am Kaiserstuhl 18G1

P2 Stadthalle, Freiburger Weg. **GPS:** n48,13830 e7,70321.⬆➡.

20 🛏 free. **Location:** Urban, simple, central.
Surface: asphalted/metalled.
Distance: 🚶200m ⊗200m.

Eppingen 16A2

Wohnmobilhalt am Parkweg, Am Altstadring.
GPS: n49,13793 e8,91402.⬆.

4 🛏 free 🚰 €1/80liter 🔌€1 Ch €1 🔌(4x)€1. **Location:** Rural,
comfortable. **Surface:** metalled. ⬛ 01/01-31/12
Distance: 🚶500m ⊗on the spot 🚌500m 🚶on the
spot.

Esslingen am Neckar 16B3

Äußerer Burgplatz, Mülbergerstraße. **GPS:** n48,74713 e9,31064.⬆.

2 🛏 free. **Location:** Urban, simple. **Surface:** metalled. ⬛ 01/01-31/12
Distance: 🚶1km 🏊1km ⊗on the spot 🛒1km 🚌300m.
Remarks: Max. 48h.

Ettenheim 18G1

Ernst Caravan und Freizeit Center, Rudolf Hell Straße 32-44.
GPS: n48,27431 e7,78161.⬆.

30 🛏 free 🚰 €1 🔌€1 Ch €1 🔌(12x)€0,50/kWh. **Location:** Highway,
simple. **Surface:** metalled. ⬛ 01/01-31/12
Distance: 🚗500m.
Remarks: Motorhome dealer, accessory shop, repairs.

Ettlingen 15H3

Wohnmobilstellplatz Am Freibad, Schöllbronner strasse.
GPS: n48,93561 e8,41747.⬆➡.

14 🛏 free 🚰 €1 Ch 🔌(8x)€1/kWh. **Location:** Urban, simple.
Surface: asphalted. ⬛ 01/01-31/12
Distance: 🚶100m 🚗3,3km ⊗100m 🛒700m ⊗on the spot 🚶on
the spot.
Remarks: Parking swimming pool, max. 48h.

Filderstadt 16A3

Parkplatz P2, Tübinger Strasse 40. **GPS:** n48,67347 e9,21456.⬆➡.

8 🛏 €7/24h 🚰 €1/80liter Ch 🔌(8x)€0,50/kWh,16Amp. 🚾
Location: Urban. **Surface:** gravel. ⬛ 01/01-31/12
Distance: 🚶500m ⊗500m 🛒500m 🚌500m.

Freiburg 18H1

Reisemobilplatz Freiburg, Bissierstrasse / Am Eschholzpark.
GPS: n47,99915 e7,82643.⬆➡.

80 🛏 €8, motorhome >7m + € 0,50/50cm 🚰€1/100liter Ch
🔌(20x)€0,50/kWh 📶free. 🚾 **Location:** Urban, comfortable.
Surface: asphalted/gravel.
⬛ 01/01-31/12
Distance: 🚶Old city centre 1,5km 🚗4,3km ⊗450m.
Remarks: Max. 72h, green zone: environmental badge obligatory.

Freiburg 18H1

WV-Südcaravan, Hanferstrasse 30, Hochdorf.
GPS: n48,04146 e7,81473.⬆.

6 🛏 free 🚰 €1/80liter Ch. **Location:** Urban, simple.
Surface: asphalted/metalled. ⬛ 01/01-31/12
Remarks: During opening hours.

Freudenberg 16A1

P. Freudenberg-Süd, Hauptstrasse. **GPS:** n49,74001 e9,31938.⬆.

10 🛏 €5/night 🚰€1/15minutes Ch 🔌(6x)€1/8h,16Amp. 🚾
Location: Rural, comfortable. **Surface:** metalled.
⬛ 01/01-31/12
Distance: 🚶50m 🏊20m 🚌20m ⊗300m 🛒500m.

Friedrichshafen 19B2

Stellplatz Friedrichshafen, Lindauerstrasse 2.
GPS: n47,65025 e9,49597.⬆➡.

20 🛏 free, 01/04-31/10 € 12 🚰€1/80liter ChWC ⬛.
Surface: asphalted/metalled. ⬛ 01/01-31/12
Distance: 🏊200m 🚌200m ⊗on the spot.
Remarks: Max. 3 nights, payment only with coins.

Gaildorf 16B2

Bleichgärten. GPS: n49,00224 e9,76587.⬆➡.

7 🛏 free 🚰 Ch 🔌(4x)free,16Amp. **Location:** Simple.
Surface: metalled. ⬛ 01/01-31/12
Distance: 🚶500m ⊗400m 🛒500m 🚌500m.

Gailingen am Hochrhein 19A2

Rheinuferpark, Strandweg. **GPS:** n47,69051 e8,75621.⬆➡.
20 🛏 € 15. 🚾 ⬛ 01/04-31/10
Distance: 🚶1km 🏊on the spot.

Gammertingen 19A1

Freizeitanlage an der Lauchert, Reutlingerstrasse.
GPS: n48,25611 e9,21056.➡.

DE

8 ⛺free ⚡(6x)€1/4h WC. **Location:** Simple. **Surface:** grassy/gravel. 🔌 01/01-31/12
Distance: 🚰1km 🏊on the spot 🛒on the spot ⊗1km 🍴700m 🚶on the spot.

Geisingen 19A2
Reisemobilstellplatz Geisingen, Am Espen 8. **GPS:** n47,92016 e8,65153.

37 ⛺€7 ⛽€1/80liter 🚽Ch included ⚡(37x)€1/4kWh. **Surface:** gravel. 🔌 01/01-31/12
Distance: 🚰300m 🏊2km 🛒50m ⊗300m 🍴300m 🚐500m 💧100m 🚶100m.

Gernsbach 15H3
Parkplatz Murginsel, Schlossstrasse/Klingelstrasse. **GPS:** n48,75934 e8,33900. ⬆️

8 ⛺€5 ⛽€1/100liter 🚽Ch ⚡(8x)€1/12h WC. 🚿 **Location:** Rural, simple. **Surface:** asphalted. 🔌 01/01-31/12
Distance: 🚰500m 🛒on the spot ⊗500m 🍴1km 🚐on the spot 💧on the spot 🚶on the spot.
Remarks: Max. 7 days.

Gernsbach 15H3
Am Schwimmbad 1, Oberstrot. **GPS:** n48,74239 e8,34186. ⬆️➡️

5 ⛺free. **Location:** Rural, simple. **Surface:** grassy. 🔌 01/01-31/12
Distance: 🚰200m ⊗200m 💧on the spot 🚶on the spot.
Remarks: At swimming pool.

Giengen 16C3
Reisemobilstation Charlottenhöhle, Lonetalstrasse 60, Hürben. **GPS:** n48,58412 e10,21203. ⬆️➡️

15 ⛺€7/night ⚡€2 🚽Ch ⚡(6x)€2/12h,16Amp WC 🚿€2. **Location:** Rural, quiet. **Surface:** gravel. 🔌 01/01-31/12
Remarks: At prehistoric cave, coins at Hölenhaus.

Giengen 16C3
Am Schießberg, Auf dem Schießberg. **GPS:** n48,62975 e10,25159. ⬆️

8 ⛺free. **Location:** Simple. **Surface:** gravel. 🔌 01/01-31/12
Distance: 🚰1,5km 🏊4,3km 🍴1,5km 💧1,5km.

Tourist information Giengen:
👁 Charlottenhöhle. Caves. 🔌 8.30-11.30h, 13.30-16.30h, Su 8.30-16.30h.

Göppingen 16B3
Hohen Staufenhalle, P1, Lorcherstrasse. **GPS:** n48,71176 e9,64816. ⬆️

10 ⛺free ⛽€1/80liter 🚽Ch. **Location:** Urban. **Surface:** asphalted. 🔌 01/01-31/12
Distance: 🚰1km ⊗1km 💧1km.
Remarks: Max. 2 nights.

Grossbottwar 16B2
Parkplatz an der Wunnensteinhalle, In den Frauengärten. **GPS:** n49,00363 e9,28739. ⬆️➡️

3 ⛺free. **Surface:** metalled. 🔌 01/01-31/12
Distance: 🚰400m ⊗400m 🚐200m.
Remarks: Max. 3 nights.

Gschwend 16B2
Naturbadesee, Frickenhofer Strasse. **GPS:** n48,93603 e9,75143. ⬆️

3 ⛺free. **Location:** Rural. **Surface:** forest soil. 🔌 01/01-31/12
Distance: 🚰1,5km.

Gschwend 16B2
Joosenhofer Sägmühle. GPS: n48,92312 e9,77393. ⬆️➡️

free ⛽€1/80liter 🚽Ch. **Surface:** asphalted. 🔌 01/01-31/12

Güglingen 16A2
Oberes Tal. GPS: n49,06492 e8,99489. ⬆️➡️

6 ⛺free ⛽€1 🚽Ch. **Location:** Rural, simple. **Surface:** metalled. 🔌 01/01-31/12
Distance: 🚰700m ⊗500m 🍴Aldi-Lidl 500m 💧on the spot 🚶on the spot.
Remarks: At swimming pool, max. 5 nights.

Haigerloch 19A1
Wohnmobilstellplatz Haigerloch, Weildorfer Kreuz 1. **GPS:** n48,36875 e8,79384. ⬆️➡️

10 ⛺free ⛽€1/60liter 🚽Ch ⚡(10x)€1/8h. **Location:** Urban, simple. **Surface:** asphalted. 🔌 01/01-31/12
Distance: 🚰300m 🚐on the spot.
Remarks: Max. 4 days.

Hardheim 16B1
Am Alten Bahnhof, Bretzinger Straße. **GPS:** n49,60245 e9,47126. ⬆️➡️

12 ⛺free ⛽€1/80liter 🚽Ch free ⚡(8x)€1/2kWh. **Location:** Rural, comfortable, noisy. **Surface:** gravel.

◘ 01/01-31/12
Distance: 🚶1km ⊗1km ⛽1km.

Haslach/Kinzigtal 18H1

Klosterplatz, Ringstraße. **GPS:** n48,27572 e8,08509.⬆.

20 free. **Location:** Urban, simple. **Surface:** metalled.
◘ 01/01-31/12
Distance: 🚶50m ⊗150m ⛽500m 🚂100m.

Haslach/Kinzigtal 18H1

Parkplatz Eichenbach-sporthalle, Strickerweg.
GPS: n48,27854 e8,07968.⬆.

10 free. **Location:** Simple. **Surface:** metalled.
◘ 01/01-31/12
Distance: 🚶500m ⊗300m.

Haslach/Kinzigtal 18H1

Waldseeparkplatz, Waldseeweg. **GPS:** n48,27161 e8,09148.⬆.

10 free. **Location:** Rural, simple. **Surface:** asphalted.
◘ 01/01-31/12
Distance: 🚶1km ⊗200m ⛽1km.

Hausach 18H1

Waldstadion, Waldstraße. **GPS:** n48,28058 e8,17829.⬆➡.

4 free ⛽WC. **Location:** Rural, simple, simple, quiet, noisy.
Surface: gravel/sand. ◘ 01/01-31/12
Distance: 🚶500m ⊗100m.

Hausach 18H1

Badepark, Schanze 3. **GPS:** n48,28620 e8,16589.⬆➡.

6 free. **Location:** Simple. **Surface:** metalled.
◘ 01/01-31/12
Distance: ⊗on the spot ⛽500m.
Remarks: Nearby swimming pool.

Hechingen 19A1

Freizeitanlage Domäne Areal, Brielhof 1.
GPS: n48,33773 e8,94966.⬆.

18 € 18 ⛽included. **Location:** Simple. **Surface:** metalled.
◘ 01/01-31/12
Distance: 🚶2km ⊘200m ⊗on the spot.
Remarks: Reduction at restaurants and Golf Park.

Hechingen 19A1

Burg Hohenzollern, K 7110. **GPS:** n48,32579 e8,96404.⬆.

3 € 4. **Location:** Rural, simple. **Surface:** asphalted.
Distance: ⊗Imbiss 🚶on the spot.

Hechingen 19A1

Zollernalbcamping, Niederhechingerstrasse.
GPS: n48,35797 e8,96093.⬆➡.

20 € 10 ⛽€1/time ⚡Ch€1/time ⚡€1/kWh WC€2,50.
Location: Simple. **Surface:** metalled.
◘ 01/31-31/12 ◘ sanitary building: 01/11-01/04
Distance: 🚶2km ⛽500m 🚲on the spot 🚶on the spot.
Remarks: Waste dump € 2/day.

Heidenheim 16C3

In den Seewiesen. **GPS:** n48,69455 e10,16410.⬆➡.

22 € 2/day ⛽€1/70liter ⚡€1 Ch ⚡(18x)€1/6h,16Amp.
Location: Rural, simple. **Surface:** asphalted/gravel.
◘ 01/01-31/12
Distance: ⊘5km ⛽1km.

Heilbronn 16A2

Wertwiesenpark, Neckarhalde. **GPS:** n49,13047 e9,20469.⬆➡.

20 free ⛽€1/100liter ⚡Ch ⚡(12x)€0,50/kWh.
Location: Comfortable. **Surface:** metalled. ◘ 01/01-31/12

Distance: 🚶2km ⊘7km ⊗100m ⛽500m.

Heiligenberg 19B2

Sennerei Schläge, Betenbrunner strasse.
GPS: n47,81892 e9,31445.⬆➡.

10 € 5/16-09h ⛽€0,50 ⚡€0,50 Ch. 🚾 **Surface:** grassy/metalled.
◘ 01/01-31/12
Distance: 🚶300m ⊘300m ⛽300m ⊗200m ⛽bakery 200m.
Remarks: Max. 2 nights.

Herbrechtingen 16C3

P7 Eselstalparkplatz, Baumschulenweg.
GPS: n48,61758 e10,17411.⬆➡.

15 € 7 ⛽€2 ⚡Ch ⚡€2/24h. **Location:** Rural, quiet.
Surface: asphalted. ◘ 01/01-31/12
Remarks: Check in at Hölenhaus.

Hessigheim 16A2

Fasanenhof, Römerweg 1. **GPS:** n49,00939 e9,18877.⬆.
15 € 5 ⛽. **Location:** Rural, simple. ◘ 01/01-31/12
Distance: ⊘3,5km ⊗on the spot ⛽shop with farm products 🚲on
the spot 🚶on the spot.
Remarks: Farm/restaurant/Biergarten/shop.

Hessigheim 16A2

Felsengarten Kellerei Besigheim e.G., Am Felsengarten 1.
GPS: n48,99612 e9,18068.⬆.

5 guests free ⛽⚡. **Surface:** asphalted. ◘ 01/01-31/12
Distance: 🚶1km ⊗on the spot ⛽1km.
Remarks: Max. 2 nights.

Heubach 16B3

Am Freibad, Mögglinger Strasse. **GPS:** n48,79802 e9,93831.

6 € 6 ⛽€1/90liter ⚡Ch€0,50. **Surface:** grasstiles.
◘ 01/01-31/12
Distance: ⊗200m ⛽Lidl 400m.

Höchenschwand 18H2

Natursportzentrum. **GPS:** n47,73652 e8,15990.⬆➡.

DE

12 €7 Ch (12x)€1/6h WC. **Location:** Rural, comfortable.
Surface: gravel. 01/01-31/12
Distance: 400m 100m 600m on the spot.

Holzmaden 16B3

Urwelt-Museum Hauff, Aichelbergerstrasse 75/90.
GPS: n48,63482 e9,52771.
6 free. **Surface:** metalled. 01/01-31/12
Distance: 3km 2,2km.
Remarks: Max. 1 night.

Hornberg 18H1

Hotel Schöne Aussicht, Schöne Aussicht 1, Niederwasser.
GPS: n48,19443 e8,18494.
4 €8 included.
Distance: on the spot.

Hüfingen 18H2

Bräunlinger Straße. **GPS:** n47,92361 e8,48707.

22 €5 €1 Ch €1. **Location:** Urban, comfortable, noisy.
Surface: grasstiles. 01/01-31/12
Distance: 300m 300m.
Remarks: Thursday market.

Hülben 16B3

Phoenix Wohnmobihafen, Kaltentalstrasse.
GPS: n48,52620 e9,41227.

10 free €0,50/80liter Ch (6x)€0,50/kWh. **Location:** Rural, simple. **Surface:** gravel. 01/01-31/12
Distance: 400m 400m 500m Vordere-Alb-Radweg on the spot on the spot.
Remarks: Max. 4 days.

Ihringen 18G1

Kaiserstuhl Camping, Nachtwaid 5. **GPS:** n48,03083 e7,65778.

6 € 14,60 + tourist tax Ch €1,80/3kWh WC included. **Location:** Rural, comfortable. **Surface:** asphalted/metalled.
31/03-30/10
Distance: 600m 200m.

Isny 19C2

Parkplatz An der Untere Mühle, Seidenstrasse 43.
GPS: n47,69457 e10,03780.

10 € 7,50 + € 1,50/pp tourist tax €1/80liter Ch (8x)€ 0,50/kWh WC. **Location:** Urban. **Surface:** asphalted/gravel.
01/01-31/12
Distance: 300m 100m 300m 200m.
Remarks: Max. 2 nights.

Isny 19C2

Caravans Dethleffs, Rangenbergweg. **GPS:** n47,69938 e10,05490.

9 € 5 + € 1,50/pp tourist tax, clients Dethleffs free Ch (9x) included. **Surface:** metalled. 01/01-31/12
Distance: 1km 1km 1km 1,4km 500m.
Remarks: Max. 3 nights.

Kaisersbach 16B2

Schwaben-Park, Hofwiesen 11, Gmeinweiler.
GPS: n48,90304 e9,65484.

10 free. 01/04-31/10
Remarks: Inclining pitches.

Tourist information Kaisersbach:
Schwaben-Park. Amusement park. Easter-Oct 9-18h.

Kappelrodeck 15H3

Wohnmobileck am Heidenhof, Grüner Winkel.
GPS: n48,58370 e8,12650.

18 € 5/day, 3 days € 10, 7 days € 20 €1/100liter Ch (8x)€ 1/2kWh. **Location:** Rural, simple, quiet. **Surface:** gravel/metalled.
01/01-31/12
Distance: 800m 150m 500m on the spot on the spot.
Remarks: Max. 6 nights.

Karlsruhe 15H2

Am Yachthafen Maxau, Maxau am Rhein.
GPS: n49,03720 e8,30583.

12 free. **Surface:** gravel. 01/01-31/12
Distance: Karlsruhe 9km on the spot 2km.
Remarks: Along the Rhine river, max. 24h.

Karlsruhe 15H2

Ettlinger Allee. **GPS:** n48,98761 e8,40412.

2 free. **Surface:** asphalted. 01/01-31/12
Distance: centre 2,5km 400m metro 400m.
Remarks: Max. 24h, small pitches.

Kehl 15G3

Am Wasserturm, Schwimbadstrasse. **GPS:** n48,56350 e7,81400.

40 € 8 €1/80liter Ch (16x)€0,50/kWh.
Location: Urban, comfortable, quiet. **Surface:** gravel. 01/01-31/12
Distance: 1km 100m 500m on the spot on the spot on the spot.
Remarks: Max. 3 days, friday market.

Kehl 15G3

Reisemobilstellplatz Hurst, An den Sportanlagen 1, Kehl-Auenheim.
GPS: n48,60653 e7,83146.

18 €7 €1 Ch (12x)€3 WC€0,50 €1,50.
Location: Rural, simple, quiet. **Surface:** asphalted/grassy.
01/01-31/12
Distance: 500m on the spot 500m on the spot on the spot.
Remarks: Check in on arrival.

Kehl 15G3

Bürstner-Service-Centrum, Elsässer strasse 80, Kehl-Neumühl.
GPS: n48,57010 e7,84042.

6 free €1/100liter Ch (6x)€1/kWh WC. **Location:** Rural.
Surface: asphalted. 01/01-31/12
Distance: 1km 100m 600m on the spot on the spot.

Kenzingen 18G1

Ritter's Weingut, Rossleiteweg 1. **GPS:** n48,18739 e7,78343.

DE

15 ⑃ € 10, 2 pers.incl, € 2/pp 🚰 ❄ ✏ €2,50/day WC ⬛included. 📷
Location: Comfortable. **Surface:** grassy/gravel. ⬛ 01/01-31/12
Distance: ⬛ 7,5km ⊗on the spot.

| 🛏 | **Kirchberg/Jagst** | 16B2 |

Wanderparkplatz Kirchberg-Tal, Hohen Loher Strasse.
GPS: n49,20367 e9,98344.⬆.

10 ⑃free. **Surface:** gravel. ⬛ 01/01-31/12

| 🛏 | **Kirchheim unter Teck** | 16B3 |

Ziegelwasen, Schlierbacher Straße. **GPS:** n48,64998 e9,45919.⬆➡.

3 ⑃free. **Location:** Urban, simple.
Surface: asphalted/metalled.
⬛ 01/01-31/12
Distance: ⬛500m Altstadt ⊗500m ⛲500m ⬛100m ❀on the spot.
Remarks: Max. 3 days.

| 🛏 S | **Kisslegg** | 19C2 |

Wohnmobilhafen Kißlegg, Strandbadweg.
GPS: n47,79602 e9,87950.⬆.
24 ⑃€ 5-7 🚰€1/100liter ❄Ch✏(5x)€0,50/kWh WC⬛.
Surface: metalled. ⬛ 01/01-31/12
Distance: ⬛800m ⛱100m ⛲100m ⊗100m ⬛1km ⛲400m.

| 🛏 S | **Kisslegg** | 19C2 |

Familiefreizeitgelände St Anna, Le Pouliguenstrasse.
GPS: n47,79119 e9,87229.⬆➡.

3 ⑃free. **Surface:** grassy/metalled. ⬛ 01/01-31/12
Distance: ⬛800m ⊗500m ⛲500m.
Remarks: Max. 2 nights.

| 🏨 | **Kisslegg** | 19C2 |

Hotel Sonnenstrahl, Sebastian Kneipp strasse 1.
GPS: n47,78421 e9,87973.
3 ⑃free. **Surface:** asphalted/metalled. ⬛ 01/01-31/12
Distance: ⬛800m ⊗on the spot ⛲800m.
Remarks: Max. 2 nights.

| 🛏 S | **Königschaffhausen** | 18G1 |

Wohnmobilgarten im Kirschenhof Schmidt, Königsweg 5.
GPS: n48,14277 e7,66273.⬆➡.

16 ⑃€ 11 + € 1/pp tourist tax 🚰❄Ch✏ WCincluded ⬛€1 📶in
Café. **Location:** Rural, comfortable. **Surface:** gravel/metalled.
⬛ 01/01-31/12
Distance: ⬛500m ⊗on the spot.
Remarks: Wifi in café.

| 🛏 S | **Königsfeld** 🌲👫 | 18H1 |

Reisemobilpark Bregnitzhof, Buchenberger Strasse 34.
GPS: n48,14028 e8,40583.⬆➡.

21 ⑃€ 8/night 🚰€0,50 ❄Ch✏€1/8h. 📷
Location: Rural, luxurious, quiet. **Surface:** gravel. ⬛ 01/01-31/12
Distance: ⬛1km ⊗10 min walking.
Remarks: Check in between 14-19h, 18-holes golf course, Saunaland-
schaft Bregnitzhof.

| 🛏 S | **Konstanz** | 19B2 |

Parkplatz Döbele, Döbeleplatz. **GPS:** n47,65794 e9,16933.⬆➡.

12 ⑃€ 1/h, € 15/24h 🚰❄Ch✏ WCincluded.
Surface: asphalted/metalled. ⬛ 01/01-31/12
Distance: ⬛1km ⛱800m ❀800m ⊗200m ⛲800m ⛲500m.
Remarks: Max. 24h.

| 🛏 S | **Korb** | 16B3 |

Reisemobilstellplatz Unterm Korber Kopf, Brucknerstrasse 14.
GPS: n48,84597 e9,35544.⬆.

6 ⑃€ 3 🚰€0,50/80liter ❄Ch✏(6x)€0,50/kWh. **Surface:** metalled.
⬛ 01/01-31/12
Distance: ⬛400m ⊗Gaststätte ⛲300m ⛲500m.
Remarks: Coins at restaurant.

| 🛏 S | **Kressbronn** | 19B2 |

Wohnmobilstellplatz Tunau, Tunau 4.
GPS: n47,58999 e9,57512.⬆➡.

40 ⑃€ 17,50-21 🚰❄Ch✏(40x)WC⬛€1,50/pp 📶included. 📷
Surface: asphalted/grassy. ⬛ 01/04-31/10
Distance: ⬛1km ⛱1km ⛲1km ⊗on the spot ⛲1km.

| CS | **Kressbronn** | 19B2 |

Gohren am See. GPS: n47,58818 e9,56256.
11 ⑃€ 12 🚰❄Ch✏€3/12h WC⬛€1/day.
Surface: grassy/gravel. ⬛ 01/04-15/10
Distance: ⛱Bodensee.

| 🛏 S | **Külsheim** | 16B1 |

Am Schloss Külsheim, Kirchbergweg. **GPS:** n49,67123 e9,52255.⬆.

12 ⑃free 🚰€0,50/80liter ❄Ch✏(12x)€0,50/kWh. **Location:** Rural.
Surface: grasstiles.
⬛ 01/01-31/12 ⬛ 10/09-25/09
Distance: ⬛300m.

| 🛏 S | **Ladenburg** 🍴 | 16A1 |

Wohnmobilstellplatz Ladenburg, Heidelberger Straße.
GPS: n49,46596 e8,61460.⬆.

34 ⑃€ 10 🚰€1/80liter ❄Ch✏€1/2kWh 📶.📷
Location: Urban, comfortable, central, quiet. **Surface:** grassy.
⬛ 01/01-31/12
Distance: ⬛Altstadt 500m, Heidelberg 10km ❀3km ⊗200m
⛲200m.

| 🛏 S | **Langenau** | 16C3 |

Karlstraße. **GPS:** n48,50193 e10,12203.⬆.
4 ⑃€ 5 🚰€0,50/70liter ✏€0,50/kWh. **Location:** Simple.
Surface: metalled. ⬛ 01/01-31/12
Distance: ⬛500m ❀3,2km ⊗300m ⛲1,2km.

| 🛏 | **Langenbrettach** | 16B2 |

Freibad Langenbeutingen, Schwabbacker Strasse 24, Langenbeutingen. **GPS:** n49,21227 e9,40767.⬆.

3 ⑃free. **Location:** Rural. **Surface:** asphalted.
Remarks: Parking swimming pool.

| 🛏 | **Langenburg** | 16B2 |

Am Freibad, In der Strut 5. **GPS:** n49,24973 e9,86681.⬆.
2 ⑃free. **Surface:** gravel. ⬛ 01/01-31/12
Distance: ⬛1km.
Remarks: Not accessible coming from the west.

| 🛏 S | **Lauchringen** 🍴 | 18H2 |

An der Wutach, Badstrasse. **GPS:** n47,62556 e8,31361.➡.

DE

20 ⌁free, 01/04-01/11 € 5 ⌁⌁Ⓒincluded ⌁(16x)€2/24h.
Location: Rural, comfortable, quiet. **Surface:** gravel.
◼ 01/01-31/12 ● service: 01/11-01/04
Distance: ⌁on the spot ⌁on the spot.
Remarks: Pay at town hall or swimming pool, caution € 20, key electricity at pool.

Lauda-Königshofen 16B1
Badstrasse, Lauda. **GPS:** n49,55886 e9,70099.⬆

4 ⌁free. **Location:** Rural, simple. **Surface:** asphalted.
◼ 01/01-31/12
Distance: ⌁1km ⌁500m.
Remarks: Parking at swimming pool.

Lauda-Königshofen 16B1
Gasthaus Zur Lamm, St. Josefstrasse 30-32, Marbach.
GPS: n49,56568 e9,72834.⬆➡

12 ⌁€ 5/24h ⌁(12x)included ⓌⒸfree, at restaurant.
Location: Rural, simple, quiet. **Surface:** asphalted.
◼ 01/01-31/12 ● Restaurant: Mo
Distance: ⊗on the spot ⌁on the spot.

Laufenburg 18H2
Laufenburg Baden P6, Andelsbachstraße.
GPS: n47,56585 e8,06677.⬆➡

6 ⌁€ 5 ⌁€2/5minutes ⌁Ch€2 ⌁(6x)€0,50/kWh. **Location:** Urban, quiet. **Surface:** concrete. ◼ 01/01-31/12
Remarks: Along the Rhine river.

Laupheim ❀ 19B1
Schloß Grosslaupheim, Klaus-Graf-Stauffenberg-Strasse.
GPS: n48,23128 e9,88872.⬆➡

7 ⌁€ 8 ⌁€0,50 ⌁€0,50 Ch€0,50 ⌁. **Location:** Rural.
Surface: metalled. ◼ 01/01-31/12
Distance: ⌁on the spot.

Leonberg 16A3
Parkplatz Steinstrasse, Steinstrasse. **GPS:** n48,79705 e9,01751.⬆

DE

5 ⌁free, Mo-Fr 8-18h € 2,50. ⌁ **Surface:** metalled. ◼ 01/01-31/12
● Sa 5-13h
Distance: ⌁400m ⊗150m ⌁300m ⌁on the spot.

Leutkirch im Allgäu 19C2
Wohnmobilstellplatz Leutkirch, Kemptener Straße.
GPS: n47,82228 e10,03939.⬆

14 ⌁€ 6 ⌁€1/100liter ⌁Ch ⌁€0,50/kWh. **Surface:** asphalted.
◼ 01/01-31/12
Distance: ⌁1km ⊗300m.

Löffingen ⛰ 18H2
Waldbad Löffingen, Am Waldbad. **GPS:** n47,90017 e8,33287.⬆➡

7 ⌁€ 8 + € 2/pp tourist tax, 01/10-31/05 free ⌁⌁⌁(4x)included
⌁€0,50, At swimming pool. **Location:** Comfortable. **Surface:** concrete.
◼ 01/01-31/12 ● service 01/10-01/05
Distance: ⌁Swimming pool ⊗on the spot.
Remarks: Check in at pay-desk of swimming pool.

Tourist information Löffingen:
☻ Schwarzwaldpark. Game preserve and summer toboggan slide (€ 1.02 a time). ◼ Easter-Oct 9-18h.

Malsch 15H3
Gast Caravanning, Daimlerstr. 20b. **GPS:** n48,89079 e8,30747.⬆

6 ⌁free ⌁€1/80liter ⌁Ch. **Location:** Simple.
Surface: asphalted/metalled. ◼ 01/01-31/12
Distance: ⌁7,6km.
Remarks: Motorhome dealer, accessory shop.

Mannheim/Friedrichsfeld 15H1
Güma Reisemobile, Steinzeugstrasse 21. **GPS:** n49,44570 e8,56780.⬆

3 ⌁free ⌁Ch ⌁Ⓦfree. **Location:** Simple, noisy.
Surface: metalled.

◼ 01/01-31/12
Distance: ⌁10km ⌁1km ⌁1km ⌁300m.
Remarks: Max. 3 nights, sanitary use during shop opening hours.

Marbach am Neckar 🐑 16A2
Parkplatz Bolzplatz, Poppenweiler/Weimarstrasse.
GPS: n48,93389 e9,26278.⬆

5 ⌁€ 5 ⌁⌁Ch ⌁ **Location:** Rural, simple. **Surface:** metalled.
◼ 01/01-31/12
Distance: ⌁1km ⌁6,2km ⊗100m ⌁600m ⌁500m.
Remarks: Max. 2 nights, service: Gruppenklärwerk Häldenmühle, L1100.

Markelsheim 16B1
Engelbergparkplatz, Engelsbergstrasse.
GPS: n49,47537 e9,83474.⬆➡

2 ⌁free. **Location:** Urban. **Surface:** asphalted. ◼ 01/01-31/12
● week of Whitsuntide
Distance: ⌁300m ⊗300m.
Remarks: At fire-station, max. 2 nights.

Meckenbeuren 19B2
Wohnmobilplatz Besenwirtschaft Georgshof, Pfingstweiderstrasse 10-12/1, Reute. **GPS:** n47,68022 e9,55308.⬆➡

9 ⌁€ 9 ⌁Ch ⌁(9x)€0,50/kWh Ⓦ ⌁€ 1. **Surface:** grassy/gravel.
◼ 01/01-31/12
Distance: ⌁on the spot ⌁Bodensee 5km ⊗200m ⌁100m.

Meersburg/Bodensee ❀ ⛵ 19B2
Ergeten, Allmendweg. **GPS:** n47,70160 e9,26898.⬆

35+60 ⌁€ 10/24h ⌁€1/100liter ⌁€ 1 Ch ⌁€0,50/kWh Ⓦ.
Surface: metalled. ◼ 01/01-31/12
Distance: ⌁1km ⊗100m ⌁50m ⌁shuttle to centre.
Remarks: At edge of city, + 2x parking Allmendweg P1 n47.70211, o 9.26983, P2 n47,70159, o 9,27172.

Meißenheim 18G1
Wohnmobilpark Ortenau, Winkelstrasse 36.
GPS: n48,41616 e7,77736.⬆➡

24+24 🏕 € 5/day 🚰€1/120liter 🔌💧(24x)€1/kWh.♿
Location: Rural, comfortable. **Surface:** gravel/metalled.
🅾 01/01-31/12
Distance: 🚶500m 🛒800m.

🛉S **Memmingen** 🍽 **19C1**

Wohnmobilstellplatz Memmingen, Colmarer Straße/Hemmerlestraße. **GPS:** n47,99531 e10,18245. ⬆➡

20 🏕 € 1/2h, € 5/24h 🚰€1/100liter 🔌Ch💧(18x)€0,50/kWh. 🚐
Location: Urban, simple. **Surface:** metalled.
🅾 01/01-31/12
Distance: 🚶900m 🚲2,2km 🛒700m 🛒Lidl 600m.
Remarks: Max. 3 days.

🛉S **Mengen** 🌳🌲 **19B1**

Südsee III, Uferweg 25. **GPS:** n48,03117 e9,28265. ⬆➡

50 🏕 € 9,50 🚰€1/80liter 🔌Ch💧(16x)€0,50/kWh WC included
📶. **Location:** Rural, comfortable, quiet. **Surface:** gravel.
🅾 01/01-31/12
Distance: 🚶500m 🏊on the spot 🛒on the spot 🛒500m 🎣on the spot.
Remarks: Incl. access Badesee.

🛉S **Messkirch** 🌿 **19A1**

Messplatz P2, Am Stachus. **GPS:** n47,99381 e9,11514. ⬆

4 🏕free 🚰€1/80liter 🔌ChWC. **Location:** Urban, simple.
Surface: metalled. 🅾 01/01-31/12, service 01/04-30/09
Distance: 🚶500m 🛒400m 🛒200m 🚌500m.

🛉S **Metzingen** 🚂🍽 **16B3**

Reisemobilplatz Outletcity Metzingen, Stetterstrasse 4.
GPS: n48,53241 e9,27574. ⬆

20 🏕 € 10 🚰🔌Chincluded 💧(6x)€3,16Amp. **Location:** Urban,

---

simple. **Surface:** gravel. 🅾 01/01-31/12
Distance: 🚶800m 🏊800m 🛒800m 🛒800m 🚐shuttle every 15 min.
Remarks: Money in envelope in mail box.

🛉S **Mosbach** 🌿🚂🍽 **16A2**

Wasemweg. GPS: n49,36139 e9,14833. ⬆

10 🏕free 🚰€1/150liter 🔌Ch💧(10x)€1/12h. **Location:** Rural, comfortable, quiet. **Surface:** concrete.
🅾 01/01-31/12
Distance: 🚶800m.

🛉S **Mössingen** **19A1**

Wohnmobilstellplatz Firstwald, Firstwaldstraße, Kernstadt.
GPS: n48,41348 e9,06915. ⬆

10 🏕free 🚰€1/50liter 🚰€1/time Ch💧(10x)€0,50/kWh,16Amp.
Location: Urban, simple. **Surface:** grasstiles.
🅾 01/01-31/12
Distance: 🚶1,5km 🛒500m 🛒1km 🚌100m.

🛉 **Muggensturm** **15H3**

Muggensturm, Vogesenstraße. **GPS:** n48,87946 e8,28721. ⬆

3 🏕free. **Location:** Urban, simple. **Surface:** gravel.
🅾 01/01-31/12
Distance: 🚶1,5km 🚲4,4km 🏊beach 100m.

🐟S **Mühlberg** 🏔 **19C1**

Ferienhof Musch, Unterer weg 7. **GPS:** n47,98534 e9,98697. ⬆

3 🏕 € 10, 2 pers.incl 🚰🔌Ch💧(3x)included WC🚽€3 📶€2,50/day. **Surface:** grassy/metalled. 🅾 01/01-31/12
Distance: 🚶10km 🏊100m 🛒100m 🛒10km 🛒10km.
Remarks: Bread-service.

🐟 **Müllheim** 🚂 **18G2**

Am Engelberg, Hügelheim. **GPS:** n47,83282 e7,62320. ⬆➡

2 🏕free. **Location:** Rural, simple, isolated, quiet.
🅾 01/01-31/12
Distance: 🚶500m 🛒1,5km.

🛉S **Müllheim** 🚂 **18G2**

Am Nüsslegarten, Am Nüsslegarten, Britzingen.
GPS: n47,82891 e7,67336. ⬆

2 🏕free. **Location:** Rural, simple, quiet. 🅾 01/01-31/12

🛉S **Müllheim** 🚂 **18G2**

Freibad Müllheim, Ziegleweg 7. **GPS:** n47,80237 e7,63403. ⬆

3 🏕free. **Location:** Urban, simple. **Surface:** asphalted.
🅾 01/01-31/12
Remarks: Next to swimming pool.

🛉S **Müllheim** 🚂 **18G2**

Parkplatz Nußbaumallee, Nußbaumallee.
GPS: n47,80942 e7,62985. ⬆

3 🏕free. **Location:** Urban, simple. **Surface:** asphalted.
🅾 01/01-31/12
Remarks: Max. 2 days.

🛉S **Müllheim** 🚂 **18G2**

Markgräfler Kräuterhof, Im Käppeleacker 3, Hügelheim.
GPS: n47,83237 e7,62045.

4 🏕free 💧free. **Location:** Urban, simple. **Surface:** grasstiles.
🅾 01/01-31/12
Distance: 🚶500m 🛒1km.
Remarks: Herbery, herb-stube.

🛉S **Münsingen** **19B1**

Wiesentalstadion, Grafenecker Straße. **GPS:** n48,40939 e9,48580. ⬆

DE

18 € 5/24h, 3 days € 12 €1/100liter Ch €1/6h.
Location: Urban, simple. **Surface:** gravel. 01/01-31/12
Distance: 1km 200m within walking distance on the spot on the spot on the spot.

Murg 18H2

Am Freibad. **GPS**: n47,55196 e8,02403.

15 € 10 €1/100liter €0,50/kWh. **Location:** Rural, comfortable, quiet. **Surface:** metalled. 01/01-31/12
Distance: 500m on the spot.

Murrhardt 16B2

Parkplatz Festhalle, Kaiser-Ludwig-Straße 25.
GPS: n48,97960 e9,57461.

3 free €1/90liter Ch. **Location:** Rural, simple.
Surface: asphalted. 01/01-31/12
Distance: 400m 100m.

Nagold 16A3

Wohnmobilhafen, Am Glockenrain. **GPS**: n48,56389 e8,72306.

12 free €1/80liter €1 Ch€1 (12x)€1/kWh.
Location: Rural, simple, quiet. **Surface:** gravel/metalled.
01/01-31/12
Distance: 1km 25m 900m 400m on the spot on the spot.

Nagold 16A3

Am Bahnhof, Bahnhofstraße. **GPS**: n48,55791 e8,72748.

4 free. **Location:** Rural, simple, noisy. **Surface:** asphalted.
01/01-31/12
Distance: 700m 100m on the spot on the spot on the spot.
Remarks: Max. 4 nights.

Nattheim 16C3

Ramensteinbad, Dieselstrasse 22. **GPS**: n48,70261 e10,23745.

4 free €1/100liter Chfree €1/2kWh. **Location:** Urban, quiet. **Surface:** metalled. 01/01-31/12 25/04-07/05
Distance: 500m 300m 200m Lidl.
Remarks: Parking swimming pool, max. 3 days.

Neckarsulm 16A2

Aquatoll, Reisachmühlweg. **GPS**: n49,18802 e9,24302.

50 free €2/60liter Ch. **Location:** Rural, simple.
Surface: asphalted/gravel. 01/01-31/12
Distance: 4km.
Remarks: Parking swimming pool, max. 24h.

Neckarwestheim 16A2

Wohnmobilstellplätze Im Bühl, Liebensteiner Strasse.
GPS: n49,04186 e9,18797.

2 free €2 Ch (4x)€2/8h. **Surface:** metalled.
01/01-31/12
Distance: 500m 200m 500m.
Remarks: From 4th night € 25/night.

Neresheim 16C3

Stellplatz Alter Bahnhof, Dischinger Straße 11.
GPS: n48,75102 e10,33957.

5 free €1 Ch (4x)€1/4h. **Location:** Noisy.
Surface: metalled. 01/01-31/12
Distance: on the spot 12km on the spot.
Remarks: Service during opening hours.

Neuffen 16B3

Am Schützenhaus, Schützenhausweg. **GPS**: n48,54726 e9,37057.

8 free €2/8minutes Ch (7x)€2/8h. **Location:** Simple.
Surface: asphalted. 01/01-31/12
Distance: 500m 500m 500m on the spot.

Neuhausen ob Eck 19A1

Beim Friedhof. **GPS**: n47,97473 e8,92397.

8 voluntary contribution €1 €1 Ch (9x).
Location: Urban, simple. **Surface:** metalled. 01/01-31/12
Distance: 300m 500m 1km 300m 2km 2km.
Remarks: Max. 3 nights.

Neunkirchen 16A2

Festplatz, Zwingenbergerstrasse. **GPS**: n49,38818 e9,01531.

8 free €1/90liter Ch. **Location:** Simple, quiet.
Surface: asphalted. 01/01-31/12
Distance: 300m.
Remarks: Service next to: Autohaus Weishaupt, Industriestrasse 3 (200m).

Nordheim 16A2

Lauffener Straße. **GPS**: n49,10461 e9,13552.

2 € 5/3 days Ch included. **Location:** Simple.
Surface: asphalted. 01/01-31/12 on the spot on the spot.
Remarks: In front of swimmingpool, max. 3 days.

Nordheim 16A2

Müllers Weingut unf Weinstube, Im Auerberg 3.
GPS: n49,10236 e9,13810.

2 € 5,with electricity and water € 8 Ch. **Location:** Rural.
Distance: 800m on the spot on the spot on the spot on the spot.

Nordrach 18H1

Schwarzwald-Panorama Wohnmobilstellplatz, Im Dorf 29.
GPS: n48,39873 e8,07927.

DE

8 free €1/10liter Ch (8x)6h. **Location:** Rural, simple, central. **Surface:** metalled. 01/01-31/12
Distance: 100m 100m.

Nürtingen 16B3

Stellplatz Plätschwiesen, B313, Plätschwiesen, Oberensingen.
GPS: n48,63645 e9,33051.

12 € 5/24h €1 Ch (8x)€1. **Location:** Urban.
Surface: metalled. 01/01-31/12
Distance: 1km on the spot 500m.
Remarks: Max. 7 days.

Oberkirch 15H3

Am Renchtalstadion, Renchallee. **GPS:** n48,52972 e8,07250.

21 € 5, € 7/2 days + € 2 tourist tax €1/80liter €1 Ch (30x)€ 0,50/kWh.
Location: Rural, simple, quiet. **Surface:** grassy/gravel.
01/01-31/12 week before and week after 1st weekend Sep
Distance: 100m 100m 100m on the spot on the spot.

Oberkirch 15H3

Waldparkplatz Schauenburg, Burgstraße 29.
GPS: n48,53812 e8,09452.

4 € 8 (4x)€2. **Location:** Simple, isolated, quiet.
Surface: grassy/sand. 01/01-31/12
Distance: 500m.
Remarks: Max. 4 days, € 8 voucher restaurant.

Oberndorf/Neckar 19A1

Neckarhalle, Austrasse 12. **GPS:** n48,28222 e8,58472.

8 free €1/70liter Ch (4x)€1/kWh. **Location:** Rural, simple, noisy. **Surface:** asphalted. 01/01-31/12
Distance: 2km 300m 200m 50m on the spot on the spot.

Oberstenfeld 16B2

Mineralfreibad, Beilsteiner Strasse 100. **GPS:** n49,03160 e9,31890.

4 free. **Surface:** asphalted. 01/01-31/12

Oberteuringen 19B2

Ferienhof Kramer, St. Georg strasse 8. **GPS:** n47,73948 e9,47278.

8 € 16, 2 pers.incl Ch (8x)€2 WC €4.
Surface: gravel/metalled. 15/04-15/09
Distance: 2km on the spot 300m 300m.

Offenburg 15H3

Strandbad Gifizsee, Platanenallee 15. **GPS:** n48,45785 e7,93663.
11 € 12 + € 3 /pp (peak season) €1/80liter Ch (11x)€ 0,50/kWh WC. **Location:** Simple. **Surface:** grasstiles.
01/04-31/10
Distance: 2,5km 3,8km 100m on the spot 150m.
Remarks: Bread-service, dog € 1,50/night.

Offenburg 15H3

Bürgerpark, Stegermattstraße 26a. **GPS:** n48,46565 e7,94566.

2 free. **Location:** Urban, simple, quiet. **Surface:** asphalted/metalled.
01/01-31/12
Distance: 500m 300m.
Remarks: In front of swimmingpool.

Offenburg 15H3

Camping Kuhn, Im Drachenacker 4. **GPS:** n48,48039 e7,92776.

10 free €0,50/50liter Ch (8x)free. **Location:** Urban, simple. **Surface:** metalled. 01/01-31/12
Distance: 2km 3,7km 500m.
Remarks: Service during opening hours.

Öhringen 16B2

P Frei- und Hallenbad, Pfaffenmühlweg.
GPS: n49,19771 e9,51137.

15 € 8 Ch included. **Location:** Rural, simple.

Surface: gravel. 01/01-31/12
Distance: 1km 100m.
Remarks: Max. 3 days, to be paid at swimming pool.
Tourist information Öhringen:
RADius. Cycle route, 18km.

Öllingen 16C3

Parking Rathaus, Hauptstrasse. **GPS:** n48,52816 e10,14813.

5 free €4 Ch. **Surface:** grasstiles. 01/01-31/12

Oppenau 15H3

Hauptstrasse. **GPS:** n48,47639 e8,16972.

6 free €1/100liter Ch (6x)€1/8h. **Location:** Rural, simple, quiet. **Surface:** gravel. 01/01-31/12
Distance: 300m 150m bakery 300m on the spot on the spot.

Oppenweiler 16B2

Caravanstation, Murrwiesenstraße 15.
GPS: n48,97999 e9,45898.

2 free €1/80liter Ch. **Surface:** asphalted. 01/01-31/12
Distance: 600m.
Remarks: Max. 2 days.

Ottenhöfen im Schwarzwald 15H3

Bauernhof Murhof, Murhof 1. **GPS:** n48,56005 e8,15350.

15 € 10, 2 pers.incl €1/100liter Ch (15x)€0,50/kWh WC €0,50. **Location:** Rural, simple, quiet. **Surface:** grassy/metalled.
01/04-31/10
Distance: 1km 500m 500m on the spot.
Remarks: Swimming pool 200m.

Pforzheim 16A3

Reisemobilplatz Oststadt am Enzauenpark, Wildersinnstraße.
GPS: n48,89784 e8,72232.

15 ☀free 🚰€1/80liter ⚡(4x)€1/kWh. **Location:** Urban, simple, noisy. **Surface:** metalled. ⬛ 01/01-31/12
Distance: 🛒1,5km ⊗200m 🍴100m 🚌on the spot 🚲on the spot 🚶on the spot.
Remarks: Max. 7 days, service 200m.

🏕🅂 Pforzheim 16A3
Parkplatz 2 Wildpark, Tiefenbronnerstraße. **GPS:** n48,87651 e8,71749.
☀€ 2-4/24h. **Location:** Urban.
Remarks: Max. 1 night.

🅂 Pforzheim 16A3
Hohwiesenweg. **GPS:** n48,89750 e8,72674. ⬆.
4 ☀€1/80liter 💧€1 Ch€1 ⚡(2x)€1/kWh. **Location:** Simple, noisy.
Surface: metalled.
Distance: 🛒1,5km ⊗50m 🍴100m 🚌on the spot 🚲on the spot 🚶on the spot.

🏕🅂 Pfullendorf 19B2
Seepark Linzgau, P-Ost, Bannholzerweg 18. **GPS:** n47,93097 e9,23728.

15 ☀€ 4/24h 🚰. **Surface:** unpaved. ⬛ 01/01-31/12

🏕🅂 Pfullingen 16A3
Wohnmobilplatz Schönbergbad, Klosterstraße.
GPS: n48,45537 e9,22812. ⬆➡.

7 ☀free 🚰€1/50liter 💧€1/time Ch ⚡€1/2kWh. **Location:** Urban, simple. **Surface:** grassy. ⬛ 01/01-31/12
Distance: 🛒1,5km ⊗nearby 🚲on the spot.
Remarks: Max. 4 days.

🏕🅂 Radolfzell 19A2
Wohmobilstellplatz in den Herzen, Zeppelinstraße.
GPS: n47,73888 e8,95331.

15 ☀€ 8/24h 🚰€1/80liter 🔌Ch ⚡(12x)€0,50/kWh.
Surface: metalled. ⬛ 01/01-31/12
Distance: 🛒1km ⚓500m 🍴1km 🚲BodenseeRadweg 🚶Bodensee-Rundwanderweg.
Remarks: Max. 2 nights.

🏕🅂 Radolfzell 19A2
Wohnmobilstellplatz Halbinsel Mettnau, Strandbadstrasse.
GPS: n47,73784 e8,98007. ⬆.

---

12 ☀€ 8/24h 🚰€1/50liter 🔌Ch ⚡(6x)€0,50/kWh.
Surface: asphalted. ⬛ 01/01-31/12
Distance: 🛒500m ⚓700m 🚤700m ⊗500m 🍴700m 🚌100m.
Remarks: Max. 2 nights.

🅲🅂 Radolfzell 19A2
Campingplatz Böhringer See, Hindenburgstrasse.
GPS: n47,76176 e8,93488. ⬆.

10 ☀€ 10-13 🚰 🔌Ch ⚡(5x)€0,50/kWh WC💧€1. **Surface:** metalled.
⬛ 01/01-31/12
Distance: 🛒1km ⊗on the spot 🍴1km.

🏕🅂 Rastatt 15H3
Leopoldring. **GPS:** n48,85409 e8,19970. ⬆➡.

5 ☀€ 5 🚰€1/10minutes 🔌Ch ⚡(8x)€1/6h. 🚲 **Location:** Simple.
Surface: metalled. ⬛ 01/01-31/12
Distance: 🛒500m 🚴3,8km.
Remarks: Check in at pay-desk of swimming pool, discount at swimming pool and sauna.

🏕🅂 Ravensburg 19B2
Wohnmobilstellplatz Ravensburg, Mühlbruckstrasse.
GPS: n47,78196 e9,60001. ⬆➡.

19 ☀€ 8 🚰€1/80liter 🔌Ch ⚡€0,50/kWh. 🚲 **Surface:** metalled.
⬛ 01/01-31/12
Distance: 🛒centre 800m ⊗500m 🍴200m 🚌250m 🚲Donau-Bodensee Radweg.
Remarks: Max. 3 nights.

Tourist information Ravensburg:
ℹ Bodensee-Erlebniskarte. Card gives free access to all boats, telpher carriers, beaches etc. Around the Lake Constance in Germany, Switzerland and Austria. 🎫 € 57/3 days.
ℹ Tourist Information, Kirchstrasse 16. City of the Tore und Turme, gates and towers.

🏕🅂 Rechberghausen 16B3
Sportpark Lindach, Am Desenbach. **GPS:** n48,72405 e9,63594. ⬆➡.

---

6 ☀free 🚰€0,50/80liter 🔌Ch ⚡(6x)€0,50/kWh. **Location:** Rural, simple. **Surface:** grassy. ⬛ 01/04-01/10
Distance: 🛒1km ⚓500m ⊗1km 🍴1km 🚌500m.

🏕🅂 Reichenau 19A2
Zum Sandseele. **GPS:** n47,69887 e9,04711. ⬆.

12 ☀€ 12/24h 🚰€1/80liter 🔌Ch ⚡(8x)€1/2kWh.
Surface: asphalted/metalled. ⬛ 01/01-31/12
Distance: 🛒1,5km ⚓on the spot 🚤on the spot ⊗100m 🍴2km.
Remarks: Max. 1 night.

🏕🅂 Reutlingen 16A3
P&R Parkplatz, Am Südbahnhof/Marktstrasse.
GPS: n48,48280 e9,22982. ⬆➡.

3 ☀free 🚰 🔌Ch. **Location:** Urban, simple, noisy. **Surface:** gravel.
⬛ 01/01-31/12
Distance: 🛒3km ⊗on the spot 🚌on the spot.
Remarks: In front of motorhome dealer Berger, max. 48h.

🏕🅂 Reutlingen 16A3
Sportpark Markwasen, Hermann-Hesse-Straße.
GPS: n48,47536 e9,19377. ⬆.

10 ☀€ 8 🚰€1/80liter 🔌Ch ⚡(8x)€0,50/kWh. 🚮
Location: Urban, simple. **Surface:** gravel. ⬛ 01/01-31/12
Distance: 🛒3km.
Remarks: Public transport included.

🏕🅂 Rheinmünster 15H3
Freizeit Center Oberrhein, Am Campingpark 1.
GPS: n48,77250 e8,04240. ⬆.

20 ☀€ 8/24h 🚰€1/80liter 🔌Ch ⚡(20x)€0,50/kWh.
Location: Rural, comfortable, quiet. **Surface:** grassy.
⬛ 01/01-31/12

Distance: ⚓on the spot ⊗200m 🏍on the spot 🚶on the spot.

| 🚐S | **Riedlingen** | 19B1 |

Stadthalle, Hindenburgstraße. **GPS:** n48,15189 e9,47766.➡️.

3 🚐free 🔌€1/100liter 🗑Ch 💧€1/4h. **Location:** Urban.
Surface: asphalted. 🅾 01/01-31/12
Distance: 🚶300m ⊗200m 🛒100m.

| 🚐S | **Rielasingen-Worblingen** 🌿 | 19A2 |

Naturbad Aachtal, Herdweg. **GPS:** n47,72127 e8,86332.⬆️.
🚐free, May-Sep € 4,50/day 🔌€1/100liter 🗑Ch 💧€0,50/kWh
🅾01/05-30/09. **Location:** Rural. **Surface:** gravel. 🅾 01/01-31/12
Distance: 🚶600m.

| 🚐S | **Rottenburg/Neckar** 🌿⛲🍽 | 16A3 |

Wohnmobilhafen Neckarufer, Ulmenweg 4.
GPS: n48,47213 e8,95010.⬆️➡️.

12 🚐€5 🔌€1/80liter 🗑Ch 💧(8x)€0,50/kWh. 🏭
Location: Urban, simple. **Surface:** asphalted. 🅾 01/01-31/12
Distance: 🚶800m ⚓800m ⊗800m 🏍on the spot.
Remarks: Max. 3 days.

| 🚐S | **Rottweil** 🌿⛲ | 19A1 |

Parkplatz, Stadionstrasse. **GPS:** n48,15556 e8,62861.⬆️➡️.

16 🚐€5 🔌€1 🗑Ch 💧(16x)€1/8h. **Location:** Urban, simple.
Surface: gravel. 🅾 01/01-31/12
Distance: 🚶1km ⊗1km ⚓1km 🛒500m.
Remarks: Parking stadium.

| ☺S | **Rust** ⛲ | 18G1 |

Europapark Rust, Europa-Parkstrasse. **GPS:** n48,27189 e7,71745.⬆️➡️.

200 🚐8-20h € 2/h (max. € 6), 20-8h € 2/h (max. € 22) 🔌€1 🗑
Ch 💧WC 🅾included. 🏭
Location: Simple. **Surface:** asphalted.
🅾 03/04-07/11, 27/11-09/01 9-18
Distance: ⊗on the spot.

Tourist information Rust:
😊 Europa-park, Europa-Park-Straße 2. Large amusement and theme
park with Europe as theme. 🅾 03/04-07/11, 27/11-09/01 9-18h.

| 🚐S | **Sankt Blasien** ⛪ | 18H2 |

Rehbach in Menzenschwand, Rehbachweg, Sankt Blasien.
GPS: n47,81306 e8,06933.⬆️.

20 🚐€6 🔌🗑Ch 💧(16x)€3/24h. **Location:** Rural, simple, quiet.
Surface: gravel.
🅾 01/01-31/12
Distance: 🚶St Blasien 8km 🍞bakery 500m 🚶on the
spot 🚶on the spot.
Remarks: At ski-lift Rehbach, in winter time not always easy to reach.

| 🚐S | **Sasbachwalden** 🌿⛲🍽 | 15H3 |

Wohnmobilstellplatz Alde Gott, Talstraße 2.
GPS: n48,61945 e8,12094.⬆️➡️.

30 🚐€7/night 🔌€1/100liter 🗑Ch 💧(20x)€2/24h. 🏭
Location: Rural, comfortable, quiet. **Surface:** gravel/metalled.
🅾 01/01-31/12
Distance: 🚶centre 300m 🚴9km 🏊9km ⊗100m ⚓250m 🏊250m
🛒100m 🏍on the spot 🚶on the spot.
Remarks: Waterfall 1km, swimming pool 800m.

| 🚐S | **Schiltach** 🏔🌿⛲ | 18H1 |

P1, Lehewiese. **GPS:** n48,29111 e8,34250.⬆️➡️.

10 🚐free 🔌💧(3x). **Location:** Simple, quiet. **Surface:** gravel.
🅾 01/01-31/12
Distance: 🚶200m ⊗50m ⚓50m 🛒on the spot 🏍on the spot 🚶on
the spot.
Remarks: Busy parking during the day.

| 🚐S | **Schluchsee** 🏔 | 18H2 |

P Aqua Fun, Faulenfürster Straße. **GPS:** n47,81569 e8,18113.⬆️.

20 🚐€8 🔌€1/100liter 💧€1/8h. 🏭 **Location:** Rural, comfortable,
central, quiet. **Surface:** asphalted.
🅾 01/01-31/12
Distance: ⚓200m.
Remarks: Max. 1 night.

| 🚐S | **Schonach im Schwarzwald** 🏔❄ | 18H1 |

Parkplatz Obertal, Schwimmbadweg. **GPS:** n48,14573 e8,18872.⬆️.

10 🚐€7 🔌€1 🗑€0,50 Ch 💧(8x)€1/8h. **Location:** Rural,
comfortable. **Surface:** grasstiles. 🅾 01/01-31/12
Distance: 🚶1km ⚓650m 🏍on the spot 🏊on the spot.
Remarks: Max. 3 nights, coins at tourist info, free entrance swimming
pool, ski-lift and public transport.

| 🚐S | **Schorndorf** | 16B3 |

Gmünder Straße 84/1. GPS: n48,80539 e9,54187.⬆️.

7 🚐€5 + € 4/pp 🔌€2 🗑Ch€2 💧WC🅾€2 🅾€2 📶€1. 🚿
Location: Simple. **Surface:** metalled. 🅾 01/01-31/12
Distance: 🚶10min.

| 🚐S | **Schramberg** 🍽 | 18H1 |

Bahnhofstraße, B462. GPS: n48,23017 e8,38323.⬆️.

2 🚐free 🔌€1/80liter 🗑€1 Ch€1. **Location:** Rural, simple, noisy.
Surface: metalled. 🅾 01/01-31/12
Distance: 🚶on the spot ⊗100m ⚓50m 🛒10m 🏍on the spot
🚶on the spot.

| 🚐S | **Schwäbisch Gmünd** | 16B3 |

Schiesstalplatz, Schiesstalstraße. **GPS:** n48,80543 e9,81308.⬆️.

8 🚐free 🔌€1/50liter 🗑Ch 💧(8x)0,50/kWh. **Location:** Rural,
simple. **Surface:** gravel. 🅾 01/01-31/12
Distance: 🚶1km ⊗50m 🛒500m.
Remarks: Motorhome < 7m, max. 5 days a month.

| 🚐S | **Schwäbisch Hall** | 16B2 |

Wohnmobilstellplatz Auwiese, Spitalmühlenstraße.
GPS: n49,12218 e9,73473.⬆️➡️.

7 🚐free. **Surface:** gravel. 🅾 01/01-31/12
Distance: 🚶1,5km ⊗100m.
Remarks: Max. 48h.

DE

Schwaigern 16A2

Wohnmobilstellplatz Schaigern, Gemminger Straße 91.
GPS: n49,14576 e9,04529. ⬆.

2 🛏free 🚰€1 🔵Ch 🔌free. **Surface:** asphalted.
🔘 01/01-31/12
Distance: 🚶1km ⊗300m 🐕 on the spot 🧍 on the spot.

Schwetzingen 15H2

Ketscher Landstrasse. **GPS**: n49,37803 e8,55820. ⬆.

12 🛏free 🚰€3/80liter 🔵Ch. **Location:** Simple.
Surface: grasstiles/metalled. 🔘 01/01-31/12
Distance: 🚶500m ⊗on the spot 🍽on the spot 🐕on the spot
🧍on the spot.
Remarks: Max. 3 nights, noisy place.

Seelbach 18H1

Reisemobil-Wellness-Stellplatz Schwarzwälder Hof, Am Tretenbach.
GPS: n48,30042 e7,94497. ⬆.

16 🛏€18 🚰€1/90liter 🔵Ch 🔌(16x)kWh WC🚽 📶 📠
Location: Rural, comfortable. **Surface:** metalled.
🔘 01/01-31/12
Distance: 🚶600m ⊗100m.
Remarks: Including access to swimming pool, use sanitary facilities,
entrance 1p wellness/sauna.

Seewald 15H3

P4, L362. **GPS**: n48,55131 e8,49522. ⬆➡.

17 🛏free WCfree. **Location:** Rural, simple, quiet. **Surface:** asphalted.
🔘 01/01-31/12 ▪ service 01/11-31/03
Distance: 🚶1,5km 🛒25m ⊗600m.

Sigmaringen 19B1

Wohnmobilplatz Sigmaringen, Georg Zimmerer Straße 4.
GPS: n48,08545 e9,21029. ⬆➡.

20 🛏€8 🚰€1/80liter 🔵Ch🔌(20x)€1/4h. 🚐 **Location:** Simple.
Surface: metalled. 🔘 01/01-31/12
Distance: 🚶500m ⊗500m 🍽200m on the spot.

Sindelfingen 16A3

Badezentrum Sindelfingen, Hohenzollernstrasse.
GPS: n48,71993 e9,01779. ⬆.

10 🛏free. **Location:** Urban, simple. **Surface:** asphalted.
🔘 01/01-31/12
Distance: ⊗on the spot 🚐on the spot 🐕on the spot 🧍on the spot.

Singen 19A2

P Landesgartenschau, Schaffhauserstrasse.
GPS: n47,75992 e8,82766. ⬆➡.

20 🛏free 🚰🔵Chfree 🔌(16x)€1/6h. **Surface:** grassy/gravel.
🔘 01/01-31/12, service 15/03-15/11
Distance: 🚶1km ⊗on the spot 🚐200m.
Remarks: Max. 72h.

Singen 19A2

Hallenbad, Waldeckstraße 4. **GPS**: n47,76472 e8,84781. ⬆.
3 🛏free. **Surface:** asphalted. 🔘 01/01-31/12
Distance: 🚶500m.
Remarks: At swimming pool.

Sinsheim 16A2

Wohnmobilpark Sinsheim, Am Ilvesbach.
GPS: n49,25022 e8,88002. ⬆.
32 🛏€6 🚰€1/100liter 🔵Ch 🔌€0,50/kWh 📶 📠
Surface: metalled. 🔘 01/01-31/12
Distance: 🚐300m.
Remarks: Discount at swimming pool.

Sinsheim 16A2

Schwimmbadweg 11b. **GPS**: n49,24778 e8,88667. ⬆➡.

5 🛏free. **Location:** Rural, comfortable, quiet. **Surface:** asphalted.
🔘 01/01-31/12
Distance: 🚶1,5km ⊗1,5km.
Remarks: Max. 48h.

Stetten 19B2

Alte Brennerei, Riedetsweilerstrasse 5. **GPS**: n47,69326 e9,29788. ⬆.

15 🛏€9 🚰€1 🔵Ch 🔌(6x)€0,50/kWh. **Surface:** grassy/gravel.
🔘 01/01-31/12
Distance: 🚶300m ⛰2km 🛒2km ⊗300m 🍽300m 🚐300m.

Stockach/Bodensee 19A2

Reisemobilhafen 'Papiermühle', Johann-Glatt-strasse 3.
GPS: n47,84169 e8,99945. ⬆.

85 🛏€10 🚰€0,50/50liter 🔵Ch 🔌(118x) WC🚽.
Surface: gravel/metalled. 🔘 01/01-31/12
Distance: 🚶1,5km ⊗on the spot 🚐700m.

Sulz am Neckar 19A1

Stellplatz Wöhrd, Ludwigstraße. **GPS**: n48,36427 e8,63681. ⬆➡.

6 🛏free 🚰€1/80liter 🔵Ch 🔌(4x)€0,50/kWh.
Location: Rural, simple, quiet. **Surface:** metalled.
🔘 01/01-31/12
Distance: 🚶300m ⊗100m 🍽100m on the spot 🐕on the spot
🧍on the spot.

Sulzburg 18G2

Camping Sulzbachtal, Sonnmatt 4. **GPS**: n47,84773 e7,69868. ⬆➡.

10 🛏€15 + tourist and eco tax 🚰🔵Ch 🔌(10x)€0,70/
kWh WC🚽 📶 included. 🚿♨ **Location:** Comfortable.
Surface: grassy/gravel. 🔘 01/01-31/12
Distance: 🚶500m ⊗on the spot.

Tauberbischofsheim 16B1

P Freibad, Vittryallee. **GPS**: n49,62155 e9,66632. ⬆.

3 🛏free 🚰🔵ChWCfree 🚽€0,50, during opening hours.
Location: Simple. **Surface:** asphalted. 🔘 01/01-31/12
Distance: 🚶500m ⊗300m 🍽100m 🚐500m.
Remarks: Service at Kläranlage ma-do 7-16 uur.

🚐 [S] Tettnang 19B2

Loretostrasse. **GPS**: n47,66425 e9,59175.[↑][→].

14 🚐 € 5 🚰 € 1 🚽 € 1 Ch € 1 🔌 (8x) € 1/8h. 🚻
Surface: grassy/metalled. ◘ 01/01-31/12
Distance: 🏘 800m 🍴 200m 🛒 200m 🚌 200m.

⛺ [S] Tettnang 19B2

Gutshof Camping Badhütten, Badhütten, Laimnau.
GPS: n47,63370 e9,64668.[↑].

70 🚐 € 20 🚰 € 1 🚽 Ch 🔌 € 1/3kWh WC 🚿 € 1. **Surface:** grassy.
◘ 01/01-31/12

⛺ [S] Titisee 18H2

Camping Bankenhof, Bruderhalde 31a, Hinterzarten.
GPS: n47,88643 e8,13046.[↑].

8 🚐 € 14, 2 pers incl 🚰 🚽 Ch 🔌 WC 🚿 included 🧺 € 3/3 📶 € 0,50/h.
Location: Rural, comfortable, quiet.
Surface: gravel/sand.
◘ 01/01-31/12
Distance: 🏘 3km 🌊 Titisee 600m 🚲 on the spot 🚶 on the spot ⛷ 3km.
Remarks: Pay at reception.

🚐 [S] Todtmoos 18H2

Jägermatt, Vordertodtmoos. **GPS**: n47,73390 e8,00285.[↑][→].

30 🚐 € 5 🚰 🚽 Ch included. 🚻 **Location:** Rural, simple, noisy.
Surface: gravel/metalled. ◘ 01/01-31/12
Distance: 🏘 1km 🛒 50m.

🚐 Triberg im Schwarzwald 18H1

Sommerauer Strasse, Nußberg. **GPS**: n48,13161 e8,25294.[↑][→].

20 🚐 free. **Location:** Rural, simple. **Surface:** gravel.
◘ 01/01-31/12
Distance: 🏘 2km 🍴 on the spot.

🚐 [S] Trochtelfingen 19B1

Eberhard-von Werderberg-Halle, Siemensstrasse.
GPS: n48,30811 e9,23546.[→].

20 🚐 € 3 🚰 € 1/80liter 🚽 Ch 🔌 (4x)free,16Amp. **Location:** Urban, simple. **Surface:** gravel. ◘ 01/01-31/12
Distance: 🏘 Old city centre 🛒 500m 🚌 500m 🚶 on the spot.
Remarks: To be paid at town hall.

🏭 Trochtelfingen 19B1

Kräuter- und Erlebnisgarten Alb-Gold Nudelfabrik, Grindel 1.
GPS: n48,32838 e9,24001.[↑].

4 🚐 free. **Location:** Rural, simple, noisy. **Surface:** metalled.
◘ 01/01-31/12
Distance: 🏘 3km 🍴 on the spot 🛒 on the spot 🚶 on the spot.

🚐 [S] Tuttlingen 19A1

Stellplatz Donaupark, Stuttgarter strasse.
GPS: n47,98490 e8,81316.[↑].

10 🚐 free 🚰 € 1/5minutes 🚽 € 1/time Ch 📶. **Location:** Urban, simple.
Surface: metalled. ◘ 01/01-31/12
Distance: 🏘 500m 🍴 500m 🛒 500m 🚌 500m 🚲 Donauradweg.
Remarks: Max. 3 nights.

🚐 [S] Überlingen 19A2

Reisemobilhafen Überlingen, Kurt-Hahn-strasse.
GPS: n47,77617 e9,15046.

20 🚐 € 6-10 🚰 € 0,50/70liter 🚽 € 0,50 Ch 🔌 (30x) € 0,50/2kWh WC. 🚻
Surface: asphalted/gravel. ◘ 01/01-31/12
Distance: 🏘 1km 🌊 1km 🎣 1km 🍴 200m 🛒 1,5km 🚌 200m.
Remarks: Max. 3 days, price incl. bus transport (max. 5 pers) to the city centre.

🚐 [S] Uhldingen-Mühlhofen 19B2

Ehbachstrasse. **GPS**: n47,72535 e9,23649.[↑].

21 🚐 8-18h € 1,50/h, max. € 5, night € 10 🚰 € 1 🚽 € 1 Ch WC.
Surface: grasstiles/metalled. ◘ 01/03-31/10
Distance: 🏘 1km 🌊 2km 🎣 2km 🍴 kiosk on the spot 🛒 300m.
Remarks: Max. 24h.

🚐 [S] Ulm 16C3

P+R Friedrichsau, Wielandstrasse. **GPS**: n48,40774 e10,00929.[↑][→].

50 🚐 free 🚰 € 1 🚽 Ch. **Location:** Urban, simple, central.
Surface: metalled. ◘ 01/01-31/12
Distance: 🍴 175m 🚌 on the spot.
Remarks: Max. 3 days, green zone: environmental badge obligatory.

🏭 [S] Ummendorf 19B1

Bräuhaus Ummendorf, Bachstrasse 10.
GPS: n48,06340 e9,83252.[↑][→].

5 🚐 free 🚰 🔌 (5x) € 3/day WC 🚿 € 3 📶. **Surface:** metalled.
◘ 01/01-31/12
Distance: 🏘 300m 🍴 on the spot 🛒 800m 🚌 100m.
Remarks: 3 days free stay.

🚐 [S] Unterkirnach 18H1

Reisemobilhafen Am Rathaus, Rathausplatz.
GPS: n48,07719 e8,36707.[↑][→].

16 🚐 € 9 🚰 🚽 Ch 🔌 included. **Location:** Urban, luxurious, quiet.
Surface: gravel.
◘ 01/01-31/12
Distance: 🏘 on the spot 🌊 400m 🎣 500m 🍴 200m 🛒 300m 🚌 200m ⛷ 150m ⛷ 400m.
Remarks: Pay at tourist office, alternative arrangement if full.

🍴 [S] Unterkirnach 18H1

Ackerloch-Grillschopf, Unteres Ackerloch 2.
GPS: n48,08473 e8,36573.[↑].

DE

20 🛏 € 4, tourist tax € 2,10/pp 🚐 Ch 🔌 WCincluded. 🧺
Location: Rural, simple. **Surface:** unpaved.
⬤ Nov
Distance: 🚶1,5km ⊗on the spot 🚶on the spot 🎿on the spot 🏊on the spot.

Untermünkheim — 16B2
Wohnmobilpark Ostertag, Kupfer Straße 20, Übrigshausen.
GPS: n49,17603 e9,71321.⬆️.

10 🛏 € 8 🚐 Ch 🔌 €0,50 🛢€1. **Location:** Rural, comfortable.
Surface: grassy/gravel. ⬤ 01/03-30/11
Distance: ⊗50m.
Remarks: At manege.

Villingen/Schwenningen — 19A1
Messegelände VS-Schwenningen, Waldeckweg.
GPS: n48,05028 e8,54056.⬆️.

4 🛏free 🚐€1 Ch. **Location:** Urban, simple, noisy.
Surface: asphalted. ⬤ 01/01-31/12
Distance: 🚶1km 🛒500m.

Vogtsburg im Kaiserstuhl — 18G1
Hauptstraße/L115, Oberrotweil. **GPS:** n48,09000 e7,64361.

8 🛏free. **Location:** Rural, simple, isolated, quiet.
⬤ 01/01-31/12
Distance: 🚶800m.

Waiblingen — 16B3
Parkplatz Hallenbad, An der Talaue. **GPS:** n48,83029 e9,32540.⬆️.

20 🛏 € 6/24h, 19-9h € 2 🚐€1/80liter Ch 🔌(6x)€1/kWh WC.
Location: Urban. **Surface:** gravel. ⬤ 01/01-31/12
Distance: 🚶500m 🏊500m 🛒50m 🛢300m 🚰600m.
Remarks: Parking swimming pool, max. 3 nights, during congresses special tariff.

Waldkirch — 18H1
Reisemobilstellplatz Am Stadpark, Am Stadtrain.
GPS: n48,09023 e7,95833.⬆️.

10 🛏free 🚐€1/80liter 🛢€1 Ch€1. **Location:** Urban, simple, central.
Surface: asphalted. ⬤ 01/01-31/12
Distance: 🚶500m.
Remarks: Max. 2 days.

Waldshut-Tiengen — 18H2
Wohmobil-Park Waldshut-Tiengen, Jahnweg 22, Waldshut.
GPS: n47,61121 e8,22513.⬆️➡️.

44 🛏 € 10 🚐€1/100liter Ch 🔌€1/kWh 🛢€0,50. **Location:** Urban, luxurious, quiet. **Surface:** metalled. ⬤ 01/01-31/12
Distance: ⊗on the spot.
Remarks: Along the Rhine river, bread-service.

Walldürn — 16B1
Basilikaplatz, Hauptstrasse. **GPS:** n49,58637 e9,36726.⬆️.

8 🛏free 🚐€1/80liter 🔌(4x)€0,50/kWh. **Location:** Rural, simple.
Surface: gravel. ⬤ 01/01-31/12
Distance: 🚶250m ⊗400m.
Remarks: Pilgrimage site.

Walldürn — 16B1
Goldschmitt Technik-Center, Industrieparkstrasse.
GPS: n49,58977 e9,39339.⬆️.

30 🛏free 🚐€1/80liter Ch 🔌(18x)€0,50/kWh.
Location: Rural, comfortable. **Surface:** asphalted/gravel.
⬤ 01/01-31/12
Distance: 🚶2,6km ⊗100m.
Remarks: Baker every morning.

Wangen im Allgäu — 19B2
P17, Am Klösterle. **GPS:** n47,68160 e9,83401.⬆️➡️.

40 🛏 € 7 + € 1,30/pp tourist tax 🚐€0,50/120liter Ch 🔌(46x) WC.
🛢 **Surface:** metalled. ⬤ 01/01-31/12

Distance: 🚶on the spot 🏊500m 🚶500m ⊗on the spot 🛒on the spot 🚰on the spot.
Remarks: Tourist tax € 1.

Tourist information Wangen im Allgäu:
ℹ️ Tourist Information, Parkplatz 1, Rathaus. Traditional small Bavarian town. Every Thursday city walk through historical city centre, 15.30-17.
🎫 free.
🎪 ⬤ Wed.

Wehr — 18H2
Ludingarten. **GPS:** n47,62515 e7,90582.⬆️➡️.

10 🛏 € 10 🚐€1/100liter Ch 🔌(8x)€1/8h WC.
Location: Simple, quiet. **Surface:** metalled. ⬤ 01/01-31/12
Distance: 🚶nearby.
Remarks: Pay at tourist office, Hauptstr. 14 or Bistro Gleis 13, Bahnhofplatz.

Weikersheim — 16B1
Parkplatz Tauberwiesen, August-Laukhuff-Straße 15.
GPS: n49,48364 e9,89706.⬆️.

30 🛏free. **Location:** Rural, simple. **Surface:** gravel.
⬤ 01/01-31/12
Distance: 🚶300m 🛒400m.

Weikersheim — 16B1
Campingplatz Schwabenmühle, Weikersheimer Strasse 21, Laudenbach. **GPS:** n49,45795 e9,92691.⬆️.

6 🛏 € 5/night 🚐€2/100liter Ch 🔌(6x)€4/12h. **Location:** Simple.
Surface: gravel. ⬤ Easter-15/10
Distance: 🚶300m 🚰200m.

Weil der Stadt — 16A3
Festplatz, Jahnstrasse. **GPS:** n48,75268 e8,87453.⬆️➡️.

4 🛏free 🚐€1/80liter 🛢€1 Ch€1 🔌(4x)€1/kWh.
Location: Urban, simple, noisy. **Surface:** asphalted.
⬤ 01/01-31/12
Distance: 🚶300m ⊗300m 🛒250m 🏍on the spot 🚶on the spot.
Remarks: Max. 3 days.

Weingarten — 19B2
Festplatz, Abt Hyller Strasse 55. **GPS:** n47,81009 e9,63041.⬆️.
8 🛏 € 5 🚐€1 🛢€1 Ch 🔌€2. **Surface:** metalled. ⬤ 01/01-31/12
Distance: 🚶1km 🚰500m 🏍on the spot 🚶on the spot.
Remarks: Max. 3 nights.

DE

Weinsberg · 16A2

Eugen-Diez-Straße 2. **GPS:** n49,14846 e9,28464. ⬆➡.
6 🚐free ⚡€1 Ch (6x)€0,50/kWh. **Location:** Rural, quiet.
Surface: grasstiles. ⬛ 01/01-31/12
Distance: 500m 2km on the spot on the spot.

Welzheim · 16B2

Aichstruter Stausee, Seiboldsweiler, Aichstrut.
GPS: n48,90020 e9,63719. ⬆.

12 🚐€5 ⚡€1/80liter ChWC. **Surface:** gravel. ⬛ 01/01-31/12
Distance: 5km on the spot on the spot on the spot.
Remarks: At artificial lake, max. 1 week.

Wertheim · 16B1

Wohnmobilstellplatz An der Taubermündung, Linke Tauberstrasse.
GPS: n49,76501 e9,51213. ⬆➡.

54 🚐€7/24h ⚡€1/90liter Ch. **Location:** Simple, noisy.
Surface: gravel.
⬛ 01/01-31/12 2nd sa of the month + high water
Distance: 500m on the spot.
Remarks: Along the Tauber river, max. 3 days.

Wertheim · 16B1

Expocamp, Wertheim Caravaning & Freizeit, Hymerring 1.
GPS: n49,77368 e9,58034. ⬆.

90 🚐free ⚡€1/90liter Ch €1/3h WC during opening hours.
Location: Rural, comfortable. **Surface:** asphalted. ⬛ 01/01-31/12
Distance: 400m 3,7km.
Remarks: Baker at 8am, Wertheim Outletcentrum 100m.
Tourist information Wertheim:
🛍 Wertheim Village, Almosenberg. Outlet-shopping.

Wildberg · 16A3

Wohnmobilstellplatz Wildberg, Klosterhof 4.
GPS: n48,62055 e8,74485. ⬆.

4 🚐free ⚡€1/100liter Ch €1/kWh.
Location: Quiet. **Surface:** asphalted/metalled.
⬛ 01/01-31/12 ⬤ service 01/11-31/03
Distance: historical centre 500m 700m 1km on the spot.
Remarks: Along river, nearby monastery.

Wolfach · 18H1

Ferienhof Bartleshof, Ippichen 6, Ippichen.
GPS: n48,30183 e8,26264. ⬆.

5 🚐€15 ⚡ Ch (4x) €2 €2. **Location:** Rural, simple,
quiet. **Surface:** grassy/gravel. ⬛ 01/01-31/12
Distance: on the spot on the spot.
Remarks: € 10, reduction at restaurant.

Wolfach · 18H1

Trendcamping Schwarzwald, Schiltacher Straße 80, Halbmeil.
GPS: n48,29053 e8,27763. ⬆.

6 🚐€15 + tourist tax ⚡ ChWC included €3 €2. **Location:** Rural, simple, quiet. **Surface:** grassy/sand.
⬛ 10/04-15/10
Distance: on the spot.

Wolfegg/Allgäu · 19B2

Reisemobilhafen Loretopark, Rötenbacher Straße.
GPS: n47,81489 e9,79802. ⬆.
12 🚐€5 ⚡€1/80liter Ch €0,50/kWh. ⬛ 01/01-31/12
Distance: 500m.

Wolfegg/Allgäu · 19B2

Hofgarten, Alttaner strasse. **GPS:** n47,82105 e9,79487. ⬆.

2 🚐€5. **Surface:** gravel/metalled.
⬛ 01/01-31/12
Distance: on the spot.
Remarks: Max. 2 nights.
Tourist information Wolfegg/Allgäu:
Ⓜ Automobilmuseum. 200 oldtimers.
⬛ 01/04-31/10 9.30-18h, 01/11-31/03 Su 10-17h.
Ⓜ Bauernhaus-museum. Open air museum.
⬛ 01/04-31/10 Tue-Su 10-18/17h ⬤ Mo Apr Oct.

Wutöschingen · 18H2

Wohnmobilplatz Degernau, Ofteringer Strasse 1, Degernau.
GPS: n47,66639 e8,37917. ⬆⬆➡.

17 🚐€8/day, 2 pers.incl ⚡€1/100liter Ch (17x)€0,50/kWh,
16Amp WC €1 €3/3 included. **Location:** Rural, comfortable,
quiet. **Surface:** grassy/gravel. ⬛ 01/03-31/10
Distance: on the spot 200m 1km 500m on the spot
on the spot on the spot.
Remarks: Sauna, solarium.

Zell am Harmersbach · 18H1

Stellplatz am Schwimmbad, Nordracher Strasse.
GPS: n48,35146 e8,05942. ⬆➡.

14 🚐€3/20-12h ⚡€1/10minutes Ch (8x)€1/10h.
Location: Rural, simple, quiet. **Surface:** gravel.
⬛ 01/01-31/12
Distance: 2km 2km.

Bavaria

Absberg · 16D2

Badehalbinsel Brombachsee, Gunzenhausen-Pleinfeld Ausfart
Absberg. **GPS:** n49,13770 e10,87389.

150 🚐€8/24h ⚡€0,20/60liter Ch (80x)€0,50/kWh WC €0,50.
Location: Rural, comfortable, quiet. **Surface:** grassy.
⬛ 01/04-01/10
Distance: 1km on the spot on the spot 1km on the spot
on the spot.

Adelsdorf · 16D1

Gasthof Niebler, Neuhauser Hauptstrasse 30.
GPS: n49,70017 e10,90221.

4 🚐€15, guests free ⚡. **Surface:** metalled.
⬛ 01/01-31/12
Distance: on the spot on the spot.

Ahorn · 11D3

Freizeitzentrum Wittmannsberg, Badstrasse 20, Eicha.
GPS: n50,22537 e10,90252.

4 🚐free. **Surface:** metalled. ⬛ 01/01-31/12
Distance: on the spot 5km.

Aichach · 16D3

Reisemobilplatz, Franz-Beck-Strasse. **GPS:** n48,45889 e11,12611. ⬆➡.

4 🚐€5 ⚡ Chfree. **Location:** Urban, simple, quiet.
Surface: grassy/gravel. ⬛ 01/01-31/12

Distance: 🚰500m ⊗500m 🚽100m.

🏕️Ⓢ **Albertshofen** 🚤 **16C1**

An der Fähre Mainstockheim-Albertshofen, Mainstraße. **GPS:** n49,77254 e10,15749.⬆️.

10 🏕️€ 5 🚰Ch 🔌included. **Location:** Rural, simple, quiet. **Surface:** gravel. ⏹️ 01/01-31/12
Distance: 🚰on the spot ⛱️on the spot 🚤on the spot ⊗50m 🏍️on the spot.
Remarks: Along Main river, closed when high water.

🍴Ⓢ **Altmannstein** **16E2**

Gasthof Forster, Schulstrasse 9. **GPS:** n48,90125 e11,69559.

20 🏕️guests free 🔌(4x)€2/night. **Surface:** asphalted.
⏹️ 01/01-31/12
Distance: 🚰on the spot ⊗on the spot 🚽3km.
Remarks: Bread-service, check in before 19h (Mo-Tue 16h).

🏕️Ⓢ **Altötting** **19G1**

Griesstraße. **GPS:** n48,22946 e12,67493.⬆️.

8 🏕️free 🚰€1/80liter 🚰Ch 🔌(8x)€1/4h WC.
Location: Urban, simple, noisy. **Surface:** grasstiles. ⏹️ 01/01-31/12
Distance: 🚰5 min ⊗on the spot 🚽on the spot.
Remarks: Max. 3 days.

🏕️Ⓢ **Altötting** **19G1**

P2 Dultplatz, Traunsteinerstrasse. **GPS:** n48,22287 e12,67921.⬆️.

7 🏕️free 🚰€1/10liter 🚰🔌(8x)€1/4h. **Location:** Urban, simple, central. **Surface:** gravel. ⏹️ 01/01-31/12
Distance: 🚰700m.
Remarks: Max. 3 days.

🏕️Ⓢ **Altusried** **19C2**

Am Freibad, Im Tal 4. **GPS:** n47,79915 e10,21934.⬆️➡️.

10 🏕️€ 5 🚰€1 🚰Ch 🔌€0,50/kWh. 🚐 **Location:** Rural, simple, quiet. **Surface:** grassy/gravel. ⏹️ 01/01-31/12
Distance: 🚰500m 🚽700m.
Remarks: Parking at swimming pool.

🏕️Ⓢ **Amberg** 🌿⚓ **16E1**

Gasfabrikstraße. **GPS:** n49,44043 e11,86198.⬆️➡️.

10 🏕️free 🚰stay 🔌(12x)€1/12h. **Location:** Urban, simple, central, quiet. **Surface:** asphalted.
⏹️ 01/01-31/12
Distance: 🚰500m 🚤50m ⊗1km 🚽1km 🏍️50m 🚶50m.

🏕️ **Amorbach** **16A1**

P Altstadt, Dr.F.A.Freundt-Straße. **GPS:** n49,64683 e9,22115.

5 🏕️free. **Location:** Urban, simple. **Surface:** asphalted.
⏹️ 01/01-31/12
Distance: 🚰500m ⊗400m 🚽Lidl.

🏕️Ⓢ **Ansbach** 🌿 **16C2**

Freizeitbad Aquella, Am Stadion 2. **GPS:** n49,30459 e10,55852.⬆️➡️.

12 🏕️free 🚰€0,50/50liter 🚰Ch 🔌(12x)€0,50/kWh.
Location: Simple, central. **Surface:** metalled.
⏹️ 01/01-31/12
Distance: 🚰1km 🚤7,7km ⊗on the spot 🚽1km 🚌on the spot.
Remarks: At swimming pool.

🍴Ⓢ **Arnbruck** 🏔️🌸❄️ **16G2**

Landhotel Rappenhof, Rappendorf 5. **GPS:** n49,13517 e12,95069.

5 🏕️€ 10 🚰🚰Ch 🔌€5 WC 🔌included. **Location:** Simple.
Surface: grassy. ⏹️ 01/01-31/12 ⏹️ 15/11-15/12
Distance: 🚰2km ⊗on the spot 🚽2km 🎿10km 🚡8km.
Remarks: Use of sauna against payment.

🏕️Ⓢ **Arnstein** **11B3**

Badesee, Am Alten Schwimmbad. **GPS:** n49,97667 e9,95917.⬆️.

12 🏕️free 🚰€1/80liter 🚰Ch 🔌(4x)€1/2kWh.
Location: Rural, simple, quiet. **Surface:** grassy/metalled.
⏹️ 01/01-31/12, service 01/04-31/10
Distance: 🚰500m ⛱️100m 🚽100m ⊗snack 100m 🗑️500m
🚶 on the spot.
Remarks: At the old swimming pool.

🏕️ **Arnstein** **11B3**

Cancale Platz. **GPS:** n49,97637 e9,96725.

5 🏕️free. **Location:** Urban. **Surface:** metalled. ⏹️ 01/01-31/12
Distance: 🚰100m ⊗100m 🚽100m.
Remarks: Max. 1 night.

🏕️ **Arzberg** **11E3**

Am Rathausplatz. **GPS:** n50,05528 e12,18870.⬆️.
2 🏕️free. **Surface:** metalled. ⏹️ 01/01-31/12
Distance: 🚰250m ⊗300m 🚽250m.

🏕️Ⓢ **Aschaffenburg** 🌿⚓🍺🌾 **11A3**

Willigesbrücke, Grossostheimerstrasse. **GPS:** n49,97139 e9,13722.⬆️.

25 🏕️€ 3/24h 🔌(18x)€0,50/kWh. 🚐📷 **Location:** Simple, quiet.
Surface: grassy/gravel. ⏹️ 01/01-31/12
Distance: 🚰historical centre 500m 🚤8km 🚌on the spot.
Remarks: Parking along the Main, near Altstadt, being indicated with small signs, max. 3 days.

🍴 **Aschheim** **19E1**

Gasthof Zur Post, Ismaningerstrasse 11. **GPS:** n48,17433 e11,71490.

2 🏕️€ 10. **Surface:** asphalted. ⏹️ 01/01-31/12
Distance: 🚰on the spot ⊗on the spot 🚽300m.

🏕️ **Auerbach** **16E1**

Franz-Josef-Strauß-Platz, Hopfenoher Straße.
GPS: n49,69171 e11,63768.⬆️.

DE

3 ⌇free. **Location:** Simple. **Surface:** grassy.
Distance: 🚰500m ⊗500m 🚿500m.

⌇S **Aufseß** 11D3

Brauerei-Gasthof Reichold, Hochstahl 24.
GPS: n49,88389 e11,26855. 🔼➡️.

38 ⌇€ 7 🚰€1/90liter ⌇Ch🧹(38x)€1,50 WC🧹€1 ⌇.
Location: Rural, comfortable, quiet. **Surface:** grassy/metalled.
🅿 01/01-31/12
Distance: 🚰on the spot ⊗on the spot 🚿on the spot 🚴on the spot 🚶Brauereienweg.
Remarks: Bread-service, breakfast buffet € 8/pp.

⌇S **Aufseß** 11D3

Brauerei Rothenbach, Im Tal 70. **GPS:** n49,88413 e11,22781. 🔼.

3 ⌇€ 5 🧹🚴 **Location:** Urban, simple. **Surface:** metalled.
🅿 01/03-30/10
Distance: 🚰on the spot ⊗on the spot 🚿on the spot 🚴on the spot 🚶on the spot.

⌇S **Augsburg** 16D3

Schillstraße 109, Lechhausen. **GPS:** n48,38914 e10,90435.

4 ⌇€ 5 🚰⌇Ch🧹€1/2kWh WC🧹 ⌇.
Location: Urban. **Surface:** gravel. 🅿 01/01-31/12
Distance: 🚴3,2km Sportgaststätte 🚿200m 🚴on the spot 🚶on the spot.
Remarks: At sports centre.

⌇S **Augsburg** 16D3

Wohnmobilstellplatz Wertach, Bürgemeister Ackermann strasse 1.
GPS: n48,36944 e10,87750. 🔼➡️.

12 ⌇€ 8 🚰€1/90liter ⌇Ch🧹€1/6h. 🏠 **Location:** Urban, simple.
Surface: gravel. 🅿 01/01-31/12
Distance: 🚰on the spot 🚴4,5km 🏊on the spot ➡️on the spot ⊗500m 🚿500m.

⌇S **Bad Abbach** 16E2

Kaiser-Therme, Kurallee 4. **GPS:** n48,92712 e12,04044. 🔼.

34 ⌇€ 10 + € 1,80/pp 🚰€1/4minutes ⌇Ch🧹(16x) WC🧹 ⌇.
Surface: grasstiles/grassy. 🅿 01/01-31/12
Distance: 🚰2km.
Remarks: Check in at pay-desk of the Therme.

⌇S **Bad Aibling** 19F1

Stellplatz an der Therme P13, Lindenstrasse/Heubergstrasse.
GPS: n47,85639 e12,00583. 🔼➡️.

25 ⌇€ 7 🚰⌇Ch🧹€0,50/kWh. **Location:** Comfortable.
Surface: grasstiles/metalled. 🅿 01/01-31/12
Distance: 🚰500m 🏊400m 🚿500m 🚿600m 🚌100m.

⌇S **Bad Bayersoien** 19D2

Wohnmobilstellplatz Bad Bayersoien, Am Bahnhof 6.
GPS: n47,68798 e10,99820. ➡️.

12 ⌇€ 9/24h 🚰€1/90liter ⌇Ch🧹€1/2kWh. **Location:** Rural, simple, quiet. **Surface:** gravel. 🅿 01/01-31/12
Distance: 🚰400m 🏊300m 🚿300m ⊗400m 🚿400m.

⌇S **Bad Birnbach** 16G3

Camping Arterhof, Hauptstraße 3, Lengham.
GPS: n48,43512 e13,10939. 🔼.

10 ⌇€ 10 🚰⌇ChWC🧹 📶included. **Location:** Rural, simple, quiet.
Surface: gravel. 🅿 01/01-31/12
Distance: ⊗on the spot.

⌇S **Bad Bocklet** 11B3

Kurgarten, Aschacherstrasse. **GPS:** n50,26490 e10,07486. 🔼➡️.

13 ⌇€ 8, tourist tax incl 🚰€1/80liter ⌇Ch🧹(13x)€0,50/kWh.
Surface: metalled. 🅿 01/01-31/12
Distance: 🚰500m 🚌Free bus to Bad Kissingen.

⌇S **Bad Brückenau** 11B3

Schlosspark König Ludwig I, Schlüchterner Straße.
GPS: n50,30556 e9,74861. 🔼➡️.

10 ⌇€ 8 + € 2,50/pp Gästekarte 🚰€1/100liter ⌇Ch🧹€0,50/kWh.
Surface: asphalted. 🅿 01/01-31/12
Distance: 🚰4km 🚿50m.

⌇S **Bad Brückenau** 11B3

Sinnflut, Industriestrasse P5. **GPS:** n50,31212 e9,79607. 🔼➡️.

8 ⌇€ 3 🚰⌇Ch🧹(8x)€1. **Surface:** gravel. 🅿 01/01-31/12
Distance: 🚰250m ⊗250m 🚿250m.
Remarks: Parking swimming pool.

⌇S **Bad Brückenau** 11B3

Stellplatz Bahnhofstrasse, Buchwaldstrasse.
GPS: n50,30667 e9,78556. 🔼.

20 ⌇€ 3 🚰€1/8h. **Surface:** metalled. 🅿 01/01-31/12
Distance: 🚰300m ⊗on the spot 🚿on the spot 🚌on the spot.

⌇ **Bad Feilnbach** 19F2

Gasthof Tiroler Hof, Aiblinger strasse 95.
GPS: n47,76476 e12,03857. 🔼🔼.

3 ⌇guests free. **Location:** Simple, isolated. **Surface:** gravel.
🅿 01/01-31/12
Distance: 🚰on the spot ⊗on the spot 🚿1km.

⌇S **Bad Füssing** 16G3

Campingplatz Holmerhof, Am Tennispark 10.
GPS: n48,35798 e13,30658. 🔼.

9 ⌇€ 9,10 🚰€1/30liter ⌇Ch🧹(9x)€2/kWh WC🧹 📶€2.
Location: Rural, simple. **Surface:** metalled. 🅿 01/01-31/12
Distance: 🚰1km ⊗on the spot 🚿1km.
Remarks: Max. 3 days, use sanitary € 5/motorhome, swimming pool

available.

⌂Ⓢ Bad Gögging ⚘ 16E2

Limes-Therme, Am Brunnenforum 1. **GPS**: n48,81857 e11,78868. ⬆.

+20 🚐 € 6, tourist tax € 1,80/pp ⚡€ 0,50/50liter 🗑Ch ⚡.
Location: Simple. **Surface:** asphalted. ☐ 01/01-31/12
Distance: 🚶150m ⊗150m ♨150m.
Remarks: Check in at pay-desk of the Therme.

⌂Ⓢ Bad Griesbach ⚘ 16G3

Mobilhafen Dreiquellenbad, Singham 40.
GPS: n48,42023 e13,19261. ⬆.

29 🚐 € 16,50 + tourist tax ⚡€ 1/80liter 🗑Ch ⚡(29x)€ 0,60/kWh
🗑included 🚿€ 5. **Location:** Rural, simple, quiet. **Surface:** metalled.
☐ 01/01-31/12
Distance: 🚶2km ⊗on the spot.
Remarks: Max. 3 days, thermal-Vital-Oase incl.

☐Ⓢ Bad Hindelang ⛰❄ 19C2

Wiesengrund Wohnmobilpark, Parkplatz Wiesengrund 1.
GPS: n47,49931 e10,37218. ⬆➡.

30 🚐 € 8-10 + tourist tax € 2,10/pp, 7><16 € 1,60, <7 € 0,90 ⚡€ 1/
100liter 🗑Ch ⚡€ 0,50/kWh WC☐€ 1 🚿. **Location:** Rural,
luxurious, quiet. **Surface:** grassy/gravel.
☐ 01/01-31/12
Distance: ⊗on the spot 🚶1km ♨on the spot.

☐Ⓢ Bad Hindelang ⛰❄ 19C2

Wohnmobilplatz Bergheimat, Passstraße 60, Oberjoch.
GPS: n47,51791 e10,42142. ⬆.

10 🚐 € 15, dog € 3,50 ⚡🗑Ch ⚡WC☐€ 1 🚿. **Location:** Rural,
simple, noisy. **Surface:** grassy/gravel.
☐ 01/01-31/12
Distance: 🌊on the spot ♨on the spot.

⌂Ⓢ Bad Kissingen 🌿♨⚘ 11B3

KissSalis Therme, Heiligenfelder Allee 16.
GPS: n50,18861 e10,06139. ⬆➡.

Surface: metalled. ☐ 01/01-31/12
Distance: ♨50m.

18 🚐 € 4 + € 3,40/pp tourist tax ⚡€ 1/90liter 🗑Ch ⚡€ 1/8h.
Surface: asphalted. ☐ 01/01-31/12
Distance: 🚶500m ⊗on the spot ♨on the spot.

⌂Ⓢ Bad Kohlgrub 19D2

Sanatorium Kurhaus Dr. Lauter, Kurhausstrasse 81.
GPS: n47,66412 e11,04315. ⬆.

4 🚐 € 12 ⚡⚡. **Location:** Rural, simple, quiet. **Surface:** gravel.
☐ 01/01-31/12
Distance: 🚶1,5km ⊗on the spot ♨1,5km 🏊1km 🚲1km.

⌂Ⓢ Bad Kohlgrub 19D2

Kur-Camping Waldruh, Sonnen 93. **GPS**: n47,65789 e11,04393. ⬆.

16 🚐 € 10,40 + € 2,50/pp ⚡🗑Ch ⚡€ 0,40/kWh WC☐🔲€ 2,50 🚿
🗑. **Surface:** gravel. ☐ 01/01-31/12
Distance: 🚶1,5km ♨1,5km.

⌂Ⓢ Bad Königshofen 11C3

Frankentherme, Am Kurzentrum 1. **GPS**: n50,30003 e10,47503. ⬆➡.

77 🚐 € 9 ⚡€ 1 🗑Ch ⚡€ 0,50/kWh WC☐.
Surface: grasstiles/metalled.
☐ 01/01-31/12
Remarks: Washing-machine/dryer available, if full 2 alternatives will
be given, special health arrangement possible.

Tourist information Bad Königshofen:
ℹ Kurverwaltung Königshofen, Am Kurzentrum 1,
www.bad-koenigshofen.de.
Traditional small town with half-timbered houses, cycle and hiking
routes in the surroundings.

⌂Ⓢ Bad Kötztingen 🌿⚘ 16G2

Aqacur, Bgm. Seidl Platz. **GPS**: n49,17539 e12,86196.

3 🚐free ⚡€ 1 🗑Ch ⚡€ 1/8h. **Location:** Urban, simple.

⌂Ⓢ Bad Neustadt 11C2

Parkplatz An der Saale. **GPS**: n50,31637 e10,22205. ⬆➡.

60 🚐 € 8 ⚡€ 1/50liter 🗑Ch ⚡(48x)included. 🚌.
Surface: grasstiles. ☐ 01/01-31/12
Distance: 🚶500m.

⌂Ⓢ Bad Reichenhall ⚘ 19G2

Wohnmobilpark Rupertus Therme, Hammerschmiedweg.
GPS: n47,73466 e12,87536. ⬆➡.

25 🚐 € 13, 2 pers.incl ⚡€ 1/80liter 🗑Ch ⚡included.
Location: Comfortable. **Surface:** gravel. ☐ 01/01-31/12
Distance: 🚶500m 🚌on the spot.

⌂Ⓢ Bad Rodach 11C2

ThermeNatur Bad Rodach, Thermalbadstrasse.
GPS: n50,33452 e10,77499.

24 🚐 € 4,50 + € 2/pp tourist tax ⚡€ 1,50 🗑Ch ⚡(16x)€ 1,50 WC☐.
Surface: metalled. ☐ 01/01-31/12, water: 01/04-30/09
Distance: 🚶on the spot ⊗on the spot ♨500m.
Remarks: Caution key service € 10, caution key electricity € 20, key
service at swimming pool.

⌂Ⓢ Bad Steben ⚘ 11E2

An der Therme, P3, Steinbacher Straße. **GPS**: n50,36250 e11,63239. ⬆.

18 🚐 € 5 + € 0,50/pp tourist tax ⚡€ 0,50/80liter 🗑Ch ⚡€ 0,50/kWh
🚿. **Surface:** metalled. ☐ 01/01-31/12
Distance: 🚶500m ⊗200m ♨500m.

☐Ⓢ Bad Tölz 🌿⚓❄ 19E2

Bürgermeister Stohlreiterpromenade. **GPS**: n47,76252 e11,55142. ⬆➡.

30 🚐 € 8/24h ⚡€ 1/50liter 🗑Ch. **Location:** Rural.

DE

Surface: asphalted. ☐ 01/01-31/12
Distance: 🚶1km ⊗500m ⚏500m ⎘500m.
Remarks: Max. 48h, incl. Kurkarte.
Tourist information Bad Tölz:
☺ Alpamare. Large swimming pool complex with wave machine, Alpa, slides, sauna etc. ☐ Su-Thu 8-21h, Fri-Sa 8-22h, 24/12-01/01 8-16h.

Bad Windsheim 🛈 16C1
Phoenix Reisemobilhafen, Bad Windsheimer Strasse 7.
GPS: n49,51361 e10,41722. ⬆➡.

100 ⛽€ 10,90 ⛽€1/100liter ⬛Ch ⚡(80x)€0,50/kWh WC⬛€1 ▣€ 2,50/2,50 📶. **Surface:** gravel. ☐ 01/01-31/12
Distance: 🚶1km ⊗100m ⚏500m.
Remarks: Bread-service.

Bad Windsheim 🛈 16C1
Fränkisches Freilandmuseum, Eisweiherweg.
GPS: n49,49705 e10,41667. ⬆⬆➡.

20 ⛽€ 5 + € 1,60/pp tourist tax. **Surface:** grassy.
☐ 01/01-31/12
Distance: 🚶1km ⊗500m ⚏500m.
Remarks: Open air museum.

Bad Wörishofen 🛈 19D1
Therme Bad Wörishofen, Thermenallee 1.
GPS: n48,02120 e10,59100. ⬆.

25 ⛽€ 9 ⛽€1/100liter ⬛Ch ⚡included WC. 🚿 **Location:** Urban, simple. **Surface:** asphalted. ☐ 01/01-31/12
Distance: 🚶1,5km ⊿4,3km ⊗on the spot ⚏500m ⎘on the spot.
Remarks: Check in at pay-desk of the Therme, max. 3 nights, max. 8M, bread-service.

Balderschwang 🏔❄ 19C2
Wohnmobilplatz Schwabenhof, Schwabenhof 23.
GPS: n47,45745 e10,12963. ⬆.

50 ⛽€ 11-16 ⚏⬛Ch ⚡€3,50/day WC⬛€0,50. 🚿
Location: Rural, comfortable, luxurious.
Surface: grassy/gravel.
☐ 01/01-31/12
Distance: 🚶3km ⊗on the spot ⚏3km ⎘100m ⚡100m ⛷100m.
Remarks: Bread-service, drying room for skis.

Bamberg 🌊 11D3
Wohnmobilplatz, Am Heinrichsdamm. **GPS:** n49,88626 e10,90296. ⬆.

25 ⛽€ 12 ⛽€1/100liter ⬛Ch ⚡€0,50/kWh. 🚐
Location: Urban, simple. **Surface:** gravel. ☐ 01/01-31/12
Distance: 🚶10 min walking ⚏on the spot ⊗on the spot ⎘on the spot.
Remarks: Max. 24h.

Bärnau 🏔🌲❄ 11F3
Gasthof und Wald-Pension Blei, Altglashütte 4.
GPS: n49,77222 e12,38880.

30 ⛽€ 10, guests free ⚏⬛Ch ⚡WC included, customers free.
Surface: asphalted/grassy. ☐ 01/01-31/12
Distance: 🚶6km ⊗on the spot ⚏6km ⎘100m.

Baunach 11D3
Sportplatz-Festplatz, Bahnhofstrasse 14-4.
GPS: n49,98750 e10,85444. ⬆.

5 ⛽free ⚏€1 ⬛Ch ⚡€1/12h. **Surface:** grassy/metalled.
☐ 01/01-31/12
Distance: 🚶200m ⊗200m ⚏200m.
Remarks: Parking at the edge of nature reserve Haßberge, in the old part of the city, max. 2 nights.

Bayerbach 🛈 16G3
Wohnmobilhafen Vital, Huckenham 11.
GPS: n48,41537 e13,13010. ⬆.

10 ⛽€ 12,50 2 pers.incl, dog € 2,50 ⚏⬛Ch ⚡(8x)€0,50/kWh WC⬛included 📶€1. **Location:** Rural, simple, quiet.
Surface: metalled. ☐ 01/01-31/12
Distance: 🚶500m ⊗on the spot.
Remarks: Max. 3 nights, use sanitary facilities at campsite.

Bayreuth ⛲🛈 11E3
P6 Stadthalle, Jean-Paul strasse. **GPS:** n49,94028 e11,57639. ⬆➡.

3 ⛽€ 0,60/30min, max € 10. 🚐 **Location:** Urban, simple, noisy.
Surface: metalled. ☐ 01/01-31/12
Distance: 🚶on the spot ⊗200m ⚏200m.

Bayreuth ⛲🛈 11E3
Lohengrin Therme Bayreuth, Kurpromenade 5.
GPS: n49,94204 e11,63493. ⬆➡.

24 ⛽€ 6 ⚏€1/50liter ⬛€1 ⬛Ch€1 ⚡€1/6h WC⬛€1,50. 🚿
Location: Rural, simple, central, quiet. **Surface:** asphalted.
☐ 01/01-31/12
Distance: 🚶1,5km ⊿3,5km ⊗500m ⚏1km ⎘on the spot 🚲on the spot 🚶on the spot.
Remarks: Bread-service.

Bayrischzell 🏔🌲❄ 19F2
Wohnmobilstellplatz Bayrischzell, Seebergstraße.
GPS: n47,67189 e12,01023. ⬆➡.

20 ⛽€ 10 ⚏€0,50/80liter ⬛Ch ⚡(12x)€0,50/kWh.
Location: Comfortable, central. **Surface:** gravel.
☐ 01/01-31/12
Distance: 🚶400m ⊗400m ⚏400m ⎘400m 🚌bus 5min ⛷on the spot.

Beilngries 🛈 16E2
Landgasthof Euringer, Dorfstrasse 23. **GPS:** n49,01054 e11,50261. ⬆.

6 ⛽guests free ⚏⬛Ch ⚡. **Location:** Urban, simple, central.
Surface: metalled. ☐ 01/01-31/12
Distance: 🚶4km ⊗on the spot ⚏4km.

Beilngries 16E2
An der Altmühl, An der Altmühl. **GPS:** n49,02655 e11,47121.

20 ⛽€ 10 ⚏⬛Ch ⚡WC⬛included. **Location:** Urban, comfortable, central, quiet. **Surface:** grassy.
Remarks: Check in at reception campsite.

Benediktbeuern 🏔🌲🛈 19E2
Wohnmobilstellplatz Benediktbeuren, Schwimmbadstraße 37.
GPS: n47,69920 e11,41556. ⬆➡.

DE

8 🛏 € 7 🚿 Ch included 🚽 € 1/6h. **Location:** Rural, comfortable, quiet. **Surface:** asphalted. 🅿 15/03-01/11
Distance: 🚶1km.
Remarks: Max. 3 nights, Alpenwarmbad 01/05-01/09 (swimming pool).

| 🍴 S | Beratzhausen | 16E2 |

Landgasthof Friesenmühle, Friesenmühle 1.
GPS: n49,08534 e11,81176. ⬆➡.

10 🛏 free, use of a meal desired 🚿🚽 (2x) WC. **Surface:** grassy/gravel. 🅿 01/01-31/12 ⬛ Wed
Distance: 🚶1km ⊗on the spot 🛒1km.
Remarks: Motorhome service: volutary contribution, apply< 22h.

| S | Berching | 16E2 |

Stellplatz Schiffsanleger, Uferpromenade.
GPS: n49,10972 e11,43910. ⬆.
12 🛏 € 5 🚿 € 1 Ch 🚽 € 1/8h. **Surface:** grasstiles/metalled.
🅿 01/01-31/12
Distance: 🚶200m 🛒50m ⊗on the spot 🛒300m 🚌100m.

| S | Berchtesgaden | 19G2 |

Reisemobilplatz Rasp, Renothenweg 15, Oberau.
GPS: n47,65172 e13,07038. ⬆➡.

20 🛏 € 8 + € 2,10/pp tourist tax 🚿 € 2 Ch 🚽 € 2 WC.
Location: Central, quiet. **Surface:** gravel.
🅿 Easter-30/11
Distance: 🚶500m 🛒500m.

| 🚏 | Bergen/Chiemgau ❄ | 19F1 |

Parkplatz Hochfelln-Seilbahn, Maria-Eck-Straße 8.
GPS: n47,79710 e12,59079. ⬆.

10 🛏 € 5. 🏧 **Location:** Simple. **Surface:** metalled.
🅿 01/01-31/12
Distance: 🚶1,2km ⊗on the spot 🚴on the spot.
Remarks: Parking ski-lift, max. 1 night.

| 🍴 S | Bernried | 16G2 |

Altes Gasthaus Artmeier, Innenstetten 45.
GPS: n48,89675 e12,90262. ⬆.

10 🛏 € 5 🚿 € 1/100liter 🗑 🚽 (4x) € 1/day. **Location:** Rural, simple, quiet. **Surface:** gravel/sand. ⬛ Tue, water: 01/11-31/03
Distance: 🚶3km ⊗on the spot 🛒on the spot.

| 🍴 S | Biesenhofen | 19D2 |

Gasthof Stegmühle, Stegmühle 2. **GPS:** n47,82437 e10,64428. ⬆.

4 🛏 € 5, free with a meal 🚿 Ch 🚽 WC 🚽. **Location:** Simple.
Surface: gravel/metalled. 🅿 01/01-31/12
Distance: 🚶1km 🛒1km ⊗on the spot 🛒1km.

| S | Bischofsgrün 🏔 🌳 ❄ | 11E3 |

Rangenweg. **GPS:** n50,05407 e11,79292. ⬆➡.

6 🛏 free, tourist tax € 1,50 to be paid at tourist office 🚿 € 1/40liter Ch 🚽 (6x) € 1/12h. **Surface:** metalled. 🅿 01/01-31/12
Distance: 🚶250m 🚴500m 🚶nearby.

| S | Bischofsheim an der Rhön | 11B2 |

Viehweg 1, Haselbach. **GPS:** n50,39506 e9,99593. ⬆➡.

12 🛏 € 5 🚿 € 1/80liter Ch. **Surface:** asphalted. 🅿 01/01-31/12
Distance: 🚶on the spot ⊗on the spot 🛒on the spot.
Remarks: Parking swimming pool in Haselbach.

| 🍴 | Bischofswiesen | 19G2 |

Götschen Alm, Kollertradte 21, Loipl. **GPS:** n47,64817 e12,93631.

20 🛏 guests free. **Surface:** gravel.
🅿 01/04-30/11
Distance: 🚶2km ⊗on the spot 🛒2km 🚴on the spot 🚶on the spot.

| S | Blaichach 🏔 | 19C2 |

Alpen-Rundblick Mobil Camping, Am Eichbichl 1.
GPS: n47,54615 e10,25917. ⬆➡.

60 🛏 € 10,50/12,50 + € 1,70 pp 🚿 € 1/80liter Ch 🚽 (54x)€ 0,60/kWh WC 🚽 € 1,60 ⬛ € 2,50. 🛁 **Location:** Luxurious.
Surface: grassy/gravel. 🅿 01/01-31/12
Distance: 🚶300m 🚴 3,3km 🏊on the spot 🛒on the spot ⊗500m 🛒500m 🚴5km 🚶1km.

| Bodenmais 🌿 🏔 🌳 ❄ | 16G2 |

Concorde-Reisemobil-Stellplatz, Kötztinger Straße.
GPS: n49,07147 e13,09273. ⬆.

12 🛏 € 7 + tourist tax 🚿 € 0,50/100liter Ch 🚽 € 0,50/kWh.
Surface: asphalted.
🅿 01/01-31/12
Distance: 🚶800m ⊗200m 🛒200m.
Remarks: Use swimming pool, sauna, fitness-studio incl.

| 🍴 S | Bodenwöhr | 16F1 |

Gasthof zum Troidlwirt, Bodenwöhrer strasse 6.
GPS: n49,28305 e12,26272. ⬆.

40 🛏 € 10 🚿 Ch 🚽 (12x)€ 1 WC 🚽 € 1. **Surface:** grassy/metalled.
🅿 01/01-31/12 ⬛ Restaurant: Sa
Distance: 🚶on the spot ⊗on the spot 🛒bakery 300m.

| S | Bogen | 16F2 |

Volksfestplatz, Kotaustraße 12. **GPS:** n48,90744 e12,68877. ⬆.

5 🛏 € 10 🚿 € 1 Ch 🚽 (4x)€ 1/5h. **Surface:** grassy/metalled.
🅿 01/01-31/12
Distance: 🚶300m 🛒Edeka 100m.
Remarks: Check in at pay-desk of swiming pool.

| S | Burgbernheim | 16C1 |

Wohnmobilstellplatz im Gründlein, Freibadstrasse.
GPS: n49,44627 e10,31869. ⬆➡.

12 🛏 free 🚿 € 1/100liter Ch 🚽 (10x)€ 0,50/kWh.

DE

Surface: grasstiles. ◘ 01/01-31/12
Distance: 🚰500m ⊗500m 💧500m 🚐500m.

| 🍴 | **Burghaslach** | 16C1 |

Hotel-Restaurant Steigerwaldhaus, Oberrimbach 2.
GPS: n49,72764 e10,53542.⬆.

10 🅿€6, guests free. **Surface:** grassy. ◘ 01/01-31/12
Distance: 🚰500m ⊗on the spot 💧5km.

| 🅿S | **Burghausen** 🌿 | 19G1 |

Waldpark Lindach, Berghamer Strasse 1.
GPS: n48,15443 e12,80859.⬆➡.

16 🅿€5/24h 🚰€1/80liter 🗑Ch ⚡(16x)€0,50/kWh WC⬜.🚌
Location: Rural, comfortable, quiet. **Surface:** gravel.
◘ 01/01-31/12 ◙ sanitary 01/11-31/03
Distance: 🚰1,5km ⊗500m 💧1,5km.
Remarks: Check in at Bürgerhaus Marktlerstr. 15a, caution key sanitary €20.

| 🅿S | **Burgkirchen** | 19G1 |

Peterhof, Peterhof 24. **GPS:** n48,15096 e12,75025.⬆.

3 🅿€12,50, 2 pers.incl 🚰🗑⚡WCincluded 📺📶. **Location:** Rural, simple, quiet. **Surface:** grassy.
◘ 01/01-31/12
Distance: 🚰2km ⊗2km 💧2km.

| 🅿S | **Burgkunstadt** 🌿 💐 | 11D3 |

Alter Postweg. GPS: n50,13965 e11,25017.⬆.

4 🅿free 🚰€1 Ch. **Location:** Rural, simple. **Surface:** gravel.
◘ 01/01-31/12
Distance: 🚰100m ⚡15km 🏊100m 🚐100m ⊗300m 💧300m 🚲on the spot 🚶on the spot.
Remarks: Max. 48h.

| 🅿S | **Bürgstadt** 🍷 | 16A1 |

Winzerfestplatz, Josef-Ullrich-Straße. **GPS:** n49,71356 e9,26405.⬆.

25 🅿free 🚰€1/80liter 🗑Ch ⚡(12x)€1/6h. **Location:** Rural, comfortable. **Surface:** asphalted. ◘ 01/01-31/12
Distance: 🚰500m ⊗200m 💧200m.

| 🅿S | **Cadolzburg** 🌿 | 16D1 |

Parkplatz Am Höhbuck, Am Höhbuck. **GPS:** n49,46123 e10,85188.
8 🅿free 🚰🗑Ch ⚡. **Surface:** metalled. ◘ 01/01-31/12
Distance: 🚰on the spot.

| 🅿S | **Coburg** | 11D3 |

Ketschenanger, Schutzenstrasse. **GPS:** n50,25306 e10,96417.⬆.

9 🅿free. **Surface:** asphalted.
Distance: 🚰on the spot ⊗on the spot.
Remarks: Parking next to gymnasium, max. 48h.

| 🅿S | **Coburg** | 11D3 |

Aral-station, Bambergerstrasse. **GPS:** n50,24833 e10,96639.

3 🅿free 🚰€1 🗑Ch. **Surface:** metalled.
◘ 01/01-31/12
Distance: 🚰on the spot

Tourist information Coburg:
📷❌ Die Veste Coburg. Medieval fortress.
❌ Schloß Ehrenburg.
◘ guided tour Tue-Su.

| 🅿S | **Deggendorf** | 16G2 |

Konstantin-Bader-Strasse, Konstantin-Bader-Straße.
GPS: n48,82656 e12,96367.⬆.

3 🅿free. **Location:** Simple. **Surface:** asphalted. ◘ 01/01-31/12
Distance: 🚰centre 500m ⊗250m.

| 🅿S | **Deggendorf** | 16G2 |

Elypso, Sandnerhofweg 4-6. **GPS:** n48,82029 e12,91098.⬆.
4 🅿€6,50 🚰€0,50/50liter ⚡€0,50/kWh. **Surface:** metalled.
◘ 01/01-31/12
Distance: 🚰5,4km ⚡4km.

| 🅿S | **Deiningen** | 16C2 |

Cowabanga, Am Sportpark. **GPS:** n48,86292 e10,58042.➡.

| 🅿S | **Denkendorf** | 16E2 |

10 🅿free 🚰⚡€2,50 WC⬜. **Location:** Urban, simple.
Surface: asphalted. ◘ 01/01-31/12
Distance: 🚰2km ⊗on the spot.
Remarks: Parking sports centre.

| 🍴S | **Denkendorf** | 16E2 |

Gasthof Lindenwirt, Hauptstrasse 43. **GPS:** n48,92806 e11,45568.⬆.

10 🅿€4 🚰⚡included. 🚲 **Location:** Urban. **Surface:** gravel/sand.
◘ 01/01-31/12
Distance: 🚰on the spot ⚡700m ⊗on the spot 💧200m 🚲on the spot 🚶on the spot.

| 🅿S | **Dettelbach** 🍷 | 16C1 |

Zur Mainfähre, Mainsondheimerstrasse.
GPS: n49,80076 e10,16751.⬆➡.

35 🅿€7 🚰€1/60liter 🗑Ch ⚡(24x)€0,50/kWh. 🚌 **Surface:** grassy.
◘ 01/01-31/12 ◙ Service: winter
Distance: 🚰100m ⊗100m 💧100m.

| 🅿S | **Dießen** 🍷 | 19D1 |

Seestraße. **GPS:** n47,95220 e11,10598.⬆.
12 🅿€8 🚰€1 🗑Ch ⚡(12x)€4/8h. 🚌 **Surface:** gravel.
◘ 01/01-31/12
Distance: 🏊200m ⊗200m 🚐150m 💧150m.
Remarks: Max. 3 days.

| 🅿S | **Dingolfing** | 16F3 |

Wohnmobilstellplatz Dingolfing, Wollanger/Prasserweg.
GPS: n48,62827 e12,50206.⬆➡.

12 🅿free 🚰€1/80liter 🗑Ch ⚡(12x)€1/12h. **Location:** Rural, comfortable, quiet. **Surface:** gravel. ◘ 01/01-31/12
Distance: 🚰400m ⚡4,6km 💧250m.
Remarks: Nearby swimming pool.

| 🅿S | **Dinkelsbühl** 🌿 | 16C2 |

Park- & Campanlage, Dürrwanger Straße.
GPS: n49,07812 e10,32906.⬆.

12 🏕 € 12 🔌 Ch ✏ included 🚿 €1,50. **Surface:** metalled.
🅿 01/01-31/12
Distance: 🚰1,5km 🏊100m 🛒500m.
Remarks: To be paid at campsite (500m).

Dittelbrunn — 11C3

Gasthaus Goldene Flasche, Strohgasse 1, Hambach.
GPS: n50,09787 e10,20763.⬆.

3 🏕 € 1. **Surface:** metalled. 🅿 01/01-31/12
Distance: 🚰on the spot ⊗on the spot 🛒200m.

Donauwörth — 16D3

Wohnmobilstellplatz am Festplatz, Neue Obermayerstrasse.
GPS: n48,71490 e10,77874.⬆➡.

20 🏕free 🔌€1/80liter 🔌Ch ✏€1/8h. **Location:** Urban, simple.
Surface: asphalted. 🅿 01/01-31/12
Distance: 🚰on the spot ⊗on the spot 🛒500m.
Remarks: Max. 1 night.

Ebermannstadt — 16D1

P2, Oberes Tor. **GPS:** n49,78222 e11,18946.⬆➡.

10 🏕free. **Surface:** metalled. 🅿 01/01-31/12
Distance: 🚰750m ⊗450m 🛒100m.
Remarks: Max. 1 night.

Ebern — 11C3

Wohnmobilhafen Ebern, Walk-Strasser-Anlage.
GPS: n50,09312 e10,79496.

20 🏕 € 6 🔌Ch ✏€1/2kWh WC included.
Surface: metalled.
🅿 01/01-31/12
Distance: 🚰on the spot 🏊1km 🚲2km ⊗100m 🛒200m 🛒100m.

Ebern — 11C3

Dietz, Bahnhofstrasse. **GPS:** n50,10167 e10,78917.

10 🏕 € 5 🔌€1/100liter 🔌Ch ✏ WC 🚿. **Surface:** asphalted/grassy.
🅿 01/01-31/12
Distance: 🛒400m.

Ebrach — 11C3

Naturbad, Schwimmbadweg. **GPS:** n49,84639 e10,48306.⬆➡.

5 🏕free 🔌€1/80liter 🔌ChWC. **Surface:** metalled.
🅿 01/01-31/12
Distance: 🚰2km ⊗2km 🛒2km 🛒500m.
Remarks: Parking swimming pool.

Eggenfelden — 16G3

P2, Birkenallee. **GPS:** n48,40185 e12,77579.⬆.

5 🏕free. **Location:** Simple, quiet. **Surface:** grassy/metalled.
🅿 01/01-31/12
Distance: 🚰1km.
Remarks: Max. 3 days.

Eggenfelden — 16G3

Tankstelle Breitner Shell, Tiefstadt 10. **GPS:** n48,39591 e12,76621.

🏕 € 3 🔌🚿. **Location:** Simple. **Surface:** asphalted.
Remarks: Max. 1 night.

Eging am See — 16G2

Bavaria Kur-Sport Camping Park, Grafenauer Str. 31.
GPS: n48,72120 e13,26519.⬆➡.

10 🏕 € 15 🔌🚿Ch ✏(10x)included. **Location:** Rural, simple, quiet.
Surface: asphalted. 🅿 01/01-31/12
Remarks: Max. 2 days, check in at reception campsite, use sanitary facilities at campsite.

Eibelstadt — 16B1

Wassersportclub Eibelstadt, Mainparkring.
GPS: n49,73146 e9,98701.⬆.

35 🏕 € 10 🔌€1/5minutes 🔌Ch ✏6Amp WC included 🚿€1/time
🔌€5. **Surface:** grassy/gravel. 🅿 01/01-31/12
Distance: 🚰2km 🚲50m ⊗50m 🛒1km.
Remarks: Along Main river.

Eichstätt — 16D2

Schottenwiese/Volkfestplatz. GPS: n48,88400 e11,19816.➡.

50 🏕 € 8 🔌Ch ✏(30x)€0,50/kWh WC 🚿€0,50.
Location: Urban, simple, central, quiet. **Surface:** metalled.
🅿 01/01-31/12 ⊙ Eichstätter Volksfest
Distance: 🚰500m 🛒500m 🚲on the spot 🧗on the spot.

Tourist information Eichstätt:
⛺ Volksfestplatz. Flea market. 🅿 10/05, 14/06, 12/07, 13/09, 04/10.
☀ Altstadtfest, Innenstad. City celebration. 🅿 28/08-06/09.
☀ Eichstätter Volksfest, Volkfestplatz. Folk festival. 🅿 02/09-11/09.
🌿 Informationszentrum Naturpark Altmühltal, Notre Dame 1, voormalig klooster. Information centre nature reserve. 🅿 01/04-31/10 Mo-Sa 9-17h, Su 10-17h, 01/11-31/03 Mo-Thu 8-12h, 14-17h, Fri 8-12h. 🅃 free.

Einsiedl — 19E2

Wohnmobilstellplatz, B11. **GPS:** n47,57000 e11,30389.⬆➡.

80 🏕 € 5 🔌€1/70liter ✏€1/6h. **Location:** Rural, comfortable, quiet.
Surface: asphalted/gravel. 🅿 01/01-31/12
Distance: 🚰500m 🏊on the spot 🚲on the spot ⊗500m 🛒3,5km
🎣1,5km 🛒1,5km.
Remarks: Max. 3 nights.

Eisenheim — 11C3

Weingut Herbert Schuler, An der Mainaue, Obereisenheim.
GPS: n49,88883 e10,17942.

60 🏕 € 5 🔌Ch ✏€0,50. **Surface:** grassy/metalled.
🅿 01/01-31/12
Distance: 🚰on the spot 🏊on the spot ⊗on the spot.
Remarks: Along Main river.

Eltmann am Main — 11C3

Parkplatz, Mainlände. **GPS:** n49,97306 e10,66250.⬆➡.

10 🛏free 🚰€1/80liter 🧹€1/6h. **Surface:** metalled.
⬛ 01/01-31/12
Distance: 🚶500m 🏊on the spot 🚉on the spot ⊗100m 🚊300m.

Enderndorf 🌿🏖🍴🏕🚻 16D2

Wohnmobilstellplatz Panorama, Kreisstraße, Spalt-Enderndorf.
GPS: n49,15028 e10,91083.⬆.

60 🛏€ 8,00 🚰€0,20/10liter 🗑Ch 🧹(60x)€1/kWh 🚿.
Surface: metalled. ⬛ 01/04-31/10
Distance: 🚶400m 🏊400m 🚉400m ⊗400m 🚊3km 🚲150m.

Enderndorf 🌿🏖🍴🏕🚻 16D2

Reisemobil-Stellplatz Enderndorf-West, Zum Hafen.
GPS: n49,14777 e10,91126.⬆.

25 🛏€ 8/24h 🚰€0,20/100liter 🗑Ch 🧹€0,50/kWh. 🔌
Location: Rural, simple, isolated, quiet. **Surface:** grasstiles.
⬛ 01/01-31/12
Distance: 🚶200m 🏊150m 🚉200m 🚊200m 🚲on the spot 🚶on the spot.

Erbendorf 11E3

Am Stadtpark, Bahnhofstraße 21. **GPS:** n49,84144 e12,04769.⬆➡.

10 🛏free 🚰€1 🗑Ch. **Surface:** gravel. ⬛ 01/01-31/12
Distance: 🚶100m ⊗200m 🚊200m.
Remarks: Max. 3 days.

Erding ♨ 19E1

Wohnmobilpark Erding, Thermenallee 1.
GPS: n48,29332 e11,88707.⬆➡.

55 🛏€ 10/day 🚰€1/80liter 🗑Ch 🧹€1/2kWh WC.
Surface: grasstiles/metalled. ⬛ 01/01-31/12
Distance: 🚶2km ⊗2km 🚉2km 🚲50m.
Remarks: Max. 7 nights.

Escherndorf 11C3

Campingplatz Escherndorf, An der Güß 9a.
GPS: n49,85996 e10,17632.⬆.

22 🛏€ 8 🚰🗑Ch 🧹. **Surface:** grassy. ⬛ 01/04-31/10
Distance: 🚶300m 🚊300m.

Ettenbeuren 19C1

Wohnmobilpark Kammelaue, Zum Sportplatz 12.
GPS: n48,37565 e10,36021.➡.

40 🛏€ 7, € 13 service incl 🚰🗑Ch🚽 🧹WC🔌. **Location:** Rural,
comfortable, quiet. **Surface:** grasstiles/metalled. ⬛ 01/04-31/10
Distance: 🚶500m ⊗on the spot 🚉500m 🚲on the spot 🚶on the spot.

Feucht 16D1

Am Freibad Feuchtasia, Chormantelweg. **GPS:** n49,37848 e11,22495.

9 🛏€ 7 🚰€1/80liter 🗑Ch 🧹(8x)€1/2kWh 🔌. **Surface:** grasstiles.
⬛ 01/01-31/12
Distance: 🚶1km 🚉900m.

Fichtelberg 11E3

Automobilmuseum, Eckert Naglerweg 9.
GPS: n49,99760 e11,85820.⬆.

15 🛏free. **Surface:** asphalted/metalled. ⬛ 01/01-31/12
Distance: ⊗100m.
Remarks: Parking museum.

Fischen 🏔🚻 19C2

Wohnmobil-Stellplatz Fischen, Mühlenstraße.
GPS: n47,44950 e10,26946.⬆.

12 🛏€ 8, tourist tax € 1,95/pp 🚰€1 🗑€1 Ch 🧹(12x)€1/12h. 🚿
Location: Rural, simple. **Surface:** asphalted.
Distance: 🚶1,2km 🏊on the spot 🚲on the spot 🚶on the spot.

Remarks: Pay at Sportpark, Mühlenstraße 55.

Forchheim 16D1

Sportinsel, An der Regnitzbrücke. **GPS:** n49,72120 e11,04939.⬆➡.

12 🛏€ 3 🚰€3 🗑ChWC 🧹€1. **Surface:** grasstiles.
⬛ 01/01-31/12 ⬛ sanitary building: 01/11-28/02
Distance: 🚶600m ⊗on the spot 🚉on the spot.

Frasdorf 19F1

Bauernhof Lederstube, Lederstube 3.
GPS: n47,79521 e12,28774.⬆⬆.

6 🛏€ 7 🚰€1,50 🗑Ch 🧹€3. **Location:** Rural, simple, isolated, quiet.
Surface: grassy/gravel. ⬛ 01/03-30/09
Distance: 🚶500m 🏊800m 🚉800m 🚲800m.

Freilassing 19G1

Stellplatz Freilassing, Salzburgerstrasse.
GPS: n47,84031 e12,98599.⬆.

5 🛏free. **Surface:** asphalted. ⬛ 01/01-31/12
Distance: 🚶6km 🚲100m.

Tourist information Freilassing:
⛺ Flea market.

Freyung 🍴🏔🚻🛶❄ 16H2

Freizeitpark Solla, Solla. **GPS:** n48,80104 e13,54125.⬆➡.

12 🛏€ 5 🚰€1/80liter 🗑Ch 🧹(12x)€0,50/kWh. **Location:** Rural,
simple, quiet. **Surface:** grasstiles. ⬛ 01/01-31/12
Distance: 🚶2km ⊗500m 🏊on the spot 🚲on the spot.

Freyung 🍴🏔🚻🛶❄ 16H2

Parking Freibad, Zuppinger Straße. **GPS:** n48,80515 e13,54102.⬆.

10 🛏free. **Location:** Urban, simple, quiet. **Surface:** metalled.
⬛ 01/01-31/12

Distance: 🚂1km ⊗1km 🚰1km.

| 🏕 | **Friedberg** | 16D3 |

Herrgottsruhstrasse. **GPS:** n48,35765 e10,99095. ➡️.

4 🏕free. **Location:** Simple. **Surface:** gravel. ⬛ 01/01-31/12
Distance: 🚂600m ⊗600m 🚰600m.

| 🏕 | **Friedberg** | 16D3 |

Seestraße. **GPS:** n48,36540 e10,96529. ⬆️➡️.

4 🏕free. **Location:** Rural, simple, quiet. **Surface:** asphalted.
⬛ 01/01-31/12
Distance: 🚂1,8km ⬿5km ⊼on the spot ⇢on the spot ⊗400m
🏊on the spot ⚲on the spot.

| S | **Friedberg** | 16D3 |

Marquardtstrasse 2/A. **GPS:** n48,34825 e10,99757.
🚱Chfree.
Distance: 🚰on the spot.

| 🏕S | **Friedenfels** ⚘🏔❄ | 11E3 |

Freibad, Badstrasse. **GPS:** n49,88639 e12,10417. ⬆️.

15 🏕€ 3,50 🚱€1. **Surface:** metalled. ⬛ 01/01-31/12
Distance: 🚂1,5km.
Remarks: Max. 3 days, service during opening hours.

| 🏕S | **Friedenfels** ⚘🏔❄ | 11E3 |

Zentral, Gemmingenstraße. **GPS:** n49,88102 e12,10297. ⬆️.

15 🏕€ 3,50 🚱💧. **Surface:** metalled.
Distance: 🚂on the spot 🚐25m.
Remarks: Max. 3 days, pay at tourist office, Café Am Steinwald, Gemmingenstr. 19.

| 🏕 | **Friedenfels** ⚘🏔❄ | 11E3 |

Stellplatz 'Ruhig', Weißensteiner Weg, Frauenreuth.
GPS: n49,89278 e12,08556. ⬆️.

5 🏕€ 3,50. **Surface:** metalled. ⬛ 01/01-31/12
Distance: 🚂1,5km ⬿Frauenreuther Weiher.
Remarks: Max. 3 days.

| 🏕S | **Füssen** ⚘🏕🍴🏔❄⚓ | 19D2 |

Camper's Stop, Abt Hafnerstrasse 9. **GPS:** n47,58186 e10,70080. ⬆️➡️.

120 🏕€ 13, trailer € 5 🚱€0,50/150liter 🚱Ch 💧€1/kWh WC 🚽€0,50
📶€2. **Location:** Urban, comfortable, noisy. **Surface:** gravel/metalled.
⬛ 01/01-31/12
Distance: 🚂1,5km ⊼600m ⬿600m ⊗terrace 🚰50m 🚐250m
🏊4km ⚲400m.

| 🏕S | **Füssen** ⚘🏕🍴🏔❄⚓ | 19D2 |

Wohnmobilstellplatz Füssen, Abt Hafnerstrasse 1.
GPS: n47,58224 e10,70355. ⬆️🚱.

30 🏕€ 13,50 🚱Ch 💧(6x)€2,50 WC 🚽€0,50 📶€2. 🏊
Location: Noisy. **Surface:** metalled. ⬛ 01/01-31/12
Distance: 🚂1,8km ⊼1km ⊗200m 🚰300m 🚐500m 🏊on the spot
⚲on the spot 🚴on the spot 🏊on the spot.

| 🏕S | **Garmisch-Partenkirchen** ⚘🏔🌲❄ | 19D2 |

Alpencamp am Wank, Wankbahnstraße 2.
GPS: n47,50573 e11,10802. ⬆️.

110 🏕€ 10 + € 2/pp tourist tax, € 1 Umwelttaxe 🚱€1/50liter 🚱Ch
💧(110x)€1/kWh WC 🚽€1 ⬛ 🏊 **Location:** Rural, comfortable.
Surface: asphalted. ⬛ 01/01-31/12
Distance: 🚂1km ⊼2km ⊗50m 🚰700m 🚐50m 🚴2,5km
🏊1,5km.

| 🏕S | **Gerolzhofen** | 11C3 |

P3 Zur Volkach, Schallfelderstrasse. **GPS:** n49,89808 e10,35169. ⬆️➡️.

6 🏕€ 5 🚱€1 🚱Ch 💧(4x)€0,50/kWh WC. **Surface:** metalled.
⬛ 01/01-31/12

Distance: 🚂100m.
Remarks: Max. 3 days.

| 🏕 | **Gerolzhofen** | 11C3 |

P1 Geomaris, Dingolshäuser Straße 2. **GPS:** n49,89980 e10,36035. ⬆️.

6 🏕free. **Surface:** asphalted. ⬛ 01/01-31/12
Distance: 🚂750m.
Remarks: Parking swimming pool.

| 🏕S | **Geslau** | 16C2 |

Bauernhof Mohrenhof, Lauterbach 3.
GPS: n49,34630 e10,32500. ⬆️➡️.

20 🏕€ 10-12 🚱Ch 💧€0,50/kWh WC 🚽€0,50 ⬛€3 📶€2,50/2h.
Surface: grassy. ⬛ Easter-31/10
Distance: 🚂500m ⊼on the spot.
Remarks: Bread-service.

| 🏕S | **Goldkronach** ⚘🏔❄ | 11E3 |

Festplatz, Schulstrasse. **GPS:** n50,01265 e11,68276. ⬆️➡️.

4 🏕free 🚱€1/10minutes 🚱Ch 💧(4x)€1/10h. **Surface:** gravel.
⬛ 01/01-31/12
Distance: 🚂50m ⊼500m 🚴2km.

| 🏕S | **Gößweinstein** ⚘ | 16D1 |

Alte Jugendherberge, Etzdorfer Straße 6.
GPS: n49,76556 e11,33028. ⬆️.

6 🏕€ 7 🚱€1/80liter 🚱Ch 💧€1/2kWh. 🏊 **Location:** Urban,
simple. **Surface:** metalled.
Distance: 🚂600m ⊗600m 🚰600m ⊼300m ⚲600m.

| 🏕S | **Grafenau** | 16G2 |

Grafenauer Kurpark, Freyunger Straße.
GPS: n48,85605 e13,40456. ⬆️➡️.

10 🏕€ 5 Kurtaxe incl 🚱€1/80liter 🚱Ch 💧included 📶free.

Location: Urban, simple, quiet. **Surface:** gravel.
☐ 01/01-31/12
Distance: 500m 600m 550m ReWe on the spot.
Remarks: Wifi in Touristinformation + 1/2h free internet in Stadt-bücherei.

S — Gräfendorf — 11B3
Volkert an der Roßmühle, Roßmühle, Weickersgrüben.
GPS: n50,10660 e9,78309.

5 €5 €2/100liter Ch (5x)included. ☐ 01/04-31/10
Distance: on the spot on the spot on the spot.
Remarks: At motorhome dealer, accessory shop, max. 24h, check in at shop.

Greding — 16D2
Am Hallenbad. **GPS:** n49,04409 e11,35551.

20 free. **Location:** Urban. **Surface:** metalled.
☐ 01/01-31/12
Distance: Old city centre 300m 500m 250m 250m on the spot on the spot.
Remarks: Parking at city wall in front of swimming pool.

Tourist information Greding:
ℹ City wall and towers.

S — Großheubach — 16A1
Weingut Gasthaus Zur Bretzel, Kirchstraße 1.
GPS: n49,72620 e9,22083.

25 €17 Ch WCincluded €1/time. **Location:** Rural, comfortable, quiet. **Surface:** grassy/gravel. ☐ 01/11-15/11
Distance: 100 m on the spot on the spot.
Remarks: To be paid at Gasthaus, € 10 euro discount coupon (restaurant, wine).

S — Großweil — 19E2
Aplengasthof Kreut-Alm, Kreut 1. **GPS:** n47,66184 e11,28286.

15 customers free . **Location:** Rural, simple, isolated, quiet.
Surface: asphalted. ☐ 01/03-31/10
Distance: 3,2km on the spot.

Großweil — 19E2
Freilichtmuseum Glentleiten, An der Glentleiten 4.
GPS: n47,66495 e11,28506.

10 free. **Surface:** gravel.
Distance: 2km 3,5km Gaststätte - Biergarten 1km.
Remarks: Open air museum, only overnight stays.

S — Günzburg — 16C3
Waldbad, Heidenheimerstrasse. **GPS:** n48,46287 e10,26944.

24 €5/24h €1/100liter (24x)€0,50/kWh. **Location:** Simple. **Surface:** gravel.
☐ 01/01-31/12 Danube Bike Trail.
Remarks: Parking swimming pool.

S — Gunzenhausen — 16D2
Surfzentrum Schlungenhof. **GPS:** n49,12790 e10,74559.

80 €10/24h €1 Ch included WC €1 .
Location: Rural, comfortable, quiet. **Surface:** grassy/gravel.
☐ 01/04-30/10
Distance: 100m on the spot 1,8km.

S — Gunzenhausen — 16D2
Altmühlsee, Seezentrum Mühr. **GPS:** n49,13145 e10,73534.

40 €3 day/€6 night. **Location:** Rural, comfortable, isolated, quiet. **Surface:** grassy. ☐ 01/01-31/12
Distance: on the spot 200m on the spot on the spot.
Remarks: Max. 3 days.

S — Hammelburg — 11B3
Am Bleichrasen, P2, Am Weiher. **GPS:** n50,11390 e9,88820.

25 €6/24h Ch included (18x)€0,50/kWh WC.
Location: Urban, simple, quiet. **Surface:** asphalted.
☐ 01/01-31/12
Distance: on the spot on the spot 200m 300m.

S — Hammelburg — 11B3
Forellenhof Reuss, Am Erlich 30, Diebach.
GPS: n50,13310 e9,81917.

18 €7 Chincluded €2 €2. **Location:** Rural, comfortable, quiet. **Surface:** grassy. ☐ 01/04-31/10
Distance: Hammelburg 7km on the spot on the spot.
Remarks: Bread-service, weekend: Gaststätte/Biergarten.

S — Hammelburg — 11B3
Schloß Saaleck, Am Schlossberg. **GPS:** n50,10998 e9,87281.

3 free WC. **Surface:** asphalted/metalled. ☐ 01/01-31/12
Distance: on the spot.

Hammelburg — 11B3
Restaurant Nöth, Morlesauer Strasse 3. **GPS:** n50,11707 e9,80313.

5 free. **Location:** Rural, simple, quiet. **Surface:** gravel.
☐ 01/01-31/12
Distance: on the spot on the spot on the spot on the spot on the spot.
Remarks: Check in at restaurant, use of a meal desired.

S — Hassfurt — 11C3
Festplatz am Gries, Ringstrasse. **GPS:** n50,03068 e10,50094.

22 €5/night €1 Ch €1 WC. **Surface:** asphalted.
☐ 01/01-31/12
Distance: 200m 10m 200m 200m.
Remarks: Along Main river.

Herrieden — 16C2
Volksfestplatz an der Altmühl, Staatsstrasse 2248.
GPS: n49,23191 e10,49588.

10 free. **Surface:** asphalted. ☐ 01/01-31/12
Distance: 100m 200m 200m.

DE

Remarks: Parking at the old mill bridge.

Hersbruck 16D1

Fackelmanntherme Hersbruck, Badestraße.
GPS: n49,51142 e11,44267.

6 €6 €1 Ch €1/6h. **Surface:** gravel.
01/01-31/12 **Distance:** on the spot 200m 200m.
Remarks: Check in at pay-desk of the Therme.

Herzogenaurach 16D1

Freizeitbad Atlantis, Würzburger Straße 35. **GPS:** n49,57251 e10,86641.
12 €6/24h Ch (12x).
Surface: gravel.
01/01-31/12
Distance: on the spot.
Remarks: € 2 reduction swimming pool.

Hilpoltstein 16D2

Seezentrum Heuberg am Rothsee, Heuberg.
GPS: n49,20954 e11,18595.

50 €7,50 Ch. **Surface:** metalled. 01/01-31/12 Service: winter
Distance: 200m 200m.

Hilpoltstein 16D2

Am Main-Donau Kanal. GPS: n49,20455 e11,18813.

30 €6. **Surface:** grassy. 15/04-30/10
Distance: 1,9km Canal 1,9km 1km on the spot
on the spot.

Tourist information Hilpoltstein:
Burgfeste. Festival with events. beginning Aug.

Hof/Saale 11E2

Park Theresienstein, Plauener Straße. **GPS:** n50,32956 e11,92041.

10 free. **Surface:** metalled. 01/01-31/12
Distance: 2,5km 1km.
Remarks: Max. 24h.

Hof/Saale 11E2

Utreusee, Wilhelm Löhe strasse. **GPS:** n50,28583 e11,91361.

10 free. **Surface:** asphalted/metalled. 01/01-31/12
Distance: 100m 50m 500m.
Remarks: Max. 24h.

Hof/Saale 11E2

Clean Park, Ernst Reuterstrasse. **GPS:** n50,32641 e11,89248.

4 €5 €1 Ch. **Surface:** metalled. 01/01-31/12
Distance: 2km 800m.
Remarks: Max. 72h.

Tourist information Hof/Saale:
Bürgerpark Theresienstein. Landscape park according English example. 9-18h, winter 9-16h.
Untreusee. Lake with water sports.

Hofheim in Unterfranken 11C3

Wohnmobilplatz Hofheim, Johannisstraße 28.
GPS: n50,14185 e10,51957.

30 €7 €1/80liter Ch €0,50/kWh WC .
Surface: grasstiles. 01/01-31/12
Distance: 750m 750m.
Remarks: Bread-service.

Hohenberg/Eger 11E3

Wiesenfestplatz, Selberstrasse. **GPS:** n50,09762 e12,22085.

10-20 voluntary contribution Ch free WC.
Surface: metalled. 01/01-31/12
Distance: 200m 50m.
Remarks: Beautiful view, porcelain museum.

Hohenburg 16E1

Sportplatz, Sportplatzweg 1. **GPS:** n49,29194 e11,80917.

6 €7 €2 WC. **Surface:** metalled. 01/01-31/12
Distance: 1km.

Remarks: Parking at sports park.

Huisheim 16D2

Waldparkplatz im Schwalbtal, Waldschenke 1, Gosheim.
GPS: n48,84932 e10,71530.

10 € 5, guests free . **Location:** Rural, simple, quiet.
Surface: asphalted. 01/01-31/12
Distance: on the spot.

Immenstadt 19C2

P 3 Viehmarktplatz, Badeweg. **GPS:** n47,56192 e10,20857.

6 free Ch WC. **Location:** Urban, simple, comfortable.
Surface: asphalted. 01/01-31/12
Distance: 700m.

Ingolstadt 16E3

Parkplatz Hallenbad, Jahnstrasse. **GPS:** n48,76025 e11,42038.

8 € 5 (9-17h), overnight stay free €1/80liter Ch included
. **Location:** Urban, comfortable. **Surface:** metalled.
01/01-31/12
Distance: on the spot 1,6km on the spot on the spot
on the spot on the spot.
Remarks: Parking at sports park, max. 3 days.

Inzell 19G1

Camping Lindlbauer, Kreuzfeldstraße 44. **GPS:** n47,76717 e12,75417.

12 € 16 Ch WC included. **Location:** Rural.
Surface: metalled. 01/01-31/12
Distance: 1km.
Remarks: Max. 1 night, health resort 500m.

Iphofen 16C1

Einesheimer Tor, Birklinger Straße. **GPS:** n49,70260 e10,26459.

8 free €1 Ch (6x)€1 WC. **Location:** Urban, simple.

DE

Surface: gravel. ☐ 01/01-31/12
Distance: 🚶200m ⊗200m 🚰200m.
Remarks: Parking at city wall.

🏕️ S Ippesheim 16C1

Kempe's Autohof Gollhofen, Industriestraße 1.
GPS: n49,58546 e10,17579.
25 🚐 € 5 🚰WC🛒. **Surface:** asphalted. ☐ 01/01-31/12
Distance: ⊗on the spot.

🏕️ S Kastl/Oberpfalz 🌿⛲ 16E1

Wanderparkplatz Am Alten Bahnhof, Amberger Straße.
GPS: n49,36657 e11,68388.⬆️.

5 🚐free 🚰🛒ChWCfree. **Surface:** gravel. ☐ 01/01-31/12
Distance: 🚶200m ⊗200m 🚰100m 🛒50m.

🏕️ S Kaufbeuren 19D1

Wohnmobilplatz Kaufbeuren, Buronstraße.
GPS: n47,89885 e10,61650.⬆️.
8 🚐free 🚰🛒Chfree 🔌(6x)€0,50/2kWh. **Location:** Urban.
Surface: gravel.
Distance: 🚶historical centre 3km.
Remarks: Max. 3 days.

🏕️ S Kelheim 🚢 16E2

Volksfestplatz, Am Pflegerspitz. **GPS:** n48,91331 e11,87657.⬆️➡️.

50 🚐€ 6 🚰🛒Ch 🔌(18x)€1/2kWh WC. **Surface:** metalled.
☐ 01/01-31/12 📍 service 01/11-31/03
Distance: 🚶500m ⊗500m.
Remarks: Max. 3 nights, hindmost part.

🏕️ S Kemnath 11E3

Wohnmobilstellplatz Kemnath, Am Eisweier 8.
GPS: n49,87219 e11,88774.

5 🚐free 🚰€1 🛒Ch 🔌(6x)€1/6h WC. **Surface:** concrete.
☐ 01/01-31/12
Distance: 🚶650m ⊗650m 🛒650m.

🏕️ S Kempten 19C2

Illerstadion, Illerdamm/Jahnstrasse. **GPS:** n47,72915 e10,31940.⬆️➡️.

10 🚐€ 5 🚰€1 🛒🏠 **Location:** Urban, simple, noisy.
Surface: metalled. ☐ 01/01-31/12
Distance: 🚶500m 🚿2,7km.

🏕️ S Kiefersfelden 🏔️🌲❄️ 19F2

Hödenauer See, Wasserstrasse. **GPS:** n47,62881 e12,18949.⬆️➡️.

10 🚐€ 5 WC🛒€0,50. **Location:** Simple. **Surface:** gravel/sand.
☐ 01/01-31/12
Distance: 🚶2km 🚿3km 🍴on the spot ⊗50m 🛒300m.
Remarks: Max. 3 days.

🏕️ S Kiefersfelden 🏔️🌲❄️ 19F2

Rathausplatz. GPS: n47,61303 e12,18981.⬆️.

20 🚐€ 10. **Location:** Simple. **Surface:** asphalted. ☐ 01/01-31/12
Distance: 🚶on the spot 🚿2km ⊗100m.
Remarks: Max. 3 days.

🏕️ S Kirchenlamitz 11E3

REWE-Markt, Weißenstädter Straße. **GPS:** n50,14905 e11,94055.⬆️➡️.

12 🚐free 🚰🛒Ch free, voluntary contribution.
Location: Comfortable. **Surface:** asphalted. ☐ 01/01-31/12
Distance: 🚶500m 🛒10m.

👁️ S Kirchham 16G3

Erlebnispark Haslinger Hof, Ed 1. **GPS:** n48,34947 e13,29115.⬆️.

25-30 🚐Overnight stay € 17 (incl. € 9 voucher) 🚰🛒Ch.
Location: Rural, simple, quiet. **Surface:** gravel.
☐ 01/01-31/12
Distance: ⊗on the spot.

🏕️ S Kitzingen 🚢 16C1

Wohnmobilpark Am Main, Bleichwasen, Etwashausen.
GPS: n49,74274 e10,16491.⬆️.

70 🚐€ 7/24h 🚰€1/80liter 🛒Ch 🔌€0,50/kWh WC.
Location: Simple. **Surface:** asphalted. ☐ 01/01-31/12
Distance: 🚶300m 🍴on the spot 🛒on the spot ⊗300m 🛒300m
🚲on the spot.
Remarks: Between Alter Mainbrücke and Nordbrücke, bread-service.

🏕️ S Klingenberg ⛵🚢 16A1

Sonja's Wohnmobilhafen, Zur Einladung.
GPS: n49,78370 e9,17805.⬆️.

55 🚐€ 7,50 🚰€1 🛒Ch 🔌(50x)€2. **Location:** Rural, comfortable,
quiet. **Surface:** grassy/gravel. ☐ 01/01-31/12
Distance: 🚶500m 🛒on the spot ⊗500m 🛒2km.

🏕️ S Königsberg 🌿🌳 11C3

Buchweg. GPS: n50,08472 e10,57028.⬆️➡️.

6 🚐€ 2 🚰Ch. **Surface:** metalled. ☐ 01/01-31/12
Distance: 🚶300m ⊗300m 🛒300m.
Remarks: Parking sports park.

🏕️ S Königsbrunn 19D1

Königsallee. GPS: n48,27243 e10,88283.⬆️➡️.

12 🚐€ 6/24h 🚰€1/100liter 🛒Ch 🔌(12x)€0,50/kWh.
Location: Noisy. **Surface:** metalled.
Distance: 🚶1km 🛒1km.

🏕️ S Kreuzwertheim 🚢 16B1

Am Mainufer, Fährgasse. **GPS:** n49,76251 e9,51840.⬆️.

10 🚐€ 5. 🐕 **Location:** Simple, quiet. **Surface:** gravel.
☐ 01/01-31/12
Distance: 🚶Wertheim centre 1,2km 🍴on the spot ⊗600m.
Remarks: Along Main river, max. 1 night.

🏕️ S Kronach 11D3

Hammermühle, Am Sand. **GPS:** n50,23195 e11,32735.⬆️➡️.

10 🚐€ 5/24h 🚰€1 🛒Ch 🔌(12x)€0,50/kWh.🏠
Location: Rural, simple. **Surface:** asphalted. ☐ 01/01-31/12
Distance: 🚶10min 🛒on the spot ⊗200m 🛒300m.

Kronach — 11D3

Lucky Stable Ranch, Mostrach 1. **GPS:** n50,21840 e11,34012.

5 €5, 2 pers.incl WCincluded €1,50 €1,50.
Location: Rural, simple, isolated, quiet. **Surface:** grassy/metalled.
01/01-31/12
Distance: 2km on the spot on the spot 2km.
Remarks: At manege.

Krün — 19E2

Tennsee Reisemobilhafen, Am Tennsee 1.
GPS: n47,49083 e11,25444.

37 €12,50-18,50 + tourist tax €1,50/pp, Umwelttaxe €0,60/pp
Ch €0,70/kWh WC €3 €3/h.
Location: Rural, comfortable, luxurious, quiet. **Surface:** grassy/gravel.
01/01-31/12 07/11-15/12
Distance: 2,5km 800m 3km on the spot on the spot
100m on the spot on the spot 5km 300m.

Kulmbach — 11D3

Wohnmobilstellplatz Kulmbach, Am Schwedensteg.
GPS: n50,11130 e11,46118.

25 €3 €1/100liter Ch (25x)€1/2kWh. **Location:** Urban,
simple. **Surface:** gravel. 01/01-31/12 water disconnected in
winter
Distance: on the spot 50m 200m 500m on the spot
on the spot 200m.

Kümmersbruck — 16E1

Wohnmobilstellplatz Kümmersbruck, Am Butzenweg.
GPS: n49,41978 e11,89651.

8 free. **Location:** Rural, simple, quiet. **Surface:** metalled.
01/01-31/12
Distance: 1km 1km.
Remarks: At sports centre.

Lalling — 16G2

Wohnmobilstellplatz Weber, Euschertsfurth 34.
GPS: n48,83222 e13,14444.

8 €8 Chincluded (10x)€0,30/kWh €1,50.
Location: Rural, comfortable, quiet. **Surface:** grassy/metalled.
01/04-30/11
Distance: 1,5km 100m.
Remarks: Swimming pool incl.

Lalling — 16G2

Lalling-Freizeitgelände, Waldstrasse. **GPS:** n48,84139 e13,13778.

2 free €1/80liter Ch €3/day. **Location:** Rural, simple,
quiet. **Surface:** metalled/sand. 01/01-31/12
Distance: 2km.
Remarks: At tennis-courts.

Lalling — 16G2

Familie Stelzer, Euschertsfurth 141. **GPS:** n48,83222 e13,13917.

4 €4 Service €1. **Location:** Rural, simple, quiet.
Surface: asphalted/grassy. winter
Distance: 1km 1km.

Lalling — 16G2

Lallinger Hof, Hauptstrasse 23. **GPS:** n48,84560 e13,13851.

4-5 guests free against payment. **Location:** Rural, simple, quiet.
01/04-31/10
Distance: 250m 250m.
Remarks: Check in at restaurant.

Lalling — 16G2

Sieglinde, Obstgarten 13, Hunding. **GPS:** n48,84502 e13,14939.

3 €5 Chincluded (2x)€2/day WC. **Location:** Rural,
simple, quiet. **Surface:** grassy. 01/04-31/12
Distance: 700m.

Lalling — 16G2

Gasthof zur Post, Pfarrweg. **GPS:** n48,84405 e13,14064.

15 free. **Location:** Rural, simple, quiet. **Surface:** metalled.
winter
Distance: 200m 200m.

Lalling — 16G2

Feng Shui Kurpark, Euschertsfurther Straße.
GPS: n48,84137 e13,13952.

€1. **Surface:** gravel. 01/01-31/12
Remarks: Not indicated.

Lalling — 16G2

Erikas Wohlfühlplatz, Kleinfeld 6, Hunding.
GPS: n48,84333 e13,17944.

10 €5 + €0,50/pp (10x)€1/day WC €3. **Location:** Rural,
simple, quiet. **Surface:** grassy/sand. 01/04-31/10
Distance: on the spot on the spot 3km 200m on the
spot on the spot.
Remarks: Check in at Kleinfeld 6.

Landau/Isar — 16F3

Am Festplatz, Harburger Straße 20/B20.
GPS: n48,67712 e12,68323.

± 20 free €1/100liter Ch (6x)€0,50/kWh.
Surface: grassy/gravel. 01/01-31/12
Distance: 1,5km 2,3km McDonalds 200m bakery 200m.

Landsberg am Lech — 19D1

Waitzinger Wiese, Gottesackerangerweg.
GPS: n48,05534 e10,87371.

8 €1/24h €1/100liter Ch (8x)€0,50/6h WC €0,50.
Location: Urban, simple. **Surface:** metalled. 01/01-31/12
Distance: 400m 300m.

⑤Ⓢ Lechbruck am See ❀⚓⛺� ❄ 19D2

Wohnmobilpark via Claudia, Via Claudia 6.
GPS: n47,71556 e10,82139.⬆➡.

52 ☜€ 12,50-13,30 2 pers.incl, dog € 3-3,50 ⛽🔲Ch 🚻WC 🔲€ 1,50 🔲€2,50 ☝🔧 **Location:** Rural, comfortable, luxurious. **Surface:** gravel. 🔲 01/01-31/12 **Distance:** 🚲5km ⚓on the spot ➤on the spot ⊗on the spot 🍺on the spot 🚐on the spot ⛳10km ☋on the spot.

⑤Ⓢ Lenggries ⛰⚐ 19E2

Dürrachstrasse, Fall. **GPS:** n47,57039 e11,53380.⬆➡.

25 ☜€ 0,50/h, € 4/24h ⛽€2 WC. **Location:** Isolated, quiet. **Surface:** metalled. 🔲 01/01-31/12 **Distance:** ⚓250m ➤250m ⊗150m 🍺8km 🍴on the spot ☋on the spot. **Remarks:** Max. 7 days.

⑤Ⓢ Lindau ⛰⚐ 19B2

Blauwiese, P1. GPS: n47,55869 e9,70130.⬆➡.

34 ☜€ 1/h, € 20/24h ⛽€0,50 🔲€0,50 ChWC. **Surface:** metalled. 🔲 01/01-31/12 **Distance:** 🚲on the spot ⚓1km ➤1km ⊗500m 🍺500m 🚐on the spot. **Remarks:** Max. 24h.

©Ⓢ Lindau ⛰⚐ 19B2

Park Camping, Frauenhoferstrasse, Lindau-Zech.
GPS: n47,53764 e9,73148.

15 ☜€ 12/24h ⛽🔲Ch 🚻WC 🔲included, on camp site. **Surface:** gravel. 🔲 15/03-31/10 **Remarks:** Max. 24h.

Tourist information Lindau:
👁 Lindau Insel. Promenade along the lake with Mangturm, 700 years old lighthouse.

⑤Ⓢ Litzendorf 11D3

ASV Naisa, Am Wetterkreuz. **GPS:** n49,91559 e11,00261.⬆.

8 ☜free. **Location:** Rural, simple, quiet. **Surface:** gravel. 🔲 01/01-31/12 **Distance:** 🚐200m 🍴on the spot.

⑤Ⓢ Litzendorf 11D3

Tiefenellern, Ellerbergstrasse. **GPS:** n49,91927 e11,07006.

3 ☜. **Location:** Rural, simple, isolated. **Surface:** gravel. 🍴on the spot 🍴on the spot.

⑤Ⓢ Lohr/Main ⚓⚐ 11B3

Lohrer Mainlände, Osttangente. **GPS:** n49,99429 e9,58053.

20 ☜€ 5 ⛽€1/100liter 🔲Ch 🚿(22x)€2/8h ☝€2/h.🔲 **Location:** Urban, noisy. **Surface:** metalled. 🔲 01/04-31/10 **Distance:** 🚲300m 🍴on the spot 🍺Aldi 800m. **Remarks:** Along Main river, max. 3 days.

⑤Ⓢ Mainbernheim ❀ 16C1

Goldgrubenweg. **GPS:** n49,71153 e10,22045.⬆➡.

10 ☜free. **Location:** Urban, simple, quiet. **Surface:** metalled. 🔲 01/01-31/12 **Distance:** 🚲on the spot ⊗200m 🍺200m 🍴100m.

⑤Ⓢ Mainstockheim ⚐ 16C1

Wohnmobilhafen Mainstockheim, Albertshöfer straße.
GPS: n49,77173 e10,15595.⬆➡.

37 ☜€ 7 ⛽🔲Ch 🚿included. 🔧 **Location:** Rural, simple, quiet. **Surface:** gravel. 🔲 01/01-31/12 **Distance:** 🚲on the spot 🚿5km ⚓on the spot ⊗100m 🍺100m 🍴on the spot. **Remarks:** Along Main river.

⑤Ⓢ Manching 16E3

Am Braunweiher. GPS: n48,71078 e11,49602.⬆.

50 ☜free ⛽€1/80liter 🔲Ch. **Location:** Simple. **Surface:** grasstiles/metalled. 🔲 01/01-31/12 **Distance:** 🚲1,5km ⚓1,3km 🍺Edeka 1km.

⑤Ⓢ Markt Wald ❀⚐ 19C1

Wohnmobilpark Markt Wald, Bürgle 1a.
GPS: n48,14602 e10,57517.⬆➡.

20 ☜€ 7 ⛽€1/100liter 🔲Ch 🚿€0,50/kWh WC 🔲€2. 🔧 **Location:** Rural, comfortable, quiet. **Surface:** grassy/gravel. 🔲 01/01-31/12 **Distance:** 🚲1km ⚓on the spot ➤on the spot ⊗on the spot 🍺1km 🚐on the spot 🍴on the spot 🍴on the spot. **Remarks:** At small lake, bread-service, use sanitary facilities at campsite.

⑤Ⓢ Marktbreit ⚐ 16C1

Am Kranen, Staatstraße. **GPS:** n49,66878 e10,14241.⬆.

3 ☜free. **Location:** Simple. **Surface:** metalled. 🔲 01/01-31/12 **Distance:** 🚲on the spot ⚓on the spot ➤on the spot ⊗on the spot 🍺500m 🍴on the spot. **Remarks:** Max. 1 day.

⑤Ⓢ Marktheidenfeld 16B1

Martinswiese, Georg-Mayr-Straße. **GPS:** n49,84918 e9,59887.⬆➡.

30 ☜€ 5/24h ⛽€1/100liter 🔲Ch 🚿(8x)€1/4h WCincluded. **Location:** Rural, comfortable, quiet. **Surface:** gravel. 🔲 01/01-31/12 🔲 during event **Distance:** 🚲600m ⚓on the spot ➤on the spot ⊗200m 🍺Lidl 650m. **Remarks:** Along Main river, max. 3 days.

⑤Ⓢ Marktheidenfeld 16B1

Georg-Mayr-Straße. **GPS:** n49,85364 e9,60025.⬆.

DE

20 🛏free. **Location:** Rural, simple, noisy. **Surface:** gravel.
⬛ 01/01-31/12
Distance: 🚶1km ⊗50m ⚡Lidl 50m.
Remarks: Max. 3 days.

▦Ⓢ Marktleuthen 11E3
Am Angerparkplatz. **GPS:** n50,12946 e11,99483. ⬆.

10 🛏free 🚰🗑Ch⚡(10x)free 🗑€0,50. **Surface:** metalled.
⬛ 01/01-31/12
Distance: 🚶250m ⊗150m ⚡200m.
Remarks: Max. 7 days, bread-service.

▦Ⓢ Marktredwitz 11E3
Wohnmobilstellplatz am Auenpark, Dörflaser Platz, Fabrikstraße.
GPS: n49,99710 e12,08640. ⬆➡.

20 🛏free 🚰€0,50 🗑€0,50 Ch€0,50 ⚡(6x)€0,50/kWh.
Surface: asphalted/gravel. ⬛ 01/01-31/12
Distance: 🚶300m ⊗50m ⚡150m.

▦ Marktredwitz 11E3
Angerplatz, Egerland-Kulturhaus, Fikentscherstrasse.
GPS: n50,00379 e12,09506. ⬆➡.

6 🛏free. **Surface:** asphalted. ⬛ 01/01-31/12
Distance: 🚶1km ⊗500m.

◎Ⓢ Massing 16F3
Am Freilichtmuseum, Spirknerstraße. **GPS:** n48,39528 e12,60056.
10 🛏free 🚰on demand.
Surface: asphalted.
Distance: ⊗Museumstüberl.
Remarks: Open air museum, busy parking during the day.

▦ Mehlmeisel 11E3
Parkplatz Am Park. GPS: n49,97615 e11,85471. ⬆.

🛏free. **Surface:** metalled. ⬛ 01/01-31/12
Distance: ⊗250m ⚡bakery 100m.
Remarks: Max. 3 nights.

▦Ⓢ Mellrichstadt 11C2
Malbachweg. **GPS:** n50,43139 e10,30972. ⬆.

7 🛏free 🚰€1/80liter 🗑Ch ⚡€0,50/kWh. **Surface:** asphalted.
⬛ 01/01-31/12
Distance: 🚶500m ⊗750m ⚡750m.

▦Ⓢ Memmelsdorf 11D3
Seehofblick, Pödeldorferstrasse 20-A. **GPS:** n49,92906 e10,95594.
4 🛏€ 5 🚰€1/80liter 🗑Ch ⚡€1/8h. **Location:** Urban, simple.
Surface: asphalted. ⬛ 01/04-31/10
Distance: 🚶on the spot ⊗250m.

▦Ⓢ Memmelsdorf 11D3
Stocksee, Stockseestrasse. **GPS:** n49,92556 e10,93417. ⬆.

5 🛏€ 5 🚰€1/80liter 🗑Chfree ⚡(4x)€1/8h. **Location:** Urban.
Surface: asphalted. ⬛ 01/01-31/12
Distance: 🚶1,2km ⊗500m ⚡100m.

▦Ⓢ Miltenberg 🌿⛲🥖 16A1
Linkes Mainufer, Jahnstrasse/Luitpoldstrasse.
GPS: n49,70464 e9,25860. ⬆➡.

20 🛏free 🚰🗑ChWCfree. **Location:** Central. **Surface:** asphalted.
⬛ 01/01-31/12
Distance: 🚶200m ⊗200m ⚡200m.

⚓ Miltenberg 🌿⛲🥖 16A1
Am Yachthafen, Steingässerstrasse. **GPS:** n49,70446 e9,25435. ⬆.

20 🛏free. **Location:** Rural, simple. **Surface:** grassy/gravel.
⬛ 01/01-31/12
Distance: 🚶800m 🏊on the spot ⊗800m ⚡500m 🚐on the spot.
Remarks: Along Main river.

▦Ⓢ Mistelgau 🐴 11D3
Therme Obernsees, An der Therme 1, Obernsees.
GPS: n49,91630 e11,37831. ⬆.

40 🛏€ 10 🚰€1/50liter 🗑Ch ⚡€1/12h WC🗑🔌♿

Location: Luxurious, quiet. **Surface:** grasstiles/metalled.
⬛ 01/01-31/12
Distance: 🚶1km ⊗Therme-Bistro 🍽on the spot 🚐on the spot 🚲on the spot 🚶on the spot.
Remarks: Bread-service, discount on access terme.

▦Ⓢ Mittenwald 🍲 19E2
Wohnmobil-Stellplatz Karwendel, Albert-Schott-Straße.
GPS: n47,43792 e11,26411. ⬆➡.

30 🛏€ 7/24h + € 4/pp tourist tax 🚰€1/80liter 🗑Ch ⚡(30x)€ 0,80/kWh. **Location:** Simple, noisy. **Surface:** asphalted/gravel.
⬛ 01/01-31/12
Distance: 🚶250m 🚐on the spot.
Remarks: Along railwayline.

▣Ⓢ Mitterteich 11E3
Freizeithugl Großbüchlberg, Großbüchlberg 32.
GPS: n49,97286 e12,22496.

23 🛏€ 12, 2 pers.incl 🚰🗑Ch ⚡WC🗑🔌♿against payment.
⬛ 01/01-31/12
Distance: ⊗200m.
Remarks: Bread-service.

▦Ⓢ Monheim 🌿⛲🍲 16D2
An der Stadthalle, Schulstraße. **GPS:** n48,84503 e10,85329. ⬆➡.

7 🛏free 🚰€1 🗑Ch ⚡€1/10h. **Location:** Simple, central.
Surface: grasstiles. ⬛ 01/01-31/12
Distance: 🚶400m ⊗500m ⚡500m.

▦Ⓢ Moosbach 🏞🌳 16F1
Am Badeweiher Tröbes, Friedhofgasse. **GPS:** n49,59076 e12,41193. ⬆➡.

6 🛏€ 5 🚰🗑Ch ⚡. **Surface:** gravel. ⬛ 01/01-31/12
Distance: 🚶250m ⊗250m ⚡250m.
Remarks: Check in at Gästeinformation.

▦Ⓢ Mörnsheim 16D2
Wohnmobilstellplatz Hammermühle, Altendorf.
GPS: n48,87455 e11,02948. ⬆.

DE

21 ⌁ € 10, dog € 1 ⌁ ⌁Ch included ⌁€0,60/kWh ⌁€2.
Location: Rural. **Surface:** unpaved. ⌁ 01/04-31/10
Distance: ⌁Altendorf 2km ⊗Imbiss, Biergarten ⌁ on the spot ⌁ on the spot.
Remarks: Nature reserve Altmühltal, bread-service.

| ⌁ S | **München** | **19E1** |

Allianz-Arena Wohnmobilstellplätze, Werner-Heisenberg-Allee 25, Munich (München). **GPS:** n48,22089 e11,62505.⌁.

110 ⌁ € 15 ⌁€0,20/20liter ⌁(10x)€1/kWh. **Surface:** asphalted.
⌁ during event
Distance: ⊗Bistro-Biergarten ⌁on the spot.
Remarks: FC Bayern Erlebniswelt (Fanmuseum).

| ⌁ S | **München** | **19E1** |

Messe Riem, De-Gasperi-Bogen, München-Riem, Munich (München).
GPS: n48,13342 e11,70746.
1000 ⌁ € 35/incl. 2 pers, € 15/pers ⌁ ⌁Ch ⌁ WC ⌁included.
Surface: metalled. ⌁ Oktoberfest
Distance: ⌁metro 300m.
Remarks: Opened 2 days before Oktoberfest.

| ⌁ S | **München** | **19E1** |

Wohnmobilstellplatz Oktoberfest, Siegenburger Straße 58, Laim, Munich (München). **GPS:** n48,12788 e11,52190.
250 ⌁ € 18 + € 3/pp ⌁ ⌁Ch ⌁ WC ⌁included.
Surface: metalled.
⌁ Oktoberfest
Distance: ⊗100m ⌁500m.
Remarks: Opened 2 days before Oktoberfest.

Tourist information Munich (München):
⌁ München Welcome Card. Card gives for free entrance on among other things public transport and 50% discounts on curiosities.
⌁ € 11/day 2 pers.
⌁ Agustinerbräu, Neuhauserstrasse 16. Brewery from 1644.
⌁ Schloß Nymphenburg.
Former summer residence of the Witelbacher monarchs.
⌁ Tue-Su 9-12.30h, 13.30-17h.
⌁ Neumarkt. Ruins of citadel dominating the city.
⌁ Oktoberfest.
Beer festival, special motorhome parking.

| ⌁ | **Münnerstadt** | **11C3** |

Lache, P1, Seminarstrasse. **GPS:** n50,24957 e10,19086.

5 ⌁free ⌁€1/90liter ⌁Ch ⌁€0,50 WC ⌁. **Surface:** metalled.
⌁ 01/01-31/12
Distance: ⌁350m.

| ⌁ S | **Murnau am Staffelsee** | **19D2** |

Am Bahnhof Murnau, Am Bahnhof. **GPS:** n47,68005 e11,19447.⌁⌁.

6 ⌁ € 1/day ⌁€1/100liter ⌁Ch ⌁€1/2kWh. **Location:** Rural, comfortable, central, quiet. **Surface:** grasstiles/metalled.
⌁ 01/01-31/12
Distance: ⌁500m ⌁10km ⊗400m ⌁300m ⌁on the spot.
Remarks: Max. 72h.

| ⌁ S | **Naila** | **11E2** |

Christian-Schlicht-strasse. **GPS:** n50,33071 e11,71127.⌁.

4 ⌁free ⌁Ch. **Location:** Urban, simple. **Surface:** metalled.
⌁ 01/01-31/12
Distance: ⌁100m ⌁50m ⌁300m ⌁300m ⌁on the spot ⌁on the spot.
Remarks: Parking left side of the station, thursday market.

| ⌁ | **Naila** | **11E2** |

Badstraße. **GPS:** n50,32965 e11,70108.⌁.

10 ⌁free. **Location:** Urban, simple, isolated. **Surface:** asphalted.
⌁ 01/01-31/12
Distance: ⌁650m.
Remarks: Thursday market.

| ⌁ S | **Nesselwang** ⌁ ⌁ ⌁ ⌁ | **19C2** |

An der Riese, Altspitzbahn. **GPS:** n47,61995 e10,49830.⌁⌁.

70 ⌁ € 8 ⌁€1 ⌁Ch ⌁(62x)€1/kWh ⌁. ⌁.
Location: Rural, comfortable. **Surface:** gravel/metalled.
⌁ 01/01-31/12
Distance: ⌁500m ⌁3,8km ⌁1km ⌁3km ⊗200m ⌁500m
⌁500m ⌁on the spot ⌁200m ⌁200m.
Remarks: Baker every morning, code internet at tourist office.

| ⌁ | **Neualbenreuth** ⌁ | **11F3** |

Reisemobilhafen Sibyllenbad, Parkplatz P2, Kurallee.
GPS: n49,98099 e12,42406.⌁.

8 ⌁free ⌁€1 ⌁Ch ⌁€1. **Surface:** gravel. ⌁ 01/01-31/12
Distance: ⌁500m ⌁500m ⌁500m ⌁500m ⌁on the spot.

21 ⌁ € 8 + € 1/pp tourist tax ⌁ ⌁Ch ⌁(20x)€0,50/kWh WC ⌁.
Surface: metalled. ⌁ 01/01-31/12
Distance: ⌁1,5km.
Remarks: Bread-service.

| ⌁ S | **Neuburg/Donau** ⌁ ⌁ | **16D3** |

Parkplatz P1, Schlösslwiese, Zur Ringmeierbucht.
GPS: n48,74022 e11,18434.

30 ⌁free ⌁€1 ⌁Ch. **Location:** Urban, simple, central, quiet.
Surface: gravel/sand. ⌁ 01/01-31/12
Distance: ⊗100m ⌁400m ⌁on the spot ⌁on the spot.
Remarks: On the Danube river.

| ⌁ | **Neumarkt/Oberpfalz** | **16E1** |

Volksfestplatz, Woffenbacherstrasse. **GPS:** n49,28118 e11,44528.⌁.

30 ⌁free. **Surface:** grassy. ⌁ 01/01-31/12
Distance: ⌁600m.
Remarks: At sports centre.

| ⌁ S | **Neumarkt/Oberpfalz** | **16E1** |

Fritz Berger, Fritz-Berger-Str. 1. **GPS:** n49,30500 e11,48444.⌁.

⌁free ⌁ ⌁Chfree. **Surface:** grassy. ⌁ 01/01-31/12
Distance: ⌁2km ⌁2km.

| ⌁ | **Neusäß** | **16D3** |

Titania-Therme, Birkenallee 1. **GPS:** n48,40089 e10,82508.

5 ⌁free. **Location:** Urban, simple, central, quiet. **Surface:** metalled.
⌁ 01/01-31/12
Distance: ⌁1,2km ⌁3km ⌁1,2km ⌁on the spot ⌁on the spot.

| ⌁ S | **Neustadt/Aisch** | **16C1** |

Am Festplatz, Bei den Sommerkeller. **GPS:** n49,58187 e10,60271.⌁.

Neustadt/Aisch · 16C1

Am Waldwad, Eilersweg. **GPS:** n49,57462 e10,62993. ⬆️➡️.

6 🚐free. **Surface:** grasstiles. ⬛ 01/01-31/12
Distance: 🚶3,5km ⊗4km 🍺4km 🚆1km.

Niederwerrn · 11C3

Jahnstrasse. **GPS:** n50,06073 e10,17526. ⬆️.

30 🚐free 🚰€3 ⚡ChWC🗑️. **Surface:** asphalted. ⬛ 01/01-31/12
Distance: 🚶on the spot ⊗on the spot.
Remarks: Near sports fields, max. 3 nights.

Nordheim am Main · 11C3

Zehnthofstrasse. **GPS:** n49,85952 e10,17909. ⬆️.

30 🚐voluntary contribution 🚰⚡Chfree. **Surface:** metalled.
⬛ 01/01-31/12
Distance: 🚶200m.
Remarks: Along Main river.

Nördlingen · 16C3

Kaiserwiese. **GPS:** n48,85488 e10,48445. ⬆️.

30 🚐free 🚰€2 ⚡€2 Ch ⚡€2/kWh WC. **Location:** Urban, simple,
quiet. **Surface:** asphalted. ⬛ 01/01-31/12
Distance: 🚶on the spot ⊗McDonalds.
Remarks: Max. 48h.

Nürnberg · 16D1

Volkspark Dutzendteich, Munchener Strasse.
GPS: n49,42403 e11,10586. ⬆️➡️.

10 🚐free. **Location:** Urban. **Surface:** asphalted. ⬛ 01/01-31/12
Distance: 🚶4km 🚆700m.
Remarks: Max. 3 nights.

Nürnberg · 16D1

Volkspark Marienburg, Kilianstrasse.
GPS: n49,47495 e11,09606. ⬆️➡️.

8 🚐free. **Location:** Urban. **Surface:** grasstiles/metalled.
⬛ 01/01-31/12
Distance: 🚶centre 4km ⊗800m 🚆800m 🍺on the spot.
Remarks: Max. 3 nights.

Nürnberg · 16D1

Wöhrder See, Rechenberganlage, Dr Gustav Heinemannstrasse.
GPS: n49,46041 e11,11548. ⬆️.

8 🚐free. **Location:** Urban. **Surface:** metalled. ⬛ 01/01-31/12
Distance: 🚶3km 🚆500m.
Remarks: Max. 3 nights.

Tourist information Nürnberg:
ℹ️ City walk through old city centre, daily from Tourist Information,
Hauptmarkt. ⬛ 14.30h.
ℹ️ Nürnberg Card. Card gives for free entrance on among other things
public transport and museums, discounts on purchases, boat trips, city
walks etc.
Ⓜ️ Spielzeugmuseum, Karlstrasse 13-15. Toy museum. ⬛ Tue-Su
10-17h, Wed 10-21h.
⚔️ Die Burg. Palace. ⬛ 01/04-30/09 9-12h, 12.45-17h, 01/10-31/03
9.30-12h, 12.45-16h. 🎫 € 3.
🐾 Tiergarten. Zoo. ⬛ 01/04-30/09 8-19.30h, 01/10-31/03 9-17h.

Oberammergau · 19D2

Campingpark Oberammergau, Ettalerstrasse 56B.
GPS: n47,59040 e11,07157. ⬆️➡️.

20 🚐€8 🚰⚡Ch ⚡WC🗑️against payment. 🏪 **Location:** Simple.
Surface: gravel. ⬛ 01/01-31/12
Distance: 🚶1,2km 🚗400m 🚆100m 🍺1,2km 🚲1km.
Remarks: Max. 24h.

Oberaudorf · 19F2

Pechler Hof, Tatzlwurmstrasse 5. **GPS:** n47,66132 e12,16890. ⬆️➡️.

5 🚐€9 🚰⚡🗑️included. **Location:** Simple, central, quiet.
Surface: grassy. ⬛ 01/01-31/12
Distance: 🚶1km 🚆500m 🍺200m 🚆100m.

Oberaudorf · 19F2

Hotel Feuriger Tatzlwurm, Tatzlwurm, B307.
GPS: n47,67223 e12,08448.

10 🚐guests free 🚰. **Location:** Rural, simple.
Surface: gravel/metalled. ⬛ 01/01-31/12
Distance: 🚶on the spot ⊗on the spot.

Oberelsbach · 11B2

Wohnmobilstellplatz Oberelsbach, Gangolfstrasse.
GPS: n50,44234 e10,11412. ⬆️.

6 🚐€5 🚰€1/80liter ⚡Ch ⚡(6x)€0,50/kWh. ⬛ 01/01-31/12
Distance: 🚶500m ⊗on the spot.
Remarks: Max. 3 days.

Obermaiselstein · 19C2

Wohnmobilplatz Allgäu, Am Goldbach 3, Niederdorf.
GPS: n47,44422 e10,24288. ⬆️➡️.

30 🚐€ 10 + € 1,30/pp tourist tax 🚰⚡Ch ⚡(25x)€2/day
WC🗑️€1⬛. 🚿 **Location:** Rural, comfortable, luxurious.
Surface: asphalted/gravel. ⬛ 01/01-31/12
Distance: ⊗on the spot.

Oberstdorf · 19C3

Rubi-Camp, Rubinger Straße 34. **GPS:** n47,42340 e10,27772. ⬆️.

80 🚐€ 23-27 + € 2,60/pp tourist tax, dog € 3 🚰⚡Ch ⚡€0,70/kWh
WC🗑️🔌🚿 **Surface:** grassy. ⬛ 01/01-31/12
Distance: 🚶150m (skibus) 🚲on the spot 🚶on the spot.
Remarks: Bread-service.

Oberstdorf · 19C3

Wohnmobilstellplatz Oberstdorf, Enzenspergerweg 10.
GPS: n47,40856 e10,28625. ⬆️.

150 🚐€ 12, tourist tax € 2,60/pp 🚰⚡Ch ⚡€2,50/24h WC🗑️🔌.
Location: Rural, luxurious. **Surface:** grassy/metalled.
⬛ 01/01-31/12
Distance: 🚶on the spot ⊗250m 🚆100m 🍺on the spot 🚲500m

≈800m.

Oberthulba 11B3

Reisemobilstellplatz Thulbatal. GPS: n50,17419 e9,92499. ⬆️

25 🅿️ € 6,50, 2 pers.incl 🔧Ch ♨️€2 WC🚽€0,80 🔌€2,30.
Surface: grasstiles. ⬛ 15/03-15/11
Distance: 🚶1km 🏊on the spot ⊗150m.

Oberviechtach 16F1

Am Freibad, Im Wiesengrund. **GPS:** n49,45296 e12,42458. ⬆️

+5 🅿️free 🔧Ch ♨️(3x)free. **Location:** Simple, isolated.
Surface: asphalted. ⬛ 01/01-31/12
Distance: 🚶1km ⊗600m.
Remarks: Max. 3 days.

Oettingen 16C2

Schießwasen. GPS: n48,95690 e10,60894. ⬆️

4 🅿️free 🔧€1/10minutes 🗄️Ch ♨️(4x)€1/8h.
Location: Simple, quiet. **Surface:** metalled.
⬛ 01/01-31/12 🚫 last weekend Jul, 1st weekend Aug
Distance: 🚶10 min walking 🚉500m.

Ostheim 11C2

Streuwiesenparkplatz, Nordheimer Straße/Alexander Straße.
GPS: n50,45820 e10,22656. ⬆️

6 🅿️€ 3 🔧€1/80liter 🗄️Ch ♨️€0,50. **Surface:** metalled.
⬛ 01/01-31/12
Distance: 🚶300m ⊗300m 🚉300m.

Ottobeuren 19C1

Parking Sportwelt, Galgenberg 4. **GPS:** n47,94907 e10,29649. ⬆️

10 🅿️free 🔧€0,50/100liter 🗄️Ch ♨️(6x)€0,50/kWh.
Location: Urban, comfortable. **Surface:** metalled.
⬛ 01/01-31/12

Distance: 🚶1km.
Remarks: Coins at Sportwelt (9-23h), village with noteworthy cathedral.

Parkstein 16E1

Basaltkegel von Parkstein, Basaltstrasse 16.
GPS: n49,73179 e12,07127.

20 🅿️free. **Surface:** metalled. ⬛ 01/01-31/12
Distance: 🚶200m ⊗50m.
Remarks: Nearbij Gasthof Bergstüberl, beautiful view.

Passau 16H3

Güterbahnhof, Regensburger strasse. **GPS:** n48,57406 e13,44495. ⬆️

15 🅿️€ 3/h, max. € 13/day 🔧Ch 🚌 **Location:** Urban, simple, noisy. **Surface:** metalled. ⬛ 01/01-31/12
Distance: 🚶500m ⊗500m 🚉500m 🚏100m.
Remarks: Price incl. bus transport to the city centre.

Passau 16H3

Halser Straße. **GPS:** n48,57895 e13,47437. ⬆️

13 🅿️€ 1/h, max. € 8/day 🔧€1/50liter 🗄️Ch ♨️€0,50/kWh.
Location: Urban, comfortable, central. **Surface:** metalled.
⬛ 01/01-31/12 🚫 high water
Distance: 🚶centre 500m ⊗500m 🚉500m 🚣on the spot.
Remarks: Max. 24h.

Passau 16H3

Winterhafen, Regensburgerstrasse/Racklau.
GPS: n48,57412 e13,42690. ⬆️➡️

60 🅿️free. **Surface:** gravel. ⬛ 01/01-31/12 🚫 high water
Distance: 🚶2km 🏊On the Danube river 🚣on the spot ⊗500m 🚉500m 🚏300m.

Peiting 19D2

Wellenfreibad, Ammergauer Strasse 22/A. **GPS:** n47,79317 e10,92227.

3 🅿️free. ⬛ 01/01-31/12
Distance: 🚶100m.
Remarks: Parking at swimming pool, max. 48h.

Petting 19G1

Stellplatz Schneiderhof, Seestrasse 11a. **GPS:** n47,91375 e12,81120.

4 🅿️€ 14 incl. 2 pers., tourist tax incl 🔧Ch ♨️€0,50/kWh
WC🚽included. **Surface:** grassy.
Distance: 🚶300m 🏊1km ⊗300m 🚉300m 🚏500m.

Petting 19G1

Wolferstätte, Stubern 1. **GPS:** n47,88988 e12,78455.

3 🅿️€ 12, 2 pers.incl 🔧€2/100liter 🗄️Ch ♨️ WC🚽. **Surface:** grassy.
⬛ 01/05-30/10
Distance: 🚶4km 🚉5km 🚏2km.

Pfronten ❄️ 19D2

Wohnmobilstellplatz Wohlfahrt, Am Wiesele 7, Weißbach.
GPS: n47,59829 e10,55240. ⬆️➡️

45 🅿️€ 10, 2 pers.incl 🔧€0,50 🗄️Ch ♨️(48x)WCincluded 🚽€0,50 🔌€
3.🛒 **Surface:** gravel. ⬛ 01/01-31/12
Distance: 🚡Skibus 🎿5km 🛒on the spot.

Plattling 16G2

Freizeit- und Sportzentrum Plattling, Georg-Ecklstrasse.
GPS: n48,77226 e12,87331. ⬆️➡️

20 🅿️free 🔧€1/80liter 🗄️Ch ♨️(4x)€0,50/kWh. **Location:** Rural, simple. **Surface:** metalled. ⬛ 01/01-31/12
Distance: 🚶500m 🚉500m.

Pleystein 16F1

Reisemobilplatz Pleystein, Vohenstraußer Straße/Galgenbergweg.
GPS: n49,64429 e12,40548. ⬆️

10 🛏free 🚰🔧WC free. **Surface:** gravel. 📷 01/01-31/12
Distance: 🚶350m.

📷 Poppenricht 🚩 16E1
Wohnmobilstellplatz an der Vils, Vilsstrasse.
GPS: n49,48184 e11,83119.⬆️

20 🛏free. **Location:** Rural, simple, quiet. **Surface:** gravel.
📷 01/01-31/12
Distance: 🚶1km ➜on the spot ⊗2km 🛒1km 🧍on the spot.
Remarks: Along the historic "Goldenen Straße" from Nürnberg to Prague, at sports centre.

📷S Pottenstein 16D1
Wohnmobilpark Pottenstein, Am langen Berg.
GPS: n49,76294 e11,40826.⬆️

25 🛏€7 🚰€1/80liter 🔧Ch€1 ⚡(6x)€1/kWh. **Location:** Rural, simple. **Surface:** grassy/metalled.
📷 01/01-31/12 ◉ Service: winter
Distance: 🚶1km 🛒Aldi 200m.

Tourist information Pottenstein:
👁 Teufelshöhle. Caves, constant temperature 9°C and atmospheric humidity 98%. 📷 01/04-31/10 9-17h.
🏰 Burg Pottenstein. 1000 Jaar oude burcht. 📷 Tue-Su 10-17h.

📷S Prichsenstadt 16C1
Wohnmobilstellplatz Schützengesellschaft 1752, Wiesentheider Straße 3. **GPS:** n49,81649 e10,34981.⬆️

5 🛏€5 🚰€1 ⚡€2,50. **Surface:** gravel. 📷 01/01-31/12
Distance: 🚶300m ⊗on the spot.

📷S Prien am Chiemsee ⛲🚩⛴ 19F1
Wohnmobilstellplatz Strandbad Schraml, Harrasser Strasse 39.
GPS: n47,85400 e12,36679.⬆️➡️

---

30 🛏€9/night, €2,50/day 🚰🔧Ch€3 🔧 WC. **Location:** Rural, simple, isolated. **Surface:** grassy/sand. 📷 01/04-15/10
Distance: 🚶1,5km ➜6km 🚗on the spot ⊗500m ➜on the spot.
Remarks: Steep ramp.

📷S Rain/Lech 16D3
Wohnmobilstellplatz Rain, Fasanenweg.
GPS: n48,69195 e10,90699.⬆️

8 🛏free 🚰€1 🔧Ch ⚡€1/6h. **Surface:** metalled.
📷 01/01-31/12
Distance: 🚶1km 🚴on the spot 🧍on the spot.

📷S Ramsthal 11B3
Festplatz, Hauptstrasse, K6-4. **GPS:** n50,13750 e10,06111.⬆️

12 🛏free 🚰€1/100liter 🔧Ch ⚡€0,50/kWh WC. **Surface:** metalled.
📷 01/01-31/12
Distance: 🚶on the spot ⊗Gasthof Wahler, Gaststätte zum Beck 🍴on the spot.

📷S Reit im Winkl 🏔❄ 19F2
Wohnmobilpark Reit im Winkl, Am Waldbahnhof 7, Groissenbach.
GPS: n47,67013 e12,48358.⬆️➡️

250 🛏€8-12 🚰€0,20/10liter 🔧Ch ⚡€0,75/kWh WC.
Location: Rural, quiet. **Surface:** grassy/metalled. 📷 01/01-31/12
Distance: 🚶1km 🛒200m ➜on the spot ⛷on the spot.
Remarks: Use sanitary €4,50-6/pppn, shuttle bus to ski-piste.

📷S Reit im Winkl 🏔❄ 19F2
Wohnmobilpark Seegatterl, Seegatterl 7.
GPS: n47,65898 e12,54213.⬆️➡️

100 🛏€8-10, tourist tax excl ⚡€0,20/10liter 🔧Ch ⚡€0,75/kWh WC. **Location:** Rural, quiet. **Surface:** grassy/gravel.
📷 17/12-10/04, 01/06-15/10
Distance: 🚶4km ⛰1,5km ⛷150m ⊗on the spot.

📷S Reit im Winkl 🏔❄ 19F2
Gasthof Stoaner, Birnbacher Straße 34. **GPS:** n47,67900 e12,44930.
15 🛏€10, 2 pers.incl., winter €12 🚰🔧Ch ⚡WC included.
Surface: unpaved.
◉ 01/11-20/12, Easter-30/04
Remarks: At golf court.

📷S Riedenburg ⛲🏔🌲 16E2
Volksfestplatz, Austraße. **GPS:** n48,96446 e11,68181.⬆️➡️

40 🛏€6 🚰🔧Ch included ⚡€1/8h.🔌 **Location:** Central.
Surface: gravel/metalled.
📷 01/01-31/12 ◉ last week of Aug
Distance: 🚶450m 🚗on the spot ⊗300m 🛒20m.
Remarks: At the Main-Danube Canal.

📷S Roding 16F2
Volksfestplatz, Jahnstraße 21. **GPS:** n49,19806 e12,51722.⬆️
4 🛏free 🚰€1/70liter 🔧€1/time Ch ⚡€0,50/kWh. **Location:** Urban, simple. **Surface:** asphalted/metalled.
📷 01/01-31/12
Distance: 🚶150m ⊗150m 🛒500m.
Remarks: Max. 1 day.

📷S Roßhaupten 🌿⛲🏠🐄🌾❄ 19D2
Wohnmobilstellplatz Miller, Augsburger Strasse 23.
GPS: n47,65889 e10,71944.⬆️

25 🛏€9, 4 pers.incl 🚰🔧Ch ⚡(3x)€2 WC 🔧€1. **Location:** Simple.
Surface: metalled. 📷 01/01-31/12
Distance: 🚶50m ⛰1,2km ➜1,2km ⊗200m 🛒150m 🚲150m ⛷1km 🐎500m.
Remarks: Next to Camping- und Freizeitmarkt, reparation work.

📷S Rothenbuch 11B3
Freizeitanlage, Heigenbrücker Weg. **GPS:** n49,97460 e9,39475.⬆️

10 🛏€7 🚰€1/80liter 🔧Ch ⚡€0,50/kWh. 🔌 **Location:** Rural, simple, quiet. **Surface:** grasstiles. 📷 01/01-31/12
Distance: 🚶250m.

📷S Rothenburg ob der Tauber 🌿 16C1
Parkplatz P2, Bensen Strasse. **GPS:** n49,37048 e10,18324.

25 🛏€10 🚰€1/45liter 🔧Ch ⚡€0,50/kWh WC. **Surface:** metalled.
📷 01/01-31/12
Distance: 🚶700m.

📷S Rothenburg ob der Tauber 🌿 16C1
Parkplatz P3, Weinsdorfer Strasse. **GPS:** n49,38222 e10,18889.⬆️

30 🛏 € 10 🚰 €1/45liter 🔧 Ch WC. **Surface:** metalled.
⊙ 01/01-31/12
Distance: 🚶on the spot.

Tourist information Rothenburg ob der Tauber:
Ⓜ Mittelalterliches Kriminalmuseum, Burggasse 3. History of 1000
years of jurisdiction.
⊙ 01/04-31/10 9.30-18h, 01/11-28/02 14-16h, 01/12-31/12, 01/03-
31/03 10-16h.
🎭 Schäfertanz. Traditional celebration.
⊙ 27/03, 15/05, 04/09.

| 🚐 S | **Rothenkirchen** | 11D2 |
Waldschwimmbad. GPS: n50,37389 e11,31583.

40 🛏 € 5 🚰 €0,50 🔧 Ch € 1 🔧 (16x) WC included.
Surface: metalled. ⊙ 01/04-31/10
Distance: 🚶1,5km.
Remarks: Parking swimming pool.

| 🚐 S | **Röthlein** | 11C3 |
Sportanlage TSV/Bundeskegelbahn, Friedhofstrasse.
GPS: n49,98694 e10,21583. ⬆

10 🛏 free. **Surface:** unpaved.
Distance: 🚶on the spot.

| 🚐 S | **Röttingen** ❀ | 16B1 |
Wohnmobilplatz an der Tauber, Neubronner Straße.
GPS: n49,50724 e9,96995.

10 🛏 free 🚰 €2,50/day WC 🔧 €2,50/day. **Location:** Rural, simple.
Surface: gravel. ⊙ 01/01-31/12
Distance: 🚶500m 🚲on the spot ⊗on the spot.
Remarks: Fishing permit available at town hall.

| Ⓒ S | **Ruhpolding** | 19G2 |
Campingplatz Ortnerhof, Ortsstraße 5.
GPS: n47,74260 e12,66303. ⬆ ➡

16 🛏 € 9 🚰 🔧 Ch 🔧 €1,50 + €0,60/kWh WC 🔧 💧€3 📶€3/24h.
Location: Rural. **Surface:** gravel. ⊙ 01/01-31/12
Distance: 🚶3km ⊗on the spot 🍴2km 🏊on the spot.
Remarks: At golf court, max. 1 night.

| 🚐 S | **Scheidegg** | 19C2 |
Wohnmobilpark am Kurhaus, Am Hammerweiher 1.
GPS: n47,57351 e9,84545. ⬆
20 🛏 € 6, tourist tax € 1,70/pp 🚰 🔧 Ch included 🔧€3 🔧€1,50 📶.
Surface: gravel/metalled. ⊙ 01/01-31/12
Distance: 🛒Minishop.
Remarks: Bread-service.

| 🚐 S | **Scheinfeld** | 16C1 |
Freibad Scheinfeld, Badstrasse 5. **GPS:** n49,67434 e10,46173.

2 🛏 € 6 🚰 🔧 Ch 🔧. **Surface:** gravel. ⊙ 01/01-31/12
Remarks: At swimming pool.

| 🚐 S | **Schliersee** 🏔🏕📷❄ | 19E2 |
Am Spitzingsee, Spitzingstraße. **GPS:** n47,66648 e11,88851. ⬆

+10 🛏 summer € 12, winter € 9 (no service) 🚰 🔧 Ch.
Location: Rural, simple, isolated, quiet. **Surface:** gravel.
⊙ 01/01-31/12 ⊙ Service: winter
Distance: 🚶5,4km 🍴on the spot ⊗500m 🚴on the spot 🚶on the
spot 🏊on the spot.
Remarks: Altitude 1085m, at lake.

| 🚐 S | **Schlüsselfeld** 🐟 | 16C1 |
Bambergerstrasse. GPS: n49,75572 e10,62267. ⬆ ⬆

5 🛏 free 🚰 €1/80liter 🔧 Ch. **Location:** Urban, simple, central.
Surface: asphalted. ⊙ 01/01-31/12
Distance: 🚶on the spot ⊗on the spot 🍴on the spot 🚴50m 🚶50m.

| 🏕 S | **Schlüsselfeld** 🐟 | 16C1 |
Concorde, Concorde-Straße 2–4. **GPS:** n49,76745 e10,56478. ⬆

20 🛏 free 🚰 €1/100liter 🔧 Ch 🔧 €0,50/kWh 📶. **Location:** Rural,
simple, quiet. **Surface:** metalled.
⊙ 01/01-31/12
Distance: 🚶1km ⊗1km 🍴1km.
Remarks: At motohome manufacturer.

| 🚐 S | **Schnelldorf** | 16C2 |
BP-Truckstop Feuchtwangen, Rudolph Dieselstrasse 1.
GPS: n49,17149 e10,24124. ⬆

20 🛏 € 7 🚰 €1/80liter 🔧 Ch 🔧 (3x) WC 🔧 €2. **Surface:** metalled.
⊙ 01/01-31/12
Distance: 🚗300m ⊗on the spot 🍴on the spot.
Remarks: Reduction at restaurant € 5, special part for motor homes.

| 🚐 S | **Schöllkrippen** 🍴 | 11A3 |
Naturerlebnisbad, Häfner-Ohnhaus-Straße.
GPS: n50,08484 e9,25247. ⬆

35 🛏 € 7/24h 🚰 €1/80liter 🔧 Ch 🔧 (24x)€0,50/kWh. 🚐
Location: Rural, comfortable, quiet. **Surface:** grassy.
⊙ 01/01-31/12
Distance: 🚶500m.

| 🚐 S | **Schongau** 🍺 | 19D2 |
Festplatz, Lechuferstrasse. **GPS:** n47,80906 e10,89815. ⬆

70 🛏 € 5 🚰 €1/5liter 🔧 Ch WC. 🚐
Location: Urban, simple.
Surface: asphalted.

DE

■ service: 20/03-05/11 ◯ 25/07-08/08
Distance: ⚊400m ⚊100m ⚊400m ⚊on the spot.
Remarks: Caution key sanitary € 30, guests free.

| 🏕️ | **Schönsee** | 16F1 |

Moorbad, Böhmerwaldstrasse. **GPS:** n49,51091 e12,55321.⬆️
5 ⏚free. **Location:** Simple. ■ 01/01-31/12
Distance: ⊗300m.
Remarks: Max. 3 days.

| 🏕️ S | **Schonungen** | 11C3 |

Behr Reisemobile, An der Kemenate 6, Abersfeld, B303.
GPS: n50,07352 e10,39366.⬆️

5 ⏚free ⛽🔌Chfree. **Surface:** metalled. ■ 01/01-31/12
Distance: 🛒8km.
Remarks: Motorhome dealer, accessory shop, after opening hours inaccessible.

| 🏕️ | **Schrobenhausen** | 16D3 |

Am Klostergarten, Rot-Kreuz-Straße.
GPS: n48,55835 e11,26234.⬆️➡️

4 ⏚free. **Location:** Simple, quiet. **Surface:** metalled.
■ 01/01-31/12
Distance: ⚊400m ⚊400m ⚊400m.

| S | **Schrobenhausen** | 16D3 |

Stadtwerke-Kläranlage, Köningslachenerweg 12.
GPS: n48,57374 e11,27519.⬆️
⛽🔌ChService€5.
Remarks: Mo-Thu 7-12h, 13-16h, Fr 7-12h.

| 🏕️ | **Schwandorf** | 16E1 |

Festplatz, Angerring, Krondorf. **GPS:** n49,33230 e12,10247.⬆️

30 ⏚free ⛽🔌Chfree.
Location: Simple. **Surface:** asphalted/grassy.
■ 01/01-31/12 ◯ week before/after Whitsuntide
Distance: ⚊500m ⚊200m ⚊500m.
Remarks: Along the Naab river.

| 🏕️S | **Schwangau** 🌿🌲🌳❄️♨️ | 19D2 |

Wohnmobilpark Schwangau, Münchenerstrasse 151.
GPS: n47,59167 e10,77250.⬆️

24 ⏚€ 14-19, tourist tax € 1,90/pp, dog € 2 ⛽🔌Ch 🧹(24x)€
2,50 WC included. 🚿 **Location:** Urban, comfortable.
Surface: grassy/gravel. ■ 01/01-31/12
Distance: ⚊2km ⚊on the spot ⚊on the spot ⊗on the spot ⚊on

the spot ⚊on the spot 🚴1km ⚤on the spot.

| 🏕️ | **Segnitz** 🌊 | 16C1 |

Mainstraße 20. **GPS:** n49,67012 e10,14242.⬆️

4 ⏚free. **Location:** Urban, simple. **Surface:** metalled.
Distance: ⚊on the spot ⚊on the spot ⚊on the spot ⊗200m.
Remarks: Max. 1 day.

| 🏕️S | **Segnitz** 🌊 | 16C1 |

Gasthaus zum Goldenen Anker, Mainstraße 8.
GPS: n49,67063 e10,14344.⬆️

17 ⏚€ 7,50 ⛽€ 0,50/50liter 🔌Ch 🧹€ 0,50. **Location:** Simple.
Surface: grassy/gravel. ■ 01/01-31/12 ◯ Restaurant: Thu
Distance: ⚊on the spot ⚊on the spot ⚊on the spot ⊗on the spot.
Remarks: Along Main river.

| 🏕️ | **Selb** | 11E1 |

Wundsiedler Weiher. **GPS:** n51,15581 e12,13455.➡️

20 ⏚free. **Surface:** gravel. ■ 01/01-31/12
Distance: ⚊2km ⊗200m.
Remarks: Hiking trails.

| 🏕️S | **Siegsdorf** | 19G1 |

Gasthof Hörterer der Hammerwirt, Schmiedstrasse, B306, Hammer.
GPS: n47,80096 e12,70392.⬆️➡️

10 ⏚guests free ⛽WC📶. **Location:** Rural. **Surface:** metalled.
■ 01/01-31/12 ◯ Wed
Distance: ⊗on the spot ⚊100m ⚊100m 🚴2,5km ⚤300m.
Remarks: Max. 3 nights.

| ⚓ | **Sonthofen** ♨️ | 19C2 |

Erlebnisbad Wonnemar, Stadionweg 5.
GPS: n47,50344 e10,27883.⬆️➡️

12 ⏚free. **Location:** Urban, simple. **Surface:** gravel.

■ 01/01-31/12
Distance: 🛒2,3km ⊗on the spot 🚴on the spot ⚤on the spot.
Remarks: Max. 1 night.

| 🏕️S | **Steinach/Straubing** | 16F2 |

Firma Hubert Brandl Caravantastic, Gewerbering 11.
GPS: n48,95639 e12,62250.⬆️

3 ⏚free ⛽€1 🔌🧹. **Location:** Simple. **Surface:** grassy.
■ 01/01-31/12
Distance: ⚊1,5km ⚊2km ⚊1km.
Remarks: Connection electricity < 18h.

| 🏕️S | **Steinberg am See** ⚓🚣🌳🌊 | 16F1 |

Movin'G'round, Am Steinberger See. **GPS:** n49,28247 e12,17357.⬆️

25 ⏚€ 7 ⛽service€2 Ch 🧹. **Location:** Rural, simple.
Surface: grassy. ■ 01/04-31/10
Distance: ⚊500m ⚊on the spot ⊗on the spot.
Remarks: Check in at pay-desk.

| 🏕️ | **Steinhausen** | 19B1 |

Parkplatz, Am Reiterhof 1. **GPS:** n48,02746 e9,69476.

5 ⏚free. **Surface:** gravel. ■ 01/01-31/12
Distance: ⊗180m.

| 🏕️S | **Sulzbach-Rosenberg** 🌿🍺 | 16E1 |

Großparkplatz, Bayreuther Straße. **GPS:** n49,50583 e11,74500.⬆️➡️

4 ⏚free ⛽€1/80liter 🔌Ch 🧹(4x)€0,50/kWh. **Location:** Urban,
simple. **Surface:** gravel. ■ 01/01-31/12
Distance: ⚊300m ⊗500m ⚊500m 🚴on the spot.

| 🏕️S | **Sulzemoos** | 19D1 |

Der Freistaat Caravaning, Ohmstrasse. **GPS:** n48,28267 e11,26084.⬆️

40 ⏚free ⛽€1/80liter 🔌Ch 🧹(20x)€1/kWh WC. **Location:** Simple.
Surface: gravel.

01/01-31/12
Distance: 800m 800m McDonalds 800m 800m 600m.
Remarks: Motorhome dealer.

Tauberrettersheim — 16B1

Brunnenstrasse. **GPS:** n49,49635 e9,93720.

6 free. **Location:** Rural, simple. **Surface:** grassy.
01/01-31/12
Distance: on the spot on the spot.

Thierstein — 11E3

Kaiserstein, Hirtweg. **GPS:** n50,10610 e12,10490.

10 €4 Ch included voluntary contribution.
Surface: metalled. **01/01-31/12** 01/10-31/03 water disconnected. **Distance:** 500m 500m 500m.
Remarks: Max. 2 nights, beautiful view.

Thüngersheim — 11B3

Parkplatz Main-Aue, Am Schwimbad. **GPS:** n49,88084 e9,83717.

20 free Ch free (16x)€0,50/kWh. **Location:** Rural, comfortable, noisy. **Surface:** grassy. **01/04-31/10**
Distance: 500m on the spot.
Remarks: Along Main river.

Traunstein — 19F1

Gasthaus Jobst, Balthasar Permoserstrasse 64, Rettenbach.
GPS: n47,91188 e12,64899.

10 €3, guests free €2 Ch €2,50. **Surface:** metalled.
01/01-31/12 Wed

Traunstein — 19F1

Firma Grüaugl, Schmidhamerstrasse 31. **GPS:** n47,88227 e12,59941.

12 €5 €2 €2 Ch €0,50/kWh. **Location:** Isolated.
Surface: metalled. **01/01-31/12**

Distance: on the spot.
Remarks: Camping equipment store.

Treuchtlingen — 16D2

Reisemobilstellplatz am Kurpark, Kästleinmühlenstrasse 20.
GPS: n48,96028 e10,91778.

56 €9,50 €1/80liter Ch €1/8h WC included.
Location: Urban, comfortable, quiet. **Surface:** grasstiles.
01/01-31/12
Distance: 800m on the spot.
Remarks: Bread-service.

Übersee/Chiemsee — 19F1

Bauernhof Steiner, Almfischer 11, Stegen.
GPS: n47,80963 e12,49136.

25 €11, 2 pers.incl Ch €0,40/kWh WC €1,50.
Surface: gravel. **01/01-31/12**
Distance: Übersee 2km 4,6km Chiemsee 6km 1km.

Übersee/Chiemsee — 19F1

Wohmobilstellplatz Dusenhof, Stegen 4.
GPS: n47,81237 e12,48843.

28 €11, 2 pers.incl Ch €0,50/kWh €1.
Surface: grassy/gravel. **01/01-31/12**
Distance: Übersee 1km 4km Chiemsee 5km.
Remarks: Bread-service.

Veitshöchheim — 16B1

Parkplatz am Fußgängersteg, Am Güßgraben.
GPS: n49,83623 e9,86916.

5 free. **Location:** Rural, simple. **Surface:** metalled.
01/01-31/12
Distance: 500m on the spot.
Remarks: Along Main river, max. 24h.

Viechtach — 16G2

P1, Stadtmitte, Bierfeldstraße. **GPS:** n49,07876 e12,88235.

---

6 free. **Surface:** metalled. **01/01-31/12**
Distance: 400m 150m 50m.
Remarks: In front of supermarket Edeka, max. 3 nights.

Viechtach — 16G2

P2, Stadthalle, Friedhofstrasse. **GPS:** n49,07722 e12,88528.

3 free. **Location:** Simple. **Surface:** metalled.
01/01-31/12
Remarks: Max. 3 nights.

Viechtach — 16G2

P5, TÜV, Karl-Gareis-Straße. **GPS:** n49,08222 e12,88306.

free. **Surface:** asphalted. **01/01-31/12**
Distance: 500m 500m.
Remarks: Max. 3 nights, small pitches.

Viechtach — 16G2

Berghütte 'Zum Pröller', Hinterviechtach 3, Kollnburg.
GPS: n49,02939 e12,83892.

3 €5 included. **Surface:** gravel. **01/01-31/12**
Distance: Viechtach 7km 20m.
Remarks: Parking at skipistes.

Viechtach — 16G2

Am Regenufer 1. **GPS:** n49,08303 e12,88824.
€1 €1 Ch. **01/01-31/12**
Tourist information Viechtach:
Stadtplatz. Week market. Wed 7-17h.

Vilseck — 16E1

Ziegelanger. **GPS:** n49,61145 e11,80068.

20 free. **Location:** Simple, central, quiet. **Surface:** asphalted/gravel.
01/01-31/12

Distance: 🚲200m ⚓on the spot ➡on the spot ⊗on the spot 🚴200m 🚶200m.

Vilshofen 16G3

Schiffanleger, Donaukade. **GPS:** n48,63833 e13,18000. ⬆➡.

12 🛏free. **Location:** Simple, noisy. **Surface:** asphalted. 🗓 01/01-31/12

Distance: 🚲500m ⚓On the Danube river ➡on the spot ⊗500m 🚰500m.

Remarks: Max. 1 night.

Vilshofen 16G3

Yachthafen Vilshofen, Am Bootshafen. **GPS:** n48,63870 e13,18785. ⬆➡.

10 🛏€12 🚰⚡Ch🚿(10x)€3/day WC⚡€1. **Location:** Comfortable, quiet. **Surface:** gravel. 🗓 01/04-30/11

Distance: 🚲500m ⚓On the Danube river.

Vohenstrauß 16F1

Stadthalle, Neuwirtshauser Weg 11. **GPS:** n49,61872 e12,34523. ⬆.

15 🛏free 🚰⚡Ch🚿free WC⚡. **Surface:** gravel. 🗓 01/01-31/12

Distance: 🚲100m 🏪800m ⊗50m 🚰100m.

Remarks: Caution key sanitary € 50.

Volkach 11C3

Mainschleife, Am Main. **GPS:** n49,86389 e10,22139. ⬆➡.

40 🛏€5,50. **Surface:** gravel. 🗓 01/01-31/12

Distance: 🚲500m ⚓on the spot ➡on the spot ⊗500m 🚰500m.

Wackersberg 19E2

Camping Demmelhof, Stallau 148. **GPS:** n47,75056 e11,49992. ⬆.

12 🛏€15, 2 pers.incl 🚰⚡Ch🚿€0,60/kWh WC⚡€0,50 💡€3. **Surface:** grassy. 🗓 01/01-31/12

Distance: 🚲5km ⊗500m 🚍600m.

Waidhaus 16F1

Barbara Sonneschein, Pfrentsch 20. **GPS:** n49,61823 e12,49040. ⬆➡.

10 🛏€5 🚰Chincluded 🚿€0,35/kWh. 🏪 **Location:** Rural, simple, quiet. **Surface:** grassy. 🗓 01/1-31/12

Distance: 🚲on the spot 🚶on the spot.

Wald 19D2

Walder Badeweiher, Am Sportplatz. **GPS:** n47,72294 e10,56348. ⬆➡.

10 🛏€5 🚰Ch. 🏪 **Location:** Rural, quiet. **Surface:** gravel. 🗓 01/01-31/12

Distance: 🚲500m ⚓on the spot ⊗250m 🚴on the spot 🚶on the spot.

Waldkirchen 16H2

Karoli-Badepark, VDK Heimstrasse 1. **GPS:** n48,72222 e13,60278. ⬆.

16 🛏free 🚰€1/50liter 🚰Ch🚿(10x)€0,50/kWh WC⚡. **Location:** Rural, simple, quiet. **Surface:** gravel. 🗓 01/01-31/12

Distance: 🚲1km ⚓25m 🏪2km ➡on the spot 🚲on the spot.

Remarks: Parking skating rink-swimming pool, use sanitary only during opening hours swimming pool, against payment.

Waldsassen 11F3

P2 Schwanenwiese, Schwanengasse. **GPS:** n50,00526 e12,30739. ⬆.

4 🛏€5 🚿(2x)€2/10h WC. **Surface:** metalled. 🗓 01/01-31/12

Distance: 🚲500m ⚓500m 🚰500m.

Remarks: Max. 3 days, pay at tourist office.

Waldsassen 11F3

P1, Joseph-Wiesnetstrasse. **GPS:** n50,00250 e12,30361. ⬆.

2 🛏free. **Surface:** metalled. 🗓 01/01-31/12

Distance: 🚲100m ⚓100m 🚰100m.

Remarks: Max. 3 days.

Wassertrüdingen 16C2

Parkplatz Entengraben. **GPS:** n49,03926 e10,59494. ⬆➡.

12 🛏voluntary contribution 🚰€1/80liter 🚰Ch🚿(6x)€1/8h. **Location:** Urban, simple, quiet. **Surface:** metalled. 🗓 01/01-31/12

Distance: 🚲on the spot ⚓on the spot ➡on the spot 🚰1km.

Weidenberg 11E3

Am Sportpark, In der Au. **GPS:** n49,93781 e11,73068. ⬆.

2-3 🛏free. **Surface:** gravel. 🗓 01/01-31/12

Distance: 🚲750m ⊗Chinese restaurant 100m 🚰1,5km.

Weilheim in Oberbayern 19D2

Reisemobilplatz, Lohgasse. **GPS:** n47,84012 e11,13583. ⬆.

8 🛏€4/24h 🚰€0,50/50liter 🚰Ch🚿€0,50/kWh WC🚗. **Location:** Urban, simple, central. **Surface:** asphalted. 🗓 01/01-31/12

Distance: 🚲Old city centre 500m ➡100m 🚰200m.

Remarks: Along the Ammer river.

Weismain 11D3

Bauhof, Burgkunstadterstrasse. **GPS:** n50,08639 e11,23872. ⬆➡.

4 🛏free 🚰€1 ⚡€0,50 Ch€0,50 🚿(6x)€0,50. **Location:** Urban, simple. **Surface:** asphalted. 🗓 01/01-31/12

Distance: 🚲on the spot ⚓on the spot ⊗200m 🚰200m 🚍200m.

Remarks: Parking in centre.

Weissenburg 16D2

Kirchweihplatz, Limesbad, Badstrasse 5. **GPS:** n49,02476 e10,97180. ⬆.

🛏free 🚰€1/80liter 🚰Ch. **Location:** Urban. **Surface:** metalled. 🗓 01/04-31/10

Distance: 🚶Old city centre 300m ⊗La Fattoria, Frauentorstrasse 11; Mai Tai, Bismarckanlage 16; Wittelsbacher Hof, Fr.Ebertstrasse 21 🍴on the spot.

🔲S Wertach 🌿⛺🏕🎿❄🌱 19C2

Camping Grüntensee, Grüntenseestraße 41.
GPS: n47,61003 e10,44704. ⬆➡.

12 🚐€ 15 + tourist tax € 1/pp 🚰🔌Ch🧹(12x)€0,50/kWh.📹🧺
Location: Rural, luxurious, quiet. **Surface:** gravel.
🔲 01/01-31/12
Distance: 🚶2,5km 🏖600m 🏊on the spot 🚣on the spot ⊗on the spot 🍴1,5km 🚲1,5km 🎠on the spot 🎣on the spot 🎿on the spot 🐟on the spot.

🔲S Wertingen 16D3

Wohnmobilpark Wertingen, Am Bahnhof 4.
GPS: n48,55948 e10,69065.

12 🚐€ 7 🚰€1 🔌Ch🧹€2/day.📹 **Location:** Urban, comfortable, central, quiet. **Surface:** grassy/gravel. 🔲 01/01-31/12
Distance: 🚶800m 🍴300m.

🔲S Wiesenttal 11D3

Wohnmobilstellplatz Streitberg, Bahnhofstrasse, B470.
GPS: n49,80782 e11,21636. ⬆➡.

7 🚐€ 2 🚰🔌Chfree. **Location:** Rural, simple, quiet. **Surface:** gravel.
🔲 01/01-31/12
Distance: 🚶500m 🚲500m ⊗500m 🍴500m 🚌300m.
Remarks: Along railwayline.

🔲S Wolnzach 16E3

Schwimm- & Erlebnisbad Wolnzach, Hanslmühlweg 6.
GPS: n48,59718 e11,62792. ⬆.

4 🚐free 🚰€1/80liter 🔌Ch🧹(4x)€0,50/kWh. **Location:** Simple.
Surface: metalled. 🔲 01/01-31/12
Distance: 🚶600m 🏖500m 🍴600m.
Remarks: Service 100m.

🏠 Wonneberg 19G1

Gasthof Alpenblick, Traunsteiner Straße 21, Weibhausen.
GPS: n47,89880 e12,69123.

5 🚐free, use of a meal desired.
Location: Simple. **Surface:** gravel.
Distance: ⊗on the spot.

🔲S Wunsiedel 11E3

Wohnmobilstellplatz Festspielstadt Wunsiedel, Ludwigstraße.
GPS: n50,03638 e11,99351. ⬆.

6 🚐€ 5/24h 🚰🔌Ch🧹included. **Surface:** gravel. 🔲 01/01-31/12
💧 water: Nov-March
Distance: 🚶600m ⊗300m 🍴1km.
Remarks: Pay at tourist office.

🔲 Würzburg 🌿⛺🏕🌱 16B1

Viehmarktplatz, Dreikronenstra. **GPS:** n49,79782 e9,92319. ⬆.

🚐6-20h € 5, overnight stay free. **Location:** Urban, simple, noisy.
Surface: asphalted. 🔲 01/01-31/12
Distance: 🚶800m 🏊on the spot ⊗50m.

Tourist information Würzburg:
👁 Würzburger Residenz, Residenzplatz. Baroque castle, Unesco World Heritage Site. 🔲 01/04-31/10 9-18h, 01/11-31/03 10-16h. 🎫 € 4.

🔲 Zeil am Main 11C3

Altstadtparkplatz, Mittelweg. **GPS:** n50,00667 e10,59583. ⬆.

5 🚐free. **Surface:** metalled. 🔲 01/01-31/12

🔲 Zeil am Main 11C3

Parkplatz Tuchanger, Oskar Winkler strasse.
GPS: n50,01083 e10,59056. ⬆➡.

20 🚐free. **Surface:** metalled. 🔲 01/01-31/12
Distance: 🚶1km ⊗1km 🍴1km.
Remarks: Parking gymnasium.

Tourist information Zeil am Main:
⊗ Brauereigasthof Göller "Zum alten Freyung". Brewery restaurant

with regional specialities and Göller-beer. 🔲 Mo-Su 9.30-01h.
🍷 Altstadt Weinfest. Wine festivals. 🔲 06/08-08/08.
🥾 Wein-Wander-Weg. Hiking trail through wine region.

🔲S Zellingen 🌱 11B3

Am Freibad, Badstraße. **GPS:** n49,89476 e9,82680. ⬆.

5 🚐free 🚰free 🧹€3/day. **Location:** Rural, simple. **Surface:** grassy.
🔲 01/01-31/12
Remarks: Check in at swimming pool (service).

🎡 Zirndorf 16D1

Playmobil Funpark, Brandstätterstrasse. **GPS:** n49,43087 e10,93935.
40 🚐€ 4. **Surface:** metalled.
Distance: ⊗on the spot.

🇩🇰 Denmark

Capital: Copenhagen
Government: Constitutional monarchy
Official Language: Danish
Population: 5,669,000 (2014)
Area: 44,000m²

General information
Dialling code: 0045
General emergency: 112
Currency: Danish Krone (DKK), 1 DKK= 100 øre,
DKK 1 = € 0,13, € 1 = DKK 7,44,
DKK1 = £ 0,11, £ 1 = DKK 9,45 (October 2015)
Payments by credit card are accepted at almost
every shop and restaurant.

Regulations for overnight stays/campsites
Overnight parking is allowed: for 1 night, if there
is no local prohibition, but no "camping" activities
are allowed.

Camping Key Europe is obligatory when using
Danish campsites: the card can be purchased
at any campsite for DKK 110 (± € 14,30/ £11,64),
valid for one year.

Additional public holidays 2016
May 1 Great Prayer Day
June 5 Danisch Constitution Day
June 23 Sankt Hans Eve

Time Zone
Winter (Standard Time) GMT+1
Summer (DST) GMT+2

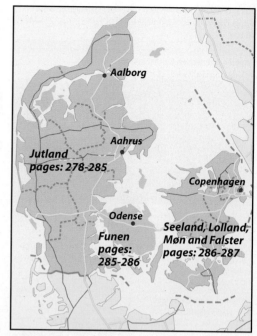

Aalborg

Aahrus

Jutland
pages: 278-285

Copenhagen

Odense

Funen
pages:
285-286

Seeland, Lolland,
Møn and Falster
pages: 286-287

DK

Jutland

Aabybro 4C3
Birthe&Leif Brinkmann, Kanalvej 164. **GPS**: n57,11947 e9,73156.⬆.

3 🚐DKK 50.♨
Location: Simple, isolated. **Surface:** grassy. ⬛ 01/01-31/12
Distance: 🚰5km.

Aalbæk 4C2
Aalbæk Havn, Sdr. Havnevej 65. **GPS**: n57,59306 e10,42686.⬆.

6 🚐DKK 170 🚰🚿(6x)WC⬛included.♨
Location: Simple, quiet. **Surface:** gravel. ⬛ 01/01-31/12
Distance: 🚰800m ⛱on the spot 🎣on the spot ⊗800m 🍺800m
🛒250m.
Remarks: Pay at harbourmaster.

Aalbæk 4C2
Galleri & Selskabslokal Gyllegaard, Hirtshalsvej 48.
GPS: n57,60619 e10,41757.⬆➡.

5 🚐DKK 100.♨
Location: Simple, isolated, quiet. **Surface:** grassy. ⬛ 01/01-31/12
Distance: 🚰4km ⛱1km ⊗4km 🍺4km.

Aarhus 5D1
Aarhus centrum parkerinsplads, Kalkværksvej 2.
GPS: n56,14815 e10,21015.⬆➡.

6 🚐free 🍺free.
Location: Urban, simple, central. **Surface:** asphalted. ⬛ 01/01-31/12
Distance: 🚰500m ⊗on the spot 🍺on the spot.
Remarks: Behind petrol station, max. 24h.

Aarhus 5D1
Marselisborg Havn, Marselisborg Havnevej 54.
GPS: n56,13927 e10,21916.
🚐🚰Ch🚿WC⬛against payment.⬛🚿
Distance: 🚰on the spot ⊗on the spot.

Aarhus 5D1
Aarhus Nord, Randersvej 400. **GPS**: n56,22672 e10,16335.
🚐DKK 100🚰Ch🚿against payment. ⬛ 01/01-31/12
Remarks: Quick-Stop: >20h - <10h.

Åbenrå 5D2
Camperstop Aabenraa, Sønderskovvej 104.
GPS: n55,02513 e9,41471.⬆.

34 🚐€ 14 🚰DKK20/120liter 🚿Ch🚿DKK 4,50/kWh WC⬛DKK
10/5minutes. **Surface:** grassy/gravel. ⬛ 01/01-31/12
Distance: 🚰2km ⊗8km ⛱400m.
Remarks: Chip-card available at campsite.

Åbenrå 5D2
Lystbådehavn, Kystvej 55. **GPS**: n55,03434 e9,42352.➡.

48 🚐€ 17 🚰🚿Ch🚿WCincluded ⬛⬛against payment 📶free. ⬛🚐
📷⛱. **Location:** Comfortable. **Surface:** gravel. ⬛ 01/04-31/10
Distance: 🚰1km ⛱on the spot 🎣on the spot ⊗on the spot 🍺50m
🛒200m 🚿on the spot 🏕on the spot.
Remarks: Harbour Åbenrå.

Augustenborg 5D2
Augustenborg Slot, Palævej. **GPS**: n54,94694 e9,85389.

70 🚐DKK 100🚰Ch🚿WC⬛.♨
Location: Rural, comfortable. **Surface:** grassy. ⬛ 01/01-31/12
Distance: 🚰1,5km 🚿on the spot 🏕on the spot.

Augustenborg 5D2
Yachthavn, Langdel 6. **GPS**: n54,94074 e9,86942.⬆.

19 🚐DKK 130 🚰🚿Ch🚿DKK 25 WC⬛.♨
Location: Luxurious, central. **Surface:** gravel. ⬛ 01/04-15/10
Distance: 🚰1km 🚿1km 🏕on the spot.

Billund 5C1
Camperpark Billund, Grenevej 5. **GPS**: n55,70480 e9,12406.⬆.
10 🚐€ 16 🚰🚿Chincluded⬛🚿DKK22.
Location: Rural, comfortable. **Surface:** grassy. ⬛ 01/01-31/12
Distance: 🚰3,5km ⊗3,5km 🍺3,5km.

Bindslev 4C3

Tannisbugt Hallen, Stadion alle 7. **GPS**: n57,54559 e10,19943.
20 ⬛ € 10 ⚡ Ch WC.
Location: Urban. **Surface**: metalled. ◼ 15/07-07/08

Bredebro 5C2

Claus Cornelsen, Galgemark 9. **GPS**: n55,04853 e8,83270. ⬆.

50 ⬛ free ⚡ Ch ✎ against payment ⬛.
Location: Rural, simple, quiet. **Surface**: gravel. ◼ 01/01-31/12
Distance: 1km.

Brovst 4C3

Vilsbæk Rideskole ved Brovst, Kanalvej 34.
GPS: n57,11895 e9,53640. ⬆.

10 ⬛ DKK 60 ⚡ Ch ✎ WC included. **Location**: Rural, simple,
isolated, quiet. **Surface**: grassy. ◼ 01/01-31/12
Distance: 2km.

Brønderslev 4C3

Serritslev Fiskepark, Agårdsvej 35. **GPS**: n57,29750 e9,99597. ⬆.

20 ⬛ DKK 50 ⚡ free WC. **Location**: Rural, simple, isolated, quiet.
Surface: grassy. ◼ 01/01-31/12
Distance: on the spot.

Bylderup-Bov 5C2

Boskov, Kvænholtvej 15. **GPS**: n54,94488 e9,06078. ⬆.

10 ⬛ DKK 60 ⚡ Ch ✎ included.
Location: Rural, simple, isolated. **Surface**: grassy/gravel.
Distance: 200m.

Bylderup-Bov 5C2

B&B Bredevad, Bredevadvej 5. **GPS**: n54,96885 e9,12138. ⬆.

2 ⬛ € 13, 2 pers.incl ⚡ Ch ✎ WC included.

Location: Rural.
Distance: 4km.

Bylderup-Bov 5C2

Kristianshåb Autocamper Park, Kristianshåbvej 5.
GPS: n54,96189 e9,06950. ➡.

50 ⬛ DKK 100 incl. 2 pers ⚡ Ch ✎ DKK 4/24h WC ⬛ ◼.
Location: Rural, comfortable, isolated.
Surface: grassy.
◼ 01/01-31/12
Distance: 6km 1km 5km.

Tourist information Bylderup-Bov:
🏰 Schackenborg Slot, Schackenborg 2, Tønder. Visit the castle garden.

Bælum 4C3

Bakgaarden, Hælskovvej 2. **GPS**: n56,83815 e10,12007. ⬆.

4 ⬛ DKK 50 ⚡ Ch ✎ included.
Surface: grassy. ◼ 01/01-31/12
Distance: 1km 1km.

Bønnerup 4D3

Bønnerup Lystbådehavn, Vestre Mole 2, Glesborg.
GPS: n56,53139 e10,71139. ⬆.

20 ⬛ DKK 150 ⚡ Ch ✎ (12x) included WC ⬛ ◼ against payment.
Location: Rural, comfortable, quiet. **Surface**: gravel.
◼ 01/01-31/12
Distance: 500m on the spot 250m 400m.
Remarks: Parking at marina.

Børkop 5D1

Brejning Lystbådehavn, Brejning Strand.
GPS: n55,67431 e9,68920. ⬆.

12 ⬛ € 16 ⚡ ✎ (12x) WC included ◼.
Location: Rural, simple, isolated, quiet. **Surface**: gravel/metalled.
◼ 01/01-31/12
Distance: Børkop 5km 4,1km 10m 10m.
Remarks: Restaurant only in summer.

Ebeltoft 5D1

Skøvgarde, Havmøllevej 5. **GPS**: n56,24475 e10,77902. ⬆ ➡.

2 ⬛ DKK 50. **Location**: Rural, simple, isolated, quiet.
Surface: grassy. ◼ 01/01-31/12 **Distance**: on the spot.
Remarks: Pay at Havmøllevej 5 or 20.

Ebeltoft 5D1

Dråby Strand, Dråby Strandvej 13. **GPS**: n56,22172 e10,73778.
⬛ DKK 150 ⚡ Ch ✎ against payment. ◼ 04/04-14/09
Remarks: Quick-Stop: >20h - <10h.

Egå 5D1

Egå Marina, Egå Havvej 35. **GPS**: n56,21069 e10,28819. ⬆.

7 ⬛ € 19 ⚡ Ch ✎ (7x) WC included ⬛ ◼.
Location: Urban, comfortable. **Surface**: asphalted. ◼ 01/01-31/12
Distance: 2km 400m on the spot on the spot 600m
600m.
Remarks: Tallycard: service, electricity, sanitary building, caution DKK 50.

Ejerslev 4C3

Ejerslev Havn, Utkærvej 5. **GPS**: n56,91855 e8,92096. ⬆ ➡.

10 ⬛ DKK 110 ⚡ Ch ✎ (10x) WC included ◼.
Location: Rural, isolated, quiet. **Surface**: gravel.
◼ 01/01-31/12
Distance: 4km on the spot 4km on the spot on the spot.
Remarks: Bread-service, last 2km gravel road, borrow cycles for free.

Engesvan 5C1

Pårup Autocamperplads, Silkeborgvej 8. **GPS**: n56,13694 e9,35028. ⬆.
4 ⬛ DKK 50 ⚡ Ch ✎ included. **Location**: Urban, simple,
central. **Surface**: gravel. ◼ 01/04-01/11
Distance: on the spot.

Erslev 4C3

Inger-Marie og Knud Erik Nielsen, Bindeleddet 4.
GPS: n56,83881 e8,68060. ⬆.

4 ⬛ DKK 40 ✎. **Location**: Rural, simple, isolated, quiet.
Surface: gravel. ◼ 01/01-31/12
Distance: 1km.

Esbjerg 5C2

Nebelso, Vestervadsvej 17 Vester Nebel.
GPS: n55,55000 e8,54361. ⬆ ➡.

DK

25 ⬛DKK 50 ⬛DKK 10 ⬛DKK 25. ⬛
Location: Rural, simple, isolated, quiet. **Surface:** grassy/gravel.
⬛ 01/04-01/11
Distance: ⬛15km ⬛on the spot.
Remarks: Fishpond, fishing license DKK90 www.nebelsoe.dk.

Fanø 5C2
Fanø Fiskesø, Storetoft 30. **GPS:** n55,43401 e8,39294.
4 ⬛€ 14 ⬛Ch ⬛WC ⬛against payment. **Surface:** gravel.
Distance: ⬛on the spot.
Remarks: At fish pond.

Fjerritslev 4C3
Erna K Nielsen, Holmsøvej 31, Haverslev. **GPS:** n57,04102 e9,39252. ⬛

6 ⬛DKK 50 ⬛included. ⬛
Location: Rural, simple, quiet. **Surface:** grassy. ⬛ 01/01-31/12
Distance: ⬛Limfjord 1,7km.

Fjerritslev 4C3
Niels Balle, Hedegardsvey 19. **GPS:** n57,12505 e9,33422. ⬛

4 ⬛DKK 70 ⬛(1x)included. ⬛
Location: Rural, simple, isolated. **Surface:** grassy. ⬛ 01/01-31/12
Distance: ⬛7km ⬛4km.

Flauenskjold 4C3
Markedsplad, Agertoften 4. **GPS:** n57,24854 e10,28477. ⬛⬛

10 ⬛DKK 50 ⬛⬛DKK 25 WC included. ⬛
Location: Rural, simple, quiet. **Surface:** grassy.
⬛ 01/01-31/12
Distance: ⬛5km.
Remarks: Money in envelope in mail box, festival and market place.

Fredericia 5D2
Lystbådehavnen, Strandvejen 115/Sanddalbakke.
GPS: n55,55246 e9,72805. ⬛

8 ⬛€ 11 ⬛Ch ⬛(8x)WC ⬛included. ⬛ ⬛ ⬛.
Location: Rural, simple, quiet. **Surface:** metalled.
⬛ 01/01-31/12
Distance: ⬛1km ⬛on the spot ⬛on the spot ⬛on the spot ⬛1km ⬛200m.
Remarks: Tallycard: service, electricity, sanitary building, caution DKK 50.

Frederikshavn 4C3
Frederikshavn Marina, Søsportsvej 8. **GPS:** n57,42375 e10,52709. ⬛.

20 ⬛DKK 150 ⬛Ch ⬛(10x)WC ⬛included. ⬛
Location: Urban, comfortable, central, quiet. **Surface:** grassy/gravel.
⬛ 01/01-31/12
Distance: ⬛800m ⬛on the spot ⬛on the spot ⬛on the spot ⬛700m.
Remarks: Pay at harbourmaster.

Gistrup 4C3
Kirsten og Karl Age, Gunderupvej 164. **GPS:** n56,93476 e9,95844. ⬛

4 ⬛DKK 100 ⬛included. ⬛
Location: Rural, simple, isolated. **Surface:** gravel.

Glejbjerg 5C2
Betina & Klaus Jørgensen, Gammelgårdsvej 3.
GPS: n55,55052 e8,78705.
4 ⬛free ⬛Chfree ⬛against payment WC ⬛.
Location: Comfortable. **Surface:** grassy/gravel. ⬛ 01/01-31/12

Grenaa 4D3
Fornæs Skibsophug, Folshøjvej. **GPS:** n56,41879 e10,91709.
10 ⬛free. **Surface:** grassy. ⬛ 01/01-31/12

Tourist information Grenaa:
⬛ Kattegat Centret. The underwater world and shark centre. ⬛ 10-16/17h ⬛ 13/12-26/12.

Haderslev 5D2
Fam. Nowak, Felstrupvej 37. **GPS:** n55,25488 e9,52556. ⬛

2 ⬛free ⬛Service DKK 30 ⬛ ⬛.
Location: Rural. **Surface:** gravel. ⬛ 01/01-31/12
Distance: ⬛3km ⬛100m ⬛on the spot.

Haderslev 5D2
Haderslev Sejl Club, Sydhavnsvej 1F. **GPS:** n55,24806 e9,50028. ⬛
6 ⬛€ 15 ⬛Ch WC ⬛included. **Surface:** gravel.
Distance: ⬛on the spot.

Tourist information Haderslev:
⬛ Sillerup Mølle, Sillerup Møllevej 33. Mill, bake bread yourself. ⬛ 15/06-15/09 Tue 10h.
⬛ Wachman's Tour. Excursion with the night watch in the old part of the city. ⬛ 01/07-31/08 Thu 21h.

Hadsund 4C3
Hvirvelkærgård, Kystvejen 202, Als. **GPS:** n56,76414 e10,28565. ⬛

10 ⬛DKK 90 ⬛DKK 30 WC ⬛included. ⬛
Location: Rural, simple, quiet. **Surface:** grassy. ⬛ 01/01-31/12
Distance: ⬛1km ⬛1km.

Hadsund 4C3
Hadsund Havn, Skovvej 67. **GPS:** n56,70988 e10,10428. ⬛.

10 ⬛DKK 130 ⬛⬛WC ⬛included. ⬛
Location: Rural, comfortable, quiet. **Surface:** grassy. ⬛ 01/01-31/12
Distance: ⬛2km ⬛2km ⬛2km.

Hadsund 4C3
Ingrid og Kristen Gade, Hobrovej 62. **GPS:** n56,70773 e10,07975. ⬛

4 ⬛DKK 100 ⬛⬛(2x)WC ⬛included. ⬛
Location: Rural, simple. **Surface:** grassy. ⬛ 01/01-31/12

Hanstholm 4C3
THy Minicamping (Rær Autocamperplads), Kærbakken 2.
GPS: n57,08945 e8,67104. ⬛⬛

20 ⬛DKK 100 ⬛Ch ⬛WC ⬛included. ⬛
Location: Rural, comfortable. **Surface:** grassy. ⬛ 01/01-31/12
Distance: ⬛Hanstholm 4km ⬛5km.

Hanstholm 4C3
Hanstholm, Hamborgvej 95. **GPS:** n57,10909 e8,66724.
⬛DKK 165 ⬛Ch ⬛against payment. ⬛ 01/03-30/09
Remarks: Quick-Stop: >20h - <10h.

Tourist information Hanstholm:
⬛ Frøstrup mini-village, Søndergade 36, Frøstrup. Miniature village.
⬛ 01/05-15/10 Wed-Thu 10-13h, 01/07-31/08 daily 13-16h.

Havndal 4C3
Udbyhøj Havn, Havnevej 62 Udbyhøj. **GPS:** n56,61111 e10,30583. ⬛.

DK

10 ⌕DKK 150 ⊞🔌Chincluded 🚿against payment WC⎅📶.🚗🧹
Location: Rural, comfortable. **Surface:** asphalted. 🅾 01/01-31/12
Distance: ⚓on the spot ⛽on the spot 🛒500m.

| ⛢S | **Havndal** 🚤 | 4C3 |

Rethe og Hans Jørn Mogensen, Klattrupgade 36, Klattrup.
GPS: n56,66397 e10,21208.⬆.

4 ⌕DKK 50 ⊞🔌Ch🚿included.🧹
Location: Rural, simple, quiet. **Surface:** grassy/gravel. 🅾 01/01-31/12
Distance: 🚶2km 🛒2km.

| ⓒS | **Havndal** 🚤 | 4C3 |

Randers Fjord, Midtvasen 21. **GPS:** n56,60997 e10,29334.
2 ⌕DKK 130 ⊞🔌Ch🚿against payment. 🅾 01/04-15/09
Remarks: Quick-Stop: >20h - <10h.

| ⛢S | **Hirtshals** 🚢🚤 | 4C2 |

Banegårdspladse, Banegårdspladsen 1.
GPS: n57,59119 e9,96308.⬆➡.

30 ⌕free.
Location: Simple, central. **Surface:** metalled. 🅾 01/01-31/12
Distance: 🚶600m 🚲4,8km 🚉600m ⚓on the spot.
Remarks: At station and ferry terminal.

| 🅿 | **Hirtshals** 🚢🚤 | 4C2 |

Willemoesvej. **GPS:** n57,59097 e9,98601.

40 ⌕free.
Location: Simple, quiet. **Surface:** unpaved. 🅾 01/01-31/12
Distance: 🚶1km ⚓Sandy beach 🚉1km.
Remarks: Parking ferry to Norway.

Tourist information Hirtshals:
Ⓜ Nordsømuseet, Willemoesvej 2. Oceanarium, large aquarium.
🅾 11/01-01/12 10-17.

| 🅴 | **Hjallerup** | 4C3 |

Peter Bastholm Galleri Retro, Alborgvej 715.
GPS: n57,17919 e10,15856.⬆.

5 ⌕DKK 100 🔌⎅.🧹
Location: Rural, isolated, quiet. **Surface:** gravel. 🅾 01/01-31/12
Distance: 🎣fish pond.

| ⛢S | **Hjørring** | 4C2 |

Somo-Art, Tverstedvej 41, Uggerby. **GPS:** n57,57523 e10,12868.⬆.
6 ⌕€ 16 ⊞🔌Chincluded 🚿free.
Location: Rural, quiet. **Surface:** grassy. 🅾 01/04-20/10
Distance: 🚶3km 🚉3km 🛒3km.

| ⛢S | **Hjørring** | 4C2 |

Thomas Lindrup, Tverstedvej 31. **GPS:** n57,57484 e10,12842.⬆➡.

6 ⌕DKK 120 ⊞🔌Ch🚿(6x)WC⎅included.🧹 **Location:** Rural,
comfortable, isolated, quiet. **Surface:** grassy. 🅾 01/01-31/12

| ⛢S | **Hobro** | 4C3 |

Hobro Camping Gattenborg, Skivevej 35. **GPS:** n56,64015 e9,78265.
3 ⌕DKK 160 ⊞🔌Ch🚿against payment. 🅾 01/04-02/10
Remarks: Quick-Stop: >20h - <10h.

| ⛢S | **Holsted** | 5C2 |

Holsted Golfbanen, Bergardsvej 4, Vejen-Esberg.
GPS: n55,52353 e8,93228.

15 ⌕€ 10 🔌🚿WC. **Surface:** gravel. 🅾 01/04-30/10
Distance: 🚶1km.

| ⛢S | **Horsens** 🚤 | 5D1 |

Lystbådehavn, Jens Hjernøes Vej 32. **GPS:** n55,85764 e9,87417.⬆➡.

5 ⌕DKK 150 ⊞🔌Ch🚿WC⎅included 🖥📶.🚗🧹
Location: Rural, comfortable, quiet. **Surface:** gravel.
🅾 01/01-31/12
Distance: 🚶3km ⚓on the spot ⛽on the spot 🚉on the spot.
Remarks: Harbour Horsen, special motorhome parking, Tallycard:
service, electricity, sanitary building, caution DKK 50.

Tourist information Horsens:
👁 Dolmen "Jættestuen", åbjerg Skov. Dolmen.
🅾 01/01-31/12.

| ⛢S | **Hoven** | 5C1 |

Kvindehojskole, Bredgade 10, Tarm. **GPS:** n55,85065 e8,75938.⬆.

6 ⌕free WCfree.
Location: Urban, simple. **Surface:** gravel. 🅾 01/01-31/12
Distance: 🚶on the spot.
Remarks: Parking and stay overnight possible at several places;
Brugsen 2/3 campers; sport hall.

| ⛢S | **Hurup** 🌿🚤 | 4B3 |

Nordisk Folkecenter, Kammersgaardsvej 16.
GPS: n56,69358 e8,41306.⬆.

8 ⌕DKK 60 🚿WCincluded.🧹 **Location:** Rural, simple, isolated,
quiet. **Surface:** gravel. 🅾 01/01-31/12
Distance: 🎣on the spot 🚉4km.
Remarks: Check in at reception, access energy-park incl.

| ⓒS | **Hvide Sande** 🚤🚤 | 5B1 |

Autocamper Fabriksvej 31, Fabriksvej 31.
GPS: n56,00245 e8,11979.⬆.
45 ⌕€ 12,50. 🚗🧹
Location: Rural, simple. **Surface:** gravel/sand. 🅾 01/01-31/12
Distance: 🚶800m ⚓500m 🛒500m.

| ⓒS | **Hvide Sande** 🚤🚤 | 5B1 |

Autocamper Fabriksvej 42. **GPS:** n56,00475 e8,11754.⬆.
20 ⌕€ 12,50. 🚗🧹 **Location:** Rural, simple.
Surface: gravel/sand.
Distance: 🚶200m ⚓on the spot 🛒200m.

| ⓒS | **Hvide Sande** 🚤🚤 | 5B1 |

Autocamper P, Tungevej 6. **GPS:** n55,99722 e8,12222.⬆.

40 ⌕DKK 75.🚗🧹 **Location:** Rural, simple, quiet.
Surface: gravel/metalled. 🅾 01/01-31/12
Distance: 🚶200m ⚓on the spot 🚉200m 🛒300m 🚶on the spot.
Remarks: Beach parking, service Hvide Sande Camping, 1km, DKK
37,50.

| ⓒS | **Hvide Sande** 🚤🚤 | 5B1 |

Bjerregaard, Sdr. Klitvej 185. **GPS:** n55,90620 e8,16565.
⌕DKK 120 ⊞🔌Ch🚿against payment. 🅾 15/04-01/10
Remarks: Quick-Stop: >20h - <10h.

| ⓒS | **Hvide Sande** 🚤🚤 | 5B1 |

Hvide Sande (Beltana), Karen Brands Vej 70. **GPS:** n55,98689 e8,13478.
⌕DKK 110 ⊞🔌Ch🚿against payment. 🅾 03/04-26/10
Remarks: Quick-Stop: >20h - <10h.

| 🅿S | **Højslev** | 4C3 |

Virksund Lystbådehavn, Sandkrogen 10. **GPS:** n56,61014 e9,29139.
12 ⌕€ 16 🔌🚿WC⎅📶included. **Surface:** gravel.
Distance: ⚓on the spot.

| ⛢S | **Ikast** | 5C1 |

Jens Jørgen Billlo, Bangsvej 50, Tulstrup. **GPS:** n56,15480 e9,16197.⬆.

DK

5 ☐free 🚰🔌Ch ⚡against payment.
Location: Rural, simple, isolated, quiet. **Surface:** grassy.
Distance: 🏖1,5km 🏊4km.

| 🏕S | Juelsminde | | 5D1 |

Havn & Marina, Havnegade 15. **GPS:** n55,71457 e10,01509.⬆.

12 ☐€ 20 🚰🔌Ch ⚡(12x)WC ☐🔌📶included. 📠🗑
Location: Rural, comfortable, central, quiet. **Surface:** gravel.
🅾 01/05-30/09
Distance: 🏖200m 🏊on the spot 🛒on the spot ⊗on the spot
🏊200m.
Remarks: Tallycard: service, electricity, sanitary building, caution DKK 50.

| 🏕S | Karup | | 5C1 |

2B Pack, Ulvedalsvej 43. **GPS:** n56,31528 e9,27361.⬆.
4 ☐€ 14 🚰🔌Ch ⚡ 🅾 23/03-29/10

| 🏕S | Kolding | | 5D2 |

Kolding Marina, Skamlingvejen 5. **GPS:** n55,48746 e9,50051.⬆.

15 ☐€ 15 🚰🔌Ch ⚡WC ☐🔌📶against payment. 📠🗑
Location: Rural, comfortable, quiet. **Surface:** grassy/gravel.
🅾 01/05-01/10
Distance: 🏖2,6km 🏊on the spot ⊗on the spot.
Remarks: Near marina, Tallycard: service, electricity, sanitary building, caution DKK 50.

| 🏕S | Kvissel | | 4C3 |

Bondegård Hansen, Mejlingvej 65. **GPS:** n57,46753 e10,39556.⬆.

10 ☐DKK 75 🚰🔌Ch ⚡WCincluded ☐DKK 10.🚽
Location: Rural, comfortable, quiet. **Surface:** grassy.
🅾 01/01-31/12
Distance: 🏖1km 🏊5km.

| 🏕S | Lemvig | | 4B3 |

Fjaltring Strand Høfte, Kjeldjergvej (Fjaltring).
GPS: n56,47596 e8,12477.⬆.

---

10 ☐free 🚰⚡WCfree ☐.
Location: Rural, simple, isolated, quiet. **Surface:** metalled.
Distance: 🏖1km 🏊on the spot 🏊1km.
Remarks: Beach parking.

| 🏕S | Lemvig | | 4B3 |

Lemvig Havn, Toldbodgade. **GPS:** n56,55395 e8,30956.
10 ☐free. **Surface:** gravel. 🅾 01/01-31/12
Distance: ⊗250m 🏊250m.
Remarks: Max. 12h.
Tourist information Lemvig:
👁 Bovbjerg Fyr, Fyrvej 27. Lighthouse.

| 🏕S | Løgstør | | 4C3 |

Løgstør Golfklub, Viborgvej 13, Ravnstrup.
GPS: n56,94689 e9,25390.⬆.

10 ☐DKK 110 ⚡(4x)included.🚽
Location: Simple, isolated, quiet. **Surface:** gravel.
Distance: 🏖2km ⊗2km 🏊2km.

| 🏕S | Løgstør | | 4C3 |

Løgstør Lysbadehavn, Kanalvejen 19. **GPS:** n56,96728 e9,24528.⬆➡.

12 ☐DKK 110 🚰🔌⚡(12x)WC ☐🔌📶included. 🚽🗑
Location: Comfortable, central. **Surface:** grassy/metalled.
🅾 01/01-31/12
Distance: 🏖200m 🏊on the spot 🛒on the spot ⊗on the spot
🏊200m.

| 🍴 | Løgstør | | 4C3 |

Café Bondestuen, Over Aggersund 49. **GPS:** n57,00835 e9,28776.⬆.

6 ☐free. **Location:** Rural, simple. **Surface:** gravel.
🅾 01/01-31/12

| 🏕S | Løkken | | 4C3 |

Hugo Ottesen, Kettrupvej 80. **GPS:** n57,31135 e9,67861.⬆.

5 ☐DKK 100 🚰⚡🚽 **Location:** Rural, simple, isolated.
Surface: grassy. 🅾 01/01-31/12

| 🏕S | Løkken | | 4C3 |

Galleri Munkens Klit, Munkensvej 11. **GPS:** n57,33871 e9,70522.⬆➡.

10 ☐DKK 100 🚰⚡DKK 5 WC ☐📶included.🚽 **Location:** Rural, comfortable, isolated, quiet. **Surface:** grassy. 🅾 01/01-31/12
Distance: 🏖3km.

| 🏕S | Løkken | | 4C3 |

Gl.Klitgaard, Lyngbyvej 331. **GPS:** n57,41784 e9,76017.
☐DKK 140 🚰🔌Ch ⚡against payment. 🅾 15/04-23/10
Remarks: Quick-Stop: >20h - <10h.

| 🏕S | Løkken | | 4C3 |

Grønhøj Strand, Kettrupvej 125. **GPS:** n57,32127 e9,67293.
☐DKK 100 🚰🔌Ch ⚡against payment. 🅾 15/04-18/09
Remarks: Quick-Stop: >20h - <10h.

| 🏕S | Løkken | | 4C3 |

Løkken Strand, Furreby Kirkevej 97. **GPS:** n57,38533 e9,72571.
☐DKK 100 🚰🔌Ch ⚡against payment. 🅾 05/05-04/09
Remarks: Quick-Stop: >20h - <10h.

| 🏕S | Løkken | | 4C3 |

Rolighed, Grønhoj Strandvej 35. **GPS:** n57,32143 e9,67818.
☐DKK 75 🚰🔌Ch ⚡against payment.
🅾 04/04-18/10
Remarks: Quick-Stop: >20h - <10h.
Tourist information Løkken:
Ⓜ Vendsyssel historiske museum "Jens Thomsens Gård", Strand-fogedgården i Rubjerg, Langelinie 2. Cultural past of the coast area. Hiking-trails. 🅾 16/06-15/09 Mo, Wed-Fri, Su 11-17h. Ⓣ free.
☸ Familiy Farm Fun Park, Lyngbyvej 86, Vittrup. Animal park.
🅾 01/05-30/09.

| 🏕S | Mariager | | 4C3 |

Kongsdl Bådelaug, Kongsdal Havn 8. **GPS:** n56,68383 e10,07023.⬆.

24 ☐DKK 120 🚰🔌Ch ⚡(24x)WC ☐DKK 5/3minutes 🔌📶included. 📠🗑 **Location:** Rural, comfortable, isolated, quiet. **Surface:** gravel.
🅾 01/01-31/12
Distance: 🏖7km 🏊on the spot 🛒on the spot.

| 🏕S | Mariager | | 4C3 |

Mariager, Ny Havnevej 5A. **GPS:** n56,65399 e9,97640.
2 ☐DKK 100 🚰🔌Ch ⚡against payment. 🅾 08/04-25/09
Remarks: Quick-Stop: >20h - <10h.

| 🏕S | Nordborg | | 5D2 |

Kvickly, Gartnervænget. **GPS:** n55,05611 e9,74150.➡.
10 ☐free. **Surface:** asphalted. 🅾 01/01-31/12
Remarks: At supermarket.

| 🏕S | Nordborg | | 5D2 |

Lone & Henning Carlsson, Kådnervej 7. **GPS:** n55,03194 e9,73111.⬆.

5 ⬛DKK 100 ⬛WC ⬛.⬛
Location: Rural, comfortable, quiet. **Surface:** gravel. ⬛ 01/01-31/12
Distance: ⬛5km.
Remarks: Narrow entrance.

Nykøbing Mors · 4C3

Morsø Sejlklub & Marin, Jernbanevej 3A.
GPS: n56,79282 e8,86370.⬛⬛

18 ⬛€ 16 ⬛Ch ⬛WC ⬛⬛included. ⬛⬛
Location: Comfortable, quiet. **Surface:** gravel. ⬛ 01/01-31/12
Distance: ⬛150m ⬛on the spot ⬛on the spot ⬛on the spot
⬛200m.
Remarks: Tallycard: service, electricity, sanitary building, caution DKK 25.

Nykøbing Mors · 4C3

Ejerslev Havn, Utkærvej 5, Ejerslev. **GPS:** n56,91868 e8,92093.
⬛€ 11 Ch ⬛€4 ⬛. ⬛ 01/01-31/12

Nørager · 4C3

Stellplads E45 Autocamper, Fyrkildevej 39, Ladelund.
GPS: n56,77505 e9,70986.⬛

15 ⬛DKK 75 ⬛included. ⬛.⬛ **Location:** Rural, simple, isolated, quiet. **Surface:** grassy. ⬛ 01/01-31/12
Distance: ⬛E45 5km.

Odder · 5D1

Jørgen Petersen, Aarhusvej 354. **GPS:** n56,01650 e10,18157.⬛⬛

3 ⬛DKK 75 ⬛⬛Ch ⬛WC⬛included. ⬛⬛ **Location:** Rural, luxurious, isolated, quiet. **Surface:** grassy/gravel. ⬛ 01/01-31/12
Distance: ⬛5km.

Odder · 5D1

Odder strand Camping, Toldvejen 50. **GPS:** n55,93891 e10,25054.
⬛DKK 150 ⬛Ch ⬛against payment. ⬛ 01/04-21/09
Remarks: Quick-Stop: >20h - <10h.

Randers · 4C3

Mellerup Bådelaug, Amtsvejen 153 Mellerup.
GPS: n56,52431 e10,22213.⬛

3 ⬛DKK 100 ⬛⬛WC ⬛included. ⬛⬛
Location: Rural, simple, quiet. **Surface:** gravel. ⬛ 01/01-31/12
Distance: ⬛Mellerup 1,2km ⬛on the spot ⬛on the spot.
Remarks: Pay at harbourmaster.

Randers · 4C3

Randers havn, Toldbodgade 14. **GPS:** n56,46229 e10,05122.⬛

10 ⬛free. **Location:** Urban, simple. **Surface:** gravel.
⬛ 01/01-31/12
Distance: ⬛500m ⬛on the spot.
Remarks: Max. 24h.

Ribe · 5C2

Fabelbo, Hølleskovvej 48. **GPS:** n55,24076 e8,86077.
⬛free ⬛free. **Location:** Isolated, quiet. **Surface:** grassy.
⬛ 01/01-31/12

Ribe · 5C2

Stampemøllevej. **GPS:** n55,32480 e8,75740.⬛

25 ⬛free ⬛⬛WC free.
Location: Urban, simple. **Surface:** asphalted.
⬛ 01/01-31/12
Distance: ⬛500m ⬛100m ⬛400m.
Remarks: Parking south of centre, max. 48h.

Ribe · 5C2

Storkesøen, Haulundvej 164. **GPS:** n55,31703 e8,76022.⬛⬛

24 ⬛DKK 140 ⬛⬛Ch ⬛included.
Location: Rural, comfortable, quiet. **Surface:** grassy. ⬛ 01/01-31/12
Distance: ⬛1km ⬛on the spot.
Remarks: At fish pond.

Ribe · 5C2

Maglegaard, Toftlundvej 6. **GPS:** n55,31067 e8,79151.

3 ⬛DKK 100 ⬛⬛DKK 20. ⬛
Location: Rural, simple, quiet. **Surface:** grassy.
Distance: ⬛3km.

Tourist information Ribe:
⬛ Vadehavscentret, Okholmvej 5. Wadden Sea centre.
⬛ 10-16/17h ⬛ 01/12-31/01.
⬛ Museet Ribes Vikinger, Odins Plads. Viking period in Denmark.
⬛ daily 10-16h, summer 10-18h ⬛ 01/11-31/03 Mo.
⬛ Ribe Vikingecenter. Open air museum.
⬛ 01/05-30/06, 01/09-15/10 Mo-Fri 10-15.30h, 01/07-31/08 daily 11-17h.
⬛ Weis Stue, Torvet 2. Oldest inn of Denmark with traditional Danish kitchen.

Ringkøbing · 5B1

Annemette & Svend Erik Jensen, Birkmosevej 6.
GPS: n56,08806 e8,26722.⬛
15 ⬛free ⬛⬛Ch against payment.
Location: Simple. **Surface:** grassy. ⬛ 01/01-31/12
Distance: ⬛500m ⬛500m ⬛200m.

Ringkøbing · 5B1

Lystbadenhavn, Fiskerstraede 60. **GPS:** n56,08611 e8,24056.⬛

10 ⬛€ 14 ⬛⬛Ch ⬛(6x)DKK 2,30/kWh WC included ⬛DKK 10/3minutes. ⬛⬛ **Location:** Urban, comfortable, quiet.
Surface: gravel. ⬛ 01/01-31/12
Distance: ⬛on the spot ⬛on the spot ⬛on the spot ⬛500m ⬛500m.
Remarks: Parking at pier.

Ringkøbing · 5B1

Autocamperplads, Vesterled 11. **GPS:** n56,09338 e8,23740.⬛

20 ⬛DKK 70. ⬛ **Location:** Urban, simple. **Surface:** gravel.
⬛ 01/01-31/12
Distance: ⬛700m ⬛400m ⬛400m ⬛700m ⬛700m.
Remarks: Pay with Danish coins.

Ringkøbing · 5B1

Søndervig, Solvej 2. **GPS:** n56,11186 e8,11760.
⬛DKK 115 ⬛⬛Ch ⬛against payment. ⬛ 04/04-25/10
Remarks: Quick-Stop: >20h - <10h.

Tourist information Ringkøbing:
⬛ Fishing and Family Park West, Hovervej 56. Recreation park with swimming pool. ⬛ 10h-sunset.

Roslev · 4C3

Sallingsund Sejlklub, Færgevej 7. **GPS:** n56,76333 e8,86667.
⬛€ 16 ⬛⬛Ch ⬛WC ⬛included. ⬛⬛
Distance: ⬛on the spot ⬛on the spot.

Roslev · 4C3

Sundsøre Lystbådehavn, Sundsørevej. **GPS:** n56,70991 e9,17324.
⬛€ 16 ⬛⬛WC ⬛included. **Location:** Isolated, quiet.
Surface: grassy/gravel. ⬛ 01/01-31/12
Distance: ⬛on the spot ⬛on the spot.
Remarks: At marina and ferry-boat.

Rødding · 5C2

Inga & Ejnar Gejl, Skodborgskovvej 25, Skodborgskov.
GPS: n55,40056 e9,15722.
4 ⬛ ⬛⬛against payment WC free.
Location: Rural, simple. **Surface:** grassy. ⬛ 01/01-31/12
Distance: ⬛5km.

Rødding · 5C2

Brændekilde, Haderslevvej 59. **GPS:** n55,35750 e9,18833.⬛

DK

10 ③free ⛽DKK 25 Ch ⚡DKK 25 WC.
Location: Rural, simple, noisy. **Surface:** metalled. ⬛ 01/01-31/12
Distance: 🚶1km.
Remarks: Max. 1 week.

Rødding 5C2
FB Camping Service, Industriparken 13. **GPS:** n55,42556 e9,16083.
15 ③free ⛽DKK 10 ⚡Ch free ⚡DKK 40.
Location: Urban, simple. **Surface:** gravel. ⬛ 01/01-31/12

Rødekro 5C2
Rødekro Fiskepark, østermarkvej 3-7. **GPS:** n55,08806 e9,30889. ➡

50 ③DKK 100 ⛽🔌Ch ⚡DKK 2/kWh WC🚽DKK 5 ⬛DKK 25. 🚿
Location: Rural, simple, quiet. **Surface:** grassy.
⬛ 01/01-31/12
Distance: 🚶2km 🏊on the spot 🚤on the spot 🎣on the spot
🚰100m.
Remarks: At fish lake.

Silkeborg 5D1
Anne & Gert Lassen, Ellinglund, Ellingvej 16, Funder Kirkeby.
GPS: n56,16546 e9,40954.
③€ 14 ⛽🔌Ch ⚡WC🚽🚿.
Location: Rural, comfortable. **Surface:** grassy. ⬛ 01/01-31/12
Distance: 🚶2km.

Silkeborg 5D1
Jørgen Engebjerg, Lemmingvej 12. **GPS:** n56,22124 e9,53991.
3 ③€ 10 ⛽⚡included.
Location: Rural. **Surface:** grassy.
⬛ 01/01-31/12
Distance: 🚶5km.
Tourist information Silkeborg:
👁 AQUA, Vejlsøvej 55. Aquarium.
⬛ 01/09-31/05 Mo-Fri 10-16h, Sa-Su 10-17h, 01/06-31/08 10-18h.

Sindal 4C3
Sindal, Hjørringvej 125. **GPS:** n57,46849 e10,17945.
3 ③DKK 120 ⛽🔌Ch against payment ⚡DKK 25. ⬛ 01/04-20/09
Remarks: Quick-Stop: >20h - <10h.

Skagen 4C2
P-plads på Grenen i Skagen, Akandevej.
GPS: n57,73895 e10,63283. ⬆

20 ③DKK 150. 🚿📷
Location: Rural, simple, isolated. **Surface:** asphalted. ⬛ 01/01-31/12
Distance: 🚶2km ⊗100m 🎣3km.

Skals 4C3
Ulbjerg, Skråhedevej 6. **GPS:** n56,64495 e9,33915.
③€ 10,50 ⛽🔌Ch ⚡against payment. ⬛ 01/01-31/12
Remarks: Quick-Stop: >20h - <10h.

Skjern 5C1
Stauning Havn, Strandvejen, Stauning. **GPS:** n55,95488 e8,37352. ⬆
6, <10m ③€ 14 ⚡Ch WC🚽included.
Surface: metalled. ⬛ 01/01-31/12

Distance: 🚶Skjern 8km ⊗on the spot.

Skærbæk 5C2
Skærbæk, Ullerupvej 76. **GPS:** n55,16584 e8,77909.
③DKK 100 ⛽🔌Ch ⚡against payment. ⬛ 01/01-31/12
Remarks: Quick-Stop: >20h - <10h.

Snedsted 4C3
Kaj Foget, Skyumvey 105. **GPS:** n56,84380 e8,59720. ⬆➡

6 ③DKK 50. 🚿 **Location:** Rural, simple, isolated, quiet.
Surface: grassy. ⬛ 01/01-31/12

Spøttrup 4C3
Gyldendal hav, Vester Hærup Strandvej 34.
GPS: n56,58107 e8,71066.⬆

15 ③€ 16 ⛽🔌Ch ⚡(4x)WC🚽🚿included. 🚿
Location: Rural, simple, quiet. **Surface:** gravel/sand. ⬛ 01/01-31/12
Distance: 🏖Sandy beach 🚤on the spot ⊗on the spot.

Storvorde 4C3
Egense Lystbådehavan, Kystvej 1. **GPS:** n56,98270 e10,30451. ⬆

6 ③DKK 110 ⛽⚡(6x) WC🚽. 🚿
Location: Rural, simple, quiet. **Surface:** metalled. ⬛ 01/01-31/12
Distance: 🏊on the spot 🚤on the spot 🎣1km.
Remarks: Pay at harbourmaster.

Stouby 5D1
Løgballe Autocamperplads, Løgballevej 12.
GPS: n55,70765 e9,84359. ⬆➡

7 ③DKK 75 ⛽DKK 15 🔌Ch ⚡(7x)DKK 30 WC. 🚿 **Location:** Rural,
simple, isolated, quiet. **Surface:** gravel. ⬛ 01/04-01/10

Strandby 4C3
Strandby havn, Søndre Havnevej 27. **GPS:** n57,49249 e10,50245. ⬆

---

6 ③DKK 120 ⛽🔌WC included. 🚿
Location: Urban, simple. **Surface:** metalled. ⬛ 01/01-31/12
Distance: 🚶on the spot 🏊on the spot 🚤on the spot ⊗on the spot
🎣on the spot.
Remarks: Pay at harbourmaster.

Struer 4C3
Holstebro-Struer Lystbådehavn, Fjordvejen.
GPS: n56,49380 e8,59068. ⬆➡

4 ③€ 16 ⛽⚡WC🚽Access sanitary building DKK 20 📷🛜included.
🚿🚰
Location: Urban, comfortable, quiet.
Surface: gravel. 📷 winter
Distance: 🚶100m 🎣100m.
Remarks: Tallycard: service, electricity, sanitary building, caution
DKK 50.
Tourist information Struer:
👁 Gimsinghoved, Gimsinghoved 1. Former large Danish farm.

Sæby 4C3
Top Plads hos Ase en Helmer, Understedvej 65, Understed.
GPS: n57,37249 e10,46447. ⬆

20 ③DKK 100 ⛽🔌Ch ⚡WC🚽📷 🚿 **Location:** Rural, comfortable, isolated, quiet. **Surface:** grassy. ⬛ 01/01-31/12

Sæby 4C3
Lene en Knut Holdensgård, Holdenggårdvej 16, Sønder.
GPS: n57,21616 e10,45253. ⬆

3 ③DKK 50 ⛽⚡🚿 **Location:** Rural, simple, isolated, quiet.
Surface: grassy. ⬛ 01/01-31/12

Sæby 4C3
Sæby Havn, Havnen 20. **GPS:** n57,33218 e10,53373. ⬆➡

20 ③DKK 150 ⛽⚡(20x)included. 🚿 **Location:** Urban, simple,
central. **Surface:** asphalted. ⬛ 01/01-31/12
Distance: 🚶100m ⊗100m 🎣100m.

Sæby 4C3
Danbjerg, Hjørringvej 160. **GPS:** n57,32544 e10,36967. ⬆➡

DK

6 ⌇DKK 50 ✏. **Location:** Rural, simple, isolated, quiet.
Surface: grassy/gravel. ☐ 01/01-31/12
Distance: 🚶1km 🚰1km.

Tarm · 5C1

Par3Golf, Grimlundvej. **GPS:** n55,83819 e8,71321.
⌇free. **Location:** Isolated, quiet. ☐ 01/01-31/12
Distance: 🚶Tarm 19km.

Tårs (Hjørring) · 4C3

Vendelbo Vans Autocampere, Damhusvej 23.
GPS: n57,38972 e10,11500.⬆.

8 ⌇DKK 50 🚰🔌Ch ✏(8x)WC ☐included. 💆🧺
Location: Urban, comfortable, central, quiet. **Surface:** grassy/gravel.
☐ 01/01-31/12
Distance: 🚶100m 🏊500m 🛒500m ⊗300m 🚰300m 🔵200m.
Remarks: At motorhome dealer, max. 48h, sanitary 9-17h.

Thorsager · 5D1

Dagli Brugsen, Thorsgade 26. **GPS:** n56,34305 e10,46286.⬆.

4 ⌇free.
Location: Urban, simple. **Surface:** gravel/metalled. ☐ 01/01-31/12
Distance: 🚶on the spot 🚰on the spot.
Remarks: Behind supermarket Brugsen.

Thyholm · 4C3

Jegindø Havn, Havnegade. **GPS:** n56,65219 e8,63575.
⌇€ 15 🚰WC☐🔵📶included. **Surface:** gravel. ☐ 01/01-31/12
Remarks: At harbour.

Tinglev · 5C2

Uge Green 2. **GPS:** n54,97365 e9,34601.

6 ⌇€ 10 🚰🔌Ch 🔵(6x)DKK 27,10Amp WC☐DKK 10 📶included.
Location: Rural. **Surface:** grassy. ☐ 01/01-31/12
Distance: ✏2km 🏊on the spot 🛒on the spot ⊗800m
🔵on the spot 🚴on the spot 🎣on the spot.

Toftlund · 5C2

Dahl, Lebækvej 2. **GPS:** n55,17839 e9,07768.
5 ⌇DKK 35 🚰🔌Ch ✏included.

Ulfborg · 5C1

Tvind Skolecenter, Skorkærvej 8. **GPS:** n56,25636 e8,28110.⬆.

---

15 ⌇free. **Location:** Rural, simple, isolated. ☐ 01/01-31/12
Distance: 🚶8km ⊗8km 🚰8km.

Ulfborg · 5C1

Rejkjær, Ringkobingvej 24. **GPS:** n56,23319 e8,30966.
⌇DKK 100 🚰🔌Ch ✏against payment. ☐ 03/04-18/10
Remarks: Quick-Stop: >20h - <10h.

Vandel · 5C1

Dagli' Brugsen, Hans Thomsens Vej. **GPS:** n55,71285 e9,21800.
⌇free. **Surface:** asphalted. ☐ 01/01-31/12
Remarks: At petrol station and supermarket, Legoland 6km.

Vandel · 5C1

Rastplads, Billundvej. **GPS:** n55,70687 e9,26709.
⌇free 🚰WCfree. **Surface:** forest soil.
☐ 01/01-31/12
Distance: 🚶on the spot 🚰4km.
Remarks: Parking in the forest with place for campfire, Legoland 10km.

Vejers Strand · 5B2

Stjerne, Vejers Havvej 7. **GPS:** n55,61915 e8,14090.
⌇DKK 115 🚰🔌Ch ✏against payment. ☐ 01/01-31/12
Remarks: Quick-Stop: >20h - <10h.

Vejers Strand · 5B2

Vejers Familicamping, Vejers Havvej 15. **GPS:** n55,61950 e8,13594.
⌇DKK 115 🚰🔌Ch ✏against payment.
☐ 01/04-18/09
Remarks: Quick-Stop: >20h - <10h.

Tourist information Vejers Strand:
👁 Tirpitz. German bunker.

Vesløs · 4C3

Amtoft Havn, Gårdbækvej 12. **GPS:** n57,00647 e8,94068.⬆.

10 ⌇€ 14 🚰🔌Ch ✏(10x)WC☐included 🔵📶free. 💆🧺
Location: Rural, comfortable, quiet. **Surface:** grassy.
☐ 01/01-31/12
Distance: 🚶on the spot 🏊on the spot 🛒on the spot 🚰on the spot.

Vesløs · 4C3

Vejlernes Grill & Kiosk, Aalborgvej 219B. **GPS:** n57,02518 e9,01585.

⌇free. **Surface:** gravel. ☐ 01/01-31/12

Vinderup · 4C3

Handbjerg Marina, Strandvejen. **GPS:** n56,47568 e8,71337.
5 ⌇DKK 10. ☐ 01/01-31/12
Distance: ⊗on the spot.

Tourist information Vinderup:
Ⓜ Hjerl Hedes Frilandsmuseum, Hjerl Hedevej 14. Open air museum.
☐ 01/04-31/10 10-17h.
⌂ Stubber Kloster, Stubbergård sø. Ruins of former Benedictine
monastery. ☐ 01/01-31/12. 🔲 free.

Voerså · 4C3

Parking Havn, Havstokken 11. **GPS:** n57,20389 e10,49389.⬆➡.

20 ⌇DKK 120 🚰🔌Ch ✏(20x)WC☐included. 💆
Location: Rural, comfortable, isolated. **Surface:** gravel.
☐ 01/04-31/10
Distance: 🚶3km 🏊on the spot 🛒on the spot ⊗3km 🚰3km.
Remarks: Money in envelope in mail box.

Funen

Aarup · 5D2

Annemette & Lars Mogensen, Frøbjerg Vænge 31.
GPS: n55,34907 e10,08323.
3 ⌇free 🔌free. **Surface:** gravel. ☐ 01/01-31/12

Assens · 5D2

Britta Bang, Lilletoftevej 7, Lilletofte Gamtofte.
GPS: n55,28165 e9,98850.
3 ⌇€ 13,50 🚰🔌Ch ✏included WC🔵.
Location: Rural. **Surface:** metalled.
Distance: 🚶7,5km ⊗7km 🚰7km.

Tourist information Assens:
Ⓜ Vestfyns Hjemstavnsgård, Klaregade 23.,Gummerup, Glamsbjerg.
Open air museum. ☐ 01/04-31/10 10-16h 🔵 Mo.

Bagenkop · 5E3

Koldkrigsmuseum Langelandsfor, Vognsbjergvej 4A.
GPS: n54,75306 e10,71583.
⌇DKK 95. **Surface:** metalled. ☐ 01/04-31/10
Remarks: Check in at museum.

Bogense · 5D2

Autocamper - Bogense, Vestre Havnevej 29-31.
GPS: n55,56806 e10,07833.⬆.
5 ⌇€ 14 🚰✏included. **Surface:** gravel. ☐ 01/01-31/12
Distance: 🚶300m 🏊on the spot.

Faaborg · 5D2

Faaborg Havn, Kanalvej 19. **GPS:** n55,09658 e10,23429.
6 ⌇DKK 120 🚰DKK 5 🔌Ch ✏DKK 3/kWh WC☐.
Surface: asphalted. ☐ 01/01-31/12
Distance: 🚶200m 🏊on the spot 🛒on the spot ⊗on the spot
🚰500m 🛒200m.
Remarks: Check in at harbourmaster.

Ferritslev · 5D2

Jørgen Christensen, Rolfvej 45. **GPS:** n55,32111 e10,56806.
47 ⌇free. **Location:** Urban, simple. **Surface:** metalled.
☐ 01/01-31/12

Gram · 5C2

Anholm Fiskesø, Folevej 11. **GPS:** n55,30564 e8,99888.⬆.

15 ⌇€ 6,75 🚰🔌Ch ✏included. 💆
Location: Rural, simple, isolated, quiet. ☐ 01/04-01/11
Distance: 🚶5km 🏊on the spot ⊗1km 🚰5km.
Remarks: At fish pond.

Gram · 5C2

Annemettes, Ribelandevej 18. **GPS:** n55,28647 e9,00098.⬆.

DK

3 ⅏ € 14 🚰🔌Ch🔧⚓
Location: Rural, simple, isolated, quiet. **Surface:** grassy/gravel.

Middelfart 5D2
Lystbådehavn, østre Hougvej 112. **GPS:** n55,49250 e9,73028.⬆️

12 ⅏ € 17 🚰🔌Ch🔧 (12x) WC🚻📶included.🚙📷
Location: Rural, luxurious, isolated, quiet.
Surface: asphalted/metalled. ⏹ 01/01-31/12
Distance: 🛒2km 🏖on the spot 🚣on the spot ⚓on the spot
🍴 on the spot.
Remarks: Harbour Middelfahrt, Tallycard: service, electricity, sanitary building, caution DKK 50.

Nyborg 5E2
GPS: n55,29734 e10,83963.

⅏free 🚰🔌Chfree. **Surface:** metalled.

Nyborg 5E2
Sulkendrup Vandmølle, Sulkendrupvej 1, Sulkendrup.
GPS: n55,29384 e10,71334.
3 ⅏ € 10 🚰DKK25🔌ChWC🚻DKK 10/time.
Location: Rural, comfortable. **Surface:** grassy. ⏹ 01/01-31/12
Distance: 🛒5km.

Tourist information Nyborg:
✕ Nyborg Fæstning, Slotsgade 1. Fortress.
✕ Nyborg Slot / Danehofslottet, Slotsgade 34. Castle, end 12th century. ⏹ 01/04-31/10 10-15/17h.

Odense 5D2
Tarup Campingcenter, Agerhatten 31. **GPS:** n55,36110 e10,46722.
20 ⅏free. **Surface:** grassy.
Distance: 🛒6km 🚲2km.

Stenstrup 5D2
Tronbjerggård Strandhave, Højbjergvej 13.
GPS: n55,12944 e10,58306.
3 ⅏against payment 🚰🔌🔧WC.

Svendborg 5D2
Mogens Nielsen, Tordensgårdevej 3. **GPS:** n55,08750 e10,55389.
10 ⅏🚰🔧WC🚻included. **Location:** Rural, comfortable.
Surface: grassy/metalled. ⏹ 01/01-31/12
Distance: 🛒5km 🚣5km ⚓on the spot.

Svendborg 5D2
Idrætshallen, Ryttervej 70. **GPS:** n55,05668 e10,57613.
🚰🔌Ch.

Tourist information Svendborg:
✕ Egeskov Slot, Kværndrup. Citadel with park and 6 museums.
⏹ 01/05-31/10 10-17/20h.
✕ Valdemars Slot, Slotsalléen 100, Troense, Tåsinge. Castle on the island Tåsinge, fully furnished. ⏹ 01/05-31/10 10-17h ⏹ May, Sep, Oct: Mo.

Varde 5C2
Fritidscenter, Lerpøtvej 55. **GPS:** n55,63294 e8,47447.
20 ⅏against payment 🚰🔧🔌against payment.
Surface: grassy. ⏹ 01/05-31/10

Remarks: At sports centre.

Varde 5C2
Jensen, Ringkøbingvej 143. **GPS:** n55,65762 e8,48942.⬆️

4 ⅏DKK 75 🚰🔧🔌WC.⚓ **Location:** Rural, comfortable, isolated, quiet.**Surface:** grassy/metalled.
Distance: 🛒5km.

Varde 5C2
Joan & Preben Christensen, Ringkøbingvej 259, Hindsig.
GPS: n55,72077 e8,49345.⬆️

5 ⅏DKK 50 🚰🔧Ch⚓ **Location:** Rural, comfortable, quiet.
Surface: grassy. ⏹ 01/01-31/12
Distance: 🛒12km 🚲3km.

Seeland, Møn, Lolland and Falster

Bogø By 5F2
Café-Restaurant Stalden, Hougårdsbanke 5.
GPS: n54,93000 e12,02806.
4 ⅏free for clients 🚰🔌Ch🔧WC📶against payment.
Location: Rural. **Surface:** grassy. ⏹ 01/01-31/12
Distance: 🛒1km ⚓on the spot.

Copenhagen 5F1
Copenhagen City Camp, Elvaerksvej 7-9.
GPS: n55,65440 e12,55697.

70 ⅏DKK 150-225 🚰🔧Ch🔌WC🚻 ⏹ 23/05-06/09
Distance: 🛒within walking distance ⚓on the spot 🍴on the spot.
Remarks: Next to harbour and new shopping center Fisketorv.

Tourist information Copenhagen:
ℹ️ Copenhagen Card. Card gives free entrance to public transport, 60 museums and attractions. Available at Tourist Offices, hotels, campsites.
😊 Dyrehavsbakken, Dyrehavevej 62, Klampenborg (ten n. van Kopenhagen). Popular amusement park, oldest park of Denmark, with among other things 100 attractions and 35 restaurants. 🚆 free.
😊 Tivoli, Vesterbrogade 3. Large amusement park in the centre of the city with among other things 32 restaurants, 26 attractions, shows, concerts etc. ⏹ 11-21/1h.

Dannemare 5E3
Hummingen, Pumpehusvej 1. **GPS:** n54,71317 e11,24606.
⅏DKK 140 🚰🔧Ch🔌against payment. ⏹ 04/04-17/10
Remarks: Quick-Stop: >20h - <10h.

Farum 5F1
Hovedgade 32. **GPS:** n55,81222 e12,36917.
3 ⅏free. **Location:** Urban, simple. **Surface:** metalled.
⏹ 01/01-31/12

Farum 5F1
Stavnsholt Renseanlæg. GPS: n55,81278 e12,40556.
🚰🔌Chfree. ⏹ Mo-Thu 7-15.30h, Fr 7-11.30h

Farø 5F2
Farø, Grøsundvej. **GPS:** n54,94876 e11,98696.
20 ⅏free 🚰🔌ChWCfree.
Location: Noisy. **Surface:** asphalted.

Frederikssund 5F1
Marbæk Lystbådehavn, Strandlystvej 26 D. **GPS:** n55,82778 e12,06389.
4 ⅏€ 17 🚰🔌Ch🔧WCincluded ⅏against payment.
Location: Comfortable. **Surface:** gravel. ⏹ 01/01-31/12

Gedser 5F3
Gedser Lystbådehavn, Vestre Strand 3. **GPS:** n54,58194 e11,92361.
5 ⅏€ 16 🚰🔧included. **Surface:** gravel. ⏹ 01/01-31/12
Distance: ⚓200m.

Gørlev 5E2
Reersø Havn, Strandvejen 101, Reersø. **GPS:** n55,51750 e11,11833.
5 ⅏against payment 🚰🔧included WC⅏against payment.
⏹ 01/11-01/04

Hundested 5E1
Hundested Havn, Havnegade 8. **GPS:** n55,96557 e11,84845.⬆️➡️
5 ⅏€ 16 🚰🔌Ch🔧⅏against payment.
Location: Comfortable. **Surface:** metalled. ⏹ 01/01-31/12
Distance: 🛒500m 🏖on the spot 🚣on the spot ⚓on the spot
🍴200m ⚓200m.

Hundested 5E1
Lynæs Havn, Lynæs Havnevej 15 B, Lynæs. **GPS:** n55,94167 e11,86667.
10 ⅏€ 16 🚰🔌Ch🔧WCagainst payment.
Surface: metalled. ⏹ 01/01-31/12

Hørve 5E1
Teglværksgårdens, Teglværksvej 9A. **GPS:** n55,75794 e11,36568.
⅏DKK 110 🚰🔌Ch🔧against payment. ⏹ 01/01-31/12
Remarks: Quick-Stop: >20h - <10h.

Kalvehave 5F2
Lystbådehavn, Kalvehave Havnevej 26. **GPS:** n54,99584 e12,16641.
2 ⅏against payment 🚰🔧against payment. **Surface:** grassy/gravel.

Karrebæksminde 5E2
Naestved Sjelklub, Ved Broen 29. **GPS:** n55,17706 e11,65018.
6 ⅏€ 18 🚰🔧Ch🔌WC🚻against payment 📶included.⚓
Distance: 🚣on the spot ⚓on the spot.

Kirke Hyllinge 5F1
Gershøj Havn, Gershøj Havnevej 5, Gershøj. **GPS:** n55,71667 e11,98000.
10 ⅏€ 8 Ch🔧against payment WC🚻included.
Location: Simple. **Surface:** gravel. ⏹ 01/01-31/12
Distance: 🛒5km.

Korsør 5E2
Pit-Stop Storebælt, Storebæltsvej 85. **GPS:** n55,34833 e11,11556.
40 ⅏€ 10. 🚙🔧 **Location:** Simple. ⏹ 01/01-31/12
Distance: ⚓500m.

Korsør 5E2
Lystbådehavn, Sylowsvej 10. **GPS:** n55,32664 e11,13190.

⅏€ 17 🚰included 🔧WC🚻against payment.
Surface: gravel. ⏹ 01/01-31/12

Tourist information Korsør:
Ⓜ The Great Belt Bridge and Nature Centre, Storebæltsvej 88. Exhibition about the construction of the bridge over the Grote Belt. ⏹ 01/03-31/12 10-17/19h.
✕ Korsør Fæstning, Korsør Coastal Battery, The Fortress, Søbatteriet 7. Fortress. ⏹ 01/04-30/11 Tue-Su 11-16h.

Lynge 5F1
Irene & Aage Andersen, Stengårdsvej 12. **GPS:** n55,81972 e12,27376.
3 ⅏free. **Location:** Simple. ⏹ 01/01-31/12

Maribo 5E3
Skelstrupgåren Bed and Breakfast, Skelstupvej 3.
GPS: n54,78774 e11,52095.
5 ⅏DKK 50 🔧against payment. **Surface:** grassy.
Distance: 🛒2,2km 🚲4km.

Munke Bjergby 5E2
Dojringevej 40a. **GPS:** n55,49637 e11,55065.

3 ⌇free WC.
Location: Simple. **Surface:** gravel. ◻ 01/01-31/12
Distance: 5km ⊗on the spot on the spot on the spot.

10 ⌇free DKK 10,07 DKK 10,07 DKK 29,83.
Surface: grassy. ◻ 01/01-31/12
Distance: 5km on the spot on the spot.
Remarks: Max. 48h.

Nykøbing 5E1
Lystbådehavn, Snekkevej 9. **GPS:** n55,91610 e11,67287.⬆.
10 ⌇DKK 110 Ch included against payment.
Surface: metalled.
Distance: ⊗on the spot.

Nykøbing F. 5F3
Toreby Sejlklub, Dæmningen 2, Sundby Lolland.
GPS: n54,76051 e11,86041.
5 ⌇€ 14 WC included. **Surface:** gravel.
Distance: ⊗on the spot on the spot on the spot.

Nykøbing F. 5F3
Falster City Camping, østre Allé 112. **GPS:** n54,76243 e11,89479.
⌇DKK 120 Ch against payment. ◻ 01/04-01/12
Remarks: Quick-Stop: >20h - <10h.

Præstø 5F2
Præstø Havn, Fjordstien 1. **GPS:** n55,12444 e12,04333.⬆.
5 ⌇€ 16 included. **Surface:** asphalted.
Distance: ⊗on the spot.

Ringsted 5E2
Mogens Madsen, Vibevej 34. **GPS:** n55,44222 e11,80667.
3 ⌇free against payment. **Surface:** metalled. ◻ 01/01-31/12
Distance: 4 km 800m.

Rødvig 5F2
Rødvig Fiskerihavn, Fiskerihavnen 8. **GPS:** n55,25417 e12,37500.
4 ⌇€ 16 Ch WC included.
Surface: metalled. ◻ 01/01-31/12
Distance: ⊗on the spot.
Remarks: Check in at harbourmaster.

Rødvig 5F2
Rødvig Camping, Højstrupvej 2 A. **GPS:** n55,24346 e12,34999.
⌇DKK 100. ◻ 01/04-28/09
Remarks: Quick-Stop: >20h - <10h.

Sakskøbing 5E3
Sakskøbing Lystbådehavn, Maltrup Vænge 38.
GPS: n54,81078 e11,61957.
5 ⌇€ 14 WC against payment included.
Distance: ⊗500m.

Sjællands Odde 5E1
Sjællands Odde Havn, Østre Havnevej 42. **GPS:** n55,97139 e11,36956.
2 ⌇€ 16 included WC against payment.
Surface: gravel. ◻ 01/01-31/12

Skælskør 5E2
Skælskør Havn, Havnevej 20. **GPS:** n55,25223 e11,28992.
15 ⌇€ 14 Ch WC included against payment.
Surface: metalled. ◻ 01/01-31/12
Distance: ⊗on the spot.

Taastrup 5F1
Park Hotel, Brorsonsvej 3. **GPS:** n55,65389 e12,30000.⬆.
10 ⌇DKK 125 DKK25 WC.
Surface: metalled. ◻ 01/01-31/12
Distance: 300m 1,5km ⊗on the spot 300m.
Remarks: Breakfast buffet DKK 75.

Tårs (Harpelunde) 5E2
Fiskeri & lystbådehavn, Tårsvej 15, Harpelunde.
GPS: n54,87811 e11,02381.
2 ⌇€ 17 WC included. ◻ 01/01-31/12
Remarks: Harbour Tårs.

Værløse 5F1
Furesø Museer, Skovgårds alle 37. **GPS:** n55,78528 e12,37722.
4 ⌇free.
Location: Urban, simple. **Surface:** metalled. ◻ 01/01-31/12
Distance: ⊗250m 250m.

Værløse 5F1
Bryggeri Skovlyst, Skovlystvej 2. **GPS:** n55,76317 e12,38365.

🏴 Spain

Capital: Madrid
Government: Constitutional monarchy
Official Language: Spanish
Population: 47,737,000 (2014)
Area: 505,782 km²

General information
Dialling code: 0034
General emergency: 112
Currency: Euro

Regulations for overnight stays
Wild camping is allowed having gained permission from the municipality, olice or property owner. Along the Mediterranean coast wild camping is almost always forbidden. Parking places (P) mentioned here can be considered as tolerated places to stay overnight.

Additional public holidays 2016
January 6 Epiphany
March 25 Good Friday
May 1 Labor Day
May 26 Corpus Christi
August 15 Assumption of the Virgin Mary
October 22 National Holiday
November 1 All Saints' Day
December 6 Constitution Day
December 8 Immaculate Conception

Time Zone
Winter (Standard Time) GMT+1
Summer (DST) GMT+2

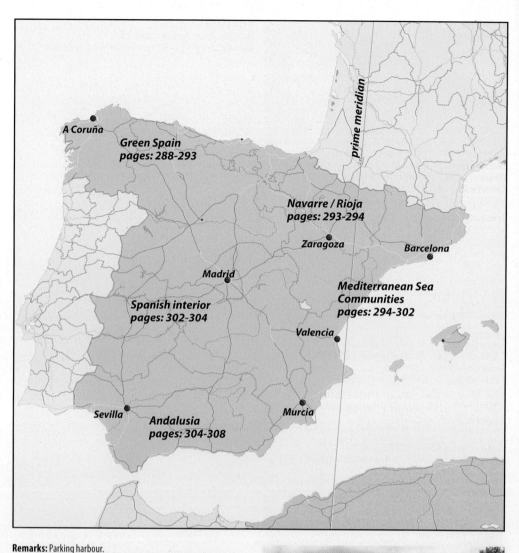

Green Spain
pages: 288-293

Navarre / Rioja
pages: 293-294

Mediterranean Sea Communities
pages: 294-302

Spanish interior
pages: 302-304

Andalusia
pages: 304-308

A Coruña · Zaragoza · Barcelona · Madrid · Valencia · Sevilla · Murcia · *Prime meridian*

Green Spain

🏕S A Coruña 🌿⛽🗑🏖 28C3
Puerto de San Pedro de Visma, Zona de O Portiño.
GPS: n38,07927 w1,25852. ⬆.

12 🅿free 🚿🍽 Chfree. **Surface**: metalled.
Distance: 🚶3km 🏖on the spot ⊗50m 🛒1km Carrefour 🚌1km.
Remarks: Max. 48h.

🏕 A Coruña 🌿⛽🗑🏖 28C3
Tore de Hercules. **GPS**: n43,38378 w8,40228.
🅿free. **Surface**: asphalted.
Distance: 🚶on the spot ⊗50m 🛒50m.

📷 A Guarda 🏖 28B2
GPS: n41,89892 w8,87825. ⬆.

5 🅿. **Location**: Urban, simple, central.
Surface: asphalted.
Distance: 🚶1km ⊗300m 🛒500m.

Remarks: Parking harbour.

🏕S A Laracha 28C1
Area de O Regado, AC-552. **GPS**: n43,24972 w8,61694. ⬆.
3 🅿free 🚿🍽 Chfree. **Surface**: asphalted.

🏕S A Pontenova 28D1
Rua de la Estación. **GPS**: n43,34739 w7,19171. ⬆➡.

8 🅿free 🚿🍽 Chfree. **Surface**: asphalted.
Distance: ⊗200m 🛒100m.
Remarks: Max. 48h.

🏕S A Rúa 28D2
Área Recreativa O Aguillón. **GPS**: n42,38800 w7,11459. ⬆.
10 🅿free 🚿🍽 Chfree. **Surface**: asphalted/grassy. 🅾 01/01-31/12
Distance: 🚶500m 🏖on the spot ⊗500m 🛒500m.
Remarks: Next to football ground.

🏕S Arcade 🏖 28C2
Rúa do Peirao. **GPS**: n42,33946 w8,61329.
5 🅿free 🚿🍽 Chfree. **Surface**: metalled. 🅾 01/01-31/12
Distance: ⊗nearby 🛒nearby.

📷 Arrigorriaga 28H2
Carretera Buia Etorbidea. **GPS**: n43,23772 w2,91938. ⬆.

🚶. **Location**: Urban, simple. **Surface**: asphalted.
🅾 01/01-31/12

🏕S As Neves 28C2
Camino del Emenjeric. **GPS**: n42,08726 w8,41374. ⬆➡.

1 🅿free 🚿🍽 Chfree. **Location**: Rural. 🅾 01/01-31/12
Distance: ⊗200m 🛒200m.
Remarks: Max. 48h.

🏕S Bakio ⚓ 28H2
Parking, BI 3101. **GPS**: n43,42783 w2,80442. ⬆.

20 ⑤free ⚡WCfree.
Location: Urban, simple. **Surface:** grasstiles. 🅾 01/01-31/12
Distance: 🚶100m 🏖200m ⊗100m 🚌on the spot.
Remarks: Behind tourist info.

| 📷S | **Barrio Cosío** 🏔🌳 | 28F2 |

Área de Autocaravanas del Valle del Nansa.
GPS: n43,23349 w4,39892.⬆.

6 ⑤first day free, then € 5 ⚡€3 ⚡Ch 〰.
Location: Rural, simple, quiet. **Surface:** metalled.
Distance: 🚶on the spot ⊗on the spot 🍺100m.
Remarks: Max. 24h.

| 📷S | **Bárzana** 🏔 | 28E1 |

Area de Bárzana-Quirós, El Felguere. **GPS:** n43,15611 w5,97306.

15 ⑤free ⚡⚡Chfree. **Location:** Rural, simple, quiet.
Surface: asphalted. 🅾 01/01-31/12 🅾 holidays
Distance: 🚶100m ⊗100m 🍺100m.
Remarks: Max. 48h.

| 🅻 | **Behobia** 🍴 | 26A2 |

N10, Calle de Aria Juncal. **GPS:** n43,34310 w1,7598.⬆.

6 ⑤€ 3/2h < 19.30, overnight stay free.
Location: Urban, simple, noisy. **Surface:** asphalted. 🅾 01/01-31/12
Distance: 🚶on the spot 🏄500m 🏖200m 🍺500m 🚌on the spot.

| 📷S | **Bermeo** 〰 | 28H2 |

Área de la Pérgola, Itsasoan Galdurakoen Lamera.
GPS: n43,42306 w2,72556.⬆➡.

10 ⑤free ⚡⚡Chfree.
Location: Urban, simple. **Surface:** asphalted. 🅾 01/01-31/12
Distance: 🚶500m ⊗500m 🍺500m 🚌300m.
Remarks: Nearby football ground, max. 48h.

| 📷S | **Bertamirans** 🍴 | 28C1 |

Paseo Fluvial. **GPS:** n42,86009 w8,64838.⬆.

15 ⑤free ⚡⚡Chfree. **Surface:** asphalted. 🅾 01/01-31/12
Distance: ⊗100m 🏖50m Carrefour ↘dir. Santiago every 30 min.
Remarks: Max. 48h.

| 📷S | **Bilbao** 〰⛱ | 28H2 |

Kobetamendi, Monte Kobeta, 31. **GPS:** n43,25961 w2,96355.⬆➡.

72 ⑤€ 15/day ⚡⚡Ch ✂included.
Location: Urban, comfortable, quiet.
Surface: grasstiles.
🅾 15/06-15/10
Distance: 🚶centre 4,5km 🏄2,8km 🚌Bilbao-bus 58.
Remarks: 16/10-14/05 free parking, asphalt, max. 72h, service passerby € 6.

Tourist information Bilbao:
🅸 Bilbao.
Capital of the Basque Country and previously centre of the iron industry.
✝ Basílica de Begoña,
Virgen de Begoña, 38, Bilbao-Vizcaya. Basilica.

| 📷S | **Boiro** 🐑🏖 | 28C2 |

Playa Jardín de Barraña. **GPS:** n42,64183 w8,89481.⬆➡.

10 ⑤€ 3-6 ⚡⚡Chfree. **Surface:** asphalted. 🅾 01/01-31/12
Distance: 🚶500m 🏖20m ⊗200m Bistro Prima 🍺400m.
Remarks: Max. 48h.

| 📷S | **Boiro** 🐑🏖 | 28C2 |

Playa Mañons, S/n 15930 Chancelas–Abanqueiro.
GPS: n42,63138 w8,85311.⬆➡.
8 ⑤free ⚡⚡Chfree.
Distance: 🏖on the spot.

| 📷S | **Bueu** | 28C2 |

PO315 dir Cabo Udra. **GPS:** n42,33460 w8,8248.
⑤free. **Surface:** sand.
Remarks: Max. 48h.

| 🅻 | **Bueu** | 28C2 |

Puerto, Avda. de Montero Rios. **GPS:** n42,32732 w8,7838.
⑤.

| 📷S | **Burela** | 28D1 |

Area de Burela, Parque de O Campón, parking Hospital de Burela.
GPS: n43,65216 w7,35891.⬆.

5 ⑤free ⚡⚡Chfree. **Surface:** asphalted.
Distance: 🚶200m ⊗300m 🍺200m.
Remarks: Max. 48h.

| 📷 | **Cabárceno** 👫🏖 | 28G2 |

Área Lago del Acebo, N634> dir Parque de la naturaleze de Cabárceno.
GPS: n43,35802 w3,81959.⬆.

30 ⑤free ⚡⚡Chfree.
Location: Rural, quiet. **Surface:** asphalted.
Distance: 🚶100m 🏖50m 🏄50m ⊗200m 🍺200m.
Remarks: Max. 48h.

| ⚓ | **Camariñas** 🏖 | 28B1 |

Puerto Club Nautico, Rúa Castelo. **GPS:** n43,12694 w9,18333.
5 ⑤free. **Surface:** asphalted.

| 📷S | **Candás** | 28E1 |

Area de La Fuente de los Angeles, Calle Estacion.
GPS: n43,58495 w5,77197.⬆.

6 ⑤free ⚡⚡ChWCfree.
Location: Urban, simple. **Surface:** asphalted. 🅾 01/01-31/12
Distance: 🚶500m 🏖1km ⊗500m 🍺500m.
Remarks: Along railwayline.

| 📷S | **Cangas de Onís** | 28F1 |

Parking Lanzadera Picos de Europa, Calle del Llreau.
GPS: n43,35211 w5,12536.⬆.

4 ⑤free ⚡⚡Chfree. **Location:** Urban. **Surface:** asphalted.
Distance: ⊗100m.
Remarks: Max. 48h.

| 📷S | **Carnota** 🏖 | 28B1 |

Area de Mar de Lira, Calle Miñarzo s/n. **GPS:** n42,80306 w9,12944.

4 ⑤free ⚡⚡Chfree. **Surface:** sand.
Distance: 🚶Carnota 5km 🏖10m ⊗on the spot.
Remarks: Parking next to hatchery.

| 📷S | **Cartelle** | 28C2 |

Camperpark O Mundil, Antigua Carretera OU-659.
GPS: n42,21444 w8,03306.

ES

24 ⌂€10 ⛽⌂Ch ✇WC⌂◉≋free.
Surface: gravel. ◖ 01/01-31/12
Distance: ⌂1km zona fluvial Río Arnoia ⊗10m.

Chantada 28C2
Champ de Sangoñedo, Ctra. De Barrela o Seixo.
GPS: n42,60598 w7,77989.⬆.
5 ⌂free ⛽⌂Chfree.
Distance: ⌂500m.
Remarks: At footballstadium.

Coaña 28D1
Area de Ortiguera, Barrio Nueva Rasa. **GPS:** n43,56082 w6,73352.⬆.
2 ⌂free ⛽⌂Chfree.
Location: Rural, simple. **Surface:** asphalted.
Distance: ⊗on the spot ⌂on the spot.

Colombres 28F1
Area de Casa Junco, N-634. **GPS:** n43,38056 w4,55472.

15 ⌂free ⛽⌂Chfree. **Surface:** asphalted.
Distance: ⊗on the spot.

Colunga 28F1
Area de Los Llanos, Avda de Asturias N-632.
GPS: n43,48472 w5,26491.⬆.

25 ⌂€4 ⛽€3 ⌂⌂€1.
Location: Simple. **Surface:** asphalted. ◖ 01/01-31/12
Distance: ⌂500m ⛵2km ⊗200m.
Remarks: Thursday market.

Cospeito 28D1
Camino de la Laguna. **GPS:** n43,23984 w7,55579.
5 ⌂free ⛽⌂Ch ✇free. **Surface:** asphalted. ◖ 01/01-31/12
Distance: ⊗300m.

Cudillero 28E1
Puerto. GPS: n43,56568 w6,1517.⬆.

5 ⌂. **Location:** Simple. **Surface:** asphalted.
Remarks: Parking in harbour.

Cudillero 28E1
Hotel Rest. Casa Fernando II, N-632. **GPS:** n43,56028 w6,17722.⬆.

5 ⌂free ⛽⌂Ch€3.
Location: Simple, quiet. **Surface:** asphalted. ◖ 01/01-31/12
Distance: ⊗on the spot.

Ferrol 28C1
Ctra. de la Malata. **GPS:** n43,49333 w8,23972.⬆.

15 ⌂free ⛽⌂Chfree. **Surface:** asphalted.
Distance: ⌂700m ⊗300m.

Finisterre 28B1
Praia de Langosteira. **GPS:** n42,92320 w9,26149.

5 ⌂free ⛲.
Distance: ⌂on the spot ⊗1km ⌂1km.
Remarks: Beach parking, max. 48h.

Fuente Dé 28F2
Picos de Europa, C621. **GPS:** n43,14433 w4,81274.
⌂free. **Surface:** sand.
Remarks: Parking funicular railway.

Gijón 28E1
Polígono Puerto Musel. **GPS:** n43,54467 w5,69562.⬆.

15 ⌂free ⛽⌂free.
Location: Urban, simple, noisy. **Surface:** asphalted. ◖ 01/01-31/12
Distance: ⌂3km ⌂on the spot ⌂on the spot.
Remarks: Max. 48h.

Gijón 28E1
Camino de las Mimosas, El Rinconin. **GPS:** n43,54708 w5,63648.

20 ⌂free.
Location: Urban, simple, central. **Surface:** asphalted. ◖ 01/01-31/12
Distance: ⌂300m.
Remarks: Baker every morning (Jul/Aug).

Gorliz 28H2
Paseo de Astondo. **GPS:** n43,41220 w2,94194.⬆.

⌂free. **Location:** Urban, simple. **Surface:** asphalted.
◖ 01/01-31/12
Distance: ⌂500m ⌂50m ⌂on the spot.
Remarks: Parking beach.

Gozon 28E1
Area Autocaravanas El Molino, Ctr. Luanco-Cabo Peñas.
GPS: n43,62541 w5,81125.⬆➡.

25 ⌂€10 ⛽⌂included ✇€4,60.
Location: Rural, comfortable, quiet. **Surface:** grassy. ◖ 01/01-31/12
Distance: ⌂500m ⊗on the spot ⌂on the spot ⌂on the spot.
Remarks: To be paid at campsite.

Guitiriz 28C1
Rua do Voluntariado. **GPS:** n43,17727 w7,88062.⬆.
5 ⌂free ⛽⌂Ch ✇free. **Surface:** gravel. ◖ 01/01-31/12
Distance: ⌂800m ⌂100m.

Hermandad De Campoo De Suso 28F2
Estación Invernal Alto Campoo, C 628 Reinosa - Espinilla, dir: Alto
Campoo. **GPS:** n43,03839 w4,37036.
20 ⌂ ⛽⌂Ch.
Distance: ⛷on the spot.

Hondarribia 26A2
Ramón Iribarren Pasalekua. **GPS:** n43,37929 w1,79768.➡⬆.

20 ⌂€12/day ⛽⌂Chincluded. ⌂
Location: Urban, simple, quiet. **Surface:** asphalted. ◖ 01/04-31/09
Distance: ⌂2km ⛵8km ⌂on the spot ⌂on the spot.
Remarks: Beautiful view.

Illano 28D1
Area de Folgueirou, Area recreativa de Folgueirou.
GPS: n43,34333 w6,85116.
30 ⌂free ⛽⌂Chincluded.
Location: Rural, simple. **Surface:** grassy/gravel. ◖ 01/01-31/12
Distance: ⊗on the spot.

Lanestosa 28G2
Area de Lanestosa, Calle Mirabueno. **GPS:** n43,21789 w3,43878.⬆.

10 ⌂free, service € 5-8/24h ⛽⌂Ch ✇WC⌂included.
Location: Rural, simple. **Surface:** gravel. ◖ 01/01-31/12
Distance: ⌂200m ⊗400m ⌂6km ⌂on the spot ⌂on the spot.

ES

⬛S Langreo 🍴 28E1
Ecomuseo Minero Valle de Samuño, Calle Puente Carbón.
GPS: n43,27835 w5,67433. ⬆.

11 🅿free 🚰🔌Chfree. **Location:** Rural, simple, quiet.
Surface: asphalted/metalled. 🅾 01/01-31/12
Distance: ⊗on the spot.
Remarks: At Ecomuseum.

⬛S Legazpi 28H2
Parque Mirandaola de Legazpi, Carretera Legazpia, GI 2630.
GPS: n43,03678 w2,33758. ⬆➡.

5 🅿free 🚰🔌Chfree.
Location: Urban, simple, noisy. **Surface:** asphalted. 🅾 01/01-31/12
Distance: 🚶1,5km ⊗on the spot 🏃on the spot.
Remarks: Max. 48h.

⬛S Lekeitio 🌊⚓ 28H2
Iñigo Artieta Etorbidea. **GPS**: n43,35849 w2,50743. ⬆➡.

14 🅿free 🚰€1/100liter 🔌Ch. **Location:** Urban, comfortable, quiet.
Surface: asphalted. 🅾 01/01-31/12
Distance: 🚶500m ⛱500m ⊗500m 🏃300m.
Remarks: Coins at tourist info.

⬛S Liérganes ⚓ 28G2
Calle de Puente Romano. **GPS**: n43,34479 w3,74183. ⬆.

10 🅿free 🚰🔌free. **Location:** Urban, simple, central.
Surface: asphalted. 🅾 01/01-31/12
Distance: 🚶200m ⛱250m 🏃350m.
Remarks: Parking nearby train station, max. 48h.

⬛S Lugo 🍷 28D1
Pabellón Municipal de Deportes, Avda. de Santiago.
GPS: n43,00452 w7,56144. ⬆.

---

10 🅿free 🚰🔌Chfree. **Surface:** asphalted.
Distance: 🚶10min 🚲5,2km 🏃10min.
Remarks: Parking gymnasium, max. 48h.

P S Lugo 🍷 28D1
Plaza de Asturias, Rúa Ánxel Fole. **GPS**: n43,00972 w7,55805.
15 🅿€12/24h 🚰🔌free. **Surface:** asphalted.

⬛S Lugones 28E1
Area de Lugones, Calle Conde de Santa Bárbara.
GPS: n43,40694 w5,81139. ⬆.

4 🅿free 🚰🔌Chincluded. **Location:** Urban, simple.
Surface: asphalted/metalled. 🅾 01/01-31/12
Distance: 🚶9 km Oviedo ⊗on the spot 🏃on the spot 🏃200m.
Remarks: Next to sports centre.

⬛S Mieres 28E1
Area de Mieres, Calle Asturias. **GPS**: n43,25194 w5,78083. ⬆.

6 🅿free 🚰🔌Chfree.
Location: Urban, simple. **Surface:** asphalted. 🅾 01/01-31/12
Distance: 🚶100m 🚲500m ⊗on the spot 🏃on the spot.
Remarks: Along railwayline.

⬛S Milladoiro 28C1
Traversia do Porto. **GPS**: n42,84512 w8,58079. ⬆.

20 🅿free 🚰🔌Chfree.
Surface: asphalted.
Distance: ⊗200m 🏃200m 🚌dir. Santiago every 15 min.
Remarks: At swimming pool, max. 48h.

⬛S Miño 28C1
AP-9 Coruña-Ferrol ><, km 15,5. **GPS**: n43,37404 w8,18736. ⬆.
12 🅿free 🚰🔌ChWC free. **Surface:** asphalted.
Distance: ⊗on the spot 🏃on the spot.
Remarks: Parking nearby motorway.

⬛S Miranda de Ebro 🌊 28G2
Calle de Burgos. **GPS**: n42,68880 w2,95403. ⬆➡.

7 🅿free 🚰🔌Chfree.
Location: Urban, simple, noisy. **Surface:** metalled. 🅾 01/01-31/12
Distance: 🚶1km 🚲3km 🚣river.

Tourist information Miranda de Ebro:
🎪 Medieval annual fair. 🅾 around May 1.
🎪 Week market. 🅾 Sa.

⬛S Mondoñedo 28D1
Calle de Vicedo. **GPS**: n43,42778 w7,37028. ⬆.
10 🅿free 🚰🔌Chfree. **Surface:** metalled.

⬛S Monforte de Lemos 🌊🌿 28D2
Auditorio Multiusos de Monforte, Calle de la Circunvalación / Calle de Santa Clara. **GPS**: n42,52750 w7,5119. ⬆.

20 🅿free 🚰🔌Chfree. **Surface:** asphalted.
Distance: ⊗500m 🏃550m 🚌300m.
Remarks: Max. 48h.

⬛S Nava 28E1
Area de Nava, Avda. de la Constitución. **GPS**: n43,35722 w5,49917. ⬆.

4 🅿free 🚰🔌Chfree.
Surface: asphalted/metalled. 🅾 01/01-31/12
Distance: 🚶900m 🚲10km.
Remarks: At sports centre, no camping activities.

⬛S Navelgas 28E1
Area de Navelgas, Recinto Ferial. **GPS**: n43,40402 w6,54167. ⬆.
15 🅿free 🚰🔌Chfree.
Location: Urban. **Surface:** asphalted/metalled.
Distance: 🚶100m.

⬛S Navia 28D1
Area de la Granja, C/ Travesía de la Granja.
GPS: n43,54528 w6,72028. ⬆.
10 🅿free 🚰🔌Chfree 📶. **Location:** Urban.
Surface: gravel/metalled.
Distance: ⊗on the spot 🏃on the spot.

🅿 Noia 🌊🌿 28C2
Rúa de Pedra Marques. **GPS**: n42,78783 w8,8906.

🅿free. **Surface:** asphalted.
Distance: 🚶on the spot ⊗50m 🏃50m 🚌Bus 20m.

Tourist information Noia:
👁 El Pendo, 5km S. Santander. Cave with petroglyphs.

⬛S O Barco 28D2
Malecón Campiño. **GPS**: n42,41063 w6,97493. ⬆➡.

12 🅿free 🚰🔌Chfree. **Surface:** unpaved. 🅾 01/01-31/12
Distance: 🚶400m 🚲250m 🏃250m.

⬛S Pajares 🏔❄ 28E2
Valgrande-Pajares, Brañillín. **GPS**: n42,97889 w5,77194. ⬆➡.

ES

15 ⊠free ⚡Chfree. **Location:** Rural. **Surface:** asphalted.

| ⊞ S | **Parada do Sil** | 28D2 |

Rural Pepe, Campo da Feira 17. **GPS:** n42,38287 w7,57106.⬆.
4 ⊠guests free ⚡Ch ⚡€2. 01/01-31/12
Distance: ⊗on the spot ⚡on the spot.

| ⊠ S | **Pobra do Brollòn** | 28D2 |

Campo Municipal de Fut. GPS: n42,56944 w7,39417.⬆.
8 ⊠free ⚡Chfree. **Surface:** metalled.

| ⊠ S | **Pola de Laviana** | 28E1 |

Area de Pola de Laviana, Av. Real Titánico.
GPS: n43,25478 w5,56836.⬆.

8 ⊠free ⚡Chfree.
Location: Rural, simple. **Surface:** grasstiles.
Distance: ⚡1500m ⚡1500m ⚡1500m.

| ⊠ S | **Posada de Valdeón** | 28F2 |

Calle del General Mola. **GPS:** n43,15285 w4,91747.⬆➡.

18 ⊠€8 ⚡Ch⚡. **Location:** Rural. **Surface:** grassy.
Distance: ⊗on the spot ⚡on the spot.
Remarks: Max. 96h, in Parque Nacional de Los Picos de Europa.

| ⊠ S | **Potes** | 28F2 |

Santo Toribio de Liébana, CA885. **GPS:** n43,15028 w4,65389.

⊠free ⚡free.
Location: Isolated, quiet.
Surface: asphalted.
Distance: ⚡Potes 3km ⚡on the spot.
Remarks: Parking monastery.
Tourist information Potes:
⚡ Local products. Mo.
⚡ Historical cattle market, since 1379. 01/08-15/08.

| ⊠ S | **Redondela** | 28C2 |

Avda. de Mendiño. **GPS:** n42,28972 w8,61055.⬆.
15 ⊠free ⚡Ch.
Distance: ⚡600m ⚡500m ⊗600m ⚡600m.

| ⊠ S | **Rentería** | 28H2 |

Área Rural de Listorreta-Barrengoloia.
GPS: n43,26800 w1,90135.⬆.

2 ⊠free ⚡Chfree. **Location:** Rural, simple, isolated, quiet.
Surface: asphalted. 01/01-31/12
Distance: ⚡Renteria 7km ⚡on the spot.
Remarks: Parking nature reserve.

| ⊠ S | **Ribadeo** | 28D1 |

Eroski, Camino de Vilar. **GPS:** n43,54000 w7,06055.
10 ⊠free ⚡Chfree. **Surface:** asphalted. 01/01-31/12
Distance: ⚡500m ⚡1km ⚡on the spot.
Remarks: At supermarket.

| ⊠ S | **Ribamontán al Monte** | 28G1 |

A8 Bilbao > Santander. **GPS:** n43,40282 w3,62877.
10 ⊠free ⚡Chfree.

| ⊠ S | **Ribamontán al Monte** | 28G1 |

A8 Santander > Bilbao. **GPS:** n43,40446 w3,62476.
10 ⊠free ⚡Chfree. **Location:** Highway. **Surface:** asphalted.

| ⊠ S | **Riosa** | 28E1 |

Area de El Angliru, Viapará s/n. **GPS:** n43,24806 w5,90667.⬆.

15 ⊠€5 ⚡Chincluded.
Location: Rural, simple, isolated, quiet. **Surface:** metalled.
01/01-31/12
Distance: ⊗on the spot. **Remarks:** No camping activities.

| ⊠ S | **San Clodio** | 28D2 |

Parque de Pena da Mula, Calle del Troque.
GPS: n42,46750 w7,28583.⬆.

3 ⊠free ⚡Chfree. **Surface:** asphalted. 01/01-31/12
Distance: ⚡200m ⚡Playa Fluvial 25m ⊗cafetaria.

| ⊠ S | **San Martín del Rey Aurelio** | 28E1 |

Área del Pozo Entrego, Avda. de la Vega, AS17.
GPS: n43,28639 w5,63889.⬆.

3 ⊠free ⚡Chfree.
Location: Urban, simple. **Surface:** asphalted.
Distance: ⚡on the spot ⊗on the spot ⚡Alcampo 1km.
Remarks: Max. 48h.

| ⊠ S | **San Sebastian** | 28H2 |

Paseo de Berio nº 2. **GPS:** n43,30797 w2,01426.⬆.

44 ⊠€ 6,45, 01/10-31/05 € 3,20 ⚡Chincluded.
Location: Urban, simple, noisy. **Surface:** grasstiles.
01/01-31/12
Distance: ⚡2km ⊗50m ⚡100m.
Remarks: Max. 48h, marked pitches, registration with licence plate number.
Tourist information San Sebastian:
⚡ Centro de Atracción y Turismo (CAT), Reina Regente, www.donostia.org. Old city with, Parte Vieja, historical city centre with numerous cafés, restaurants and tapa bars.
Ⓜ Palacio del Mar. Museum for oceanografics. 10-19h, Sa-Su 10-21h, 15/06-15/09 10-21h.
⚡ Su-morning.

| ⊠ S | **Santander** | 28G1 |

Marina de Santander, Calle Tramo de Unión, Camargo.
GPS: n43,42736 w3,80537.⬆.

20 ⊠ ⚡Ch⚡(2x) €5 ⚡€4/30minutes.
Location: Simple. 01/01-31/12
Distance: ⊗100m ⚡3km.

| P S | **Santiago de Compostela** | 28C1 |

Rúa Manuel María. **GPS:** n42,89560 w8,5317.
100 ⊠8-20h € 3 ⚡€3 ⚡Ch.
Surface: asphalted.
01/01-31/12
Distance: ⚡centre 2,5km ⚡3km ⊗50m ⚡line 1 > centre.
Remarks: Ticket for overnight stay € 12.
Tourist information Santiago de Compostela:
⚡ Oficina de Turismo, Rúa del Villar, 43, www.santiagoturismo.com. City known for the termination of the pilgrime route.
⚡ Plaza de la Quintana. Impressive square.
⚡ Fiesta del Apóstol Santiago.
Most important festival of Galicia.
15/07-31/07.

| ⊠ S | **Santillana del Mar** | 28G1 |

Ctra. C6316. **GPS:** n43,38895 w4,10721.

⊠€ 2/24h. **Surface:** asphalted.

| ⊠ S | **Sanxenxo** | 28B2 |

Área de Cachadelos, PO-308. **GPS:** n42,41652 w8,86833.⬆➡.
65 ⊠€ 10 ⚡Ch⚡included. **Surface:** grassy.
Distance: ⚡200m ⊗2km ⚡on the spot.

| ⊠ S | **Sarria** | 28D2 |

Calle de Castelo. **GPS:** n42,77194 w7,41028.⬆.

ES

12 ⬛free 🚐 ⚡Chfree. **Surface:** asphalted.
Distance: ⛽800m 🏖on the spot ⊗800m.

♿S Saturrarán 🌊 28H2
GPS: n43,31968 w2,41165. ⬆.

5 ⬛free WC.
Location: Rural, simple. **Surface:** grasstiles. ◻ 01/01-31/12
Distance: ⛽500m 🏖on the spot 🍴700m.
Remarks: Parking beach.

♿S Suesa 28G1
Area de Autocaravanas Suesa, Mojante 25.
GPS: n43,44736 w3,72788. ⬆.

66 ⬛€9 🚐 ⚡Chincluded ⚡(10x)€3 WC 📶.
Location: Comfortable. **Surface:** grasstiles. ◻ 01/01-31/12
Distance: ⛽1km 🏖1,8km 🏪1,5km ⊗1km 🍴1km.
Remarks: Max. 96h, pay at reception campsite.

♿S Tapia 28D1
Area de Playa Grande, Av. de la Playa. **GPS:** n43,56667 w6,94639. ⬆.
15 ⬛free 🚐 ⚡Chfree. **Location:** Rural.
Surface: grasstiles.
Distance: ⛽500m ⊗500m 🍴500m.

♿S Teverga 🏔 28E1
Parking Senda del Oso, Entrago. **GPS:** n43,16954 w6,09755. ⬆.

20 ⬛free 🚐 ⚡Chfree 🚿€3.
Location: Simple, noisy. **Surface:** asphalted. ◻ 01/01-31/12
Distance: ⊗on the spot 🚲on the spot.
Remarks: Max. 48h.

♿S Tui 28C2
Puente Tripes, Avenida de Portugal. **GPS:** n42,04333 w8,64656. ⬆.

3 ⬛free. **Location:** Urban, simple. **Surface:** asphalted.

◻ 01/01-31/12
Distance: 🚲1,3km ⊗500m 🛒Lidl 1,5km.
Remarks: Max. 48h.

♿S Vegadeo 28D1
Area de Vegadeo, Calle Emilio Cotarelo, s/n.
GPS: n43,46667 w7,05167. ⬆.
8 ⬛free 🚐 ⚡Chfree.
Location: Urban. **Surface:** asphalted/metalled.
Distance: ⊗on the spot 🍴on the spot.
Remarks: Max. 72h.

♿S Vilalba 28D1
Rua da Feira. **GPS:** n43,29556 w7,67694. ⬆.
15 ⬛free 🚐 ⚡Chfree. **Surface:** asphalted.
Distance: ⊗300m 🍴300m.

♿S Villanueva de Oscos 28D1
Area de Villanueva, Lugar de Villanueva. **GPS:** n43,31056 w6,98583. ⬆.
2 ⬛free 🚐 ⚡Chfree. **Surface:** gravel.
Remarks: Max. 48h.

♿S Vitoria Gasteiz 🌿🏖🛒 28H2
Área de Lakua, Portal de Foronde. **GPS:** n42,86684 w2,68539. ⬆➡.

10 ⬛free 🚐 ⚡Chfree. **Location:** Urban, comfortable, central, quiet.
Surface: asphalted. ◻ 01/01-31/12
Distance: ⛽2km 🚲5km ⊗100m 🍴bakery 50m 🚌50m.
Remarks: Max. 72h, market Wednesday.

♿S Zumaia 🌊 28H2
Calle de la Estación. **GPS:** n43,29279 w2,24684. ⬆➡.

25 ⬛free 🚐 ⚡Chfree.
Location: Simple, noisy. **Surface:** asphalted. ◻ 01/01-31/12
Distance: ⛽2km 🚲4,4km 🏖on the spot 🚶on the spot.

Navarre and Rioja

♿ Aínsa 🌿 31A1
Plaza del Castillo.
GPS: n42,41916 e0,13515.
⬛free.
Surface: sand.
Tourist information Aínsa:
ℹ The capital of a medieval kingdom by surrounded fortress walls.
🚶 ◻ Tue.

🏛 Albarracín 🌿 31A2
Quesería Sierra de Albarracín, Pol. Los Rubiales, 1.
GPS: n40,43286 w1,4405.

6 ⬛free. ◻ 01/01-31/12
Distance: ⛽1km ⊗200m 🍴1km 🚌1km.

⛺ Alquézar 🌿 31A1
Alquézar, Ctra.Barbastro,. **GPS:** n42,17097 e0,02382.
⬛€21-25. ◻ 01/01-31/12
Tourist information Alquézar:
ℹ Historical city.

🏛S Ansó 26B3
Ctra. de Ansó a Fago. **GPS:** n42,75648 w0,83102.
2 🚐.

🏨🍴S Aoiz 26A3
Hotel Ekai. **GPS:** n42,77624 w1,38536. ⬆.

10 ⬛free 🚐 ⚡🚿📶free.
Location: Rural, simple. **Surface:** gravel/metalled. ◻ 01/01-31/12
Distance: ⛽3km ⊗on the spot.

♿S Arguedas 🌿🏖 31A1
Aparcamiento Municipal de Autocaravanas de Arguedas, Calle Bordón. **GPS:** n42,17270 w1,5913. ⬆➡.

9 ⬛free 🚐€2/100liter ⚡Ch.
Location: Rural, simple, quiet. **Surface:** gravel. ◻ 01/01-31/12
Distance: ⛽800m ⊗800m 🍴800m.
Remarks: At Parque de Bardenas Reales, max. 48h.

♿S Ariza 29H1
Area de Servicios La Cadiera, A2 Madrid > Zaragoza.
GPS: n41,31210 w2,00329.
5 🚐.

♿S Arnedillo 🏔 28H3
Calle Miguel del Pozo. **GPS:** n42,21361 w2,23972. ⬆➡.

40 ⬛€10 🚐 ⚡Ch 🚿(40x)€1/4h WC 📶,cold shower 📶included. 🛝
Location: Rural, comfortable. **Surface:** asphalted.
◻ 01/01-31/12
Distance: ⛽200m ⊗200m 🍴200m 🚶on the spot.
Remarks: Follow the signs in the village.

♿S Berriozar 🌿 26A3
Av. Berriozar. **GPS:** n42,84043 w1,66557. ⬆➡.

20 ⬛free 🚐€2/100liter ⚡Ch.
Location: Urban, simple. **Surface:** concrete. ◻ 01/01-31/12
Distance: ⛽4km Pamplona 🚌500m.
Remarks: Max. 72h, coins at sports centre (9-21h).

🏛 Bielsa 26D3
Calle Mayor. **GPS:** n42,63437 e0,21893.
3 🚐.

🏛 Botaya 31A1
Parking Monasterio de San Juan la Peña. **GPS:** n42,50699 w0,66414.

ES

3 🛏free.

🛏S Cascante 28H3

Av. Fuentes Dutor Parking Termolúdico. **GPS**: n41,99372 w1,68669.⬆

40 🛏free ⛽🛏free.
Location: Urban, simple. **Surface:** asphalted. ⬛ 01/01-31/12
Distance: 🚶750m ⊗800m.

🛏 Estelle 🌿 28H2

Calle St. Barbara Calea. **GPS**: n42,67306 w2,03972.

3 🛏free. **Surface:** asphalted. ⬛ 01/01-31/12

Tourist information Estelle:
🚶 Puebte la Reine. ⬛ Sa.

🛏S Falces 28H3

Calle la Mota. **GPS**: n42,39295 w1,79574.⬆
6 🛏free ⛽🛏Chfree.
Location: Simple. **Surface:** metalled. ⬛ 01/01-31/12
Distance: 🚶700m 🚰300m.

🛏S Haro 🌿🛁 28H2

LR111. **GPS**: n42,57253 w2,86739.⬆

10 🛏free ⛽free.
Location: Rural, simple, quiet. **Surface:** gravel. ⬛ 01/01-31/12
Distance: 🚶1,5km ⊗1,3km 🚰1,5km.

🛏S Haro 🌿🛁 28H2

Parking centro deportivo, Av de los Ingenieros del Ministerio Obras Públicas, LR-111. **GPS**: n42,57677 w2,85222.⬆

4 🛏free ⛽free.
Location: Urban, simple.
Surface: asphalted.
⬛ 01/01-31/12

Distance: 🚶500m ⛽14km ⊗on the spot.
Remarks: At sports park, Haro, Rioja Wine Capital, wine museum, wine cellars.

Tourist information Haro:
ℹ Capital of Rioja wine.

🛏S Irura 28H2

Area del Frontón, Calle Zilar. **GPS**: n43,16778 w2,0652.⬆➡

4 🛏free ⛽🛏Chfree. **Location:** Urban, simple, noisy.
Surface: asphalted. ⬛ 01/01-31/12
Distance: ⛽100m.

🛏S Logroño 28H3

Avenue de la Sonsierra, LR132. **GPS**: n42,47916 w2,4571.⬆

3 🛏free ⛽🛏Chfree. **Location:** Urban, simple, noisy.
Surface: metalled. ⬛ 01/01-31/12
Distance: 🚶700m 🏊100m ⊗400m 🚰300m 🚌20m.
Remarks: Max. 48h.

🛏 Logroño 28H3

Emblase de la Grajera, Pontano de la Grajera.
GPS: n42,44909 w2,50189.⬆

15 🛏free.
Location: Rural, simple. **Surface:** concrete. ⬛ 01/01-31/12
Distance: 🚶7km ⛽1km 🚣on the spot.
Remarks: Parking at lake, golf court and park La Grajera.

🛏 Navarrete 🌿 28H3

Calle de la Carretera. **GPS**: n42,42458 w2,55584.⬆

🛏free.
Location: Urban, simple. **Surface:** asphalted. ⬛ 01/01-31/12
Distance: 🚶1km ⊗3km ⊗600m 🚌800m.
Remarks: Parking at sports park.

🛏 Roncesvalles ⛰ 26A3

Paseo Ibaneta. **GPS**: n43,02018 w1,32401.⬆

5 🛏.
Location: Rural, simple. **Surface:** asphalted. ⬛ 01/01-31/12
Distance: 🚶1,5km.
Remarks: Beautiful view.

🛏 Zaragoza 31A1

Parque de Atracciones de Zaragoza. **GPS**: n41,61994 w0,90122.
10 🛏.
Distance: ⛽4,5km.

Mediterranean Sea Communities

🛏S Alcover 31B1

Avinguda Catalunya 2. **GPS**: n41,26315 e1,17324.⬆

5 🛏€ 5/24h ⛽🛏Chincluded. **Location:** Rural, simple, central, quiet.
Surface: concrete. ⬛ 01/01-31/12
Distance: 🚶on the spot ⛽700m ⊗350m 🚰100m 🚌280m.
Remarks: Max. 48h.

🛏S Alicante 31A3

Villafranqueza, Av. Pintor Gastón Castelló 41.
GPS: n38,37808 w0,48822.⬆

25 🛏€7 ⛽🛏Ch 🔌WC 📶included.
Location: Noisy. ⬛ 01/01-31/12
Distance: ⛽1km ⊗50m 🚌50m.
Remarks: Next to petrol station.

🛏S Altafulla 31B1

Área de Servicio Mèdol, AP-7 km 237, Barcelona > Taragona.
GPS: n41,14157 e1,34590.
10 🛏free ⛽🛏Chfree. **Location:** Highway. **Surface:** asphalted
⬛ 01/01-31/12
Distance: ⊗on the spot 🚰on the spot.

🛏S Altafulla 31B1

Área de Servicio Mèdol, AP-7 km 237, Taragona > Barcelona.
GPS: n41,14054 e1,34746.
10 🛏free ⛽🛏Chfree. **Surface:** asphalted. ⬛ 01/01-31/12
Distance: ⊗on the spot 🚰on the spot.

🛏S Altea 〰 31A3

San Antonio Camperpark, Ctra. del Albir 5/6, CV7651.
GPS: n38,58544 w0,05989.⬆

ES

50 ⌇€ 15, 2 pers.incl ⊢▭Ch ⌁€0,45/kWh,10Amp WC ⌇▭€3
⌇included. Location: Comfortable. ☐ 15/09-30/04
Distance: ⌁Altea > 1km < Albir ⌁100m ⌇500m ⌇500m
⌇200m, tram 1km.
Remarks: Bread-service, discount longer stays.

⌇S | Amposta | 31B2
Casa de Fusta, Partida L'Encanyissada. GPS: n40,65851 e0,67475. ⬆➡

70 ⌇free ⊢€3 ▭Ch ⌁ ⌇. Location: Rural, comfortable, isolated,
quiet. Surface: gravel/sand. ☐ 01/01-31/12
Distance: ⌇on the spot ⊗on the spot ⌇on the spot ⌇on the spot
⌇on the spot.
Remarks: Bread-service.

⌇S | Ascó | 31B1
C/ Alcalde Tomas Biarnes Radua. GPS: n41,18673 e0,56802. ⬆➡

25 ⌇free ⊢▭Chfree. Location: Simple, central, noisy.
Surface: asphalted. ☐ 01/01-31/12
Distance: ⌇100m ⌇200m ⌁200m ⊗500m ⌇500m.

⌇S | Avinyo | 31B1
Area Municipal de Avinyó, Calle Industria.
GPS: n41,86556 e1,97472. ⬆
10 ⌇free ⊢€1/50liter ▭Chfree. Surface: gravel/sand.
Distance: ⌇300m ⊗300m ⌇300m.

⌇S | Avinyonet del Penedès | 31B1
Area Cellar Can Battle - Artcava, Masia Can Batlle s/n, BV2411.
GPS: n41,36790 e1,77306. ⬆➡

10 ⌇free ⊢▭Chfree. Location: Rural, simple, isolated, quiet.
Surface: gravel. ☐ 01/01-31/12
Distance: ⌇1km ⌁6km ⊗1km ⌇1km.
Remarks: Wine tasting.

⌇S | Ayora | 31A3
El Nogal, Romeral 5. GPS: n39,05870 w1,0324.

20 ⌇€ 10 ⊢▭Chincluded ⌁€2/day ⌇.
Location: Rural, comfortable, isolated, quiet. Surface: grassy.
Distance: ⌇2km ⌇2km ⌇on the spot ⌇on the spot.

⌇S | Barberà de la Conca | 31B1
Area de la Cooperativa Barberá, Calle Comercio 40.
GPS: n41,41025 e1,22734. ⬆

10 ⌇free ⊢▭Chfree. Location: Rural, simple, central, quiet.
Surface: gravel. ☐ 01/11-31/08
Distance: ⌇on the spot ⌇500m.

⌇S | Barcelona | 31B1
CityStop, Rambla Guipúzcoa. GPS: n41,42433 e2,20748. ⬆
80 ⌇€ 30 ⊢▭Ch ⌁€4 WC ⌇.
Location: Urban, comfortable. Surface: asphalted.
Distance: ⌇on the spot.

⌇S | Barcelona | 31B1
Park & Ride del Besòs, Carrer del Taulat, B10 > salida 24 / 25, Sant Adrià
del Besos. GPS: n41,41565 e2,22363. ⬆

20 ⌇€ 30/24h, € 3/h ⊢▭Ch ⌁ WC ⌇included ▭.
Location: Urban. Surface: metalled. ☐ 01/01-31/12
Distance: ⌇1km ⊗300m ⌇300m ⌇Tram 100m, metro 500m.
Remarks: Max. 72h, monitored parking.

⌇S | Bellcaire d'Empordà | 31C1

Àrea Massís del Montgrí - Camper Park
Bellcaire d'Empordà

- **Located in nature reserve**
- **Wifi included**
- **Swimming pool**

www.massisdelmontgri.cat
info@massisdelmontgri.cat

Àrea Massís del Montgrí, Camí Vell d'Ullà, 21.
GPS: n42,07521 e3,09748. ⬆
36 ⌇€ 8, 01/06-30/09 € 10 ⊢▭Ch ⌁€4 WC ⌇..
Surface: grassy. Distance: ⌇500m ⌁5km ⊗500m.

⌇S | Bellvei | 31B1
Bellvei del Penedès, Camino Plains. GPS: n41,24613 e1,56992. ⬆➡

30 ⌇€ 6 ⊢▭Chincluded ⌁€3 ⌇€1/day. Location: Comfortable,
isolated, quiet. Surface: grassy/gravel. ☐ 01/01-31/12
Distance: ⌇1km ⌁6,5km ⌇5km ⊗1,2km ⌇1km ⌇on the spot.

⌇S | Benagéber | 31A2
Ctra. CV-3930. GPS: n39,70913 w1,10136. ⬆➡

70 ⌇free ⊢▭Chfree. Location: Rural, simple, isolated, quiet.
Surface: gravel/sand. ☐ 01/01-31/12
Distance: ⌇100m ⌇400m ⌇on the spot ⌇on the spot.
Remarks: Max. 72h, picnic and barbecue place.

⌇S | Bicorp | 31A3
Junto al Polideportivo. GPS: n39,13278 w0,79056. ⬆

20 ⌇€ 5 ⊢▭Chincluded WC ⌇.
Location: Rural, isolated. Surface: gravel.
Distance: ⌇200m.

⌇S | Cadaqués | 31C1
Parking, Riera de Sant Vicenç. GPS: n42,28964 e3,27260.

⌇€ 20,20/24h WC ⌇. ▭ ▭ Surface: asphalted.
Distance: ⌇100m ⌁1km ⌇1,5km ⊗100m ⌇100m.

Tourist information Cadaqués:
⌖ La Riera. Week market. ☐ Mo 8-14h.

⌇S | Calaf | 31B1
Area Calaf Barcelona, Calle Doctor Fleming, 6.
GPS: n41,72940 e1,52610. ⬆
10 ⌇€ 10 ⊢▭Chincluded ⌁ ⌇free.
Location: Rural, simple. Surface: asphalted. ☐ 01/01-31/12
Distance: ⌇500m ⌇300m.

⌇S | Calaf | 31B1
Calle de Leida-Girona. GPS: n41,73306 e1,52667. ⬆

5 ⌇free ⊢▭Chfree. Location: Comfortable. Surface: asphalted.
Remarks: At petrol station.

⌇S | Calaf | 31B1
Carrer Berlin. GPS: n41,73500 e1,51389. ⬆

4 ⌇free ⊢▭Chfree. Surface: gravel/metalled.

ES

Remarks: Max. 24h, market Saturday.

Callosa d'en Sarrià   31A3

Fonts de l'Algar, Partida Segarra s/n. **GPS:** n38,65430 w0,09289.

40 ⌁ € 14 ⟷ Ch ⚡€4 WC ⌁ €2 ⟋ included.
Location: Comfortable, isolated. 01/01-31/12
Distance: 700m 700m.

Calnegre   30H2

Camperpark Taray, RM-D21, Puntas de Calnegre.
GPS: n37,51520 w1,3985.

50 ⌁ € 6 ⟷ €1/100liter Ch €4.
Location: Simple. **Surface:** sand. 01/01-31/12
Distance: 100m 500m 500m.

Calnegre   30H2

Puntas Calnegre, Ctra. Puntas de Calnegre, nº 42.
GPS: n37,51179 w1,41198.

17 ⌁ € 6,50, 01/06-30/09 € 8 ⟷ Ch ⚡ included.
Surface: metalled. 01/01-31/12
Distance: 600m.

Calpe   31A3

Mediterráneo Camper, Calle Partida Colari 7E.
GPS: n38,65126 e0,06942.

75 ⌁ € 9-12, Jul/Aug € 14 ⟷ Ch ⚡ WC included €3/3 ⟋ €2/
day. **Surface:** gravel. 01/01-31/12
Distance: beach 750m 75m Mercadona 300m.
Remarks: Discount longer stays.

Calpe   31A3

Paraiso Camper Calpe

- 800m to the sandy beach
- Comfortable motorhome stopover
- Reservations possible

www.paraisocamper.com
calpe@paraisocamper.com

Paraiso Camper, Urbanización Los Almendros, 9A.
GPS: n38,64893 e0,06665.
58 ⌁ € 11 (discount longer stays) ⟷ Ch ⚡(58x)€0,20/kWh
WC included €0,20 €3/3 ⟋€2/day
Location: Comfortable, central. **Surface:** gravel. 01/01-31/12
Distance: 1,8km 7km 800m 800m 400m 250m
400m 1km.

Calpe   31A3

Nautica caravanning, Ctra. N233. **GPS:** n38,65578 e0,03660.

20 ⌁ € 10 ⟷ Ch ⚡ €2 ⟋ Location: Simple, central.
Surface: asphalted. 01/01-31/12 Sa-Su
Distance: 500m 400m.
Remarks: Motorhome dealer, arrival during opening hours.

Cambrils   31B1

Camperpark Las Moreras, Carretera N-340, Km. 1.139,1.
GPS: n41,04471 e0,99437.

120 ⌁ € 11,45, Jul € 11,25 + € 6,15/pp, Aug € 11,25 + € 8,60/pp ⟷
Ch ⚡ WC €4/3 ⟋€1/h.
Location: Comfortable, isolated, quiet. 01/01-31/12
Distance: 4km on the spot on the spot on the spot 4km
on the spot on the spot.

Cambrils   31B1

Area de Cambrils, A7. **GPS:** n41,08542 e1,03777.
10 ⌁ free, 20-8h € 15 ⟷ Ch ⚡ included.
Location: Highway. **Surface:** asphalted. 01/01-31/12
Distance: on the spot.
Remarks: Monitored parking.

Tourist information Cambrils:
ℹ️ Oficina de Turismo, Paseo les Palmeres, nº 1, www.turcambrils.info.
Bathing resort in traditional Mediterranean style.

Cañada de Callego   30H2

Loma de St.Antonio, Camino de Perchèles. **GPS:** n37,53542 w1,37226.

⌁ free. **Location:** Simple, isolated. **Surface:** sand.
Remarks: Parking at sea.

Carcaixent   31A3

Hort de Soriano. GPS: n39,07045 w0,40918.

15 ⌁ free ⟷ Ch free.
Location: Comfortable, quiet. **Surface:** sand. Mo, Aug
Distance: 7km on the spot.
Remarks: Max. 48h, picnic and barbecue place. At recreation area,
first drive into Carrer Julián Ribera (39°7'19"N 00°27'04'W) ± 5km, than
follow Hort de Soriano.

Cartagena   31A3

Area Autocaravanas Cartagena. GPS: n37,65373 w1,00345.

30 ⌁ € 10 ⟷ Ch ⚡ WC €4 ⟋ included.
Surface: gravel. 01/01-31/12
Distance: centre 5km, port 8km 400m 400m 400m
on the spot on the spot.
Remarks: Bread-service, sunday market Bohio 500m, Thursday market
Dolores 1km.

Cartagena   31A3

Área Belmonte Plus, Ctra. de Tentegorra, 1.
GPS: n37,61500 w1,00555.

15 ⌁ € 10 ⟷ Ch ⚡ included.
Location: Noisy. **Surface:** asphalted.
Distance: 500m on the spot.

Ceutí   30H2

Ceutí, Pz José Virgili 1. **GPS:** n38,08099 w1,26717.

20 ⌁ free ⟷ Ch ⚡ WC free.
Location: Simple. **Surface:** asphalted. 01/01-31/12
Distance: 300m 4,5km 170m 200m.

ES

🅂 Daimús — 31A3

Area Camper Dunes, Carrer Garbi 2a. **GPS:** n38,96981 w0,14509. ⬆️

65 ⏚€9 ⛽Ch ⚡€3 WC included ⊙€3 🚿€1/3h.
Location: Comfortable. **Surface:** gravel/metalled.
Distance: ⛱350m ⊗50m ⊖100m ⓢon the spot.

🅂 Deltebre — 31B2

Agrobotiga del Delta, Avda. Les Goles de l'Ebre, 2.
GPS: n40,72605 e0,72261. ⬆️➡️

50 ⏚free ⛽Ch free. **Location:** Rural, simple, central.
Surface: concrete. ⬛ 01/01-31/12
Distance: ⛽800m ⛵19km ⛱1,5km ⊗600m ⓢon the spot.

🅂 El Campello 🌿🌊 — 31A3

Camper Área Campello Beach
El Campello

- **Located directly on the beach**
- **Comfortable motorhome stopover**
- **Sanitary facilities**

www.camperareacampellobeach.com
info@camperareacampellobeach.com

Camper Area Campello Beach, Calle Juan de la Cierva.
GPS: n38,39479 w0,40985.
45 ⏚€12, Jul-Aug €14 ⛽Ch ⚡€2/day WC included ⬛€3 ⊙€3/3
🚿€2. 💧 **Location:** Luxurious. **Surface:** gravel/sand.
⬛ 01/01-31/12. **Distance:** ⛽1km ⛵5km ⛱on the spot ⊗500m
ⓢ500m ⊖on the spot.

🅂 El Campello 🌿🌊 — 31A3

Camper Park Alicante, Carrer Llauradors 113.
GPS: n38,42599 w0,40914. ⬆️

35 ⏚€7,50 ⛽€3 Ch ⚡€2,50/day WC ⊙€2 🚿free.
Location: Comfortable. **Surface:** gravel. ⬛ 01/01-31/12
Distance: ⛽500m ⛵5km ⛱1,8km ⊗500m ⓢ1km.

🅂 El Campello 🌿🌊 — 31A3

Bar-Restaurant, N332 km124. **GPS:** n38,45746 w0,36129. ⬆️

5 ⏚€5 ⛽⚡WC 🚿included. **Surface:** sand.
Distance: ⊗on the spot.
Remarks: 3 days free.

🅂 El Catllar 🌿 — 31B1

Area de El Catllar, Cami de la Foni. **GPS:** n41,17658 e1,32685. ⬆️

10 ⏚free ⛽Ch free.
Location: Simple, central, quiet. **Surface:** metalled. ⬛ 01/01-31/12
Distance: ⛽200m ⊗200m 🚲on the spot 🚶on the spot.

🅂 El Masroig — 31B1

Celler El Masroig, Passeig de Arbre 3. **GPS:** n41,12658 e0,73385. ⬆️➡️

10 ⏚free ⛽Ch WC.
Location: Rural, simple. **Surface:** gravel. ⬛ 01/01-31/12
Distance: ⛽on the spot ⊗200m ⓢ200m.
Remarks: Sale of wines.

🅂 El Palomar — 31A3

Font de Sis, Avenida Riuet. **GPS:** n38,85749 w0,5032.

17 ⏚€5 ⛽Ch ⬛€3/day 🚿€2/day.
Location: Isolated. ⬛ 01/01-31/12
Distance: ⛽200m ⊗on the spot ⓢ200m.
Remarks: Picnic and barbecue place.

🅂 Els Muntells — 31B2

Carrer Major. GPS: n40,66852 e0,75903. ⬆️

10 ⏚€6 ⛽Ch included. **Location:** Rural, simple, isolated, quiet.
Surface: asphalted/gravel. ⬛ 01/01-31/12
Distance: ⛽500m ⛱1,2km ⊗400m ⓢ600m 🚲on the spot 🚶on the spot.

🅂 Figueres — 31C1

Parking Supermercado Esclat, Avda. de los Paisos Catalans, N260.
GPS: n42,26042 e2,95096.

---

5 ⏚free. **Surface:** asphalted.
Distance: ⛽on the spot ⊗500m ⓢon the spot ⊖50m.
Remarks: Max. 48h.

Tourist information Figueres:
- 🎪 Rambla. Antiques market. ⬛ 3rd Sa of the month.
- 🎪 Plaza Catalunya en Plaza del Gra. ⬛ Tue-Thu-Sa 9-14h.

🅂 Garrigàs — 31C1

Área del Empordà Norte, A7 km-35. **GPS:** n42,17333 e2,93194. ⬆️
10 ⏚free ⛽WC free. **Surface:** metalled. ⬛ 01/01-31/12

🅂 Garrigàs — 31C1

Área del Empordà Sur, A7 km-35. **GPS:** n42,17456 e2,93074. ⬆️

10 ⏚free ⛽WC free. **Surface:** metalled. ⬛ 01/01-31/12

🅂 Ibi — 31A3

Área Chambit, Calle Pedro Valdivia. **GPS:** n38,62222 w0,56694. ⬆️

25 ⏚free ⛽Ch free.
Location: Simple. **Surface:** sand. ⬛ 01/01-31/12
Distance: ⛵2,3km.

🅂 Jalance — 31A2

N330. GPS: n39,18740 w1,0761. ⬆️

10 ⏚free ⛽Ch free.
Location: Isolated. **Surface:** asphalted. ⬛ 01/01-31/12
Distance: ⛽300m.
Remarks: Parking next to swimming pool, max. 48h.

🅂 Jávea — 31A3

Avda.de Nancy. GPS: n38,77024 e0,18945.

10 ⏚. **Surface:** unpaved.
Distance: ⊗100m ⓢ100m.

L'Alqueria de la Comtessa — 31A3

Camperpark KM Zero, Metge Panella nº 1.
GPS: n38,93878 w0,15276. ➡️.

35 🛏️€ 8 🚰🚽Ch 🔌💧(35x)€3/day,6Amp WC🚽included 🔲€3/3 📶€1/day. **Location:** Comfortable. **Surface:** asphalted.
🔲 01/01-31/12 🔲 01/07-31/08
Distance: 🏪100m 🚲1,5km 🏊4km ⊗200m 🚏200m 🚌150m 🚊300m 🎣500m.
Remarks: Car rental.

L'Olleria — 31A3

Carrer J Bautista Ferrere. **GPS:** n38,91572 w0,55402.

5 🛏️free 🚰🚽Ch. **Location:** Urban. **Surface:** asphalted.
Distance: 🏪300m 🚲2km ⊗250m.
Remarks: Max. 48h.

La Azohia — 31A3

Carretera a La Azohía. **GPS:** n37,56332 w1,17393.

50 🛏️free. **Location:** Simple. **Surface:** unpaved.
Distance: 🏊50m ⊗100m 🚏100m.

La Marina — 31A3

Finca La Escuera, Escuera 300. **GPS:** n38,14360 w0,66939.

11 🛏️€ 14 🚰🚽Ch 🔌€0,26/kWh WC🚽🔲€4 📶.
Surface: sand.
🔲 01/01-31/12
Distance: 🏪300m 🏊3km ⊗300m 🚏300m 🚌300m 🚶on the spot.

La Marina — 31A3

La Marina Elche, Cami del Molar o Pinet. **GPS:** n38,15628 w0,63791.

20 🛏️€ 8 🚰🚽Chincluded 🔌€0,50/kWh,16Amp.
🔲 winter

La Marina — 31A3

Camino del Pinet, La Marina nord. **GPS:** n38,15087 w0,63276.

40 🛏️free. **Surface:** asphalted.

La Romana — 31A3

Camperpark EuroPeCa, Cuevas de San Anton 2.
GPS: n38,35662 w0,90378.

7 🛏️€ 9 🚰🚽Ch 🔌€0,30/kWh WC🚽€1 🔲€4 📶included.
Location: Rural, comfortable, isolated.
Surface: gravel.
🔲 01/01-31/12
Distance: 🏪1,5km ⊗1,5km 🚏1,5km 🚶on the spot.
Remarks: Possibility for reservation: 0034638278693.

La Salzadella — 31A2

Av. Tomas Molins. **GPS:** n40,41611 e0,17305. ⬆️➡️.

6 🛏️free 🚰🚽Chfree. **Location:** Rural, simple, quiet.
Surface: asphalted.
Distance: 🏪250m ⊗250m 🚏250m.
Remarks: Village of cherries: cherry soap, cherry jam.

La Sénia — 31A2

Carrer dels Domenges. **GPS:** n40,63897 e0,28502. ⬆️➡️.

10 🛏️free 🚰€2 🚽Ch.
Location: Rural, simple, quiet. **Surface:** gravel. 🔲 01/01-31/12
Distance: 🏪800m ⊗200m 🚏200m.

La Seu d'Urgell — 31B1

Portal de cerdanya. **GPS:** n42,35888 e1,46447.
8 🛏️.

Lavern — 31B1

Cava Quilera, Masia Ca l'Artigas. **GPS:** n41,39848 e1,77038. ⬆️.
4 🛏️free. 🔲 01/01-31/12
Distance: ⊗1,5km.
Remarks: At wine-grower.

Lleida — 31B1

AP-2 Zaragoze > Barcelona km 143. **GPS:** n41,54111 e0,63917.
10 🛏️🚰🚽Ch.
Distance: 🚲on the spot.

Lleida — 31B1

Autocaravanas Miguel, Ctra. N-Ila 456. **GPS:** n41,58945 e0,57591.
🛏️🚰🚽Ch🚽. **Surface:** grassy/gravel. 🔲 01/01-31/12

Distance: 🚲4,5km ⊗750m 🚌on the spot.
Remarks: Camping equipment store.

Lorca — 30H2

Caravanas Lorca, Pl. Saprelorca Buzón 233. **GPS:** n37,61205 w1,75993.
20 🛏️free 🚰€2 🚽€2 Ch 🚽. **Surface:** gravel. 🔲 Su
Distance: 🏪7km 🚲300m 🚏20km ⊗50m.
Remarks: At motorhome dealer.

Lorquí — 30H2

Parque de la Constitución. **GPS:** n38,07909 w1,25918.

15 🛏️free 🚰🚽Chfree. **Location:** Simple, central.
Surface: asphalted/metalled. 🔲 Mo 07-15h , market
Distance: 🏪500m 🚲5km ⊗300m.

L'Alfàs del Pi — 31A3

Camper Park Costa Blanca, Cami des Alguers, 79.
GPS: n38,58389 w0,08139. ⬆️➡️.

38 🛏️€ 13 🚰🚽Ch 🔌(42x)€2 WC🚽€0,25 🔲€3/3 📶included.
Location: Rural, comfortable, quiet. **Surface:** metalled.
🔲 01/01-31/12
Distance: 🏪L'Alfàs del Pi 2km 🚲5km 🏖️sandy beach 2,5km 🚌2km ⊗500m 🚏1km 🚊Tram 600m.
Remarks: Bread-service, discount longer stays.

L'Alfàs del Pi — 31A3

Camper Park Orange Grove, Cami d'Alguers 65.
GPS: n38,58526 w0,08405. ⬆️.

42 🛏️€ 12 🚰🚽Ch 🔌€2,5Amp WC🚽🔲€3/3 📶€4/day. 🐕♿
Location: Comfortable, quiet. **Surface:** gravel. 🔲 01/01-31/12

L'Arboç — 31B1

Área del Penedés Norte, AP7 dir Barcelona. **GPS:** n41,28794 e1,59117.
10 🛏️🚰🚽Chfree. **Surface:** metalled. 🔲 01/01-31/12
Distance: ⊗on the spot 🚏on the spot.

L'Arboç — 31B1

Área del Penedés Sur, AP7 dir Taragona. **GPS:** n41,29029 e1,59235.

10 🛏️🚰🚽Chfree. **Surface:** asphalted. 🔲 01/01-31/12
Distance: ⊗on the spot 🚏on the spot.

Mataro — 31B1

Autocaravanas del Sol, Calle de Torrent de Madá, El Cros.
GPS: n41,53564 e2,41790. ⬆️.

4 🏕€ 10 ⊞⚡Ch ⚓ WC 📶included. ☐ 01/01-31/12
Distance: 🚉300m ⊳ Barcelona 100m.
Remarks: At motorhome dealer, max. 7 nights.

Montblanc — 31B1
Restaurant Masia Poblet, C14, La Guardia dels Prats.
GPS: n41,41464 e1,17479.⬆.

10 🏕€ 10, guests free ⊞⚡Ch included ⚓€3,10Amp.
Location: Rural, comfortable, isolated, quiet.
Surface: grassy/metalled. ☐ 01/01-31/12
Distance: 🚉5km ⊗on the spot ⚓5km.

Montblanc — 31B1
Área de Autocaravanas Sam, Avda. Lluis Companys.
GPS: n41,36933 e1,17180.⬆.

10 🏕€ 10 ⊞⚡Ch ⚓ WC 📶included.
Location: Simple. **Surface:** asphalted. ☐ 01/01-31/12
Distance: 🚉800m ⚡350m 🚉800m ⚓400m.
Remarks: At motorhome dealer.

Montseny — 31B1
Área de Montseny, AP7-Nord km-117 > Francia.
GPS: n41,64700 e2,42586.⬆.

20 🏕free ⊞⚡free. **Surface:** metalled. ☐ 01/01-31/12
Distance: ⊗on the spot ⚓on the spot.

Montseny — 31B1
Área de Montseny, AP7-Sur>Barcelona. **GPS:** n41,65000 e2,44222.⬆.

20 🏕free ⊞⚡free. **Surface:** metalled. ☐ 01/01-31/12
Distance: ⊗on the spot ⚓on the spot.

Morella ⚜ 🛁 — 31A2
N232. **GPS:** n40,62398 w0,09141. ⬆➡.

30 🏕free ⊞⚡Chfree. **Location:** Rural, simple, isolated, quiet.
Surface: grassy/metalled. ☐ 01/01-31/12
Distance: 🚉1,5km ⚡1,5km ⚓1,5km 🚶on the spot.
Remarks: Max. 72h.

Mula — 30H2
Camino de las Curtis. **GPS:** n38,03972 w1,48139.⬆.

5 🏕free ⊞⚡Chfree.
Location: Simple. **Surface:** asphalted. ☐ 01/01-31/12
Distance: 🚉500m ⚓500m.

Murcia — 31A3
Camperpark Casablanca, F16. **GPS:** n38,00189 w1,01939.⬆.

120 🏕€ 12 ⊞⚡Ch ⚓ WC 📺 📥€3/3 📶included. 🚲
Location: Comfortable, central. **Surface:** gravel.
☐ 01/01-31/12
Distance: 🚉Murcia 11km ⚡500m ⚓15km ⊗500m 🚌on the spot
🚲on the spot 🚶on the spot.
Remarks: 24/24 surveillance.

Murcia — 31A3
Camperpark Huerta de Murcia, Carril los Cánovas, Rincón de Almodóvar, Los Ramos. **GPS:** n38,00520 w1,04229.

45 🏕€ 12 ⊞⚡Ch ⚓ WC 📺 📥€3/3 📶included. 🚲
Location: Comfortable. **Surface:** gravel. ☐ 01/01-31/12
Distance: 🚉Alquerías 1,7km ⊗500m ⚓500m 🚌on the spot.
Remarks: Bread-service.

Navarcles — 31B1
Calle de la Font de la Cura. **GPS:** n41,75661 e1,90833.⬆.

5 🏕free ⊞⚡Ch ⚓ free. **Location:** Isolated, quiet. **Surface:** gravel.
Distance: 🚉500m 🚶on the spot.

Navata — 31C1
Restaurante Can Janot, Ctra. de Olot nº 2.
GPS: n42,22600 e2,86325.⬆.

20 🏕€ 4 ⚡€2 📶. **Location:** Quiet. **Surface:** grassy.
Distance: ⊗on the spot ⚓100m.
Remarks: Guests free.

Oliva — 31A3
Area Camper Kikopark, C/ Assagador de Carro.
GPS: n38,93282 w0,09742.⬆.

15 🏕€ 18-26,50 ⊞⚡Ch ⚓ WCincluded. ☐ 01/01-31/12
Distance: ⚓on the spot ⊗on the spot.
Remarks: Stop & Go arrival >15h, departure <15h.

Palamós — 31C1

EmpordArea, C/ Pui Gorgoll s/n - C/ Pla del Llop s/n.
GPS: n41,85740 e3,11467.
40 🏕€ 12, 17/07-28/08 € 17 ⊞⚡Ch ⚓8Amp WC 📥€1 📥€4
📶included. **Surface:** grassy/gravel. ☐ 01/01-31/12
Distance: 🚉1km ⚡1,3km ⚓1km ⊷1km ⊗700m ⚓350m
🚌500m 🚲1,2km 🚶1,2km.

Peñíscola — 31A2
Camper Park Los Pinos, C/ Abellers, 2.
GPS: n40,37912 e0,38827.⬆➡.

30 🏕15/09-15/06 € 10, 16/06-14/09 tariff camp site ⊞⚡Ch
⚓,10Amp WC 📥€4,50/4,50 📶included. **Location:** Rural, luxurious,
quiet. **Surface:** gravel/metalled. ☐ 01/01-31/12
Distance: 🚉1,5km ⚓2km 🚉1,5km ⚓800m.

Peñíscola — 31A2
Area camper Vizmar, Cami de la Volta.
GPS: n40,39357 e0,40778.⬆➡.

ES

25 ⛺ € 7 🚰 ⬛Ch 💧 € 4/day WC ⬛included 🚿€3,95/day.
Location: Rural, comfortable, quiet. **Surface:** gravel.
◻ 01/01-31/12
Distance: 🚶3km ⛱500m ⊗300m 🛒300m 🚌300m.

Peñíscola 31A2
Stop&Go La Volta, Camino de la Volta 20.
GPS: n40,39793 e0,40316. ⬆➡.

70 ⛺ € 7, 01/07-31/08 € 10, 2 pers incl., 1 pers + € 1-2 🚰 ⬛Ch
💧 €3,6Amp WC ⬛ ◻€4/4 🚿included. **Location:** Rural, comfortable,
isolated, quiet. **Surface:** grassy/gravel. ◻ 01/01-31/12
Distance: 🚶4km, Peñíscola 5km ⛱1km ⊗2km 🛒4km 🚌1km.

Platja d'Aro 31C1
Calle Roma. **GPS:** n41,81028 e3,05767. ⬆.

30 ⛺ € 8 🚰 ⬛Chincluded.
Location: Comfortable, quiet. **Surface:** asphalted.
Distance: ⛱750m.
Remarks: Max. 2 days.

Quart 31C1
Avinguda de la Bóbila. **GPS:** n41,93944 e2,83917. ⬆.

4 ⛺free 🚰 ⬛Chfree. **Surface:** metalled. ◻ 01/01-31/12
Distance: 🚶on the spot 💧6,5km ⊗on the spot 🛒on the spot.
Remarks: Max. 48h, max. 8M.

Ramonete 30H2
Wo-Mo Puerto Villa Brisa, Los Curas, D21, Puntas de Calnegre.
GPS: n37,52589 w1,4336. ⬆➡.

50 ⛺ € 7 🚰€0,10/10liter ⬛Ch 💧€0,50 ◻€2 ◻€4/4 🚿. ⬛
Location: Simple, isolated. **Surface:** gravel. ◻ 19/09-30/05
Distance: 🚶5km ⛱5km ⊗5km 🚌5km.
Remarks: Bread-service.

Rialp 31B1
Paseig del Pallars. **GPS:** n42,43925 e1,13384.
5 ⛺free 🚰 ⬛Ch 💧. **Surface:** gravel.
Distance: 🚶200m ⊗200m 🛒200m 🚌100m.
Remarks: Next to football ground.

Ripoll 31B1
Raval de Barcelona. **GPS:** n42,20008 e2,18695. ⬆.

5 ⛺free. **Surface:** asphalted.
Distance: 🚶300m ⊗500m 🚌500m.
Remarks: Max. 24h, no camping activities.

Tourist information Ripoll:
⛪ Centrum. Week market. ◻ Sa-morning.

San Feliu de Guixols 31C1
Parking Narcis Massanas, Ronda Narcis Massanas.
GPS: n41,78020 e3,02303. ⬆.

15 ⛺free 🚰 ⬛Chfree.
Location: Simple, quiet. **Surface:** unpaved.

San Fulgencio 31A3
Camper Park San Fulgencio, Mar Cartabrico 7, Centro Comercial las
Dunas. **GPS:** n38,12080 w0,66005. ⬆.

40 ⛺first day € 14, then € 12 🚰 ⬛Ch 💧WC ⬛ ◻€3 🚿included.
Location: Comfortable. **Surface:** gravel.
◻ 01/01-31/12
Distance: ⛱1,5km ⊗200m 🛒150m 🚌150m.

San Fulgencio 31A3
Oasis, Caminal del Convenio. **GPS:** n38,11972 w0,66194. ⬆.

14 ⛺ € 10, 15/06-15/09 € 14 🚰 ⬛Ch 💧€0,40/kWh,16Amp WC ⬛
◻€3/2 🚿included.
Location: Comfortable. **Surface:** gravel. ◻ 01/01-31/12
Distance: 🚶San Fulgencio 7km ⛱beach 1,5km ⊗200m 🛒200m
🚌300m.

San Raphael del Río 31A2
Restaurante Spätzle-Fritz, Planes del Reine, San Jorge, CV-11.
GPS: n40,57507 e0,39333. ⬆.

50 ⛺ € 8, guests free 🚰€2 ⬛€2 Ch 💧€4 WC ⬛€2 🚿.
Location: Rural, comfortable, isolated, quiet. **Surface:** gravel.
◻ 01/01-31/12
Distance: 🚶3,5km 💧7km ⛱9km ⊗on the spot.

Sant Hilari Sacalm 31B1
Carretera de la Font Picant. **GPS:** n41,88417 e2,50778. ⬆.

10 ⛺free 🚰 ⬛Chfree 💧.
Location: Rural. **Surface:** gravel/sand. ◻ 01/01-31/12
Distance: 🚶200m ⊗200m 🛒200m.
Remarks: Max. 48h.

Santa Coloma de Cervelló 31B1
Santa Coloma de Cervelló, Can Julià, s/n.
GPS: n41,36495 e2,02512. ⬆➡.

6 ⛺free 🚰 ⬛Chfree. **Location:** Simple, isolated, quiet.
Surface: asphalted. ◻ 01/01-31/12
Distance: 🚶500m 💧5km ⊗400m 🚌500m.

Santa Cristina d'Aro 31C1
Costa Brava Park, Carretera Platje d'Aro. **GPS:** n41,81306 e3,01119. ⬆.

46 ⛺ € 15 🚰€3 ⬛Ch 💧included 🚿€6. **Surface:** metalled/sand.
Distance: ⛱6km ⊗100m.

Segorbe 31A2
Area de Segorbe, Escalera de la Estación.
GPS: n39,84805 w0,48166. ⬆➡.

12 ⛺free 🚰 ⬛Chfree. **Location:** Simple, central, quiet.
Surface: asphalted/metalled. ◻ 01/01-31/12
Distance: 🚶1km 💧2km ⊗800m 🛒800m 🚌on the spot.
Remarks: Max. 48h.

Simat de la Valldigna 31A3
Carrer dels Brolls. **GPS:** n39,04120 w0,308. ⬆.

ES

20 🅼free 🚰🗑Chfree. **Surface:** sand. 🅿 01/01-31/12
Distance: 🚶500m ⊗450m 🛒500m.

🅂 **Sitges** 31B1
Avda. del Cami Pla. **GPS:** n41,25083 e1,81838.⬆

10 🅼€ 5 1/11-31/3, € 8 1/4-31/10 🚰🗑Ch 🗑.
Location: Simple. **Surface:** asphalted. 🅿 01/01-31/12
Distance: 🚶800m ⌅2,5km 🛒50m.
Remarks: Industrial area, max. 7 days, Barcelona 40km.

🅂 **Sta.Pola** 31A3
Europa-Area, Carrer dels Electricistas. **GPS:** n38,20805 w0,57416.⬆➡

33 🅼€ 9 🚰🗑Ch 🗑€3 WC🗑⊡€4 📶.🚿
Location: Comfortable. **Surface:** gravel/metalled. 🅿 01/01-31/12
Distance: 🚶1,7km ⌅1,8km ⊗1,7km.

🅂 **Tortosa** 31A2
Área de Tortosa, Cami de la Toia. **GPS:** n40,80277 e0,51388.⬆➡

30 🅼free 🚰🗑Chfree. **Location:** Simple, central, quiet.
Surface: asphalted. 🅿 01/01-31/12
Distance: 🚶1,1km ⌅10km ⊗900m 🛒1km.

🅂 **Totana** 30H2
Camperstop Sierra Espuña, Morti s/n Camino del Polideportivo.
GPS: n37,79380 w1,51139.⬆

25 🅼€ 7 🚰🗑Chincluded 🗑€3/day WC🗑€1 ⊡€3 📶free.
Location: Comfortable. **Surface:** gravel.
Distance: 🚶2,5km ⌅5km ⊗450m.

🅂 **Tremp** 31B1
Passeig de Conca de Tremp. **GPS:** n42,16312 e0,89043.⬆

10 🅼free 🚰🗑free 🗑€1/2h. **Surface:** asphalted.
Remarks: Max. 48h.

🅂 **Turis** 31A2
Carretera de Silla Tunis. **GPS:** n39,38944 w0,69777.⬆

10 🅼free 🚰🗑Chfree.
Location: Simple. **Surface:** unpaved. 🅿 01/01-31/12
Distance: 🚶500m.

🅂 **Valencia** 🌿🚿⛲🍦🛍 31A2

Valencia Camper Park
Valencia

Excellent location for city visit
Wifi included
Open all year

www.valenciacamperpark.com
valcampark@gmail.com

Valencia Camper Park, Calle Universo, Bétera.
GPS: n39,57958 w0,44494.⬆
78 🅼€ 12 🚰€0,50/40liter 🗑Ch 🗑(52x)€3/24h,4Amp,6Amp€5
WC🗑⊡€3 📶included 🗑.🚿🗑
Location: Urban, luxurious. **Surface:** gravel. 🅿 01/01-31/12
Distance: 🚶Valencia 12km ⌅1,5km 🚂train 300m.
Remarks: Swimming pool (summer).

🅂 **Valencia** 🌿🚿⛲🍦🛍 31A2
Area Camping-car La Marina, Carrer del Rio 556B, El Saler.
GPS: n39,38666 w0,3321.⬆

70 🅼€ 11 🚰🗑ChWC🗑 📶. **Surface:** gravel.
Distance: 🚶Valencia 6km ⌅beach 150m ⊗600m 🛒500m
🚂on the spot 🚲on the spot 🚶on the spot.
Remarks: Discount longer stays.

🅂 **Valencia** 🌿🚿⛲🍦🛍 31A2
Parking Valencia, Avda. Peris y Valero, 27.
GPS: n39,45627 w0,37806.⬆

8-10 🅼€ 25 🚰🗑Ch 🗑WCincluded.
Location: Urban, central, noisy. **Surface:** asphalted/gravel.
Distance: 🚶city centre 1,7km ⌅2,5km 🚂200m.
Remarks: Monitored parking.

🅂 **Vallirana** 31B1
Carrer Major, N340. **GPS:** n41,38239 e1,92719.⬆➡

6 🅼. **Location:** Simple, noisy. **Surface:** asphalted.
🅿 01/01-31/12
Distance: 🚶800m ⊗300m 🛒800m.

🅂 **Vic** 31B1
Carrer de la Fura. **GPS:** n41,93444 e2,24000.⬆➡

10 🅼€ 5 🚰€2/100liter 🗑Ch 🗑€6/3h. **Surface:** grassy.
Distance: 🚶1,8km ⊗400m.
Remarks: Max. 48h.

🅂 **Viladrau** 🏔 31B1
Carrer Montseny s/n. **GPS:** n41,84544 e2,38732.⬆

16 🅼free 🚰🗑Ch📶free.
Location: Rural. **Surface:** gravel/sand. 🅿 01/01-31/12
Distance: 🚶500m ⊗500m 🛒500m.
Remarks: Max. 48h, nature reserve.

🅂 **Vilafranca del Penedès** 31B1
Vilafranca del Penedès, Avda. Tarragona, N-340a.
GPS: n41,34001 e1,69147.⬆➡

10 🅼free 🚰🗑Ch. **Location:** Rural, simple, central, quiet.
Surface: gravel/sand. 🅿 01/01-31/12
Distance: 🚶500m ⌅1,2km ⊗900m 🛒850m Lidl 🚲on the spot
🚶on the spot.

ES

Yecla 31A3

Finca Caravana, Paraje Fuente del Pinar A-14.
GPS: n38,71443 w1,11948.

10 🛏€ 8 🚰🗑Ch included. **Location:** Rural, simple, isolated.
Surface: gravel/sand. ⬤ 05/06-30/06

Spanish interior

Aguilar de Campoo 28F2

N611, Ctra Palencia-Aguillar de Campoo.
GPS: n42,78631 w4,25757. ⬆➡.

10 🛏free 🚰🗑Ch free.
Location: Urban, simple. **Surface:** asphalted. ⬛ 01/01-31/12
Distance: 🛒1km 🚲 3,1km ⊗1km 🍽1km.
Remarks: Max. 48h.

Aldeadávila de la Ribera 29D1

GPS: n41,22028 w6,61333. ⬆.

5 🛏free 🚰🗑Ch free. **Surface:** asphalted. ⬛ 01/01-31/12
Distance: ⊗on the spot 🍽200m.
Remarks: Max. 48h.

Almazán 29H1

Camino Viejo del Cubo de la Solana. **GPS**: n41,49259 w2,53385.
🗑.
Remarks: Parking at swimming pool.

Ampudia 28F3

Area de San Martín, Glorieta. S. Martín.
GPS: n41,91130 w4,78082. ⬆➡.

6 🛏free 🚰🗑Ch free.
Location: Rural, simple. **Surface:** gravel/metalled. ⬛ 01/01-31/12
Distance: 🛒400m.
Remarks: No camping activities.

Astorga 29E2

Parking plaza de Toros. **GPS**: n42,45138 w6,06593. ⬆➡.

15 🛏free 🚰🗑Ch free. **Surface:** metalled.
Distance: 🛒500m 🚲 1,4km ⊗500m 🍽500m.
Remarks: Max. 48h.

Astudillo 28F3

Area de la Joya, Urbanizacion de don Bosco. **GPS**: n42,18944 w4,3. ⬆.

10 🛏free 🚰🗑Ch free.
Location: Rural, simple. **Surface:** gravel.
Distance: 🛒1km 🍽300m.
Remarks: No camping activities.

Avila 29F1

Parking del Palacio de Congresos, Calle Molino dell Carril.
GPS: n40,66111 w4,70472.

10 🛏free.
Surface: asphalted.
Distance: 🚲2,2km.

Tourist information Avila:
ℹ Small medieval town
surround by ramparts.
⛪ The San Vicenta basilica
is a Roman building.

Baltanàs 28F3

Area de la Ermita de Revilla, Plaza Arrañales de Revilla.
GPS: n41,93472 w4,2475. ⬆➡.

5 🛏free 🚰🗑Ch free.
Location: Rural, simple. **Surface:** concrete. ⬛ 01/01-31/12
Remarks: No camping activities.

Bretocino 28E3

Area para Autocaravanes, Cuesta de los Nogales.
GPS: n41,88654 w5,75517. ⬆.

---

5 🛏€ 7 🚰🗑Ch 🔌 included WC🔲. 🚿 **Location:** Rural,
comfortable, quiet. **Surface:** concrete. ⬛ 01/01-31/12
Distance: 🛒300m 🍽300m.
Remarks: Service passerby € 3, swimming pool.

Burgo de Osma 29G1

Calle de Santos Iruela. **GPS**: n41,58662 w3,07338. ⬆.

10 🛏free 🚰
Location: Rural, simple. **Surface:** metalled. ⬛ 01/01-31/12
Distance: 🛒500m ⊗200m 🍽500m.

Burgos 28G3

N120, Calle de Cartuja de Miraflores. **GPS**: n42,34037 w3,69361.

5 🛏€ 0,60/h, max. € 2,60, 20-10h free. **Surface:** asphalted.
Distance: 🚲2,6km.
Remarks: Parking beside river.

Tourist information Burgos:
ℹ City, 8th century, with a lot of curiosities such as the cathedral, the
castle and Monasterio de las Huelgas.

Cabrerizos 29E1

Don Quijote, Ctra. Aldealengua km 4. **GPS**: n40,97500 w5,60306.
🛏€ 22 🚰🗑Ch. ⬛ 01/03-31/10
Remarks: Formula Camper.

Cáceres 29D2

Avda. Lope de Vega. **GPS**: n39,48041 w6,36649. ⬆➡.

15 🛏free 🚰🗑Ch 🔲 free. **Surface:** asphalted.
Distance: 🛒600m 🚲 6,7km.
Remarks: Monitored parking.

Tourist information Cáceres:
ℹ Oficina de Turismo, Plaza Mayor, nº 3, www.inedito.com/caceres/.
City with historical centre.
🎭 PeroPalo. Traditional celebration. ⬛ 21/02-24/02.

Carrión de los Condes 28F3

C/ Las Huertas. **GPS**: n42,33875 w4,60808. ⬆➡.

10 🛏free 🚰🗑Ch free.
Location: Rural, simple. **Surface:** metalled.
Distance: 🛒200m ⊗200m 🍽200m.
Remarks: Max. 48h.

Cervera de Pisuerga 28F2

C/ El Maderao. **GPS**: n42,87139 w4,49972. ⬆.

ES

10 ⏱free ⚡ ⛽Chfree.
Location: Rural, simple, isolated. **Surface:** sand.
Distance: 🚉500m ⊗500m 🏪500m.
Remarks: Along river, max. 48h.

| 🅿 | **Coca** ⛲ | **29F1** |

GPS: n41,21348 w4,52733. ⬆.

5 ⏱free.
Location: Urban, simple. **Surface:** metalled. ⬛ 01/01-31/12
Remarks: Parking castle.

| 🅿 | **Consuegra** | **29G3** |

GPS: n39,45339 w3,6106.
⏱free. **Surface:** sand.
Remarks: Isolated parking at foot of hill with windmills.

| 🚐 S | **Cuellar** ⛲ | **29F1** |

Área El Castillo, Calle del Alamillo, 40. **GPS:** n41,40083 w4,32028. ⬆.

6 ⏱free ⚡ ⛽free.
Location: Rural, simple. **Surface:** metalled.
Distance: 🚲2km.
Remarks: At castle.

| 🚐 S | **Don Benito** | **29D3** |

Avda. de los Deportes. **GPS:** n38,96250 w5,86305. ⬆➡.
3 ⏱free ⚡ ⛽Chfree. **Surface:** metalled. ⬛ 01/01-31/12
Distance: ⊗on the spot 🏪on the spot 🚌on the spot.

| 🚐 S | **Espinosa de los Monteros** | **28G2** |

Parking Las Cocinas, BU-570 > Bárcenas. **GPS:** n43,08556 w3,5575. ⬆.

10 ⏱free ⚡ ⛽Chfree.
Location: Simple, isolated. **Surface:** asphalted. ⬛ 01/01-31/12
Distance: 🚉1km ⊗1km 🏪1km 🚶on the spot.
Remarks: Max. 48h, tuesday market.

| 🚐 S | **Foncastín** | **28F3** |

Estación de Servicios La Loba, A6, salida 175.
GPS: n41,44131 w4,97957. ⬆.

5 ⏱free ⚡ ⛽Chfree.
Location: Rural, simple. **Surface:** asphalted. ⬛ 01/01-31/12
Distance: 🚲250m ⊗on the spot.

| 🚐 S | **Frómista** 🌿 | **28F3** |

Paseo de Julio Senador, P-980. **GPS:** n42,26494 w4,41198. ⬆➡.

6 ⏱free ⚡ ⛽Chfree.
Location: Urban, simple. **Surface:** metalled. ⬛ 01/01-31/12
Distance: 🚉600m 🚲200m ⊗500m 🏪500m.
Remarks: At sports park, max. 48h, weigh bridge nearby € 0,50.

| 🚐 S | **La Alberca** | **29D1** |

Casa del Parque. **GPS:** n40,48833 w6,11583. ⬆.
10 ⏱free ⚡ ⛽Chfree. **Surface:** metalled.
Distance: 🚉300m.
Remarks: Max. 48h.

| 🚐 S | **La Joyosa** | **31A1** |

Área de Marlofa, Calle Sobradiel. **GPS:** n41,73744 w1,06664. ⬆➡.
21 ⏱free ⚡ ⛽Ch 🔧€3 WC🚽. **Surface:** asphalted/grassy.
Distance: 🚲9km.

| 🚐 S | **Lagartera** | **29E2** |

Camino de la Estacion. **GPS:** n39,91151 w5,19978. ⬆.

3 ⏱free ⚡ ⛽free. **Surface:** asphalted. ⬛ 01/01-31/12
Distance: 🚉on the spot 🚲1,4km 🏪100m.
Remarks: Max. 48h.

| 🚐 S | **León** | **28E2** |

Avda. De los Peregrinos, 5. **GPS:** n42,60471 w5,58525. ⬆.

10 ⏱free ⚡ ⛽Chfree. **Surface:** metalled.
Distance: ⊗300m.
Remarks: Max. 48h.

| 🚐 S | **Logrosán** | **29E3** |

El Palomar, Calle Palomar. **GPS:** n39,33188 w5,48044. ⬆➡.
10 ⏱free ⚡ ⛽free. ⬛ 01/01-31/12
Remarks: Max. 48h.

| 🚐 S | **Olmedo** | **29F1** |

Parque del Mudejar, N601, km 148,1. **GPS:** n41,29167 w4,68194. ⬆.

9 ⏱free ⚡ ⛽Chfree.
Location: Rural, simple. **Surface:** metalled. ⬛ 01/01-31/12
Distance: ⊗100m 🏪200m.

| 🚐 S | **Osorno** | **28F2** |

Los Chopos, N611 Osorno > Herrera de Pisuerga.
GPS: n42,41694 w4,35111. ⬆.

30 ⏱free ⚡ ⛽Chfree. **Surface:** asphalted.
Distance: 🚉700m 🚲2,2km ⊗on the spot.
Remarks: Max. 48h, monitored parking.

| S | **Palazuelos de Eresma** | **29F1** |

Calle Cordel. **GPS:** n40,92848 w4,05529. ⬆➡.

⚡€1 ⛽Chfree. ⬛ 01/01-31/12
Distance: 🚲4km.

| 🚐 S | **Palencia** | **28F3** |

Parque Isla Dos Aguas, Avda. Ponce de León, 12.
GPS: n42,00389 w4,53333. ⬆➡.

23 ⏱free ⚡ ⛽Chfree. **Surface:** asphalted.
Distance: 🚉on the spot 🚲4km ⊗on the spot 🏪El Arbol 50m
🚗100m.
Remarks: Max. 48h.

| 🅿 | **Peñafiel** | **28F3** |

Calle de Los Destiladeros. **GPS:** n41,59440 w4,11582. ⬆.

5 ⏱free.
Location: Rural, simple. **Surface:** asphalted. ⬛ 01/01-31/12
Distance: ⊗150m.
Remarks: Parking castle.

| 🚐 S | **Peñaflor** | **31A1** |

Parking Surrecreo, Urbanizacion Los Rosales Peñaflor.
GPS: n41,72777 w0,79194. ⬆➡.

150 🛏 € 15 🚰 Ch 🔧 WC included.
Distance: 🚶8 km.

🛏 S Pollos 28E3
Estación de Servicios La Loba 2000, A62, salida 169.
GPS: n41,41004 w5,13396. ⬆.

10 🛏 free 🚰 🔧 Ch free.
Location: Highway, simple. **Surface:** metalled. 🅾 01/01-31/12
Distance: 🚗200m ⊗on the spot 🍷on the spot.
Remarks: At petrol station.

🛏 S Ribaseca 28E2
Carretera la Bañeza. **GPS:** n42,54439 w5,5882.
🛏 15-25 🚰 🔧 Ch 🔧 WC ⃞ 📶 included. **Surface:** asphalted.
🅾 01/01-31/12
Distance: 🚶8km ⊗2,3km 🚌800m.
Remarks: At motorhome dealer, car rental, motorhome washing place.

🛏 S Salamanca 29E1
Parking Turismus, Avenida del Padre Ignacio Ellacuria.
GPS: n40,95758 w5,67646. ⬆.

15 🛏 free. **Location:** Urban. **Surface:** asphalted.
Distance: 🚶city centre 1,5km 🍷50m Lidl/Mercadona 🚌on the spot.

🛏 S Saldaña 28F2
Calle de los Sauces. **GPS:** n42,51882 w4,74125. ⬆.

6 🛏 free 🚰 🔧 Ch.
Location: Rural, simple. **Surface:** concrete. 🅾 01/01-31/12
Distance: 🚶1km ⊗1 km.
Remarks: Next to sports fields, max. 48h.

🍴 S Sancti-Spiritus 29D1
Hostal-Restaurante La Ponderosa, Carretera nacional 620 km303.
GPS: n40,73481 w6,36093.

🛏 customers free 🚰 🔧.
Distance: 🚗3km.
Remarks: Daily menu € 8.

Sepúlveda 🌿 29G1
Calle de el Postiguillo. **GPS:** n41,29897 w3,74479.

ES

10 🛏 free. **Surface:** asphalted.
Distance: 🚶300m 🚗12km ⊗100m.

🖼 Soria 28H3
Monte de las Animas. **GPS:** n41,76769 w2,45391.

🛏 free. **Surface:** gravel.

🛏 S Terradillos 29E1
Area del Encinar, Paseo de Poniente. **GPS:** n40,88000 w5,58194. ⬆.
10 🛏 free 🚰 🔧 Ch free. **Location:** Simple. **Surface:** asphalted.
Distance: ⊗200m.

🛏 S Teruel 31A1
Area en Andorra. GPS: n40,98384 w0,44724.
🛏 free 🚰 €0,20/130liter 🔧 free Ch.
Surface: asphalted. 🅾 01/01-31/12
Distance: 🚶1km 🚗13km ⊗1,2km.
Remarks: Coins at petrol station.

🛏 Toledo 🌿 29F2
Parking de la Estación, Avda. de Castilla la Mancha.
GPS: n39,86472 w4,01944.
50 🛏 free.
Surface: asphalted.
Distance: 🚗1,3km.
Tourist information Toledo:
✝ Catedral.
Cathedral known for its richness.
⌒ El Alcázar. Roman castle ruins, 16th century.

🛏 S Turégano 29F1
CL603. **GPS:** n41,15241 w4,00749. ⬆.

10 🛏 free 🚰 🔧 Ch free.
Location: Rural, simple. **Surface:** asphalted. 🅾 01/01-31/12
Distance: ⊗200m.
Remarks: Behind former grain factory, max. 48h.

🛏 S Valencia de Don Juan 28E2
Area de Coyanza, Calle Tres de Abril. **GPS:** n42,28750 w5,51333. ⬆ ➡.

7 🛏 free 🚰 🔧 Ch free.
Location: Urban, simple. **Surface:** concrete. 🅾 01/01-31/12
Distance: 🚶500m ⊗300m.
Remarks: Max. 48h.

🛏 S Valladolid 🌿 🍽 28F3
San Lorenzo, Avda. Ramon Pradera, 6. **GPS:** n41,65583 w4,73722. ⬆.

10 🛏 € 2,50/24h 🚰 🔧 included.
Location: Urban. **Surface:** asphalted.
Distance: 🚶city centre 1km 🚗3,2km ⊗400m.
Remarks: Max. 48h.

🛏 S Villada 28F3
C/ San Fructuoso, Calle del Ferial Nuevo 10.
GPS: n42,25533 w4,9649. ⬆ ➡.

5 🛏 free 🚰 🔧 Ch free.
Location: Rural, simple, quiet. **Surface:** gravel. 🅾 01/01-31/12
Distance: 🚶200m ⊗200m 🍷200m.
Remarks: Max. 48h, no camping activities.

🛏 Villalpando 28E3
Area de Servicios Villalpando, A6, salida 236.
GPS: n41,85906 w5,41993. ⬆.
5 🛏 free. **Location:** Highway, simple, isolated, noisy.
Surface: asphalted. 🅾 01/01-31/12
Distance: 🚗200m ⊗on the spot 🍷on the spot.
Remarks: At petrol station.

🛏 S Zafra 30D1
Ctra. de los Santos de Maimona, Ex101. **GPS:** n38,42527 w6,41083. ⬆.

30 🛏 free 🚰 🔧 Ch free. **Surface:** asphalted. 🅾 01/01-31/12

🛏 S Zafra 30D1
Ferial Zafra, Ctra. Badajoz-Granada. **GPS:** n38,42558 w6,4116. ⬆ ➡.
30 🛏 free 🚰 🔧 Ch free. **Location:** Urban. **Surface:** asphalted.

🖼 Zamora 🍽 28E3
Estadio Barrio 3 Arboles, Calle de los Pisones.
GPS: n41,50337 w5,75585.

18 🛏 free. **Location:** Urban, simple, central.
Surface: asphalted.
Distance: 🚶1km ⊗1km.
Remarks: Playground.

Andalusia

🖼 S Abla 🌿 30G2
Area de Abla, A-92A. **GPS:** n37,14455 w2,77347. ⬆.
7 🛏 free 🚰 🔧 Ch free. **Surface:** asphalted. 🅾 01/01-31/12
Distance: 🚶on the spot 🚗1,5km ⊗100m.

🛉Ⓢ Abla 🌿   30G2
Area de Montagón, Carretera ALP-503.
GPS: n37,15415 w2,77716. ⬆️➡️.

13 🅿free 🚰🗑Chfree.
Location: Rural, simple, quiet. **Surface:** asphalted. ⬜ 01/01-31/12
Distance: 🚶1,5km 🏖2km ⊗1,5km 🛒1,5km.
Remarks: Next to football ground.

📷 Agua Amarga 🏖   30H3
Calle Ensenada. **GPS:** n36,93883 w1,93657. ⬆️.

20 🅿free.
Location: Rural, simple, quiet. **Surface:** gravel/sand. ⬜ 01/01-31/12
Distance: 🚶on the spot 🏖100m ⊗50m 🛒500m 💧2km.
Remarks: Riverbed.

🛉Ⓢ Alanís 🏔   30D1
Area de Alanís de la Sierra, Alameda del Parral.
GPS: n38,03729 w5,71057. ⬆️.
5 🅿free 🚰🗑Chfree.
Location: Simple. **Surface:** metalled. ⬜ 01/01-31/12
Distance: 🚶on the spot ⊗200m.

🛏Ⓢ Alcalá de Guadaíra   30D2
Autocaravanas Hidalgo, A92 Sevilla><Malaga km 7.
GPS: n37,32856 w5,8056.

18 🅿€ 10 🚰€0,50 Ch🧹included 📶.
Distance: 🏖170m exit 15.
Remarks: Motorhome dealer, max. 2 nights.

🛉Ⓢ Algar   30D3
Complejo Tajo del Aguila. GPS: n36,65111 w5,66555. ⬆️.
🅿€ 20 🚰🗑Ch🧹WC included. ⬜ 01/01-31/12
Distance: 🚶1km ⊗on the spot 🚶on the spot.
Remarks: Max. 7 nights.

📷 Alicún de las Torres   30G2
GR6104. **GPS:** n37,50836 w3,10802.

3 🅿free. **Surface:** metalled. ⬜ 01/01-31/12
Distance: 🚶100m ⊗100m.
Remarks: Next to the spa resort.

🛉Ⓢ Almayate 🏖   30F3
Area AMB, Carretera Nacional 340, km 266,5.
GPS: n36,72372 w4,13999. ⬆️.

40 🅿€ 7, 01/06-30/09 € 10 🚰🗑Ch🧹📶included. 🚿
Location: Rural, simple. **Surface:** gravel.
Distance: 🚶700m 🏖100m ⊗100m 🛒2km 🚌200m.
Remarks: At motorhome dealer.

🍴Ⓢ Almensilla   30D2
San Diego, A-8054. **GPS:** n37,31361 w6,09333.
15 🅿free 🚰🗑Chfree.
Remarks: At petrol station BP and restaurant, restaurant visit appreciated.

⚓Ⓢ Almerimar 🛥🏖   30G3
Area del Puerto Deportivo Almerimar, Torre del puerto.
GPS: n36,69612 w2,79425. ⬆️.

20 🅿€ 12,69 🚰🗑Ch🧹WC included 📶€3,50/24h.
Location: Urban, simple. **Surface:** asphalted. ⬜ 01/01-31/12
Distance: 🏖on the spot ⊗100m 🛒300m 💧100m 🚌100m.
Remarks: Check in at harbourmaster 9-14h, 16-21h.

🛉Ⓢ Antequera 🏛   30E2
Area de Antequera, Calle Miguel de Cervantes.
GPS: n37,02139 w4,57191. ⬆️.

12 🅿free 🚰🗑Chfree.
Location: Urban, simple, noisy. **Surface:** asphalted. ⬜ 01/01-31/12
Distance: 🚶on the spot 🏖6,5km ⊗50m 🛒500m.
Remarks: Next to football ground.

🛉Ⓢ Archidona 🌿   30E2
A7200. **GPS:** n37,09097 w4,38879. ⬆️.

12 🅿free 🗑Chfree.
Location: Rural, simple. **Surface:** concrete. ⬜ 01/01-31/12
Distance: 🚶250m 🏖1km 🛒500m 💧1km 🚶on the spot.

🛉Ⓢ Benarrabá 🏔   30E3
Area Autocaravanas Benarrabá, Carretera Comarcal MA-538.
GPS: n36,54935 w5,27901. ⬆️.
5 🅿free 🚰🗑Chfree. **Surface:** gravel. ⬜ 01/01-31/12
Distance: 🚶500m ⊗600m.

🛉Ⓢ Cabo de Gata   30H3
Cabo de Gata Camper Park, Carrertera de San José.
GPS: n36,81639 w2,14918. ⬆️.

50 🅿€ 7-10 🚰🗑Ch🧹(50x)WC 🗑3,50/3,50 📶included.
Surface: gravel. ⬜ 01/01-31/12
Distance: 🚶5km 🏖7km 🚴7km ⊗on the spot 🛒5km 🚌on the spot 🚶on the spot 🚶on the spot.
Remarks: Service passerby € 3, bicycle rental.

🛉Ⓢ Cabra 🌿   30F2
Area de Cabra II, Calle de la Libertad. **GPS:** n37,47602 w4,44271.

🅿free 🚰🗑Chfree.
Location: Urban. **Surface:** asphalted. ⬜ 01/01-31/12 ◉ Mo 07-13h
Distance: 🚶600m ⊗200m.

🛉Ⓢ Cabra 🌿   30F2
Auditorio Municipal Alcalde Juan Muños, Juanita la Larga.
GPS: n37,46608 w4,42361. ⬆️➡️.

4 🅿free 🚰🗑Chfree.
Location: Urban, simple, quiet. **Surface:** asphalted. ⬜ 01/01-31/12
Distance: 🚶500m 🏖300m 🛒500m.
Remarks: Max. 48h.

📷 Cala de Mijas 🛥🏖   30E3
Av. del Mediterraneo. **GPS:** n36,50496 w4,68344. ⬆️.

50 🅿free.
Location: Urban, simple. **Surface:** sand. ⬜ 01/01-31/12
Distance: 🚶500m 🏖500m 🏖800m ⊗50m 🛒100m 🚌50m.
Remarks: Market Wednesday and Saturday.

🛉Ⓢ Canjáyar 🌿🏔   30G3
Paraje de la Alcoholera, A-348. **GPS:** n37,01400 w2,74523. ⬆️.

7 🅿free 🚰🗑Chfree.
Location: Rural, simple, quiet. **Surface:** asphalted/metalled.
Distance: 🚶1km ⊗450m.
Remarks: At tennis-courts.

ES

Chipiona 30D2

Carretera de la Playa. **GPS:** n36,70442 w6,42915.

8 🅂free. **Surface:** asphalted. ⏱ 01/01-31/12
Distance: 🚿4km ⚓on the spot ⊗on the spot 🍴1,5km.

Conil de la Frontera 30D3

Avda. del Rio. **GPS:** n36,27282 w6,08994.

20 🅂free. **Surface:** asphalted. ⏱ 01/01-31/12
Distance: ⚓on the spot ⊗500m 🍴500m.
Remarks: Parking along coast road.

Córdoba 30E1

Avda. de los Custodios. **GPS:** n37,87528 w4,78778.
30 🅂€ 11. **Surface:** asphalted/gravel. ⏱ 01/01-31/12
Distance: 🚿historical centre 300m ⚓2,3km.
Remarks: In front of police station.

P Córdoba 30E1

Avda. del Campo de la Verdad/Calle del Compositor Rafael Castro.
GPS: n37,87515 w4,76626.
🅂free. **Surface:** asphalted.
⏱ 01/01-31/12
Distance: 🚿1km.

Tourist information Córdoba:
Ⓜ Museo Municipal Taurino, Plaza de las Bulas. Museum about bull-fighting. ⏱ Tue-Sa 8.30-15h, Su 8.30-14.30h ⊙ Mo. Ⓣ € 4.
Ⓜ Torre de la Calahorra. Urban museum. ⏱ 10-14, 16.30-20.30. Ⓣ € 4,50.
✖ Oficina de Turismo, Torrijos, 10 (Palacio de Congresos), www.ayuncordoba.es. Historical and culturally rich city, city of the flamenco and bull-fighting.
✖ Palacio del Marqués de Viana. Palace with collections of leather, silverware, porcelain etc. ⏱ Mo-Sa 10-19h, Su 10-15h. Ⓣ € 8.
✝ Mezquita. World-famous Moorish mosque. ⏱ 10-19h.

Cuevas de San Marcos 30F2

GPS: n37,26059 w4,40237.

15 🅂free. ⛽🍴free.
Location: Rural, simple, isolated. **Surface:** asphalted.
Distance: 🚿1km ⊗500m 🍴1km.
Remarks: Parking at swimming pool.

Cullar 30G2

Venta de Peral2, A-92. **GPS:** n37,55336 w2,6144.

20 🅂free WC🍴free. **Surface:** asphalted. ⏱ 01/01-31/12
Distance: 🚿3km ⊗10m 🍴10m.

Dólar 30G2

Area de Venta de Dólar, A92. **GPS:** n37,19521 w2,98397.

30 🅂free ⛽🍴Chfree.
Location: Highway, simple. **Surface:** metalled. ⏱ 01/01-31/12
Distance: 🚿2km ⊗50m ⊗on the spot.
Remarks: At petrol station.

Doña Mencía 30F2

Area de Esparcimiento Dona Mencia. **GPS:** n37,54656 w4,35237.

7 🅂free ⛽free.
Location: Rural, comfortable, quiet. **Surface:** gravel. ⏱ 01/01-31/12
Distance: 🚿500m ⊗La Cantina ☕on the spot.

El Bosque 30D3

Calle de Juan Ramón Jiménez. **GPS:** n36,75670 w5,51056.

5 🅂free ⛽🍴Chfree. **Surface:** metalled. ⏱ 01/01-31/12
Distance: 🚿on the spot ⊗100m 🍴300m.

El Puerto de Santa Maria 30D3

Parking Pasarela, Av. de Europa. **GPS:** n36,59840 w6,2212.

50 🅂€ 6.
Location: Urban, simple. **Surface:** asphalted. ⏱ 01/01-31/12
Distance: 🚿500m ⊗200m Burgerking 🍴300m 🚌200m.

Gelves 30D2

Puerto Gelves, Calle de Puerto Gelves. **GPS:** n37,33934 w6,02405.

20 🅂€ 12 ⛽🍴Ch ✂€2,80 WC🔲 📶 ⚡
Surface: asphalted. ⏱ 01/01-31/12
Distance: 🚿on the spot ⚓4,3km ⊗on the spot 🍴on the spot 🚌on the spot.
Remarks: Sevilla 10km, good bus connection.

Granada 30F2

Área de Geysepark-Cármenes, Torre de Comares.
GPS: n37,15136 w3,59533.

100 🅂€ 16/day 🚿🍴Chservice:€5 ⚡€2/48h. 🚲
Location: Urban, simple. **Surface:** asphalted.
⏱ 01/01-31/12
Distance: 🚿200m ⚓2km ⊗200m 🍴200m 🚌200m.
Remarks: Covered parking, entrance motorhomes 2nd ramp, max. ^3.10m, advice: pre-order entrance tickets Alhambra.

P Granada 30F2

Alhambra, P5. **GPS:** n37,17168 w3,57974.

50 🅂€ 53/24h, 01/10-01/05 € 29/24h.
Location: Rural, simple. **Surface:** gravel.
⏱ 01/01-31/12
Distance: 🚿1,5km ⊗200m 🍴200m 🚌100m.

Tourist information Granada:
👁 Alhambra. Most important curiosity of the city, the best kept Arab palace. ⏱ 9-20h, winter, Sa 20-22h, Su 9-18h, summer Tue,Thu, Sa 22-24h.
👁 Cuevas del Sacromonte. Caves in Sacromonte mountain, gypsies previously lived here. Now important tourist attraction and stage of flamenco shows.
👁 El Albaicín. Moorish district facing the Alhambra.

Grazalema 30E3

Calle Juan de la Rosa. **GPS:** n36,75807 w5,36365.

4 🅂free. **Surface:** asphalted. ⏱ 01/01-31/12
Distance: 🚿300m ⊗200m 🍴500m.

Huelva 30C2

Monumento a Colón, Avenida Francesco Montenegro.
GPS: n37,21333 w6,93972.

15 🅂free. **Surface:** asphalted. ⏱ 01/01-31/12
Distance: 🚿6km ⚓50m ⊗on the spot 🍴6km 🚌500m.

Huércal-Overa 30H2

Travesía de la Alameda. **GPS:** n37,39823 w1,94672.

10 � free ⌐ €0,50/100liter ⌐Ch. **Location:** Urban, simple.
Surface: metalled. ☐ 01/01-31/12 ☐ Mo 09-14h , market
Distance: ⌐200m ⊗200m ⌐200m on the spot ⌐on the spot.
Remarks: Max. 72h, coins at El Pabellon Municipal.

La Isleta 30H3
Playa del Pénom blanca, Carreta Noria. **GPS:** n36,81670 w2,05146.⬆.

15 ⌐free. **Location:** Rural, simple. **Surface:** gravel.
Distance: ⌐100m ⌐sandy beach 20m ⊗150m ⌐300m.
Remarks: Parking at sea.

La Línea de Concepción 30D3
Av. Principe de Asturias. **GPS:** n36,15583 w5,34553.

50 ⌐€ 1/h, € 15/24h. **Surface:** metalled. ☐ 01/01-31/12
Distance: ⌐500m ⌐1km ⊗200m ⌐1km.
Remarks: Market Wednesday.

La Línea de Concepción 30D3
Area de Alcaidesa Marina, Av. Principe de Asturias.
GPS: n36,15528 w5,35389.
60 ⌐€ 12 ⌐Chincluded. **Surface:** metalled.
Distance: ⊗on the spot ⌐on the spot.

Málaga 30E3
Area de Los Patios, Calle Montejaque. **GPS:** n36,68706 w4,46045.⬆.

10 ⌐free ⌐€1/50liter ⌐Ch.
Location: Urban, simple. **Surface:** asphalted. ☐ 01/01-31/12
Distance: ⌐on the spot ⌐1,7km ⊗on the spot ⌐Carrefour
⌐400m.

Tourist information Málaga:
ℹ Oficina de Turismo, Pasaje de Chinitas, 1, www.andalucia.org. Old sparkling port city with fine beaches.
Ⓜ Alcazaba. Moorish castle complex with archeological museum.
Ⓜ Museo casa natal de Pablo Picasso, Plaza de la Merced. House where the painter was born. ☐ Mo-Sa 10-20h ☐ Su-afternoon.
Ⓜ Palacio de los Condes de Buena Vista, Calle San Agustin, 6. Art-historical museum.
⌐ ☐ Su.

Marchena 30E2
Calle Sevilla s/n. **GPS:** n37,33083 w5,42416.⬆.
20 ⌐free ⌐Chfree. **Surface:** metalled.
Distance: ⌐1km.

Olvera 30E2
Vía Verde de la Sierra. **GPS:** n36,94138 w5,25305.⬆.
48 ⌐€ 5 ⌐Ch ⌐included. ☐ 01/01-31/12
Distance: ⌐1km.

Peñarroya-Pueblonuevo 30E1
El Pantano. GPS: n38,27694 w5,27722.⬆.

20 ⌐€ 5-7 ⌐Ch Service€1,50 ⌐€2 ⌐included.
Location: Comfortable, isolated, quiet.
☐ 01/01-31/12
Distance: ⌐4km ⌐lake ⌐on the spot ⌐on the spot ⌐on the spot.
Remarks: Direct access to the lake, motorhome washing place € 1, swimming pool.

Priego de Córdoba 30F2
Parque Niceto Alcalá - Zamora, Calle del Carrusel s/n.
GPS: n37,44361 w4,21186.⬆.

10 ⌐free ⌐Chfree.
Location: Urban, simple. **Surface:** concrete. ☐ 01/01-31/12
Distance: ⌐500m ⊗500m ⌐500m.

Tourist information Priego de Córdoba:
⌐ Iglesia de la Aurora.

Rute 30F2
Calle de Jésus Obrero. **GPS:** n37,33113 w4,37323.⬆⌐.

6 ⌐free ⌐Chfree.
Location: Rural, simple. **Surface:** asphalted.
Distance: ⌐500m ⊗500m ⌐300m.
Remarks: Parking next to police station, max. 48h.

San Juan de los Terreros 30H2
Playa de Entrevista, A332. **GPS:** n37,35083 w1,67972.

>20 ⌐free ⌐. **Surface:** gravel/sand. ☐ 01/01-31/12
Distance: ⌐500m ⌐100m ⊗2km ⌐2,5km.
Remarks: Parking beach.

Sancti Petri La Barrosa 30D3
Carretera de la Barossa. **GPS:** n36,38612 w6,2053.

20 ⌐free. **Surface:** metalled. ☐ 01/01-31/12
Distance: ⌐2km ⌐200m ⊗1km ⌐5km.
Remarks: Parking beach.

Sanlúcar de Barrameda 30D2
Sanlúcar AC Parking, Camino de la Reyerta, s/n.
GPS: n36,76195 w6,39617.⬆.

58 ⌐01/07-30/09 € 12, 01/04-30/06 € 10, 01/10-31/03 € 8 ⌐Ch
⌐(30x)€3/day,5Amp WC ⌐€3/3 ⌐included. ☐ 01/01-31/12
Distance: ⌐4km ⌐100m ⌐100m ⊗300m ⌐350m ⌐400m
⌐500m.

Sevilla 30D2
Area Ac Sevilla Centro, Carretera de la Esclusa, Seville (Sevilla).
GPS: n37,36239 w5,99452.

100 ⌐€ 12 ⌐Ch ⌐(40x)€3 WC ⌐included.
Surface: asphalted.
☐ 01/01-31/12
Distance: ⌐200m ⊗200m ⌐300m ⌐on the spot ⌐200m ⌐200m.

Sevilla 30D2
Parking Kansas City, Avda. de Kansas City, Seville (Sevilla).
GPS: n37,39194 w5,97333.
⌐€ 18/24h.
Surface: asphalted.

Tourist information Seville (Sevilla):
⌐ Alcazar, Plaza del Triumpho.
⌐ Italica. Roman ruins, 9 km at north of Sevilla on N630.
⌐ Almeda de Hercules. ☐ Su-morning.
⌐ Parque de los Descubrimientos. Theme park science, in pavilion of Expo 1992. ☐ Fri-Su, summer Tue-Thu from 18h ☐ 10/01-28/02.
⌐ Calle de las Sierpes. Famous shopping street.

Sierra Nevada 30F2
Los Peñones de San Francisco. GPS: n37,09995 w3,3947.⬆⌐.

60 ⌐€ 10/day ⌐Chincluded.
Surface: asphalted.
Distance: ⌐3km ⊗1km ⌐300m.
Remarks: Shuttle bus to village.

Tourist information Sierra Nevada:
⌐ Parc Natural de Sierra Nevada. Large nature park with Europe's most southern ski resort.

⁕S Taberno 30H2

Área El Rancho, Los Llanos (La Carrasquilla), Santopetar.
GPS: n37,46028 w2,03833. ⬆️➡️.

8 🅿️ € 8 ⟊🔋Ch 🧹 (4x)WC 🗑️ 📶 included.
Location: Rural, simple, quiet. **Surface:** gravel. ⬤ Mo
Distance: 🚶600m 🚲13km ✕on the spot.
Remarks: Entrance swimming pool € 2.

🖼️ Tarifa 🌿 30D3

GPS: n36,06804 w5,6856.

20 🅿️ free. **Surface:** sand. ⬤ 01/01-31/12
Distance: 🚶10km 🏖️on the spot ✕50m 🛒100m.
Remarks: Parking beach.

Tourist information Tarifa:
ℹ️ Tourist Office, Duke of Kent House, Cathedral Square, Gibraltar, www.gibraltar.gi. British colony at the northwest end of the Rock of Gibraltar.
👁️ Siege Tunnels, Gibraltar. Labyrinth of tunnels, ingenious defence system.

🏯S Torre de Benagalbón ⛵🏖️ 30F3

Camper Areas M&H El Rincón, Cortijo Casillas De Los Rubios.
GPS: n36,71658 w4,23799. ⬆️➡️.

35 🅿️ € 12/24h ⟊🔋Ch included 🧹€3/24h 📺€7,50/time 📶€1/24h.
🚿 **Location:** Rural, comfortable, quiet. **Surface:** gravel.
⬤ 01/01-31/12
Distance: 🚶1km 🚲3km 🏖️700m ✕100m 🛒700m 🚌750m.

⟊S Valverde del Camino 30C1

Ctra. de Zalamea. **GPS**: n37,58111 w6,75138. ⬆️.

10 🅿️ free ⟊🔋Ch free.
Surface: asphalted/sand. ⬤ 01/01-31/12
Distance: 🚶500m.

⟊S Vélez-Rubio 🌿🏞️ 30H2

Área Puerta Oriental de Andalucía, Calle Granada.
GPS: n37,65194 w2,07555. ⬆️.

10 🅿️ free ⟊🔋Ch free. **Location:** Rural, simple, quiet.
Surface: metalled. ⬤ 01/01-31/12 ⬤ 1st week Aug
Distance: 🚶500m 🚲2,2km ✕500m 🛒500m.

⟊S Vera 30H2

Acvera Motorhome Park & Aire. GPS: n37,26030 w1,85347. ⬆️.
150 🅿️ € 7-9 ⟊🔋Ch 🧹 included.
Location: Rural, comfortable. **Surface:** metalled.
Distance: 🚶Vera 2km 🚲4,7km 🏖️beach 7km ✕on the spot.
Remarks: Tennis & padel lessons, 11 tennis courts.

⟊S Vera 30H2

Oasis al Mar, Av del Salar. **GPS**: n37,22731 w1,82819. ⬆️.
50 🅿️ € 7-9, trailer € 1 ⟊🔋Ch 🧹€3/day 📺€3 📶 included.
Location: Rural, comfortable. **Surface:** gravel. ⬤ 01/10-01/05
Distance: 🚶centre Vera 4,4km 🏖️2km.
Remarks: Motorhome washing place € 4.

⟊S Villanueva de Algaidas 🏞️ 30E2

Calle de la Archidona, A-7201. **GPS**: n37,17810 w4,45021. ⬆️.
20 🅿️ free ⟊🔋Ch free.
Location: Rural, simple. **Surface:** asphalted.
Distance: 🚶500m ✕50m.
Remarks: Max. 48h.

Finland

Capital: Helsinki
Government: parliamentary constitutional
republic
Official Language: Finnish and Swedish
Population 5,269,000 (2014)
Area: 336,855 Km²

General information
Dialling code: 0358
General emergency: 112
Currency: Euro
Credit cards are accepted almost everywhere.

Regulations for overnight stays
Wild camping is in general allowed in the National
Parks, on private land with permission of the
owner.

Camping Key Europe is obligatory when using
campsites: the card can be purchased at any
campsite for € 16 (± £11,42), valid for one year.

Additional public holidays 2016
March 25 Good Friday
March 28 Easter Monday
May 1 Labour Day
June 24 Midsummer Eve
June 25 Midsummer
December 6 Independence Day

Time Zone
Winter (Standard Time) GMT+2
Summer (DST) GMT+3

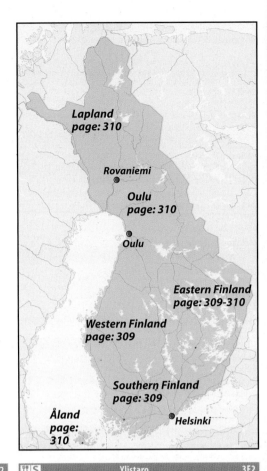

Lapland
page: 310

Rovaniemi

Oulu
page: 310

Oulu

Eastern Finland
page: 309-310

Western Finland
page: 309

Southern Finland
page: 309

Åland
page:
310

Helsinki

Southern Finland

Hamina 3F2
Aallokko Caravan, Helsingintie. **GPS**: n60,56039 e27,18280.
€ 10 Ch €3 1/h. 01/04-31/10
Distance: 1km on the spot on the spot 1km.

Imatra 3F2
ABC Imatra, Tiedonkatu 2. **GPS**: n61,18627 e28,74008.
Surface: asphalted.
Distance: on the spot.

Karjaa 3E3
ABC Karjaa, Lepinpellonkatu 2. **GPS**: n60,05489 e23,64809.
Surface: asphalted.
Distance: on the spot.

Lepaa 3E2
Kyläkauppa Pikkuakka. GPS: n61,11587 e24,34537.
12 € 20
Distance: on the spot.

Liikkala 3F2
Onnelan Tila, Hakalantie 37. **GPS**: n60,70986 e27,01708.
2 € 20. **Location:** Isolated, quiet.
Distance: 2km 2km.

Parikkala 3F2
Tukkikuja. **GPS**: n61,55500 e29,49748.
free
Distance: on the spot on the spot on the spot.
Remarks: At harbour.

Särkisalmi 3F2
Oronmyllyn Toimintakeskus, Oronmyllyntie 250.
GPS: n61,62059 e29,37868.
12 € 10 €10 WC . **Location:** Isolated, quiet.
Distance: 7km on the spot.

Western Finland

Hanhikoski 3E2
Maatilamatkailu Koivusalo, Vanhatie 386. **GPS**: n62,96175 e22,77427.
€ 20 WC .
Distance: 4km.

Hattu 3G1
Arhipan Pirtti. GPS: n62,92948 e31,28065.
€ 14 €4 WC .
Distance: 300m on the spot.

Huittinen 3E2
ABC Huittinen, Loimijoentie 89. **GPS**: n61,16713 e22,68061.
Ch . **Surface:** asphalted.
Distance: on the spot.

Ikaalinen 3E2
Ikaalisten Kylpylä Rantasipi, Hämyläntie 2.
GPS: n61,77586 e23,01928.
20 € 12.
Distance: on the spot on the spot.

Ilmarinen 3E3
Ilmaristen Matkailutila, Väänteläntie 45.
GPS: n60,49801 e22,37492.
6 € 15. **Surface:** gravel.

Kangasala 3E2
Mobilan Auto Kylä, Kustaa Kolmannen tie 75.
GPS: n61,44124 e24,12997.
free.
Distance: 6km 100m 100m.
Remarks: At museum.

Killinkoski 3E2
Killinkosken Kyläyhdistys, Inkantie 60. **GPS**: n62,40382 e23,89105.
20 free €5.

Lempäälä 3E2
Kärppälän Rustholli, Kärppäläntie 50. **GPS**: n61,33448 e23,67716.
8 € 25 WC included. **Surface:** grassy.
Distance: 6km.

Mieto 3E2
Hakunin kotieläintila, Hakunintie 193. **GPS**: n62,57169 e22,26394.
€ 10 included. **Location:** Isolated, quiet.
Remarks: Sauna € 10.

Nokia 3E2
ABC Nokia Kolmenkulma, Rounionkatu 140.
GPS: n61,50143 e23,56800.
Ch . **Surface:** asphalted.
Distance: on the spot.

Tuuri 3E2
Veljekset Keskinen Oy, Onnelantie 45. **GPS**: n62,60595 e23,71426.
10 € 10 €5 WC . **Surface:** asphalted. 01/01-31/12
Remarks: Swimming pool and sauna on site.

Vaajakoski 3E2
ABC Vaajakoski, Vaajakoskentie 850. **GPS**: n62,22871 e25,90290.
10 Ch . **Surface:** asphalted.
Distance: on the spot on the spot.

Ylistaro 3E2
Meijeriranta majoitus, Lahdentie 5. **GPS**: n62,95396 e22,52998.
20 € 15, dog € 10 WC included.
Distance: 2km on the spot 2km.

Ylönkylä 3E3
Katiskanmäki, Särkisalontie 2. **GPS**: n60,16479 e22,99639.
30 € 6 + € 5/pp WC included €7/5. **Surface:** gravel.
Distance: on the spot.

Eastern Finland

Heinävesi 3F2
Heinäveden satama, Kermarannantie 48.
GPS: n62,43835 e28,63796.
€ 10 € 8 WC .
Distance: 800m on the spot.

Iisalmi 3F1
Untamonkatu 6. **GPS**: n63,56465 e27,19025.
10 free € 10. **Location:** Urban. **Surface:** gravel.
Distance: on the spot 800m 250m 250m.
Remarks: At gymnasium.

Iisalmi 3F1
Luuniemenkatu 11. **GPS**: n63,55102 e27,18841.
10 free. **Surface:** gravel.
Distance: on the spot on the spot 500m.

Ilomantsi 3F1
Hyvinvointikeskus Toivonlahti, Henrikintie 4.
GPS: n62,67684 e30,91145.
12 € 10.
Distance: on the spot on the spot 200m.

Karhunpää 3F1
Laitalan Lomat, Laitalantie 85. **GPS**: n63,61440 e28,86089.
€ 12 € 2/day.

Lieksa 3F1
ABC Lieksa, Kalliokatu 8. **GPS**: n63,32240 e30,00854.
Ch . **Surface:** asphalted.
Distance: on the spot.

Rantasalmi 3F2
Hotelli Rinssi-Eversti, Ohitustie 5. **GPS**: n62,06390 e28,30890.
6 € 10 € 5 WC included .
Distance: 100m on the spot.
Remarks: Use of sauna against payment.

Sulkava 3F2
Alanteentie. **GPS**: n61,78528 e28,37769.

5 � € 14 ⚡included WC ⬚. **Surface:** asphalted.
Distance: 🚶500m ⚓on the spot ⛵on the spot ⊗100m.

Oulu

| 🏠 S | **Kontiomäki** | 3F1 |

Shell, Viitostie 2. **GPS:** n64,31988 e28,04344.
20 ⌐表 € 6 ⚡ WC included 📶. **Location:** Highway.
Distance: ⚓on the spot.
Remarks: At petrol station.

| 🏠 S | **Puolanka** | 2D3 |

Pororajan Majoitus, Pudasjärventie 1. **GPS:** n64,87494 e27,64344.⬆.
8 ⌐表 € 12 ⚡💧€3 WC ⬚🔲. **Surface:** asphalted. ⬛ 01/01-31/12
Distance: 🚶1km ⊗1km ⚑1km 〰on the spot.

| 🏠 S | **Sanginkylä** | 3E1 |

Valkeisen virkistysalueella, Puolangantie 207.
GPS: n64,86477 e26,74733.
⌐表 € 10 💧⚡€2 📶.
Distance: ⚓on the spot ⛵on the spot.

| 🏠 S | **Siikajoki** | 3E1 |

Ruokolahden lava, Limingantie 197, Paavola.
GPS: n64,61267 e25,23947.⬆.
8 ⌐表 Ch ⚡€5 WC ⬚€15. **Location:** Rural. **Surface:** gravel.
⬛ 23/05-06/09
Distance: 🚶2km ⚓on the spot ⛵on the spot.
Remarks: Key at kiosk.

| 🍴 S | **Ylivieska** | 3E1 |

Hotelli Käenpesä, Lintutie 1. **GPS:** n64,06782 e24,52621.
4 ⌐表 € 20 ⚡ WC ⬚.
Distance: 🚶800m ⊗on the spot.
Remarks: Check in at hotel.

Lapland

| 🍴 S | **Anetjärvi** 👥 | 2D3 |

Aneen Loma, Anetjärventie 72A. **GPS:** n65,91851 e27,98786.
10 ⌐表 € 25 ⚡ WC ⬚included. **Location:** Rural.
Distance: ⚓on the spot ⛵on the spot.
Remarks: At the beach, sauna incl.

| 🏠 S | **Tanhua** | 2C2 |

Tanhuan Erämajat, Pessijoentie 2. **GPS:** n67,52802 e27,53691.⬆.
10 ⌐表 €5 💧🔲Ch WC ⬚. **Surface:** grassy.
Distance: ⊗300m.
Remarks: Use of sauna against payment.

| 🏠 S | **Tanhua** | 2C2 |

Tanhuan Erämajat, Pessijoentie 2. **GPS:** n67,52802 e27,53691.⬆.
10 ⌐表 €5 💧🔲Ch WC ⬚. **Surface:** grassy.
Distance: ⊗300m.

Åland

| 🏠 S | **Keitele** | 3E1 |

Matkailukeskus Lossisaari, Sininentie 205.
GPS: n63,18941 e26,34270.⬆.
13 ⌐表 € 16 Ch ⚡ WC ⬚ 📶. **Surface:** grassy. ⬛ 01/01-31/12
Distance: 🚶1,5km ⚓on the spot ⛵on the spot ⊗on the spot
⚑1,5km.
Remarks: Behind petrol station, bread-service.

FI

🇫🇷 France

Capital: Paris
Government: Unitary republic
Official Language: French
Population: 66,300,000 (2014)
Area: 543,965 km²

General information

Dialling code: 0033
General emergency: 112
Currency: Euro
Payments by credit card are accepted almost everywhere, however chip and pin systems are non-compatible with British cards and fuel for example can only be bought at supermarkets during opening hours.

Regulations for overnight stays

Wild camping is accepted almost everywhere throughout inland France. Special regulations for motor homes you can find on signs by entering the town. It is permitted to stopover at motorway services, be aware that toll roads often issue time-constrained tickets.

Additional public holidays 2015

March 25 Good Friday
May 1 Labor Day
May 8 Liberation Day
July14 National Holiday
August15 Assumption of the Virgin Mary
November 1 All Saints Day
November 11 Armistice Day 1918

Time Zone

Winter (Standard Time) GMT+1
Summer (DST) GMT+2

Nord-Pas-de-Calais
pages: 311-314
Lille

Picardie
pages: 314-315

Normandie
pages: 328-340

Champagne-Ardenne
pages: 315-319
Metz

Lorraine
pages: 319-326

Alsace
pages: 326-328

Brittany
pages: 340-360
Rennes

Ile-de-France
page: 340
Paris

Pays-de-la-Loire
pages: 360-373

Centre
pages: 373-381

Bourgogne
pages: 381-385
Dijon

Franche-Comté
pages: 385-389

Poitou-Charentes
pages: 389-397

Limousin
pages: 397-401

Auvergne
pages: 401-410

Lyon

Rhône-Alpes
pages: 410-422

Bordeaux

Aquitaine
pages: 422-437

Midi-Pyrénées
pages: 437-449

Montpellier

Provence-Alpes-Côte d'Azur
pages: 459-468

Languedoc-Roussillon
pages: 449-459

Marseille

prime meridian

Andorra
page: 449

Corsica
pages 468

Ajaccio

FR

Nord-Pas de Calais

| Ambleteuse | 12C2 |
D940 > Wimereux. **GPS**: n50,80638 e1,61484.⬆.

7🛏€5. **Location**: Rural. **Surface**: grassy.
Distance: 🚶750m ⚓1,2km.

| Arques | 12D2 |
Rue Michelet. **GPS**: n50,74551 e2,30459.⬆➡.

20🛏€3,50 ⛽€1,50 🚿Ch. **Surface**: gravel. ⬛ 01/04-31/10
Distance: 🚶2km 🚲100m.
Remarks: Behind camp site Beauséjour.

| Arras | 12D3 |
Rue des Rosati. **GPS**: n50,29463 e2,78812.⬆.

10🛏free ⛽€2/100liter 🚿Ch 🚽€2/1h. **Surface**: asphalted.
⬛ 01/01-31/12
Distance: 🚶700m ⊗500m.
Tourist information Arras:
👁 Hôtel de Ville. Town hall in Gothic style. Also guided tours of the subterranean passages of Arras.
🎪 ⬛ Wed, Sa.

| Bailleul | 12D2 |
Rue du collège. **GPS**: n50,74010 e2,73170.

20🛏free. **Surface**: asphalted. ⬛ 01/01-31/12
Distance: 🚶700m ⚓2,8km.
Remarks: At commemorative monument.

| Banteux | 10A3 |
GPS: n50,06259 e3,20106.⬆.

5🛏€4 ⛽🚿Chfree. **Location**: Rural, simple.
Surface: grassy/gravel. ⬛ 01/01-31/12 ◉ service 01/11-31/03
Distance: 🚶500m ⚓2,5km 🚴on the spot 🚶on the spot.

| Bavay | 10B3 |
Chemin de Ronde. **GPS**: n50,30004 e3,79551.⬆.
10🛏free ⛽🚿Chfree. **Surface**: gravel. ⬛ 01/01-31/12
Distance: 🚶200m ⊗200m.

| Berck-sur-Mer | 12C3 |
Baie d'Authie, Chemin aux Raisins. **GPS**: n50,39701 e1,56431.⬆➡.

80🛏€10 ⛽🚿Chincluded. 🚻 **Surface**: gravel. ⬛ 01/01-31/12
Distance: 🚶1,5km ⚓100m 🍟friteur 100m.
Remarks: Baker every morning.

| Berck-sur-Mer | 12C3 |
Parking Terminus, Rue Dr. Calot, Berck-Nord.
GPS: n50,42361 e1,56750.⬆.

40 🛏 € 10 🚰 🔌Ch included. **Location:** Simple. **Surface:** gravel.
⬛ 01/01-31/12
Distance: 🏖beach 200m.
Remarks: Beach parking.

Berck-sur-Mer 12C3

Chez Mireille, Chemin Genty. **GPS:** n50,41654 e1,57696.

80 🛏 € 7 🚰 🔌Ch 🔌(4x)€2/kWh 📶free. **Surface:** grassy.
⬛ 01/04-31/10
Distance: 🏪600m 🏖800m ⊗on the spot.
Remarks: To be paid at bar.
Tourist information Berck-sur-Mer:
😊 Bagatelle, CD 940. Amusement park. ⬛ Easter-Sep 10-18.30h.

Bergues 12D2

Rue Maurice Cornette. **GPS:** n50,96543 e2,43596.⬆️➡️.

50 🛏free. **Surface:** gravel. ⬛ 01/01-31/12
Distance: 🏪500m ⚓2,2km.
Remarks: Behind football ground, max. 48h.

Boulogne-sur-Mer 12C2

Parking Moulin Wibert, Boulevard Sainte Beuve, D940.
GPS: n50,74308 e1,59688.⬆️.

40 🛏 € 5,25/24h 🚰 € 3/10minutes 🔌Ch 🧹. **Surface:** metalled.
Distance: 🏪centre 2,5km ⚓5,5km 🏖on the spot 🚌on the spot.

Boulogne-sur-Mer 12C2

Boulevard Chanzy. **GPS:** n50,72194 e1,60027.⬆️.

🛏free. **Surface:** asphalted.
Distance: 🏪500m ⚓4,5km.
Remarks: Nearby casino.
Tourist information Boulogne-sur-Mer:
🏛 Boulevard Clocheville. ⬛ Wed-morning.

🏛 place Dalton, centre. ⬛ Wed + Sa morning.
🏛 place Vignon. ⬛ Su-morning.

Boussois 10B3

Rue du Rivage. **GPS:** n50,28845 e4,04544.⬆️.
4 🛏 🚰 Ch. **Surface:** gravel. ⬛ 01/01-31/12
Distance: 🏪1km.

Calais 12C2

Digue Gaston Berthe. **GPS:** n50,96688 e1,84406.

60 🛏free, 01/04-31/10 € 7/24h 🚰🔌Ch 🚽WC included.
Surface: asphalted.
Distance: 🏪500m 🏖100m ⊗100m 🍺100m.

Calais 12C2

Quai Edmond Pagniez. **GPS:** n50,96050 e1,84466.⬆️.

100 🛏free, 01/04-31/10 € 7/24h 🚰🔌Ch 🚽included.
Surface: asphalted. ⬛ 01/01-31/12
Distance: 🏪300m ⊗350m.
Remarks: Service: Digue Gaston Berthe.
Tourist information Calais:
Ⓜ Centre d'Information Eurotunnel. Exhibition about the Channel tunnel.
🏛 ⬛ Wed, Thu, Sa.

Cambrai 10A3

Grand Carré. **GPS:** n50,18515 e3,22587.⬆️.
6 🛏 € 8 🚰🔌Ch 🔌included. 🚐 **Location:** Comfortable, quiet.
Surface: asphalted. ⬛ 01/01-31/12
Distance: 🏪1,5km ⊗750m.

Cassel 12D2

Route d'Oxelaere, C301. **GPS:** n50,79328 e2,48852.⬆️➡️.

5 🛏free 🚰€2 🔌Ch 🚽€2. **Location:** Isolated, quiet.
Surface: gravel. ⬛ 01/01-31/12
Distance: 🏪1km.
Remarks: At sports park, coins at tourist info.

Catillon-sur-Sambre 10A3

Avenue de la Groise, N43. **GPS:** n50,07624 e3,64615.⬆️.

5 🛏 € 5 🚰🔌Ch 🔌included. **Surface:** asphalted. ⬛ 01/01-31/12
Distance: 🏪200m 🏖on the spot.
Remarks: At the canal, max. 72h.

Catillon-sur-Sambre 10A3

Rue de la Gare. **GPS:** n50,07699 e3,64404.⬆️➡️.

20 🛏free. **Surface:** gravel. ⬛ 01/01-31/12
Distance: 🏪500m 🔌on the spot.
Remarks: At the canal.

Embry 12C2

Les Salons de l'Embryenne, D108. **GPS:** n50,49534 e1,96610.⬆️.

8 🛏 € 6 🚰€2,50 🔌Ch 🔌€2,50/4h 🚽WC €2,50 🧹 🚿 **Location:** Isolated, quiet. **Surface:** gravel. ⬛ 01/01-31/12

Equihen-Plage 12C2

Plage de la Crevasse, Rue du Beurre Fondu.
GPS: n50,67993 e1,56830.⬆️➡️.

20 🛏 € 5 🚰€3/10minutes 🔌Ch 🔌(6x)€3/12h.
Surface: grassy/gravel. ⬛ 01/01-31/12
Distance: 🏪100m 🏖100m 🍺100m.

Grand-Fort-Philippe 12D2

Bd François Lévêque. **GPS:** n51,00142 e2,10851.⬆️.
8 🛏free. **Surface:** asphalted. ⬛ 01/01-31/12
Distance: 🏪on the spot 🏖600m.
Remarks: At the canal, >3,5t not allowed.

Gravelines 12D2

Parking des Miaules, Rue des Islandais/Rue du Port.
GPS: n50,98766 e2,12232.⬆️.

20 🛏 € 3, 01/04-01/10 € 6. 🚐 🧹 **Location:** Rural, simple, quiet.
Surface: gravel.
Distance: 🏪500m 🔌nearby ⊗300m.

Gravelines 12D2

Rue de la Gendarmerie. **GPS:** n50,99342 e2,13177.⬆️➡️.
🚰€2 🔌Ch 🧹.

Hardelot 12C2

Place R.L. Peeters. **GPS:** n50,63500 e1,59888.⬆️.

🚿free. **Surface:** asphalted. ⬛ 01/01-31/12
Distance: ⛱1,7km.

| 🅿️🅂 | Hondschoote | 12D2 |

Impasse Spinnewyn. **GPS:** n50,97628 e2,58033. ⬆️➡️.

8 🚿free 🚰€2/100liter 🗑Ch 🔌€2/1h. **Surface:** asphalted.
Distance: 🚶800m 🍽nearby.
Remarks: Behind Moulin de la Victoire, coins available, addresses indicated on the spot.

| 🅿️ | Landrecies | 10B3 |

Avenue Dumey. **GPS:** n50,12715 e3,69007.
4 🚿. ⬛ 01/01-31/12

| 🅿️🅂 | Le Portel | 12C2 |

Rue des Champs. **GPS:** n50,71188 e1,57485. ⬆️➡️.

40 🚿€ 3, 01/06-30/09 € 4 🚰€2/100liter 🗑Ch 🚿€2/4h 🧺📱💳
Surface: metalled. ⬛ 01/01-31/12
Distance: 🚶200m ⛱300m ⊗300m 🍽300m.
Remarks: Next to sports fields, 300m from beach (stairs).

| �ⓘ🅂 | Le Touquet-Paris Plage 🏖🍦🍴🧺 | 12C2 |

Parc International de la Canoke, Boulevard de la Canche.
GPS: n50,52648 e1,59869. ⬆️.

100 🚿€ 9 🚰€2/100liter 🗑Ch 🔌€2/55minutes 🧺.
Surface: grassy/gravel. ⬛ 01/01-31/12
Distance: 🚶10 min walking ⛱on the spot ⊗on the spot 🍽on the spot 🍴on the spot.

| 🅸🅂 | Le Touquet-Paris Plage 🏖🍦🍴🧺 | 12C2 |

Centre Nautique du Touquet Base Nord, Avenue Jean Ruet.
GPS: n50,53588 e1,59285. ⬆️➡️.

60 🚿€ 13 🚰€2/100liter 🗑Ch 🔌€2/55minutes. **Surface:** asphalted.
⬛ 01/01-31/12

Distance: 🚶10 min walking ⛱on the spot ⊗on the spot 🍽on the spot 🍴on the spot.

Tourist information Le Touquet-Paris Plage:
🅾️ Aqualud. Leisure pool park. ⬛ 15/02-30/11 10-18h.

| 🅿️🅂 | Le-Cateau-Cambrésis | 10A3 |

Avenue du Maréchal Leclerc, N43. **GPS:** n50,10197 e3,55491. ⬆️.

5 🚿free 🚰🗑Ch 🚿free. **Surface:** asphalted. ⬛ 01/01-31/12
Distance: 🚶1km.

| 🅿️🅂 | Lens | 12D3 |

Stade Bollaert-Delelis P6, Rue Maurice Fréchet.
GPS: n50,43192 e2,82057.

6 🚿free 🚰🗑Chfree 🚿against payment 🧺. **Surface:** asphalted.
⬛ 01/01-31/12
Distance: 🚶500m ⊗on the spot 🍽1km 🍴on the spot.
Remarks: Max. 24h.

| 🅸🅂 | Longfossé | 12C2 |

Ferme du Louvet, 5, Route de Wierre, D52 Desvres > Samer.
GPS: n50,64667 e1,79062. ⬆️➡️.

8 🚿€ 6 🚰€3 🗑Ch 🚿included. **Location:** Rural, isolated, quiet.
Surface: gravel.
Remarks: Narrow entrance.

| 🅿️ | Merlimont | 12C3 |

Place de la Gare. **GPS:** n50,46026 e1,58053. ⬆️.

12 🚿free. **Surface:** gravel. ⬛ 01/01-31/12

| 🅿️🅂 | Montreuil-sur-Mer | 12C3 |

Avenue des Garennes. **GPS:** n50,45944 e1,75939.

8 🚿free 🚰€2/100liter 🗑Chfree 🚿(2x)against payment.
Surface: asphalted. ⬛ 01/01-31/12

Distance: 🚶500m ⛱300m 🍴450m.

| 🅿️🅂 | Nuncq-Hautecôte | 12D3 |

La Pommeraie, 13, route nationale. **GPS:** n50,30516 e2,29375. ⬆️➡️.

5 🚿€ 5 🚰€2 🗑Ch 🚿€5 🔌free. **Location:** Rural, comfortable, quiet. **Surface:** gravel. ⬛ 01/01-31/12
Distance: ⊗50m.
Remarks: Covered pool € 3.

| 🅿️ | Oye-plage 🌊 | 12D2 |

Les Huttes d'Oye Plage. GPS: n50,99703 e2,04228. ⬆️.

10 🚿free. **Surface:** gravel.
⬛ 01/01-31/12
Distance: ⛱on the spot ⊗100m.
Remarks: Beach parking, service Oye-Plage: 50,97713 2,03966.

| 🅿️🅂 | Richebourg 🌿 | 12D2 |

Rue de la Briqueterie. **GPS:** n50,58028 e2,74639. ⬆️➡️.

6 🚿free 🚰€2/100liter 🔌€2/55minutes 📶included. **Location:** Rural, comfortable. **Surface:** grassy. ⬛ 01/01-31/12
Distance: 🚶500m 🚲on the spot 🚶on the spot.
Remarks: Max. 48h.

| 🅿️ | Stella-plage | 12C3 |

Cours des Champs Elysées. **GPS:** n50,47470 e1,57726. ⬆️.

30 🚿free. **Location:** Simple, isolated. **Surface:** asphalted.
Distance: 🚶1km ⛱on the spot ⊗650m.
Remarks: Parking at dune.

| 🅿️🅂 | Tardinghen | 12C2 |

Le site des 2 caps, La Ferme d'Horloge, 1615 Route d'Ausques, D249.
GPS: n50,86250 e1,64890. ⬆️➡️.

30 🚿€ 5/24h 🚰€3 🗑Ch 🚿€3/24h 📶. **Surface:** metalled.
⬛ 01/01-31/12

Distance: 🚶1,6km.
Remarks: Swin-golf € 5.

| 🏕 | Tardinghen | 12C2 |

Le site des 2 caps, La Fleur des Champs.
GPS: n50,85639 e1,65139.⬆.

50 🛢€ 5/24h. **Surface:** grassy. ⬜ 01/01-31/12
Distance: 🚶2km ⛱2km.

| 🏕 | Tardinghen | 12C2 |

Le site des 2 caps, Le Fond de Sombre, Hervelinghen > Wissant.
GPS: n50,89361 e1,68972.⬆.

10 🛢€ 5/24h. **Surface:** grassy. ⬜ 01/01-31/12
Distance: ⛱1km.

| 🏕 S | Wissant | 12C2 |

Parking Wissant, Avenue Georges Clémenceau.
GPS: n50,88684 e1,67064.⬆➡.

FR

30 🛢free 🔧Chfree. **Surface:** metalled. ⬜ 01/01-31/12
Distance: 🚶700m ⛱1,1km.

Picardie

| 🏕 S | Bellicourt | 10A3 |

Hameau de Riqueval, D1044. **GPS:** n49,95156 e3,23519.⬆.

2 🛢free 🔧Ch🔧Service € 4. **Surface:** asphalted. ⬜ 01/01-31/12
🔘 service: 01/10-31/03
Distance: 🚶300m ⊗on the spot 🚌on the spot.
Remarks: Coins at tourist info.

| 🏕 S | Bourseville | 12C3 |

Lotissement le Village. **GPS:** n50,10350 e1,52702.⬆➡.

35 🛢€ 5 🔧€2 🔧Ch 🔧€3. 🔧 **Location:** Isolated, quiet.
Surface: asphalted. ⬜ 01/01-31/12

Distance: 🚶500m ⛱3km ⊗500m 🛒500m.

| 🏕 | Bruyères-et-Montberault | 15A1 |

Avenue de Verdun. **GPS:** n49,52538 e3,66080.⬆➡.

4 🛢free. **Surface:** asphalted. ⬜ 01/01-31/12
Distance: 🚶100m ⊗100m 🛒200m.

| 🏕 S | Cayeux-sur-Mer | 12C3 |

Rue Faidherbe. **GPS:** n50,20300 e1,52612.⬆➡.

30 🛢€ 7 🔧€3 🔧Ch. **Surface:** gravel. ⬜ 01/01-31/12
Distance: 🚶2km ⛱At the sea, no beach ⊗2km 🛒2km.
Remarks: To be paid at campsite.

| 🏕 | Cayeux-sur-Mer | 12C3 |

Route blanche, Le Hourdel, D102. **GPS:** n50,21448 e1,55208.➡.

30 🛢free. **Location:** Simple, isolated, quiet. **Surface:** gravel.
⬜ 01/01-31/12
Distance: 🚶500m, Cayeux 6km ⛱sea 50m ⊗500m 🛒3km.

| 🏕 S | Château-Thierry | 15A2 |

Aire de Château. **GPS:** n49,03657 e3,38365.⬆➡.

13 🛢€ 6,50 🔧Ch 🔧€1,50/12h WC🔧included. 🔧 🔧
Location: Urban, comfortable. **Surface:** asphalted. ⬜ 01/01-31/12
Distance: 🚶centre 1,8km ⛱on the spot 🚌on the spot ⊗on the spot
🛒on the spot 🚲on the spot 🚶on the spot.
Remarks: Along the Marne river.

| 🏕 S | Conty | 14G1 |

Rue du Marais. **GPS:** n49,74333 e2,15583.⬆.

30 🛢free 🔧€2/100liter 🔧Ch WC. **Surface:** grassy. ⬜ 01/01-31/12
Distance: 🚶200m ⛱6,5km 🚌300m ⊗300m 🛒300m.
Remarks: Coins at tourist info, town hall and bakery.

| 🏕 S | Coucy-le-Château-Auffrique | 15A1 |

Chemin du Val Serain. **GPS:** n49,52037 e3,31150.⬆.

6 🛢€ 5 🔧Ch 🔧included. 🔧 🔧 **Location:** Rural, comfortable.
Surface: gravel. ⬜ 01/01-31/12
Distance: 🚶500m ⊗on the spot 🛒500m.
Remarks: Castle 1km.

| 🏕 S | Doullens | 12D3 |

Rue du Pont à l'Avoine, N25-Arras-Amiens. **GPS:** n50,15390 e2,34260.⬆.

4 🛢free 🔧free. **Surface:** asphalted.

| 🏕 S | Fort Mahon Plage | 12C3 |

Plage Parking de la Dune, Rue de la Bistouille.
GPS: n50,33833 e1,55611.⬆.

60 🛢€ 9 🔧ChWCfree. 🔧 **Surface:** gravel. ⬜ 01/01-31/12
Distance: 🚶200m ⛱600m ⊗200m.

| 🏕 | Laôn | 15A1 |

Promenade de la Couloire. **GPS:** n49,56313 e3,62967.⬆➡.

6 🛢free. **Surface:** metalled.
Distance: 🚶300m ⊗500m.
Remarks: Near city wall.

| 🏕 S | Le Crotoy | 12C3 |

Camping-Car Park le Tarteron, Route de Rue.
GPS: n50,22972 e1,64128.⬆.
24 🛢€ 12 🔧Ch 🔧included. **Location:** Quiet. **Surface:** gravel.
⬜ 01/01-31/12
Distance: 🚶2km ⛱2km ⊗2km.

| 🏕 S | Le Crotoy | 12C3 |

Aire Camping-car, Bassin des Chasses. **GPS:** n50,21800 e1,63300.⬆.

50 🛢€ 5/24h 🔧€2/100liter 🔧Ch 🔧€2/1h. 🔧 **Surface:** sand.

◯ 01/01-31/12
Distance: 🚶5 min walking ⛱15 min walking ⊙Laverie Crotelloise, 20, avenue du Gal de Gaulle.

| 🖳Ⓢ | Le Crotoy ⚓🌊 | 12C3 |

Aire Camping-car, Chemin du Marais. **GPS:** n50,22886 e1,61253.⬆.

35 🍴€ 5/24h 🚰€2/10minutes 🔌Ch🔲€2/1h. **Surface:** sand.
◯ 01/01-31/12
Distance: 🚶1,5km ⊗on the spot ✕1,5km ⊙Laverie Crotelloise, 20, avenue du Gal de Gaulle.

| 🖳Ⓢ | Le Nouvion-en-Thiérache | 10B3 |

Allée du S/l François d'Orléans. **GPS:** n50,00542 e3,78078.⬆.
5 🍴🚰€3 🔌Ch🔲. **Location:** Rural. **Surface:** asphalted.
◯ 01/01-31/12
Distance: 🚶2km.
Remarks: Coins at campsite.

| 🅲Ⓢ | Long | 12C3 |

Camping Municipal La Peupleraie, Rue de la Chasse à Vaches.
GPS: n50,03457 e1,98313.

8 🍴€ 5 🚰€2 🔌Chfree ✂€2/h WC🔲⊙. **Surface:** grassy/gravel.
◯ 01/01-31/12 ● service: 16/10-30/04
Distance: ⛱on the spot 🚶on the spot.

| 🖳Ⓢ | Longpont | 15A2 |

Rue Saint-Louis, D17. **GPS:** n49,27395 e3,22129.⬆.

3 🍴free 🚰🔌Chagainst payment. **Location:** Rural. **Surface:** gravel.
◯ 01/01-31/12
Distance: 🚶100m.
Remarks: Max. 72h, abbey 150m.

| 🖳Ⓢ | Mers-les-Bains 🌊 | 12C3 |

Chemin de la Petite Allée. **GPS:** n50,06175 e1,40150.⬆.

50 🍴€ 5,50 🚰€2 🔌Ch. **Location:** Comfortable. **Surface:** gravel.
◯ 01/01-31/12
Distance: 🚶1,3km ⛱sandy beach 1,5km 🛒Auchan 600m.

| 🖳Ⓢ | Morienval | 14H2 |

Route de Pierrefonds 32. **GPS:** n49,30352 e2,92309.⬆➡.

21+9 🍴€ 8 🚰€2/100liter 🔌Ch🔲✂(21x)€2/day.🚿
Location: Rural, comfortable, quiet. **Surface:** grassy/gravel.
◯ 22/03-16/11
Distance: 🚶500m ⊗500m 🛒500m.
Remarks: In case of absence, money in an envelope in mail box.

| 🖳Ⓢ | Neuilly-Saint-Front | 15A2 |

Chemin de la Chantraine. **GPS:** n49,16713 e3,26003.
20 🍴free 🚰€3 🔌Ch🔲€3/55minutes. **Surface:** grassy.
Distance: 🚶600m.

| 🖳Ⓢ | Picquigny | 12D3 |

Rue de la Cavée d'Airaines. **GPS:** n49,94388 e2,13496.⬆.

8 🍴€ 5 🚰🔌Ch ✂€2 WC🔲included. 🚿 **Location:** Rural.
Surface: grassy.
Distance: 🚶500m 🛒500m.

| 🖳Ⓢ | Quend | 12C3 |

Ferme de la Grande Retz. **GPS:** n50,32893 e1,61811.⬆➡.

10 🍴€ 7 🚰Ch ✂€3 📶included. **Surface:** grassy. **◯** 01/01-31/12
Distance: 🚶3km ⛱9km 🚲9km 🛒2km.

| 🖳Ⓢ | Quend-plage-les-Pins | 12C3 |

Plage des Pins. **GPS:** n50,32410 e1,55545.⬆.

100 🍴€ 7/24h 🚰€3/10minutes 🔌Ch🔲€3/1h. **Surface:** gravel.
◯ 01/01-31/12
Distance: 🚶800m ⛱beach 900m 🛒on the spot.

| 🖳Ⓢ | Saint-Valery-sur-Somme 🌿⛱🌊 | 12C3 |

Rue de la Croix l'Abbé. **GPS:** n50,18220 e1,62881.⬆➡.

180 🍴€ 9/24h 🚰🔌Chincluded. 🏧🌊 **Location:** Rural.
Surface: gravel. **◯** 01/01-31/12
Distance: 🚶1km ⊗nearby 🛒nearby.
Remarks: Market on Sunday.

| 🖳Ⓢ | Villers-Côtterets 🌿⛱ | 15A2 |

Rue Alfred Juneaux. **GPS:** n49,26052 e3,08713.⬆➡.

6 🍴free 🚰€3/10minutes 🔌Chfree 🔲€3/1h 🧹. **Location:** Urban, comfortable, quiet. **Surface:** gravel/metalled.
◯ 01/01-31/12
Distance: 🚶on the spot ⊗600m 🛒600m.
Remarks: Max. 72h, service 50m.

| 🖳Ⓢ | Villers-Côtterets 🌿⛱ | 15A2 |

Grand Bosquet Parc du Château, Place Aristide Briand.
GPS: n49,25483 e3,09400.⬆.

6 🍴free. **Location:** Urban, simple, central, noisy.
Surface: grassy/metalled. **◯** 01/01-31/12
Distance: 🚶on the spot 🚲20km ⊗200m 🛒500m 🚍100m.

Champagne Ardenne

| 🅲Ⓢ | Arc-en-Barrois 🌊 | 18C2 |

Camping municipal, D3/D159. **GPS:** n47,95056 e5,00528.⬆➡.

25 🍴€ 5 🚰🔌ChWC🔲included, on campsite. 🚿 **Location:** Simple.
Surface: gravel. **◯** 01/01-31/12 ● Whitsuntide
Distance: 🚶500m ⊗500m 🛒500m.

| 🖳Ⓢ | Attigny | 15C1 |

D987. **GPS:** n49,48583 e4,58077.⬆.

4 🍴free 🚰🔌Chfree. **Location:** Rural, simple.
Distance: 🚶800m ⊗800m 🛒900m.

| 🖳Ⓢ | Avize | 15B3 |

Place du Bourg Joli. **GPS:** n48,97175 e4,00999.⬆.

5 🍴free 🚰🔌Chfree. **Location:** Urban, simple, central, quiet.
Surface: asphalted. **◯** 01/01-31/12
Distance: 🚶on the spot ⊗200m 🛒bakery 50m.

Remarks: Next to town hall.

Bar-sur-Aube 18C1
7, Rue des Varennes. **GPS:** n48,23491 e4,70065. ↑→.

1 free €3,50/100liter Ch €3,50/1h. **Location:** Simple.
Surface: asphalted. 01/01-31/12
Distance: on the spot on the spot on the spot.

Beaunay 15B3
Ferme Du Bel Air, Rue Principale. **GPS:** n48,88177 e3,87475. ↑.

12 €6 Ch (6x)included. **Location:** Rural, simple,
isolated, quiet. **Surface:** gravel. 01/01-31/12
Distance: 2km 2km 2km.

Bogny-sur-Meuse 15C1
Rue de la Meuse. **GPS:** n49,85780 e4,74225. ↑.

6 free €2/100liter Ch €2/2h, only 2-euro coins.
Location: Rural, simple, quiet. **Surface:** asphalted.
01/01-31/12
Distance: on the spot on the spot 250m 400m 500m.
Remarks: Along the Meuse river, service 75m.

Brienne-le-Château 18C1
Rue de la Gare. **GPS:** n48,39617 e4,53130. ↑→.

10 free €3/10minutes Ch €3/55minutes. **Location:** Simple,
noisy. **Surface:** asphalted. 01/01-31/12 water disconnected in
winter
Distance: 300m 400m 300m.
Remarks: At former station, coins at tourist info, supermarket
Champion.

Cerisières 18C1
D186, Froideau. **GPS:** n48,29921 e5,06339. ↑→.

20 free Ch free. **Location:** Rural, simple, isolated, quiet.

Surface: gravel. 01/01-31/12
Distance: 2km.

Chamery 15B2
Salle Polyvalente, Rue du Château Rouge.
GPS: n49,17475 e3,95446. ↑.

5 free €2/100liter Ch €2/2h. **Location:** Rural, simple,
quiet. **Surface:** gravel. 01/01-31/12
Distance: 300m 400m.
Remarks: In front of community centre.

Champigny-lès-Langres 18D2
Rue du Port, D74. **GPS:** n47,88167 e5,33861. ↑.

6 free WC. **Location:** Simple, noisy. **Surface:** gravel.
01/01-31/12
Distance: 400m 800m.

Chaource 18B1
Chemin de Ronde/Rue des Roises. **GPS:** n48,05944 e4,13861. ↑→.

10 free €2/100liter Ch €2/1h.
Location: Comfortable, quiet.
Surface: grassy.
Distance: 100m on the spot on the spot on the spot on
the spot.
Remarks: Coins at tourist info, 2, Grande rue, monday-morning market.

Charleville-Mézières 15C1
Rue des Pâquis. **GPS:** n49,78056 e4,72056. ↑.

8 free €2/100liter Ch €2/55minutes €5,40, ask at camp
site. **Surface:** asphalted.
01/01-31/12 electricity: 01/11-31/03
Distance: 800m on the spot 500m 2km 600m Nearby
campsite Nearby campsite.
Remarks: Service only with 2-euro coins, ask for electricity at campsite.
Tourist information Charleville-Mézières:
Musée Ardennes, Place Ducale. Regional museum. 10-12, 14-18
Mo.
place Ducale. Regional products. Tue, Thu, Sa.

Chaumont 18D1
Port de la Maladière, RN74 Neufchâteau > Chaumont.
GPS: n48,11815 e5,15437. ↑.

12 €6,50, €0,20/pp tourist tax Ch included WC €
2,40 €2,20/3,20 free. **Location:** Quiet. **Surface:** metalled.
01/04-31/10
Distance: 4km Canal de la Marne 100m nearby.
Remarks: Baker every morning.

Chavanges 15C3
Ruelle du Fief Berthaux. **GPS:** n48,50691 e4,57627. ↑→.

8 free €3 Ch. **Location:** Simple, quiet.
Surface: asphalted/gravel. 01/01-31/12
Distance: 300m 400m.
Remarks: Coins at the shops.

Colombey-les-deux-Eglises 18C1
Rue de Général de Gaulle. **GPS:** n48,22316 e4,88619. ↑.

10 free Ch WC free. **Location:** Simple, quiet.
Surface: asphalted/gravel. 01/04-30/11
Distance: on the spot 50m 50m.
Remarks: Museum and Memorial Général De Gaulle 800m.

Corgirnon 18D2
Allée du Parc. **GPS:** n47,80681 e5,50308. ↑→.

8 €4 Ch included. **Location:** Rural, comfortable,
isolated, quiet. **Surface:** gravel. 01/01-31/12 water
disconnected in winter
Distance: 500m 10km 500m, baker on site (Tue-Su).
Remarks: Bread-service.

Dolancourt 18C1
Nigloland, RN19. **GPS:** n48,26086 e4,60945. ↑.

28 €6/24h, free with a meal Ch included.
Location: Simple, isolated. **Surface:** asphalted. 03/04-03/11
Distance: on the spot.

Remarks: Parking amusement park, max. 24h.

🏕️Ⓢ Donjeux 🚣 18D1

Halte Nautique, D67a. **GPS**: n48,36586 e5,14891.⬆️.

4 🚐free 🚰🚻Ch 🚿(4x)free. **Location:** Comfortable, quiet.
Surface: gravel/metalled. ⬜ 01/01-31/12
Distance: 🚶1km 🛶Canal de la Marne 🎣on the spot ⊗1km 🛒800m
🧍on the spot.
Remarks: Baker every morning.

🏕️Ⓢ Épernay 🍦 15B2

Rue Dom Pérignon. GPS: n49,03602 e3,95130.⬆️.

3 🚐free 🚰€2/100liter 🚻Ch ➕€2/1h WC€0,50/time.
Location: Urban, simple, central, noisy.
Surface: asphalted.
Distance: 🚶within walking distance 🚉Avenue Jean Jaurès.
Remarks: Behind church St.Pierre-St.Paul, coins at tourist info.

Tourist information Épernay:
👁 Cave de Catellane, 154, avenue de Verdun.
👁 Mercier, 70, avenue de Champagne.
⬜ Mo-Sa 9.30-11.30h, 14-16.30h,
Su/holidays 9.30-11.30h, 14-17.30h.

🏕️Ⓢ Esternay 15A3

Place des Tilleuls, D48, Rue de la Paix. GPS: n48,73196 e3,55719.⬆️.

8 🚐free 🚰🚻free. **Location:** Urban, simple, central, quiet.
Surface: gravel. ⬜ water: 15/03-15/11
Distance: 🚶within walking distance ⊗200m 🛒400m.
Remarks: Behind church.

🏕️ Froncles 18D1

Halte Nautique. GPS: n48,29954 e5,15246.⬆️.

10 🚐€3 🚰€3/day 🚻Ch 🚿(8x)€3/1day 🚽€2,50/stay 🔌€3/3 🛜.📶
Location: Comfortable. **Surface:** gravel. ⬜ 01/01-31/12
Distance: 🚶500m 🏖river-beach 🎣on the spot ⊗on the spot
🛒1km 🧍on the spot.
Remarks: Baker on site (Tue-Su).

🏕️ Fumay 10C3

Quai des Carmélites. GPS: n49,99736 e4,70986.⬆️.

+10 🚐free. **Surface:** unpaved. ⬜ 01/01-31/12
Distance: 🚶400m.
Remarks: Along the Meuse river.

🏕️Ⓢ Giffaumont-Champaubert ⛵🚣 15C3

Site de Chantecoq, Rue du grand Der. **GPS**: n48,56880 e4,70294.⬆️.

50 🚐free 🚰€3,80/80liter 🚻Ch ➕€3,80/45minutes WC.
Location: Rural, simple. **Surface:** metalled.
⬜ 01/01-31/12
Distance: 🏊on the spot ⊗900m.
Remarks: At lake Der de Chantecoq, coins at tourist info.

🏕️Ⓢ Giffaumont-Champaubert 🚣🚣 15C3

Station Nautique, Rue du Port. **GPS**: n48,55354 e4,76715.⬆️.

50 🚐€7,50 20-8h, parking free 🚰🚻Ch 🛜included 🍽.📶📶
Location: Rural. ⬜ 01/01-31/12
Distance: 🏊on the spot ⊗200m 🛒8km Montier-en-Der 🚲on the
spot 🧍on the spot.

🏕️ Givet 10C3

Rue Jean Jaurès. GPS: n50,13593 e4,82138.⬆️.

12 🚐free. **Location:** Urban, simple, central, quiet. **Surface:** asphalted.
⬜ 01/01-31/12

🏕️Ⓢ Givet 10C3

Camping Municipal, Rue Berthelot. **GPS**: n50,14291 e4,82611.⬆️.

5 🚐free 🚰€3/100liter 🚻Ch ➕€3/h. **Location:** Rural, simple.
Surface: asphalted. ⬜ 01/01-31/12
Distance: 🚶750m ⊗750m 🛒1km.
Remarks: Coins at campsite.

🏕️Ⓢ Goncourt 🚣 18D1

Rue des Lottes, D74. GPS: n48,23685 e5,60998.⬆️.

30 🚐€2 ➕€2 🚻Ch. **Location:** Rural, comfortable.
Surface: asphalted/gravel. ⬜ 01/01-31/12
Distance: 🚶100m 🏊on the spot ⊗100m 🛒100m.
Remarks: Along the Meuse river, max. 48h, baker at 8am.

🏕️Ⓢ Haybes 10C3

Halte Fluviale, Quai du Docteur Adolphe Hamai.
GPS: n50,01093 e4,70762.⬆️.

4 🚐free 🚰🚻Ch€2,05 🔌€3,30/3,30. **Surface:** metalled.
⬜ 01/01-31/12
Distance: 🚶200m ⊗50m 🛒bakery 200m.
Remarks: Along the Meuse river, service at camping municipal.

🏕️Ⓢ Javernant 🌿 18B1

Le Cheminot, N77. GPS: n48,14789 e4,01046.⬆️.

5 🚐free 🚰free. **Location:** Simple. **Surface:** asphalted.
⬜ 01/01-31/12
Remarks: 2013: during inspection service out of order.

🏕️Ⓢ Joinville 🌿🚣🚣 18D1

Halte Nautique, Rue des Jardins. **GPS**: n48,44583 e5,15000.⬆️.

12 🚐free 🚰€2 🚻Ch ➕€2 🍽.📶 **Location:** Simple, quiet.
Surface: gravel/metalled. ⬜ 01/01-31/12
Distance: 🚶500m 🏊on the spot 🎣on the spot ⊗800m 🛒100m
🧍on the spot.

🏕️Ⓢ Juzennecourt 18C1

Place de la Mairie. GPS: n48,18429 e4,97890.⬆️.

4 🚐free 🚰Ch 🚿WC. **Location:** Simple, quiet. **Surface:** metalled.
⬜ 01/01-31/12
Distance: 🚶on the spot 🛒bakery in the village 🧍on the spot.
Remarks: Parking townhall.

⬛S La Cheppe — 15C2

Champ d'Attila, Rue de Champo d'Attila. **GPS**: n49,04892 e4,49377.⬆

5 ⊠free ⚲€2/100liter ⬛Ch ⬛€2/2h WC ⬛. **Location:** Rural, simple, quiet. **Surface:** asphalted.
⬛ 01/01-31/12
Distance: 🚶500m.

⬛S La Gault-Soigny — 15A3

Rue de la Liberté, D373. **GPS**: n48,81758 e3,59072.⬆

8 ⊠free ⚲⬛Chfree. **Location:** Rural, simple, quiet.
Surface: asphalted. ⬛ 01/01-31/12
Distance: 🚶on the spot.
Remarks: Near Salle des Fêtes, service 50m.

⬛S Langres 🍂 — 18D2

Ruelle de la Poterne. **GPS**: n47,85795 e5,32989.⬆➡

15 ⊠free ⚲⬛Chfree. **Location:** Simple, quiet. **Surface:** asphalted
⬛ 01/01-31/12
Distance: 🚶800m.

⬛ Langres 🍂 — 18D2

Parking Panorama, Allée des Marronniers.
GPS: n47,86104 e5,33674.⬆

⊠free. **Location:** Simple, quiet. **Surface:** asphalted.
⬛ 01/01-31/12
Distance: 🚶on the spot ⬛on the spot.
Remarks: Inclining pitches, free elevator to old town.

⬛ Langres 🍂 — 18D2

Place de Bel Air. **GPS**: n47,85885 e5,33225.⬆

⊠free WC. **Location:** Urban, simple, noisy. **Surface:** asphalted.
⬛ 01/01-31/12
Distance: ⬛on the spot ⬛on the spot.

⬛ ⬛ Fri.

Launois-sur-Vence — 15C1

Avenue Louis Jolly. **GPS**: n49,65467 e4,54005.⬆

10 ⊠free. **Location:** Rural, simple, quiet. **Surface:** unpaved.
⬛ 01/01-31/12
Distance: 🚶on the spot ⬛50m.
Remarks: In front of tourist office, max. 48h.

S Launois-sur-Vence — 15C1

Rue du Thin. **GPS**: n49,65810 e4,53987.⬆➡
⚲€2/100liter ⬛Ch ⬛€2/1h. ⬛ water: frost
Remarks: Coins at tourist info.

Tourist information Launois-sur-Vence:
⬛ Relais de Poste. Monthly antiques and flea market. ⬛ 3rd Su of the month 9-18h.

⬛S Les Riceys ⬛ ⬛ — 18B2

D452. **GPS**: n47,99222 e4,36458.⬆➡

40 ⊠free ⚲€2 ⬛Ch ⬛€2. **Location:** Simple, isolated, quiet.
Surface: asphalted. ⬛ 01/01-31/12
Distance: 🚶500m ⬛500m ⬛500m.

⬛S Mareuil-sur-Ay ⬛ — 15B2

Relais nautique, Place Charles de Gaulle. **GPS**: n49,04522 e4,03490.⬆

8 ⊠free ⚲⬛Ch ⬛€5/3h. **Location:** Urban, comfortable, central, quiet. **Surface:** asphalted. ⬛ 01/01-31/12 ⬛ water disconnected in winter
Distance: 🚶on the spot ⬛on the spot ⬛on the spot ⬛on the spot ⬛on the spot.
Remarks: On the canal, in village, coins at supermarket.

⬛ Mesnil-Saint-Père ⬛ — 18B1

Rue du Lac. **GPS**: n48,25524 e4,34090.

50 ⊠free. **Location:** Simple. **Surface:** asphalted. ⬛ 01/01-31/12
Distance: ⬛beach 400m.
Remarks: Nearby lake Orient.

⬛ Monthermé — 15C1

Rue du Général de Gaulle, D989. **GPS**: n49,88136 e4,72979.⬆

---

6 ⊠free. **Location:** Rural, simple, quiet. **Surface:** grassy.
⬛ 01/01-31/12
Distance: 🚶900m ⬛on the spot.
Remarks: Along the Meuse river, max. 24h.

⬛S Monthermé — 15C1

Etape fluviale, Quai A. Briand. **GPS**: n49,88608 e4,73593.⬆

± 20 ⊠€3 + € 0,20/pp tourist tax ⚲€2,80/day ⬛€1,50 ⬛€ 3,50/3,50. **Surface:** grasstiles.
Distance: 🚶300m.
Remarks: Along the Meuse river, check in at harbourmaster.

⬛S Montier-en-Der 🍂 — 18C1

Rue de l'Isle. **GPS**: n48,47861 e4,76861.⬆

6 ⊠free ⚲€2,60/8minutes ⬛Ch ⬛€2,60/55minutes WC.
Location: Simple. **Surface:** gravel.
Distance: 🚶on the spot ⬛500m ⬛500m.
Remarks: Coins at tourist info.

⬛ Mouzon — 15C1

Halte fluviale. **GPS**: n49,60687 e5,07710.
8 ⊠€7,80, 01/11-31/03 free ⚲⬛Ch ⬛WC ⬛ ⬛ included.
Surface: asphalted. ⬛ 01/01-31/12 ⬛ Service: winter
Distance: 🚶100m.
Remarks: Along the Meuse river, sanitary and wifi code at harbour master, felt museum 100m (May-Sep).

⬛S Mutigny — 15B2

Aire de l'étang, Route de Montflambert.
GPS: n49,06894 e4,02669.⬆➡

8 ⊠free ⚲€5/100liter ⬛€5/3h ⬛. **Location:** Rural, simple, isolated, quiet. **Surface:** asphalted. ⬛ 01/01-31/12
Distance: 🚶1km ⬛3km ⬛3km.

⬛S Nogent-sur-Seine — 15A3

Parking camping/piscine, Rue du camping.
GPS: n48,50388 e3,50888.⬆

5 ⌂ € 6,58/night, € 2,99/3h ⛽🚰 Chfree ⚡(2x)included3h.♨
Location: Urban, simple, quiet. **Surface:** asphalted.
⚪ 01/01-31/12
Distance: 🚉1,5km 🏊2km ⊗1,5km 🛒1,5km 🚲2km.
Remarks: Max. 48h.

		Peigney 🅿🌊		18D2

Lac de la Liez, D284, rue Côté de Recey.
GPS: n47,87272 e5,38077. ⬆➡

8 ⌂ € 10,50 ⛽🚰Ch⚡📶€2.♨ **Location:** Simple.
Surface: asphalted. ⚪ 01/01-31/12
Distance: 🚉500m 🏊on the spot 🍴on the spot ⊗on the spot 🛒on the spot.

		Piney	18B1

Place des Anciens Combattants, Rue du Général de Gaulle.
GPS: n48,35878 e4,33442. ⬆➡

3 ⌂free ⛽€3/10minutes 🚰Ch🛒€3/1h. **Location:** Simple.
Surface: metalled. ⚪ 01/01-31/12 ◉ water: frost
Distance: 🚉500m 🏊500m 🛒500m.
Remarks: Coins at Office de Tourisme Mesnil-Plage and restaurant le Tadorne.

		Reims	15B2

Parc du CIS de la Comédie, Esplanade André Malraux, chaussée
Bocquaine. **GPS:** n49,24881 e4,02110. ⬆➡

7 ⌂free ⛽🚰Chfree. **Location:** Urban, simple, central, noisy.
Surface: metalled.
Distance: 🚉15 min walking ⚡1,4km ⊗350m 🛒100m.
Remarks: Max. 48h, call for entrance code, noisy place.

		Saint-Dizier 🌿	15C3

Centre Loisirs Caravanning, Route de Villiers en lieu.
GPS: n48,64255 e4,91035. ➡

6 ⌂free ⛽🚰Ch🛒WCfree. **Location:** Simple. **Surface:** asphalted.
⚪ 01/01-31/12
Distance: 🚉1,5km 🛒400m.
Remarks: At motorhome dealer, coins during opening hours.

		Sainte-Livière	15C3

1 rue Sainte Libaire. **GPS:** n48,59941 e4,82468. ⬆
19 ⌂ € 8 ⛽🚰Ch⚡(19x)📶included. **Location:** Rural, isolated,
quiet. **Surface:** gravel. ⚪ 01/01-31/12
Distance: 🏊2km Lake Der-Chantecoq 🛒2km.
Remarks: Service passerby € 3.

		Sainte-Marie-du-Lac-Nuisement	15C3

Port de Nuisement, D13A. **GPS:** n48,60285 e4,74922.
6 ⌂free ⛽🚰Ch⚡. **Surface:** asphalted. ⚪ 01/01-31/12
Distance: 🚉4km 🏊on the spot.

		Sapignicourt 🌿	15C3

Rue Deperthes à Larzicourt. **GPS:** n48,65111 e4,80583. ⬆

4 ⌂ ⛽€2,50/10minutes 🚰Ch€2,50/55minutes. **Location:** Rural,
simple, isolated, quiet. **Surface:** grassy.
Distance: 🚉500m.
Remarks: Coins at town hall and Mr. Bauer, 14, grande rue.

		Sedan 🌿	15C1

Rue Hue Tanton. **GPS:** n49,70145 e4,95092. ⬆
⌂free. ⚪ 01/01-31/12
Remarks: Parking places around the castle of Sedan.

		Sézanne	15B3

Place du Champ Benoist. GPS: n48,72222 e3,72125. ⬆

7 ⌂free ⛽€2/100liter 🚰Ch🛒€2/1h WCfree. **Location:** Urban,
simple, central, noisy. **Surface:** asphalted. ⚪ 01/01-31/12 ◉ Sa
market
Distance: 🚉on the spot ⊗50m 🛒300m 🚌50m.

		Suippes	15C2

Rue de l'Abreuvoir. **GPS:** n49,13074 e4,53419. ⬆

10 ⌂free ⛽€2/liter 🚰Ch€2/1h 🧺. **Location:** Urban, simple.
Surface: asphalted. ⚪ 01/01-31/12
Distance: 🚉on the spot ⊗200m 🛒200m.

		Vendeuvre-sur-Barse	18C1

Place du 8 mai 1945, Rue du Pont Chevalier.
GPS: n48,23727 e4,46646. ⬆➡

5 ⌂free ⛽€3 🚰Ch🛒€3. **Location:** Urban, simple, simple.
Surface: asphalted. ◉ tue-evening, wed-morning (market)
Distance: 🚉100m 🛒on the spot 🛒ATAC 🚌on the spot.

		Viéville 🌿🌊	18D1

Halte Nautique La Licorne. GPS: n48,23825 e5,12988. ⬆

6 ⌂ € 1,50 🚰€1,50/day ⚡(6x)€1,50/day.♨
Location: Rural, simple, quiet.
Surface: gravel.
Distance: 🚉on the spot ⊗3km 🛒500m 🚲on the spot 🚶on the spot.

		Villeneuve-Renneville-Chevigny	15B3

Champagne Leclère-Massard, 12, rue du Plessis.
GPS: n48,91488 e4,05959. ➡

6 ⌂ € 5 ⛽🚰Ch⚡included 📶€2/day.♨ **Location:** Comfortable.
Surface: asphalted.
Distance: 🚉3km 🛒2km ⊗3km 🛒3km 🚶on the spot.
Remarks: Tu-Su fresh bread, champagne tastery.

		Villers-sous-Châtillon	15B2

Halte camping-cars, Rue du Parc. **GPS:** n49,09642 e3,80078. ⬆➡

5 ⌂free ⛽€3/100liter 🚰Ch🛒€3/1h. **Location:** Rural, simple,
quiet. **Surface:** asphalted. ⚪ 01/01-31/12
Distance: 🚉1,2km 🛒50m ⊗1,2km 🛒2km.
Remarks: Coins at town hall and restaurant du Commerce.

Lorraine

		Allarmont	18F1

Le Meix du Haut Regard, 21, rue du Haut Regard.
GPS: n48,48070 e7,01381.
2 ⌂ ⛽🚰Ch⚡€5/24h ◉€4 📶free. **Location:** Comfortable,
luxurious. **Surface:** gravel.
Distance: 🚉400m ⊗400m 🛒400m.
Remarks: Swimming pool available.

		Amnéville 🏛	15E2

Rue de l'Europe. **GPS:** n49,24780 e6,13842. ⬆

10 ⊠free ⌐€3 ⬚Ch. **Location:** Rural, simple, quiet.
Surface: grassy. ☐ 01/01-31/12
Distance: ⬚1,8km.
Remarks: Behind tourist info, max. 48h.

| ⊠ | **Ancerville** | 15C3 |

Impasse des Pransons. **GPS:** n48,63641 e5,01582.⬆.

2 ⊠free. **Location:** Urban, simple, quiet. **Surface:** metalled.
☐ 01/01-31/12
Distance: ⬚on the spot ⊗400m ⬚400m.

| � | **Avocourt** | 15D2 |

Restaurant La Terrasse, Rue du Moulin. **GPS:** n49,20417 e5,14227.⬆.
4 ⊠free. **Location:** Rural, simple. **Surface:** unpaved.
☐ 01/01-31/12
Distance: ⬚on the spot ⊗on the spot.

| ⊠S | **Baccarat** | 18F1 |

Place du General Le'Clerc. **GPS:** n48,44667 e6,74000.⬆.

15 ⊠€ 5/night ⌐€2/100liter ⬚Ch ⬚€2/3minutes WC.⬚
Surface: asphalted. ☐ 01/01-31/12 ☐ Fri-morning market
Distance: ⬚300m ⬚on the spot ⬚on the spot ⊗300m ⬚300m.
Remarks: Along river, max. 24h.
Tourist information Baccarat:
M Musée du Cristal. Crystal museum. ☐ Mo-Sa 10-18h. ⬚ € 2,50.

| ⊠S | **Bar-le-Duc** | 15D3 |

Halte du port fluvial, Rue du débarcadère.
GPS: n48,77536 e5,16654.⬆➡.

8 ⊠free ⌐€2/100liter ⬚Ch ⬚€2/55minutes. **Location:** Urban,
simple, noisy. **Surface:** asphalted.
☐ 01/01-31/12
Distance: ⬚on the spot ⬚on the spot ⊗150m ⬚150m ⬚150m
⬚on the spot.
Remarks: At the canal, coins at tourist info, 7 rue Jeanne d'Arc.

| ⊠ | **Beaulieu-en-Argonne** ⬚⬚⬚ | 15C2 |

Parking Mairie, Grande Rue, D2B. **GPS:** n49,03183 e5,06665.⬆.

6 ⊠free. **Location:** Urban, simple, central, quiet. **Surface:** asphalted.
☐ 01/01-31/12
Distance: ⬚on the spot ⊗50m ⬚on the spot ⬚on the spot.
Remarks: In front of police station.

| ⊠ | **Beaulieu-en-Argonne** ⬚⬚⬚ | 15C2 |

Parking St. Rouin, D2. **GPS:** n49,03554 e5,02975.⬆.

4 ⊠free. **Location:** Isolated. **Surface:** gravel.
Distance: ⬚Beaulieu 6km.
Remarks: Isolated parking.

| ⊠S | **Bitche** | 15G2 |

Rue Bombelles. **GPS:** n49,05431 e7,43446.⬆.
5 ⊠free ⌐€2 ⬚Ch ⬚€2. **Location:** Comfortable, isolated, quiet.
Surface: gravel.
Distance: ⬚750m ⊗750m ⬚750m.

| ⊠S | **Bruley** | 15E3 |

D118, rue Saint-Martin. **GPS:** n48,70640 e5,85554.⬆.

10 ⊠free ⌐€3/10minutes ⬚Ch ⬚(2x)€3/8h. **Surface:** gravel.
☐ 01/01-31/12
Distance: ⬚200m ⊗300m ⬚300m.
Remarks: Max. 48h.

| ⊠S | **Bulgnéville** ⬚ | 18E1 |

Étang des Récollets, Rue des Récollets.
GPS: n48,20733 e5,83899.⬆➡.

10 ⊠€ 3/24h ⌐ ⬚ChWCincluded. **Location:** Rural, luxurious, quiet.
Surface: asphalted. ☐ 15/04-31/12
Distance: ⬚700m ⬚1,8km ⬚on the spot ⬚on the spot ⊗100m
⬚700m.

| ⊠S | **Certilleux** | 18D1 |

Rue de l'Église. **GPS:** n48,31193 e5,72679.⬆.

8 ⊠free ⌐free. **Location:** Urban, simple. **Surface:** asphalted.
☐ 01/01-31/12
Distance: ⬚on the spot
Remarks: Beautiful view.

| ⊠ | **Champougny** | 15D3 |

D145f. **GPS:** n48,54410 e5,69277.⬆.

3 ⊠free. **Location:** Rural, simple, quiet. **Surface:** grassy.
☐ 01/01-31/12
Distance: ⬚200m ⬚25m.

| ⚓S | **Charmes** | 18E1 |

Port de plaisance. **GPS:** n48,37334 e6,29542.⬆.

100 ⊠€ 7 ⌐included ⬚Ch ⬚(80x)€2 WC ⬚€1,50 ⬚€3/day.
Surface: gravel/metalled. ☐ 01/01-31/12
Distance: ⬚1km ⬚1,5km ⬚on the spot ⬚on the spot ⬚within
walking distance.
Tourist information Charmes:
⬚ ☐ Fri-morning.

| ⊠S | **Commercy** | 15D3 |

Rue du Docteur Boyer. **GPS:** n48,76374 e5,59616.⬆.

4 ⊠free ⌐€3/15minutes ⬚Ch ⬚(4x)€3/4h ⬚free.
Location: Comfortable. **Surface:** asphalted. ☐ 01/01-31/12
Distance: ⬚800m ⬚on the spot ⬚on the spot ⊗600m ⬚100m.
Remarks: On the canal.

| ⊠S | **Contrisson** ⬚ | 15C3 |

Ballastière. GPS: n48,80530 e4,94714.⬆.

10 ⊠free WC. **Location:** Rural, simple, isolated, quiet.
Surface: unpaved. ☐ 01/01-31/12
Distance: ⬚800m ⬚on the spot ⬚on the spot ⊗1km ⬚1km.
Remarks: At small lake.

| ⊠S | **Damvillers** | 15D2 |

Rue de L'Ile d'Envie, D905. **GPS:** n49,33790 e5,39752.⬆.

FR

4 🛏 free 🚰 €2/100liter 🚽Ch 🚮 €2. **Location:** Urban, simple, central.
Surface: asphalted. 🅿 01/01-31/12
Distance: 🛒 on the spot ⊗ on the spot 🚰 on the spot.

| 🛈 | Damvillers | 15D2 |

Etang, D905. **GPS:** n49,34978 e5,39970.⬆.
10 🛏 free. **Location:** Isolated. **Surface:** grassy. 🅿 01/01-31/12
Distance: 🛒 Damvillers 1km.

| ⚓S | Dieue-sur-Meuse | 15D2 |

Port de plaisance, Route des Dames. **GPS:** n49,07110 e5,42634.⬆.

15 🛏 free 🚰 free. **Location:** Rural, simple, quiet. **Surface:** gravel.
🅿 01/01-31/12
Distance: 🛒 200m ⊿ on the spot ➤ on the spot ⊗ 200m 🚰 200m.
Remarks: At the canal.

| 🛈S | Dun-sur-Meuse 🌿🐚 | 15D2 |

Rue du Vieux Port. **GPS:** n49,38919 e5,17787.⬆.

16 🛏 €7 🚰🚽Ch 🧹 (8x)WC 🗑 included 🔌.💧 **Location:** Rural,
comfortable, central, quiet. **Surface:** gravel. 🅿 01/01-31/12
🅿 sanitary building: 01/11-01/04
Distance: 🛒 600m ⊿ on the spot ➤ on the spot ⊗ 400m 🚰 600m.

| 🛈S | Épinal | 18E1 |

Camping-Car Park, Chemin du Petit Chaperon Rouge.
GPS: n48,17969 e6,46865.⬆.
50 🛏 €12 🚰🚽Ch 🧹 (20x)📶 included. 🗑 💳 🅿 01/01-31/12
Distance: 🛒 1,5km.

| ⚓S | Épinal | 18E1 |

Port d'Épinal, Quai de Dogneville, D12. **GPS:** n48,18671 e6,44493.⬆.

5 🛏 summer € 5, winter € 8 🚰🚽Ch 🧹 Service €3/15min 💳.
Surface: asphalted.
Distance: 🛒 1km ⊿ 3,5km.
Remarks: Max. 48h.

| | Etain | 15D2 |

Allée du champ de foire, D631. **GPS:** n49,20942 e5,63755.
6 🛏 free. **Location:** Simple, noisy. **Surface:** metalled.
🅿 01/01-31/12
Distance: 🛒 on the spot ⊗ 500m 🚰 500m.

| 🛈S | Etival-Clairefontaine | 18F1 |

Rue du Vivier. **GPS:** n48,36355 e6,86504.⬆.

---

20 🛏 free 🚰🚽Chfree. **Surface:** gravel. 🅿 01/01-31/12 🔵 water
disconnected in winter
Distance: 🛒 on the spot.
Remarks: Behind town hall.

| 🛈 | Fains-Veel 🐚 | 15D3 |

Halte Fluviale, Rue du Stade. **GPS:** n48,79298 e5,12503.⬆.

2 🛏 free. **Location:** Simple, quiet. **Surface:** metalled.
🅿 01/01-31/12
Distance: 🛒 450m ⊿ on the spot ➤ on the spot ⊗ on the spot 🚰 on
the spot.

| 🛈 | Favières | 18E1 |

Base de Loisirs. GPS: n48,46660 e5,96124.⬆.

8 🛏 free 🚰 €2 🚽Ch 🚮 €2 WC 📶. **Location:** Rural, comfortable,
central, quiet. **Surface:** gravel/metalled.
Distance: 🛒 200m ⊿ 13km ⊿ on the spot ➤ on the spot ⊗ on the
spot 🚰 bakery 300m 🚲 on the spot 🚶 on the spot.

| 🛈S | Fénétrange | 15F3 |

Wally Services, Route de Sarre Union. **GPS:** n48,85365 e7,02723.⬆.
5 🛏 free 🚰 €2 🚽Ch 🚮 €2. **Surface:** grassy/metalled.
Remarks: Max. 48h.

| 🛈S | Fraize | 18F1 |

Impasse de la Gare/ Place Jean Sonrel. **GPS:** n48,18188 e7,00360.

6 🛏 free 🚰 €3 🚽Ch 🚮 €3 WC. **Surface:** asphalted.
🅿 01/01-31/12
Distance: 🛒 100m ⊗ 100m 🚰 100m.
Remarks: Behind tourist info.

| 🛈S | Gérardmer 🚡🐚❄ | 18F1 |

Chemin de la Rayée, La Mauselaine. **GPS:** n48,05846 e6,88862.⬆.

100 🛏 € 4,50/24h 🚰 €2/100liter 🚽Ch. **Surface:** asphalted.

🅿 01/01-31/12
Distance: 🛒 Gérardmer 1,7km.
Remarks: Parking at skipistes, coins at tourist info.

| 🛈S | Gérardmer 🚡🐚❄ | 18F1 |

Parking de la Prairie, Boulevard d'Alsace.
GPS: n48,07199 e6,87333.⬆.

100 🛏 € 4,50 🚰 €2/100liter 🚽ChWC 🧹. **Surface:** asphalted/gravel.
🅿 01/01-31/12
Distance: 🛒 on the spot.
Remarks: Coins at tourist info.
Tourist information Gérardmer:
🏕 🅿 Thu, Sa.

| 🛈 | Gondrecourt-le-Château 🍦 | 15D3 |

Parking Musée du Cheval, Rue Saint Blaise. **GPS:** n48,51390 e5,50975.
2 🛏 free. **Surface:** metalled.
Distance: 🛒 on the spot ⊗ 50m 🚰 50m.

| 🛈 | Gondrecourt-le-Château 🍞 | 15D3 |

Rue du Général Leclerc. **GPS:** n48,51373 e5,50386.
3 🛏 free. **Location:** Urban. **Surface:** unpaved.
🅿 01/01-31/12
Distance: 🛒 on the spot ⊗ on the spot 🚰 on the spot.

| 🛈S | Haironville 🌿🐚 | 15D3 |

GPS: n48,68438 e5,08586.⬆.

5 🛏 free 🚰 €2/10minutes 🚽Ch 🚮 €2/50minutes. **Location:** Rural,
simple, central, quiet. **Surface:** gravel.
🅿 01/01-31/12
Distance: 🛒 200m 🚰 200m.
Remarks: Coins at the shops in the village.

| 🛈S | Heudicourt sous les Côtes 🐚 | 15D3 |

Ste Nautique de Madine. GPS: n48,93549 e5,71548.⬆.

50 🛏 first night € 10, € 7 each additional night 🚰🚽ChWC 🗑.
💧 **Location:** Rural, comfortable, quiet. **Surface:** grassy/gravel.
🅿 01/04-31/10
Distance: 🛒 3km ⊿ on the spot ➤ on the spot ⊗ on the spot.
Remarks: View on Lac de Madine.

| 🛈S | Heudicourt sous les Côtes 🐚 | 15D3 |

Entrée 2, D133. **GPS:** n48,94035 e5,71741.⬆.

50 🛏 € 7. 💧 **Location:** Rural, simple, quiet. **Surface:** grassy.
🅿 01/04-31/10

FR

Distance: 3km 100m 100m.
Remarks: Next to campsite.

S **Hombourg-Haut** 15F2
Rue des Suédois. **GPS:** n49,12448 e6,77888.

7 free €2/100liter Ch €2/4h. **Surface:** asphalted.
01/01-31/12
Distance: 400m 200m on the spot.
Remarks: Max. 48h.

Issoncourt 15D3
Parking Relais de la Voie Sacrée. GPS: n48,97070 e5,28776.

4 free. **Location:** Rural, simple, quiet. **Surface:** gravel.
Distance: 50m.

La Bresse 18F1
Route de Lispach. **GPS:** n48,04354 e6,93348.
free. **Surface:** grassy/gravel. 01/01-31/12
Remarks: At cross-country skiing circuit.

CS **La Bresse** 18F1
Camping Belle Hutte. GPS: n48,03500 e6,96268.

20 € 12,50-22,50 Ch WC against payment.
Surface: grassy/gravel. 01/01-31/12
Distance: 9km 100m 500m.
Remarks: Summertime on campsite, wintertime in front of campsite.

CS **La Bresse** 18F1
Camping du Haut Des Bluches, 5, route des Planches.
GPS: n48,00005 e6,91718.

18 € 5 12.00-12.00h Ch WC included. 01/01-31/12
05/11-14/12
Remarks: Zone camping-car.

S **La Bresse** 18F1
Route de Niachamp. **GPS:** n47,99430 e6,85431.
€2/100liter Ch. 01/01-31/12

S **La Croix-sur-Meuse** 15D3
Auberge de la Truite, Route de Seuzey. **GPS:** n48,98267 e5,53393.

4 free (4x)€3/24h WC. **Location:** Rural, comfortable,
quiet. **Surface:** grassy. 01/01-31/12
Distance: 2km on the spot on the spot.

Lachaussée 15E2
Domaine du Vieux Moulin, Grande Rue. **GPS:** n49,03507 e5,81735.
4. **Location:** Rural, simple. **Surface:** gravel.
Distance: 100m 50m on the spot.
Remarks: Along Étang de Lachaussée.

Laheycourt 15C3
Rue de la Gare. **GPS:** n48,88903 e5,02165.

3 free. **Location:** Rural, simple, quiet. **Surface:** grassy.
01/01-31/12
Distance: on the spot 50m 50m.
Remarks: Along the Chée river.

S **Les Islettes** 15C2
Route du Lochères. **GPS:** n49,12122 e5,03684.

16 € 5/24h Ch WC included. **Location:** Rural,
comfortable. **Surface:** gravel. 01/01-31/12
Distance: 3km 10,5km 3km 3km.

S **Ligny-en-Barrois** 15D3
Relais Nautique, Rue Jean Willemert. **GPS:** n48,68787 e5,31943.

8 free €2/10minutes Ch €2/55minutes.
Location: Comfortable, central, quiet. **Surface:** asphalted.
Distance: 200m on the spot 200m 200m on the spot
on the spot.
Remarks: Along Canal de la Marne au Rhin.

Ligny-en-Barrois 15D3
Aire de Pilvetus, Chemin des Pains de Seigle.
GPS: n48,69262 e5,33621.
10 free. **Location:** Simple, isolated. **Surface:** gravel.
01/01-31/12
Distance: 1,2km.

Loison 15D2
Parking Camp Marguerre. GPS: n49,28962 e5,56737.

6 free.
Location: Rural, simple, isolated.
Remarks: Isolated parking, Camp Marguerre: militair erfgoed '14-18.

Longeville-en-Barrois 15D3
Gr Grande Rue. **GPS:** n48,74201 e5,20645.

10 free. **Location:** Urban, simple, quiet. **Surface:** gravel.
Distance: on the spot on the spot on the spot 100m
100m on the spot on the spot.
Remarks: Along the Ornain river.

S **Longuyon** 15D2
Parking Salvador Allende, N18. **GPS:** n49,44802 e5,59973.

2 free Ch WC.
Location: Urban, simple, central, noisy.
Surface: asphalted.
Distance: on the spot on the spot 100m.
Remarks: Parking next to tourist info, not suitable for big motorhomes.

S **Longwy** 15D1
Stade Municipal, Avenue du 8 Mai 1945.
GPS: n49,52656 e5,76559.

7 free €2,50/20minutes Ch €2,50/4h. **Location:** Urban,
simple, central, noisy. **Surface:** asphalted.
01/01-31/12
Distance: on the spot 400m 350m.
Remarks: At football ground.

CS **Lunéville** 15F3
Les Bosquets, Quai des Petits Bosquets. **GPS:** n48,59652 e6,49865.

15 € 5,50/24h Ch included free.
01/01-31/12
Distance: 700m 600m.

Ⓜ✖ Château Petit Versailles. Castle, 18th century and museum.
◯ 10-12h, 14-18h ◉ Tue.

Marbotte 15D3

Parking de la Mairie, Rue Principale, D12.
GPS: n48,83445 e5,58142.⬆.

2 free. **Location:** Simple, quiet. **Surface:** unpaved.
Distance: on the spot.

Maxey-sur-Meuse 18D1

GPS: n48,44861 e5,69500.⬆.

4 free. (4x)free. **Location:** Simple. **Surface:** gravel.
◯ 14/05-31/12
Distance: 2km 2km 500m.

Maxey-sur-Vaise 15D3

Grande Rue. **GPS**: n48,53836 e5,66705.⬆.

6 free. **Location:** Simple, central, quiet.
◯ 01/01-31/12
Distance: on the spot.

Metz 15E2

Allée Metz Plage. **GPS**: n49,12371 e6,16887.⬆.

8 free. Chfree.
Surface: asphalted.
Distance: 350m 1,5km 300m.
Remarks: At entrance campsite, max. 48h, inclining pitches.
Tourist information Metz:
👁 Place St Louis. Square surrounded by houses from the 14th century.
✝ Cathédrale St Etienne. Cathedral.

Millery 15E3

Avenue de la Moselle, D40. **GPS**: n48,81507 e6,12716.⬆.

5 free Chfree. **Surface:** asphalted. ◯ 01/04-31/10
◉ water: 01/11-31/03
Distance: on the spot 3,5km.
Remarks: Along Mosel.

Mirecourt 18E1

Place Thierry. **GPS**: n48,29945 e6,13591.⬆.
20 €6 Ch WCincluded. **Location:** Comfortable, central.
Surface: gravel.
Distance: on the spot.

Monthureux-sur Saône 18E1

D460. **GPS**: n48,03199 e5,97390.⬆➡.

8 free Ch WCfree €3/48h,Wifi-Stop.
Location: Comfortable, quiet. ◯ 01/01-31/12
Distance: on the spot on the spot 200m 75m.
Remarks: At football ground.

Montigny-lès-Vaucouleurs 15D3

Rue de la Côte. **GPS**: n48,58875 e5,63007.⬆.

10 free. **Location:** Rural, simple, quiet. **Surface:** gravel.
◯ 01/01-31/12
Distance: 700m.

Montplonne 15D3

Rue du Four. **GPS**: n48,68630 e5,16934.⬆.

4 free. **Location:** Rural, simple. **Surface:** gravel.
Distance: on the spot.
Remarks: Next to cemetery.

Morley 15D3

Parking Lavoir, D5A. **GPS**: n48,57848 e5,24878.⬆.

5 free. **Location:** Rural, simple, central, quiet.
Distance: on the spot.

Nancy 15E3

Parking Faubourg les III Maisons, Rue Charles Keller.
GPS: n48,70403 e6,17598.⬆.

€ 0,60-4,80, overnight stay free. **Surface:** asphalted.
◯ 01/01-31/12
Distance: city centre ± 1km.

Nancy 15E3

Port Saint Georges, N57, boulevard du 21ème Régiment d'Aviation.
GPS: n48,69221 e6,19318.

6 € 10/night Ch WC included. **S**urface: asphalted.
◯ 01/05-01/11
Distance: 500m on the spot on the spot 100m 100m
100m.
Remarks: Max. 5 nights, check in at harbourmaster.
Tourist information Nancy:
Ⓜ Musée Historique Lorraine, Palais Ducal. Regional museum.
◯ 15/06-15/09 ◉ Tue.
⊕ Zoo Haye, Velaine-en-Haye. Zoo with centre for wild birds.

Nant-le-Grand 15D3

Grand Rue, D169A. **GPS**: n48,67530 e5,22382.⬆.

4 free. **Location:** Rural, simple, quiet. **Surface:** gravel.
Distance: on the spot.

Niderviller 15F3

Marina Niderviller, Avenue de Lorraine. **GPS**: n48,71748 e7,09901.
12 € 10 €1/100liter Ch €0,50/kWh WC.

Nonsard Lamarche 15D3

Base de Loisirs, Base de Loisirs de Madine.
GPS: n48,93064 e5,74873.⬆.

30 €7 €3 Ch. **Location:** Rural, simple, isolated, quiet.
Surface: grassy/metalled. ◯ 01/04-31/10
Distance: 700m on the spot on the spot on the spot.
Remarks: At lake Madine, coins at campsite.

Nubécourt 15D2

D151, Rue Raymond Poincaré. **GPS**: n48,99704 e5,17256.⬆➡.

FR

10 🅿free. **Location:** Rural, simple, central, quiet. **Surface:** metalled.
⬛ 01/01-31/12
Distance: 🚰on the spot 🛒200m 🚮 on the spot ⚶ on the spot.

🅱🆂 Phalsbourg 15G3
Avia, ZAC Louvois, Route du Luxembourg. **GPS:** n48,77047 e7,24198.
🅿free 🚰€2 🚽Ch 🔌€2. **Surface:** asphalted. ⬛ 01/01-31/12
Distance: ⊗on the spot.

🅱 Pierre-Percée 18F1
D182A. **GPS:** n48,46723 e6,92911.

± 8 🅿free. **Surface:** asphalted.
Distance: 🚮on the spot 🛒on the spot.
Remarks: Picnic area at artificial lake.

🅱 Plombières-les-Bains ♨ 18F2
Avenue des Etats-Unis. **GPS:** n47,96208 e6,45411.⬆

5 🅿€ 8/24h 🚰 🔌(5x)included. **Surface:** asphalted.
⬛ 01/04-15/10

🅱🆂 Pompierre 18D1
Chemin de la Corvée. **GPS:** n48,25691 e5,67188.⬆➡

3 🅿free 🚰 🔌free. **Location:** Urban, simple, noisy.
Surface: asphalted. ⬛ 01/01-31/12
Distance: 🚮1km 🛒500m 🚮500m.

🅱🆂 Pont-à-Mousson 🌿⛵〰 15E3
Port de plaisance, Avenue des Etas Unis, D910.
GPS: n48,90296 e6,06088.⬆

42 🅿€ 9,50 🚰🚽Ch 🔌 WC 🔋📶included. **Location:** Luxurious.
Surface: asphalted. ⬛ 01/04-31/10
Distance: 🚮400m 🚲 3,4km 🛒on the spot ⊗400m 🚮400m 🚮on the spot.
Remarks: Check in at reception, bread-service.

🅱🆂 Rebeuville 18D1
Rue du Cougnot. **GPS:** n48,33530 e5,70128.⬆➡.

3 🅿free 🚰🚽Ch 🔌free. **Location:** Rural, comfortable, isolated.
Surface: asphalted. ⬛ 01/01-31/12
Distance: 🚮5km 🛒on the spot ⊗5km 🚮5km 🚮500m.

🅱🆂 Remiremont 18F1
Rue du Lit d'Eau. **GPS:** n48,01540 e6,60208.⬆.
30 🅿€ 6 🚰🚽Ch 🔌€3. 🛒 **Surface:** gravel.
Distance: 🚮1km.
Remarks: At small lake.

🅱🆂 Revigny-sur-Ornain 🛒 15C3
Stade/Office de Tourisme, Rue de l'Abattoir.
GPS: n48,82642 e4,98330.⬆➡

2 🅿free 🚰€3 🚽Ch 🔌€3. **Location:** Urban, simple, central, quiet.
Surface: asphalted. ⬛ 01/01-31/12
Distance: 🚮on the spot 🛒100m 🚮on the spot 🚮on the spot 🚮on the spot.
Remarks: Coins at tourist info.

🅱🆂 Rhodes 15F3
Port Municipal, Rue Principale. **GPS:** n48,75784 e6,90053.
30 🅿€ 18/24h 🚰🚽Ch 🔌 WC 🔋included. **Surface:** grassy.
⬛ Easter-01/10
Distance: 🚮on the spot 🛒on the spot.
Remarks: Along Etang du Stock.

🅱🆂 Richardmenil 15E3
Chemin de la Maize. **GPS:** n48,59457 e6,16078.⬆

5 🅿free 🚰🚽Ch 🔌(4x)free. **Surface:** asphalted.
⬛ 01/01-31/12
Distance: 🚮1km 🚮on the spot 🛒on the spot ⊗500m 🚮1km 🚮1km.

🅱🆂 Rollainville 18D1
Rue de la Cure. **GPS:** n48,36185 e5,73842.⬆➡

1 🅿free 🚰🔌free. **Location:** Urban, simple, central.
Surface: asphalted. ⬛ 01/01-31/12
Distance: 🚮on the spot.
Remarks: Baker at 8am.

🅱🆂 Rupt-sur-Moselle 18F2
Quai de la Parelle. **GPS:** n47,92061 e6,66194.⬆.

6 🅿free 🚰€3/10minutes 🚽Ch 🔌(4x)€3/3h WC.
Surface: asphalted.
Distance: ⊗350m 🚮250m 🚮on the spot ⚶ Voie Verte.
Remarks: Coins at the shops and town hall.

🅲🆂 Saint-Mihiel 15D3
Chemin Gué Rapeau. **GPS:** n48,90227 e5,53960.⬆➡.

4 🅿€ 3 🚰🚽Chfree 🔌€3/24h. **Location:** Rural, simple, isolated,
quiet. **Surface:** asphalted. ⬛ 01/01-31/12
Distance: 🚮1,5km ⊗1km 🚮1,5km.
Remarks: Directly at the river, nearby sluices, next to camping
municipal, max. 24h.

🅱🆂 Saint-Nabord 18F1
Rue de la Croix Saint Jacques. **GPS:** n48,04527 e6,58175.⬆.

3 🅿free 🚰€3/80liter 🚽Ch 🔌€3. **Surface:** asphalted.
⬛ 01/01-31/12
Distance: 🚮300m ⊗200m 🚮50m.

🅱🆂 Saint-Nicolas-de-Port 15E3
Rue du jeu de Paune. **GPS:** n48,63515 e6,30048.⬆➡.

10 🅿free 🚰€4 🚽Ch 🔌. **Location:** Urban, simple, central, quiet.
Surface: gravel. ⬛ 01/01-31/12
Distance: 🚮on the spot ⊗150m 🚮200m 🚮100m.

🅱🆂 Sarralbe 15F2
Rue de la Sarre. **GPS:** n49,00171 e7,03240.⬆.
4 🅿free. **Surface:** asphalted. ⬛ 01/01-31/12
Distance: 🚮350m ⊗350m.
Remarks: At sports centre.

Seuil-d'Argonne 15C3
Rue du Commandant Laflotte, D2/D20. **GPS:** n48,98294 e5,06215.⬆.

5 🅿free. **Location:** Urban, simple, quiet. **Surface:** gravel.

FR

◻ 01/01-31/12
Distance: ⊗650m ⬛650m 650m 650m.
Remarks: In fron of sports fields.

| 🅿️ | **Sierck-les-Bains** | 15E2 |

Place de la Gro. **GPS:** n49,44424 e6,36217.⬆️

8 free. **Location:** Simple. **Surface:** asphalted. ◻ 01/01-31/12
Distance: 200m ⊗200m ⬛350m.
Remarks: Along ther Moselle river, nearby police station.

| 🅿️ | **Souilly** | 15D2 |

Route de St.André-en-Barrois, D159. **GPS:** n49,02730 e5,27985.⬆️
6 free. **Surface:** gravel. ◻ 01/01-31/12
Distance: 600m.

| 🅿️ S | **Stenay** 🌊 | 15D1 |

Aire Camping-car, D947. **GPS:** n49,48979 e5,18323.⬆️➡️

47 €8 Ch WC €4/4 included. **Location:** Rural,
comfortable, quiet. **Surface:** metalled. ◻ 01/01-31/12
Distance: 150m 150m ⬛800m, bakery 300m.
Remarks: Pay and entrance code at harbourmaster, musée Européen de la Bière, beer museum.

| ⚓ S | **Stenay** 🌊 | 15D1 |

Port de plaisance, Rue du Port. **GPS:** n49,49096 e5,18312.⬆️➡️

6 €8 Ch WC €4/4 included. **Location:** Comfortable,
quiet. **Surface:** asphalted. ◻ 01/01-31/12
Distance: on the spot ⊗200m ⬛500m.
Remarks: Pay at harbourmaster.

Tourist information Stenay:
Ⓜ Musée de la Bière. Beer museum.
✠ Château, Louppy-sur-Loison. Renaissance castle, 17th century.

| 🅿️ | **Tannois** 🌿 | 15D3 |

Parking du Belvédère, D169. **GPS:** n48,71977 e5,22967.⬆️

10 free. **Location:** Rural, simple, isolated, quiet. **Surface:** gravel.
◻ 01/01-31/12
Distance: 1,3km 1,5km on the spot on the spot.

| 🅿️ S | **Thaon-les-Vosges** | 18E1 |

Aire du Coignot, Rue du Coignot. **GPS:** n48,24889 e6,42611.⬆️➡️

20 free Ch free. **Surface:** asphalted/gravel.
◻ 01/03-01/10
Distance: 1,5km ⬛400m.
Remarks: Next to port fluvial.

| 🅿️ | **Thierville-sur-Meuse** | 15D2 |

Thierville sur-meuse, Avenue de l,etangbleu.
GPS: n49,17499 e5,36357.⬆️

20 free. **Location:** Rural, simple, central. **Surface:** gravel.
◻ 01/01-31/12
Distance: 100m ⊗50m 50m on the spot on the spot.
Remarks: Along the Meuse river.

| 🅿️ S | **Tilleux** | 18D1 |

Grande Rue. GPS: n48,29300 e5,72250.⬆️➡️

8 free free. **Location:** Simple. **Surface:** gravel.
◻ 01/01-31/12
Distance: 100m.
Remarks: Inclining pitches, entrance road max. 3,5t.

| 🅿️ S | **Toul** | 15E3 |

Avenue du Colonel Péchot. **GPS:** n48,67939 e5,88806.

9 €7 Ch (8x)included. **Surface:** asphalted.
◻ 01/01-31/12
Distance: 4km.
Remarks: In front of police station.

| 🅿️ S | **Val-et-Châtillon** | 15F3 |

Rue de Petitmont. **GPS:** n48,55704 e6,96566.⬆️
6 free €3 Ch €3. **Surface:** gravel. ◻ 01/01-31/12
Distance: ⬛3,5km on the spot.
Remarks: Max. 4 days, bread-service.

| 🅿️ S | **Vaucouleurs** 🌊 | 15D3 |

Rue du Cardinal Lépicier. **GPS:** n48,60179 e5,66737.⬆️➡️

3 €5 €2/100liter Ch €2 WC. **Location:** Urban, simple,
central. **Surface:** asphalted. ◻ 01/01-31/12
Distance: on the spot ⊗500m ⬛500m.

| 🅿️ | **Vauquois** 🌿 | 15C2 |

Parking municipal, D212. **GPS:** n49,20405 e5,07398.⬆️➡️

8 free. **Location:** Rural, simple. **Surface:** gravel.
Distance: on the spot.

| 🅿️ | **Velaines** | 15D3 |

D120A. **GPS:** n48,70589 e5,29804.⬆️

4 free. **Location:** Simple, central. **Surface:** gravel.
Distance: on the spot ⬛on the spot.

| 🅿️ S | **Ventron** ⛷️ | 18F2 |

Chemin du Plain. **GPS:** n47,93906 e6,86900.⬆️
10 free €2/100liter Ch €2/55minutes. **Location:** Simple,
central, quiet. **Surface:** asphalted. ◻ 01/01-31/12
Remarks: Coins at tourist info.

| 🅿️ S | **Ventron** ⛷️ | 18F2 |

Route de Frère Joseph. **GPS:** n47,92495 e6,86364.⬆️
free. **Surface:** asphalted. ◻ 01/01-31/12
Distance: Ventron 3,2km on the spot.
Remarks: Parking at skipistes.

| 🅿️ | **Verdun** | 15D2 |

Dragées Braquir, Rue du Fort de Vaux, D112.
GPS: n49,15955 e5,39989.⬆️

10 free. **Location:** Urban, simple, central.
Surface: metalled.
Distance: on the spot.
Remarks: Max. 1 night.

| 🅿️ | **Vigneulles-les-Hattonchat** | 15D2 |

Rue Miss Skinner. **GPS:** n48,99200 e5,70122.⬆️
5 free. **Location:** Isolated, quiet. **Surface:** gravel.
Distance: 2km.

| 🅿️ S | **Void-Vacon** | 15D3 |

Rue de la Gare. **GPS:** n48,68240 e5,61960.⬆️➡️

20 ⅃free ⚡€2/100liter ☒Ch▥€2. **Location:** Rural, simple, isolated, quiet. **Surface:** grassy/gravel.
☐ 01/01-31/12
Distance: ⚲700m ⚲10m ⚲10m.
Remarks: Coins at shop/town hall.

Alsace

Benfeld   18G1
Concessionnaire CLC Alsace, 9, Rue de Hollande, RN83 dir Strasbourg-Colmar. **GPS:** n48,37772 e7,59778. ⬆➡
5 ⅃free ⚡☒Ch⚲free. **Surface:** gravel/metalled.
☐ 01/01-31/12
Distance: ⚲2km ⚲2km ⚲2km.
Remarks: At motorhome dealer.

Bourbach-le-Haut   18F2
Route Joffre. **GPS:** n47,79463 e7,02868. ⬆

5 ⅃€6 ⚡☒Ch▥included. ⚲ **Surface:** asphalted.
☐ 15/03-15/11
Distance: ⚲50m ⚲100m ⚲100m ⚲5km.
Remarks: In front of fire-station.

Chavannes-sur-l'Etang   18F2
Aire pique-nique La Porte d'Alsace, RD419, Rue d'Alsace. **GPS:** n47,63325 e7,01858. ⬆➡

15 ⅃€7 (19-9 h) ⚡☒Ch⚲WCfree. **Surface:** asphalted.
☐ 01/01-31/12
Distance: ⚲900m ⚲1km.
Remarks: Parking picnic area.

Colmar   18G1
Rue de la Cavalerie. **GPS:** n48,08218 e7,35990. ⬆

20 ⅃€3, overnight stay free. **Location:** Central, noisy.
Surface: asphalted.
Distance: ⚲200m ⚲on the spot ⚲on the spot ⚲on the spot.

Colmar   18G1
Rue Henry Wilhelm. **GPS:** n48,08366 e7,35527. ⬆
16 ⅃€3, overnight stay free. **Location:** Urban, simple, central.
Surface: asphalted.
Distance: ⚲400m ⚲400m ⚲400m.

Colmar   18G1
Port de Plaisance de Colmar, 6 rue du Canal. **GPS:** n48,08054 e7,37599.

---

25 ⅃€11-15 + €0,22/pp tourist tax ⚡☒Ch⚲WC▥€3/2 ⚲included. **Location:** Comfortable, quiet. **Surface:** asphalted.
☐ 01/01-31/12
Distance: ⚲1,3km ⚲Lidl 400m.

Eguisheim   18G1
Bannwarth, Rue de Bruxelles 3. **GPS:** n48,04456 e7,30478.

6 ⅃free. **Surface:** metalled.
Distance: ⚲100m.

Ferrette   18G3
Rue de Lucelle. **GPS:** n47,48882 e7,31118. ⬆

5 ⅃free ⚡€2/10minutes ☒Ch▥€2/55minutes. **Location:** Simple, isolated, quiet. **Surface:** asphalted.
Distance: ⚲700m ⚲2km ⚲2km.

Fessenheim   18G2
Allée de la Guyane. **GPS:** n47,91833 e7,53139. ⬆

30 ⅃free ⚡€2 ☒Ch▥€2. **Surface:** asphalted/gravel.
☐ 01/01-31/12
Distance: ⚲700m ⚲700m ⚲200m.
Remarks: Coins available at swimming pool, supermarket.

Guebwiller   18G2
Avenue Maréchal Foch. **GPS:** n47,90554 e7,21869. ⬆

⅃free. **Surface:** gravel.
☐ 01/01-31/12
Distance: ⚲300m ⚲on the spot ⚲300m ⚲300m ⚲300m ⚲5km.

Guewenheim   18F2
Le Doller. **GPS:** n47,75612 e7,09855.

10 ⅃free ⚡€3,50 ☒Ch⚲WC▥. **Surface:** gravel.
☐ 01/01-31/12
Distance: ⚲2km ⚲1km ⚲2km ⚲2km.

Harskirchen   15F3
Port de Plaisance, Rue de Bissert. **GPS:** n48,93930 e7,02759. ⬆➡
2 ⅃€10 ☒Ch ⚲⚲included. **Surface:** gravel.
☐ 15/03-11/11 ⚲on the spot.
Remarks: At canal Houillères de la Sarre, max. 24h.

Hartmannswiller   18G2
Grand Rue. **GPS:** n47,86311 e7,21494. ⬆
4 ⅃free ⚡€4,30 ⚲€4,30 ⚲ **Surface:** asphalted.

Heiligenstein   18G1
Lieu-dit Lindel, D35. **GPS:** n48,42780 e7,45147. ⬆

3 ⅃free. **Surface:** gravel. ☐ 01/01-31/12
Distance: ⚲800m ⚲300m ⚲500m.
Remarks: Hiking trails and wine tasting.

Hirtzbach   18G2
Place de la Gare. **GPS:** n47,60061 e7,22542.
10 ⅃free ⚡☒Chfree. ☐ 01/01-31/12

Kaysersberg   18G1
Aire Camping-car P1, Place de l'Erlenbad.
GPS: n48,13565 e7,26325. ⬆➡

80 ⅃€7/24h ⚡☒ChWC⚲free. ⚲ **Surface:** asphalted.
☐ 01/01-31/12
Distance: ⚲300m ⚲300m ⚲300m.
Remarks: Wifi at Office de Tourisme.

Tourist information Kaysersberg:
Ⓜ Musée Albert Schweitzer. The life of Albert Schweitzer.

Le Bonhomme   18F1
Col du Bonhomme, D148, route des Crètes. **GPS:** n48,16495 e7,07971.

⅃free. **Surface:** gravel.
Distance: ⚲on the spot.

Linthal   18F2
Rue du Markstein, D430. **GPS:** n47,94495 e7,12783. ⬆
4 ⅃free ⚡€4,30 ▥€4,30 ⚲. **Location:** Simple, quiet.
Surface: asphalted.

Michelbach   18F2
Salle des polyvalente, Rue Principale. **GPS:** n47,75800 e7,11000. ⬆

5 ⅃free. **Surface:** metalled. ☐ 01/01-31/12
Distance: ⚲250m ⚲2km ⚲2km ⚲1km ⚲1km.
Remarks: Behind community centre.

FR

Mittelbergheim — 18G1

Parking Zotzenberg, Rue Ziegelscheuer. **GPS:** n48,39869 e7,44194.⬆.

4 free. **Surface:** asphalted.
Distance: 300m 3,1km ⊗300m 300m on the spot.
Remarks: At cemetery, wine tasting.

Munster — 18G1

Aire Aire de camping-cars Munster, Rue du Dr Heid.
GPS: n48,03779 e7,13471.⬆.
54 €6 €3 Ch €3 WC €1,50 . **Surface:** gravel.
01/01-31/12
Distance: on the spot ⊗on the spot on the spot on the spot.

Munster — 18G1

Place de la salle des Fêtes. GPS: n48,03944 e7,13944.⬆.

8 free. **Surface:** asphalted. 01/01-31/12
Distance: 300m ⊗300m 300m on the spot.

Murbach — 18G2

Abbaye de Murbach, Rue de Guebwiller. **GPS:** n47,92321 e7,16059.⬆.

20 free Service €4,30 Ch . **Location:** Isolated, quiet.
Surface: gravel/metalled. 01/01-31/12
Distance: 350m on the spot ⊗on the spot 500m 5km.

Obernai — 18G1

Parking de l'Altau, Route d'Ottrott. **GPS:** n48,46239 e7,47369.⬆.
free. **Location:** Urban, simple, central. **Surface:** asphalted.
01/01-31/12
Distance: 600m ⊗600m 600m.
Remarks: Video surveillance.

Obernai — 18G1

Parking des Remparts, Rue Poincaré. **GPS:** n48,45972 e7,48667.⬆➡.

50 free. **Surface:** gravel. 01/01-31/12
Distance: 300m 2,7km ⊗300m 300m 200m.
Remarks: Large parking in centre, video surveillance.

Obernai — 18G1

Camping municipal Le Vallon de l'Ehn, 1, rue de Berlin.
GPS: n48,46471 e7,46757.⬆➡.
€2 Ch. 01/01-31/12

Oltingue — 18G3

Place Saint Martin. **GPS:** n47,49158 e7,39068.⬆.

---

3 free €2/10minutes, €2/55minutes.
Surface: asphalted. 01/01-31/12
Distance: 100m ⊗200m.

Orbey — 18F1

Hôtel Restaurant Les Terrasses du Lac Blanc, Lac Blanc.
GPS: n48,13540 e7,08957.⬆.

8 €5, free with a meal included Ch (8x)€2,50.
Surface: grassy/gravel.
Distance: 500m 500m on the spot.
Remarks: Guests free.

Orschwihr — 18G2

Rue de la Source. **GPS:** n47,93722 e7,23083.⬆➡.

4 free Ch €4,30 . **Surface:** asphalted. 01/01-31/12
Distance: 200m ⊗200m 500m.
Remarks: Max. 48h.

Pfaffenheim — 18G2

Aire du Winzerhof, Rue de la Tuilerie. **GPS:** n47,98639 e7,29167.

5 free €3 Ch (5x)€2 WC . **Surface:** gravel/metalled.
01/01-31/12
Distance: 400m ⊗400m 500m.

Ribeauvillé — 18G1

Route de Guémar. **GPS:** n48,19231 e7,32867.⬆.

15 €1,50/5h, €1,50/night €2 Ch. **Location:** Simple.
Surface: gravel. 01/01-31/12
Distance: 400m ⊗on the spot on the spot.
Remarks: Next to Cave de Ribeauvillé.

Tourist information Ribeauvillé:
Sa.

Riquewihr — 18G1

Avenue Jacques Preiss. **GPS:** n48,16608 e7,30175.⬆.

6 €2/5h, €4/night €2 Ch €2. **Surface:** asphalted.
01/01-31/12
Distance: 200m ⊗200m 200m.
Remarks: Motorhomes <7m, video surveillance.

Tourist information Riquewihr:
Office de Tourisme, Rue de 1ère Armée. Picturesque street with houses of the 16th century.

Sainte-Marie-aux-Mines — 18G1

Place des Tisserands. **GPS:** n48,24700 e7,18322.⬆.

4 free. **Surface:** asphalted. 01/01-31/12
Distance: 300m ⊗300m 300m.
Remarks: Max. 24h.

Tourist information Sainte-Marie-aux-Mines:
Office de Tourisme, 86, rue Wilson, www.tourisme.fr/office-de-tourisme/sainte-marie-aux-mines-68.htm. Mineral city with silvermine, Mine d'Argent Sainte-Barthélemy.

Saverne — 15G3

Rue des Emouleurs. **GPS:** n48,74512 e7,36854.
free. **Surface:** gravel/sand. 01/01-31/12
Distance: centre 650m.

Saverne — 15G3

Camping Les Portes d'Alsace, Rue du Père Liebermann.
GPS: n48,73131 e7,35504.⬆.
15 €8, Jul/Aug €10 Ch WC included.
Surface: gravel. 01/04-30/09
Remarks: Service passerby €3.

Tourist information Saverne:
Château de Rohan. Museum, former summer residence of the bishops of Strasbourg.

Soufflenheim — 15H3

Rue des Menuisiers. **GPS:** n48,82940 e7,95395.⬆➡.

3 free €2 Ch €2. **Surface:** asphalted. 01/01-31/12
Distance: 300m ⊗200m 300m 200m.

Soultz — 18G2

Rue de la Marne. **GPS:** n47,88806 e7,23139.⬆.

30 free Service €4,10 Ch . **Surface:** asphalted.
01/01-31/12

FR

Distance: 🚶500m ⊗500m 🛒500m 📮500m 🚍500m.
Remarks: Payment only by bank card.

🏭S Strasbourg 🌿⛵🚽 15G3

Parking Auberge de Jeunesse des Deux Rives (Parc du Rhin), Rue des Cavaliers. **GPS:** n48,56659 e7,79975.⬆️.

20 🛏free 🚰💧Ch ⚡€2,50/100liter 🔧Ch ⚡€2,50/1h ⚡.
Surface: grassy/sand. ⬛ 01/01-31/12
Distance: 🚶Strasbourg centre 5km 🚍bus 21 + tram.
Tourist information Strasbourg:
👁⊗ Maison Kammerzell. Restaurant, 1467-1589, one of the most beautyfull half-timbered houses in the Alsace region.
Ⓜ️ Musée Alsacien. Folk art and handycrafts.
✝ Cathédrale de Nôtre-Dame.

🏭S Thann 🌿🏖⛵🌳🌾 18F2

Place du Bungert, Rue des Pélerins. **GPS:** n47,81159 e7,10450.

10 🛏free 🚰💧Ch ⚡free. **Surface:** asphalted. ⬛ 01/01-31/12
⬛ Sa-morning market
Distance: 🚶600m 🅿on the spot 🛒500m 💧500m 🚍500m.

🏭S Thann 🌿🏖⛵🐾🌾 18F2

Rue du Général de Gaulle. N66. **GPS:** n47,80889 e7,10460.⬆️.
30 🛏free 🚰💧Ch Service€4 ⚡. **Location:** Noisy.
Surface: asphalted. ⬛ 01/01-31/12
Distance: 🚶250m 🛒50m 💧50m.

🏭S Trois Épis 🌿🏖🐾🌾 18G1

Place des Antonins. **GPS:** n48,10101 e7,22948.⬆️➡️.

25 🛏free 🚰€2 💧Ch 🔌€3/55minutes WC ⬛€1. **Surface:** asphalted.
⬛ 01/01-31/12
Distance: 🚶150m 🛒150m 💧150m.

📷 Turckheim ⛵🌾 18G1

Quai de la gare. **GPS:** n48,08555 e7,27739.

6 🛏free. **Location:** Noisy. **Surface:** metalled.
⬛ 01/01-31/12
Distance: 🚶historical centre 250m 🛒250m 💧300m 🚍on the spot.

S Turckheim ⛵🌾 18G1

Camping municipal Les Cigognes, 4, quai de la Gare.
GPS: n48,08539 e7,27535.
🚰€5,40 💧Ch. ⬛ 15/03-31/10

♿S Ungersheim 18G2

Ecomusée. GPS: n47,85200 e7,28400.⬆️➡️.

20 🛏€6 🚰💧included. **Surface:** gravel/metalled. ⬛ 01/01-31/12
Distance: 🚶6km.
Remarks: Check in at hotel.

🏭S Villefranche-sur-Saône 21C3

Camping-car Park, 2788 Route de Riottier.
GPS: n45,97278 e4,75135.⬆️.
128 🛏€12 🚰💧Ch ⚡📶included. 🏪🏬 **Location:** Urban, luxurious. ⬛ 15/05-15/09
Distance: 🛣A6 1,3km 🚉Station > Lyon 3,4km.
Remarks: Wifi code: 692712.

🏭S Westhalten 🏖 18G2

Rue St Blaise, D18, Vallée Noble, dir Soultzmatt..
GPS: n47,95626 e7,25135.

6 🛏free 🚰€2 💧Ch 🔌€2. **Location:** Noisy. **Surface:** asphalted.
⬛ 01/03-30/11
Distance: 🛒nearby ⊗nearby 💧on the spot.
Remarks: Max. 48h.

🏭S Willer-sur-Thur 🌾 18F2

Place de l'Eglise. **GPS:** n47,84315 e7,07292.⬆️➡️.

3 🛏free 🚰💧Chfree. **Surface:** asphalted.
⬛ 01/01-31/12
Distance: 🚶250m 🛒500m 💧500m, bakery 50m 🚍500m 🚲500m.

Normandie

🏭S Agon-Coutainville 🌾 14B2

Flot Bleu Park, Boulevard Louis Lebel-Jéhenne.
GPS: n49,05176 w1,59123.⬆️➡️.

25 🛏€6,30/24h 🚰💧Ch ⚡included 🏪🏬 **Location:** Comfortable. **Surface:** grassy. ⬛ 01/01-31/12
Distance: 🚶800m.
Remarks: Service passerby € 2,70.

♿S Angiens 🌾 14F1

Aire de Château d'Iclon, Impasse des Roseaux.
GPS: n49,84390 e0,81945.⬆️➡️.

10 🛏€5 + € 1/pp 🚰€2,50 💧€2,50 Ch ⚡€3. **Surface:** grassy/gravel.
⬛ 01/01-31/12
Distance: 🚶3km.

🏭S Ardevon 14B3

La Bidonnière, Route de la Rive 5. **GPS:** n48,60352 w1,47612.⬆️.

50 🛏€10, 01/11-31/03 €6 🚰💧Ch 🔌 ⚡(40x)€3,70/24h WC ⬛€3/stay 📶included. **Location:** Rural, luxurious, quiet.
Surface: grassy/gravel.
⬛ 01/01-31/12
Distance: 🚶on the spot 🛒3km ⊗1km 💧3km 🚍1,5km 🚲on the spot ⛺on the spot.
Remarks: Bread-service, free bicycles available, view on Mt.St.Michel.

🏭S Arromanches-les-Bains 🌿🏖🌾 14C1

Rue François Carpentier. **GPS:** n49,33904 w0,62553.⬆️.

14 🛏free 🚰€2/10minutes 💧Ch 🔌€2/1h 📶free15minutes.
Surface: asphalted. ⬛ 01/01-31/12
Distance: 🚶150m 🅿100m ⊗100m 💧250m.
Remarks: Next to camping municipal.

📷 Arromanches-les-Bains 🌿🏖🌾 14C1

Arromanches 360, Cinéma Circulaire, Chemin du Calvaire / D514.
GPS: n49,33924 w0,61419.⬆️.

20 🛏€6. 🚐 **Location:** Rural, comfortable. ⬛ 01/01-31/12
Distance: 🚶400m 🅿300m.
Remarks: Beautiful view.

📷 Auderville 14B1

D901. **GPS:** n49,71431 w1,93481.⬆️.

15 🛏free. **Location:** Rural, simple. **Surface:** grassy/gravel.
⬛ 01/01-31/12
Distance: 🚶300m 🅿700m ⊗600m.

FR

⬛Ⓢ Auffay 🍴 14F1

Place de Bleckede. **GPS**: n49,71755 e1,10055. ⬆️➡️

6 🚐free 🚰€3/100liter 🚽Ch. **Surface**: asphalted. ⬜ 01/01-31/12
Distance: 🛒on the spot ⊗100m 🚉100m.

⬛Ⓢ Avranches 🌿♨ 14B3

Centre Culturel, Boulevard Jozeau Marigné.
GPS: n48,68585 w1,367. ⬆️➡️

8 🚐free 🚰€2/10minutes 🚽Ch. **Location**: Urban, simple.
Surface: gravel/metalled. ⬜ 01/01-31/12
Distance: 🛒200m 🚆1,9km ⊗200m 🚉200m.
Remarks: Behind community centre, max. 1 night, attractive medieval centre.

Tourist information Avranches:
- 👁 Jardins des Plantes. Garden with exotic plants.
- ✝ Basilique St Germain. ⬜ 9-12h, 14-16h.
- 🎪 place des Halles. ⬜ Sa + Tue-morning.

⬛ Bagnoles-de-l'Orne 🌿♨🎋♨ 14D3

Avenue du Dr Paul Lemuet. **GPS**: n48,55558 w0,40973. ⬆️

6 🚐free. **Location**: Simple, noisy. **Surface**: asphalted.
⬜ 01/01-31/12
Distance: 🛒400m ⊗400m 🔲900m 🚶on the spot.

⬛ Bagnoles-de-l'Orne 🌿♨🎋♨ 14D3

D235. **GPS**: n48,55821 w0,4129. ⬆️➡️

6 🚐free. **Location**: Urban, simple. **Surface**: gravel.
⬜ 01/01-31/12
Distance: 🛒on the spot ⊗400m 🔲400m 🚶on the spot.
Remarks: Behind tourist info, Place du Marché.

⬛Ⓢ Bagnoles-de-l'Orne 🌿♨🎋♨ 14D3

D916. **GPS**: n48,55034 w0,40202. ⬆️

3 🚐 🚰🚽Ch. **Location**: Simple. **Surface**: asphalted.
⬜ 1/1-31/12
Distance: 🛒900m 🚉on the spot 🔲on the spot 🚐on the spot.

⬛Ⓢ Barfleur 14C1

Route Alfred Rossel, D1. **GPS**: n49,66998 w1,26355.

8 🚐free 🚰ChWC. **Location**: Urban, simple.
Surface: metalled.
Distance: 🛒200m.

Barneville-Carteret 14B1

Quai Émile Valmy, rue du port. **GPS**: n49,37300 w1,789.

12 🚐free. **Location**: Urban, simple. **Surface**: asphalted.
Distance: 🛒600m ⊗on the spot 🚐on the spot 🔲600m.
Remarks: In front of the Gare Maritime.

Ⓢ Barneville-Carteret 14B1

Carrefour Market, Route du Pont Rose. **GPS**: n49,38553 w1,75239.
🚰€2 🚽Ch 🔲€2/1h. **Location**: Simple. ⬜ 01/01-31/12

⬛Ⓢ Bayeux 🌿♨🍴 14C2

Place Gauquelin-Despallières. **GPS**: n49,28044 w0,70775. ⬆️

5 🚐free 🚰🚽ChWCfree. **Location**: Urban. **Surface**: asphalted.
⬜ 01/01-31/12
Distance: 🛒on the spot ⊗100m 🚉100m 🚐on the spot.
Remarks: Max. 12h.

Tourist information Bayeux:
- Ⓜ Musée Memorial 1944. Battle of Normandy, June 6 till August 22, 1944. ⬜ 9.30-17h, 01/05-30/09 9-19h.
- ✝ Cathédrale Nôtre Dame. Gothic cathedral.

⬛Ⓢ Beauvoir 14B3

Aire de camping-car du mont St Michel, Route de Mont St Michel.
GPS: n48,59426 w1,5122. ⬆️

122 🚐€12,50 🚰🚽Ch 🔌(122x)included 📶free. 🛢♻
Location: Rural, comfortable, luxurious, quiet. **Surface**: grassy/gravel.
⬜ 01/01-31/12
Distance: 🛒500m ⊗500m.
Remarks: Service passerby €4,50, le Mont Saint Michel 5km.

⬛Ⓢ Beauvoir 14B3

Le Mont-St-Michel, Rue Au Bis. **GPS**: n48,60841 w1,50681.

220 🚐€20/24h 🚉. **Surface**: asphalted.
⬜ 01/01-31/12
Distance: ⊗on the spot 🚐on the spot.
Remarks: Free shuttle to Le Mont-Saint-Michel 07.30-00.30h.

🍴Ⓢ Beauvoir 14B3

La Ferme Saint Michel, Route du Mont Saint Michel, D976.
GPS: n48,61112 w1,50978. ➡️

35 🚐guests free 🚰🚽ChWC 📶. **Location**: Simple. **Surface**: gravel.
⬜ 01/01-31/12 🔲 Mo
Distance: 🛒600m ⊗on the spot 🚉600m 🚐on the spot.

⬛ Bernières-sur-Mer 🌿♨ 14D2

Rue Victor Tesnière. **GPS**: n49,33472 w0,41984. ⬆️

35 🚐free. **Location**: Urban, simple. **Surface**: gravel.
Distance: 🛒on the spot 🚲100m ⊗100m 🚉on the spot 🔲100m 🚐on the spot 🐾on the spot 🚶on the spot.

⬛Ⓢ Beuvron-en-Auge 🌿♨ 14D2

Parking de la Gare, Avenue de la Gare. **GPS**: n49,18560 w0,0495. ⬆️

16 🚐€6 🚰🚽Chincluded. 🛢 **Location**: Rural, comfortable, quiet.
Surface: gravel. ⬜ 01/01-31/12
Distance: 🛒200m ⊗on the spot 🚉on the spot.
Remarks: Pay and coins at Tabac-Presse 200m.

⬛Ⓢ Bretteville-sur-Odon 14D2

Camping-car service, 4-6 Avenue des Carrières.
GPS: n49,18449 w0,41465. ⬆️

6 🚐free 🚽Chfree. **Location**: Urban, simple. **Surface**: metalled.
⬜ 01/01-31/12
Distance: 🛒1km 🚐500m.

⬛Ⓢ Bréville-les-Monts 14D2

Rue des Dentellières. **GPS**: n49,24167 w0,228. ⬆️

FR

4 ⚌free ⬡€2/10minutes 🚿Ch. **Location:** Simple, comfortable.
Surface: asphalted. ☐ 01/03-15/11
Distance: 🚶on the spot.
Remarks: Max. 72h, (may-july-aug) 48h, coins at tourist info Merville and harbour.

Bricquebec 🌿 14B1
Bas de Cattigny, D900, route de Cherbourg.
GPS: n49,47402 w1,64674.⬆

6 ⚌free ⬡🚿Ch💧(2x)free. **Location:** Comfortable, quiet.
Surface: gravel.
Distance: 🚶1km 🚲on the spot.

Broglie 14E2
Parc de la bibliothèque. **GPS:** n49,00563 e0,52948.⬆➡

8 ⚌€ 5/night ⬡€2,50/100liter 🚿Ch💧€2,50/1h.
Surface: grassy/metalled.
☐ 01/03-31/10 7-22h, 01/11-28/02 7.30-19h
Distance: 🚶200m ⊗200m 🛒200m, 7.30-19h.
Tourist information Broglie:
⌂ ☐ Fri 7-13h.

Buchy 14F1
D919, Route de Forges. **GPS:** n49,58538 e1,36417.⬆

6 ⚌free ⬡€2 🚿Ch💧€2. **Surface:** asphalted. ☐ 01/01-31/12
Distance: 🚶500m ⊗500m 🛒500m.

Cabourg 🏖 🌳 14D2
Avenue Michel d'Ornano. **GPS:** n49,28225 w0,11994.⬆

6 ⚌free ⬡€2/10minutes 🚿Ch 🧹. **Location:** Rural, comfortable, quiet. **Surface:** asphalted. ☐ 01/01-31/12
Distance: 🚶centre 900m 🚲7,5km 🏊1,6km 🚲on the spot.
Remarks: Nearby Hippodrome.

Cambremer 14D2
Place de l'Europe/Avenue des Tilleuls. **GPS:** n49,14991 e0,04729.⬆

7 ⚌free ⬡€2/100liter 🚿Ch💧€2/1h. **Location:** Rural, simple, central, quiet. **Surface:** gravel.
☐ 01/01-31/12
Distance: 🚶50m ⊗100m 🛒bakery 100m.
Remarks: Coins at the shops and town hall.

Campigny 14E2
Chemin de la Motte. **GPS:** n49,31139 e0,55223.⬆

3 ⚌free ⬡🚿Chfree. **Surface:** grassy. ☐ 01/01-31/12
Remarks: On inner court of old presbytery, max. 24h.

Carentan 14C1
Camping-Car Park de Carentan, Chemin du Grand Bas Pays.
GPS: n49,30937 w1,2392.⬆

12 ⚌€ 13,60 ⬡🚿Ch📶included. 🛝 **Location:** Comfortable, quiet. **Surface:** gravel/metalled. ☐ 01/01-31/12
Distance: 🚶500m 🏊500m.
Remarks: Service passerby € 5.

Carolles 14B3
Rue du Mont Dol. **GPS:** n48,75931 w1,57062.⬆➡

15 ⚌€ 8 ⬡€3/100liter 🚿Ch💧€3/55minutes. 🛝
Location: Comfortable. **Surface:** grassy/gravel. ☐ 01/01-31/12
Distance: 🏊150m ⊗on the spot 🛒on the spot.
Remarks: Only exact change.

Carolles 14B3
La Guériniére, Residence les Jaunets. **GPS:** n48,74989 w1,55695.⬆
5 ⚌free ⬡€2 🚿Ch💧€2. **Surface:** asphalted. ☐ 01/01-31/12
Distance: 🚶on the spot 🏊2km.
Remarks: In front of town hall.

Caumont-l'Éventé 🌿 14C2
Souterroscope des Ardoisières, Route de Saint Lô, D71.
GPS: n49,08868 w0,81645.➡

3 ⚌free ⬡€2/10minutes 🚿Ch💧€2/55minutes
WC. **Location:** Simple, isolated. **Surface:** asphalted.
☐ 01/01-31/12, service 15/02-15/11
Distance: ⊗on the spot 🏊500m 🚶on the spot.

Cerisy-la-Forêt 14C2
GPS: n49,19806 w0,93389.⬆

10 ⚌free ⬡€2 🚿Ch💧€2. **Location:** Rural, simple. **Surface:** gravel.
☐ 01/01-31/12
Distance: 🚶500m 🛒500m.
Remarks: Near abbey.

Cherbourg 🌿 🏖 🍵 〰 14B1
Musée Cité de la Mer, Llée du President Menut.
GPS: n49,64740 w1,61782.

40 ⚌free. **Location:** Urban, simple. **Surface:** asphalted.
Distance: 🚶1km 🚲on the spot ⊗1km 🛒on the spot.
Remarks: Max. 1 night.
Tourist information Cherbourg:
Ⓜ Musée Fort du Roule. War museum. ☐ 9.30-12h, 14-17.30h.

Clecy 🌳 14D2
Rue du Stade. **GPS:** n48,91886 w0,48114.⬆➡

5 ⚌free ⬡€2/20minutes 🚿Ch💧 **Location:** Simple, quiet.
Surface: gravel. ☐ 01/01-31/12
Distance: 🚶100m ⊗100m 🏊300m 🚌200m.
Remarks: Coins at the shops in the village.

Clères 14F1
Rue Edmond Spalikowski, Côte du Mont Blanc.
GPS: n49,60228 e1,11667.⬆⬆➡

10 ⚌free ⬡€5/100liter 🚿Ch💧€5/6h. **Surface:** gravel.
☐ 01/01-31/12 🔲 service: 01/11-28/02

Distance: 🚶500m ⊗500m 🚰500m.
Remarks: Nearby football ground, max. 72h, coins at bakery, butcher and Bar-Tabac.

🏕️🆂 Colleville-Montgomery 14D2

Rue de Saint-Aubin/Rue les Petites Rues.
GPS: n49,27166 w0,29891. ⬆️➡️

9🚐€5 🚰🗑️Chfree. **Location:** Rural, simple, quiet. **Surface:** grassy.
🅿️ 01/01-31/12
Distance: 🚶200m 🚰450m.

Tourist information Colleville-Montgomery:
Ⓜ️ Musée Omaha Beach, St.Laurent-sur-Mer. Collection of military vehicles, weapons and costumes.

🏕️🆂 Cormeilles 〰️ 14E2

Route du Château de Malou, D810. **GPS:** n49,24926 e0,37371. ➡️

8🚐free 🚰🗑️Chfree. **Surface:** asphalted. 🅿️ 01/01-31/12
Distance: 🚶400m 🌊river 🚰400m.

🏕️🆂 Coudeville-sur-Mer 〰️🏖️🌳 14B2

Avenue de la Mer D351. **GPS:** n48,88707 w1,56607. ⬆️

10🚐€5,65/24h 🚰🗑️Ch🔌included 🗑️.🚮🗑️ **Location:** Rural.
Surface: grassy/gravel. 🅿️ 01/01-31/12
Distance: 🚶500m 🌊200m ⛽200m ⊗500m 🚰500m.

🏕️🆂 Courseulles-sur-Mer 〰️🏖️ 14D2

Avenue de la Libération. **GPS:** n49,33440 w0,44551. ⬆️

13🚐€6,20 🚰🗑️Chincluded. **Location:** Urban, comfortable, central.
Surface: asphalted. 🅿️ 01/01-31/12
Distance: 🚶50m 🌊200m ⊗pizzeria 50m.
Remarks: Nearby entrance campsite, max. 24h.

🏕️🆂 Courseulles-sur-Mer 〰️🏖️ 14D2

Juno Beach, Voie des Français Libres. **GPS:** n49,33694 w0,46502. ⬆️

✈️ Normandic market. 🅿️ Sa 8-14h.

25🚐free. **Location:** Central, quiet. **Surface:** metalled.
🅿️ 01/01-31/12
Distance: 🚶100m 🌊50m.

🏕️🆂 Couterne 14D3

Place de la Mairie. **GPS:** n48,51223 w0,41417. ➡️

10🚐free 🚰🗑️ChWCfree. **Location:** Urban, simple.
Surface: asphalted. 🅿️ 01/01-31/12
Distance: 🚶on the spot ⊗nearby 🚰nearby ⛽on the spot.
Remarks: Max. 1 night, closed when frosty.

🏕️🆂 Criel-sur-Mer 🏖️ 12C3

Rue de la Plage, D222. **GPS:** n50,03241 e1,31000. ⬆️

75🚐free. **Surface:** grassy/gravel. 🅿️ 01/01-31/12
Distance: 🚶500m 🌊on the spot ⛽on the spot ⊗500m 🚰1km.

🏕️🆂 Deauville 🏖️ 14D2

Boulevard des Sports. **GPS:** n49,35727 e0,08417. ⬆️

8🚐free 🚰🗑️Ch 🔌(6x)free. **Location:** Urban, simple, quiet.
Surface: gravel. 🅿️ 01/01-31/12
Distance: 🚶on the spot 🌊800m 🚰500m.
Remarks: Behind stadium, max. 24h.

🏕️🆂 Dieppe 🏖️ 12B3

Quai de la Marne. **GPS:** n49,93014 e1,08667. ⬆️

45🚐€7/24h 🚰🗑️Chfree 🗑️.🚮 **Surface:** metalled.
🅿️ 01/01-31/12
Distance: 🚶500m 🌊on the spot ⛽on the spot ⊗500m 🚰500m.
Remarks: Max. 48h, wifi card available at harbour master.

Tourist information Dieppe:
🏰 Château Dieppe. Castle, 15th century, with maritime museum.
🕙 10-12h, 14-18h 🅿️ 01/10-31/05 Tue.
✈️ 🅿️ Tue, Thu 8-14h.

🏕️🆂 Dives-sur-Mer 🏖️ 14D2

Rue de l'avenir. **GPS:** n49,29028 w0,10345. ⬆️➡️

10🚐free 🚰€2/10minutes 🗑️Ch 🗑️. **Location:** Rural, comfortable, quiet. **Surface:** asphalted. 🅿️ 01/01-31/12
Distance: 🚶500m 🌊900m.
Remarks: Nearby Port Guillaume.

🏕️🆂 Doudeville 14E1

Place du Mont Criquet, centre-ville. **GPS:** n49,72000 e0,78750. ⬆️

25🚐free 🚰€3,50/100liter 🗑️Ch. **Surface:** asphalted.
🅿️ 01/01-31/12
Distance: 🚶100m ⊗100m 🚰100m.

🏕️🆂 Dragey-Ronthon 🏖️ 14B3

Route de la Plage. **GPS:** n48,70945 w1,5139. ⬆️

8🚐free. **Location:** Simple, simple, isolated. **Surface:** grassy/sand.
🅿️ 01/01-31/12
Distance: 🚶2km 🌊on the spot ⛽on the spot 🚶‍♂️on the spot.
Remarks: Max. 24h.

🏕️🆂 Ducey 🌳 14B3

P du Domaine, Rue St Quentin. **GPS:** n48,62513 w1,294. ⬆️➡️

30🚐free 🚰€2/100liter 🗑️Ch🚽€2 WC. **Location:** Simple, noisy.
Surface: gravel/metalled. 🅿️ 01/01-31/12
Distance: 🚶500m ⊗500m 🚰500m 🚶‍♂️on the spot.
Remarks: Only exact change.

🏕️🆂 Englesqueville-la-Percée 14C1

Ferme de la Rouge Fossé, D514. **GPS:** n49,38781 w0,94829. ⬆️

6🚐€5 🚰🗑️Ch€3/time 🔌(6x)included24h. 🚲
Location: Comfortable, isolated, quiet. **Surface:** grassy/gravel.
🅿️ 01/01-31/12

Distance: 🏊500m.

Equeurdreville 14B1

Rue Jean Bart. **GPS:** n49,65465 w1,65044.⬆.

6 🅿free 🚰🗑Chfree. **Location:** Urban, simple.
Surface: gravel/sand.
Distance: 🚶1km 🏊1km 🛒on the spot.

Etretat 14E1

Aire de stationnement Maupassant, Rue Guy de Maupassant.
GPS: n49,70009 e0,21579.⬆➡.

30 🅿€ 8/24h 🚰€3/100liter 🗑Ch🔌€3/55minutes.
Surface: grassy/metalled. 🅾 01/10-31/12
Distance: 🚶1km 🏊1,2km 🛒1km 🍴1km.
Remarks: Next to camping municipal, max. 24h.

Etretat 14E1

Pl. de la Gare. **GPS:** n49,70843 e0,21524.⬆.
10 🅿free. **Surface:** metalled. 🅾 01/01-31/12
Distance: 🚶900m 🏊1km.

Tourist information Etretat:
ℹ Office de Tourisme, Place Maurice Guillard, www.etretat.net. The cliffs which have the shape of an arch are a well-known tourist attraction.

Fécamp 14E1

Parking de la Mâture, Chaussée Gayant. **GPS:** n49,76024 e0,37412.⬆.
+10 🅿free 🚰€3 🗑Ch. **Location:** Urban. **Surface:** asphalted.
Distance: 🚶on the spot.

Fécamp 14E1

Quai Sadi Carnot. **GPS:** n49,76087 e0,37157.⬆.

10 🅿free. **Surface:** asphalted. 🅾 01/01-31/12
Distance: 🚶200m 🏊on the spot 🛒on the spot 🍴200m 🛒500m.
Remarks: Between pier and marina.

Tourist information Fécamp:
ℹ Office de Tourisme, 113, rue Alexandre le Grand, www.fecamptourisme.com. City against the chalk-cliff of the Côte d'Albâtre, fishing-port is now mainly a marina.
Ⓜ✖ Palais Bénédictine. Museum with Bénédictine distillery and tasting-pub. 🅾 01/07-31/08 10-18h, 01/09-30/06 10.30-11.30h, 14-17h.

Fermanville 14B1

Le Cap Lévi. **GPS:** n49,69002 w1,4673.⬆➡.

6 🅿€ 3. ⚓ **Location:** Rural, simple, quiet. **Surface:** grassy.

🅾 01/01-31/12

Fervaches 14C2

La Vallée. **GPS:** n48,99550 w1,0826.⬆.
8 🅿€ 3 🚰🗑ChWC included 📶free. **Location:** Rural, comfortable.
Surface: grassy/gravel.
Distance: 🚶150m 🛒150m.
Remarks: Wifi code at grocery.

Forges-les-Eaux 14G1

Aire de camping car de la Minière, Boulevard Nicolas Thiessé.
GPS: n49,60569 e1,54288.⬆.

35 🅿€ 6,77, 01/11-15/03 free 🚰🗑Ch 🧹included.
Surface: asphalted. 🅾 01/01-31/12
Distance: 🚶2km.
Remarks: Max. 48h.

Formigny 14C1

La Ferme du Lavoir, D517. **GPS:** n49,34041 w0,89654.⬆.

6 🅿€ 10/night 🚰🗑Ch 🧹 WC 📶included. ⚓ **Location:** Rural, comfortable, quiet. **Surface:** asphalted/grassy.
Distance: 🚶300m 🏊3km.
Remarks: Organic orchards, cider production.

Gacé 14E3

Rue du Marché aux Bestiaux. **GPS:** n48,79500 e0,29583.⬆.

30 🅿free 🚰€2 🗑Ch. **Surface:** asphalted. 🅾 01/01-31/12
Distance: 🚶on the spot 🚲2,6km 🍴50m.
Remarks: In front of tourist office, max. 24h.

Gavray 14B2

D38. **GPS:** n48,91113 w1,34641.⬆.

8 🅿free 🚰€4/10minutes 🗑Ch. **Location:** Urban, comfortable.
Surface: asphalted. 🅾 01/01-31/12
Distance: 🚶400m 🏊200m 🍴600m 🛒100m.
Remarks: In front of police station.

Gisay-la-Coudre 14E2

D35. **GPS:** n48,95001 e0,62670.➡.

6 🅿free 🚰€2/100liter 🗑Ch. **Surface:** asphalted.
🅾 01/01-31/12
Distance: 🛒on the spot ⊗300m.
Remarks: Coins available at restaurant La Tortue.

Gournay-en-Bray 14G1

Avenue Sadi Carnot. **GPS:** n49,48055 e1,72640.
10 🅿free 🚰🗑Chfree. **Surface:** asphalted. 🅾 01/01-31/12 🅾 Thu-morning closed because of market + 2nd weekend Sep
Distance: 🚶on the spot ⊗on the spot 🍴on the spot 🛒on the spot.
Remarks: Max. 48h.

Gournay-en-Bray 14G1

Route du Vieux Saint-Clair. **GPS:** n49,50106 e1,72245.⬆.
🅿€ 6 🚰€1 🗑€2. **Location:** Rural, simple, isolated, quiet.
Distance: 🚶2,5km.

Gouvets 14C2

Le Bourg D454. **GPS:** n48,93133 w1,09492.⬆.

20 🅿🚰🗑🧹WCfree. **Location:** Rural, simple, isolated, quiet.
Surface: asphalted/metalled. 🅾 01/01-31/12
Distance: 🚶on the spot ⊗6km 🚶on the spot.

Gouville-sur-Mer 14B2

Chemin du Beau Rivage. **GPS:** n49,09970 w1,60896.⬆➡.

40 🅿€ 5/19-10h 🚰liter 🗑Ch🔌minutes WC included. ⚓
Location: Urban. **Surface:** gravel. 🅾 01/01-31/12
Distance: 🏊on the spot 🍴on the spot 🚌50m.

Grainville-Langannerie 14D2

Rue de Lapford. **GPS:** n49,01438 w0,26805.⬆➡.

6 🅿free 🚰€2/10minutes 🗑Ch🔌€2/55minutes.
Location: Rural, comfortable. **Surface:** metalled.
🅾 01/01-31/12
Distance: 🚶100m.
Remarks: Near Salle des Fêtes.

Grandcamp-Maisy 14C1

Rue du Moulin Odo. **GPS:** n49,38620 w1,03782.➡.

14 ⬛free 🚰€2 ♨Ch. **Location:** Rural, comfortable, quiet.
Surface: asphalted/gravel.
Distance: 🚰500m ⬛500m.
Remarks: Coins at tourist info, rue Aristide Briand.

⬛Ⓢ **Granville** 〰️⛱️🎏🌊 **14B2**
Haute Ville, Rue du Roc. **GPS:** n48,83530 w1,6095.⬆️.

20 ⬛€6 🚰€2/10minutes ♨Ch➕€2/55minutes 🗑️.
Location: Simple. **Surface:** asphalted/gravel. ⬤ 01/01-31/12
Distance: 🚰500m ⊗500m ⬛500m on the spot.
Remarks: Motorhome parking behind sea aquarium, upper city,
Atlantic Wall 50m, max. 24h.
Tourist information Granville:
ℹ️ Office de Tourisme, 4, Cours Jonville, www.ville-granville.fr. The
old centre, Haute-Ville, is surrounded by ramparts. The lower city is a
bathing resort.
🏹 ⬤ Wed, Sa.

⬛Ⓢ **Gréville-Hague** **14B1**
D402. **GPS:** n49,67509 w1,80127.⬆️.

10 ⬛free 🚰€2 ♨Ch➕€2 WC. **Location:** Rural, comfortable.
Surface: metalled.
Distance: 🚰on the spot ⬛100m.
Remarks: Next to sports fields.

⬛Ⓢ **Grigneuseville** **14F1**
La Plaine d'Hermesnil, 7 rue de la Plaine.
GPS: n49,64427 e1,19900.⬆️➡️.

7 ⬛€6 🚰♨Ch included. **Surface:** gravel.
Distance: 🚰2,5km ⊗2,5km ⬛2,5km.

⬛Ⓢ **Grossville** **14B1**
Bar-Epicerie Caladjo, Rue des Touzés. **GPS:** n49,50659 w1,74311.⬆️.

---

15 ⬛€6 🚰€2 ♨Chfree 🗑️€2. **Location:** Rural, simple.
Surface: gravel. ⬤ 01/01-31/12
Distance: ⊗on the spot ⬛on the spot.

⬛Ⓢ **Guilberville** **14C2**
D159. **GPS:** n48,98871 w0,94844.⬆️➡️.

15 ⬛free 🚰€2/100liter ♨Ch➕€2/1h. **Location:** Rural, simple,
quiet. **Surface:** gravel.
⬤ 01/01-31/12 ⬤ service: 01/11-01/03
Distance: 🚰300m ⚓1,5km ⊗300m ⬛300m.
Remarks: Coins at tourist info, Bistro and bakery.

⬛Ⓢ **Hermanville-sur-Mer** **14D2**
Rue Verte. **GPS:** n49,28592 w0,31243.⬆️.

6 ⬛free 🚰♨Chfree. **Location:** Simple, central, quiet.
Surface: asphalted. ⬤ 01/01-31/12
Distance: 🚰on the spot ⬛200m.
Remarks: Tuesday market.
Tourist information Hermanville-sur-Mer:
🏹 ⬤ Tue morning.

⬛Ⓢ **Hérouvilette** **14D2**
Place l'Aiguillon, Avenue de Caen, D 513A.
GPS: n49,21983 w0,24497.⬆️➡️.

8 ⬛free 🚰♨Chfree. **Location:** Rural, comfortable.
Surface: asphalted. ⬤ 01/01-31/12
Distance: 🚰250m ⬛200m.

⬛Ⓢ **Heurteauville** **14E1**
Les Cerisiers, Rue de Village. **GPS:** n49,44777 e0,81333.⬆️➡️.

12 ⬛€8 🚰♨Chincluded 🗑️€2. **Surface:** grassy/gravel.
⬤ 01/04-31/10
Distance: 🚰3km ⬛20m ⬛20m ⊗3km ⬛3km.
Remarks: Along the Seine river.

⬛Ⓢ **Honfleur** 〰️⛱️🌊 **14E1**
Bassin de l'Est, Quai de la cale. **GPS:** n49,41916 e0,24166.⬆️.

---

120 ⬛€10 🚰♨Ch 🗑️(60x)included. 📷🎥 **Location:** Urban,
simple, central. **Surface:** gravel.
⬤ 01/01-31/12 ⬤ service in winter
Distance: 🚰500m ⚓2,7km ⊗300m ⬛500m.

⬛Ⓢ **Isigny-sur-Mer** 🌊 **14C1**
Quai Neuf. **GPS:** n49,32150 w1,10456.⬆️.

6 ⬛free 🚰€2/100liter ♨Ch.
Location: Rural. **Surface:** asphalted.
Distance: 🚰300m ⬛on the spot ⬛200m.

⬛Ⓢ **Jobourg** **14B1**
Nez de Jobourg, D202. **GPS:** n49,67722 w1,93806.

10 ⬛free 🚰WCfree. **Surface:** metalled. ⬤ 01/01-31/12
Distance: ⬛500m ⬛500m.

⬛Ⓢ **Jumièges** **14E1**
Rue Alphonse Callais. **GPS:** n49,43106 e0,81452.⬆️➡️.

20 ⬛free 🚰€3/100liter ♨Ch. **Surface:** grassy/gravel.
⬤ 01/03-30/11
Distance: 🚰1km ⬛500m ⊗200m ⬛200m.
Remarks: Coins at Tourist Info and bakery.

©Ⓢ **La Ferrière-aux-Etangs** 🌊 **14C3**
Camping du Lac, Rue de l'Etang. **GPS:** n48,65931 w0,51706.⬆️➡️.

7 ⬛free 🚰€2/10minutes ♨Ch 🗑️€2/1h. **Location:** Simple, quiet.
Surface: metalled.
⬤ 01/01-31/12
Distance: 🚰400m ⊗400m ⬛400m 🎣on the spot.
Remarks: At lake, at tennis-court, only exact change.

©Ⓢ **La Ferté-Macé** 〰️ **14D3**
Ruelle des Fournelles, D916. **GPS:** n48,59018 w0,35528.⬆️.

FR

15 free ChWC free. **Location:** Urban, simple.
Surface: asphalted. ◘ 01/01-31/12
Distance: on the spot on the spot on the spot.
Remarks: Parking at church.

La Lucerne-d'Outremer · 14B3
D35. **GPS:** n48,78437 w1,42727.

6 free, voluntary contribution Ch voluntary contribution
WC free. **Location:** Urban, simple. **Surface:** asphalted.
◘ 01/01-31/12
Distance: on the spot 100m 100m.
Remarks: Next to castle, max. 2 days.

La Mailleraye-sur-Seine · 14E1
Quai Paul Girardeau. **GPS:** n49,48444 e0,77333.

34 € 5, 1/11-31/3 free €3/10minutes Ch .
Surface: grassy.
◘ 01/01-31/12 ◘ 2nd weekend April/May
Distance: 200m on the spot on the spot on the spot
200m.
Remarks: Along the Seine river, coins at town hall and shops.

La Poterie-Cap-d'Antifer · 14E1
GPS: n49,68317 e0,16480.

4 free. **Location:** Simple, quiet. **Surface:** grassy/gravel.
◘ 01/01-31/12
Distance: 2km.

La Vespière · 14E2
Chemin de la Grand Mare/Campaugé. **GPS:** n49,02763 e0,42221.

2 free €2/100liter Ch €2/1h. **Location:** Simple,
comfortable. **Surface:** asphalted. ◘ 01/01-31/12
Distance: 300m A28 2,2km Carrefour 200m.

La-Rivière-Saint-Sauveur · 14E1
Parking de l'Orange - Place Albert Harel, Chemin des Bancs, D580.
GPS: n49,40856 e0,26926.

20 free €5/100liter Ch €5/30minutes . **Location:** Rural,
simple, central, quiet. **Surface:** asphalted.
◘ 01/01-31/12
Distance: on the spot 700m supermarket + bakery 100m.
Remarks: Coins at the shops in the village.

Langrune-sur-Mer · 14D2
Rue du Colonel Pierre Harivel. **GPS:** n49,32474 w0,36814.

3 free. **Location:** Comfortable, central.
Surface: asphalted/metalled. ◘ 01/01-31/12
Distance: on the spot beach 50m 50m.

Le Billot · 14D2
D39. **GPS:** n48,96948 e0,07217.

4 free €2,50 Ch €2,50 WC. **Location:** Rural, simple.
Surface: gravel/metalled. ◘ 01/01-31/12
Distance: 200m.
Remarks: Coins at Relais du Billot 200m, beautiful view.

Le Havre · 14D1
Chaussée John Kennedy. **GPS:** n49,48499 e0,10673.

10 free, July-Aug € 10 Ch . **Surface:** asphalted.
◘ 01/01-31/12
Distance: 1km 200m 200m 1km 1km.

Le Mont-Saint-Michel · 14B3
Aire Camping-car du Mont-Saint-Michel. **GPS:** n48,61401 w1,50773.

€ 12,50/24h Ch . **Surface:** grassy.
◘ 23-06h
Distance: La Rotisserie on the spot.

Le Mont-Saint-Michel · 14B3
Parking Véolia, La Jacotière Ardevon. **GPS:** n48,61388 w1,5058.

50 € 20,60/24h. **Location:** Rural. **Surface:** metalled.
◘ 01/01-31/12
Distance: 100m.
Remarks: Free shuttle to Le Mont-Saint-Michel.

Tourist information Le Mont-Saint-Michel:
 Office de Tourisme, Corps de Garde des Bourgeois, www.mont-saint-michel.net. Town with abbey on a cliff in the sea.

Le Noyer-en-Ouche · 14E2
Ferme Lesur, La Godinière, D140. **GPS:** n49,01017 e0,72444.

5 € 7,50 €3 €3. **Surface:** grassy. ◘ 01/01-31/12

Le Sap · 14E2
Les Terriers, Rue Nicolas Lesieur, D12. **GPS:** n48,89525 e0,33249.

4 free Ch free. **Surface:** gravel. ◘ 01/01-31/12
Distance: 500m on the spot 500m 500m.
Remarks: Next to fire-station.

Le Tréport · 12C3
Du Funiculaire, Route Touristique, D126E. **GPS:** n50,05777 e1,36222.

19 € 6 Ch €5 . **Location:** Simple, central.
Surface: asphalted. ◘ 01/01-31/12
Distance: 5 min walking on the spot on the spot 200m
200m.
Remarks: Max. 48h.

Tourist information Le Havre:
 Musée de l'Ancienne Havre, rue Jerome Bellarmato. History of the
city. Wed-Su 14-18h.
 Canyon Parc, CD34, Epretot. Family park in western style.

Le Mesnil-Jumièges · 14E1
Base de loisirs UCPA, Route de Mesnil. **GPS:** n49,41172 e0,84494.

FR

25 ⌷€ 6 ⌷€2,10/100liter ⌷Ch⌷€2,10/55minutes ⌷⌷.
Location: Comfortable, isolated, quiet. **Surface:** grasstiles.
Distance: ⌷Le Tréport centre 2km ⌷2km ⌷100m.
Remarks: Free cableway to city centre, max. 48h.

⌷⌷ **Le Tréport** ⌷ 12C3
Parc Sainte Croix, Rue Pierre Mendès France.
GPS: n50,05954 e1,38919. ⌷⌷.

61 ⌷€ 9,50, tourist tax incl ⌷⌷Ch⌷(61x)included. ⌷⌷
Location: Comfortable, isolated, quiet. **Surface:** asphalted.
⌷ 01/01-31/12
Distance: ⌷700m ⌷700m ⌷500m Mr.Ed.
Remarks: Industrial area, near camping municipal, max. 48h.
Tourist information Le Tréport:
⌷ Château d'Eu, Eu. Royal castle, 19th century.
⌷ 15/03-01/11 ⌷ Sa.

⌷ **Les Pieux** ⌷ 14B1
Plage Sciotot. GPS: n49,50722 w1,84731.
6 ⌷free. **Location:** Simple. **Surface:** metalled.
⌷ 01/01-31/12
Distance: ⌷beach 50m.
Remarks: Large parking, 50m from beach.

⌷S **Les Pieux** ⌷ 14B1
Intermarché, Route de Cherbourg. **GPS:** n49,51736 w1,79797. ⌷.

6 ⌷free ⌷€2/100liter ⌷Ch. **Surface:** asphalted.
Distance: ⌷on the spot.

⌷S **Lessay** 14B2
Place Saint Cloud. GPS: n49,21850 w1,53548. ⌷⌷.

4 ⌷free ⌷⌷Ch⌷WCfree. **Location:** Urban, simple.
Surface: asphalted. ⌷ 01/01-31/12
Distance: ⌷on the spot ⌷150m ⌷200m.
Remarks: Check in at town hall (service).

⌷S **Lion-sur-Mer** ⌷ 14D2
Rue du General Gallieni. **GPS:** n49,30174 w0,31316. ⌷.

4 ⌷free.
Location: Urban, central, noisy. **Surface:** asphalted.
⌷ 01/01-31/12
Distance: ⌷on the spot ⌷on the spot ⌷100m.
Remarks: At sea, parking townhall, only overnight stay allowed.

⌷S **Lisieux** 14E2
Parking du Carmel, Rue d'Alençon. **GPS:** n49,14413 e0,22788. ⌷⌷.

⌷free ⌷€3/100liter ⌷Ch⌷€3/1h WC. **Surface:** asphalted.
⌷ 01/01-31/12
Distance: ⌷on the spot ⌷river ⌷on the spot ⌷on the spot.

⌷S **Luc-sur-Mer** 14D2
Route de Lion-sur-Mer. **GPS:** n49,31430 w0,34346. ⌷⌷.

4 ⌷free. **Location:** Rural, simple. **Surface:** asphalted.
⌷ 01/01-31/12
Distance: ⌷200m.

⌷ **Lyons-la-Fôret** 14F2
La Cuette. **GPS:** n49,39908 e1,47912.
⌷free.
Distance: ⌷100m ⌷100m ⌷100m.

⌷S **Lyons-la-Fôret** 14F2
Les Grandes Molaises, Les Hogues. **GPS:** n49,41312 e1,42562. ⌷.

20 ⌷€ 8 + € 0,20/pp tourist tax ⌷⌷included. **Location:** Rural,
isolated. **Surface:** grassy.

⌷S **Marigny** 14B2
Rue Auguste Eudeline, D53. **GPS:** n49,09911 w1,24776. ⌷⌷.

10 ⌷free ⌷€2/10minutes ⌷Ch⌷€2/55minutes. **Location:** Urban,
simple. **Surface:** metalled. ⌷ 01/01-31/12
Distance: ⌷700m ⌷200m ⌷700m ⌷700m ⌷on the spot.

⌷S **Merville Franceville** ⌷ 14D2
Boulevard Wattier. **GPS:** n49,28483 w0,21071. ⌷.

6 ⌷free ⌷€2/10minutes ⌷Ch. **Location:** Comfortable, quiet.
Surface: asphalted. ⌷ 01/03-15/11
Distance: ⌷75m.

⌷S **Montebourg** 14B1
Parking Louis Lecacheux. GPS: n49,48486 w1,37449. ⌷.

10 ⌷free ⌷⌷Chfree. **Location:** Simple. **Surface:** metalled.
⌷ 01/01-31/12

⌷⌷S **Montfiquet** 14C2
Hotel-Restaurant Relais de la Fôret, L'Embranchement, D572.
GPS: n49,19400 w0,863. ⌷.

60 ⌷€ 14 ⌷⌷Chincluded WC€2/time,use sanitary€2.
Surface: asphalted. ⌷ 01/01-31/12
Distance: ⌷1km ⌷1km.
Remarks: Pay at reception, picnic tables available.

⌷S **Montville** ⌷⌷⌷ 14F1
Place de l'Abbé Kerebel. **GPS:** n49,54710 e1,07304. ⌷⌷.

15 ⌷free ⌷€4,50/100liter ⌷Ch⌷€4,50/h ⌷free,(8-22.30).
Surface: gravel.
⌷ 01/01-31/12
Distance: ⌷400m ⌷400m.
Remarks: Coins at mairie, restauration Hexagone, museum.
Tourist information Montville:
⌷ ⌷ Mo-morning.

⌷S **Mortain** ⌷ 14C3
Place du Château. **GPS:** n48,64887 w0,94489. ⌷⌷.

6 ⌷free ⌷⌷Ch⌷WCfree. **Location:** Urban, simple.
Surface: asphalted. ⌷ 01/01-31/12

FR

Distance: ⬛on the spot ⊗on the spot ⬛on the spot ⬛on the spot.
Remarks: Max. 48h.
Tourist information Mortain:
ℹ️ Office de Tourisme, Rue du Bourglopin, www.ville-mortain.fr. Hiking trail to the Grande and Petite Cascade, waterfalls.

🅂 Nonancourt — 14F3
D53, Rue Hippolyte Lozier. **GPS:** n48,77269 e1,19261.
4 ⬛free ⬛⬛Ch free ⬛. **Surface:** asphalted.
Distance: ⬛200m.

🅂 Notre-Dame-de-Courson 👜 — 14E2
D4. **GPS:** n48,99021 e0,25922. ⬆️.

9 ⬛free ⬛€2/20minutes ⬛Ch⬛€2/20minutes. **Location:** Rural, comfortable, quiet. **Surface:** gravel.
📅 01/01-31/12
Distance: ⬛200m ⊗Le Tournebroche 200m.
Remarks: Service only with 1-euro coins.

🅂 Oissel 🌿 — 14F2
Rue du Bras St.Martin. **GPS:** n49,33783 e1,09183. ⬆️.

2 ⬛free ⬛€2/100liter ⬛Ch⬛€2/55minutes.
Surface: gravel.
📅 01/01-31/12
Distance: ⬛200m ⬛on the spot ⬛on the spot ⊗200m ⬛200m.
Remarks: <7m, coins at the bakery: 1, Rue du Maréchal Foch.

🄿 Orbec — 14E2
Parc de Loisirs, Rue St. Pierre, D915. **GPS:** n49,01758 e0,40506. ⬆️.

6 ⬛free. **Surface:** unpaved. 📅 01/01-31/12

🅂 Ouistreham 🏖 — 14D2
Rue des Dunes/Boulevard Maritime. **GPS:** n49,28716 w0,24968. ⬆️.

45 ⬛€10 ⬛⬛Chincluded. ⬛ ⬛ **Location:** Urban, comfortable, noisy. **Surface:** asphalted/gravel. 📅 01/01-31/12
Distance: ⬛650m ⊗150m ⬛2km.
Remarks: Near car ferry.

🅂 Pirou-Plage 🏖 — 14B2
Rue des Hublots. **GPS:** n49,16522 w1,58937. ⬆️➡️.

6 ⬛free ⬛€2/10minutes ⬛Ch⬛€2/55minutes. **Location:** Simple.
Surface: asphalted. 📅 01/01-31/12
Distance: ⬛500m ⬛500m ⊗500m ⬛500m.
Remarks: Coins at campsite Clos Marin and restaurant La Marée, market on Sunday.

🅂 Pont-d'Ouilly 🏖 — 14D2
Rue de la Libération. **GPS:** n48,87794 w0,41304. ⬆️➡️.

43 ⬛€11/24h ⬛€2 ⬛Ch⬛(43x)included ⬛. ⬛ ⬛
Location: Rural, comfortable, quiet. **Surface:** gravel.
📅 01/01-31/12
Distance: ⬛550m ⬛on the spot ⊗550m ⬛550m.
Remarks: Along the Orne river.

🄿 Pont-l'Éveque — 14E2
Les Mouettes, Avenue de Verdun. **GPS:** n49,28563 e0,18769. ⬆️⬆️.

6 ⬛free. **Location:** Urban, simple, central.
📅 01/01-31/12
Distance: ⬛on the spot ⬛6km ⊗100m ⬛150m.

🄿 Port-en-Bessin-Huppain 🏖 — 14C1
Rue du 11 Novembre. **GPS:** n49,34583 w0,75861. ⬆️➡️.

17 ⬛€3,50/night. ⬛ **Location:** Rural, simple. **Surface:** sand.
📅 01/01-31/12
Distance: ⬛300m ⬛400m ⊗400m ⬛500m.

🄿 Port-en-Bessin-Huppain 🏖 — 14C1
Super U, Avenue du Général de Gaulle. **GPS:** n49,34307 w0,75212. ⬆️.

12 ⬛free ⬛€3/time ⬛Ch⬛€3/24h. **Location:** Simple.
Surface: gravel/metalled. 📅 01/01-31/12
Distance: ⬛200m ⬛400m ⊗400m ⬛on the spot.

🅂 Portbail 🏖 — 14B1
Rue Gilles Poerier. **GPS:** n49,33776 w1,69273. ⬆️.

4 ⬛free ⬛€2 ⬛Ch⬛€2/1h. **Location:** Simple, quiet.
Surface: asphalted.
Distance: ⬛200m.
Remarks: At fire-station.

🅂 Rauville-la-Bigot — 14B1
D900. **GPS:** n49,51723 w1,68368.

10 ⬛free ⬛⬛Chfree. **Location:** Comfortable, quiet.
Surface: asphalted.
Distance: ⬛500m.

🅂 Réville — 14C1
Ferme de la Froide Rue, 165, Rue des Monts.
GPS: n49,62583 w1,25278. ⬆️.

6 ⬛€7 ⬛⬛Ch⬛ ⬛ **Location:** Rural, comfortable.
Surface: grassy. 📅 01/01-31/12
Distance: ⬛1km.

🅂 Rots — 14D2
Centre Commercial Cora, Chemin de la Croix Vautier, RN13.
GPS: n49,19985 w0,46027. ⬆️.

⬛free ⬛⬛Chfree ⬛.
Location: Noisy. **Surface:** asphalted.
📅 01/01-31/12
Distance: ⬛1km ⊗on the spot ⬛on the spot.
Remarks: Terrain with video surveillance.

🅂 Rugles — 14E3
Place de la Liberté. **GPS:** n48,82230 e0,70846. ⬆️.

4 ⬛free ⬛⬛Ch⬛free. **Surface:** metalled. 📅 01/01-31/12
Distance: ⬛on the spot ⊗200m ⬛200m.
Remarks: Max. 48h.

FR

Saint Fromond 14C2
Rue des Gabariers, D8. **GPS**: n49,22202 w1,08956.⬆️.

50 🛏free ⛽€2 ⚡Ch🚻€2. **Location**: Rural, simple.
Surface: asphalted/gravel. ⏹ 01/01-31/12
Distance: 🛒on the spot ⊗50m on the spot.

Tourist information Saint Fromond:
ℹ️ Office de Tourisme, Bd de Verdun, Carentan, www.ot-carentan.fr.
Old bishop city with Gothic cathedral.

Saint-André-de-l'Eure 14F3
Boulevard Verdun. **GPS**: n48,90644 e1,26927.⬆️.

10 🛏free ⛽⚡Chfree. **Location**: Urban, comfortable, noisy.
Surface: metalled. ⏹ 01/01-31/12
Distance: 🛒1km on the spot 🌳1km on the spot.
Remarks: Along railwayline.

Saint-Hilaire-du-Harcouët 14C3
Place de la Motte. **GPS**: n48,57602 w1,09086.⬆️➡️.

10 🛏free ⛽€2 ⚡Ch🚻€2. **Location**: Urban, simple.
Surface: asphalted/metalled. ⏹ 01/01-31/12
Distance: 🛒on the spot ⊗on the spot 🌳on the spot.
Remarks: Behind church.

Saint-Jean-le-Thomas 14B3
Boulevard Stanislas. **GPS**: n48,72567 w1,52296.⬆️➡️.

17 🛏€8 ⛽€2 ⚡Ch🚻€2 WC.🚿 **Location**: Rural, comfortable.
Surface: asphalted/grassy.
Distance: 🛒500m ⊘100m ⊗100m 🌳500m 🚲on the spot 🚶on the spot.

Saint-Jouin-Bruneva 14E1
Rue des Pruniers. **GPS**: n49,65099 e0,16322.⬆️.

20 🛏free ⛽€2 ⚡Ch🚻€2. ⏹ 01/01-31/12

Distance: 🛒1km ⊘1km 🌳1km.

Saint-Jouin-Bruneva 14E1
Plage de Bruneval. **GPS**: n49,64970 e0,15349.⬆️.

30 🛏free. **Surface**: gravel. ⏹ 01/01-31/12
Distance: 🛒4km ⊘pebbled beach 🛒on the spot ⊗100m 🌳4km.

Saint-Lô 14C2
Place de la Vaucelle. **GPS**: n49,11351 w1,10309.⬆️➡️.

10 🛏free ⛽€2/10minutes ⚡Ch🚻€2/h 🚿 **Location**: Urban,
comfortable. **Surface**: asphalted. ⏹ 01/01-31/12
Distance: 🛒100m ⊗100m 🌳100m on the spot.
Remarks: Along river.

Tourist information Saint-Lô:
👁 Haras National, Rue du Maréchal Juin. National Stud farm established by Napoleon in 1806. ⏹ 01/06-30/09 14-18.
Ⓜ Musée de la Libération, place du Champ de Mars. Invasion in 1944. ⏹ 10-19h, winter 14-19h Ⓣ Tue. Ⓣ free.
✝ Nôtre Dame. Renovated church 13th century.

Saint-Martin de Bréhal 14B2
Av. de l'Hippodrome. **GPS**: n48,89829 w1,56583.⬆️➡️.

20 🛏€ 4/24h ⛽⚡free. 🚿 **Location**: Urban. **Surface**: asphalted.
⏹ 01/01-31/12
Distance: 🛒300m ⊘beach 150m ⊗300m 🌳400m.

Saint-Nicolas-d'Aliermont 14F1
Place du 19 Mars 1962, Rue d'Arques. **GPS**: n49,88045 e1,22092.⬆️.

2 🛏free ⛽€2 ⚡Ch🚻€2. **Surface**: asphalted.
⏹ 01/01-31/12
Distance: 🛒200m ⊘12km ⊗200m 🌳200m.
Remarks: Behind town hall, max. 48h, coins at town hall and library.

Saint-Nicolas-de-Bliquetuit 14E1
Route du Bac. **GPS**: n49,52083 e0,72777.⬆️➡️.

12 🛏free ⛽€2 ⚡Ch🚻€2. **Surface**: asphalted. ⏹ 01/01-31/12
Distance: 🛒1,4km ⊘on the spot 🛒on the spot ⊗2km 🌳2km 🚶on
the spot.
Remarks: Along the Seine river, coins at town hall.

Saint-Pair-sur-Mer 14B2
Avenue Léon Jozeau-Marigné. **GPS**: n48,81711 w1,56988.⬆️➡️.

30 🛏€ 5 ⛽€2/10minutes ⚡Ch🚻€2/55minutes. 🚐
Location: Urban, simple. **Surface**: asphalted/gravel.
⏹ 01/01-31/12
Distance: 🛒500m ⊘beach 500m ⊗500m 🌳on the spot.
Remarks: Parking at tennis-court, max. 48h.

Saint-Pierre-Église 14B1
Parking du 8 Mai 1945. **GPS**: n49,66897 w1,40387.➡️.

6 🛏free ⛽€2/100liter ⚡Ch. **Location**: Urban. **Surface**: metalled.
⏹ 01/01-31/12
Distance: 🛒300m 🌳on the spot.

Saint-Pierre-le-Vieux 14F1
Ferme du Moulin, D237. **GPS**: n49,85816 e0,88000.⬆️➡️.

5 🛏€ 5 + € 1/pp ⛽⚡Ch 🚿€3. **Surface**: grassy/gravel.
⏹ 01/01-31/12
Distance: 🛒1km ⊘1km 🌳1km.

Saint-Pierre-sur-Dives 14D2
Aire Camping-Cars de la Halle Médiévale, Place du Marché.
GPS: n49,01713 w0,03047.⬆️.

12 🛏€ 5/24h ⛽⚡Ch.🚐🚿 **Location**: Urban, simple, central.
Surface: gravel. ⏹ 01/01-31/12 🔘 Mo-morning market
Distance: 🛒on the spot ⊗50m 🌳150m.
Remarks: Service passerby € 3.

Saint-Saire 14F1

Rue de la Gare, D7. **GPS:** n49,69677 e1,49476.

☐free ⚡🔌Ch 🚿. **Location:** Rural, comfortable, quiet.
Surface: asphalted/grassy. ☐ 01/01-31/12
Distance: 🚶300m ⊗on the spot 🚲Avenue Verte.

Saint-Sauveur-le-Vicomte 14B1

Place Auguste Cousin. **GPS:** n49,38678 w1,52947.

☐free ⚡🔌Chfree. **Surface:** asphalted.
Distance: 🚶on the spot.
Remarks: Next to town hall, max. 48h.

Saint-Sever-Calvados 14C2

Place de la Mairie. **GPS:** n48,84169 w1,04842.

15 ☐free ⚡🔌Chfree. **Location:** Urban, simple, noisy.
Surface: gravel. ☐ 01/01-31/12
Distance: 🚶100m 🚲15km 🍴100m.

Saint-Vaast-la-Hougue 14C1

Aire de la Gallouette, Rue Galouette. **GPS:** n49,58400 w1,267.

27 ☐€7/night ⚡€2/10minutes 🔌Ch 🍴€2/1h.
Location: Comfortable. **Surface:** metalled.
☐ 01/01-31/12
Distance: 🚶300m 🍴300m.
Remarks: Near campsite Gallouette.

Tourist information Saint-Vaast-la-Hougue:
ℹ️ Office de Tourisme, 1, place Gen. de Gaulle, www.saint-vaast-reville.com. Important port for allied forces in 1944. Now large marina.
👁️ Île de Tatihou, Port. Island in front of the coast, maritime museum and bird hide. ☐ 01/04-30/09 10-18h.

Saint-Valery-en-Caux 14E1

Quai d'Aval. **GPS:** n49,87220 e0,70898.

---

40 ☐free, weekend 01/03-31/10 € 6/day, 16/05-30/09 € 6/day + € 0,20/pp ⚡€3 🔌Ch. **Surface:** asphalted. ☐ 01/01-31/12
Distance: 🚶600m 🚿on the spot 🛒on the spot ⊗500m 🥖bakery 600m.
Remarks: Max. 48h, coins at tourist info.

Saint-Vigor-le-Grand 14C2

Les Peupliers, Rue de Magny. **GPS:** n49,29949 w0,67436.

7 ☐€6, € 9 service incl ⚡🔌Ch 🚿included. 💧 **Location:** Rural, comfortable, isolated, quiet. **Surface:** gravel. ☐ 01/01-31/12
Distance: 🚶2km.
Remarks: Baker every morning, service passerby € 4, Bayeux centre 3,5km, Arromanches beaches 6,5km.

Sainte-Honorine-des-Pertes 14C1

Garage Vally, Route d'Omaha Beach, D514, dir Colleville-sur-Mer. **GPS:** n49,34868 w0,81635.

32 ☐€6 ⚡€1,50/100liter 🔌Ch 🚿(32x)included. 💧
Location: Rural, comfortable, quiet. **Surface:** grassy.
☐ 01/01-31/12
Distance: 🚶200m 🚿500m ⊗on the spot.
Remarks: Automatic bread distributor, service passerby € 2,50.

Sainte-Marie-du-Mont 14C1

Camping-car Park, La Madeleine, D913. **GPS:** n49,41417 w1,18643.

49 ☐€12 ⚡🔌Ch 📶€4/3,50 🌐included. 📱 **Location:** Simple, quiet. **Surface:** grassy/gravel. ☐ 01/01-31/12
Distance: 🚿500m.
Remarks: Code wifi: f2d1941a5c.

Tourist information Sainte-Marie-du-Mont:
Ⓜ️ Musée du Débarquement, Utah-Beach. Landing museum.

Sainte-Mère-Église 14B1

Super U, ZA les Crutelles. **GPS:** n49,40461 w1,32223.

⚡€2 🔌Ch.
Surface: asphalted.
Distance: 🚶1km 🛒on the spot.
Remarks: Motorhome washing place max. ^3.80m.

Tourist information Sainte-Mère-Église:
ℹ️ Borne 0 de la voie de la Liberté. Marker 0, start of the Libery Road.
ℹ️ Office de Tourisme, 2, Rue Eisenhower, www.sainte-mere-eglise.info. Village well-known for the paratrooper who landed on the church-tower.
Ⓜ️ Musée Airborne. Exhibition about the invasion at St.-Mère-Eglise.

☐ 10-12h, 14-18h.

Sallenelles 14D2

Boulevard Maritime D514. **GPS:** n49,26474 w0,22694.

2 ☐free ⚡€2/10minutes 🔌Ch. **Location:** Rural, simple, quiet.
Surface: asphalted. ☐ 01/01-31/12
Distance: 🚶100m 🚿on the spot 🍴300m.
Remarks: Max. 48h.

Sideville-Lorimier 14B1

Camping-car l'Orimier, Route du Pont Roger, D152.
GPS: n49,58722 w1,69222.

6 ☐€7/night ⚡🔌Ch 🚿(6x)included. **Location:** Comfortable, quiet. **Surface:** asphalted/grassy.
Remarks: Regional products.

Siouville-Hague 14B1

Avenue des Peupliers. **GPS:** n49,56356 w1,8442.

30 ☐free ⚡€2 🔌Ch. **Surface:** grassy.
Distance: 🚿200m.

Soumont-Saint-Quentin 14D2

Rue de la Mine. **GPS:** n48,97840 w0,25.

20 ☐€6 + € 0,20/pp tourist tax ⚡🔌Ch 📶included. 💧
Location: Simple. **Surface:** grassy. ☐ 01/01-31/12
Distance: 🚶1km.
Remarks: Former iron mine.

Sourdeval 14C3

Parc Saint-Lys, Rue Jean Baptiste Janin.
GPS: n48,72603 w0,92308.

8 ☐free ⚡🔌Ch 🚿free. **Location:** Urban, simple.
Surface: gravel/metalled. ☐ 01/01-31/12
Distance: 🚶100m ⊗400m 🍴400m.

FR

Surtainville 14B1

Rue des mielles. **GPS:** n49,46373 w1,82871.

10 ☐free ☐€4,16/10minutes ☐Ch ☐€4,16/55minutes ☐.
Location: Urban. **Surface:** metalled.
Distance: ☐on the spot ☐100m.
Remarks: Coins at camping municipal.

Tinchebray 14C3

Rue André Breton, D911. **GPS:** n48,76302 w0,73753. ☐☐.

3 ☐free ☐☐Ch ☐free. **Location:** Urban, simple.
Surface: asphalted. ☐ 01/01-31/12
Distance: ☐on the spot ☐300m.

Tourlaville 14B1

Espace Loisirs Colignon, piscine-camping municipal, Rue des Algues. **GPS:** n49,65398 w1,56606.

☐free ☐€2 ☐Ch. **Location:** Simple. **Surface:** asphalted.
Remarks: Coins at campsite or swimming pool.

Tourlaville 14B1

Quai Amiral Kniskern/Boulevard Maritime. **GPS:** n49,64549 w1,59976.

☐free.
Remarks: Parking at ferry-boat.

Tréauville 14B1

1, La Chaussee, D65. **GPS:** n49,54444 w1,83472. ☐.

10 ☐€6,50 ☐☐Ch ☐included. **Surface:** grassy/metalled.
Distance: ☐2,5km.

Valognes 14B1

Place Félix Buhot. **GPS:** n49,51159 w1,47813. ☐.

7 ☐free ☐€2 ☐Ch ☐€2.
Location: Simple. **Surface:** asphalted.
Distance: ☐1km ☐on the spot.
Remarks: Next to supermarket Champion.

Valognes 14B1

Zone Artisanale d'Armanville, Chemin de la Brique.
GPS: n49,51433 w1,50004. ☐.

☐€5/24h ☐€2 ☐Ch ☐€2 WC. **Location:** Simple.
Surface: asphalted. ☐ 01/01-31/12
Distance: ☐1km.
Remarks: Motorhome washing place.

Veules-les-Roses 12B3

Parking des Falaises. **GPS:** n49,87555 e0,79269. ☐☐.

☐free. **Surface:** grassy. ☐ 01/01-31/12
Distance: ☐500m ☐on the spot ☐on the spot ☐500m ☐500m.

Veules-les-Roses 12B3

Camping des Mouettes, Avenue Jean Moulin.
GPS: n49,87596 e0,80289. ☐☐.

15 ☐€10/24h ☐€3 ☐Ch. **Surface:** metalled. ☐ 01/01-31/12
Distance: ☐300m ☐500m ☐500m ☐300m ☐300m ☐on the spot.
Remarks: Max. 48h, coins at campsite, 12-14h closed.

Veulettes-sur-Mer 14E1

Chemin des Courses. **GPS:** n49,85233 e0,60165. ☐.

15 ☐€5 ☐€3,50/100liter ☐Ch ☐€3,50/1h ☐(16x). ☐
Surface: asphalted. ☐ 01/01-31/12
Distance: ☐200m ☐100m ☐100m ☐100m ☐200m.
Remarks: Behind Syndicat d'Initiative, coins at tourist info, campsite and supermarket.

Veulettes-sur-Mer 14E1

Parking de la Plage, D10. **GPS:** n49,85488 e0,60702. ☐.

50 ☐€5 ☐€3,50/10minutes ☐☐€3,50/1h. ☐ **Surface:** grassy.
☐ 01/01-31/12
Distance: ☐200m ☐50m ☐50m.
Remarks: Beach parking, max. 24h.

Villedieu-les-Poêles 14B2

Parc de la Commanderie, Rue Taillemarche.
GPS: n48,83682 w1,22436. ☐.

5 ☐free. **Location:** Urban, simple. **Surface:** asphalted.
☐ 01/01-31/12
Distance: ☐on the spot ☐2,4km ☐100m ☐100m.

Villers-Bocage 14C2

Rue du Canada. **GPS:** n49,07973 w0,6609. ☐☐.

5 ☐free ☐€2/10minutes ☐Ch ☐€2/55minutes ☐.
Location: Urban, simple, quiet. **Surface:** asphalted.
☐ 01/01-31/12
Distance: ☐1,5km ☐on the spot ☐400m ☐on the spot.
Remarks: Max. 48h.

Villers-sur-Mer 14D2

Paleospace l'Odyssee, Rue des Martois.
GPS: n49,32910 e0,01273. ☐☐.

14 ☐€10 ☐€4 ☐Ch ☐included ☐€1 ☐☐☐
Location: Urban, comfortable, quiet. **Surface:** metalled.
☐ 01/01-31/12
Distance: ☐1km ☐beach 250m ☐bakery 1,5km.
Remarks: Max. 48h.

Vimoutiers 14E2

D916, Avenue du Dr. Dentu. **GPS:** n48,93152 e0,19604. ☐.

FR

6 ⬛free 🚰⬛Ch ⚡(2x)WCfree. **Location:** Urban, simple, central.
Surface: asphalted. ⬛ 01/01-31/12
Distance: 🚶400m ⚡500m ⬛Carrefour 200m.
Remarks: Major centre in the Camembert-region, Camembert museum.

⬛⬛ **Vire** **14C2**
Place du champ de foire. **GPS:** n48,84084 w0,88862. ⬆➡

25 ⬛free 🚰⬛Chfree. **Location:** Urban, simple, noisy.
Surface: asphalted. ⬛ 01/01-31/12 ⬛ Fri-Sa
Distance: 🚶on the spot ⊗on the spot ⬛on the spot.
Remarks: Water closed during wintertime, friday-Saturday market.

Ile-de-France

⬛⬛ **Bray-sur-Seine** **18A1**
Quai de l'Ile. **GPS:** n48,41713 e3,23745.

20 ⬛free 🚰⬛Chfree ⬛. **Surface:** asphalted.
Distance: 🚶100m ⊗100m.
Remarks: Max. 72h.

Tourist information Bray-sur-Seine:
⛺ ⬛ Fri 8-13h.

⬛⬛ **Coupvray** **14H3**
Parking Disneyland Paris, Boulevard du Parc.
GPS: n48,87500 e2,79700. ⬆

⬛€ 30/day 🚰⬛ChWC⬛included. **Surface:** asphalted.
⬛ 01/01-31/12
Remarks: Motorhome area at amusement park, note: tariffs will be charged per day, even if you arrive in the evening.

Tourist information Coupvray:
😊 Disneyland Paris, Marne-la-Vallée. Attractions and themepark.

⬛⬛ **Milly-la-Forêt** **17H1**
Route de Nemours. **GPS:** n48,39798 e2,48021. ⬆
6 ⬛free 🚰⬛Chfree. **Location:** Rural. **Surface:** asphalted.
⬛ 01/01-31/12
Distance: 🚶1km ⚡9,4km A6.
Remarks: In front of Conservatoire Nationale des Plantes, gate opens automatically.

⬛⬛ **Milly-la-Forêt** **17H1**
Total, 49-51 Avenue de Ganay. **GPS:** n48,40720 e2,46782. ⬆

⬛€ 3,50 🚰⬛Ch. **Surface:** grassy. ⬛ 01/01-31/12

Distance: 🚶centre 500m ⚡7,7km A6.
Remarks: Behind petrol station, gate open 6-21h.

⬛⬛ **Nemours** **17H1**
Les Colverts de Kabaya, Route de Moret. **GPS:** n48,27866 e2,69893. ⬆
6 ⬛€ 6 🚰⬛€3. **Surface:** grassy. ⬛ 01/01-31/12
Distance: 🚶1,6km ⚡2,3km ⊗200m ⬛200m.

⬛⬛ **Provins** **15A3**
Parking Office de Tourisme, Chemin de Villecran.
GPS: n48,56189 e3,27993. ⬆➡

30 ⬛€ 8 🚰€3,50 ⬛Ch ⚡€3,50 ⬛.⬛ ⬛ **Surface:** gravel.
⬛ 01/01-31/12 ⬛ service: frost
Distance: 🚶500m ⊗500m.
Tourist information Provins:
⛺ Sa 8-14h.

⬛⬛ **Saint-Cyr-sur-Morin** **15A3**
Avenue Daniel Simon. **GPS:** n48,90627 e3,18516.
4 ⬛free 🚰⬛Chfree. **Surface:** grassy. ⬛ 01/01-31/12
Distance: ⬛on the spot.
Remarks: Behind church.

⬛⬛ **Saint-Fargeau-Ponthierry** **14H3**
Base de loisirs Seine-Ecole, Avenue Max Pierrou.
GPS: n48,53610 e2,55065. ⬆
5 ⬛€ 5,20 🚰⬛Chincluded. **Surface:** grassy.
Distance: 🚶850m.
Remarks: Recreation park.

⬛⬛ **Souppes-sur-Loing** **17H1**
GPS: n48,18083 e2,72343. ⬆➡

5 ⬛€ 5 🚰⬛Ch ⚡included. ⬛⬛ **Surface:** asphalted.
Remarks: Max. 72h.

Britanny

⬛⬛ **Antrain** ⬛ **14B3**
Route de Pontorson. **GPS:** n48,46307 w1,47938. ⬆

2 ⬛free 🚰⬛Ch⬛WCfree. **Location:** Urban, simple, central, quiet.
Surface: asphalted.
Distance: 🚶100m ⛰100m ⬛100m ⊗100m ⬛1km ⬛on the spot
⬛2km.

⬛⬛ **Arzal** **17A2**
Barrage d'Arzal, D139. **GPS:** n47,50089 w2,38074. ⬆

15 ⬛free. **Location:** Rural, simple, quiet. **Surface:** asphalted.
⬛ 01/01-31/12
Distance: 🚶1,5km ⛰50m ⬛50m ⊗50m ⬛50m.

⬛⬛ **Arzon** **13D3**
Aire d'accueil des Camping-cars de Kermor, Avenue de Kerlun, Kerjouanno. **GPS:** n47,53886 w2,88028. ⬆➡

49 ⬛€ 7/24h 🚰⬛Ch ⚡(16x) ⬛included. ⬛⬛ **Location:** Rural, comfortable, quiet. **Surface:** asphalted. ⬛ 01/01-31/12
Remarks: Nearby Plage du Fageo, June/Sep max. 72h.

⬛⬛ **Audierne** ⬛ **13B2**
Rue Lamartine. **GPS:** n48,02733 w4,53721. ⬆

10 ⬛free 🚰€2/10liter ⬛Ch⬛. **Location:** Simple.
Surface: unpaved. ⬛ 01/01-31/12
Distance: 🚶1,5km ⊗500m.

⬛⬛ **Auray** ⬛⬛ **13D3**
Chemin de Bellevue. **GPS:** n47,66365 w2,97393. ⬆➡

5 ⬛free 🚰€3/20minutes ⬛Ch⬛€3/h WC ⬛. **Location:** Simple.
Surface: asphalted. ⬛ 01/01-31/12
Distance: 🚶200m.
Remarks: Small pitches.

⬛⬛ **Auray** ⬛⬛ **13D3**
Place du Golhéres. **GPS:** n47,66524 w2,99036. ⬆➡

3 ⬛free 🚰€2 ⬛Ch. **Location:** Urban, simple. **Surface:** asphalted.
⬛ 01/01-31/12
Distance: 🚶500m ⬛on the spot.
Remarks: During inspection 2015 service out of order.
Tourist information Auray:
⛺ ⬛ Mo.

Availles-sur-Seiche 🏕️Ⓢ | 17B1

D106. **GPS:** n47,96248 w1,19902.⬆️.
6🏕️free 🔌🗑️Chfree. **Surface:** unpaved. 🅾️ 01/01-31/12
Distance: 🛒100m ⊗300m.

Baud | 13D2

Rue du Champ de Foire. **GPS:** n47,87375 w3,02008.⬆️➡️.

10🏕️free. **Location:** Central. **Surface:** metalled.
🅾️ 01/01-31/12
Distance: 🛒on the spot 🚉1,5km ⊙200m 🚌on the spot.

Baud Ⓢ | 13D2

Rue de Pont Augan. **GPS:** n47,87580 w3,02518.⬆️➡️.
🚰🗑️Chfree. 🅾️ 01/01-31/12

Bazouges-la-Pérouse 🌿🏕️ | 14B3

Boulevard de Castel Marie. **GPS:** n48,42416 w1,57408.⬆️➡️.

7🏕️free 🔌🗑️Ch🚿free. **Location:** Urban, simple, central, quiet.
Surface: asphalted. 🅾️ 01/01-31/12
Distance: 🛒200m ⊗150m 🚉200m.

Bécherel 🏕️ | 14A3

La Feronière. **GPS:** n48,29769 w1,93971.⬆️.

40🏕️free. **Location:** Rural, simple, simple. **Surface:** gravel.
🅾️ 01/01-31/12
Distance: 🛒700m ⊗700m 🚌on the spot 🚶200m.

Bédée 🏕️Ⓢ | 17A1

Rue de Dinan. **GPS:** n48,18099 w1,94416.⬆️➡️.

6🏕️free 🔌🗑️Chfree. **Location:** Urban, simple.
Surface: asphalted.
Distance: 🚴1km ⊗200m 🚌50m.
Remarks: Nearby cemetery.

Belle-Isle-en-Terre 🏕️Ⓢ | 13D1

Les Jardins du Guer, Rue Guerveur, D33.
GPS: n48,54332 w3,39417.⬆️➡️.

10🏕️2 days free, then € 5/day 🔌🗑️Ch🚿free.
Location: Comfortable, central, quiet. **Surface:** gravel.
🅾️ 01/01-31/12 🅾️ service: 01/11-01/04
Distance: 🛒100m ⛵10m 🚉350m 🚲 mountainbike trail.
Remarks: Narrow entrance.

Belz 🏕️ | 13D3

Parc de Loisirs, Rue des Sports. **GPS:** n47,66940 w3,17744.⬆️➡️.

10🏕️free. **Location:** Simple. **Surface:** gravel/metalled.
🅾️ 01/01-31/12

Berric 🏕️Ⓢ | 13D3

Chemin de l'Étang. **GPS:** n47,63294 w2,52905.⬆️➡️.

6🏕️€ 5 🔌€2/10minutes 🗑️Ch➕€2/55minutes. 🚿 **Location:** Rural,
comfortable, quiet. **Surface:** asphalted.
🅾️ 01/04-30-09
Distance: 🛒500m ⛵on the spot 🚌on the spot ⊗500m 🚉500m.
Remarks: Along river, coins at the shops in the village, access via Rue
du Grand Pont.

Binic 🏕️🍴🏖️ | 13D1

Aire camping-car de l'Ic, Rue de l'Ic. **GPS:** n48,60059 w2,83573.⬆️➡️.

50🏕️free 🔌🗑️Chfree. **Location:** Urban, simple, central, quiet.
Surface: gravel. 🅾️ 01/01-31/12
Distance: 🛒500m ⊗700m 🚌500m 🚶500m.

Tourist information Binic:
🏕️ 🅾️ Thu.

Bourg-Blanc 🏕️Ⓢ | 13B1

Rue de Brest. **GPS:** n48,49188 w4,50312.⬆️.

6🏕️free 🔌🗑️Chfree. **Surface:** sand. 🅾️ 01/01-31/12
Distance: 🚌fish pond 🚉100m.

Bréal-sous-Montfort 🏕️🏖️ | 17A1

Les Jardins de Brocéliande, Les Mesnils.
GPS: n48,05384 w1,88963.⬆️➡️.

12🏕️€ 6 🔌🗑️Ch. 🚐 **Location:** Rural, simple, quiet.
Surface: unpaved. 🅾️ 01/01-31/12
Distance: 🛒2,5km 🚴3,5km ⛵on the spot 🚲on the spot 🚶on the
spot.

Brech 🏕️Ⓢ | 13D3

Rue de Pont Douar/Avenue des Pins, D768.
GPS: n47,71917 w3,00111.⬆️➡️.

6🏕️free 🔌🗑️Ch. **Location:** Simple. **Surface:** grassy.
🅾️ 01/01-31/12
Distance: 🛒100m ⊗200m 🚉200m.
Remarks: Parking nearby small lake, plan d'eau, coins at the bakery,
during inspection 2015 service out of order.

Brest 🅿️ | 13B1

Parking Océanopolis, Rue du Cormoran. **GPS:** n48,38893 w4,43535.⬆️.

24🏕️free. **Surface:** asphalted. 🅾️ 01/01-31/12
Distance: ⛵on the spot 🚲on the spot 🚌300m.
Remarks: Busy parking during the day, gate closes at 18h.

Brest Ⓢ | 13B1

Port du Moulin Blanc, Rue Eugène Berest.
GPS: n48,39174 w4,43612.⬆️.

🔌🗑️Ch➕free. 🅾️ 01/01-31/12

Tourist information Brest:
👁️ Tour Tanguy. Diorama old Brest. 🅾️ daily, 01/10-31/05 Wed, Su
afternoon.
☻ Océanopolis. Sea-centre, penguin and seals. 🅾️ 01/04-31/08 9-18h,
01/09-31/03 10-17h 🅾️ Mo.

Brillac 🏕️Ⓢ | 13D3

Rue Saint-Maur. **GPS:** n47,54143 w2,81748.⬆️.

7 🚐 free. **Location:** Urban, simple, quiet. **Surface:** asphalted.
📅 01/01-31/12
Distance: 🏘 on the spot 🏖 400m 🍴 450m 🚌 on the spot 🚶 on the spot.

[S] Callac (22) 13C1

Av Ernest Renan. **GPS**: n48,40200 w3,43737.[→].

6 🚐 free 🚰 €2 Ch 🔌 €2. **Location:** Simple, quiet. **Surface:** gravel.
📅 01/01-31/12
Distance: 🏖 200m 🎣 200m 🚶 on the spot.
Remarks: Lac Verte Vallée.

[S] Camaret-sur-Mer 13B1

Rue Georges Ancey. **GPS**: n48,27513 w4,60793.[↑][→].

75 🚐 01/04-31/10 € 6 🚰 €2/100liter Ch 🔌 €2/55minutes.
Location: Rural, comfortable, quiet. **Surface:** gravel.
📅 01/01-31/12
Distance: 🏘 1km 🏖 500m 🍴 500m 🛒 500m 🚲 on the spot 🚶 on the spot.
Remarks: Max. 72h.

[S] Campénéac 17A1

Rue de l'Étang. **GPS**: n47,95736 w2,29039.[↑][→].

30 🚐 free 🔌 €2 WC. **Location:** Rural. **Surface:** grassy.
📅 01/01-31/12
Distance: 🏘 250m 🍴 250m 🛒 250m.
Remarks: Coins at Fauchoux, rue nationale 32.

[S] Campénéac 17A1

Rue de la Fontaine. **GPS**: n47,95674 w2,29364.[↑][→].
🚰 €2 Ch WC.
Distance: 🏘 on the spot 🍴 on the spot 🛒 on the spot.
Remarks: Coins at town hall and supermarket.

[S] Cancale 14B3

Aire camping-car Ville Ballet, Rue des Français Libres.
GPS: n48,67004 w1,86583.[↑][→].

30 🚐 € 10 🚰 10minutes Ch 🔌 55minutes,€3,40 💳.
Location: Simple. **Surface:** grassy. 📅 01/01-31/12
Distance: 🏖 300m 🍴 1km 🛒 800m 🚌 100m.
Remarks: Bread-service.

Tourist information Cancale:
👁 La Ferme Marine. Guided tour oyster farm. 📅 summer 11h,15h,17h Français, 14h English, 16h Deutsch.

[S] Carantec 13C1

Aire du Meneyer, Rue Castel an Dour. **GPS**: n48,65967 w3,9138.

20 🚐 free 🚰 €3/15minutes Ch 🔌 €3/55minutes.
Surface: gravel/metalled. 📅 01/01-31/12
Distance: 🏖 500m.
Remarks: Max. 48h.

Carantec 13C1

Chemin du Roch Glaz. **GPS**: n48,65235 w3,90308.

10 🚐 free. **Surface:** asphalted. 📅 01/01-31/12
Distance: 🏖 beach 300m 🚶 on the spot.
Remarks: Max. 24h, seaview.

Carantec 13C1

Rue Pen Al Lann. **GPS**: n48,66861 w3,895.

15 🚐 free. **Surface:** asphalted. 📅 01/01-31/12
Distance: 🏘 500m 🏖 150m 🎣 150m 🍴 1km 🛒 1km.
Remarks: At tennis-courts, max. 48h.

Carantec 13C1

Square du Grand Sacconex, Rue du Kélenn. **GPS**: n48,66892 w3,91085.

10 🚐 free. **Surface:** unpaved.
Distance: 🏘 300m 🏖 on the spot 🎣 on the spot 🍴 on the spot 🛒 300m 🏪 on the spot.
Remarks: At gymnasium.

Tourist information Carantec:
[M] Musée Maritime. Navigation museum. 📅 15/05-15-09 ● Thu.

[S] Carhaix-Plouguer 13C2

Rue de Bazeilles/Rue des Augustins. **GPS**: n48,27829 w3,57257.[↑].

10 🚐 free 🚰 Ch 🔌 free. **Location:** Urban, simple, central.
Surface: asphalted. 📅 01/01-31/12
Distance: 🏘 200m 🍴 200m 🛒 200m.

[S] Carnac 13D3

Square d'illertissen. **GPS**: n47,58505 w3,08242.[↑][→].

40 🚐 free 🚰 €2/10minutes Ch 🔌 €2/2h. **Location:** Simple.
Surface: asphalted.
📅 01/01-31/12
Distance: 🏘 50m 🏖 1,5km 🍴 50m 🛒 50m.
Remarks: Max. 1 night.

Tourist information Carnac:
[i] Office de Tourisme, 74, avenue des Druides, www.carnac.fr. Seaside resort and important place of finding of 30.000 prehistoric menhirs.
[M] Musée de la Préhistoire. Prehistoric museum. 📅 10-12.30h and 14-18h ● 01/12-01/04. [T] € 6.

[S] Caulnes 14A3

Lavoir Fontaine, Rue de Dinan. **GPS**: n48,28655 w2,15517.[↑][→].

10 🚐 free 🚰 €2/10minutes Ch 🔌 €2/1h WC. **Location:** Urban, simple, quiet. **Surface:** gravel.
📅 15/03-15/11
Distance: 🏘 500m 🍴 100m 🛒 100m 🚌 200m.
Remarks: Max. 24h.

[S] Cesson-Sévigné 17B1

Route de La Valette. **GPS**: n48,11802 w1,59121.[↑].

8 🚐 free 🚰 €2,30/10minutes Ch 🔌 €2,30/55minutes 💳.
Location: Rural, simple, central, quiet. **Surface:** metalled.
📅 01/01-31/12
Distance: 🏘 500m 🏖 on the spot 🎣 on the spot 🍴 100m 🛒 100m 🚌 500m 🚶 on the spot.

Châteauneuf-du-Faou 13C2

Penn ar Pont. **GPS**: n48,18286 w3,81576.[↑][→].

FR

15 ⌇free. **Location:** Simple, quiet. **Surface:** gravel.
◘ 01/01-31/12
Distance: ⊾1,3km ♿ on the spot ⋏ on the spot.

| ⌇S | Châtillon-en-Vendelais ◢ | 17B1 |

D108. **GPS:** n48,23112 w1,17959.

10 ⌇free ⛽free ⬛Chfree. **Location:** Rural, simple, quiet.
Surface: asphalted.
Distance: ⊾2km ▱lake ⊷on the spot ⋏ on the spot.
Remarks: At the lake, next to campsite.

| ⌇S | Cléden-Cap-Sizun | 13B2 |

Place du 19 mars 1962, Rue de la ville d'ys.
GPS: n48,04803 w4,65008.⬆.

20 ⌇free ⛽€2/10minutes⬛ChWC. **Location:** Rural, simple, quiet.
Surface: asphalted/metalled. ◘ 01/01-31/12
Distance: ⊾on the spot.

| ⌇S | Cléden-Cap-Sizun | 13B2 |

Pointe du Van, D7. **GPS:** n48,05936 w4,70727.⬆.

20 ⌇free WC. **Surface:** gravel. ◘ 01/01-31/12
Distance: ⊾Cléden-Cap-Sizun ± 5km ▱on the spot ⋏ on the spot.

| ⌇S | Cléden-Cap-Sizun | 13B2 |

Route de Kastel Koz, Beuzec-Cap-Sizun. **GPS:** n48,08473 w4,51844.⬆.

10 ⌇free. **Location:** Rural, simple, isolated. **Surface:** grassy/gravel.
◘ 01/01-31/12
Distance: ▱on the spot ⋏ on the spot.

| ⌇S | Cléden-Poher | 13C2 |

Route du Stade. **GPS:** n48,23686 w3,67165.⬆➡.

4 ⌇free ⛽⬛Ch ✎(4x)free. **Location:** Simple, quiet.
Surface: asphalted. ◘ 01/01-31/12
Distance: ⊾300m ⊗50m ⬛bakery 200m ⬛400m.
Remarks: Voluntary contribution.

| ⌇S | Clohars-Carnoët | 13C2 |

D16, Rue de Quimperlé. **GPS:** n47,79810 w3,58516.
⌇free. **Surface:** asphalted. ◘ 01/01-31/12

| ⌇S | Clohars-Carnoët | 13C2 |

Place de NAVA, Rue de Quimperlé. **GPS:** n47,79790 w3,585.⬆➡.

4 ⌇free ⛽€2 ⬛Ch⬛€2. **Location:** Simple. **Surface:** asphalted.
◘ 01/01-31/12
Distance: ⊾200m ⚐10km ▱4,5km ⬛bakery 200m.

| ⌇S | Combrit | 13B2 |

Place du 19 mars 1962, Hent Ty Plouz. **GPS:** n47,88755 w4,1546.

10 ⌇free ⛽€2/10minutes ⬛Ch⬛€2. **Location:** Simple, quiet.
Surface: metalled. ◘ 01/01-31/12
Distance: ⊾on the spot.
Remarks: Coins at the shops in the village.

| ⌇S | Commana ⬛⬛ | 13C1 |

Place du salles de Sports, D11. **GPS:** n48,41611 w3,96139.⬆➡.

5 ⌇free ⛽free. **Location:** Rural, simple, isolated, quiet.
Surface: grassy. ◘ 01/01-31/12
Distance: ⊾200m ⊗300m ⬛bakery 300m ♿ on the spot ⋏ on the spot.

| ⌇S | Concarneau ⬛⬛ | 13C2 |

Le Porzou, Allée Jean Bouin. **GPS:** n47,86320 w3,9051.⬆➡.

40 ⌇free ⛽€4/10minutes ⬛Ch⬛€4/55minutes WC ✎.
Location: Urban, simple. **Surface:** asphalted. ◘ 01/01-31/12
Distance: ⊾city centre 2km ▱on the spot.

Remarks: Foot ferry to centre.

| ⌇S | Concarneau ⬛⬛ | 13C2 |

Parking de la Gare, Avenue de la Gare. **GPS:** n47,87864 w3,9202.⬆➡.

47 ⌇€ 2/20-08h ⛽€4 ⬛Ch⬛€4/55minutes ✎⬛ ✎
Location: Simple. **Surface:** asphalted. ◘ 01/01-31/12
Distance: ⊾500m ▱beach 1,4km ♿ on the spot ⋏ on the spot.
Remarks: Parking station.

Tourist information Concarneau:
⋏ ◘ Mo, Fri.

| ⌇S | Crac'h | 13D3 |

Intermarché, AC Les Alizés. **GPS:** n47,60421 w2,99669.⬆➡.

8 ⌇free ⛽€2/10minutes ⬛Ch✎. **Surface:** asphalted.
◘ 01/01-31/12
Distance: ⊗on the spot ▱on the spot.

| ⌇S | Crozon ⬛⬛ | 13B1 |

Parking du Loc'h, Rue de l'Atlantique, Morgat.
GPS: n48,22523 w4,50851.⬆.

30 ⌇€ 4,08 ⛽€3,20/10minutes ⬛Ch⬛€3,20/55minutes.⬛
Location: Simple. **Surface:** asphalted. ◘ 01/01-31/12
Distance: ⊾300m ⊷on the spot ⊗on the spot ▱100m.
Remarks: Max. 48h, market Wednesday.

| ⌇S | Crozon ⬛⬛ | 13B1 |

Le Fret, Le Sillon, D55. **GPS:** n48,28457 w4,50934.⬆.

6 ⌇free ⛽€2,08/10minutes ⬛Ch. **Location:** Rural, simple, quiet.
Surface: unpaved. ◘ 01/01-31/12
Distance: ⊾on the spot ⊗Resto 250m.

| ⌇S | Crozon ⬛⬛ | 13B1 |

Parking office de tourisme, Boulevard de Pralognan, D887.
GPS: n48,24770 w4,4934.⬆.

FR

20 free €2 €2 **Location:** Urban, simple.
Surface: asphalted. 01/01-31/12
Distance: on the spot.
Remarks: Nearby Office de Tourisme, max. 48h.

10 €7 €2 Ch (10x)€2/night WC. **Location:** Rural, simple, isolated, quiet. **Surface:** grassy. 01/01-31/12
Distance: 1,1km.

12free €2/10minutes Ch €2/55minutes. **Surface:** asphalted. 01/01-31/12
Distance: on the spot.

Damgan 13D3
Parking de Kervoyal. GPS: n47,51465 w2,56038.

Erdeven 13D3
Parc Kerhillio, Boulevard d'Atlantique. GPS: n47,61429 w3,15958.

Fougères 14B3
Allée des Fêtes. GPS: n48,35660 w1,20242.

76 €7,50 Chincluded. **Location:** Rural, comfortable, quiet.
Surface: metalled/sand. 01/01-31/12
Distance: 600m Sandy beach.
Remarks: Parking at the beach, max. 48h.

70 €6,50/24h Ch included. **Location:** Rural, simple. **Surface:** grassy. 01/01-31/12
Distance: 500m 200m 200m on the spot on the spot.

25 free ChWCfree. **Location:** Urban, simple.
Surface: asphalted. 01/01-31/12
Distance: 500m 200m 200m.

Dinan 14A3
Rue du Port, D12. GPS: n48,45450 w2,0389.

Erquy 14A3
Caroual Plage, Rue des Hirondelles. GPS: n48,62120 w2,4724.

Fougères 14B3
Parking de la Poterne, Boulevard de Rennes.
GPS: n48,35524 w1,2113.

30 €0,30/30min 9-19h, overnight stay free. **Location:** Urban, simple, central. **Surface:** asphalted. 01/01-31/12
Distance: 800m 800m on the spot 500m.

44 €6/24h €2/100liter Ch €2. **Location:** Urban, comfortable, central. **Surface:** asphalted/metalled.
Distance: 2,5km on the spot.
Remarks: Beach parking, max. 48h, baker at 8am.

16 free Chfree. **Location:** Urban, simple, central.
Surface: metalled. 01/01-31/12
Distance: on the spot 250m 300m on the spot.
Remarks: Castle of Fougères 500m.

Dol-de-Bretagne 14B3
Place Jean Hamelin. GPS: n48,54736 w1,75442.

Étel 13D3
Camping municipal, Rue de la Barre. GPS: n47,65100 w3,202.

Fréhel 14A3
La Ville Oie, Rue des Sports, D117, Pléhérel-plage.
GPS: n48,65032 w2,35241.

16 free €2 Ch €2. **Location:** Urban, simple, noisy.
Surface: asphalted. 01/01-31/12
Distance: on the spot 100m 100m 150m.

25 €7/night €2/100liter Ch (16x)against payment.
Location: Rural, simple. **Surface:** grassy. 01/04-30/09
Distance: 500m 200m on the spot on the spot.
Remarks: Baker every morning (Jul/Aug).

40 €6 80liter Ch 1h, service:€4.
Location: Rural, simple, isolated. **Surface:** gravel/metalled. 01/01-31/12
Distance: 1,1km beach 1,2km on the spot.

Elven 13D3
Avenue des Martyrs de la Résistance, Le Guého.
GPS: n47,73879 w2,58134.

Fouesnant 13C2
Plage Mousterlin, Chemin de Kerneuc. GPS: n47,85144 w4,04662.

Gâvres 13C3
Les Joncs, Rue des Filets Bleus. GPS: n47,69515 w3,35097.
40 €5-7,60, 16/06-31/08 tariff camp site €2 Ch included.
Surface: grassy. 01/01-31/12
Distance: 100m 100m.

Glomel 13C2
Etang du Coronc, Rue du Lac. GPS: n48,22052 w3,38972.

7+25 €1 + €1,50/pp €3 Ch (12x)€2/4h.
Location: Rural, simple, quiet. **Surface:** grassy/gravel.
parking 01/01-31/12 service 01/07-31/08
Distance: 1,5km 950m 950m.

15 free. **Surface:** grassy/sand.
Distance: beach 50m.
Remarks: Beach parking, max. 48h.

Fouesnant 13C2
Leclerc, D45, Route de Quimper. GPS: n47,90234 w4,02938.

Erdeven 13D3
Chemin De Kerouriec. GPS: n47,62717 w3,17988.

12 ⛺free ⛽€2/100liter ⚡Ch💧€2/1h 🗑. **Location:** Rural, simple, quiet. **Surface:** asphalted/gravel. 🅾 01/01-31/12 **Distance:** 🚶150m 🍽400m. **Remarks:** At lake.

🅂 Goulven 13B1

Aire Naturelle Ty Poas. GPS: n48,63109 w4,30833. ⬆➡.

15 ⛺€ 5 + tourist tax ⛽€2 ⚡Ch💧€2 WC🧺. **Location:** Comfortable, quiet. **Surface:** grassy/metalled. 🅾 15/06-30/09 **Distance:** 🚶500m 🏖beach 200m 🍽500m.

🅂 Grand-Fougeray 17B2

Rue Camille de Jourdan. **GPS:** n47,72233 w1,7298. ⬆.
5 ⛺free ⚡Ch. **Surface:** asphalted. 🅾 01/01-31/12 **Distance:** 🚶300m ⊗300m.

🅂 Gueltas 13D2

Boju, Keriffe. **GPS:** n48,10406 w2,79064. ⬆➡.

16 ⛺ ⛽⚡Ch WC free. **Location:** Rural, simple, quiet. **Surface:** gravel. 🅾 01/01-31/12 **Distance:** 🚶1km ⛽on the spot. **Remarks:** At the Nantes-Brest Canal.

🅂 Gueltas 13D2

Cité des Écureuils, D125. **GPS:** n48,09667 w2,80111. ⬆➡.

10 ⛺free ⛽⚡Ch free. **Location:** Rural, simple, isolated, quiet. **Surface:** gravel. **Distance:** 🍽200m. **Remarks:** Nearby sports park.

🅂 Guern 13D2

Kervazo, Rue de la Vallée, D1. **GPS:** n48,02815 w3,09215. ⬆.

8 ⛺free ⛽⚡Ch free. **Location:** Rural, simple, quiet. **Surface:** asphalted. 🅾 01/01-31/12 **Distance:** 🚶250m 🍽bakery 300m.

Guern 13D2

Etang du Ponterre, D1. **GPS:** n48,03472 w3,0975. ⬆.

6 ⛺free. **Location:** Rural, simple. **Surface:** gravel. 🅾 01/01-31/12 **Distance:** 🚶700m ⛽on the spot 🍽700m bakery.

🅂 Guichen 17B1

Le Boel, Pont Réan. **GPS:** n48,00221 w1,77336. ⬆➡.

5 ⛺€5 ⛽⚡Ch WC free. **Location:** Simple, quiet. **Surface:** metalled. 🅾 01/01-31/12 **Distance:** 🚶500m 🛶on the spot ⛽on the spot ⊗on the spot 🍽bakery 150m. **Remarks:** Max. 48h.

Guidel 13C2

D152, Guidel-Plage > Fort-Bloqué. **GPS:** n47,75035 w3,50574. ⬆➡.

15 ⛺free. **Location:** Rural, simple. **Surface:** gravel/sand. 🅾 01/01-31/12 **Distance:** 🚶1,5km 🏖100m ⊗1,5km 🚴on the spot 🚶on the spot. **Remarks:** Behind Résidence Maéva, beach parking, max. 24h.

Guidel 13C2

La Falaise, Guidel plage. **GPS:** n47,76640 w3,5258. ⬆.

7 ⛺free. **Location:** Simple. **Surface:** metalled. 🅾 01/01-31/12 **Distance:** 🏖on the spot. **Remarks:** Behind yachting school, max. 24h.

Guidel 13C2

Plage du Loc'h, D152. **GPS:** n47,75650 w3,5159. ⬆➡.

8 ⛺free. **Location:** Quiet. **Surface:** sand. 🅾 01/01-31/12 **Distance:** 🏖250m.

🅂 Guidel 13C2

Arc-en-Ciel, ZA de Pen Mané. **GPS:** n47,80980 w3,4633.

⛽service €2, during opening hours ⚡Ch💧WC. 🅾 01/01-31/12

🅂 Guimiliau 🌳 13C1

Parking Salle Polyvalente, Rue des Bruyeres. **GPS:** n48,48676 w3,99665. ⬆➡.

15 ⛺free ⛽⚡free. **Location:** Simple, central, noisy. **Surface:** metalled. 🅾 01/01-31/12 **Distance:** 🚶on the spot ⊗400m 🍽400m 🚴on the spot 🚶on the spot. **Remarks:** Max. 2 nights.

🅂 Guingamp 🌿 13D1

Place du Vally. **GPS:** n48,56024 w3,1489. ⬆➡.

⛺free ⛽⚡Ch free WC. **Location:** Simple, central. **Surface:** asphalted. 🅾 01/01-31/12 🅿 Fri market **Distance:** 🚶on the spot. **Remarks:** Max. 24h.

🅂 Guiscriff 13C2

La Gare de Guiscriff, Rue de la Gare. **GPS:** n48,05722 w3,65401. ⬆.

4 ⛺free ⛽⚡Ch 💧(4x)€5. **Location:** Rural. **Surface:** metalled. 🅾 01/01-31/12 **Distance:** 🚶1km 🍽bakery 1km 🚴on the spot 🚶on the spot.

🅂 Guissény 13B1

Rue de Plouguerneau. **GPS:** n48,63299 w4,41127. ⬆.

⛺free ⛽€2 ⚡Ch. **Location:** Comfortable. **Surface:** gravel. 🅾 01/01-31/12 **Distance:** 🚶on the spot 🏖beach 550m 🍽250m bakery. **Remarks:** Coins at the shops and town hall.

🅂 Hédé-Bazouges 14B3

La Magdelaine. **GPS:** n48,30592 w1,79218.

50 🛏free. **Location:** Rural, simple. **Surface:** grassy/gravel.
🗓 01/01-31/12
Distance: 🚉1km ⚓on the spot 🛒on the spot ⊗50m 🚲on the spot ⚕on the spot.

⬛Ⓢ Hillion 13D1

Le Tertre Piquet, Lermot-plage. **GPS:** n48,53098 w2,66387. ⬆➡

20 🛏free. 🗑ChWCfree. **Location:** Simple, isolated. **Surface:** grassy.
🗓 01/01-31/12
Distance: ⚓sandy beach 100m.
Remarks: Beach parking, no camping activities.

⬛Ⓢ Hillion 13D1

Rue Olivier Provost. **GPS:** n48,51743 w2,66772. ⬆

7 🛏free. 🗑Chfree. **Location:** Simple, central, quiet. **Surface:** gravel.
🗓 01/01-31/12
Distance: 🚉500m ⚕100m 🚲on the spot.

⬛Ⓢ Hirel 14B3

D155. **GPS:** n48,60841 w1,82032. ⬆➡

100 🛏free, night € 6 🚰€2/100liter 🗑Ch 🛁€2/55minutes. 🚙
Location: Rural, simple. **Surface:** grassy/gravel.
🗓 01/01-31/12
Distance: 🚉700m ⚓200m ⚕200m.

⬛Ⓢ Huelgoat 🌿⛺🌳🖐 13C1

Place du Camping-cars, Route du Fao, D769a.
GPS: n48,36115 w3,75612. ⬆➡

30 🛏free. 🚰€5/10minutes 🗑Ch 🛁1h. **Location:** Rural, simple,
quiet. **Surface:** metalled. 🗓 01/01-31/12
Distance: 🚉500m ⚓on the spot 🛒on the spot ⊗500m ⚕500m ⛽500m 🚲500m ⚕500m.
Remarks: In front of campsite municipal, service 100m.

⬛Ⓢ Janzé 17B1

Aire du Hardier, D41. **GPS:** n47,97258 w1,53825. ⬆

5 🛏€ 10 🚰€2 🗑ChWCfree. 🚙 **Location:** Highway, simple, simple.
Surface: asphalted.
Distance: ✏on the spot.
Remarks: At petrol station.

⬛Ⓢ Josselin ⛺ 13D2

Josselin, Place St.Martin. **GPS:** n47,95639 w2,55056. ⬆➡

50 🛏free 🚰€2,50 🗑Ch 🛁€2,50/h WC ⚑. **Location:** Urban,
central. **Surface:** metalled.
🗓 01/01-31/12 ⚫ Sa 9-14h
Distance: 🚉300m ✏N24 900m ⚕300m ⚕bakery 300m ⚕1km ⛽on the spot.
Remarks: Castle of Josselin 400m.

Tourist information Josselin:
ℹ Office de Tourisme, Place de la Congregation, www.paysdejosselin.com. City is dominated by the castle of Rohan.

⬛Ⓢ Kerlouan 13B1

Lestonquet. **GPS:** n48,66952 w4,36161.

🛏free 🚰€2 🗑Ch. **Surface:** grassy. 🗓 01/01-31/12
Remarks: Former campsite.

⬛ Kerlouan 13B1

La Digue. **GPS:** n48,66195 w4,37879. ⬆

4 🛏free. **Location:** Isolated. **Surface:** gravel. 🗓 01/01-31/12
Distance: ⚓100m 🚲on the spot ⚕on the spot.

⬛Ⓢ Kernascléden 🖐 13C2

Domaine du Scroff, Canquisquelen. **GPS:** n47,99785 w3,31845. ⬆
2 🛏€ 10 🗑Ch WC ⚑included. **Location:** Comfortable.
🗓 01/01-31/12
Distance: 🚉1km ⊗on the spot ⚕on the spot.
Remarks: Heated pool.

⬛Ⓢ La Chèze ⚑ 13D2

Chemin d'Alénor, Allée du 19 mars 1962.
GPS: n48,13419 w2,65787. ⬆➡

10 🛏€ 4, weekend/holidays free 🚰🗑Ch 🛁(6x)WCfree. 🚙
Location: Simple, quiet. **Surface:** asphalted.
🗓 01/01-31/12
Distance: 🚉200m ⚕200m 🚲mountainbike trail.
Remarks: Parking at small lake.

⬛Ⓢ La Fontenelle 14B3

Rue de Chevrigné. **GPS:** n48,46575 w1,50495. ⬆

6 🛏free 🚰€2/10minutes 🗑Ch 🛁€2/55minutes. **Location:** Rural,
simple, quiet. **Surface:** asphalted.
🗓 01/01-31/12
Distance: 🚉on the spot ⊗350m 🚲on the spot ⚕on the spot.
Remarks: Next to cemetery, adjacent walking and bicycle area.

⬛Ⓢ La Martyre 13C1

Route de Ploudiry, D35. **GPS:** n48,44801 w4,15694. ⬆

10 🛏free 🚰🗑Ch 🛁WCfree. **Surface:** gravel.
🗓 01/01-31/12
Distance: 🚉100m ⊗100m ⚕100m.
Remarks: Nearby Maison du Plateau.

⬛ La Roche-Bernard 🌿⛺🖐 17A2

Place du Dôme. **GPS:** n47,51753 w2,29733. ⬆

>20 🛏free. **Location:** Urban, simple, central. **Surface:** asphalted.
🗓 01/01-31/12
Distance: 🚉50m ⊗100m ⚕50m.

⬛Ⓒ Ⓢ La Roche-Bernard 🌿⛺🖐 17A2

Halte Camping-car, Rue du Patis. **GPS:** n47,52012 w2,30466. ⬆➡

15 🛏€ 9,60, 01/07-25/08 € 11,10 🚰🗑Ch 🛁€4,60 WC.
Location: Urban, comfortable, quiet. **Surface:** grassy.
🗓 02/04-16/09
Distance: 🚉100m ⚓50m 🛒50m ⊗100m ⚕100m.

FR

Remarks: Next to campsite du Patis.

Tourist information La Roche-Bernard:
ℹ️ Small town especially known for the beautiful hanging bridge over the Vilaine river, 50m high and over 400m long.

La Roche-Derrien — 13D1
Rue du Jouet. **GPS:** n48,74696 w3,25976.⬆️

12 🛏️€2 🚰€2 🚿Ch🔧(6x) 📶. **Location:** Rural, simple, central, quiet. **Surface:** gravel. 🔵 01/01-31/12
Distance: 🛒100m ⊗100m 🚶100m.
Remarks: Coins at the shops and town hall.

Lampaul-Plouarzel — 13B1
Aire de Porspaul, Rue de Beg ar Vir. **GPS:** n48,44667 w4,77722.⬆️➡️

50 🛏️free, 15/04-15/10 € 3,50, Jul/Aug + € 0,30/pp 🚰€2/20minutes 🚿Ch🔧€2/55minutes WC🔧€1,60 💧€3/3,50. **Location:** Comfortable. **Surface:** grassy. 🔵 01/01-31/12
Distance: 🛒150m 🏊100m ⊗200m 🚲500m 🚴 on the spot 🚶 on the spot.
Remarks: Shower and washing machine Jul/Aug.

Landerneau — 13B1
Rue du Calvaire. **GPS:** n48,44694 w4,25667.⬆️

25 🛏️€ 5, incl. electricity 🚰€2 🚿Ch🔧included 📖🚰
Location: Comfortable. **Surface:** grassy/gravel. 🔵 01/01-31/12
Distance: 🛒500m 🏊river ⊗500m 🚲500m 🚶on the spot.

Landivisiau — 13C1
P de Keravel, Rue du Manoir. **GPS:** n48,51015 w4,0758.

3 🛏️free 🚰🚿Chfree. **Surface:** asphalted. 🔵 01/01-31/12
Distance: 🛒on the spot ⊗on the spot 🚲100m 💧centre.

Landudec — 13B2
Super U, Rue des Écoles. **GPS:** n48,00143 w4,34088.⬆️

5 🛏️free 🚰€2/10minutes 🚿Ch🔧€2/55minutes. **Location:** Rural, simple. **Surface:** asphalted. 🔵 01/01-31/12
Distance: 🛒1km ⊗on the spot 🚲on the spot.
Remarks: Motorhome washing place.

Lanfains — 13D1
Étang du Pas, Le Pas, D7. **GPS:** n48,36466 w2,87938.⬆️

6 🛏️free 🚿Ch WCfree. **Location:** Simple, quiet.
Surface: asphalted/grassy. 🔵 01/01-31/12
Distance: 🏊on the spot 🚲on the spot.
Remarks: Parking at small lake.

Languidic — 13D2
Zone Lanveur, Place du Bouilleur de Cru.
GPS: n47,83722 w3,16188.⬆️➡️

20 🛏️free 🚰🚿Chfree. **Location:** Highway, simple, noisy.
Surface: metalled. 🔵 01/01-31/12
Distance: 🛒700m 🛣️N24 300m.

Lanloup — 13D1
Rue de Saint-Roch. **GPS:** n48,71359 w2,96389.⬆️
2 🛏️free. **Location:** Rural, simple, quiet. **Surface:** gravel.
🔵 01/01-31/12

Lannilis — 13B1
Aire Fontaine Rouge. **GPS:** n48,55667 w4,50528.⬆️➡️

12 🛏️free 🚰🚿Ch WC. **Surface:** metalled. 🔵 01/01-31/12
Distance: 🛒1km 🏊1,5km 🚲1,5km.

Lannilis — 13B1
Rue Haie Blanche. **GPS:** n48,57125 w4,52151.

🛏️free 🚰🚿Chfree. **Surface:** asphalted. 🔵 01/01-31/12
Distance: 🛒100m 🚲bakery 150m.
Remarks: In front of cemetery.

Lanvallay — 14A3
Rue du terrain des sports. **GPS:** n48,45420 w2,03028.⬆️

5 🛏️free 🚰€2/100liter 🚿Ch€2. **Location:** Urban, simple.
Surface: asphalted. 🔵 01/01-31/12
Distance: 🛒50m ⊗50m 🚲50m.

Larmor-Baden — 13D3
Route d'Auray. **GPS:** n47,58816 w2,89868.⬆️➡️

3 🛏️free. **Location:** Simple. **Surface:** asphalted. 🔵 01/01-31/12
Distance: 🛒50m ⊗100m 🚲100m.
Remarks: Max. 6,5m.

Larmor-Plage — 13C3
Parking les Pins, Rue des Pins. **GPS:** n47,70970 w3,3791.⬆️➡️

4 🛏️free 🚰🚿Ch WCfree. **Location:** Central. **Surface:** asphalted.
🔵 01/01-31/12
Distance: 🛒on the spot 🏊50m ⊗100m 🚲100m.
Remarks: Nearby plage de Toulhars, max. 72h.

Le Conquet — 13B1
Parking Parklec'H, Rue Général Leclerc. **GPS:** n48,36055 w4,7701.⬆️

+10 🛏️free 🚰€2/100liter 🚿Ch🔧€2/1h. **Surface:** gravel.
🔵 01/01-31/12
Distance: 🛒200m 🏊beach 800m ⊗400m 🚲bakery 300m 🚴on the spot.
Remarks: Coins at tourist info and town hall.

Le Croisty — 13C2
Aire de pique-nique, D132, Kergoff. **GPS:** n48,06510 w3,38144.

8 🛏️free 🚰€2 🚿Ch🔧€2/55minutes WC🔧. **Location:** Comfortable, isolated, quiet. **Surface:** asphalted. 🔵 01/01-31/12
Distance: 🛒1,5km 🚶on the spot.

Le Faou 13C1
Rue de la Grève. **GPS**: n48,29529 w4,18501.⬆️.
5 ⏚15/06-15/09 € 3,50 🚰service€2 🔌Ch. **Location:** Simple.
Surface: metalled. 🅾 01/01-31/12
Distance: 🚶800m ⊗600m 🚲1,5km.

Le Faouët 13C2
Restaurant Ty Blomen, Le Grand Pont. **GPS**: n48,03575 w3,48125.⬆️.

15 ⏚free 🚰€2 🔌Ch. **Location:** Rural, simple. **Surface:** asphalted.
🅾 01/01-31/12
Distance: ⊗on the spot.

Le Folgoët 13B1
Parking Frepel, Route de Gorrékear. **GPS**: n48,56002 w4,33507.⬆️➡️.

30 ⏚free 🚰🔌Ch.✏️free. **Surface:** gravel/metalled.
🅾 01/01-31/12
Distance: 🚶on the spot ⊗100m 🚲100m.
Remarks: Nearby basilica.

Le Trévoux 13C2
Rue des Sports. **GPS**: n47,89683 w3,64228.⬆️.

4 ⏚free 🚰🔌Chfree. **Location:** Simple. **Surface:** gravel.
🅾 01/01-31/12
Distance: 🚶on the spot.
Remarks: Nearby tennis-courts, max. 48h.

Le Trévoux 13C2
Plan d'Eau, Rue de Quimperlé. **GPS**: n47,89356 w3,6386.➡️.

10 ⏚free. **Location:** Simple. **Surface:** gravel. 🅾 01/01-31/12
Distance: 🏊on the spot 🚲bakery.
Remarks: At lake.

Le Vivier-sur-Mer 14B3
Camping-Car Park, Rue de l'Abri des Flots.
GPS: n48,60291 w1,77255.⬆️.

49 ⏚€ 8,40, 01/06-30/09 € 9,60 🚰🔌Ch✏️(49x)📶included.
🏠 **Location:** Rural, comfortable, quiet. **Surface:** asphalted.
🅾 01/01-31/12
Distance: 🚶on the spot 🏊100m 🚤100m ⊗150m 🚲150m on
the spot.

Léhon 14A3
Parking Club de Tennis. **GPS**: n48,44177 w2,04233.⬆️➡️.

6 ⏚free 🚰🔌Chfree. **Location:** Urban, simple. **Surface:** asphalted.
🅾 01/01-31/12
Distance: 🚶on the spot 🚲bakery 100m.

Les Forges 13D2
Place de l'Église, D117. **GPS**: n48,01820 w2,6482.⬆️.

5 ⏚free 🚰🔌✏️WCfree. **Surface:** metalled. 🅾 01/01-31/12
Distance: 🚶100m 🚲100m.

Lézardrieux 13D1
Rue de l'Île à Bois. **GPS**: n48,83002 w3,08165.⬆️.

5 ⏚free. **Location:** Simple, isolated, quiet. **Surface:** gravel/sand.
🅾 01/01-31/12
Distance: 🚶Lézardrieux 6km 🏊50m 🚶on the spot.
Remarks: Max. 24h.

Lézardrieux 13D1
Camping Municipal, Cité des Gardiens de Phare.
GPS: n48,78021 w3,1147.⬆️➡️.

4 ⏚€ 3 🚰€3,20 🔌Ch.✏️WC🔌€1,26. **Surface:** asphalted.
🅾 01/01-31/12
Distance: 🚶500m 🏊200m ⊗300m 🚲300m 🚶on the spot.

Liffré 17B1
Intermarché. **GPS**: n48,22459 w1,50165.⬆️➡️.

⏚free 🚰🔌Ch🔌free. **Location:** Urban, simple.
Surface: asphalted. 🅾 01/01-31/12
Distance: ✏️300m 🚲on the spot.

Locmaria-Plouzané 13B1
Plage de Portez, Rue de Portez, Porsmilin.
GPS: n48,35501 w4,67269.⬆️➡️.

8 ⏚€ 4,40 🚰🔌Chincluded. **Surface:** gravel. 🅾 01/01-31/12
Distance: 🚶3,5km 🏊beach 50m 🚶on the spot 🚶on the spot.
Remarks: To be paid at campsite.

Locmaria-Plouzané 13B1
Zône détente Ty Izella, Rue de la Fontaine.
GPS: n48,37306 w4,64306.⬆️.

12 ⏚free 🚰€2 🔌Ch🔌€2. **Location:** Quiet. **Surface:** gravel.
🅾 01/01-31/12
Distance: 🚶100m ⊗250m 🚲250m.
Remarks: Coins at town hall.

Locmariaquer 13D3
Aire de Pierres Plates, > Route des Plages.
GPS: n47,55720 w2,9486.⬆️➡️.

18 ⏚free. **Location:** Simple. **Surface:** metalled.
🅾 01/01-31/12
Distance: 🏊beach 50m 🚤on the spot.
Remarks: Max. 24h, 500m from 'Les Pierres Plates'.

Locmariaquer 13D3
Résidence de Cresidui. **GPS**: n47,57204 w2,95328.
🚰€2/100liter 🔌Ch.

Tourist information Locmariaquer:
ℹ️ Office de Tourisme, Rue de la Victoire,
www.ot-locmariaquer.com. Port city with many megalithics, signed
dolmen.

Locminé 13D2
Rue Laennec / rue du Pont Person. **GPS**: n47,88788 w2,83174.⬆️.

6 ⌂free ⚭Chfree. **Location:** Simple. **Surface:** gravel.
◻ 01/01-31/12
Distance: 🚶1km ☐ N24 1,4km 🛒600m.
Remarks: Max. 48h.

Locmiquelic 13C3

Port de Ste. Catherine, Quai Rallier du Baty.
GPS: n47,72364 w3,34958. ⬆.

⌂free. **Location:** Simple. **Surface:** asphalted.
Distance: 🚶on the spot ☐on the spot ⊗on the spot.
Remarks: Parking at marina, max. 1 night.

Locqueltas 13D3

Rue de la Fontaine. **GPS:** n47,75841 w2,76901. ⬆.

6 ⌂free ⚭Ch 🚰(4x)€3,50 WCfree. **Location:** Rural, simple,
quiet. **Surface:** gravel.
◻ 01/01-31/12
Distance: 🚶100m ⚓600m ⊗100m 🛒100m.
Remarks: Max. 24h, coins at Bar-Tabac, 18 Place de la Mairie, town hall.

Locronan 13B2

Parking de la Croix de Mission, Rue du Prieuré.
GPS: n48,09811 w4,21245.

10 ⌂free, 01/06-15/10 € 5/24h ⚭€2 Ch🛒€2 WC.
Surface: grassy/sand. ◻ 01/01-31/12
Distance: ⊗50m.

Loctudy 13B2

Plage des Sables Blancs, Rue du Beau Rivage.
GPS: n47,79883 w4,19739. ⬆.

6 ⌂free. **Location:** Rural, simple. **Surface:** asphalted.
◻ 01/01-31/12
Distance: 🚶4km ⚓beach 80m.

Remarks: Beach parking.

Loudéac 13D2

Parking de la Gare, Boulevard de la Gare.
GPS: n48,18058 w2,76277. ⬆➡.

3 ⌂free ⚭Chfree. **Location:** Urban, simple. **Surface:** asphalted.
◻ 01/01-31/12
Distance: 🚶600m ⚓50m ⊗200m 🛒200m 🚌on the spot.

Maël-Carhaix 13C2

Place de l'école, Route de Rostrenen. **GPS:** n48,28344 w3,42148. ⬆➡.

5 ⌂free ⚭€2 ChWC. **Location:** Urban, simple.
Surface: asphalted. ◻ 01/01-31/12
Distance: 🚶100m ⚓100m 🛒100m.
Remarks: At fire-station, coins at town hall.

Malansac 17A2

Rue Saint Fiacre. **GPS:** n47,67820 w2,29942. ⬆➡.

5 ⌂free ⚭Chfree. **Location:** Rural, comfortable, quiet.
Surface: grassy.
Distance: 🚶100m ⚓100m 🛒100m.

Malestroit 17A1

Chemin des Tanneurs. **GPS:** n47,80772 w2,37885. ⬆➡.

12 ⌂free. **Location:** Comfortable, quiet. **Surface:** gravel/metalled.
◻ 01/01-31/12
Distance: 🚶500m ⚓on the spot ⊗350m.
Remarks: Max. 48h.

Malestroit 17A1

Chemin de l'Écluse. **GPS:** n47,81250 w2,38197. ⬆➡.

12 ⌂free. **Location:** Rural, comfortable, quiet.
Surface: gravel/metalled. ◻ 01/01-31/12
Distance: 🚶100m ⚓on the spot 🚰on the spot ⊗100m 🛒100m

🛒200m.
Remarks: Max. 48h.

Malestroit 17A1

Rue de Narvik. **GPS:** n47,80896 w2,37591. ⬆➡.
⚭Chfree. **Surface:** asphalted.
Distance: 🚶1,5km ⚓600m 🚰600m ⊗2km 🛒1km.

Marzan 17A2

Rue de la Source. **GPS:** n47,54023 w2,32383. ⬆.

+20 ⌂free ⚭ChWCfree. **Location:** Urban, simple, quiet.
Surface: asphalted.
Distance: 🚶50m 🛒20m.

Maure-de-Bretagne 17A1

Rue de Campel, D65. **GPS:** n47,89230 w1,99031. ⬆➡.

3 ⌂free ⚭Chfree. **Location:** Urban, simple, central, quiet.
Surface: gravel. ◻ 01/01-31/12
Distance: 🚶200m ⚓on the spot ⊗200m 🛒200m 🚌on the spot
🚲on the spot 🚶on the spot.

Mauron 17A1

Rue de la Libération. **GPS:** n48,08024 w2,27677. ⬆➡.

12 ⌂free ⚭€2,50/100 ⚭ChWC. **Location:** Rural, simple,
comfortable, quiet. **Surface:** asphalted.
Distance: 🚶150m ⚓on the spot 🚰on the spot ⊗150m 🛒150m
🚲on the spot 🚶on the spot.

Mégrit 14A3

Rue des Granitiers. **GPS:** n48,37817 w2,24722. ⬆.
⌂free ⚭Chfree. **Surface:** asphalted/gravel. ◻ 01/01-31/12
Distance: 🛒on the spot.

Mellé 14B3

Rue Rouviel. **GPS:** n48,48919 w1,18814. ⬆.

6 ⌂free ⚭ChWCfree. **Surface:** metalled.
Distance: 🚶200m 🛒200m.
Remarks: Nearby football ground, max. 48h.

Meslin 13D1

Allée des Loisirs, D28. **GPS:** n48,44363 w2,56994. ⬆.

10 🛏free 🚰🔌Chfree. **Location:** Urban, simple, central.
Surface: metalled. 🅾 01/01-31/12
Distance: 🚰300m ⊗bar/crêperie 50m 🍴50m.

| 🅂 | Moëlan-sur-Mer 🏖 | 13C2 |

Kerdoualen, Route de l'Île Percée. **GPS:** n47,79045 w3,70314.⬆.

4 🛏free. **Location:** Rural. **Surface:** gravel. 🅾 01/01-31/12
Distance: ⚓200m.

| 🅂 | Moëlan-sur-Mer 🏖 | 13C2 |

Rue de Beg Tal Gward. **GPS:** n47,77749 w3,64404.⬆➡.

4 🛏free. **Location:** Rural, isolated, quiet. **Surface:** asphalted.
🅾 01/01-31/12
Distance: 🚰Moëlan 5km ⚓sea 50m.

| 🅂 | Moncontour | 13D2 |

Camping la Tourelle, Rue François Lorant.
GPS: n48,35271 w2,63719.⬆➡.

4 🛏€2 🚰€2 🔌Ch🔌€2/55minutes 🧺. **Location:** Rural, simple,
quiet. **Surface:** gravel. 🅾 01/01-31/12
Distance: 🚰1,5km ⊗1,5km 🍴1,5km.
Remarks: Max. 48h.

| 🅂 | Morlaix 🍴🏖 | 13C1 |

Rue de Brest. **GPS:** n48,57422 w3,8316.⬆.

5 🛏free 🚰🔌Chfree. **Location:** Urban, simple, central, noisy.
Surface: asphalted. 🅾 01/01-31/12
Distance: 🚰on the spot 🚉on the spot ⊗200m 🍴100m 🚌200m
🚲on the spot 🚶on the spot.

| 🅂 | Mûr-de-Bretagne | 13D2 |

L'ancienne Gare, Place de la Gare. **GPS:** n48,19814 w2,98961.⬆.
4 🛏free 🚰🔌Ch. **Location:** Urban, simple. **Surface:** metalled.
🅾 01/01-31/12

Distance: 🚰700m ⊗500m.

| 🅂 | Mûr-de-Bretagne | 13D2 |

Anse de Leandroanec, Plage de Leandroanec.
GPS: n48,20969 w3,01309.⬆.
10 🛏free. **Location:** Rural, simple, quiet. **Surface:** metalled.
🅾 01/01-31/12
Distance: 🚰2,5km ⚓on the spot.

| 🅂 | Mûr-de-Bretagne | 13D2 |

Place Ste Suzanne. **GPS:** n48,20260 w2,98835.⬆.
4 🛏free. **Location:** Urban, simple. **Surface:** metalled.
🅾 01/01-31/12
Distance: 🚰300m ⊗100m.

| 🅂 🅂 | Neulliac | 13D2 |

Rue des Deux Croix, D767. **GPS:** n48,12812 w2,98552.⬆➡.

4 🛏free 🚰€2 🔌Ch🔌€2. **Location:** Simple, isolated, quiet.
Surface: asphalted.
Distance: 🚰300m ⊗300m.

| 🅂 | Névez | 13C2 |

Rue de Port Manech, Impasse du Stade. **GPS:** n47,81560 w3,7894.⬆.

20 🛏free 🚰€2/10minutes 🔌Ch🔌€2/55minutes WC. **Location:** Simple. **Surface:** asphalted. 🅾 01/01-31/12
Remarks: Parking next to stadium, max. 24h, service only with 2-euro coins.

| 🅂 | Névez | 13C2 |

Plage de Dourveil, Rue de Dourveil, D1. **GPS:** n47,79407 w3,8101.⬆.

5 🛏free. **Surface:** sand.
Distance: ⚓on the spot.
Remarks: Max. 24h, no camping activities.

| 🅂 | Névez | 13C2 |

Plage de Tahiti, Kerstalen. **GPS:** n47,79287 w3,79011.⬆.

± 11 🛏free. **Location:** Simple. **Surface:** grassy/sand.
🅾 01/01-31/12
Distance: ⚓beach 150m.
Remarks: Beach parking, max. 24h.

| 🅂 | Névez | 13C2 |

Rue de la Plage. **GPS:** n47,80499 w3,74261.⬆.

5 🛏free. **Location:** Rural, simple. **Surface:** sand.
🅾 01/01-31/12
Distance: ⚓50m.
Remarks: Max. 24h.

| 🅂 | Névez | 13C2 |

Rue des Iles, Raguénez. **GPS:** n47,78908 w3,80174.⬆.

10 🛏free. **Location:** Simple. **Surface:** asphalted. 🅾 01/01-31/12
Distance: ⚓sea 10m, beach 150m ⊗100m.
Remarks: Max. 24h.

| 🅂 🅂 | Noyal-Pontivy 🏖 | 13D2 |

Le Valvert, Caudan. **GPS:** n48,07833 w2,91583.⬆➡.

20 🛏free 🚰🔌WCfree. **Location:** Rural, comfortable, isolated, quiet.
Surface: asphalted. 🅾 01/01-31/12
Distance: 🚰Noyal-Pontivy 4,5km ⚓on the spot 🚉on the spot
⊗50m.
Remarks: At small lake.

| 🅂 🅂 | Paimpol | 13D1 |

Parking Pierre Loti, Rue Pierre Loti. **GPS:** n48,78404 w3,0463.

15 🛏free 🚰€3,30/100liter 🔌Ch🔌€3,30/55minutes.
Surface: gravel/sand. 🅾 01/01-31/12
Distance: 🚰on the spot ⚓1km 🚉400m 🚌100m 🚲on the spot
🚶on the spot.
Remarks: Service 100m.

| 🅂 | Paimpol | 13D1 |

Parking de Goas Plat, Rue de Goas Plat. **GPS:** n48,77535 w3,04009.⬆.

37 🛏free. **Location:** Urban, simple, central, quiet. **Surface:** asphalted.
Distance: 🚰centre 500m ⚓2km ⊗500m 🍴500m.
Remarks: Max. 24h.

Paimpont 🌊 17A1

Rue de l'Enchanteur Merlin. **GPS:** n48,02286 w2,17128. ⬆️

70 🛏️€ 3, 01/05-27/09 € 4 🚰€3,70/10minutes 🏕️Ch WC.
Location: Simple. **Surface:** gravel.
Distance: 🚶200m 🏖️200m 🛒200m 🍴200m 🚉200m 🚲 on the spot 🏃100m.
Remarks: Coins at tourist info and supermarket.

Pénestin 🌊 13D3

Allée du Grand Pré. **GPS:** n47,48111 w2,47361. ⬆️➡️

7 🛏️free, € 6/night + € 0,20/pp 🚰€2,50/100liter 🏕️Ch 🚽€2,50/1h.
Location: Urban. **Surface:** asphalted.
Distance: 🚶500m 🏖️1,5km 🚉500m.
Remarks: Check in all aires in Pénestin: Office de tourisme; Bar-PMU Le Narval, Rue Calvaire; Café O 20 100 O, Port de Tréhiguier, max. 48h, coins at tourist info.

Pénestin 🌊 13D3

Aire camping-car de la Pointe du Bile, Route de l'Espernel.
GPS: n47,44524 w2,48029. ⬆️

🛏️free, € 6/night + € 0,20/pp. **Location:** Rural, simple, quiet.
Surface: grassy/sand. 📅 01/01-31/12
Distance: 🏖️100m.
Remarks: Max. 48h.

Pénestin 🌊 13D3

Allée de Poudrantais. **GPS:** n47,46681 w2,48716. ⬆️

4 🛏️free, € 6/night + € 0,20/pp. **Location:** Urban, simple, quiet.
Surface: gravel/metalled.
Distance: 🏖️50m.
Remarks: Max. 48h.

Pénestin 🌊 13D3

Chemin de Camaret. **GPS:** n47,49386 w2,49075. ⬆️

4 🛏️free, € 6/night + € 0,20/pp. **Location:** Urban, simple, quiet.
Surface: gravel.
Distance: 🏖️100m.
Remarks: Max. 48h.

Pénestin 🌊 13D3

Plage de la Source, Allée du Maro. **GPS:** n47,48158 w2,49005. ⬆️

10 🛏️free, € 6/night + € 0,20/pp. **Location:** Rural, simple, quiet.
Surface: grassy/metalled.
Distance: 🏖️300m.
Remarks: Max. 48h.

Pénestin 🌊 13D3

Plage du Palandrin, L'Isle du Clos Parc, Kerséguin.
GPS: n47,45000 w2,46417. ⬆️➡️

6 🛏️free, € 6/night + € 0,20/pp tourist tax. **Location:** Rural, simple, isolated. **Surface:** grassy/sand.
📅 01/01-31/12
Distance: 🏖️Sandy beach 🚉1km.
Remarks: Pay at tourist office.

Pénestin 🌊 13D3

Route du Loguy. **GPS:** n47,49050 w2,49667. ⬆️

20 🛏️free, € 6/night + € 0,20/pp. **Location:** Rural, simple, quiet.
Surface: grassy/metalled.
Distance: 🏖️150m.
Remarks: Max. 48h.

Penmarch 🌊 13B2

Aire du Viben, Rue de la Plage. **GPS:** n47,82390 w4,3708. ⬆️

30 🛏️9-19h free, 19-9h € 4. ♿ **Location:** Rural, simple, quiet.
Surface: metalled. 📅 01/01-31/12
Distance: 🥖bakery 1km 🚉900m 🚲 on the spot 🏃on the spot.

Penmarch 🌊 13B2

Aire de Port du Bouc, Route du Ster Kérity.
GPS: n47,79981 w4,34794. ⬆️

10 🛏️€ 4/19-9h. ♿ **Location:** Rural. **Surface:** grassy/gravel.
📅 01/01-31/12
Distance: 🚶1,5km 🏖️50m 🚉1km 🚉5km.

Penmarch 🌊 13B2

Aire de Kerameil, Rue du Pont Nevez. **GPS:** n47,81369 w4,36077. ⬆️

🚰€2/10minutes 🏕️Ch WC. **Location:** Rural, simple.
📅 01/01-31/12
Distance: 🚶3km.
Remarks: Only overnight stays 19-9h.

Penvins 🌊 13D3

Camping La Gree Penvins, Chemin du Marais 20.
GPS: n47,49746 w2,68606. ⬆️➡️

22 🛏️€ 5. **Location:** Urban, comfortable, quiet. **Surface:** grassy.
📅 01/01-31/12
Distance: 🏖️on the spot 🚉350m.
Remarks: Max. 48h.

Penzé 🌊 13C1

Rue du Dossen. **GPS:** n48,59811 w3,93439.

5 🛏️free 🚰€2 🏕️Ch 🚽€2 WC. **Location:** Simple, quiet.
Surface: asphalted. 📅 01/01-31/12
Distance: 🚶100m 🏖️on the spot 🍴on the spot 🚉50m 🚉250m 🚲on the spot 🏃on the spot.
Remarks: Nearby port.

Piré-sur-Seiche 🌊 17B1

Rue de Boistrudan. **GPS:** n48,00719 w1,42871.

15 🛏️free 🚰 🏕️Chfree.

FR

Location: Rural, simple. **Surface:** metalled.
Distance: 🚰300m 🚮on the spot 🗑300m ♻500m.
Remarks: At fish lake.

🅢 **Plabennec** 13B1

Rue de l'Aber. **GPS:** n48,50155 w4,43374.⬆

5 🚐free 🚰🗑Chfree. **Location:** Simple. **Surface:** metalled.
⭕ 01/01-31/12 ♻on the spot.
Remarks: Parking at small lake.

🅢 **Planguenoual** 14A3

Bien y Vient. GPS: n48,53447 w2,54506.⬆

6 🚐€5 🚰♻€2/24h. 🚿 **Location:** Rural, comfortable, isolated,
quiet. **Surface:** grassy. ⭕ 01/01-31/12 ♻on the spot.

🅢 **Planguenoual** 14A3

Ferme Gesbert, D786. **GPS:** n48,54883 w2,5556.⬆➡

6 🚐free 🚰€2 🗑Ch ♻€2 📶. **Location:** Rural.
Surface: grassy/gravel. ⭕ 01/01-31/12
Distance: 🚰1km ⊗1km 🛒1km.
Remarks: Regional products.

🅢 **Plémet** 13D2

Rue de l'Étang, D16. **GPS:** n48,17897 w2,58918.⬆➡

15 🚐free 🚰€2/100liter 🗑Ch 📧€2/55minutes. **Surface:** gravel.
⭕ 01/01-31/12
Remarks: Parking at small lake.

🅢 **Pléneuf-Val-André** 14A3

Avenue du Général Leclerc. **GPS:** n48,58355 w2,55669.⬆➡

30 🚐€6 🚰€2 🗑Ch. 📧 ♻ **Location:** Urban, simple, central, quiet.
Surface: grassy/gravel. ⭕ 01/01-31/12
Distance: 🚰1km ⚓450m.
Remarks: Max. 72h.

🅢 **Plérin** 13D1

Sous la Tour, Rue de la Tour, D24. **GPS:** n48,53146 w2,72483.⬆

16 🚐free 🚰🗑Chfree. **Location:** Simple, quiet. **Surface:** gravel.
⭕ 01/01-31/12
Distance: ⚓on the spot ⊗300m 🛒1km.

🅢 **Pleslin-Trigavou** 14A3

D28. **GPS:** n48,53631 w2,05009.⬆

20 🚐free 🚰🗑Chfree.
Location: Urban, simple. **Surface:** asphalted.
Distance: 🚰on the spot 🛒400m ♻on the spot 🚶on the spot.
Remarks: Cycle and hiking routes: voie verte, Circuit des Mégalithes.

🅢 **Plessala** 13D2

Rue de l'Étang. **GPS:** n48,27394 w2,62427.⬆➡

12 🚐free 🚰🗑Chfree. **Location:** Urban, simple, quiet.
Surface: gravel. ⭕ 01/01-31/12
Distance: 🚰200m 🚮on the spot.
Remarks: At fish lake, max. 48h, fishing permit available.

🅢 **Plestin-les-Grèves** 13C1

Voie Communale de l'Armorique. **GPS:** n48,68157 w3,63411.⬆

🚐free. **Surface:** unpaved. ⭕ 01/01-31/12
Distance: 🚰3km ⚓50m ⊗2km 🚶on the spot.
Remarks: Beach parking, max. 24h.

🅢 **Plestin-les-Grèves** 13C1

Du Grand Rocher, Avenue de la Lieue de Grève.
GPS: n48,66968 w3,5858.
🚐free. **Location:** Simple, isolated, quiet.
Distance: 🚰1,3km ⚓100m ⊗1,3km.

🅢 **Plestin-les-Grèves** 13C1

Route de la Corniche. **GPS:** n48,67235 w3,63602.⬆

6 🚐free. **Location:** Rural, simple, quiet. **Surface:** grassy/sand.
⭕ 01/01-31/12
Distance: 🚰1km ⚓on the spot ⊗300m 🛒Lidl 2km.
Remarks: Max. 24h.

🅢 **Plestin-les-Grèves** 13C1

Rue de Guergay. **GPS:** n48,66232 w3,62562.
🚰€2/10minutes 🗑Ch ♻€2/1h.
Remarks: Motorhome washing place.

🅢 **Pleubian** 13D1

Port Béni. **GPS:** n48,84834 w3,17053.⬆

4 🚐free. **Location:** Rural, simple, isolated, quiet. **Surface:** asphalted.
⭕ 01/01-31/12
Distance: 🚰Pleubian 2,5km ⚓on the spot ⊗2,5km 🚶on the spot.
Remarks: Max. 24h.

🅢 **Pleubian** 13D1

Rue de Kermagen, Kermagen. **GPS:** n48,85667 w3,14194.⬆

4 🚐free. **Surface:** grassy. ⭕ 01/01-31/12
Distance: 🚰Pleubian 1,6km ⚓beach 100m 🚶on the spot.
Remarks: Max. 24h.

🅢 **Pleubian** 13D1

Rue de Pen Lan, Lanéros. **GPS:** n48,85760 w3,07883.⬆

4 🚐free. **Surface:** asphalted.
Distance: 🚰Pleubian 5,5km ⚓on the spot 🚶on the spot.
Remarks: Max. 24h.

🅢 **Pleumeur-Bodou** 13C1

Parking de Toul ar Stang, Rue de Toul ar Stang, Ile Grande.
GPS: n48,79868 w3,58342.⬆➡

6 🚐€6/night 🚰€2/10minutes 🗑Ch 📧€2/1h. 🚿 **Location:** Rural,
simple, quiet. **Surface:** grassy.

FR

◻ 01/01-31/12

Distance: ⚙Plemeur-Bodou 6km ⚓sandy beach 150m ⊗150m 🚶on the spot.

| ⚙S | **Pleumeur-Bodou** 🚐🌊 | **13C1** |

Cosmopolis-Parc Scientifique, Route du Radome.
GPS: n48,78297 w3,52587.⬆.

20 🚐parking free, € 5/night 🚰🔌Ch 🧹WC 🗑.
Surface: gravel/sand. ◻ 01/01-31/12
Distance: ⚙1km ⚓1km ⊗on the spot 🚶on the spot.

| P | **Plévenon** 🌿🌊 | **14A3** |

Parking Cap Fréhel. GPS: n48,68174 w2,31811.

40 🚐free, 01/06-30/09 € 4. **Surface:** metalled.
Distance: ⚓50m.
Remarks: Max. 1 night.

| ⚙S | **Ploemeur** | **13C2** |

Aire de la Vraie Croix, Route de Larmor. **GPS:** n47,72784 w3,41423.⬆.
🚐free 🚰🔌Chfree.
Remarks: Industrial area, max. 48h.

| ⚙S | **Ploemeur** | **13C2** |

Rue Louis Lessart. **GPS:** n47,73681 w3,43051.⬆.

7 🚐free. **Surface:** asphalted. ◻ 01/01-31/12
Distance: ⚙on the spot.
Remarks: Parking centre, max. 24h.

| ⚙ | **Ploemeur** | **13C2** |

Golf Ploemeur, D152, Boulevard de l'Atlantique.
GPS: n47,72316 w3,48156.⬆➡.

9 🚐free.
Location: Rural, quiet. **Surface:** gravel.
◻ 01/01-31/12
Distance: ⚙Ploemeur 5km ⚡N165 10km ⚓beach 300m 🛒1,8km.

| ⚙S | **Plogoff** 🚐 | **13B2** |

Aire Naturelle Kerguidy Izella, Rue Guillaume Pennamen.
GPS: n48,03694 w4,68139.⬆.

30 🚐€ 12 🚰🔌Ch🔌WC🗑📶included. **Location:** Rural, comfortable. **Surface:** grassy. ◻ 01/01-31/12
Distance: ⚙2km.
Remarks: 9><20h.

| ⚙S | **Plogoff** 🚐 | **13B2** |

Parking de l'Eglise, Rue Cleder cap Sizum.
GPS: n48,03727 w4,6652.⬆➡.

4 🚐free 🚰€2/10minutes 🔌Ch. **Location:** Rural, comfortable.
Surface: asphalted. ◻ 01/01-31/12
Distance: ⚙centre.

| ⚙S | **Plogoff** 🚐 | **13B2** |

Aire de la Pointe du Raz, Route des Langoustiers.
GPS: n48,03651 w4,7173.⬆.

40 🚐€ 5 day/€ 5 night. **Location:** Rural, simple. **Surface:** metalled.
◻ 01/01-31/12
Distance: ⚙3km ⊗50m.

| ⚙S | **Plogoff** 🚐 | **13B2** |

Parking du Stade, Rue du 19 Mars 1962. **GPS:** n48,03245 w4,66316.⬆.

50 🚐free. **Location:** Rural, simple, quiet. **Surface:** grassy/metalled.
◻ 01/01-31/12
Distance: ⚙on the spot ⊗450m 🛒450m bakery.

| ⚙S | **Plomelin** | **13B2** |

Plomelin, Rue Hent Keramer. **GPS:** n47,93410 w4,1515.⬆.

5 🚐free 🚰€2/10minutes 🔌Ch🔌€2. **Location:** Rural, simple, quiet.
Surface: asphalted. ◻ 01/01-31/12
Remarks: Parking sports park, max. 24h.

| ⚙S | **Plonévez-Porzay** | **13B2** |

Plonévez-Porzay, Rue des Eglantines. **GPS:** n48,12469 w4,22414.⬆.

15 🚐free 🚰€2/10minutes 🔌Ch 🔌. **Location:** Rural, comfortable.
Surface: grassy. ◻ 01/01-31/12
Distance: ⚙600m 🛒450m bakery + Spar.

| ⚙ | **Plonévez-Porzay** | **13B2** |

Kervel Izella. GPS: n48,11570 w4,28065.⬆.

10 🚐free. **Location:** Rural, simple, simple. **Surface:** grassy/sand.
◻ 01/01-31/12
Distance: ⚙5,5km ⚓50m 🚐on the spot.
Remarks: Beach parking, max. 48h.

| ⚙S | **Plouarzel** | **13B1** |

Aire de camping-car de Ruscumunoc, Route de Ruscumunoc.
GPS: n48,42232 w4,78486.⬆➡.

🚐free, 15/05-15/09 € 4,60 🚰€2,50/10minutes 🔌Ch🔌€
2,60/50minutes 🗑€1 📶 🚿 **Location:** Comfortable, quiet.
Surface: grassy. ◻ 01/01-31/12
Distance: ⚙3km ⚓100m.

| ⚙S | **Ploubalay** | **14A3** |

Rue des Ormelets. **GPS:** n48,58057 w2,14524.⬆.

3 🚐free 🚰🔌Chfree. **Location:** Simple. **Surface:** asphalted.
◻ 01/01-31/12
Distance: ⚙250m ⊗100m 🛒500m 🚐on the spot.

| ⚙ | **Ploubazlanec** 🚐🌊 | **13D1** |

Park Nevez, Cité de Lan ar Mendy. **GPS:** n48,80085 w3,03054.⬆.
3 🚐free. **Location:** Simple. ◻ 01/01-31/12
Distance: 🛒bakery.
Remarks: Max. 24h.

| ⚙ | **Ploubazlanec** 🚐🌊 | **13D1** |

Pointe de l'Arcouest, Route de l'Embarcadère.
GPS: n48,82102 w3,01948.⬆.

20 🛏free, 30/06-30/09 € 6/24h. **Location:** Simple, isolated, quiet.
Surface: grassy. ⭕ 01/01-31/12
Distance: 🚰2km ⚓50m 🚶on the spot.

Ploubazlanec 13D1

Rue du Port Loguivy. **GPS:** n48,82011 w3,06279.
6 🛏free. **Surface:** asphalted.
Distance: 🚰100m ⚓on the spot ⊗100m 🛒100m.

Plouescat 13C1

Rue de Pen an Théven. **GPS:** n48,65902 w4,21863.⬆️.

6 🛏free. **Surface:** metalled. ⭕ 01/01-31/12
Distance: 🚰3,5km ⚓100m.

Plouescat 13C1

Intermarché, La Rocade-Kerchapalain.
GPS: n48,65083 w4,18444.⬆️➡️.

4 🛏free 🚰€2 Ch €2 ⊡€5/1. **Location:** Comfortable.
Surface: asphalted. ⭕ 01/01-31/12
Distance: 🚰500m ⊗600m on the spot ⊡on the spot.
Remarks: Parking supermarket.

Plouézec 13D1

Parking A. Le Calvez. GPS: n48,74980 w2,98409.
3 🛏free. ⭕ 01/01-31/12
Distance: 🚰on the spot ⊗on the spot 🛒on the spot.

Plouézec 13D1

Parking de la Corniche, Bréhec. **GPS:** n48,72662 w2,94849.
5 🛏free. ⭕ 01/01-31/12
Distance: ⚓on the spot ⊗on the spot.

Plouézec 13D1

Place du 19 mars 1962. **GPS:** n48,74788 w2,9853.⬆️.

3 🛏free. **Surface:** asphalted. ⭕ 01/01-31/12
Remarks: Service at camping municipal.

Plougasnou 13C1

Parking de la Métairie, Rue Charles de Gaulle.
GPS: n48,69404 w3,79209.⬆️.

7 🛏free 🚰€2/10minutes Ch €2/1h WC. **Location:** Rural.
Surface: gravel. ⭕ 01/01-31/12
Distance: 🚰on the spot ⚓sandy beach 1,4km ⊗200m 🛒250m
bakery on the spot 🚶on the spot.
Remarks: Tuesday morning market.

Plougasnou 13C1

Rue des Grands Viviers, Le Diben. **GPS:** n48,70811 w3,82731.⬆️.

7 🛏free 🚰€2 Ch. **Location:** Rural, simple, isolated, quiet.
Surface: asphalted. ⭕ 01/01-31/12
Distance: 🚰300m ⚓on the spot on the spot ⊗300m 🚶on the spot.
Remarks: Max. 48h, coins at town hall.

Plougastel-Daoulas 13B1

Rue de la Fontaine Blanche. **GPS:** n48,37111 w4,36428.

15 🛏free 🚰 Ch 📶free. **Surface:** asphalted.
⭕ 15/05-15/10
Distance: 🚰450m ⊗450m 🛒450m.
Remarks: Parking at sports grounds.

Plougonvelin 13B1

Rue de Bertheaume. **GPS:** n48,33792 w4,70742.⬆️➡️.

50 🛏€6 Ch WC included. **Location:** Comfortable, quiet. **Surface:** grassy/sand. ⭕ 01/01-31/12
Distance: 🚰1km ⚓beach 650m.

Plougonvelin 13B1

Intermarché, Rue du Stade. **GPS:** n48,34245 w4,72248.

🛏€7 🚰€2/100liter Ch €1/1h ⊡€5.
Surface: asphalted.
Distance: 🛒on the spot.

Plouguerneau 13B1

Lilia. **GPS:** n48,61891 w4,55341.⬆️➡️.

10 🛏free 🚰€4/10minutes Ch €4/55minutes.
Location: Comfortable. **Surface:** asphalted. ⭕ 01/01-31/12
Distance: 🚰400m ⚓850m 🛒450m.

Plouha 13D1

Plage de Palus, Route du Palus. **GPS:** n48,67667 w2,88556.⬆️.

10 🛏free. **Location:** Rural, simple, isolated, quiet. **Surface:** grassy.
⭕ 01/03-31/10
Distance: 🚰3km ⚓sandy/pebbled beach 100m ⊗50m 🚶on the spot.
Remarks: Max. 3 days.

Ploumoguer 13B1

Rue Huon de Kermadec, D28. **GPS:** n48,40507 w4,72492.⬆️➡️.

30 🛏free, July-Aug € 3 🚰€2/80liter Ch €2/45minutes WC €2
⊡€4/2,30. **Surface:** metalled. ⭕ 01/04-30/11
Distance: 🚰200m ⊗200m 🛒200m.
Remarks: Next to stadium, max. 48h, coins at town hall, supermarket, bakery and Tabac.

Plouvorn 13C1

Plan d'Eau de Lanorgant. **GPS:** n48,57722 w4,03056.⬆️➡️.

15 🛏free 🚰€2 Ch €2 WC. **Location:** Simple, quiet.
Surface: metalled. ⭕ 01/01-31/12
Distance: 🚰500m ⚓100m 100m ⊗500m 🛒500m.
Remarks: Parking at small lake.

Pluméliau 13D2

Allée du vieux Blavet. **GPS:** n47,98229 w3,04209.⬆️.

15 🛏free 🚰 Ch free. **Location:** Rural, comfortable.
Surface: gravel. ⭕ 01/01-31/12
Distance: 🚰500m on the spot ⊗250m on the spot 🚶on the spot.
Remarks: Along the Blavet river, attention: max. ^3.1m.

Pont-Aven 13C2

Rue Louis Lomenech. **GPS:** n47,85401 w3,74333.➡️.

30 🛏free 🚰€2,45/10minutes Ch €2,45/55minutes.

Location: Simple. **Surface:** asphalted.
◻ 01/01-31/12
Distance: 🚉450m ⊗450m.
Remarks: Parking near stadium Sinquin, coins at tourist info (D783).

Pont-Aven 13C2

Rue des Abbès Tanguy. **GPS:** n47,85646 w3,75203. ⬆.

🅂free. **Location:** Simple. **Surface:** asphalted. ◻ 01/01-31/12
Distance: 🚉400m.

Pont-Croix 13B2

Place de la Métairie. **GPS:** n48,04207 w4,48549. ⬆.

40 🅂free 🚰€2/10minutes 🅲h⊟ 🗑. 🛢 **Location:** Urban, simple.
Surface: metalled. ◻ 01/01-31/12
Distance: 🚉10min ⊗on the spot.
Remarks: Thursday market.

Tourist information Pont-Croix:
🛈 ◻ Thu.

Pont-l'Abbé 13B2

Parking de la Gare, Rue de la Gare. **GPS:** n47,87070 w4,22506. ⬆.

5 🅂free 🚰🅲h⊟free. **Location:** Urban. **Surface:** asphalted.
◻ 01/01-31/12
Distance: 🚉on the spot.

Pont-l'Abbé 13B2

Leclerc, Route de Saint Jean Trolimont. **GPS:** n47,86414 w4,23646. ⬆.

13 🅂free 🚰€2 🅲h⊟€2 🔊. **Location:** Urban, simple.
Surface: asphalted. ◻ 01/01-31/12
Distance: 🚉on the spot 🍽on the spot.
Remarks: At supermarket.

Pontivy 13D2

Rue de la Fontaine. **GPS:** n48,06758 w2,96941. ⬆.

6 🅂free 🛢free. **Location:** Urban, simple. **Surface:** asphalted.
◻ 01/01-31/12
Distance: 🚉800m ⚡on the spot 🥖bakery 300m ⊗on the spot.

Port-Louis 13C3

Aire de la Côte Rouge, D781 Port-Louis > Riantec.
GPS: n47,70873 w3,34295. ⬆.

14 🅂€ 5/24h, 01/06-15/09 € 10/24h 🚰🅲h🔌(4x)included 🗑.🛢
🗑 **Surface:** asphalted. ◻ 01/01-31/12
Distance: 🏖on the spot 🍽on the spot.

Port-Louis 13C3

Aire des Remparts, Promenade Henri François Buffet.
GPS: n47,70496 w3,35602. ⬆.

30 🅂€ 5/24h, 01/06-15/09 € 10/24h 🚰🅲h🔌included 🗑.🛢
Location: Urban. ◻ 01/01-31/12
Distance: 🏖100m 🚉100m ⚓on the spot.
Remarks: In front of campsite.

Portsall 13B1

Aire camping-cars Kerros, Rue de Porsguen.
GPS: n48,56583 w4,69944. ⬆➡.

37 🅂€ 5,20/24h 🚰🅲h⊟included 🗑. **Location:** Comfortable,
quiet. **Surface:** grassy. ◻ 01/01-31/12
Distance: 🚉on the spot 🏖350m ⊗200m 🍽200m.
Remarks: Max. 3 days.

Poullaouen 13C1

D236, Rue de Ty Meur. **GPS:** n48,33672 w3,64218. ⬆➡.

5 🅂free 🚰🅲hfree. **Location:** Rural, comfortable, quiet.
Surface: gravel. ◻ 01/01-31/12
Distance: 🚉200m ⊗150m 🚴Véloroute Roscoff-Nantes ⚓on the spot.

Primelin 13B2

Camping Municipal de Kermaléro, Route de l'Océan.
GPS: n48,02550 w4,61821.

15 🅂free 🚰€2 🅲h⊟€2. **Location:** Simple. **Surface:** metalled.
◻ 01/01-31/12

Priziac 13C2

Base de Loisirs du Lac du Bel Air, Etang du Bel Air.
GPS: n48,06183 w3,41132. ⬆.

🅂€ 5,50 🚰🅲hincluded.
Distance: ⊗300m.

Quiberon 13D3

Rue de Port Kerné. **GPS:** n47,49165 w3,13941. ⬆➡.

140 🅂€ 6,40/24h 🚰€1/2minutes 🅲h 🗑. **Location:** Rural, simple.
Surface: gravel.
◻ 01/01-31/12 ⊙ service: 15/10-01/04
Distance: 🚉2km 🏖sea 250m ⊗2km 🍽2km 🚉on the spot 🚴on
the spot ⚓on the spot.
Remarks: Next to camping municipal, max. 3 days, bread-service only
in summer, seaview.

Quimperlé 13C2

Aire Saint Nicolas, Rue du Viaduc. **GPS:** n47,86640 w3,54334. ⬆➡.

3 🅂free 🚰🅲hfree. **Location:** Simple. **Surface:** metalled.
◻ 01/01-31/12

Quintin 13D1

Place du Champ de Foire. **GPS:** n48,40056 w2,90222. ⬆➡.

7 🅂free 🚰🅲hfree. **Location:** Urban, simple, quiet.
Surface: asphalted. ◻ 01/01-31/12 ⊙ Service: winter
Distance: 🚉on the spot 🏖on the spot.
Remarks: Next to swimming pool, near the lake, tuesday market.

FR

FR

Tourist information Quintin:
⚐ ◻ Tue-morning.

Radenac 13D2

Sente Verte, Les Gambris. **GPS:** n47,95778 w2,71333. ⬆.

5 🚐free. **Location:** Rural, simple, quiet. **Surface:** gravel.
◻ 01/01-31/12
Distance: 🚶700m ⛽on the spot 🚲 on the spot ⚑ on the spot.
Remarks: At small lake.

Redon 17A2

Quai Surcouf. **GPS:** n47,64510 w2,0897. ⬆➡.

10 🚐free ⛽🍽Chfree. **Location:** Simple. **Surface:** asphalted.
◻ 01/01-31/12
Distance: 🚶500m ⛵on the spot ⛽100m ⊗200m ⚱200m.
Remarks: In front of Bureau du Port de Plaisance.

Tourist information Redon:
👁 Manoir de l'Automobile de Loheac. Car collection: Ferrari, Lamborghini, Porsche, Maserati.

Réguiny 13D2

Base de Loisirs, Rue de la Piscine. **GPS:** n47,96843 w2,73828. ⬆.

10 🚐free ⛽🍽Chfree. **Location:** Rural, simple, quiet.
Surface: unpaved. ◻ 01/01-31/12
Distance: 🚶1,3km ⚱bakery 1,3km 🚲 on the spot ⚑on the spot.

Rennes 17B1

Rue du Professeur Maurice Audin. **GPS:** n48,13531 w1,64542. ⬆.

5 🚐free ⛽€2/100liter 🍽Ch ▦€2/1h ⟲€1/30minutes.
Location: Rural, simple. **Surface:** asphalted. ◻ 01/01-31/12
Distance: 🚶3km ⛵100m ⊗100m ⚱3km ⚑on the spot.
Remarks: In park, max. 48h.

Tourist information Rennes:
Ⓜ Musée de Bretagne. Regional museum.
⚐ ◻ Tue-Sa.

Riantec 13C3

Leclerc, Rond-point de Kersabiec. **GPS:** n47,72611 w3,32137. ⬆.

10 🚐free ⛽€2 🍽Ch ▦€2/55minutes ⬜. **Location:** Simple.
Surface: asphalted. ◻ 01/01-31/12
Distance: ✂on the spot ⚱on the spot.

Riantec 13C3

Route de Plouhinec. **GPS:** n47,71163 w3,29858. ⬆➡.

4 🚐free ⛽€2/10minutes 🍽Ch ▦€2/55minutes ⬜.
Location: Rural, simple. **Surface:** metalled. ◻ 01/01-31/12
Distance: 🚶1,5km.
Remarks: Near old laundry place (still operational!), max. 24h.

Rochefort-en-Terre 17A2

Parking des Grées, Rue du Souvenir. **GPS:** n47,69975 w2,33384. ⬆.

>100 🚐€ 2/24h. 🏠 **Location:** Rural, simple, quiet. **Surface:** gravel.
◻ 01/01-31/12
Distance: 🚶200m.

Rohan 13D2

Port de Plaisance, Rue Saint-Gouvry. **GPS:** n48,07187 w2,75559. ⬆➡.

14 🚐free ⛽🍽ChWCfree. **Location:** Rural, comfortable, quiet.
Surface: asphalted. ◻ 01/01-31/12
Distance: 🚶500m ⛵on the spot ⛽on the spot ⊗500m 🚲on the
spot.
Remarks: At the Nantes-Brest Canal.

Romagné 14B3

Allée des Prunus, D812. **GPS:** n48,34409 w1,27415. ⬆.

5 🚐free ⛽🍽ChWCfree. **Location:** Urban, simple.
Surface: metalled. ◻ 01/01-31/12
Distance: 🚶100m ✂1,7km ⊗200m 🚐50m.

Roscoff 13C1

Route du Laber. **GPS:** n48,71215 w3,99918. ⬆.

30 🚐free ⛽🍽Chfree. **Location:** Isolated. **Surface:** asphalted.
◻ 01/01-31/12
Distance: 🚶2km.
Remarks: Service 200m.

Tourist information Roscoff:
ℹ Office de Tourisme, 46, rue Gambetta, www.roscoff-tourisme.com.
Seaside resort and former pirates town.
⚐ ◻ Wed.

Rostrenen 13D2

Rue Rosa l'Hénaff, D23. **GPS:** n48,23318 w3,32019. ⬆➡.

6 🚐free ⛽€2/100liter 🍽Ch ▦€2/1h. **Location:** Urban, simple.
Surface: gravel.
◻ 01/01-31/12
Distance: 🚶400m ⚱100m.
Remarks: Coins at tourist info, town hall, maison de presse, tabac.

Sains 14B3

Rue du Puits Rimoult. **GPS:** n48,55305 w1,58603. ⬆➡.

10 🚐€ 5, tourist tax € 0,20/pp ⛽🍽Chfree. 🛁 **Location:** Rural,
simple, quiet. **Surface:** grassy/metalled.
◻ 01/01-31/12
Distance: 🚶100m ✂2km ⊗150m ⚱150m 🚐on the spot 🚲100m
⚑on the spot.

Saint Aignan 13D2

Place de l'Église. **GPS:** n48,18306 w3,01361. ⬆➡.

20 🚐free ⛽🍽ChWCfree. **Location:** Comfortable, quiet.
Surface: asphalted. ◻ 01/01-31/12
Distance: 🚶100m 🚲on the spot ⚑on the spot.
Remarks: Square behind the church.

Saint Gérand 13D2

Keroret, D322. **GPS:** n48,11333 w2,89028. ⬆.

12 free Ch WC free. **Location:** Rural, comfortable, quiet.
Surface: gravel. 01/01-31/12
Distance: 800m on the spot 150m on the spot on the spot.
Remarks: At the Nantes-Brest Canal.

S Saint-Aubin-d'Aubigné 17B1

Rue de Rennes. **GPS**: n48,26147 w1,60621.

5 free Ch WC free. **Location:** Urban, simple.
Surface: asphalted. 01/01-31/12
Distance: on the spot 100m on the spot on the spot.

S Saint-Barnabé 13D2

Place du Vieux Chêne, Rue Pierre Loti. **GPS**: n48,13672 w2,70146.

10 free Ch free. **Location:** Urban, simple, central.
Surface: gravel. 01/01-31/12
Distance: 200m bakery 50m.

S Saint-Benoît-des-Ondes 14B3

Rue Bord de Mer. **GPS**: n48,61681 w1,84714.

10 free €3/50liter Ch €3/15minutes. **Location:** Rural, simple. **Surface:** asphalted.
Distance: 100m on the spot on the spot 100m 200m on the spot on the spot.

S Saint-Brice-en-Coglès 14B3

Espace Jules Verne, Rue de Normandie, D102.
GPS: n48,41126 w1,36252.

8 free €2/100liter Ch €2/55minutes WC.
Location: Urban, simple, central. **Surface:** asphalted/metalled.
01/01-31/12
Distance: 300m 500m 400m 300m on the spot.

S Saint-Carreuc 13D1

Rue de la Lande, D27. **GPS**: n48,40300 w2,73923.

12 free €2/10minutes Ch €2/55minutes. **Location:** Rural, simple, isolated, noisy. **Surface:** metalled.
01/01-31/12
Distance: 300m on the spot on the spot.
Remarks: At Etang-du-Plessis, max. 24h.

S Saint-Derrien 13C1

GPS: n48,54820 w4,1817.

20 free €3 Ch €3 WC. **Location:** Quiet.
Surface: gravel/metalled. 01/05-31/10
Distance: 100m on the spot on the spot 300m 300m.
Remarks: Nearby recreation area.

S Saint-Gelven 13D2

Rue de l'Ecole, D95. **GPS**: n48,22442 w3,09589.

10 free Ch free. **Location:** Urban, simple. **Surface:** gravel.
01/01-31/12
Remarks: Service 100m.

Saint-Gelven 13D2

Tregnanton, D117. **GPS**: n48,21153 w3,08457.

free.
Location: Rural, isolated, quiet. **Surface:** grassy/metalled.
Distance: 2,5km on the spot on the spot on the spot.

S Saint-Gildas-de-Rhuys 13D3

Camping municipal de Kerver, Route du Rohu.
GPS: n47,52238 w2,85803.

35 € 6/24h €2 Ch . **Location:** Rural, simple, quiet.
Surface: asphalted. 15/03-04/11
Distance: 4km 50m 400m 4km.

S Saint-Guyomard 13D3

Route de Malestroit, D112. **GPS**: n47,78166 w2,51188.

20 € 5/night €3 Ch €3. **Location:** Rural, simple, quiet.
Surface: asphalted.
Distance: 300m 100m.
Remarks: Behind church, check in at town hall.

Saint-Jacut-de-la-Mer 14A3

Rue de la Manchette. **GPS**: n48,58969 w2,18947.

26 € 6 Ch included. **Location:** Comfortable.
Surface: grassy/gravel. 01/01-31/12
Distance: 1km 500m.
Remarks: Baker at 8am.

S Saint-Malo 14A3

Les Iltots, Avenue de la Guimorais, Rothéneuf.
GPS: n48,68109 w1,96348.

50 € 7 €3 Ch included . **Location:** Rural, comfortable. **Surface:** grassy. 28/03-12/11
Distance: sandy beach 100m 100m 200m.

S Saint-Malo 14A3

Parking Paul Féval, Rue Paul Féval. **GPS**: n48,64341 w1,99385.

200 € 7,50, overnight stay 19-9h free €2,50 Ch.
Location: Urban, simple. **Surface:** gravel. holidays + 01/07-07/09
Distance: 800m 800m on the spot.
Remarks: Free bus to centre.

Tourist information Saint-Malo:
Château. Castle, 14/15th century, historical museum. 10-12h, 14-18h. € 4,50.
Fort National. Fort designed by Vauban. At ebb accessible by foot. € 5.

S Saint-Pierre-Quiberon 13D3

Rue du Stade. **GPS**: n47,51160 w3,13903.

FR

40 € 5/24h €2/10minutes Ch €2/45minutes.
Location: Simple. **Surface:** asphalted. 01/01-31/12
Distance: 1km 1,5km on the spot on the spot.
Remarks: Max. 48h.

S Saint-Pol-de-Léon 13C1

Quai de Pempoul. **GPS**: n48,68361 w3,97083.

30 free €2 Ch €2 WC. **Surface:** metalled.
01/01-31/12
Distance: 800m on the spot on the spot 800m 800m.
Remarks: At sea.

S Saint-Pol-de-Léon 13C1

Rue Hervé Mesguen. **GPS**: n48,67919 w3,99749.

8 free €2/10minutes Ch €2/55minutes.
Location: Comfortable. **Surface:** asphalted. 01/01-31/12
Distance: on the spot.
Remarks: In front of supermarket Leclerc.

S Saint-Renan 13B1

Route de l'Aber. **GPS**: n48,43878 w4,63063.

10 free €2 Ch €2. **Surface:** gravel.
01/01-31/12
Remarks: Jul/Aug max. 48h.

S Saint-Rivoal 13C1

D42. **GPS**: n48,34930 w3,99782.

6 free Ch free1h. **Surface:** grassy/metalled.
01/01-31/12
Distance: 200m.

S Saint-Servais 13C1

Cité Yan d'Argent. **GPS**: n48,50984 w4,15434.

10 free Ch free WC. **Location:** Simple, quiet.
Surface: gravel/metalled. 01/01-31/12
Distance: 200m 200m 200m.

S Saint-Thégonnec 13C1

Park an Iliz, D118. **GPS**: n48,52215 w3,94637.

25 free Ch free. **Location:** Urban, comfortable, central, quiet. **Surface:** gravel. 01/01-31/12
Distance: on the spot 150m 150m on the spot on the spot.
Remarks: Free coins available at shops.

Tourist information Saint-Thégonnec:
Fri.
Crêperie Steredenn, Rue de la Gare 6.

S Santec 13C1

Bistrot à Crèpes, Rue de Méchouroux. **GPS**: n48,70102 w4,03868.

15 €3 €2 Ch included WC. **Location:** Quiet.
Surface: grassy. 01/01-31/12
Distance: Beach Staol 50m on the spot 800m.

S Sarzeau 13D3

Aire du Rohaliguen, Rue du Raker/Rue du Pont Neui.
GPS: n47,49769 w2,76748.

10 € 5,50/18-10h Ch WC free. **Location:** Rural, simple, quiet.
Surface: metalled. 01/01-31/12
Distance: on the spot 200m.

S Sarzeau 13D3

Rue de Brénudel. **GPS**: n47,52969 w2,7598.

20 € 5,50/24h €2 Ch €2. **Location:** Urban, simple, quiet.
Surface: asphalted. 01/01-31/12 school hours (8-16h)
Distance: on the spot 750m.

S Sarzeau 13D3

Rue du Port St.Jacques, Kerbodo. **GPS**: n47,48906 w2,79297.

15 € 5,50/18-8h Ch WC free €2. **Location:** Urban, comfortable, quiet. **Surface:** asphalted. 01/01-31/12
Distance: 200m 500m 100m 200m.
Remarks: Nearby port, max. 48h.

S Sarzeau 13D3

Rue du Stang, St.Colombier. **GPS**: n47,54665 w2,72151.

5 € 5,50/18-10h Ch free. **Location:** Urban, simple, quiet.
Surface: asphalted.
Distance: St.Colombier 100m 50m 50m 50m.
Remarks: Max. 48h.

S Scaër 13C2

Rue Louis Pasteur. **GPS**: n48,02774 w3,6951.

free €2/10minutes Ch €2/55minutes WC. **Location:** Rural, simple, quiet. **Surface:** asphalted.
01/01-31/12
Distance: 500m bakery 200m on the spot on the spot.
Remarks: Max. 72h, coins at camping municipal.

Sérent 13D2

Du Pont Salmon, Rue du Général De Gaule,.
GPS: n47,82445 w2,50194.

10 free. **Location:** Urban, simple, quiet. **Surface:** asphalted.
01/01-31/12
Distance: 400m 400m 400m on the spot.

S Silfiac 13D2

P Salle Polyvalente, Rue du Résistant P. le Bourlay.
GPS: n48,14816 w3,15668.
free Ch free. **Location:** Simple. **Surface:** asphalted.
01/01-31/12
Distance: 150m 150m on the spot on the spot.

Silfiac 13D2

Etang de pont Samuel, Pont Samuel. **GPS**: n48,12847 w3,17109.

FR

5 ⛺. **Location:** Rural, simple, isolated. **Surface:** unpaved.
🅿 01/01-31/12
Distance: � 300m ⊗200m 🚶200m.

| ⛺S | **Sougéal** | 14B3 |

Le Placis, D15. **GPS:** n48,50651 w1,52562. ⬆➡.

30 ⛺free 🚰 Ch WC free. **Location:** Rural, simple, quiet.
Surface: gravel/metalled. 🅿 01/01-31/12
Distance: 🚰on the spot ⊗300m 🍴bakery 300m.
Remarks: Bakery 500m.

| ⛺S | **Sulniac** | 13D3 |

Salle des Fêtes, Rue des Écoles. **GPS:** n47,67756 w2,56642. ⬆➡.

15 ⛺free 🚰 Ch free. **Location:** Rural, simple, quiet.
Surface: asphalted. 🅿 01/01-31/12
Distance: 🚰400m 🍴bakery 500m.

| ⛺S | **Theix** | 13D3 |

Allée de Noyalo. **GPS:** n47,62726 w2,66183. ⬆➡.

4 ⛺free 🚰 Ch free. **Location:** Urban, simple, quiet.
Surface: asphalted. 🅿 **Service:** winter
Distance: 🚰500m ⊗500m 🍴500m 🚶50m 🚴50m.

| ⛺S | **Tinténiac** | 14B3 |

Quai de la Donac. **GPS:** n48,33168 w1,83202. ⬆.

10 ⛺€3 🚰 Ch free. 🚻 **Location:** Rural, simple.
Surface: grassy/gravel. 🅿 01/04-31/10
Distance: 🚰500m ⛵Along river 🚉on the spot ⊗100m 🍴550m.

| ⛺S | **Trébeurden** ⚓ | 13C1 |

Route de Lannion, D65. **GPS:** n48,76711 w3,5514. ⬆.

5 ⛺parking free, € 5/night 🚰€4,20 Ch 🚽€4,20 🚿.
Location: Rural, comfortable, central, quiet.
Surface: asphalted.
Distance: 🚰on the spot ⛱1,4km ⊗1,5km 🍴1km bakery, Intermarché 1,5km.

| ⛺S | **Trébeurden** ⚓ | 13C1 |

Plage Goas-Treiz, Chemin de Crec'h Hellen.
GPS: n48,78231 w3,57714. ⬆➡.

12 ⛺parking free, € 5/night. 🚻 **Location:** Rural, simple, isolated.
Surface: unpaved. 🅿 01/01-31/12
Distance: 🚰Trébeurden 2km ⛱sandy beach 80m ⊗2km 🚶on the spot.
Remarks: Beach parking.

| ⛺S | **Trégastel** ⚓ | 13C1 |

Rue de Poul-Palud. **GPS:** n48,82437 w3,49874. ⬆.

56 ⛺€ 4, 01/03-15/11 € 7,50 🚰€2 Ch. 🧺 🚿 **Location:** Rural, comfortable, isolated, quiet. **Surface:** asphalted. 🅿 01/01-31/12
Distance: 🚰1km ⊗1km 🍴Super U 🚶on the spot.
Remarks: Aug max. 3 nights, max. 5 nights.

| ⛺S | **Tréguier** | 13D1 |

Boulevard Anatole le Braz. **GPS:** n48,78932 w3,23144.

20 ⛺free 🚰 Ch free. **Surface:** asphalted. 🅿 01/01-31/12
Distance: 🚰100m ⛱20m 🚉20m ⊗100m 🍴100m.

| S | **Tréguier** | 13D1 |

Super U, Boulevard Jean Guehenno. **GPS:** n48,77892 w3,23346. ⬆.
🚰€1/10minutes Ch €1/55minutes. 🅿 01/01-31/12
Distance: ⊗200m 🍴on the spot.

| ⛺S | **Trégunc** | 13C2 |

Parking Quentel, Place de la Mairie, Rue de Pont-Aven.
GPS: n47,85472 w3,85139. ⬆.

---

6 ⛺free 🚰€3 Ch 🚽€3 🚿. **Surface:** metalled.
🅿 01/01-31/12
Remarks: Behind town hall, max. 24h.

| ⛺S | **Trégunc** | 13C2 |

Parking de Pouldohan, Route de Pouldohan.
GPS: n47,84435 w3,88832. ⬆⬆➡.

5 ⛺free. **Location:** Rural, simple, isolated. **Surface:** grassy.
🅿 01/01-31/12
Distance: ⛱400m 🚰400m.

| ⛺S | **Trégunc** | 13C2 |

Plage Ster Greich. GPS: n47,84918 w3,88656. ⬆.
6 ⛺free. **Surface:** sand. 🅿 01/01-31/12
Distance: ⛱on the spot.
Remarks: Max. 24h.

| ⛺S | **Trégunc** | 13C2 |

Route de Kerlaëron. **GPS:** n47,82964 w3,8872. ⬆.

6 ⛺free. **Location:** Rural, simple. **Surface:** grassy.
🅿 01/01-31/12
Distance: ⛱200m.
Remarks: Max. 24h.

| ⛺S | **Trégunc** | 13C2 |

Rue de Porzh Breign. **GPS:** n47,84079 w3,89736. ⬆➡.

5 ⛺free. **Location:** Rural, simple, quiet. **Surface:** grassy.
🅿 01/01-31/12
Distance: ⛱200m.
Remarks: Max. 24h.

| ⛺S | **Trégunc** | 13C2 |

Supermarché Casino, Route de Concarneau, D783.
GPS: n47,85633 w3,86343. ⬆.

FR

4 ⚡free ⚡€2 📧€2/55minutes ♿. **Location:** Simple.
Surface: asphalted.
Distance: 🍴on the spot.

| 🚑S | Tremblay | 14B3 |

Route de Fougères. **GPS:** n48,42328 w1,47095. ⬆.

15 ⚡free ⚡€2/10minutes 🔌Ch📧€2/55minutes. **Location:** Urban,
simple. **Surface:** asphalted. ⬛ 01/01-31/12
Distance: 🚶400m 🍴200m on the spot.

| 🚑S | Trémuson | 13D1 |

Aire du Buchon, Rue de Brest, D712. **GPS:** n48,52250 w2,85278. ⬆➡.

5 ⚡free ⚡🔌Chfree. **Location:** Urban, simple. **Surface:** asphalted.
⬛ 01/01-31/12
Distance: 🚶500m ⊗50m 🍴200m.
Remarks: Max. 48h.

| 🚑S | Val-d'Izé | 17B1 |

Rue du Château. **GPS:** n48,17904 w1,30133. ⬆.

3 ⚡free ⚡🔌Ch🚿WCfree. **Location:** Urban, simple, quiet.
Surface: asphalted. ⬛ 01/01-31/12
Distance: 🚶100m 🚐on the spot ⊗100m 🍴100m 🚶on the spot.
Remarks: Next to sports fields.

| 🚑S | Vannes | 13D3 |

Camping-car Parc, Avenue du Maréchal Juin.
GPS: n47,63283 w2,77996. ⬆.

34 ⚡€ 9,60, Jul/Aug € 12 ⚡🔌Ch🚿€4 WCincluded 📶. 📠
♿ **Location:** Urban, comfortable, quiet. **Surface:** asphalted.
⬛ 01/01-31/12
Distance: 🚶Vannes 4km 🏊200m ⊗200m 🍴1km 🚐on the spot
🚲on the spot 🚶on the spot.
Remarks: Note: access only after buying entrance (3 formulas) via
www.campingcarpark.com (wifi available), free shuttle (summer).

Tourist information Vannes:
ℹ Office de Tourisme, 1, rue Thiers, www.tourisme-vannes.com. The
old district is surrounded by ramparts with gates and parks with historical wash places.
✝ Cathédrale St Pierre.

Pays de la Loire

| 🚑S | Abbaye Royale de Fontevraud | 23B2 |

Centre LeClerc, Avenue de l'Europe. **GPS:** n44,61659 w1,11339. ⬆.

---

15 ⚡free ⚡€2/10minutes 🔌Ch🚿€2/30minutes.
Surface: asphalted.
Distance: ⊗on the spot 🍴on the spot.

| 🚑S | Angers | 17C2 |

Boulevard Olivier-Couffon. **GPS:** n47,46616 w0,56549. ⬆.

20 ⚡€ 4/4h, € 7/10h 🔌Chfree. 🛁 **Location:** Urban, noisy.
Surface: asphalted. ⬛ 01/01-31/12
Distance: 🚶centre 950m 🏊3km.
Remarks: Max. 36h, Château d'Angers 600m.
Tourist information Angers:
◉ Haras National du Lion d'Angers. National stud-farm. ⬛ 15/04-
11/09 daily, 12/09-14/04 Sa-Su 10.30h, 14.30h, 16h.
✖ Château d' Angers. Fortified castle, museum for contemporary art.
⬛ 10-17.30h. 🎫 € 6.

| 🚑S | Angrie 🌳 | 17C2 |

Route du Vieux Bourg. **GPS:** n47,57176 w0,97312. ⬆➡.

10 ⚡free ⚡🔌Chfree. **Location:** Rural. **Surface:** gravel/metalled.
⬛ 01/01-31/12
Distance: 🚶400m 🚲on the spot.
Remarks: Max. 48h.

| 🚑S | Arnage | 17D1 |

Rue du Port. **GPS:** n47,93035 e0,18418. ⬆.

2 ⚡free ⚡€2 🔌Ch📧€2/15minutes ♿. **Location:** Urban, simple,
quiet. **Surface:** asphalted. ⬛ 01/01-31/12
Distance: 🚶250m 🚐on the spot 📧500m 🚶on the spot.

| 🚑S | Assérac 🌊 | 13D3 |

Camping-Car Park de la Baie, Chemin du Bas Village.
GPS: n47,42472 w2,44364. ⬆.
10 ⚡€ 12 ⚡🔌Ch🚿WC📶included. 📠♿ **Location:** Rural,
comfortable, quiet. **Surface:** metalled. ⬛ 01/01-31/12
Distance: 🚶Assérac 5km 🏊sandy beach 350m.

| 🚑S | Assérac 🌊 | 13D3 |

Pen-Bé. **GPS:** n47,42556 w2,45528. ⬆.

5 ⚡free WC. **Location:** Simple. **Surface:** grassy.
⬛ 01/01-31/12
Distance: 🚶50m 🏊100m 🚐100m ⊗200m 🍴200m.

| 🚑S | Assérac 🌊 | 13D3 |

Chemin de la Marché aux Bœufs. **GPS:** n47,43111 w2,45194.

⚡free WC. **Surface:** metalled.
Distance: 🚶1km 🏊300m 🚐300m 🏊2km 🚲2km.

| | Aubigné-sur-Layon | 17C3 |

Rue de 17 mars 1962. **GPS:** n47,21167 w0,46383. ⬆.

3 ⚡free ⚡🔌Chfree. **Surface:** metalled. ⬛ 01/01-31/12
Distance: 🚶100m.

| 🚑S | Averton 🌳 | 17D1 |

Étang des Perles. **GPS:** n48,34744 w0,24468. ➡.

10 ⚡free ⚡€2,50 🔌Ch📧€2,50 WC. **Location:** Rural.
Surface: gravel. ⬛ 01/01-31/12
Distance: 🏊lake 🚐on the spot 🚲on the spot 🚶on the spot.

| 🚑S | Batz-sur-Mer 🌊 | 13D3 |

Route de la Govelle. **GPS:** n47,26747 w2,4537. ⬆➡.

8 ⚡free ⚡€2 🔌Ch📧€2 WC. **Location:** Simple. **Surface:** metalled.
⬛ 01/01-31/12
Distance: 🚶1,5km 🏊100m ⊗100m 🍴1,5km 🚐50m.
Remarks: Max. 48h.

| | Batz-sur-Mer 🌊 | 13D3 |

Baie du Manéric, Route du Dervin. **GPS:** n47,27028 w2,46139.
± 10 ⚡free. **Surface:** grassy. ⬛ summer
Distance: 🏊50m.

| 🚑S | Baugé 🌳 | 17D2 |

Chemin du Pont des Fées. **GPS:** n47,53886 w0,09637. ⬆.

10 ⚡free ⚡€3/15minutes 🔌Ch📧€3/15minutes. 📠♿
Location: Rural. **Surface:** gravel.
Distance: 🚶2km ⊗400m.

| 🚑S | Baugé 🌳 | 17D2 |

Rue de la Croix de Mission, Le Vieil Baugé. **GPS:** n47,53066 e0,11899.

FR

8 ⟳free 🚰 🔌Ch free.
Location: Rural. **Surface:** gravel.
🅿 01/01-31/12
Distance: 🚶on the spot 🛒bakery 100m.
Remarks: Service 50m.

Bazouges-sur-le-Loir 17D2
Voie de la Liberté. **GPS:** n47,68994 w0,16952.⬆⬆⬆.

⟳free. **Location:** Rural, quiet. **Surface:** gravel.
🅿 01/01-31/12
Distance: 🚶200m ⊗200m.

Beauvoir-sur-Mer 17A3
Rue de Nantes. **GPS:** n46,91685 w2,0465.➡.

24 ⟳free, overnight stay € 5 🚰€2,50/3minutes 🔌Ch🔲€
2,50/15minutes WC 🔲€. **Location:** Urban, simple.
Surface: asphalted. 🅿 01/01-31/12
Distance: 🚶400m ⊗800m 🛒800m.
Remarks: Max. 48h.

Belleville-sur-Vie 20B1
Rue des Écoliers. **GPS:** n46,78160 w1,42875.⬆➡.

15 ⟳free. **Surface:** grassy/gravel. 🅿 01/01-31/12
Distance: 🚶500m ⊗500m 🛒200m.
Remarks: Near Salle des Fêtes.

Benet 20C2
Rue de la Gare. **GPS:** n46,36896 w0,59482.

10 ⟳free 🚰🔌ChWC free. **Location:** Rural, simple.
Surface: asphalted.
Distance: 🚶300m ⊗300m 🛒on the spot 🚐50m.

Blain 17A2
Place Jollan de Clerville, Rue Victor Schoelcher.
GPS: n47,47444 w1,76139.⬆.

30 ⟳free 🚰🔌Ch free. **Surface:** gravel. 🅿 01/01-31/12
Distance: ⊗100m 🛒100m.

Blaison-Gohier 17E3
Rue de Thibaut de Blaison. **GPS:** n47,39923 e0,37515.⬆➡.

5 ⟳free 🚰🔌Ch free. **Surface:** asphalted. 🅿 01/01-31/12
Distance: 🚶on the spot ⊗200m 🛒200m.

Bouchemaine 17C2
Rue Chevrière. **GPS:** n47,41913 w0,61117.⬆➡.

40 ⟳free, 01/03-30/11 € 10 🚰€0,50/50liter 🔌Ch 🔹WC 🔲€
1 🔌included. 🛏 🛒 **Surface:** grassy/gravel. 🅿 01/01-31/12
⚫ service: 01/12-28/02
Distance: 🚶50m.
Remarks: Along the river Maine, former campsite, baker every morning
(Jul/Aug).

Bouin 17A3
GPS: n47,00918 w2,02782.⬆.

10 ⟳free. **Location:** Rural, simple. **Surface:** grassy/gravel.
🅿 01/01-31/12
Distance: 🏊on the spot.

Bouin 17A3
GPS: n46,99821 w2,03314.⬆.

10 ⟳free.
Location: Simple. **Surface:** metalled.
🅿 01/01-31/12
Distance: 🚶on the spot 🚐on the spot.

Bouin 17A3
Port du Bec, Rue du Port du Bec. **GPS:** n46,93696 w2,07182.

⟳free. **Surface:** gravel. 🅿 01/01-31/12

Bourgneuf-en-Retz 17A3
D758. **GPS:** n47,04028 w1,95704.⬆.

10 ⟳free 🚰🔌ChWC free. **Location:** Simple. **Surface:** asphalted.
🅿 01/01-31/12 ⚫ Service: winter
Distance: 🚶300m 🚐200m ⊗300m 🛒300m.
Remarks: Parking tourist info, max. 48h.

Boussay 17B3
Place des Marronniers. **GPS:** n47,04240 w1,18648.⬆➡.

4 ⟳free 🚰€2/100liter 🔌Ch🔲€2/60minutes. **Location:** Simple.
Surface: asphalted. 🅿 01/01-31/12
Distance: 🚶200m ⊗200m 🛒200m 🚲on the spot.
Remarks: Max. 48h, coins at town hall, poste.

Brétignolles-sur-Mer 20A1
Parking de la Normandelière, Rue de la Source.
GPS: n46,61664 w1,85974.⬆.

25 ⟳free. **Location:** Simple. **Surface:** metalled.
🅿 01/01-31/12
Distance: 🚶1,5km 🏖sandy beach 500m 🛒1,5km 🚲on the spot
🚶on the spot.
Remarks: Service: Super U D38, GPS 46,62537 -1,85787.

Tourist information Brétignolles-sur-Mer:
🏛 🅿 Thu, Su.

Briollay 17C2
Plage de Briollay. GPS: n47,56766 w0,50733.⬆.
10 ⟳free 🚰€2 🔌Ch. **Surface:** grassy/gravel. 🅿 01/01-31/12
Remarks: Along Sarthe River, closed when frosty and high water.

Brissac-Quincé 17C3
Rue de l'Aubance. **GPS:** n47,35465 w0,4463.⬆➡.

FR

2 🚐free 🚿🗑Ch. **Surface:** asphalted. ◘ 01/01-31/12
Distance: 🚶300m ⊗300m.

📷S Chailland 17C1
Coccimarket. GPS: n48,22139 w0,86583.⬆➡.

4 🚐free 🚿🗑Chfree. **Location:** Rural, simple. **Surface:** asphalted.
◘ 01/01-31/12
Distance: 🚶300m ⊗300m 🚰on the spot.
Remarks: Max. 24h.

📷S Chaille-les-Marais 20B2
Rue du 8 Mai 1945. **GPS:** n46,39228 w1,02127.⬆.

20 🚐free 🚿€3 WCfree. **Location:** Simple, quiet. **Surface:** grassy.
◘ 01/01-31/12 ◙ Thu-morning
Distance: 🚶100m ⊗100m 🚰300m 🚌50m.
Remarks: At fire-station and sports park.

📷S Challans 17A3
Parking du Viaud Marais. **GPS:** n46,85027 w1,8742.⬆➡.

15 🚐free 🚿🗑Chfree. **Location:** Urban. **Surface:** asphalted.
◘ 01/01-31/12
Distance: 🚶1km ⊗500m 🚰500m 🚌100m.
Remarks: Max. 3 days.

📷S Chalonnes-sur-Loire 17C3
Le Champ du Bois, D751. **GPS:** n47,35105 w0,74466.⬆.
40 🚐€9 🚿€2 🗑Ch 🔌. **Location:** Comfortable. **Surface:** grassy.
◘ 01/01-31/12
Distance: 🚶1km 🚶on the spot ⊗1km 🚰on the spot.
Remarks: Nearby camp site.

📷S Chambretaud 17C3
Aire des Diamants, Rue Notre Dame. **GPS:** n46,92300 w0,9717.⬆➡.

5 🚐free 🚿€2/150liter 🗑ChWC. **Location:** Rural, simple.

Surface: asphalted. ◘ 01/01-31/12
Distance: 🚶1km 🚴5km ⊗on the spot 🚰1km.

📷S Champtocé-sur-Loire 17C2
Rue de la Hutte. **GPS:** n47,41143 w0,86958.⬆➡.

8 🚐free 🚿🗑Chfree. **Location:** Rural, simple. **Surface:** asphalted.
◘ 01/01-31/12
Distance: 🚶300m 🚴5,7km ⊗400m 🚰400m.
Remarks: At stadium.

📷S Champtoceaux 17B3
Parking Champalud, Place de Niederheimbach.
GPS: n47,33816 w1,2649.⬆➡.

5 🚐free 🚿🗑Ch 🔌€3/24h WC. **Surface:** asphalted.
◘ 01/01-31/12
Distance: 🚶150m 🚴23km.
Remarks: Square behind the church, max. 48h.

🍴S Champtoceaux 17B3
Le Port du Moulin, Le Cul du Moulin, D751.
GPS: n47,33913 w1,27445.⬆.

3 🚐free WCfree. **Surface:** metalled. ◘ 01/01-31/12
Distance: 🚶1,5km 🏊on the spot 🚶on the spot ⊗on the spot
🚰1,5km.
Remarks: Along Loire river, max. 48h.

📷S Changé 17C1
Parking du plan d'eau du Port, Rue du Bac.
GPS: n48,10047 w0,78584.⬆.

10 🚐free 🚿🗑Chfree. **Location:** Urban, simple.
Surface: gravel/sand. ◘ 01/01-31/12
Distance: 🚴5km 🚰800m.
Remarks: Along the Mayenne river.

📷S Chantonnay 20B1
Rue de l'Arc en Ciel. **GPS:** n46,68754 w1,04104.⬆➡.

5 🚐free 🚿€2/100liter 🗑Ch 🚻€2/60minutes. **Location:** Rural,
simple, noisy. **Surface:** asphalted. ◘ 01/01-31/12
Distance: 🚶1km ⊗500m 🚰1km.
Remarks: Next to sports fields, coins at tourist info.

📷S Chanzeaux 17C3
Aire de Ploizeau, D121. **GPS:** n47,25548 w0,63848.⬆.

6 🚐free 🚿€2/100liter 🗑Ch. **Surface:** metalled.
◘ 01/01-31/12
Distance: 🚶1km 🚶on the spot ⊗1km 🚰1km.

📷S Château-d'Olonne 20A1
Rue des Plesses. **GPS:** n46,49132 w1,74293.⬆➡.

20 🚐€6,10/night, €10,20/2 nights 🚿€2/6minutes 🗑Ch 🚻€
3/10minutes. 🚌 **Location:** Simple. **Surface:** asphalted.
◘ 01/01-31/12
Distance: 🚰500m.

📷 Château-Gontier 17C2
Quai-du-Docteur Lefevre. **GPS:** n47,82450 w0,70206.⬆.

30 🚐free. **Location:** Urban, simple, central. **Surface:** asphalted.
◘ 01/01-31/12
Distance: 🚶200m 🚶on the spot ⊗50m.
Remarks: Along the Mayenne river.

📷S Chavagne-en-Paillers 17B3
Place des Arcades. **GPS:** n46,89083 w1,24917.⬆➡.

3 🚐free 🚿€2/10minutes 🗑Ch 🚻€2/55minutes.
Location: Simple, central, quiet.
Surface: asphalted.
◘ 01/01-31/12
Distance: 🚶300m ⊗50m 🚰100m 🚌300m.
Remarks: Coins at tourist office/Rest. Le petit Marmiton/Boulanger de

Quartier, 8 rue G de Gaulle/ Carrefour Express, 197 rue G de Gaulle.

⚿S **Chavagnes les Eaux** 17C3

Place de la Mairie. **GPS:** n47,27024 w0,45437. ⬆➡.

3 ⛺free ⛲ 🚽Chfree. **Surface:** metalled. 🅾 01/01-31/12
Distance: 🛒on the spot 🍴150m.
Remarks: Behind church.

⚿S **Chênehutte-Trèves-Cunault** 17D3

Rue Beauregard, D751, Cunault. **GPS:** n47,32685 e0,19459. ⬆➡.

40 ⛺free ⛲€3/100liter 🚽Ch ⚡€3/6h. **Surface:** grassy.
🅾 01/01-31/12
Distance: 🛒500m ⊗500m 🍴500m.

⚿S **Chenillé-Changé** 17C2

Le Pin, D78. **GPS:** n47,69919 w0,66693. ⬆➡.

8 ⛺€2,80-4 ⛲€2,80 🚽Ch. **Location:** Simple. **Surface:** gravel.
🅾 01/01-31/12
Distance: 🛒on the spot ⊗100m.
Remarks: Along the Mayenne river, coins at cafe.

⚿S **Coëx** 20G1

Rue des Goélettes. **GPS:** n46,69717 e1,76410. ⬆.

4 ⛺free ⛲€2/10minutes 🚽Ch €2/55minutes. **Location:** Rural.
Surface: asphalted. 🅾 01/01-31/12
Distance: 🛒200m ⊗500m 🍴500m.
Remarks: Max. 48h, coins at town hall.

⚿S **Combrée** 17C2

Rue de Bretagne, Bel-Air. **GPS:** n47,71281 w0,9989. ➡.

3 ⛺free ⛲🚽ChWCfree. **Location:** Rural. **Surface:** unpaved.
🅾 01/01-31/12
Distance: 🛒100m.

⚿S **Combrée** 17C2

D203. **GPS:** n47,70321 w1,02755. ⬆.

3 ⛺free. **Location:** Rural, quiet. **Surface:** asphalted.
🅾 01/01-31/12
Distance: 🛒200m ⊗50m.
Remarks: Behind tennis-court.

⚿S **Concourson-sur-Layon** 17C3

Place du Prieuré. **GPS:** n47,17405 w0,34317. ➡.

10 ⛺free ⛲€2 🚽ChWC. **Surface:** asphalted. 🅾 01/01-31/12
Distance: 🛒400m ⊗400m 🍴400m.

⚿S **Dampierre-sur-Loire** 17D3

L'Aigrette, Route de Montsoreau. **GPS:** n47,24157 w0,0232. ⬆.

60 ⛺€5 ⛲🚽Chfree WC. **Surface:** forest soil.
🅾 01/04-31/10
Distance: 🛒on the spot ⊗on the spot 🍴on the spot 🚿on the spot.
Remarks: On the river Loire, behind town hall.

⚿S **Deux-Evailles** 17C1

Site de la Fenderie, Champ de Vigne, D129.
GPS: n48,20203 w0,52018. ➡.

20 ⛺free ⛲€2 🚽Ch €2 WC. **Location:** Rural, comfortable, quiet.
Surface: grassy/gravel. 🅾 01/01-31/12
Distance: 🛒1km 🏊20m 🛒20m ⊗20m 🍴5km Montsurs 🚶on the
spot.
Remarks: Coins at Auberge.

⚿S **Doué-la-Fontaine** 17D3

Rue Jean Gaschet. **GPS:** n47,18280 w0,25742.
3 ⛺free ⛲🚽Chfree.

⚿ **Durtal** 17D2

Rue du Petit Port. **GPS:** n47,66842 w0,24172. ⬆.

5 ⛺free. **Location:** Rural, quiet. **Surface:** asphalted.
Distance: 🛒300m 🚲2,4km.

⚿S **Durtal** 17D2

Rue Beausite. **GPS:** n47,67139 w0,2406. ⬆.

2 ⛺free ⛲€2/10minutes 🚽Ch €2/60minutes. **Location:** Simple.
Surface: asphalted. 🅾 01/01-31/12
Distance: 🛒300m 🚲2,4km.
Remarks: Inclining pitches.

⚿S **Ernée** 17C1

Plan d'eau d'Ernée, Plan d'eau d'Ernée. **GPS:** n48,29670 w0,93997.

2 ⛺free ⛲WCfree. **Location:** Urban, simple, quiet.
Surface: asphalted. 🅾 01/01-31/12
Distance: 🛒500m 🛒on the spot ⊗500m 🍴500m.
Remarks: Parking at small lake.

⚿S **Faye d'Anjou** 17C3

Chateau du Fresne, D55, Rue des Monts.
GPS: n47,29923 w0,53806. ⬆➡.

10 ⛺free ⛲🚽Chfree. **Surface:** gravel. 🅾 01/01-31/12
Distance: 🛒2km ⊗3km.

⚿S **Feneu** 17C2

Port Albert. **GPS:** n47,56560 w0,60994. ⬆.

6 ⛺free ⛲€2 🚽Ch. **Location:** Rural, quiet. **Surface:** gravel.
🅾 01/01-31/12
Distance: 🛒1,5km.
Remarks: Along the Mayenne river.

⚿S **Fontaines** 20C2

Place du Champ de Foire. **GPS:** n46,42291 w0,81952.

FR

20 🚐 free 🚰 ⬇ Ch WC free.
Location: Rural, simple. **Surface:** gravel.
Distance: 🛣 2km.

[🚐] [S] **Fontenay-le-Comte** 🐚 **20C1**

Avenue du Général de Gaulle. **GPS**: n46,46203 w0,80544. →.

10 🚐 € 5 🚰 €2/4minutes ⬇ Ch 🔌 included. **Location:** Simple, isolated, noisy. **Surface:** asphalted. 📅 01/01-31/12
Distance: 🏘 500m 🍴 500m 🥖 500m.
Remarks: In front of police station, max. 24h, centre.

[🚐] [S] **Fontevraud l'Abbaye** **17D3**

Allée des Bruyères. **GPS**: n47,18444 e0,04917. ↑→.

9 🚐 free 🚰 ⬇ Ch WC free. **Surface:** asphalted.
Distance: 🏘 400m 🍴 400m 🥖 400m.

[🚐] [S] **Foussais-Payré** **20C1**

Place du Prieuré. **GPS**: n46,53000 w0,68275. ↑→.

20 🚐 free 🚰 ⬇ Ch free. **Location:** Rural, simple. **Surface:** gravel.
📅 01/01-31/12
Distance: 🏘 500m 🍴 500m 🥖 200m.

[🚐] [S] **Fresnay-sur-Sarthe** **17D1**

Rue de la Gare. **GPS**: n48,28171 e0,02978. →.

8 🚐 free 🚰 ⬇ Ch free. **Location:** Simple. **Surface:** gravel.
📅 01/01-31/12
Distance: 🏘 600m 🍴 600m 🥖 50m.

[🚐] [S] **Gené** **17C2**

Escale du Haut Anjou, La Petite Fenouillère.
GPS: n47,63770 w0,79641. ↑→.

7 🚐 € 12 🚰 ⬇ Ch 🔌 included. 🐄 **Location:** Rural, simple.
Surface: gravel. 📅 01/01-31/12
Distance: 🏘 1,2km 🐟 fish pond.
Remarks: Cheese farm.

[🚐] [S] **Grez-en-Bouère** **17C2**

Place A. Peigné. **GPS**: n47,87306 w0,52306. →.

6 🚐 free 🚰 ⬇ Ch 🔌 free WC. **Location:** Rural, simple.
Surface: asphalted. 📅 01/01-31/12, service: 01/04-30/11
Distance: 🏘 50m 🍴 50m 🥖 100m.
Remarks: Max. 48h.

[🚐] [S] **Grez-Neuville** **17C2**

Rue du Port, D291. **GPS**: n47,60119 w0,68504. ↑→.

8 🚐 free 🚰 ⬇ Ch free. **Location:** Rural, simple. **Surface:** grassy.
📅 01/01-31/12
Remarks: Former campsite.

[🚐] [S] **Guenrouet** **17A2**

Rue des Hauts du Port. **GPS**: n47,52198 w1,94978. ↑.

2 🚐 free 🚰 €2 ⬇ Ch 🚿 €2. **Surface:** asphalted. 📅 01/04-31/10
Distance: 🏘 200m 🐟 50m 🍴 200m 🥖 200m.
Remarks: Along canal of Nantes/Brest, next to campsite Saint Clair, max. 24h.

[🚐] [S] **Guérande** 🐚 ⛱ 🧺 **13D3**

Avenue de la Brière, D99E. **GPS**: n47,33389 w2,42083. ↑→.

20 🚐 free 🚰 €5/100liter ⬇ Ch 🚿 €5/1h 💳. **Location:** Simple, noisy.
Surface: asphalted/grassy. 📅 01/01-31/12
Distance: 🏘 1km.
Remarks: Max. 48h.

[🚐] [S] **Jans** **17B2**

Place de l'Église. **GPS**: n47,62222 w1,61222. ↑.

6 🚐 free 🚰 ⬇ Ch WC free. **Surface:** gravel. 📅 01/01-31/12
Remarks: Behind town hall.

[🚐] [S] **Jard-sur-Mer** ⛱ 🐚 **20A1**

Route des Goffineaux. **GPS**: n46,41074 w1,59358. ↑→.

16 🚐 € 6,20/24h, € 10,40/48h 🚰 €2,10/10minutes ⬇ Ch 💳. 🚐 💳
Location: Rural, simple. **Surface:** asphalted.
📅 01/01-31/12
Distance: 🏘 1km 🏖 50m 🍴 1,5km 🥖 1,5km.

[🚐] [S] **Juvigné** **17C1**

Plan d'Eau de Saint Martin, Rue de la Croixille, D29.
GPS: n48,22806 w1,03806. ↑.

20 🚐 free 🚰 ⬇ Ch WC free. **Location:** Urban, simple. **Surface:** gravel.
📅 01/01-31/12
Distance: 🏘 200m 🐟 20m 🍴 200m 🥖 100m 🚶 on the spot.
Remarks: Max. 72h.

[🚐] [S] **La Baconnière** **17C1**

Place de l'Eglise. **GPS**: n48,18361 w0,89139. →.

5 🚐 free 🚰 ⬇ Ch 🔌 free. **Location:** Urban, simple.
Surface: asphalted.
📅 01/01-31/12
Distance: 🏘 on the spot 🥖 100m.
Remarks: Behind church, service (winter) on demand (town hall).

[🚐] [S] **La Baule** **13D3**

Boulevard Guy de Champsavin, La Baule-Escoublac.
GPS: n47,28196 w2,42509. ↑→.

20 🚐 free 🚰 €3 ⬇ Ch 🔌 (20x)€3/55minutes 💳.
Location: Comfortable, quiet. **Surface:** metalled.
Distance: 🏖 beach 700m.

FR

La Bernerie-en-Retz — 17A3

Parking Wilson, Avenue de Jean d Arc. **GPS**: n47,07871 w2,03399.⬆️

37 🏕️ € 5,33-6,56 🚰 €3,30 ♻️Ch🚐€3,30 WC ♻️ Surface: asphalted. ⏹️ 01/01-31/12
Distance: 🛒300m 🏖️100m ⊗300m ⚓300m 🚌on the spot.
Remarks: Max. 48h.

La Chapelle-Saint-Florent — 17B3

Aire du Stade, Rue de l'Evre. **GPS**: n47,33411 w1,05178.⬆️➡️

6 🏕️free 🚰♻️Ch. **Surface**: gravel/metalled. ⏹️ 01/01-31/12
Distance: 🛒300m 🏖️300m ⚓50m.

La Daguenière — 17C2

Chemin de Beausse, Rue de Stade. GPS: n47,42222 w0,43936.⬆️

12 🏕️free 🚰♻️Chfree. **Location**: Rural. **Surface**: asphalted.
⏹️ 01/01-31/12
Distance: 🛒200m 🏖️300m ⚓300m.
Remarks: Next to sports fields.

La Daguenière — 17C2

Port Maillard. GPS: n47,41743 w0,43781.⬆️

6 🏕️free WC. **Location**: Rural. **Surface**: unpaved.
⏹️ 01/01-31/12
Remarks: Along Loire river.

La Flèche — 17D2

Promenade du Maréchal Foch. GPS: n47,69767 w0,07875.⬆️

10 🏕️free 🚰free. **Location**: Urban. **Surface**: asphalted.
⏹️ 01/01-31/12 🔴 Wed, market
Distance: 🛒100m ⊗100m ⚓100m.

La Fresnaye-sur-Chédouet — 14E3

La forêt de Perseigne, Les Ventes du Four, D236.
GPS: n48,43469 e0,25972.⬆️

20 🏕️free 🚰♻️Chfree. **Location**: Rural, quiet. **Surface**: gravel.
⏹️ 01/01-31/12
Distance: 🛒La Fresnaye 1,5km 🚶on the spot.

La Meilleraie-Tillay — 20C1

Rue des Ombrages. GPS: n46,73923 w0,84578.⬆️➡️

6 🏕️free 🚰€2/5minutes ♻️ChWC 🚐€1. **Location**: Simple, isolated,
quiet. **Surface**: asphalted. ⏹️ 01/04-31/10
Distance: 🛒700m ⊗700m ⚓700m.

La Plaine-sur-Mer — 17A3

Boulevard des Nations Unies. GPS: n47,13994 w2,19057.⬆️➡️

8 🏕️free 🚰♻️Chfree. **Location**: Simple, isolated.
Surface: asphalted. ⏹️ 01/01-31/12
Distance: 🛒300m ⊗800m ⚓500m.
Remarks: Max. 24h.

La Poitevinière — 17C3

Place de la Fontaine, D15. GPS: n47,22750 w0,897.⬆️

4 🏕️free 🚰♻️Ch🚐WCfree. **Surface**: asphalted.
⏹️ 01/01-31/12
Distance: 🛒50m ⊗on the spot ⚓50m.
Remarks: Coins available at bar.

La Roche-sur-Yon — 20B1

Boulevard Italie. GPS: n46,66833 w1,41861.⬆️

20 🏕️free 🚰♻️Ch🧹free. **Location**: Urban. **Surface**: metalled.
⏹️ 01/01-31/12
Distance: 🛒500m ⊗500m ⚓500m.
Remarks: Max. 36h.

La Séguinière — 17C3

Avenue de Nantes. GPS: n47,06005 w0,93668.⬆️➡️

10 🏕️free 🚰€2/100liter ♻️Ch🚐€2/1h WC. **Location**: Simple.
Surface: asphalted.
Distance: 🛒100m ⊗on the spot ⚓50m.

La Suze-sur-Sarthe — 17D2

Rue du Camping. GPS: n47,88917 e0,03040.⬆️➡️

10 🏕️€ 3 ♻️Ch🚐free WC. **Location**: Urban, simple.
Surface: grassy/gravel. ⏹️ 01/01-31/12
Distance: 🛒300m ⊗300m 🚲on the spot 🚶on the spot.
Remarks: Along Sarthe River, in harbour.

La Tranche-sur-Mer — 20B2

Boulevard de la Petite Hollande. GPS: n46,34965 w1,44769.⬆️➡️

20 🏕️free, 14/06-14/09 € 10 🚰€3,50/10minutes ♻️Ch ♻️ **Location**: Simple, quiet. ⏹️ 01/01-31/12
Remarks: Max. 7 days.

La Tranche-sur-Mer — 20B2

Parking du Stade, Avenue du Général de Gaulle.
GPS: n46,35028 w1,43688.⬆️➡️

30 🏕️free, 14/06-14/09 € 10 🚰€3,50 ♻️Chfree. **Location**: Rural.
Surface: asphalted.
Distance: 🛒1km.
Remarks: Max. 7 days.

La Tranche-sur-Mer — 20B2

Parking de la Baleine, Place des Baleines.
GPS: n46,34340 w1,46222.⬆️

10 🏕️free, 14/06-14/09 € 10 🚰stay. **Location**: Rural, quiet.
Surface: gravel. ⏹️ 01/01-31/12
Distance: 🏖️200m ⊗on the spot ⚓on the spot.

Remarks: Max. 7 days.

S **La Turballe** 13D3

Boulevard de la Grande Falaise. **GPS:** n47,33106 w2,49919. ⬆️.
6 🚐free, June-Sep € 3 🚰⚡Ch🚻included. **Location:** Simple.
Surface: gravel. ⏰ 01/01-31/12
Distance: 🚶2km.
Remarks: Max. 5 nights.

S **La Turballe** 13D3

Rue Alphonse Daudet. **GPS:** n47,34870 w2,50804. ⬆️.

15 🚐free, June-Sep € 3 🚰⚡Chfree. **Location:** Simple, quiet.
Surface: gravel. ⏰ 01/01-31/12
Distance: 🚶800m 🏊500m ⊗100m 🍴100m.
Remarks: Max. 5 days.

S **Lassay-les-Châteaux** 14C3

Allée du Haut Perrin. **GPS:** n48,43777 w0,49822. ⬆️.

🚐free 🚰€2 ⚡Ch. **Location:** Urban, simple, central.
Surface: asphalted. ⏰ 01/01-31/12
Distance: 🚶100m.
Remarks: Coins at Tourist Info and bakery.

S **Laval** 17C1

Parking de la Halte Fluviale, Rue du Vieux Saint-Louis.
GPS: n48,07589 w0,77142. ⬆️➡️.

10 🚐free 🚰⚡Chfree. **Location:** Urban, simple. **Surface:** asphalted.
⏰ 01/01-31/12
Distance: 🚶300m 🛒on the spot ⊗on the spot 🍴on the spot.
Remarks: Parking nearby viaduct.

Tourist information Laval:
M Vieux Château. Medieval castle, museum with collection of naive art. ⏰ 10-12h, 14-18h.

S **Le Coudray Macouard** 17D3

Route de Bron. **GPS:** n47,18806 w0,11722. ⬆️➡️.

5 🚐free 🚰⚡. **Location:** Rural, isolated, quiet. **Surface:** grassy.
⏰ 01/01-31/12
Distance: 🚶800m 🍴800m.

S **Le Croisic** 13D3

Le Lin Gorzé, Rue du Lin Gorzé. **GPS:** n47,29917 w2,52194. ⬆️➡️.

9 🚐€ 6,30, € 0,75/pp tourist tax 🚰€2 ⚡Ch. **Location:** Simple, quiet. **Surface:** asphalted. ⏰ 01/01-31/12
Distance: 🚶500m 🏊500m ⊗500m 🍴800m.
Remarks: Max. 48h.

S **Le Croisic** 13D3

Les Courlis, Rue des Courlis. **GPS:** n47,29000 w2,505. ⬆️➡️.

15 🚐€ 6,30, € 0,75/pp tourist tax 🚰€2 ⚡Ch. **Location:** Simple.
Surface: gravel. ⏰ 01/04-31/10
Distance: 🚶500m 🏊500m ⊗500m 🍴500m.
Remarks: Max. 48h.

S **Le Croisic** 13D3

La Vigie, Avenue de Pierre Longue, D45. **GPS:** n47,28917 w2,53667. ⬆️.

9 🚐€ 6,30, € 0,75/pp tourist tax. 🚐 **Location:** Simple.
Surface: asphalted. ⏰ 01/01-31/12
Distance: 🚶3km 🏊50m ⊗3km 🍴3km.
Remarks: Max. 48h.

S **Le Croisic** 13D3

P1 Kerdavid, Rue Kerclavid 1. **GPS:** n47,29835 w2,51995. ⬆️.

8 🚐€ 6,30, € 0,75/pp tourist tax. 🚐 **Location:** Urban, simple, quiet. **Surface:** asphalted. ⏰ 01/01-31/12
Distance: 🚶500m 🏊500m 🛒500m 🍴800m.

Tourist information Le Croisic:
😊 Océarium du Croisic. Sea aquarium. ⏰ 01/06-31/08 10-19h, 01/05-31/05, 01/09-30/09 10-12h, 14-18h, 01/10-30/04 14-18h.

S **Le Guédéniau** 17D2

Rue du Lavoir. **GPS:** n47,49405 w0,04488. ⬆️➡️.

15 🚐free 🚰⚡Chfree. **Location:** Rural. **Surface:** metalled.
⏰ 01/01-31/12
Distance: 🚶on the spot.

Remarks: Recreation area at lake.

S **Le Mans** 17D1

Quai de l'Amiral Lalande. **GPS:** n48,00233 e0,18915. ⬆️.

7 🚐free 🚰⚡Chfree. **Location:** Urban, simple. **Surface:** asphalted.
⏰ 01/01-31/12
Distance: 🚶centre 1km 🍴8km.
Remarks: Along Sarthe River.

Le Mans 17D1

Rue Denfert Rochereau. **GPS:** n48,01111 e0,19750. ⬆️.

🚐free. **Location:** Urban, simple, noisy. **Surface:** asphalted.
⏰ 01/01-31/12
Distance: 🚶500m ⊗500m 🍴500m.
Remarks: Max. 24h, sunday morning market.

Tourist information Le Mans:
M Circuit Le Mans. Motorcar museum.
⛪ Place des Jacobins. ⏰ Wed + Su-morning, Fri.

S **Le Pallet** 17B3

Rue Pierre Abelard. **GPS:** n47,13494 w1,3305. ⬆️.

20 🚐free 🚰€1 ⚡Ch. **Location:** Rural, simple. **Surface:** asphalted.
⏰ 01/01-31/12
Distance: 🚶500m ⊗500m 🍴500m on the spot on the spot.
Remarks: Wine museum, coins at the shops in the village.

S **Le Poiré-sur-Vie** 20B1

Rue de Roc. **GPS:** n46,76773 w1,51162. ⬆️➡️.

5 🚐free 🚰⚡Ch free. **Location:** Central, quiet. **Surface:** gravel.
⏰ 01/01-31/12
Distance: 🚶500m ⊗500m 🍴500m.

S **Le Puy-Notre-Dame** 17D3

Place du Gâte Argent. **GPS:** n47,12390 w0,23155. ⬆️.
15 🚐free 🚰⚡Chfree. **Surface:** metalled. ⏰ 01/01-31/12
Distance: 🚶100m ⊗200m 🍴200m.
Remarks: Next to cemetery.

S **Le Puy-Notre-Dame** 17D3

Cave-Champignonnière St.Maur, 1, Rue du Chateau, Sanziers.
GPS: n47,11755 w0,20526. ⬆️➡️.

8 🛏free 🚰🔧 WC free. **Surface:** metalled. ⬛ 01/03-30/10
Distance: 🛒2km.
Remarks: At mushroom grower.

🛁S Le Puy-Notre-Dame 17D3
Domaine de la Renière, Les Caves. **GPS:** n47,13429 w0,24256. ⬆

5 🛏€5 🚰🔧 included. **Surface:** metalled. ⬛ 01/03-01/11
Distance: 🛒700m.

🛁S Le Puy-Notre-Dame 17D3
Domaine du Vieux Tuffeau, Les Caves. **GPS:** n47,13498 w0,24704. ➡

6 🛏free 🚰🔧. **Surface:** metalled. ⬛ 01/01-31/12
Distance: 🛒1km.

🛁 Le Puy-Notre-Dame 17D3
Domaine de la Girardrie, Rue Fontaine de Cix.
GPS: n47,11616 w0,24127. ⬆

5 🛏free. **Surface:** gravel. ⬛ 01/01-31/12
Distance: 🛒1km ⊗1km 🍺1km.

🛁 Le Vaudelnay 17D3
Domaine du Vieux Pressoir, 235, Rue Château d'Oiré.
GPS: n47,14669 w0,25239. ➡

4 🛏free. **Surface:** metalled. ⬛ 01/01-31/12
Distance: 🛒3km ⊗3km 🍺3km.

🛁S Les Epesses 20C1
Le Puy du Fou, D27. **GPS:** n46,89425 w0,92506. ⬆➡
100 🛏€5 🚰€2/100liter 📡Ch (36x)€2/12h. 🏪
Location: Simple, isolated, noisy.
Surface: grassy.
Remarks: Baker at 8am, free shuttle to Puy du Fou.

🛁S Les Essarts 20B1
Rue de la piscine. **GPS:** n46,77380 w1,23499. ⬆➡

10 🛏free 🚰€2/10minutes 📡Ch (2x)€2/55minutes.
Location: Rural, simple. **Surface:** asphalted. ⬛ 01/01-31/12
Distance: 🛒600m 🚲5,6km ⊗600m 🍺600m.
Remarks: At swimmingpool and campsite.

🛁S Les Herbiers 20B1
Rue Saint Exupéry. **GPS:** n46,87410 w1,01765. ⬆➡

8 🛏free 🚰📡Ch free. **Location:** Simple. **Surface:** asphalted.
⬛ 01/01-31/12
Distance: 🛒600m ⊗600m 🍺600m.
Remarks: Max. 24h.

🛁S Les Sables-d'Olonne 20A1
Les Salines, 120 route de l'Aubraie. **GPS:** n46,51635 w1,80533. ⬆➡

20 🛏€5 🚰📡Ch included 🔧€4 free. 🛝 **Location:** Rural.
Surface: sand.
⬛ 01/04-30/09
Distance: 🏖600m 🚲on the spot.
Remarks: Baker every morning, july/Aug only overnight stays (18-11h).

🛁S Les Sables-d'Olonne 20A1
Parking Vinci Parc, Rue Printanière. **GPS:** n46,49646 w1,77493. ➡

150 🛏€12, winter free 🚰📡Ch 🔧WC included. 🏪
Location: Simple. **Surface:** metalled. ⬛ 01/01-31/12 ⬤ service 06/11-31/03
Distance: 🏖beach 400m.

🛁 Les Sables-d'Olonne 20A1
Parking de la Sablière. **GPS:** n46,50585 w1,78796.
🛏free. **Surface:** asphalted.
Tourist information Les Sables-d'Olonne:
🛈 Cours Dupont. ⬛ Wed + Sa morning.
😊 Zoo d'Olonne. Zoo.

🛁S Liré 17B3
Le Haut Fief, Square Espéranto. **GPS:** n47,34130 w1,16751. ⬆

5 🛏free 🚰📡Ch 🔧WC free. **Surface:** asphalted.
⬛ 01/01-31/12
Distance: 🛒500m ⊗250m 🍺50m.
Remarks: Max. 48h.

🛁S Longué-Jumelles 17D3
Boulevard Victor Hugo. **GPS:** n47,38119 w0,11254. ⬆➡

10 🛏free 🚰📡ChWC free. **Location:** Simple, quiet. **Surface:** gravel.
⬛ 01/01-31/12
Distance: 🛒100m 🚲3,3km ⊗on the spot 🍺on the spot.
Remarks: Service 300m: N 47,38046 W -0,11488, attention: follow the signs.

🍴S Luçon 20B1
Domaine des Guifettes. **GPS:** n46,43339 w1,18189. ⬆➡

🛏€10,50, dog €2,60 🚰📡Ch 🔧 included 📶.
Location: Rural, comfortable, isolated, quiet.
Surface: gravel/metalled.
Distance: 🏊on the spot 🛒on the spot ⊗on the spot 🍺on the spot 🍴on the spot 🚲on the spot.
Remarks: Free entrance swimming pool, jacuzzi, sauna, midget golf.
Tourist information Luçon:
🛈 Centre Ville. ⬛ Wed + Sa morning.

🛁S L'Aiguillon-sur-Mer 20B2
Centre de Voile, Avenue Amiral Coubert.
GPS: n46,33238 w1,30726. ⬆➡

50 🛏€5 🚰€2/100liter 📡ChWC. **Location:** Rural, simple.
Surface: asphalted. ⬛ 01/01-31/12
Distance: 🛒300m 🏖300m 🛒on the spot ⊗300m 🍺300m.
Remarks: At lake, yachting school.

🛁S Maillé 20C2
La Petite Cabane. **GPS:** n46,34082 w0,79349.

⬛S €8 ⌐⌐ Ch included. **Location:** Rural, simple, quiet.
Surface: grassy.
Distance: 500m 200m.
Remarks: Check in at harbourmaster, service passerby € 3, bicycle rental 500m.

⬛S **Maillezais** 20C2
Rue de l'Ecole. **GPS:** n46,37081 w0,74123.→

20 free ⌐€2/100liter Ch. **Location:** Simple.
Surface: asphalted. ◻ 01/01-31/12
Distance: 500m 500m 200m.

⬛S **Maisdon-sur-Sèvre** 17B3
Domaine des Croix, Les Croix. **GPS:** n47,10710 w1,38757.↑

12 free ⌐ Ch €4/24h WC €1. **Location:** Rural.
Surface: gravel. ◻ 01/01-31/12
Distance: 1km.
Remarks: Max. 72h, wine tasting.

⬛S **Mamers** 17E1
Rue de la Piscine. **GPS:** n48,35523 e0,37187.↑→

8 €7/night, € 18/3 nights ⌐ Ch included. **Location:** Rural, comfortable. **Surface:** grassy/gravel.
◻ 01/01-31/12
Distance: 1km 500m 500m 1km 1km.
Remarks: Entrance code available at campsite.

⬛S **Martigné-Briand** 17C3
Jardin des Vieux Pressoirs, Rue d'Anjou.
GPS: n47,23584 w0,42851.↑→

4 free ⌐ Ch free. **Surface:** metalled. ◻ 01/01-31/12
Distance: 200m 200m 100m.
Remarks: Closed when frosty.

⬛S **Mayenne** 17C1
Quai Carnot. **GPS:** n48,30000 w0,62.↑

4 free ⌐€1,50 Ch. **Location:** Urban, simple, noisy.
Surface: asphalted. ◻ 01/01-31/12
Distance: 1km 10m.
Remarks: Max. 24h, coins at tourist info.

⬛S **Mervent** 20C1
Chemin du Chêne Tord. **GPS:** n46,52385 w0,76432.↑

free ⌐€2/100liter Ch. **Location:** Rural, simple, isolated, quiet.
Surface: gravel.
Distance: 1km.
Remarks: At cemetery, coins at tourist info.

⬛S **Mesnard-la-Barotière** 20B1
Base de Loisirs de la Tricherie. **GPS:** n46,85280 w1,11764.↑

free ⌐€3 Ch. **Location:** Rural, simple.
Surface: grassy.
Distance: 2km beach on the spot on the spot on the spot.
Remarks: At lake of Tricherie.

⬛S **Mezeray** 17D2
Rue de la Vezanne. **GPS:** n47,82300 w0,01485.↑→

8 free ⌐€2 Ch €2. **Location:** Rural, simple. **Surface:** gravel.
◻ 01/01-31/12
Distance: 300m.

⬛S **Montfort-le-Gesnois** 17E1
Parc des Sittelles. **GPS:** n48,03763 e0,41375.↑→

16 € 10 ⌐ Ch included. **Location:** Rural, simple, quiet.
Surface: forest soil. ◻ 01/01-31/12
Distance: 50m.

⬛S **Montreuil-Bellay** 17D3
Rue Georges Girouy. **GPS:** n47,13272 w0,15835.↑

20 free ⌐€2 Ch. **Surface:** gravel/metalled. ◻ 01/01-31/12
◉ 15/06-15/09 10-19h
Distance: 150m 150m 150m.
Remarks: Along river, nearby campsite Les Nobis.

⬛S **Montreuil-Bellay** 17D3
Caveau de la Prévoté, Rue du Cohu 55, Méron.
GPS: n47,13522 w0,11121.↑

3 free ⌐ Ch free. **Surface:** metalled.
◻ 01/01-31/12
Distance: 50m 3km 3km.

Tourist information Montreuil-Bellay:
ℹ Office de Tourisme, Place du Concorde, www.ville-montreuil-bellay.fr. City with a fortress from 1025.

⬛S **Montreuil-Juigné** 17C2
Rue Saint Jean Baptiste. **GPS:** n47,54132 w0,61526.↑→

8 free ⌐ Ch free. **Location:** Rural, simple.
Surface: gravel/metalled. ◻ 01/01-31/12
Distance: 1km 50m 800m.
Remarks: Along the Mayenne river.

⬛ **Montsoreau** 17D3
Domaine de la Perruche, 29, Rue de la Maumenière.
GPS: n47,21828 e0,05079.↑
Distance: 500m 500m.
Remarks: 10.30><18.30h.

⬛S **Moutiers-sur-le-Lay** 20B1
Palias. **GPS:** n46,55375 w1,15483.→

6 free ⌐ Ch WC free. **Location:** Simple. **Surface:** grassy.
◻ 01/01-31/12
Distance: 400m 400m 400m 200m.
Remarks: At gymnasium.

⬛S **Mouzillon** 17B3
Route de la Vendée. **GPS:** n47,13944 w1,28194.↑→

12 ⓢfree 🚰€2 💧Ch. **Location:** Simple. **Surface:** asphalted.
Distance: 🚰200m ⊗200m 🛒200m 🎣 on the spot.

🚿S | **Nantes** 🚤🍴 | **17B3**

Camping-car park du Petit Port, Boulevard du Petit Port.
GPS: n47,24252 w1,5568.⬆️➡️.

15 ⓢ€ 12/24h 🚰🞂Ch▨included. **Location:** Urban, simple, central.
Surface: grassy/metalled. 🅾️ 01/01-31/12
Distance: 🚰on the spot 🚲3,5km ⊗on the spot 🛒300m 🚋tram 150m.
Remarks: Wifi code: 44-2207, entrance code 2207A.

Tourist information Nantes:
Ⓜ Musée Jules Verne.

🚿S | **Noirmoutier-en-l'Ile** 🚤🍴 | **17A3**

Place des Ormeaux, L'Epine. **GPS:** n46,98060 w2,26404.⬆️.

40 ⓢ€ 7/24h, € 13/48h, € 19/72h 🚰100liter 🞂Ch▨🔲
included50minutes WC. 🏠♨️ **Surface:** metalled. 🅾️ 01/01-31/12
Distance: 🚰100m 🏊1,3km 🛒on the spot ⊗200m 🛒3km.
Remarks: Max. 72h.

🚿S | **Noirmoutier-en-l'Ile** 🚤🍴 | **17A3**

Place Florent Caillaud, Noirmoutier-en-l'Ile.
GPS: n47,00139 w2,25167.⬆️.

182 ⓢ€ 5, 01/04-30/09 € 8, parking free 🚰€2/100liter 🞂Ch🔲€
2/2h ♨️free. 🏠 **Surface:** asphalted. 🅾️ 01/01-31/12
Distance: 🚰750m 🏊sandy beach 2,5km 🛒750m.
Remarks: Max. 7 days.

🚿S | **Noirmoutier-en-l'Ile** 🚤🍴 | **17A3**

Place R. Ganachaud, l'Herbaudière. **GPS:** n47,02016 w2,30061.⬆️.

18 ⓢ€ 5, 01/04-30/09 € 8, parking free 🚰€2/100liter 🞂Ch🔲€2/1h.
🏠 **Surface:** asphalted. 🅾️ 01/01-31/12

Distance: 🏊on the spot⊗350m.
Remarks: Parking behind town hall.

🚿S | **Noirmoutier-en-l'Ile** 🚤🍴 | **17A3**

Rue de la Tresson, La Guérinière. **GPS:** n46,96591 w2,21482.⬆️.

20 ⓢ€ 5, 01/04-30/09 € 8, parking free 🚰🞂Chfree 🔲4.🏠♨️
Surface: gravel. 🅾️ 01/01-31/12
Distance: 🏊sandy beach 450m ⊗200m 🛒100m.
Remarks: Max. 48h.

Tourist information Noirmoutier-en-l'Ile:
ⓘ Place de la République. 🅾️ Fri.
🐚 Sealand Aquarium, Le Vieux Port.

🚿S | **Nort-sur-Erdre** 🍴 | **17B2**

13 Place du Bassin. **GPS:** n47,43746 w1,49546.⬆️.

15 ⓢfree 🚰€2 🞂ChWC▨free. **Location:** Simple, quiet.
Surface: asphalted. 🅾️ 01/01-31/12
Distance: 🚰300m 🛒100m 🛒300m 🔲300m.
Remarks: Max. 24h.

🚿S | **Notre-Dame-de-Monts** | **17A3**

Aire de la Clairière, Rue de la Clairière.
GPS: n46,83460 w2,14282.⬆️➡️.

35 ⓢ€ 5/20-8h 🚰🞂Chfree. 🏠♨️ **Location:** Rural, simple.
Surface: gravel. 🅾️ 01/01-31/12
Distance: 🚰800m 🏊200m 🛒200m ⊗800m 🛒800m.
Remarks: Motorhome parking at the beach.

🚿S | **Notre-Dame-de-Monts** | **17A3**

Aire Place de Gaulle, Rue des Maraichins.
GPS: n46,83118 w2,13006.⬆️.

20 ⓢ€ 5/20-8h 🚰🞂ChWCfree. 🏠♨️ **Surface:** asphalted.
🅾️ 01/01-31/12
Distance: 🚰300m ⊗500m 🛒300m.

🚿S | **Nozay** | **17B2**

Étang de Nozay. **GPS:** n47,57500 w1,62528.⬆️.

16 ⓢ€ 5 🚰🞂Ch♨️(16x)WCincluded. **Surface:** gravel.
🅾️ 01/01-31/12 🔲 service: frost
Distance: 🚰200m 🚲2km 🛒10m ⊗200m 🛒200m.

🚿S | **Olonne-sur-Mer** 🍴 | **20A1**

Aire de Camping-car Olonne Escale, Rue des Anciens Combattants
d'Afrique du Nord. **GPS:** n46,53814 w1,77517.⬆️➡️.

21 ⓢ€ 8/24h 🚰🞂Ch♨️included. 🏠♨️ **Location:** Simple.
Distance: 🚰300m 🛒600m.
Remarks: Jul/Aug max. 48h, max. 72h.

🚿S | **Pellouailles-les-Vignes** | **17C2**

Rue Nationale, D323. **GPS:** n47,52141 w0,43698.⬆️.

3 ⓢfree 🚰🞂Chfree. **Location:** Rural. **Surface:** asphalted.
🅾️ 01/01-31/12
Distance: 🚰on the spot 🚲1,4km ⊗100m 🛒bakery 50m.

🚿S | **Piriac-sur-Mer** 🚤🍴 | **13D3**

Parking de Brambel, Avenue du Général de Gaulle, D452.
GPS: n47,39647 w2,51292.⬆️.

12 ⓢ€ 6 🚰€2/100liter 🞂ChWC. **Location:** Comfortable.
Surface: metalled. 🅾️ 01/01-31/12
Distance: 🚰2km 🏊50m ⊗2km 🛒2km.
Remarks: Parking to sea.

🚿S | **Piriac-sur-Mer** 🚤🍴 | **13D3**

Parking de Lérat, Route de Mesquêne, D99, Lieu-dit Lérat.
GPS: n47,36807 w2,53273.⬆️.

25 ⓢ€ 6 🚰€2/100liter 🞂Ch. **Location:** Simple. **Surface:** metalled.
🅾️ 01/01-31/12
Distance: 🚰2,5km 🏊600m 🛒600m ⊗500m 🛒500m.

🚿S | **Piriac-sur-Mer** 🚤🍴 | **13D3**

Port de Piriac, Rue de la Tranchée. **GPS:** n47,37861 w2,5422.⬆️.

FR

10 🛏 € 6 🚰 €2/100liter 🔌Ch. 🚽 ◻ 01/01-31/12
Distance: 🚲500m 🏊500m 🛒500m.
Tourist information Piriac-sur-Mer:
ℹ ◻ 01/06-30/09 Mo + Wed + Sa-morning, 01/10-30/05 Tue.
🎪 Arts market. ◻ 01/07-31/08 Thu-evening.

🛏S	**Pornic**	17A3

Le Val Saint-Martin. **GPS:** n47,12053 w2,09162. ⬆➡.

7 🛏free 🚰€2/100liter 🔌Ch 📦 **Location:** Comfortable, isolated.
Surface: asphalted. ◻ 01/01-31/12
Distance: 🚲city centre 1,5km.
Remarks: Next to swimming pool.

🛏S	**Pouancé** 🏖	17B2

Rue de l'hippodrôme, Aubin. **GPS:** n47,75223 w1,18007. ⬆➡.

10 🛏€ 2,75 🔌Ch 🚰(4x)WCfree. **Location:** Rural, simple, quiet.
Surface: grassy. ◻ 01/01-31/12
Distance: 🚲500m 🏊small beach 20m 🛶20m ⊗1km 🛒1km.
Remarks: Along étang de Saint-Aubin.

🛏S	**Pouzauges**	20C1

Parking de la Vallée, D49/D203. **GPS:** n46,77639 w0,82861. ⬆➡.

10 🛏free 🚰🔌Chfree. **Location:** Simple. **Surface:** asphalted.
◻ 01/01-31/12
Distance: 🚲1km ⊗1km 🛒1km.

🛏S	**Préfailles**	17A3

Camping-Car Park de La Pointe, Chemin du Port aux Anes.
GPS: n47,13872 w2,22213. ⬆.

49 🛏€ 12/24h 🚰🔌Ch🔌included 📶.📦📦 **Location:** Comfortable. **Surface:** grassy/gravel. ◻ 01/01-31/12

🛏	**Préfailles**	17A3

Aire de Biochon, Chemin de Levertrie. **GPS:** n47,12973 e2,19028.

75 🛏€ 3. 🏖 **Location:** Rural, simple, quiet. **Surface:** gravel/sand.
◻ 01/01-31/12
Distance: 🚲3km 🏊500m 🛶500m ⊗3km 🛒3km.
Remarks: Max. 48h, baker every morning.

🛏	**Préfailles**	17A3

Aire de la Pointe St-Gildas, D313, chemin des Pinettes.
GPS: n47,13663 w2,23843.

45 🛏€ 5. 🏖 **Location:** Rural, simple, quiet. **Surface:** grassy/gravel.
◻ 01/01-31/12
Distance: 🚲3km 🏊50m ⊗200m 🛒3km.
Remarks: Max. 48h, baker every morning.

🛏S	**Préfailles**	17A3

Rue de la Prée. **GPS:** n47,13439 w2,2117.
🚰€2,50/100liter 🔌Ch. **Location:** Simple. ◻ 01/01-31/12
Remarks: Coins at tourist info.

🛏S	**Rablay sur Layon**	17C3

D54. **GPS:** n47,29772 w0,57767. ⬆➡.
10 🛏free 🚰🔌ChWCfree. **Location:** Rural, simple.
Surface: gravel/sand.
Distance: 🚲300m.

🛏S	**Riaille**	17B2

Rue de la Benate. **GPS:** n47,51412 w1,28803. ⬆➡.

5 🛏free 🚰🔌ChWC🛏free. **Location:** Rural, simple, quiet.
Surface: gravel. ◻ 01/01-31/12
Distance: 🚲700m ⊗700m 🛒700m.
Remarks: Max. 48h.

🛏S	**Rouans** 🏖	17A3

Aire naturelle de Messan, Route des Marais.
GPS: n47,19272 w1,85419. ⬆➡.

8 🛏€ 3 🚰🔌ChWCfree. **Location:** Rural, simple.
Surface: grassy/metalled. ◻ 01/01-31/12
Distance: 🚲1km 🛶on the spot ⊗on the spot 🛒1km.
Remarks: To be paid at town hall.

🛏S	**Saint-Aubin-de-Luigné**	17C3

Domaine La Biquerie, D17. **GPS:** n47,30843 w0,70211. ⬆.

30 🛏free 🚰🔌Chfree. **Surface:** grassy. ◻ 01/01-31/12
Distance: 🚲5km.

🛏S	**Saint-Calais** 🏖	17E2

Boulevard du Docteur Gigon. **GPS:** n47,92416 e0,74459. ⬆➡.

4 🛏free 🚰🔌ChWCfree. **Location:** Rural, simple.
Surface: asphalted. ◻ 01/01-31/12
Distance: 🚲400m 🚶on the spot.

🛏S	**Saint-Calais** 🏖	17E2

Le Champ Long, D249. **GPS:** n47,93375 e0,74568. ⬆.

15 🛏free WC. **Location:** Rural. **Surface:** asphalted.
◻ 01/01-31/12
Distance: 🚲1,6km 🏊lake 🛶on the spot 🚶on the spot.

🛏S	**Saint-Clément-des-Levées**	17D3

Rue de la Laiterie. **GPS:** n47,33064 w0,18042. ⬆➡.

10 🛏free 🚰€2 🔌Ch. **Surface:** metalled. ◻ 01/01-31/12
Distance: 🚲300m.
Remarks: Coins at the shops and town hall.

🛏S	**Saint-Cyr-en-Bourg**	17D3

Cave de Saumur, Route du Mureau. **GPS:** n47,19642 w0,07266. ⬆➡.

15 🛏free 🚰🔌ChWCfree. **Surface:** asphalted. ◻ 15/03-15/09
Distance: 🚲3km.
Remarks: Max. 48h, wine tasting 300m.

🛏S	**Saint-Georges-sur-Loire**	17C2

Rue de la Villette. **GPS:** n47,40610 w0,76301.

FR

20 free 🚰♨Ch free. **Location:** Rural, simple. **Surface:** asphalted. 📅 01/01-31/12
Distance: 🛒300m 🏊100m ⊗300m 🍺300m.
Remarks: Next to the old abbey, max. 24h.

| 📷S | Saint-Gilles-Croix-de-Vie ⛵🏖 | 20A1 |

La Rabalette, Rue de la Rabalette. **GPS:** n46,70302 w1,94728. ⬆.

35 🅿15/03-15/11 € 5/night 🚰€2,60/10minutes ♨Ch. 🚐 📷
Location: Urban, simple. **Surface:** asphalted. 📅 01/01-31/12
Distance: 🛒500m 🏊1km ⊗500m 🍺500m.
Remarks: Nearby lake Soudinière, coins at tourist info.

| 📷S | Saint-Gilles-Croix-de-Vie | 20A1 |

Stade de la Chapelle, Rue du Bois. **GPS:** n46,69449 w1,92716.
🅿€5 🚰€2,60 ♨Ch. **Surface:** asphalted.
📅 01/04-30/09 weekend and school holidays
Distance: 🛒centre 500m.
Remarks: Coins at tourist info, 2013: during inspection service out of order.

Tourist information Saint-Gilles-Croix-de-Vie:
🏛 📅 St.Gilles: Tue, Thu, Su; Croix de Vie; Wed, Sa.

| ©S | Saint-Hilaire-de-Chaléons | 17A3 |

Rue Eloi Guitteny, D61. **GPS:** n47,10389 w1,86639. ⬆.

2 free 🚰♨Ch WC free. **Surface:** asphalted. 📅 01/01-31/12
Distance: 🛒100m ⊗500m 🍺100m.
Remarks: Next to campsite de l'Etoile, max. 24h.

| 📷S | Saint-Hilaire-de-Riez ⛵🏖 | 20A1 |

Base des vallées, Chemin des Vallées. **GPS:** n46,73154 w1,91132. ⬆.

10 free 🚰€2,60/10minutes ♨Ch 📷. **Location:** Rural, simple.
Surface: asphalted. 📅 01/01-31/12
Distance: 🛒St.Hilaire 3,7km 🏊7km.

| 📷S | Saint-Hilaire-de-Riez ⛵🏖 | 20A1 |

Parking des Becs, Avenue des Becs. **GPS:** n46,76040 w2,02656. ⬆.
20 🅿€5/24h 🚰€2,60/10minutes ♨Ch. 🚐 **Location:** Rural.
Surface: asphalted. 📅 01/01-31/12
Distance: 🏊sandy beach 750m ⊗200m.
Remarks: Max. 3 nights.

| 📷S | Saint-Hilaire-de-Riez ⛵🏖 | 20A1 |

Allée de la Plage de la Parée Préneau. **GPS:** n46,72865 w1,99167. ⬆.

48 free, night € 5. 🚐 **Location:** Rural. **Surface:** metalled.
📅 01/01-31/12
Distance: 🏊on the spot.
Remarks: Beach parking.

| 📷S | Saint-Hilaire-de-Riez ⛵🏖 | 20A1 |

Champ Gaillard, Avenue de Baisse. **GPS:** n46,76903 w2,03337. ⬆.

28 free. **Location:** Rural, isolated. **Surface:** gravel.
📅 01/01-31/12
Distance: 🏊sandy beach 1km.

| 📷S | Saint-Jean-de-Monts | 20A1 |

Le Repos des Tortues, Route de Notre Dame de Monts 38.
GPS: n46,79879 w2,07344. ⬆.

98 🅿€ 8, 01/07-31/08 € 12 🚰♨Ch 🚿 🛁(49x),4Amp WC ⎯€
5/stay 🚮€4 included. 🚐 **Location:** Rural, luxurious.
Surface: grassy/gravel. 📅 01/01-31/12
Distance: 🛒800m 🏊1,5km 🍺50m 🚉2km.
Remarks: Video surveillance.

| 📷S | Saint-Jean-de-Monts | 20A1 |

Aire de stationnement des Pimprenelles, Rue des Pimprenelles.
GPS: n46,78882 w2,07939.
20 🅿€8 🚰♨Ch 🚿 included. 🚐 **Location:** Comfortable.
📅 01/01-31/12
Distance: 🏊sandy beach 200m.

Tourist information Saint-Jean-de-Monts:
🏛 📅 Wed, Sa.

| 📷S | Saint-Jean-sur-Mayenne | 17C1 |

Les Marchanderies. **GPS:** n48,12793 w0,75244. ⬆➡.

25 🅿€7,60 🚰♨Ch 🚿 WC ⎯included. **Location:** Rural, luxurious, quiet. **Surface:** grassy/gravel. 📅 01/01-31/12
Distance: 🛒500m 🚚on the spot ⊗300m 🍺400m bakery 🚶on the spot.
Remarks: Along the Mayenne river.

| 📷S | Saint-Léonard-des-Bois | 17D1 |

Aire Municipale, Le Gué Plard. **GPS:** n48,35318 w0,08127. ⬆.

10 free 🚰♨Ch WC free. **Location:** Simple, quiet.
📅 01/01-31/12
Distance: 🛒500m 🏊on the spot 🚚on the spot ⊗500m 🍺on the spot 🚲 on the spot 🚶 on the spot.

| 📷S | Saint-Loup-du-Gast | 14C3 |

Zone d'Activité du Creusot. **GPS:** n48,38750 w0,58548. ⬆➡.

6 free 🚰♨Ch free. **Location:** Rural, simple.
Surface: asphalted/grassy. 📅 01/01-31/12
Distance: 🛒350m.
Remarks: Departure Vélorail, € 15 per bike for 4 pers.

| 📷S | Saint-Mars-la-Jaille | 17B2 |

Rue Neuve. **GPS:** n47,52327 w1,18357.

12 free 🚰♨Ch WC free. **Location:** Rural. **Surface:** asphalted.
📅 01/01-31/12
Distance: 🛒200m 🚚on the spot.
Remarks: Parking at small lake.

| 📷S | Saint-Michel-Chef-Chef | 17A3 |

Camping-Car Park Le Thar-Cor La Plaine sur Mer, Avenue Cormier.
GPS: n47,16017 w2,16881. ⬆.

24 🅿€ 12/24h 🚰♨Ch 🚿 included. **Location:** Simple, isolated, quiet. 📅 01/01-31/12
Distance: 🏊sandy beach 400m 🍺400m 🚉400m.

| 📷S | Saint-Michel-Chef-Chef | 17A3 |

Rue du Chevecier. **GPS:** n47,18209 w2,14664. ⬆.

30 free, 20-8h € 6 🚰€2,95/100liter ♨Ch. **Location:** Simple.
Surface: asphalted. 📅 01/01-31/12
Distance: 🛒300m ⊗300m 🍺300m.
Remarks: Parking townhall, coins at tourist info and town hall.

Saint-Michel-Chef-Chef — 17A3

Camping Clos Mer et Nature, Route de Tharon.
GPS: n47,17309 w2,15779.

€6 €2/100liter Ch €2. **Location:** Simple, quiet.
Surface: grassy. 01/01-31/12
Distance: 500m sandy beach 400m 300m.
Remarks: Check in at reception campsite.

Saint-Michel-en-l'Herm — 20B2

Route de la Mer D60. **GPS**: n46,36155 w1,24929.
6 free €2 Ch.
Distance: 200m 200m.
Remarks: Coins at the shops.

Saint-Michel-Mont-Mercure — 20C1

Place du Sommet. **GPS**: n46,83222 w0,88222.

50 free €2/150liter Ch. **Location:** Simple, isolated.
Surface: gravel/sand. 01/01-31/12
Distance: 500m on the spot 500m.

Saint-Nazaire — 17A3

Route de l'Océan, D292, Saint-Marc-sur-Mer.
GPS: n47,23700 w2,30033.

15 free €3/100liter Ch €3/1h. **Location:** Rural, simple,
quiet. **Surface:** gravel. 01/01-31/12
Distance: 2km 100m 100m.

Saint-Nazaire — 17A3

Bois-Joalland, Route de Quelmer. **GPS**: n47,27669 w2,25771.
3 free. **Location:** Rural, simple, quiet. **Surface:** unpaved.
01/01-31/12
Distance: 1km 5m on the spot on the spot.
Remarks: Nearby base nautique.

Saint-Nazaire — 17A3

Parking du Théâtre, Boulevard Paul Leferme.
GPS: n47,27760 w2,20362.

8 free. **Location:** Urban, simple, isolated. **Surface:** asphalted.
01/01-31/12
Distance: on the spot 500m 50m.

Saint-Nazaire — 17A3

Quai du Port de Méan. **GPS**: n47,29937 w2,18333.
6 free. **Surface:** metalled.
Distance: 4km 1km 150m.

Saint-Nazaire — 17A3

Route du Bois Joalland. **GPS**: n47,27954 w2,26229.

5 free. **Location:** Simple, central. **Surface:** gravel.
01/01-31/12
Distance: 500m 10m 10m on the spot on the spot.

Saint-Philbert-de-Grand-Lieu — 17B3

Chemin de la Plage. **GPS**: n47,04500 w1,64172.

10 free Chfree. **Surface:** gravel. 01/01-31/12
Distance: 1km on the spot on the spot 550m 1km.

Saint-Rémy-la-Varenne — 17D3

Rue St Aubin-D132. **GPS**: n47,39805 w0,31612.

3 free ChWCfree. **Surface:** asphalted. 01/01-31/12
Distance: on the spot 100m 100m.

Saint-Saturnin-sur-Loire — 17C3

Route de Saumur, D751. **GPS**: n47,39267 w0,43285.

3 free Chfree. **Surface:** metalled. 01/01-31/12
Distance: on the spot 100m 100m.

Saint-Viaud — 17A3

Rue du Parc des Sports. **GPS**: n47,25917 w2,015.

10 free Ch (2x). **Location:** Rural, comfortable, quiet.
Surface: metalled. 01/01-31/12
Distance: 500m 100m 500m 500m.
Remarks: At recreational lake, max. 8 days.

Saint-Vincent-sur-Jard — 20B1

Chemin des Roulettes, Le Goulet. **GPS**: n46,41038 w1,5413.

43 €0,35/h €2/10minutes Ch €2/55minutes
Location: Rural, simple. **Surface:** metalled. 01/01-31/12
Service: winter
Distance: 1km 100m 400m.

Saulgé l'Hôpital — 17C3

Terrain de Loisirs, Chemin de la Planche.
GPS: n47,29853 w0,38344.

15 free Chfree. **Surface:** gravel. 01/01-31/12
Distance: 100m 100m 100m.

Segré — 17C2

Aire de l'Europe, D775. **GPS**: n47,68497 w0,85719.

free ChWCfree. **Location:** Rural. **Surface:** asphalted.
01/01-31/12
Distance: 1km.

Segré — 17C2

Place du Moulin sous la Tour, Rue Emile Zola.
GPS: n47,68409 w0,87436.

10 free Chfree. **Location:** Rural, simple. **Surface:** gravel.
01/01-31/12 Service: winter
Distance: 300m on the spot 100m on the spot.

Sillé-le-Guillaume — 17D1

2, Place de la Gare. **GPS**: n48,18167 w0,13111.

8 free €2 Ch €2. **Location:** Urban, simple.
Surface: asphalted. 01/01-31/12
Distance: 300m 300m 400m train 50m.
Remarks: May 2012 during inspection service out of order.

Talmont-Saint-Hilaire — 20A1

Parking des Gâtines, Rue des Gâtines. **GPS**: n46,46761 w1,61718.

16 ⓂⒹ€ 5/24h 🚰€3/100liter ⓌCh🔌€3/50minutes.🚿🛒
Location: Rural, simple. **Surface:** asphalted. ⭕ 01/01-31/12
Distance: 🏊500m 🎣Small lake (100m) 🛒100m.

ⓈⒹ | **Talmont-Saint-Hilaire** | **20A1**

Parking du Château Guibert, Avenue de la Plage.
GPS: n46,44098 w1,66351. ⬆️➡️

16 ⓂⒹ€ 5/24h 🚰€3 ⓌChWC 🛒🚿🛒 **Location:** Rural, simple.
Surface: metalled. ⭕ 01/04-31/10
Distance: 🎣1km.
Remarks: Max. 48h.

ⓈⒹ | **Turquant** | **17D3**

Rue des Ducs d'Anjou. **GPS:** n47,22393 e0,02858. ⬆️

20 ⓂⒹfree 🚰€2,50 ⓌCh. **Surface:** metalled. ⭕ 01/01-31/12
Distance: 🏊100m ⊗50m 🛒50m 🚌on the spot.
Remarks: Behind church, coins at the shops in the village.

ⓈⒹ | **Vaiges** | **17C1**

Rue Robert Gletron, D57. **GPS:** n48,04189 w0,48285. ⬆️

5 ⓂⒹfree 🚰€2 ⓌCh. **Location:** Urban, simple, noisy. **Surface:** gravel.
⭕ 01/01-31/12
Distance: 🏊500m 🛥1,7km 🛒20m 🛒700m bakery.

ⓈⒹ | **Valanjou** | **17C3**

Aire de Plaisance, Rue de la Mairie. **GPS:** n47,21658 w0,60326. ⬆️

6 ⓂⒹfree 🚰ⓌChWCfree. **Surface:** metalled. ⭕ 01/01-31/12
Distance: 🏊200m.
Remarks: Nearby town hall.

ⓈⒹ | **Venansault** | **20B1**

Rue Pierre Nicolas Loué. **GPS:** n46,68250 w1,51472.

5 ⓂⒹfree. **Surface:** sand. ⭕ 01/01-31/12
Distance: 🏊500m 🎣100m ⊗300m 🛒500m.

ⓈⒹ | **Vendrennes** | **20B1**

Route de l'Océan. **GPS:** n46,82690 w1,1217. ⬆️

5 ⓂⒹfree 🚰€3/150liter ⓌChfree. **Location:** Rural, simple, quiet.
Surface: metalled/sand. ⭕ 01/01-31/12
Distance: 🏊200m.
Remarks: Coins at the bakery.

ⓈⒹ | **Vihiers** | **17C3**

Rue Champ de Foire des Champs. **GPS:** n47,14355 w0,5358. ⬆️➡️

5 ⓂⒹfree 🚰ⓌChWC. **Location:** Urban. **Surface:** asphalted.
⭕ 01/01-31/12
Distance: 🏊50m ⊗100m 🛒100m.

ⓈⒹ | **Villeveque** | **17C2**

Rue du Port. **GPS:** n47,56222 w0,42257. ⬆️
6 ⓂⒹfree 🚰€1 ⓌChWC. ⭕ 01/01-31/12
Distance: 🏊100m ⊗50m 🛒bakery 200m.

ⒸⓈⒹ | **Villiers-Charlemagne** | **17C1**

Village Vacances et Pêche, Rue des Haies.
GPS: n47,92083 w0,68167. ⬆️➡️

25 ⓂⒹ€ 8,10, first night free 🚰€2 ⓌCh🔌.
Location: Rural, comfortable, quiet.
Surface: grassy.
⭕ 01/01-31/12
Distance: 🎣on the spot 🛥day pass available 🛒500m 🏃on the spot.

ⓈⒹ | **Vouvant** | **20C1**

Rue de Château Neuf. **GPS:** n46,57462 w0,77462. ⬆️➡️

20 ⓂⒹfree 🚰ⓌChfree. **Surface:** gravel. ⭕ 01/01-31/12
Distance: 🏊500m ⊗500m 🛒500m.

Centre

ⓈⒹ | **Ainay-le-Vieil** | **20H1**

La Tuilerie. **GPS:** n46,66159 e2,55582. ⬆️➡️

6 ⓂⒹfree 🚰ⓌChWCfree. **Location:** Rural, simple, quiet.
Surface: grassy. ⭕ 01/01-31/12
Distance: 🏊850m ⊗800m.

ⓈⒹ | **Allogny** 🍴 | **17G3**

D944. **GPS:** n47,21913 e2,32329. ⬆️➡️

3 ⓂⒹfree 🚰WCfree. **Location:** Rural, simple, isolated, noisy.
Surface: asphalted. ⭕ 01/01-31/12
Distance: 🏊800m 🎣50m 🛒50m.

ⓈⒹ | **Amboise** 🌿🚣🍴🏖 | **17E3**

Vinci Park, Allée de la Chapelle Saint-Jean.
GPS: n47,41761 e0,98742. ⬆️

20 ⓂⒹ€ 12/24h 🚰ⓌChincluded 🛥(20x)€2 🚿.
🚿🛒 **Location:** Rural, comfortable, central, quiet.
Surface: asphalted/grassy. ⭕ 01/01-31/12
Distance: 🏊200m 🎣200m ⊗200m 🛒200m 🚴on the spot 🏃on the spot.
Remarks: Next to campsite, castle 500m.

ⓈⒹ | **Amboise** 🌿🚣🍴🏖 | **17E3**

Parking St. Jean, Avenue Leonardo da Vinci 43 , D61.
GPS: n47,40814 e0,98986. ⬆️➡️

11 ⓂⒹfree. **Location:** Urban, simple, isolated, quiet. **Surface:** asphalted.
⭕ 01/01-31/12
Distance: 🏊on the spot ⊗1,5km 🛒1,5km 🚴on the spot.

ⓈⒹ | **Angé** | **17F3**

Place de la Mairie. **GPS:** n47,33239 e1,24450. ⬆️➡️

20 ⬛free ⬛€3/100liter ⬛Ch⬛. **Location:** Simple, isolated, quiet.
Surface: sand. ⬛ 01/01-31/12
Remarks: Coins at town hall and supermarket.

| ⬛S | Ardentes | 20G1 |

Avenue de Verdun. **GPS:** n46,74682 e1,82826.⬛.
⬛⬛⬛Ch⬛⬛
Distance: ⬛on the spot ⬛on the spot.

| ⬛ | Argenton-sur-Creuse | 20F1 |

Rue de la Grenouille. **GPS:** n46,58715 e1,52497.⬛⬛.

50 ⬛free. **Surface:** gravel. ⬛ 01/01-31/12
Distance: ⬛50m ⬛3,4km ⬛50m ⬛50m.

| S | Argenton-sur-Creuse | 20F1 |

Alleé du Champ de Foire. **GPS:** n46,58501 e1,52283.⬛.
⬛⬛ChWCfree. ⬛ 01/01-31/12
Distance: ⬛on the spot.

| ⬛S | Athée-sur-Cher | 17E3 |

Aire d'Athée-sur-Cher, D83, Rue de Cigogné.
GPS: n47,31439 e0,91756.⬛⬛.

3 ⬛free ⬛⬛Chfree. **Location:** Rural, simple, isolated, quiet.
Surface: metalled. ⬛ 01/01-31/12
Distance: ⬛800m ⬛11km ⬛1,5km ⬛1km ⬛on the spot.
Remarks: Max. 24h.

| ⬛S | Aubigny-sur-Nère | 17H3 |

Parc des Sports, D7. **GPS:** n47,48201 e2,44995.⬛⬛.

9 ⬛free ⬛⬛Chfree. **Location:** Rural, simple, isolated, quiet.
Surface: asphalted. ⬛ 01/01-31/12
Distance: ⬛1km ⬛1km ⬛2km ⬛on the spot ⬛on the spot.
Remarks: Playground.

| ⬛S | Aubigny-sur-Nère | 17H3 |

Parking du Pré qui Danse, Mail Guichard.
GPS: n47,49140 e2,43830.⬛.

17 ⬛free ⬛⬛ChWCfree. **Location:** Urban, simple.
Surface: asphalted. ⬛ 01/01-31/12
Distance: ⬛200m ⬛200m ⬛200m ⬛100m.

| ⬛S | Avoine | 17D3 |

Avenue de la République. **GPS:** n47,21287 e0,17706.⬛.

11 ⬛€4 ⬛€2/10minutes ⬛Ch⬛(11x)€4/24h ⬛⬛.
Location: Rural, comfortable, luxurious, isolated, quiet.
Surface: asphalted/metalled. ⬛ 01/01-31/12
Distance: ⬛1km ⬛Lac Mousseau 300m ⬛300m.
Remarks: Max. 3 nights.

| ⬛S | Azay-le-Rideau | 17E3 |

Camping municipal Le Sabot, Rue du Stade.
GPS: n47,25925 e0,46992.⬛⬛.

8 ⬛free ⬛€3/100liter ⬛Ch⬛€1,70,on camp site. **Location:** Urban,
comfortable, central, quiet. **Surface:** asphalted.
⬛ 01/04-01/10
Distance: ⬛200m ⬛300m ⬛on the spot ⬛on the spot.
Remarks: Max. 24h, coins at camping (9/16h), castle 300m.

| ⬛S | Azé | 17F2 |

M et Mme Hersant, Les Places, D957 Épuisay-Galette.
GPS: n47,86451 e0,97659.⬛⬛.

6 ⬛€ 10 ⬛⬛Ch⬛included. ⬛ **Location:** Rural, comfortable,
isolated, quiet. **Surface:** grassy/gravel. ⬛ 01/01-31/12
Distance: ⬛7km ⬛on the spot.

| ⬛S | Barlieu | 17H3 |

Base de loisirs de Badineau. **GPS:** n47,47918 e2,63168.⬛.

15 ⬛first night € 3,50, € 2,50 each additional night ⬛€2/liter
⬛Ch⬛€2/h WCfree. ⬛ **Location:** Rural, simple, quiet.
Surface: grassy/gravel. ⬛ Easter-01/11
Distance: ⬛1km ⬛on the spot ⬛nearby.

| ⬛S | Bessais-le-Fromental | 20H1 |

Base de loisirs de l'Étang de Goule, Champ de la Croix.
GPS: n46,73402 e2,80034.⬛⬛.

50 ⬛free ⬛€2 ⬛Ch. **Location:** Simple, isolated, quiet.

Surface: asphalted/grassy. ⬛ service: frost
Distance: ⬛4km ⬛on the spot ⬛on the spot ⬛on camp site ⬛on
camp site.

| ⬛S | Blois | 17F2 |

P2, Rue Jean Moulin. **GPS:** n47,58653 e1,32641.⬛.

20 ⬛€ 5/24h ⬛⬛Chfree. **Surface:** asphalted. ⬛ 01/05-30/09
Distance: ⬛on the spot ⬛6,9km ⬛100m ⬛100m ⬛on the spot.

Tourist information Blois:
⬛ Château de Blois.
⬛ Cathédrale St Louis.
⬛ Quatier Coty. ⬛ Wed 7-13h.

| ⬛S | Bonneval | 17F1 |

Rue de la Grève. **GPS:** n48,17980 e1,38840.⬛.
8 ⬛free ⬛⬛ChWCfree. **Surface:** asphalted. ⬛ 01/01-31/12
Distance: ⬛200m ⬛200m ⬛350m.

| ⬛S | Bonny-sur-Loire | 17H2 |

Chemin de la Cheuille. **GPS:** n47,55925 e2,83967.⬛.

6 ⬛free ⬛€2/liter ⬛Ch⬛€2/30minutes WC. **Location:** Rural,
simple, central. **Surface:** gravel. ⬛ 01/05-30/09
Distance: ⬛150m ⬛50m ⬛300m ⬛on the spot ⬛on the spot.
Remarks: Along La Cheuille river.

| ⬛S | Boulleret | 17H3 |

Place des Charmes. **GPS:** n47,42304 e2,87244.⬛⬛.

4 ⬛free ⬛€2/100liter ⬛Ch⬛(4x)€2/6h WC. **Location:** Urban,
simple, central. **Surface:** asphalted.
⬛ 01/01-31/12
Distance: ⬛on the spot ⬛on the spot ⬛on the spot ⬛on the spot
⬛on the spot.
Remarks: Coins at the shops and restaurant.

| ⬛S | Bourges | 17H3 |

Rue Jean Bouin. **GPS:** n47,07597 e2,39897.⬛.

50 ⬛free ⬛⬛Ch⬛free. **Location:** Urban, simple, central.
Surface: asphalted. ⬛ 01/01-31/12
Distance: ⬛50m ⬛500m ⬛500m.
Remarks: Max. 48h.

Tourist information Bourges:
⬛ Ballades de Bourges. Festivities and market in the city centre.
⬛ 01/07-31/08.

⚓S Brézolles · 14F3

Rue de Verneuil, D939. **GPS:** n48,69083 e1,06972.⬆️.

10 🅿free ⌁🔌Chfree. **Surface:** gravel. ⬛ 01/01-31/12
Distance: 🚶200m ⊗200m.

⚓S Briare-le-Canal ☸⚓ · 17H2

Flot Bleu Park, Boulevard Lereou. **GPS:** n47,64304 e2,72270.⬆️.

12 🅿€7/24h ⌁🔌Chincluded. 📷✎ **Location:** Urban,
comfortable, quiet. **Surface:** grassy. ⬛ 01/01-31/12
Distance: 🚶on the spot ✦4,5km ⚓on the spot ⬅on the spot
⊗800m 🛒800m 📺100m 🚌500m.
Remarks: Max. 72h.

⚓S Briare-le-Canal ☸⚓ · 17H2

Rue des Vignes. **GPS:** n47,63215 e2,73981.⬆️.

40 🅿free ⌁€2/100liter 🔌Ch✎. **Location:** Urban, simple.
Surface: gravel. ⬛ 01/01-31/12
Distance: 🚶300m ✦4,5km ⬅50m ⊗500m 📺800m 🚌on the spot
⛵on the spot.

⚓S Briare-le-Canal ☸⚓ · 17H2

Port du Commerce, Quai de Mazoyer. **GPS:** n47,63470 e2,74030.⬆️.

10 🅿free ⌁WCfree. **Location:** Simple. **Surface:** asphalted.
⬛ 01/01-31/12
Distance: 🚶200m ✦4,5km ⬅on the spot ⊗on the spot 📺800m
⛵on the spot ⚓on the spot.

⚓S Brou ((•)) · 17F1

Madison Cars 28. GPS: n48,21379 e1,14681.⬆️➡️.

15 🅿€5 ⌁€1/100liter 🔌€1 Ch€1 ✎(4x)€3/24h 📺€1.🔧
Location: Rural, comfortable, isolated, quiet. **Surface:** gravel.
⬛ 01/01-31/12
Distance: 🚶1km ⬅1km ⊗on the spot.

Remarks: In front of Swin de Brou, bread-service.

⚓S Chabris ⚓ · 17F3

Place du Champ de Foire. **GPS:** n47,25317 e1,65211.
🅿free ⌁€2 🔌Ch€2.
Location: Rural.
Distance: 🚶on the spot ⊗250m 🛒250m.
Remarks: Coins at Tourist Info and Maison de la Presse (250m).

⚓ Chambord · 17F2

Château de Chambord, Place St.Louis. **GPS:** n47,61608 e1,51057.

100 🅿<7.90m € 7/day + € 10/night, >7.90m 45/day + € 45/night.
Surface: asphalted.
Distance: ⊗100m 🛒100m.
Remarks: Parking castle, max. 1 night.

⚓S Champigny-sur-Veude · 17D3

Place du Chapeau Rouge, Rue de la Bonne Dame.
GPS: n47,06499 e0,31773.⬆️.
8 🅿free ⌁🔌Ch. **Surface:** asphalted. ⬛ 01/01-31/12
Remarks: At small lake.

⚓S Chaon · 17G2

La Maison du Braconnage, Rue des Genêts, D129.
GPS: n47,60942 e2,16611.⬆️➡️.

10 🅿free ⌁🔌Chfree. **Location:** Rural, isolated, quiet.
Surface: grassy/metalled. ⬛ 01/01-31/12
Distance: 🚶200m ⊗200m 🛒bakery 50m.
Remarks: Video surveillance.

⚓S Châteaudun ☸⚓☕ · 17F1

Aire de Châteaudun, Rue des Fouleries.
GPS: n48,07172 e1,32421.⬆️➡️.

15 🅿free ⌁€2/100liter 🔌Ch⊞€2/20minutes WC.
Location: Urban, comfortable, central, quiet. **Surface:** asphalted.
⬛ 01/01-31/12
Distance: 🚶400m ⚓Canoe rental ⬅on the spot ⊗on the spot.
Remarks: Along Loir river, castel of Châteaudun 300m.

⚓S Châteauroux · 20F1

17, Avenue de Parc des Loisirs. **GPS:** n46,82278 e1,69507.⬆️.

5 🅿free ⌁€2,50 🔌Ch⊞€2,50/1h ✎. **Surface:** asphalted.
⬛ 01/05-31/10
Distance: 🚶3,6km ⊗2km 🛒2km.

⚓S Châtillon-sur-Loire ⚓ · 17H2

Rue du Port. **GPS:** n47,59128 e2,76044.⬆️.

± 6 🅿€ 9 ⌁🔌Ch ✦WCincluded. **Location:** Rural, comfortable,
quiet. **Surface:** asphalted/gravel.
Distance: 🚶800m ✦9km A77 ⊗400m 🛒bakery 500m.
Remarks: At the canal.

⚓ Chenonceaux ☸⚓ · 17F3

Aire de Chenonceaux, Chemin de la Varenne.
GPS: n47,33053 e1,06824.⬆️.

10 🅿free. **Location:** Rural, simple, isolated, noisy. **Surface:** grassy.
⬛ 01/01-31/12
Distance: 🚶500m ⊗500m ⬅on the spot ⚓on the spot.
Remarks: Along railwayline.

P Chenonceaux ☸⚓ · 17F3

Rue du Château. **GPS:** n47,33020 e1,06648.⬆️.

20 🅿free. **Location:** Rural, simple, isolated. **Surface:** metalled.
⬛ 01/01-31/12
Distance: 🚶500m ⊗500m ⚓on the spot.
Remarks: Parking at castle of Chenonceaux.
Tourist information Chenonceaux:
♜ Castle.

⚓ Cheverny · 17F2

Château Cheverny P3, D102. **GPS:** n47,49762 e1,46097.

20 🅿free. **Surface:** metalled.
⬛ 9.30-12h, 14.15-17h, Apr-Sep 9.30-18.15h
Distance: 🚶100m ⊗100m.

Tourist information Cheverny:
♜ Château Cheverny. Castle. ⬛ 9.30-12h, 14.15-17h, Apr-Sep 9.30-
18.15h.

⚓S Chouzé-sur-Loire · 17D3

Aire de Chouzé-sur-Loire, Rue de l'Église.
GPS: n47,23809 e0,12649.⬆️➡️.

6 �free ⌿€2 ⌫Ch. **Location:** Rural, comfortable, central, quiet. **Surface:** gravel. ☐ 01/01-31/12 **Distance:** ⌿on the spot ⊗250m ⌷on the spot ⌖on the spot ⌇on the spot. **Remarks:** Coins at the shops and town hall.

🏕️S	**Cloyes-sur-le-Loir**	17F1

Rue du Colonel Boussa. **GPS:** n47,99172 e1,23218. ⬆️➡️ 5 ⌿free. **Surface:** asphalted. ☐ 01/01-31/12 **Distance:** ⊗450m ⌷800m.

🏕️	**Coullons**	17H2

Place du Monument. **GPS:** n47,62012 e2,49319. ⬆️➡️

3 ⌿free ⌿⌫ChWCfree. **Location:** Urban, simple, quiet. **Surface:** gravel. ☐ 01/01-31/12 **Distance:** ⌿on the spot ⊗500m ⌷50m ⌖50m ⌇on the spot.

🏕️S	**Courville-sur-Eure**	14F3

Avenue Thiers. **GPS:** n48,44600 e1,24166. ⬆️ 6 ⌿free ⌿€2,50/100liter ⌫Ch ⌷€2,50/55minutes. **Surface:** asphalted. ☐ 01/01-31/12 **Remarks:** Coins at campsite and shops.

FR 🏕️	**Culan**	20G2

Place du Champ de Foire. **GPS:** n46,54727 e2,34630. ⬆️

20 ⌿free ⌿€1,50 ⌫Ch ⌷€1,50 WC ⌗. **Surface:** asphalted. ☐ 01/01-31/12 **Distance:** ⌿50m ⊗50m ⌷50m. **Remarks:** Near office de tourisme.

🏕️	**Cuzion** 🌿⛺	20F2

Base de Loisirs Pont des Piles, Rue des Petites Côtes. **GPS:** n46,45639 e1,61167. ⬆️➡️

6 ⌿free. **Location:** Isolated, quiet. **Surface:** grassy/metalled. ☐ 01/01-31/12 **Remarks:** Max. 1 night.

🏕️	**Dampierre-en-Burly** 🌿⛺	17H2

Etang du Bourg, Rue nationale. **GPS:** n47,76250 e2,51413. ⬆️

6 ⌿free ⌿⌫Ch ⌖WCfree. **Location:** Rural, simple, quiet. **Surface:** gravel. ☐ 01/01-31/12 **Distance:** ⌿1km ⌱on the spot ⌷on the spot ⊗1km ⌷1,5km ⌇500m ⌖on the spot.

🏕️S	**Dry** ⛺	17G2

Rue de Meung. **GPS:** n47,79824 e1,71419. ⬆️➡️

10 ⌿free ⌿€2/10minutes ⌫Ch ⌷€2/55minutes. **Location:** Simple. **Surface:** metalled. ☐ 01/01-31/12 **Distance:** ⌿on the spot ⌱1km ⊗50m. **Remarks:** Coins at town hall.

🏕️S	**Épineuil-le-Fleuriel**	20H1

Le Bourg. **GPS:** n46,55690 e2,58265. ⬆️ 5 ⌿free ⌫Chfree. **Location:** Rural. **Surface:** gravel. ☐ 01/01-31/12

🏕️S	**Esvres-sur-Indre** 🍴	17E3

Salle des Fêtes, Impasse Auguste Noyant. **GPS:** n47,28291 e0,78418. ⬆️

7 ⌿free ⌿⌫free. **Location:** Urban, simple, central, quiet. **Surface:** gravel. ☐ 01/01-31/12 ⬛ water disconnected in winter **Distance:** ⌿on the spot ⊗100m ⌷250m ⌇on the spot ⌖on the spot ⌇on the spot.

🏕️S	**Genillé**	17F3

Ferme Jouvin, La Galerie, D 764 Loches> Montrichard. **GPS:** n47,21409 e1,10871. ⬆️

⌿€2 ⌿service €3 ⌫Ch ⌗included. ⌂ **Location:** Rural, simple, isolated, quiet. **Surface:** grassy. ☐ 01/01-31/12 **Distance:** ⌿2,7km ⌷on the spot.

🏕️S	**Germigny-des-Prés**	17G2

21 Route de Saint-Benoît. **GPS:** n47,84430 e2,26798. ⬆️

5 ⌿free ⌿⌫Chfree. **Location:** Rural, simple, quiet.

Surface: gravel/metalled. ☐ 01/01-31/12 **Distance:** ⌿100m ⌷1,5km, bakery 600m.

🏕️S	**Gien** ⛺	17H2

Quai de Nice. **GPS:** n47,67985 e2,64308. ⬆️.

8 ⌿free ⌿€2,10 ⌫Ch ⌷€2,10. **Location:** Urban, noisy. **Surface:** asphalted. ☐ 01/01-31/12 **Distance:** ⌿2km ⌷on the spot. **Remarks:** Max. 48h, coins at swimming pool.

🏕️S	**Gizeux** 🌿⛺	17D3

Aire de Gizeux, Route du Lavoir. **GPS:** n47,39275 e0,19689. ⬆️➡️

20 ⌿free ⌿€3/100liter ⌫Ch ⌷€3/1h. **Location:** Rural, comfortable, central, quiet. **Surface:** gravel. **Distance:** ⌿200m ⌷500m ⊗In village ⌇on the spot ⌖on the spot. **Remarks:** Coins at the shops and town hall, Château de Gizeux 400m.

🍴S	**Guilly**	17G3

Le Prieuré Chambres d'Hôtes, Rue du Prieuré. **GPS:** n47,07920 e1,72100. ⬆️

10 ⌿€5 ⌿€3 ⌫Ch ⌷. **Surface:** grassy/metalled. **Distance:** ⌿150m ⌷10m ⌷150m.

🏕️S	**Humbligny**	17H3

Chemin des Faviots, D44. **GPS:** n47,25451 e2,65850. ⬆️

8 ⌿free ⌿€2/100liter ⌫Ch ⌷€2/60minutes. **Location:** Rural, simple. **Surface:** gravel. ☐ 01/01-31/12 **Distance:** ⌿on the spot ⊗1km ⌷3km ⌇50m. **Remarks:** Coins at town hall.

🏕️S	**La Chapelle-Saint-Mesmin** 🍴⛺	17G2

Aire camping-cars, Chemin de Fourneaux. **GPS:** n47,88550 e1,83990. ⬆️➡️

23 ⬛€ 5/24h, € 9/48h, € 12/72h 🚰🔌Ch 🔌included. 🗑️ 🧹
Location: Urban, comfortable, quiet. **Surface:** grassy.
🅿️ 01/04-31/12
Distance: 🚶500m, Orléans 5km 🚲 2,7km 🏊50m 🚲50m ⊗500m
🍽️500m 🎣 on the spot 🚶 on the spot.
Remarks: Along Loire river, market Saturday.

⬛	La Châtre	20G1

Rue du Champ de Foire. **GPS:** n46,58250 e1,98250.

10 ⬛€ 2. **Surface:** asphalted.
Distance: 🚶50m ⊗50m 🍽️50m.

🏠 S	La Châtre	20G1

Supermarché Super U, Avenue d'Auvergne, D943.
GPS: n46,58278 e2,00139.
10 ⬛free 🚰€2/10minutes 🔌Ch🔌€2/1h. **Surface:** asphalted.
🅿️ 01/01-31/12
Distance: 🚶800m 🍽️50m.

🏠	La Ferté-Beauharnais	17G2

D922. **GPS:** n47,54455 e1,84882. ⬆️

12 ⬛free 🚰€2/10minutes 🔌Ch🔌€2/55minutes WC.
Location: Simple, noisy. **Surface:** grassy/metalled.
🅿️ 01/01-31/12
Distance: 🚶300m 🏊on the spot 🚲on the spot ⊗250m 🍽️100m.
Remarks: At small lake.

🏠	La Ferté-Saint-Cyr	17G2

D925, Rue Faubourg de Bretagne. **GPS:** n47,65623 e1,67249. ⬆️
4 ⬛. **Surface:** metalled.

🏠 S	La Loupe	14F3

Place du 8 mai, Docteur Moenner St. **GPS:** n48,47262 e1,01768.
3 ⬛ 🚰€2,20 🔌Ch🔌€2,20. **Surface:** asphalted. 🅿️ 01/01-31/12
Distance: 🚶300m ⊗100m 🍽️800m.
Remarks: Coins at tourist info.

🏠 S	La Pérouille	20F1

Étang de la Roche, Le Champ Perrot. **GPS:** n46,70507 e1,52259.
⬛free 🚰€2 🔌ChWC.
Location: Rural, isolated, quiet.
Surface: grassy/gravel.
Distance: 🚶750m 🚲5km A20 ⊗750m.
Remarks: At small lake, coins at town hall and restaurant (750m).

🏠 S	Lailly-en-Val	17G2

Place de l'Église. **GPS:** n47,77023 e1,68544. ⬆️

30 ⬛free 🚰🔌ChWC free. **Surface:** gravel. 🅿️ 01/01-31/12
Distance: 🚶100m 🚲50m ⊗300m 🍽️200m.

🏠 S	Lamotte-Beuvron 🍴	17G2

Aire municipale, Chemin de Maisonfort. **GPS:** n47,59795 e2,02524. ⬆️

---

10 ⬛free 🚰🔌ChWC 📶free. **Location:** Urban, central.
Surface: metalled. 🅿️ 01/01-31/12 ⬤ Fri-morning, water
disconnected in winter
Distance: 🚶200m 🚲4,5km 🏊on the spot 🚲on the spot ⊗200m
🍽️300m 🚲100m.
Remarks: At the canal.
Tourist information Lamotte-Beuvron:
🏠 Avenue de la Republique. Market. 🅿️ Fri-morning.

🏠 S	Langon (Loir-et-Cher)	17G3

Parking Canal du Berry, D976. **GPS:** n47,28253 c1,82862. ⬆️

7 ⬛free 🚰€2/10minutes 🔌Ch🔌€2/1h. **Surface:** asphalted.
🅿️ 01/01-31/12 ⬤ Service: winter
Distance: 🚶50m 🚲20m ⊗100m 🍽️100m.
Remarks: Coins at the shops and town hall.

🏠 S	Le Blanc 🌿🚣	20E1

Place du Général de Gaulle. **GPS:** n46,63154 e1,06164. ⬆️
⬛free 🚰€2/100liter 🔌Ch🔌€2/1h. **Location:** Central, noisy.
Surface: asphalted.
🅿️ 01/01-31/12 ⬤ service: 01/11-01/04
Distance: 🚶on the spot 🍽️250m.

🏠 S	Le Châtelet 🌿	20G1

Le Tivoli, Avenue de la Gare. **GPS:** n46,64502 e2,27863. ⬆️

5 ⬛free 🚰€2 🔌Ch 🎣. **Surface:** asphalted. 🅿️ 01/01-31/12
Distance: 🚶50m ⊗50m 🍽️300m.

🛥️ S	Léré 🚣	17H3

Le Port, Rue du Champ des Noyers. **GPS:** n47,47485 e2,87477. ⬆️

4 ⬛free 🚰🔌Ch🔌free. **Location:** Rural, simple, quiet.
Surface: asphalted. 🅿️ 01/01-31/12
Distance: 🚶400m 🚲on the spot 🎣on the spot.
Remarks: At the canal.

🏠	Les Bordes 🚣	17H2

Etang du Petit Moulin, Route de Gien.
GPS: n47,81041 e2,40729. ⬆️➡️

---

6 ⬛free 🚰🔌Ch free. **Location:** Rural, simple, quiet.
🅿️ 01/01-31/12
Distance: 🚶400m 🏊100m ⊗150m 🍽️2km 🚲500m 🚶on the spot
🚶 on the spot.

🏠 S	Les Montils 🍴	17F2

Camping-Car Park des Montils, Route de Seur.
GPS: n47,49308 e1,30571. ⬆️
45 ⬛€ 12 🔌Ch 🔌(36x) 📶included. 🗑️ 🧹 **Location:** Rural.
Surface: grassy.
Distance: 🚶500m.
Remarks: Along river, former campsite.

🏠 S	Levet 🍴	20H1

Chemin du Crot A Thibault. **GPS:** n46,92306 e2,40639. ⬆️

3 ⬛free 🔌(3x). **Location:** Rural, simple, isolated, quiet.
Surface: gravel. 🅿️ 01/03-31/10
Distance: 🚶250m ⊗250m 🍽️250m.
Remarks: Max. 24h.

🏠	Loches 🌿🚣🍴	17E3

Allée du Maquis Césario. **GPS:** n47,12656 e1,00221.
4 ⬛free. 🅿️ 01/01-31/12
Distance: 🚶700m ⊗700m.

🏠	Loches 🌿🚣🍴	17E3

Avenue Louis XI. **GPS:** n47,13315 e1,00023. ⬆️
5 ⬛free. **Surface:** gravel. 🅿️ 01/01-31/12
Distance: 🚶centre 250m.
Remarks: Max. 24h.

🏠	Loches 🌿🚣🍴	17E3

Rue de l'Amiral de Pointis. **GPS:** n47,13744 e1,00115. ⬆️
4 ⬛free. **Location:** Simple, noisy. **Surface:** asphalted.
🅿️ 01/01-31/12
Distance: 🚶1,4km 🚲1,4km.

S	Loches 🌿🚣🍴	17E3

Avenue Aristide Briand. **GPS:** n47,12240 e1,00164. ⬆️

🚰🔌Ch🔌free. 🅿️ 01/01-31/12

🏠 S	Louzouer	17H1

Cidre Chivet, 323 Les Mussereaux. **GPS:** n48,02833 e2,87062.

5 ⬛€ 5 🚰€3 🔌Ch. **Location:** Comfortable.
Surface: asphalted/metalled. 🅿️ 15/03-31/12
Distance: 🚶1,5km.

Remarks: Max. 24h.

⚙S Luant `20F1`
L'Étang Duris. **GPS:** n46,72222 e1,57338.⬆.
10 ⅀free ⏸€2 🚻Ch⊟€2. **Location:** Isolated, quiet.
Surface: gravel.
🅿 01/01-31/12
Distance: 🚲3km ⊘3,3km A20 🛶lake ⊗bar/brasserie 🅰on the spot.

⚙S Marboué 🌳 `17F1`
L'Espace Loisirs des Fontaines, Rue du Croc Marbot.
GPS: n48,11240 e1,32870.⬆➡.

13+5 ⅀free ⏸€2/10minutes 🚻Ch⊟€2/50minutes.
Location: Rural, comfortable, central, quiet. **Surface:** grassy/metalled.
🅿 01/01-31/12
Distance: 🚲on the spot ⊶500m ⊗150m 🚃on the spot 🅰on the spot.

⚙S Marcilly-en-Villette 🌳 `17G2`
Rue du Lavoir. **GPS:** n47,76197 e1,02448.⬆➡.

6 ⅀free ⏸🚻Chfree. **Location:** Rural, simple, quiet.
Surface: gravel. 🅿 01/01-31/12
Distance: 🚲200m ⊗400m ⊶500m 🅰on the spot.
Remarks: At tennis-court.

⚙S Martizay `20E1`
Aire de Loisirs, Rue des Afrique du Nord. **GPS:** n46,80528 e1,03806.⬆.

9 ⅀free ⏸🚻Ch🔧(4x)WCfree. **Location:** Quiet.
Surface: metalled/sand. 🅿 01/01-31/12
Distance: ⊶on the spot ⊷bakery 500m.

⚙S Mehun-sur-Yèvre `17G3`
Quai du Canal. **GPS:** n47,14409 e2,21010.⬆.
6 ⅀€2 ⏸🚻Ch. **Surface:** asphalted. 🅿 01/01-31/12
Distance: 🚲500m ⊗400m.
Remarks: At the canal.

⚙S Menetou-Salon `17H3`
Rue de la Liberté. **GPS:** n47,23162 e2,49002.⬆➡.

6 ⅀free ⏸🚻Ch🔧(6x)free. **Surface:** gravel/metalled.
🅿 01/04-31/10
Distance: 🚲on the spot ⊗50m ⊷100m 🚃100m.

⚙S Mennetou-sur-Cher 🌼 `17G3`
Place du 11 Novembre, N76. **GPS:** n47,26861 e1,86472.⬆➡.

8 ⅀free ⏸€2/10minutes 🚻Ch⊟€2/1h. **Surface:** sand.
🅿 01/01-31/12
Distance: 🚲150m ⊶100m ⊗150m 🚃150m.
Remarks: Coins at shops and tourist office, small fortified town.

⚙S Méry-sur-Cher `17G3`
Chemin Lucien Bonneau/N76. **GPS:** n47,24586 e1,98989.⬆.

6 ⅀€5/24h ⏸🚻Ch🔧WCincluded. ⚡ **Surface:** metalled.
🅿 01/01-31/12
Distance: 🚲150m 🚃100m.

⚙S Meung-sur-Loire 🌿 `17G2`
Chemin des Grèves. **GPS:** n47,82327 e1,69814.⬆.
8 ⅀free ⏸€2 🚻Ch. **Location:** Rural. **Surface:** gravel.
🅿 01/01-31/12
Distance: 🚲250m ⊗300m 🚃250m bakery.
Remarks: At swimming pool.

⚙S Montigny `17H3`
Le Vieux Château. **GPS:** n47,24283 e2,68627.⬆➡.

2 ⅀free ⏸€2/100liter ⊟€2/60minutes. **Location:** Rural, simple,
isolated, quiet. **Surface:** gravel. 🅿 01/01-31/12
Distance: ⊗800m 🚃850m.
Remarks: Coins at town hall, poste.

⚙S Montoire-sur-le-Loir 🌼🌿 `17E2`
Avenue de la République. **GPS:** n47,75750 e0,86928.⬆.

15 ⅀free ⏸🚻Chfree⊟€1. **Location:** Urban, comfortable, quiet.
Surface: asphalted. 🅿 01/01-31/12
Distance: 🚲on the spot ⊗500m 🚃500m ⊶on the spot.
Remarks: At former station.

⚙S Montoire-sur-le-Loir 🌼🌿 `17E2`
Aire de Montoire-sur-le-Loir, Boulevard des Alliés, Quartier Marescot.
GPS: n47,74990 e0,86317.⬆➡.

8 ⅀free. **Location:** Urban, simple, central, quiet. **Surface:** asphalted.
🅿 01/01-31/12
Distance: 🚲50m ⛱on the spot ⊶on the spot ⊗500m 🚃500m
🚃on the spot 🅰on the spot.

⚙S Montrésor 🌿 `17F3`
Rue du 8 Mai. **GPS:** n47,15750 e1,20169.⬆.
10 ⅀free ⏸🚻Chfree. **Surface:** asphalted. 🅿 01/01-31/12
Distance: 🚲200m.

⚙S Morogues `17H3`
Route des Aix, D46. **GPS:** n47,23990 e2,59857.⬆.

4 ⅀free ⏸€2/100liter 🚻Ch⊟€2/60minutes. **Location:** Rural,
simple, quiet. **Surface:** gravel. 🅿 01/01-31/12
Distance: 🚲on the spot ⊗200m ⊶1km ⊷800m.
Remarks: Coins at tourist info Henrichemont (12km).

⚙S Neuillay-les-Bois `20F1`
Route de Buzançais, D1. **GPS:** n46,76917 e1,47333.

5 ⅀free ⏸🚻Ch🔧WCfree. **Surface:** metalled.
🅿 01/05-31/10
Distance: 🚲50m ⊶50m ⊗50m 🚃50m.
Remarks: Max. 24h.

⚙S Neuillé-Pont-Pierre `17E2`
Parc Chauvin, Rue De Gaulle, D766. **GPS:** n47,54756 e0,55209.⬆⬆.

10 ⅀free ⏸🚻Ch🔧(12x)free WC. **Location:** Urban, simple, noisy.
Surface: asphalted. 🅿 01/01-31/12
Distance: 🚲on the spot ⊘3,5km ⊗on the spot 🚃on the spot.

⚙S Neuvy-Le-Barrois `20H1`
La Prairie, Le Pénisson, D45. **GPS:** n46,86159 e3,03930.⬆➡.

6 ⅀€6 ⏸€2/100liter 🚻Ch⊟€4/24h ⊟€2/time. **Location:** Rural,
comfortable, isolated, quiet. **Surface:** gravel/metalled.

FR

▣ 01/01-31/12
Distance: 🏙200m 🍴200m.

[S] Neuvy-Pailloux 20G1

Les Gloux, RN151. **GPS**: n46,88278 e1,83682.[↑].
15 🚐free 🚰 🚽Ch WC free. **Location:** Simple, isolated.
Surface: asphalted. ▣ 01/01-31/12

[S] Nogent-le-Roi 14F3

Rue du Pont des Demoiselles. **GPS**: n48,65059 e1,52894.[↑].
4 🚐free 🚰 🚽Ch ⚡free. **Surface:** asphalted.
Distance: 🏙400m 🍴400m 🥖400m.
Remarks: Next to sports fields.

Nogent-sur-Vernisson 17H2

Rue du Gué Mulet. **GPS**: n47,84055 e2,73996.[↑][→].

6 🚐free. **Location:** Simple, quiet. **Surface:** gravel.
▣ 01/01-31/12
Distance: 🏙1km 🏊on the spot 🎣on the spot 🥖1km.

[S] Nogent-sur-Vernisson 17H2

Rue Georges Bannery. **GPS**: n47,85363 e2,74014.
🚰€2 🚽Ch ⚡€2.
Remarks: Coins at tourist info, PMU Rue Bannery or bar in Rue A. Briand.

Nouan-le-Fuzelier 17G2

Rue des Peupliers. **GPS**: n47,53324 e2,03437.[↑][→].

6 🚐free. **Location:** Urban, simple. **Surface:** asphalted/metalled.
▣ 01/01-31/12
Distance: 🏙300m 🍴300m 🥖300m.

[S] Oulches 20F1

Impasse de l'Étang. **GPS**: n46,61339 e1,29547.[↑].
🚐free 🚰€2 🚽Ch ⚡€2. **Location:** Rural. **Surface:** gravel.
Distance: 🏙on the spot 🍴100m.

[S] Ouzouer-sur-Trézée 17H2

Parking halte nautique, Rue Saint-Roche.
GPS: n47,67000 e2,80888.[↑].

5 🚐free 🚰 🚽Ch WC 🚿free. **Location:** Urban, comfortable, quiet.
Surface: asphalted. ▣ 01/04-31/10
Distance: 🏙500m 🎣on the spot 🍴500m 🥖700m 🚌50m.
Remarks: At canal 'de Briare', max. 48h.

[S] Ouzouer-sur-Trézée 17H2

Camping municipal, Chemin du Rochoir.
GPS: n47,66819 e2,80611.[↑][→].

6 🚐€ 4,50 🚰 🚽Ch ⚡€2,60 WC 🚿included ▣.
Surface: grassy/gravel. ▣ 01/04-31/10

[S] Paucourt 17H1

Rue de l'Église. **GPS**: n48,03441 e2,79179.[↑].

🚐free 🚰 🚽Ch free. **Location:** Rural. **Surface:** asphalted.
▣ 01/01-31/12
Distance: 🏙on the spot 🚲4,5km.

[S] Pont-de-Ruan 17E3

D17. **GPS**: n47,26373 e0,57632.[↑].
🚐free 🚰€2 🚽Ch ⚡€2. **Location:** Simple, isolated.
Surface: gravel/sand.
Distance: 🏙300m.

[S] Pouligny-Saint-Pierre 20E1

Route du Blanc, D950, Bénavent. **GPS**: n46,65591 e1,02054.[↑][→].
10 🚐free 🚰€2 🚽€2 Ch€2 ⚡€2. **Location:** Rural, quiet.
Surface: gravel.
Distance: 🥖bakery 50m.
Remarks: Coins at the bakery.

[S] Reignac-sur-Indre 17E3

Rue Louis de Barberin, D58. **GPS**: n47,22922 e0,91585.[↑].

5 🚐free 🚰€2/100liter 🚽Ch. **Location:** Rural, simple, central, noisy.
Surface: asphalted. ▣ 01/01-31/12
Distance: 🏙300m 🚲20km 🚌on the spot 🚴on the spot 🥾on the spot.
Remarks: Max. 24h, coins at the shops in the village.

[S] Restigné 17D3

Rue Basse. **GPS**: n47,28041 e0,22614.[↑][→].

10 🚐free 🚰€2/100liter 🚽Ch. **Location:** Rural, simple, central, quiet.
Surface: gravel. ▣ 01/01-31/12
Distance: 🏙on the spot 🍴on the spot 🚴on the spot 🥾on the spot.
Remarks: Coins at town hall.

[S] Saint-Amand-Montrond 20H1

Base de Loisirs Virlay, Etangs de Goule.
GPS: n46,73362 e2,48851.[↑][→].

21 🚐free 🚰 🚽Ch free. **Location:** Rural, simple, quiet.
Surface: asphalted/grassy. ▣ 01/01-31/12
Distance: 🏙1km 🚲5km 🍴500m 🥖500m 🚴on the spot 🥾on the spot.

[S] Saint-Amand-Montrond 20H1

Quai Lutin, via Avenue Maréchal Foch. **GPS**: n46,71818 e2,50480.[↑][→].

4 🚐free 🚰 🚽Ch free. **Location:** Urban, simple.
Surface: asphalted/gravel. ▣ 01/01-31/12
Distance: 🏙200m 🏊on the spot 🎣on the spot 🍴200m 🥖200m.
Remarks: On the canal.

[S] Saint-Benoît-du-Sault 20F2

Place du Champ de Foire. **GPS**: n46,44117 e1,39249.
🚐 🚰 🚽Ch. ▣ 01/01-31/12
Distance: 🏙300m 🥖300m.

[S] Saint-Brisson-sur-Loire 17H2

Rue des Ruets, route d'Autry, D52. **GPS**: n47,64680 e2,68028.[↑][→].

6 🚐free 🚰 🚽Ch free ⚡. **Location:** Urban, simple, quiet.
Surface: asphalted. ▣ 01/01-31/12
Distance: 🏙100m 🍴100m 🥖100m 🚌50m.
Remarks: Parking nearby town hall.

[S] Saint-Claude-de-Diray 17F2

Rue du Moulin D98. **GPS**: n47,61356 e1,41402.[↑].
4 🚐free 🚰 🚽Ch free.
Location: Simple, quiet. **Surface:** gravel.
Distance: 🏙500m.
Remarks: Next to cemetery.

[S] Saint-Denis-les-Ponts 17F1

Aire de Saint Denis-les-Ponts, Rue Jean Moulin.
GPS: n48,06643 e1,28950.[↑][→].

+10 🚐free 🚰€2/100liter 🚽Ch. **Location:** Urban, comfortable, central, quiet. **Surface:** gravel.
▣ 01/01-31/12 ▣ Service: winter
Distance: 🏙Châteaudun 3km 🏊on the spot 🎣on the spot 🍴100m 🚌on the spot 🥾on the spot.
Remarks: Coins at the shops in the village, Châteaudun (city and castle) 4km.

[S] Saint-Genouph 17E3

Rue de l'Auberdière. **GPS**: n47,37702 e0,60200.[↑].
🚐free 🚰 🚽Ch. **Surface:** metalled. ▣ 01/01-31/12

FR

Distance: 350m 350m.

Saint-Georges-sur-Arnon 20G1

Allée de la Presle. **GPS:** n46,99999 e2,09884.
10 free Chfree. **Location:** Rural, isolated, quiet.
Surface: gravel. 01/01-31/12
Distance: on the spot on the spot.
Remarks: At small lake, former campsite, max 3,5t.

Saint-Georges-sur-Arnon 20G1

N151. **GPS:** n46,97740 e2,06908.

10 free Ch WC free. **Location:** Simple, isolated.
Surface: asphalted.

Saint-Georges-sur-Moulon 17H3

Route de Ville. **GPS:** n47,18596 e2,41786.

2 free Chfree. **Location:** Simple, isolated, quiet.
Surface: gravel. 01/01-31/12
Distance: 1,5km 1km 1,5km.

Saint-Gondon 17H2

Rue de Sully. **GPS:** n47,69808 e2,53876.

3 free Chfree. **Location:** Rural, simple, quiet.
Surface: asphalted. 01/01-31/12
Distance: 300m 300m 200m.
Remarks: Max. 48h.

Saint-Gondon 17H2

Rue du Petit Clou. **GPS:** n47,69995 e2,54356.

10 free Chfree. **Location:** Rural, simple. **Surface:** metalled.
01/01-31/12
Distance: 100m.
Remarks: In front of cemetery.

Saint-Jean-le-Blanc 17G2

Base de loisirs de l'Ile Charlemagne, Levée de la Chevauchée.
GPS: n47,89437 e1,93870.

free €2/100liter Ch. **Location:** Simple, isolated.
Surface: sand. 01/01-31/12
Distance: Orléans 3km on the spot on the spot.

Saint-Saturnin 20G2

Route de Perassay. **GPS:** n46,50565 e2,23585.
free €2 Ch. **Surface:** grassy. 01/01-31/12
Distance: 300m.

Sainte-Maure-de-Touraine 17E3

Aire du Bois Chaudron, D910, Le Bois Caudron.
GPS: n47,09315 e0,61275.

40 €2,50, 2 pers.incl €2 €1 Ch €3 (4x)€2/12h WC €
2 €4/3 **Location:** Rural, comfortable, isolated, quiet.
Surface: grassy. 01/01-31/12
Distance: 1,5km 4,4km 1,5km 1,5km on the spot.
Remarks: Bread-service.

Sainte-Maure-de-Touraine 17E3

Parking Ronsard, Rue de la Métairie. **GPS:** n47,11096 e0,61640.

15 free Chfree WC. **Location:** Urban, simple, central, quiet.
Surface: asphalted. 01/01-31/12
Distance: 200m 3km 200m 200m on the spot.

Sainte-Sévère-sur-Indre 20G2

Place du Champ de Foire, rue de Verdun. **GPS:** n46,48724 e2,07167.
free €2 Ch.
Location: Rural. **Surface:** gravel/sand.
Distance: 100m 180m.

Sancoins 20H1

Quai du Canal. **GPS:** n46,83356 e2,91568.

20 free €2,50/100liter Ch WC. **Location:** Simple, quiet.
Surface: gravel/metalled. 01/01-31/12
Distance: 200m on the spot on the spot 200m 150m
on the spot on the spot.

Saran 17G2

Allée Claude Bernard. **GPS:** n47,95106 e1,87315.

10 free Chfree. **Location:** Simple, central. **Surface:** gravel.
01/01-31/12
Distance: on the spot on the spot 1,5km 1km 800m
on the spot on the spot.

Selles-sur-Cher 17F3

Avenue Kleber-Loustau, D856. **GPS:** n47,27639 e1,55889.

15 €5 €4,50 Ch €4,50 WC. **Surface:** asphalted/grassy.
01/01-31/12
Distance: 500m 200m 500m 500m.
Remarks: Coins at camping, tourist info and town hall.

Sully-sur-Loire 17H2

Espace Loisirs Georges Blareau, Chemin de la Salle Verte.
GPS: n47,77139 e2,38451.

16 free Chfree. **Location:** Comfortable, quiet.
Surface: gravel/metalled. 01/01-31/12
Distance: 800m on the spot on the spot 800m 800m.
Remarks: Nearby castle of Sully, narrow entrance.

Sury-prés-Léré 17H3

Route de Savigny. **GPS:** n47,48301 e2,86527.

6 free €2/100liter Ch €2/60minutes. **Location:** Rural,
simple, quiet. **Surface:** asphalted. 01/01-31/12
Distance: 1,5km 50m 1,5km.
Remarks: Coins at town hall and restaurant.

Ternay 17E2

Plan d'eau, Rue Saint Père. **GPS:** n47,73114 e0,77617.

10 free Chfree WC. **Location:** Rural, simple, central, quiet.
Surface: gravel. 01/01-31/12
Distance: on the spot on the spot on the spot.

FR

Theillay · 17G3

Chemin du Ronaire. **GPS**: n47,31849 e2,03775.⬆.

10 free ⛽ Chfree. **Surface**: gravel/metalled.
◯ 01/01-31/12
Distance: 250m 250m.

Thenay · 20F1

Rue de la Paix, D48. **GPS**: n46,63199 e1,43096.
free ⛽€2 Ch €2. **Surface**: metalled.
Distance: 200m.
Remarks: Coins at the shops and town hall.

Thiron-Gardais · 17F1

Aire de Thiron-Gardais, Avenue de la Gare.
GPS: n48,31194 e0,99583.⬆➡.

10 free ⛽ Chfree.
Location: Urban, simple.
Surface: asphalted.
Distance: 100m 300m 300m on the spot 100m.

Tour-en-Sologne · 17F2

Rue de la Mairie. **GPS**: n47,53786 e1,49973.

10 free ⛽€2,50/100liter Ch €2,50/h WC.
Surface: gravel.
Distance: 50m 200m bakery 100m.
Remarks: Coins at townhall and bakery.

Tours · 17E3

Parking relais du Lac, Avenue du Général Niessel.
GPS: n47,36700 e0,70007.⬆.
6 € 2,60 ⛽€2/100liter Ch. **Surface**: asphalted.
Distance: 2,5km.

Vailly-sur-Sauldre · 17H3

Rue du Pont. **GPS**: n47,45727 e2,64665.⬆.

20 € 3,50 ⛽ Chfree €2,50 WC €0,80.
Location: Comfortable, central. **Surface**: gravel/metalled.
◯ 01/04-31/10
Distance: 300m on the spot nearby nearby.
Remarks: Along the Sauldre river.

Tourist information Vailly-sur-Sauldre:
🚶 ◯ Fri.

Valençay · 17F3

Avenue de la Résistance. **GPS**: n47,16080 e1,56163.⬆.

10 free ⛽€2 Ch. **Surface**: metalled. ◯ 01/01-31/12
Distance: 100m 100m 100m.
Remarks: Nearby entrance castle.

Tourist information Valençay:
Château. Castle, 15th-18th century. ◯ 01/03-30/11.

Veigné · 17E3

Camping de la Plage, D50. **GPS**: n47,28921 e0,73436.
3 free ⛽€2/100liter Ch €2/10minutes.
Location: Comfortable, noisy. **Surface**: metalled.
Distance: on the spot on the spot on the spot 100m 100m.

Vendôme · 17F2

Aire de Vendôme, Rue Geoffroy Martel. **GPS**: n47,79111 e1,07528.⬆.

5 free. **Location**: Urban, simple, central. **Surface**: asphalted.
◯ 01/01-31/12
Distance: 500m.

Villaines les Rochers · 17E3

Aire de Villaines-les-Rochers, Place de la Mairie/ Rue des Ecoles.
GPS: n47,22083 e0,49583.⬆➡.

6 free ⛽ ChWCfree. **Location**: Urban, comfortable, central,
quiet. **Surface**: asphalted. ◯ 01/01-31/12
Distance: on the spot 100m 100m on the spot on the
spot.
Remarks: Max. 24h.

Villandry · 17E3

Aire de Villandry, Rue Principale. **GPS**: n47,34100 e0,51127.⬆.

25 free ⛽€2/100liter ChWC.
Location: Rural, comfortable, central, quiet.
Surface: grasstiles.
◯ 01/01-31/12
Distance: 50m 3,1km 300m 90m 90m on the spot
on the spot on the spot.
Remarks: Coins at tourist info(100m), Château de Villandry 200m.

Villedômer · 17E2

Aire de Loisirs de Lavoir, Rue du Lavoir.
GPS: n47,54465 e0,88727.⬆➡.

5 free, 15/06-15/09 € 5 ⛽€2/100liter Ch €4/1h.
Location: Rural, simple, central, quiet. **Surface**: metalled.
◯ 01/01-31/12
Distance: 100m 8,1km 100m 200m 200m on the
spot on the spot.
Remarks: Max. 24h, coins at town hall (200m), bakery (200m) and
supermarket (50m).

Villequiers · 17H3

L'Étappe Berrichonne, Le Petit Azillon.
GPS: n47,08828 e2,77429.⬆➡.

6 €7 ⛽ Ch included. **Location**: Isolated, quiet.
Surface: gravel/metalled. ◯ 01/01-31/12
Distance: 3km.

Vitry-aux-Loges · 17G2

Rue des Érables. **GPS**: n47,93915 e2,27078.
free ⛽ Chfree. **Location**: Rural. **Surface**: asphalted.
◯ 01/01-31/12
Distance: 100m 100m on the spot on the spot.
Remarks: At canal of Orléans.

Vouvray · 17E3

Parking Bec de Cisse, Rue Bec de Cisse.
GPS: n47,40929 e0,79735.⬆➡.

3 free ⛽€2/100liter Ch €2/1h WC. **Location**: Rural,
comfortable, central, quiet. **Surface**: asphalted. ◯ 01/01-31/12
◉ Service: winter
Distance: on the spot 8,5km 500m 150m 150m on
the spot on the spot.
Remarks: Max. 48h, coins at campsite and tourist info.

Bourgogne

Anost · 18B3

Place Centrale. **GPS**: n47,07778 e4,09869.⬆.

10 free ⛽ Chfree. **Location**: Rural, simple, quiet.
Surface: metalled. ◯ 01/01-31/12
Distance: on the spot.

Autun · 21B1

Route de Chalon. **GPS**: n46,95548 e4,31667.⬆➡.

FR

17 ⓈⒻfree ⌐€3,50 ⒸⒽWC. **Location:** Urban, simple.
Surface: asphalted.
◻ 01/01-31/12
Distance: ⌂city centre 2km ⌐100m ⊗100m ⌂supermarket 900m ⌂on the spot ⚓ on the spot.
Remarks: Parking at small lake Le Vallon at N80, in front of McDonalds.
Tourist information Autun:
◖ Musée Rolin. Roman and Medieval excavations.
⚓ ◻ Wed, Fri, Su.

ⓈⓈ | **Auxerre** 🍀 🖐 | **18A2**

Quai de l'Ancienne Abbaye. **GPS:** n47,79742 e3,57738.⬆.

10 ⓈⒻfree. **Surface:** asphalted. ◻ 01/01-31/12
Distance: ⌂300m ⊗300m ⌂300m.
Remarks: Along the Yonne river.
Tourist information Auxerre:
⚓ ◻ Tue, Fri.

ⓈⓈ | **Beaune** 🍱 | **21C1**

Parking Charles de Gaulle. **GPS:** n47,01731 e4,83628.⬆.

5 ⓈⒻfree ⌐€3,50 ⒸⒽ🖳€3,50/2h 🗒.
Location: Urban, simple, central.
Surface: asphalted.
Distance: ⌂500m 🚲2,6km ⊗200m ⌂centre commercial 300m.
Remarks: 5 special pitches, all parking places permitted.
Tourist information Beaune:
◉Ⓜ Hôtel Dieu et Musée. Former hospital, 15th century, museum.
♜ Château de Meursault, Meursault. Castle with vineyard and wine tastery.

ⓈⓈ | **Beaurepaire-en-Bresse** | **21D1**

Le Bourg. **GPS:** n46,66966 e5,38985.⬆.

5 ⓈⒻfree ⌐🖳ⒸⒽ⚡ WC. **Location:** Simple, noisy.
Surface: asphalted. ◻ 01/01-31/12 ◉ Service: winter
Distance: ⌂bakery.

ⓈⓈ | **Chablis** | **18B2**

Route d'Auxerre, D235. **GPS:** n47,81711 e3,78425.⬆.

---

5 ⓈⒻfree ⌐🖳free.
Location: Simple, quiet. **Surface:** asphalted.
Distance: ⌂centre 500m ⊗on the spot.

ⓈⓈ | **Chalon-sur-Saône** 🍱 | **21C1**

P Ville Historique, Promenade Sainte Marie.
GPS: n46,78365 e4,86046.⬆.

2 ⓈⒻfree ⌐🖳ⒸⒽfree. **Location:** Simple. **Surface:** asphalted.
◻ 01/01-31/12
Distance: ⌂500m ⊗50m.
Remarks: Free shuttle to centre.

ⒸⓈ | **Charolles** ⛩ | **21B2**

Route de Viry. **GPS:** n46,43956 e4,28203.⬆.

8 ⓈⒻ€3 ⌐🖳ⒸⒽ🖳€3. **Location:** Simple. **Surface:** gravel.
◻ 01/04-01/10
Distance: ⌂300m.
Remarks: Max. 48h.

ⓈⓈ | **Château-Chinon** | **18B3**

Rue Jean Sallonnyer. **GPS:** n47,06304 e3,93627.⬆.

10 ⓈⒻfree ⌐🖳ⒸⒽfree WC. **Location:** Simple. **Surface:** metalled.
◻ 01/01-31/12
Distance: ⌂200m ⊗250m ⌂250m.
Remarks: Max. 24h.

ⓈⓈ | **Châtillon-en-Bazois** | **21A1**

Place Pierre Saury. **GPS:** n47,05310 e3,65511.⬆.

5 ⓈⒻfree ⌐🖳ⒸⒽ. **Surface:** metalled. ◻ 01/04-31/10
Distance: ⌂50m.

ⓈⓈ | **Chiddes** | **21B1**

Le Bourg. **GPS:** n46,86108 e3,94091.⬆➡.

---

4 ⓈⒻfree ⌐🖳ⒸⒽfree WC. **Location:** Simple. **Surface:** gravel.
◻ 01/01-31/12
Distance: ⌂on the spot ⊗on the spot.
Remarks: Max. 48h, free coins available at restaurant.

ⓈⓈ | **Clamecy** 🍀 | **18A3**

Rue de l'Abattoir. **GPS:** n47,46222 e3,52250.⬆.

6 ⓈⒻfree. **Location:** Simple. **Surface:** gravel. ◻ 01/01-31/12
Distance: ⌂350m ⊗150m.

ⓈⓈ | **Digoin** | **21B2**

Place de la Grève, Route de Vichy. **GPS:** n46,48102 e3,97288.⬆➡.

± 15 ⓈⒻfree ⚡(4x) WC. **Location:** Simple, central.
Surface: asphalted. ◻ 01/01-31/12
Distance: ⌂on the spot ⊗on the spot ⌂on the spot ▣on the spot.
Remarks: Next to office de tourisme.

ⒸⓈ | **Dijon** 🍱 | **18C3**

Aire de Dijon, 3, Boulevard Chainoine Kir. **GPS:** n47,32125 e5,01090.⬆.

16 ⓈⒻ€10/24h ⌐🖳ⒸⒽ⚡(17x)included. 🖼 **Location:** Urban, comfortable, noisy. **Surface:** asphalted. ◻ 01/01-31/12 ◉ water: frost
Distance: ⌂centre Dijon 1,5km 🚲10km ⛰300m ⌐300m ⊗500m ⌂500m ➤Dijon 150m ⚓10m.
Remarks: Attention: motorhomes ^3m take access road from southerly direction.
Tourist information Dijon:
ⓘ Office de Tourisme, Place Darcy, www.dijon-tourism.com. City worth a visit with a number of large mansions and streets with half-timbered houses.
Ⓜ Musée de Moutarde Amora, 48, quai Nicolas-Rolin. History of mustard and the Amora factory. ⓣ free.

ⓈⓈ | **Ecuisses** | **21C1**

Place Marcel Pagnol, Route du Bourg. **GPS:** n46,76019 e4,52283.⬆.

20 ⌕free ╞═╗free. **Location:** Simple. **Surface:** metalled.
▢ 01/01-31/12
Remarks: Max. 48h.

Étang-sur-Arroux 21B1
Place du Mousseau. **GPS:** n46,86631 e4,18946. ⬆➡.

⌕free ╞═╗Chfree. **Location:** Simple. **Surface:** asphalted.
▢ 01/01-31/12
Distance: 🚶100m 🚊100m.

Fontaine-Française 18D3
Rue Berthault. **GPS:** n47,52487 e5,36768. ⬆➡.

5 ⌕free ╞═€3 ╗Ch. **Location:** Rural, simple.
Surface: asphalted/grassy. ▢ 01/01-31/12
Distance: 🚶100m 🚲16km ╼on the spot 🚊250m bakery.
Remarks: Along river and betwee 2 lakes, coins at shops in the village 08-21h.

Fours 21A1
Rue des Saules, D981. **GPS:** n46,81720 e3,71806. ⬆.

10 ⌕free ╞═╗Chfree. **Location:** Simple. **Surface:** gravel.
▢ 01/01-31/12
Distance: 🚶200m 🛒200m 🚊200m.

Génelard 🌾 21B2
Place du Bassin, D974. **GPS:** n46,57750 e4,23500. ⬆➡.

2 ⌕free ╞═╗Ch✂free. **Location:** Simple. **Surface:** asphalted.
▢ 01/01-31/12
Distance: 🚶on the spot.

Gilly-sur-Loire 21B2
Le Gatefer. **GPS:** n46,53768 e3,78218. ⬆.
10 ⌕free ╞═╗Chfree. **Surface:** metalled. ▢ 01/01-31/12

Givry 21C1
Relais camping-car, Rue de la Gare. **GPS:** n46,78000 e4,74830. ⬆.

15 ⌕free ╞═€2/100liter ╗Ch╼€2/1h. **Location:** Comfortable.
Surface: asphalted. ▢ 01/01-31/12
Distance: 🚶on the spot ⊗300m 🚊bakery 300m ♨on the spot 🏃on the spot.
Remarks: Coins at restaurant.
Tourist information Givry:
⚐ Marché. Market. ▢ Thu.
🚲 La Voie Verte de Givry à Cluny. Cycle route on former railway,.

Gron 18A1
Rue des Petits Prés. **GPS:** n48,16011 e3,25636. ⬆.
5 ⌕free ╞═╗ChWC. **Location:** Simple, quiet. **Surface:** asphalted.
▢ 01/01-31/12

Gurgy 18A2
Quai des Fontaines. **GPS:** n47,86348 e3,55376. ⬆➡.

20 ⌕€7 ╞═╗Chincluded 🔌🚿. **Surface:** grassy/gravel.
▢ 01/04-31/10
Distance: 🚶50m 🚲7km ╼on the spot ⊗500m 🚊300m.
Remarks: Along the Yonne river, coins at supermarket.

Heuilley-sur-Saône 18D3
Rue Condé. **GPS:** n47,32800 e5,45471. ⬆.

20 ⌕free ╞═€3 ╗ChWC. **Location:** Rural, quiet.
Surface: gravel/sand. ▢ 01/01-31/12
Distance: 🚶on the spot ╼100m ⊗100m.
Remarks: Coins at town hall.

La Chapelle-de-Guinchay 21C2
Le Clos Meziat. **GPS:** n46,21017 e4,76720. ⬆.

± 10 ⌕free ╞═╗ChWCfree. **Location:** Rural, comfortable, quiet.
Surface: gravel/metalled. ▢ 01/01-31/12
Distance: 🚶centre 1,2km 🚲A6 10km ⊗1,2km 🚊1,2km.

La Charité-sur-Loire 17H3
Quai Romain Mollot. **GPS:** n47,17483 e3,01123.

5 ⌕free ╞═€4 ╗Ch╼€4/55minutes ✂. **Surface:** asphalted.
▢ 01/01-31/12
Distance: 🚶250m 🏊on the spot ╼on the spot ⊗on the spot 🚊on the spot 🛒on the spot.
Remarks: Parking at the river, max. 24h.

La Charité-sur-Loire 17H3
Quai de la Tête de l'Ourth. **GPS:** n47,17577 e3,01254.
3 ⌕free. **Surface:** asphalted. ▢ 01/01-31/12
Remarks: Parking at river.

Laignes 🌊 18B2
Chemin du Moulin Neuf, D965. **GPS:** n47,84850 e4,36132. ⬆➡.

6 ⌕free. **Location:** Simple, quiet. **Surface:** grassy.
▢ 01/01-31/12
Distance: 🚶1km 🏊on the spot.
Remarks: Parking at river, max. 24h.

Louhans 21D1
Halte nautique, Rue du Port. **GPS:** n46,62952 e5,21302. ⬆.

22 ⌕ ╞═╗ChWCincluded. **Location:** Comfortable, quiet.
Surface: gravel.
Distance: 🚶400m ╼on the spot.
Remarks: To be paid at Halte Nautique, sanitary building: 01/05-30/09.

Luzy 21B1
Place du champ De Foire. **GPS:** n46,79028 e3,96840. ⬆➡.

4 ⌕free ╞═╗ChWCfree. **Location:** Simple. **Surface:** metalled.
▢ 01/01-31/12
Distance: 🚶centre 300m ⊗100m 🚊200m 🛒500m.
Remarks: Max. 48h, coins at the shops and restaurant.

Mailly-le-Château 18A2
L'espace naturel du Beauvais, Rue du Beauvais.
GPS: n47,59308 e3,63059. ⬆.
⌕free ╞═€3 ╗Ch╼€3 ✂. **Location:** Isolated, quiet.
Surface: grassy. ▢ 01/01-31/12
Distance: 🚶650m.
Remarks: Coins at the shops.

Marsannay-la-Côte 18C3
Espace du Rocher, Rue du Rocher. **GPS:** n47,27099 e4,99224. ⬆➡.

FR

5 🛏free 🚰🔌Chfree. **Location:** Urban, simple, quiet.
Surface: asphalted. ⭕ 01/01-31/12
Distance: 🚶500m 🚲3,5km 🛒750m.

Marsannay-la-Côte 18C3
Rue de Mazy, D122. **GPS:** n47,27027 e4,98761.
🛏free. **Surface:** asphalted. ⭕ 01/01-31/12
Distance: 🚶on the spot 🚲5km.
Remarks: Parking next to Office du Tourisme.

Nolay 21C1
Avenue de la Liberté. **GPS:** n46,95016 e4,62828.⬆

± 10 🛏free 🚰🔌Ch service€2. **Location:** Urban, simple.
Surface: gravel. ⭕ 01/01-31/12
Distance: 🚶100m ✖300m 🛒300m.
Remarks: Coins at town hall.

Tourist information Nolay:
Site Champetre du Bout du Monde, Vauchignon. Water falls.

Nuits-Saint-Georges 18C3
Rue de Cussigny. **GPS:** n47,13178 e4,95189.⬆➡

10 🛏free 🚰🔌Chfree. **Location:** Urban, simple. **Surface:** asphalted.
⭕ 01/01-31/12
Distance: 🚶400m 🚲2,1km ✖500m 🛒Intermarché 300m.

Tourist information Nuits-Saint-Georges:
🚉 S Fri.

Pougues-les-Eaux 18A3
D907. **GPS:** n47,08315 e3,09382.⬆

5 🛏free 🚰€2/10minutes 🔌Ch €2/10minutes
Surface: asphalted. ⭕ 01/01-31/12
Distance: 🚶250m 🚲1,4km ✖100m.
Remarks: Coins at campsite and tourist info.

Prissé 21C2
Cave de Prissé. **GPS:** n46,32226 e4,75257.⬆

5 🛏free 🚰🔌ChWCfree. **Location:** Rural, simple.
Surface: asphalted. ⭕ 01/01-31/12
Distance: 🚶500m 🚲3km.
Remarks: Max. 24h.

Pruzilly 21C2
La Croix Blanche, salle des Fêtes. **GPS:** n46,25708 e4,69792.⬆

6 🛏free 🚰🔌ChWCfree. **Location:** Rural, simple, quiet.
Surface: asphalted. ⭕ 01/01-31/12
Distance: 🚶on the spot ✖on the spot.
Remarks: Max. 48h, vins de Côte de Beaujolais.

Quarre-les-Tombes 18B3
Rue des Ecoles. **GPS:** n47,36853 e3,99936.
6 🛏free 🚰🔌free. **Surface:** metalled. ⭕ 01/04-31/10
Distance: 🚶100m ✖100m 🛒100m.

Rogny-les-Sept-Écluses 17H2
Quai Sully. **GPS:** n47,74673 e2,88104.⬆
4 🛏free 🚰🔌Chfree. **Location:** Simple, quiet. **Surface:** grassy.
⭕ 01/01-31/12
Distance: 🚶on the spot ✖350m.
Remarks: At the canal.

Rouvray 18B3
Place du Champs de foire, D906. **GPS:** n47,42271 e4,10412.⬆➡

4 🛏free 🚰🔌Chfree. **Surface:** metalled.
Distance: 🚶on the spot.
Remarks: Max. 48h.

Saint-Fargeau 18A2
Rue de Laveau, D18. **GPS:** n47,63968 e3,06999.⬆

10 🛏free 🚰🔌ChWCfree. ⭕ 01/01-31/12
Distance: 🚶50m ✖50m.

Saint-Gengoux-le-National 21C1
GPS: n46,60624 e4,66844.⬆

16 🛏free 🚰€3/15minutes 🔌Ch 💧€3/50minutes WC
Location: Simple, quiet. **Surface:** gravel. ⭕ 01/01-31/12
Distance: 🚶500m.
Remarks: At former station.

Tourist information Saint-Gengoux-le-National:
🚲 La Voie Verte. Cycle route on former railway,.

Saint-Honoré-les-Bains 21B1
Allée de la Cressonnière. **GPS:** n46,90471 e3,84059.⬆➡

4 🛏free 🚰€2 🔌Ch 💧€2. **Location:** Simple. **Surface:** gravel.
⭕ 01/01-31/12
Distance: 🚶300m ✖300m 🛒50m.
Remarks: Max. 48h, coins at town hall and supermarket.

Saint-Julien-du-Sault 18A1
Stade Jean Sax, Rue du Stade. **GPS:** n48,02906 e3,30116.
13 🛏free 🚰🔌Chfree. ⭕ 01/01-31/12

Saint-Léger-sur-Dheune 21C1
Route de Saint-Bérain. **GPS:** n46,84648 e4,63248.⬆

12 🛏€ 7/24h 🚰🔌Ch included. ⭕ 01/01-31/12
Distance: 🚶on the spot.

Savigny-le-Sec 18C3
Rue de la Mare. **GPS:** n47,43365 e5,04607.⬆

10 🛏€ 3,50 🚰€2 🔌ChWC. **Location:** Rural, simple, isolated,
quiet. **Surface:** asphalted/gravel. ⭕ 01/01-31/12
Distance: 🚶1,3km 🛒bakery 1,3km.

Semur-en-Auxois 18B3
Avenue Pasteur. **GPS:** n47,49506 e4,34945.⬆

30 🛏free 🚰🔌Chfree. **Location:** Simple, quiet. **Surface:** asphalted.
⭕ 01/01-31/12 🚰 water: Nov-March

FR

Distance: 🚶historical centre 1,3km ⚓10km ⊗800m ⛟800m.
Remarks: At football ground.
Tourist information Semur-en-Auxois:
⌂ Alise-Ste-Reine. Findings of Gallo-Roman city. ▢ 01/04-31/10 daily.

| 📷S | Seurre ⛵ | 21D1 |

Rue de la Perche à l'Oiseau. **GPS:** n47,00405 e5,14318.⬆➡.

15 🅿free 🚰🔌Ch 🧹Service €4/20min 🔧. **Location:** Rural, simple, quiet. **Surface:** asphalted. ▢ 01/01-31/12
Distance: 🚶800m ⛱100m ⛟100m ⊗700m ⛟700m.

| 📷S | Treigny | 18A2 |

Rue du Champ de Foire. **GPS:** n47,54982 e3,18159.⬆.
2 🅿free 🚰🔌Ch. **Location:** Simple, quiet. **Surface:** asphalted.
▢ 01/01-31/12
Distance: 🚶200m ⊗200m ⛟200m.

| 📷S | Vinzelles | 21C2 |

Clos Bonin. **GPS:** n46,27145 e4,77008.⬆.

10 🅿free 🚰🔌Chfree. **Location:** Rural, simple. **Surface:** asphalted.
▢ 01/01-31/12
Distance: 🚶200m ⚓A6 2,8km ⊗on the spot ⛟on the spot 🚌on the spot.

Franche Comté

| 📷S | Arc-et-Senans | 21E1 |

Grande rue. **GPS:** n47,03343 e5,78120.⬆.

10 🅿free 🚰€2 🔌Ch. **Location:** Simple. **Surface:** gravel.
▢ 01/01-31/12
Distance: 🚶500m ⛟500m.
Remarks: Coints at mairie, supermarket and campsite.

| 📷S | Arinthod | 21D2 |

Rue de la Prélette. **GPS:** n46,39654 e5,57013.⬆➡.

5 🅿€6 🚰🔌Ch 🧹included. **Location:** Rural. **Surface:** gravel.
▢ 01/01-31/12
Distance: 🚶100m.
Remarks: Near sports fields.

| 🍴S | Arsure-Arsurette ❄ | 21E1 |

Châlet des Arches, Route de l'Aliance de vie blanc.
GPS: n46,72168 e6,08402.⬆➡.

10 🅿free 🚰€2 WC🔌. **Location:** Isolated. **Surface:** asphalted.
▢ 01/01-31/12

| 📷S | Baume-les-Dames 🌿⛱⛵ | 18E3 |

Quai du Canal. **GPS:** n47,34023 e6,35778.⬆➡.

44 🅿€ 8,80 + € 0,20/pp tourist tax 🚰🔌Ch 🧹WCincluded 🔌€
1,70. **Location:** Rural, comfortable. **Surface:** asphalted/grassy.
▢ 01/01-31/12
Distance: 🚶on the spot ⚓5,3km ⛟on the spot 🚲on the spot 🚶on the spot.
Remarks: Bread-service.
Tourist information Baume-les-Dames:
👁 Abbaye Nôtre Dame. Historical monument, 18th century.

| 📷 | Baume-les-Messieurs 🌿⛱⛵ | 21D1 |

Cascade des Tufs, Rue des Moulins. **GPS:** n46,69124 e5,63946.⬆.

10 🅿free. **Location:** Simple.

| 📷S | Belvoir | 18F3 |

Chateaux Belvoir. **GPS:** n47,32139 e6,61097.⬆➡.

3 🅿free. **Location:** Rural, simple. **Surface:** asphalted/gravel.
▢ 01/01-31/12

| 📷S | Besançon 🌿🍴 | 18E3 |

Parking du Crous, Cité Carnot, Quai Veil Picard.
GPS: n47,23702 e6,01644.⬆.

12 🅿€5/24h 🚰🔌Chfree. 🛒 **Location:** Urban, simple.
Surface: asphalted. ▢ 01/01-31/12
Distance: 🚶on the spot ⊗500m ⛟500m 🚶on the spot.
Tourist information Besançon:
👁 Jardin Botanique, avenue de la Paix. Botanical gardens.
🏛 Château, Vaire-le-Grand. ▢ 15/08-18/09, 19/09-14/08 by agreement.

⛺ 🅿 Tue, Fri, Su.
😊 Parc Zoologique de la Citadelle, Citadelle. Zoo. ▢ 10-17/19h. 🎫 € 7.

| 📷S | Bois-d'Amont 🌿⛄ | 21E2 |

Impasse de l'Eglantine. **GPS:** n46,53771 e6,13934.⬆➡.

10 🅿free 🚰€2 🔌Ch 🔌€2. **Location:** Rural, comfortable, quiet.
Surface: asphalted. ▢ 01/01-31/12
Distance: ⊗on the spot 🅿on the spot 🎿on the spot 🚶on the spot.

| 📷S | Brognard ⛵ | 18F2 |

Base de Loisirs de la Savoureuse, Rue de Paquis.
GPS: n47,52834 e6,85652.⬆.

3 🅿free 🚰🔌Chfree. **Location:** Rural, noisy. **Surface:** asphalted.
▢ 01/01-31/12.
Distance: ⛱50m ⛟1,3km.
Remarks: Max. 48h.

| 📷S | Bucey-les-Gy | 18E3 |

Chemin de Tranot 1. **GPS:** n47,42456 e5,83974.⬆.

5 🅿free 🚰€2/20minutes 🔌Chfree 🧹(5x)€2/4h.
▢ 01/01-31/12
Remarks: Coins available at the shop.

| 📷S | Champagnole | 21E1 |

20, Rue Georges Vallerey. **GPS:** n46,74633 e5,89918.⬆.

5 🅿free, 01/04-30/09 € 6 🚰€4 🔌Ch 🔌€4 WC🔌€3.
Location: Simple. **Surface:** gravel/sand. ▢ 01/01-31/12
Distance: 🚶500m ⛟250m.
Remarks: Max. 1 night, coins at campsite.

| 📷S | Clairvaux-les-Lacs | 21E1 |

Route de Lons-le-Saunier, D678. **GPS:** n46,58246 e5,74660.⬆.

6 🅿free 🚰🔌Chfree. **Location:** Urban, simple.
▢ 01/01-31/12

Distance: nearby.
Remarks: On entering village, nearby police station.

Conliège 🌿⛴🏖 21D1

Rue du Saugeois. **GPS:** n46,65270 e5,59981. ⬆➡.

2 🚐free 🚰🗑Ch WCfree. **Location:** Urban, simple.
Surface: asphalted.
Distance: ⊗100m.

Consolation-Maisonnettes ⚓ 18F3

Parc du Seminaire du Cirque de Consolation., D377.
GPS: n47,15848 e6,60600.⬆.

10 🚐€ 10/24h 🚰🗑Ch 🧹 WCincluded 🗑. **Location:** Rural, simple.
Surface: asphalted.
Distance: 🏊on the spot.
Remarks: Check in at shop.

Corravillers 18F2

Rue de la Mairie. **GPS:** n47,89431 e6,62162. ⬆➡.

2 🚐free 🚰€2/23minutes 🗑Chfree 🧹€2/23minutes.
Location: Rural, simple. **Surface:** grassy/gravel.
🔘 01/01-31/12
Distance: ⊗500m 🛒500m.

Corre 18E2

Fluvial Loisirs, Pré le Saônier. **GPS:** n47,91402 e5,99308. ⬆➡.

32 🚐€ 6 01/11-31/03, € 8 01/04-31/10 🚰🗑Ch 🧹included 🗑€
1,50 🔘€4 🔌€3/2day🚿. **Location:** Rural, comfortable, quiet.
Surface: gravel. 🔘 01/01-31/12
Distance: 🚶200m 🚲50m ⊗50m 🛒bakery 300m, supermarket
500m 🛒100m.

Cousance 21D2

Grande rue, Champs de foire. **GPS:** n46,52929 e5,39154.⬆.

---

4 🚐free 🚰🗑Ch WCfree. **Surface:** asphalted. 🔘 01/01-31/12
Distance: 🚶100m 🚲6,6km 🛒100m.

Crosey-le-Petit 18F3

Rue de begin. **GPS:** n47,35039 e6,48913. ⬆➡.

1 🚐free. **Location:** Rural, simple. **Surface:** asphalted/gravel.
🔘 01/01-31/12 🐕on the spot 🏊on the spot.

Dôle 🍴🏖 18D3

Parking de Lahr, Avenue de Lahr. **GPS:** n47,08983 e5,49641. ⬆➡.

20 🚐free. **Location:** Simple, central, noisy. **Surface:** asphalted.
🔘 Village fair: mid-May
Distance: 🚶on the spot 🏊on the spot.

Tourist information Dôle
Ⓜ Maison natale de Louis Pasteur, 43 de la rue Pasteur. Birth house
Pasteur, museum. 🔘 1/4-31/10 10-12h, 14-18h, 01/11-31/03 Sa-Su
14-18h 🔘 Su-morning. Ⓣ free.

Esmoulières 18F2

D236. **GPS:** n47,85243 e6,61502.⬆.

2 🚐free. **Location:** Rural, simple. **Surface:** asphalted.
🔘 01/01-31/12

Faucogney-et-la-Mer 18F2

Rue des Chars. **GPS:** n47,83735 e6,56003. ⬆➡.

6 🚐free 🚰€2/23minutes 🗑Chfree 🧹€2/20minutes.
Location: Rural, simple. **Surface:** grassy/gravel.
🔘 01/01-31/12
Distance: 🚶800m.

Gray 18D3

Rue de la Plage. **GPS:** n47,46045 e5,61874. ⬆➡.

12 🚐free 🚰🗑Chfree. **Location:** Comfortable.

Surface: grassy/gravel. 🔘 01/01-31/12
Remarks: Near camping municipal.

Jeurre 21D2

35, Rue Principale. **GPS:** n46,36662 e5,70769. ⬆➡.

40 🚐€ 5 🚰€2 🗑Ch€2 🧹€3/day. **Location:** Rural, simple.
Surface: grassy. 🔘 01/05-31/10

La Chapelle des Bois ❄ 21E1

Station de ski, Chemin du Marais Blanc. **GPS:** n46,60307 e6,11317.⬆.

🚐free. **Surface:** unpaved.
Distance: 🏊on the spot.

La Montagne 18F2

D136. **GPS:** n47,92581 e6,58710.

2 🚐free. **Location:** Rural, simple. **Surface:** asphalted.
🔘 01/01-31/12
Remarks: Parking at skipistes.

La Pesse 21E2

Rue de l'Epicéa, D25. **GPS:** n46,28400 e5,84764.⬆.

15 🚐free 🚰€2 🗑Ch WC. **Location:** Rural, simple. **Surface:** unpaved.
🔘 01/01-31/12
Distance: 🚶on the spot 🎿on the spot.
Remarks: At start of langlauf circuit.

La Pesse 21E2

Ferme Auberge de La Combe aux Bisons, Lieu-dit Pré Reverchon.
GPS: n46,29278 e5,86011.

3 🚐guests free 🚰. **Location:** Simple, isolated. 🔘 01/01-31/12
🔘 Mon, Tue
Distance: ⊗on the spot.

FR

Lamoura ❄ 21E2

Route de Prémanon, D25. **GPS:** n46,41107 e5,99458. ⬆.

20 🛏free 🚰💧Chfree WC. **Location:** Rural, simple.
Surface: asphalted.
Distance: ⊗winter 🎿on the spot 🚡on the spot.
Remarks: Service sportcentre La Serra, only in winter time.

Lamoura ❄ 21E2

Route de Prémanon, D25. **GPS:** n46,40139 e5,98561.

6 🛏free 🚰.
Distance: 🎿on the spot 🚡on the spot.

Le Vernois 21D1

Caveau des Byards. **GPS:** n46,73342 e5,59405. ⬆.

2 🛏 🚰free. **Location:** Urban, simple.
Surface: grassy/gravel.

Les Rousses 🌿🎿❄ 21E2

Parking l'Aube, Route du Lac. **GPS:** n46,48779 e6,06690. ⬆➡.

30 🛏free, € 4/Winter 🚰€3,60/100liter 💧Ch 💧€3,60/1h 🧹
Location: Simple. **Surface:** asphalted. 📅 01/01-31/12
Distance: 🚰500m ⊗500m 🛒200m.

Les Rousses 🌿🎿❄ 21E2

Porte du Balanciers, Route Blanche, N5. **GPS:** n46,44852 e6,07591. ⬆.

30 🛏free, € 4/Winter 🚰€3,50 💧Ch 💧WC.
Surface: asphalted.
📅 01/01-31/12
Distance: ⊗Restaurant 🚡5km.
Remarks: Coins at tourist info, ski station, ski rental, ski school.

Luxeuil-les-Bains 🌿🎿 18E2

Place de l'Etang de la Poche, Rue Gambetta.
GPS: n47,81679 e6,38659. ⬆.

20 🛏free 🚰€2/100liter 💧Ch 💧€2/1h. **Location:** Simple, quiet.
Surface: gravel. 📅 01/01-31/12
Distance: 🚶1km 🏊100m ⊗1km 🛒Auchan/Aldi 500m 🍴1km.

Tourist information Luxeuil-les-Bains:
ℹ Fougerolles. Since the 16th century the small town is the centre of distilleries (Kirsch and cherry brandy).

Maisod 🌿🎿🚣 21D2

La Mercantine. **GPS:** n46,46500 e5,68864.

40 🛏€ 6 🚰€2 💧Ch.
Location: Rural, simple. **Surface:** gravel.
Distance: 🏊100m ⊗200m.
Remarks: At lake Vouglans, max. 24h.

Mesnay 🚣 21E1

Rue Vermot. **GPS:** n46,89834 e5,80036. ⬆➡.

5 🛏free 🚰€2/10minutes 💧Chfree 🔌€2/55minutes 🧹.
Location: Simple. 📅 01/01-31/12
Distance: 🚰500m, 2,5km Arbois.

Montbéliard 🌿 18F3

Parking du Champ de Foire. **GPS:** n47,50663 e6,79128. ⬆.

4 🛏free 🚰€1,60 💧Ch 💧€1,60. **Location:** Urban.
Surface: asphalted.
Remarks: Max. 48h.

Montreux-Château 🚣 18F2

D11. **GPS:** n47,60283 e7,00252. ⬆.

8 🛏€ 5/24h 🚰€5/10minutes 💧Ch 🔌(8x) WCincluded. 🚮 **Location:** Simple. **Surface:** gravel.

Moussières 🌿🎿 21E2

GPS: n46,32111 e5,89778. ⬆.

6 🛏free 🚰€2 💧Ch 💧€2. **Location:** Rural, simple. **Surface:** gravel.
📅 01/01-31/12
Distance: 🚡on the spot.
Remarks: In front of cheese farm.

Mouthe 🏔 21E1

Place de l'Eglise. **GPS:** n46,71042 e6,19570. ⬆➡.

20 🛏free 🚰€3 💧Ch 💧. **Location:** Rural, simple.
Surface: asphalted.
Remarks: Coins at the bakery, supermarket, tourist office.

Nozeroy 21E1

Rue des Remparts. **GPS:** n46,77249 e6,03516. ⬆➡.

10 🛏€ 6 🚰💧Ch 🔌included, 2Amp. **Location:** Rural, isolated, quiet.
Surface: grassy/gravel. 📅 01/01-31/12
Distance: 🚰200m.

Orgelet 21D2

Place Ancien Champ de Foire, Rue du Faubourg de l'Orme.
GPS: n46,52232 e5,60860. ⬆.

20 🛏free 🚰💧ChWCfree. **Location:** Simple.
Surface: grassy/metalled. 📅 01/01-31/12
Distance: 🚰300m.
Remarks: Closed when frosty.

Raddon-et-Chapendu 18F2

GPS: n47,84899 e6,47427.

6 🛏free 🚰€2/23minutes 🔌€2/23minutes. **Location:** Rural, simple.
Surface: gravel.
Remarks: Near sports fields.

Randevillers 18F3
Rue de la Cote. **GPS:** n47,30944 e6,52707. ⬆️➡️.

3 🚐free. **Location:** Rural. **Surface:** asphalted/gravel.

Saint-Bresson 18F2
La Rue Saint Bresson. **GPS:** n47,86999 e6,50226. ⬆️➡️.

2 🚐. **Location:** Rural, simple. **Surface:** asphalted.

Saint-Claude 21E2
Avenue de la Libération, D436. **GPS:** n46,38049 e5,85209. ⬆️➡️.

3 🚐free 🚰🔌Ch🗑️free. **Location:** Urban, simple, noisy.
Surface: asphalted. 🅿️ 01/01-31/12
Distance: 🛒1km.
Tourist information Saint-Claude:
ℹ️ Tourist town, production of pipes.
👁️ Musée du Pipe et Diamant. Pipes and diamond exhibition.
🅿️ 01/06-30/09 9.30-12h, 14-18.30h, 01/10-31/05 14-18h ⬛ Su.

Saint-Loup-sur-Semouse 18E2
Rue de Champ de Tir. **GPS:** n47,88643 e6,27051.

4 🚐free 🚰€3 🔌Ch🗑️. **Surface:** asphalted. 🅿️ 01/03-30/11
Distance: 🛒on the spot 🏊500m ⊗on the spot 🚰on the spot 🚌on the spot.
Remarks: Behind church, max. 24h.

Saint-Point-Lac 21E1
Aire d'acceuil pour camping-cars, Rue du lac.
GPS: n46,81268 e6,30375.

40 🚐€ 6 🚰10minutes 🔌Ch🛠️55minutes 🚽free.🗑️
Surface: gravel/sand. 🅿️ 01/03-30/11
Distance: 🏊on the spot.
Remarks: Max. 3 nights, no camping activities.

Sainte-Marie-en-Chanois 18F2
Rue de la Lolonge. **GPS:** n47,83663 e6,51216. ⬆️➡️.

5 🚐free. **Location:** Rural, simple. **Surface:** asphalted.

Salins-les-Bains 21E1
Rue de la République, D472. **GPS:** n46,93254 e5,87899. ⬆️.

8 🚐free 🚰🔌Ch🗑️free. **Location:** Simple. **Surface:** asphalted.
🅿️ 01/01-31/12
Distance: 🛒50m.
Remarks: Permitted to park/stay overnight on all parkings.

Sancey-le-Grand 18F3
D-31. **GPS:** n47,29040 e6,57742. ⬆️.

2 🚐free. **Location:** Rural, simple. **Surface:** gravel.
🅿️ 01/01-31/12
Distance: 🛒500m.

Sancey-le-Long 18F3
D31/D464. **GPS:** n47,30513 e6,59477. ⬆️.

2 🚐free 🚰€2 🔌Ch🗑️€2.
Location: Rural, simple. **Surface:** gravel.
Remarks: Coins at supermarket, cafe, centre commercial.

Saulx 18E2
Place de l'Eglise. **GPS:** n47,69620 e6,28030. ⬆️➡️.

4 🚐free 🚰€2/100liter 🔌🗑️€2/2h 🚽free. **Location:** Simple, quiet.
Surface: metalled.
Distance: ⊗on the spot 🥖baker on site.

Sermamagny 18F2
Rue Alfred Lallemand. **GPS:** n47,68351 e6,81416. ⬆️.

30 🚐free. **Surface:** grassy.

Thoirette 🏔️ 21D2
Grande Rue. **GPS:** n46,26924 e5,53529. ⬆️.

5 🚐€6 🚰🔌Ch🗑️🛠️included.
Location: Simple. **Surface:** gravel.
Distance: 🛒25m 🏊50m 🚰25m.

Vaivre-et-Montoille 🏔️ 18E2
Avenue des Rives du Lac. **GPS:** n47,62938 e6,12701. ⬆️.

7 🚐free 🚰€2,50 🔌Ch. **Location:** Rural, simple, quiet.
Surface: sand. 🅿️ 01/01-31/12
Distance: 🛒1,5km 🏊beach 100m 🚲100m ⊗25m 🚣on the spot
🎣on the spot.
Remarks: Swimming pool complex, lake.

Vaivre-et-Montoille 🏔️ 18E2
Avenue du Lac. **GPS:** n47,63718 e6,10752. ⬆️.

5 🚐free. **Location:** Rural. **Surface:** asphalted. 🅿️ 01/01-31/12
Distance: 🛒on the spot 🚣on the spot 🎣on the spot.
Remarks: Directly at lake.

Vellevans 18F3
D464. **GPS:** n47,31042 e6,49139. ⬆️.

2 🚐free. **Location:** Rural. **Surface:** grassy/gravel.

Villers-le-Lac 🏔️ 18F3
Vedettes Panoramiques, Rue du Clos Rondot.
GPS: n47,05948 e6,67195. ⬆️.

FR

8 ⃞free ⃞€2 ⃞Ch ⃞free ⃞. **Location:** Simple.
Surface: concrete. ⃞ 01/01-31/12
Distance: ⃞50m.
Remarks: Small pitches.

Villers-le-Lac 18F3

Bateaux du Saut du Doubs. GPS: n47,05500 e6,67000.⃞.

50 ⃞€ 8, free with boat trip ⃞€3,50/time ⃞Ch ⃞at office/shop.⃞
Location: Simple, central. **Surface:** grassy/gravel.
⃞ 01/04-31/10
Distance: ⃞100m.
Remarks: Check in at Bateaux.

Poitou Charentes

Agris 20D3

Le Pont d'Agris, D6. **GPS:** n45,78619 e0,33944.⃞.

6 ⃞free ⃞€2 ⃞Ch ⃞€2. **Surface:** asphalted. ⃞ 01/01-31/12
Distance: ⃞on the spot ⃞on the spot ⃞on the spot.

Aigre 20D3

Parc Les Charmilles, Rue des Charrières. **GPS:** n45,89341 e0,00578.⃞.

10 ⃞€ 5,50 ⃞Ch ⃞(4x)WCincluded ⃞. **Surface:** metalled.
⃞ 01/04-31/10
Distance: ⃞on the spot ⃞on the spot ⃞on the spot.
Remarks: 4th night free.

Airvault 20D1

Rue Faubourg des Cyprès. **GPS:** n46,82516 w0,14219.⃞.

10 ⃞free ⃞ChWCfree. **Location:** Urban, simple, central.
Surface: asphalted. ⃞ 01/01-31/12
Distance: ⃞250m ⃞250m ⃞250m.

Angliers 17D3

Aire de repos de la Briande, D347. **GPS:** n46,95861 e0,10472.⃞⃞.

8 ⃞free ⃞Ch ⃞WCfree. **Location:** Rural, comfortable, quiet.
Surface: asphalted. ⃞ 01/01-31/12
Distance: ⃞Angliers 1km ⃞50m.

Angoulins 20B2

Rue du Chay. **GPS:** n46,10623 w1,13565.⃞.

17 ⃞free. **Location:** Rural, simple. **Surface:** asphalted.
Distance: ⃞1km ⃞20m.

Arçais 20C2

Aire camping-cars du Coursault, Rue de Coursault.
GPS: n46,29583 w0,69.⃞.

20 ⃞€ 8 ⃞ChWCfree.⃞ **Location:** Simple, quiet.
Surface: grassy. ⃞ 01/01-31/12
Distance: ⃞400m ⃞on the spot ⃞nearby ⃞nearby.

Aubeterre-sur-Dronne 23D1

Base de Loisirs, D2, Route de Ribérac. **GPS:** n45,26934 e0,17586.⃞⃞.

7 ⃞free ⃞Chfree. **Location:** Rural, simple, isolated, quiet.
Surface: gravel/metalled. ⃞ 01/01-31/12
Distance: ⃞500m ⃞on the spot ⃞300m ⃞500m.
Remarks: At tennis-courts.
Tourist information Aubeterre-sur-Dronne:
⃞ Place de Village. ⃞ Thu, Su.

Aulnay 20C2

Rue de Salles. **GPS:** n46,02239 w0,34528.⃞.

10 ⃞free ⃞Chfree. **Surface:** gravel.
Distance: ⃞200m ⃞200m ⃞200m.
Remarks: Max. 24h.

Aulnay 20C2

Place Charles de Gaulle, Rue Haute de l'Eglise.
GPS: n46,02306 w0,35444.⃞.

10 ⃞free. **Surface:** metalled. ⃞ 01/01-31/12
Distance: ⃞200m ⃞200m ⃞200m.

Aytré 20B2

Route de la Plage. **GPS:** n46,11311 w1,12331.⃞⃞.

30 ⃞free ⃞Chfree. **Location:** Rural, simple. **Surface:** asphalted.
⃞ 01/01-31/12
Distance: ⃞on the spot.
Remarks: Max 3,5t, max. 48h.

Barbezieux-Saint-Hilaire 23C1

E.Leclerc, Rue du Commandant Foucaud. **GPS:** n45,47047 w0,16032.⃞.

8 ⃞free ⃞€2/100liter ⃞Ch. **Location:** Urban, simple, central, noisy.
Surface: asphalted. ⃞ 01/01-31/12
Distance: ⃞500m ⃞on the spot ⃞on the spot.

Boismé 20C1

Rue des Essarts. **GPS:** n46,77765 w0,43347.⃞⃞.

4 ⃞free ⃞ChWCfree. **Location:** Rural, isolated, quiet.
Surface: metalled. ⃞ 01/01-31/12
Distance: ⃞on the spot ⃞500m ⃞500m ⃞on the spot ⃞on the spot.
Remarks: At small lake, playground.

Bougon 20D2

Musée des Tumulus, La Chapelle. **GPS:** n46,37845 w0,06825.⃞.

10 ⃞free ⃞free. **Location:** Rural, simple, isolated.
Surface: asphalted. ⃞ 01/01-31/12
Distance: ⃞3km.
Remarks: Parking museum.

FR

Bourcefranc-le-Chapus · 20B3

Bois de Pin, Prise du Portail Rouge. **GPS:** n45,82611 w1,14278. ↑.

20 free € 6. Location: Isolated, quiet. Surface: gravel.
01/01-31/12
Distance: 4km on the spot on the spot 3km.

Bourcefranc-le-Chapus · 20B3

Rue du Président Kennedy. **GPS:** n45,84546 w1,14929. ↑.

10 free. **Location:** Urban, simple, central. **Surface:** asphalted.
01/01-31/12
Distance: 250m 750m 250m 250m.
Remarks: Max. 24h.

Bourcefranc-le-Chapus · 20B3

Camping de la Giroflée, Fief de Bonnemort.
GPS: n45,83112 w1,15073. ↑.
€2,60/100liter Ch. 01/05-31/10
Distance: 2,5km on the spot.
Remarks: Coins at tourist info and town hall.

Bressuire · 20C1

Place Labâte. **GPS:** n46,84417 w0,49086. ↑.

5 free Chfree. **Location:** Urban, simple, noisy. **Surface:** sand.
01/01-31/12
Distance: 400m 400m 400m.

Cellefrouin · 20D3

D739. **GPS:** n45,89361 e0,38639. ↑→.

50 free ChWCfree. **Location:** Simple, isolated, quiet.
Surface: gravel. 01/01-31/12
Distance: 300m.

Celles-sur-Belle · 20D2

Place de l'Aumônerie, Rue des Halles.
GPS: n46,26278 w0,20806. ↑→.

10 free Chfree. **Location:** Urban, simple, quiet.
Surface: gravel. 01/01-31/12
Distance: 100m 100m 100m.

Chabanais · 20E3

Chemin des Tanneries, N141. **GPS:** n45,87447 e0,72008. ↑.

4 free. **Location:** Rural, simple. **Surface:** asphalted. 01/01-31/12
Thu
Distance: on the spot 100m 100m.
Remarks: Along the river Vienne.

Château-Larcher · 20D2

Val de Clouère. **GPS:** n46,41444 e0,31556. ↑→.

10 free € 5 Ch WCincluded. **Location:** Rural, comfortable, isolated, quiet. **Surface:** grassy/gravel.
01/03-31/11
Distance: 300m 100m 300m 300m.
Remarks: At small lake, former campsite, baker every morning.

Châtelaillon-Plage · 20B2

Avenue de l'Hippodrome. **GPS:** n46,07253 w1,07886. ↑.

54 free € 12 Chincluded free. **Location:** Rural, simple.
Surface: asphalted/grassy. 01/01-31/12
Distance: 700m 800m 700m.

Châtelaillon-Plage · 20B2

Parking de l'Office du Tourisme, Avenue de Strasbourg.
GPS: n46,07679 w1,08859. →.

5 free . **Location:** Urban, simple. **Surface:** metalled.
01/01-31/12
Distance: on the spot 500m on the spot on the spot.

Châtelaillon-Plage · 20B2

Les Boucholeurs, Avenue de l'Abbé Guichard.
GPS: n46,05538 w1,08738. ↑.

7 free. **Surface:** asphalted. 01/01-31/12
Distance: 150m 150m 150m.
Remarks: Max. 48h.

Chef-Boutonne · 20D2

Aire camping-cars, Chemin du Parc. **GPS:** n46,10982 w0,07869. ↑→.

20 free Ch WCfree. **Surface:** grassy/gravel.
01/04-31/10
Distance: 800m 300m 800m on the spot.

Cherves-Richemont · 20C3

Allee des Coquelicots. **GPS:** n45,74030 w0,35607. ↑→.

6 free Chfree. **Surface:** asphalted. 01/01-31/12
service 01/11-15/04
Distance: 500m 100m 500m.

Chey · 20D2

Place de la Liberté. **GPS:** n46,30412 w0,05002. ↑→.

4 free Ch WCfree. **Location:** Rural, comfortable, quiet.
Surface: asphalted. 01/01-31/12
Distance: on the spot.

Clérac · 23C1

Étang des Prés de Réaux, Route des Vignes.
GPS: n45,17906 w0,228. ↑.

8 free Chfree. **Location:** Rural, simple, isolated, quiet.
Surface: gravel. 01/01-31/12
Distance: 200m on the spot 100m 100m on the spot
on the spot.
Remarks: At small lake, max. 1 night.

FR

⬛S Cognac 20C3

Place de la Levade, Quartier Saint-Jacques. **GPS**: n45,69847 w0,33265.⬆

4 ⬛free ⛽€2 🚰Ch. **Location:** Urban, simple, central.
Surface: asphalted. 📅 01/01-31/12
Distance: 🛒100m ⊗on the spot 🍽100m 🏧500m 🚌on the spot.

Tourist information Cognac:
👁 Otard. Cognac distillery in 16th century castle. Guided tour and tasting. 📅 daily ● 01/10-31/03 weekend.
Ⓜ Cognac-musée. Culture around the Cognac. 📅 01/10-31/05 14-17.30h, 01/06-30/09 10-12h, 14-18h.

⬛S Confolens 🌿🎭〰 20E2

Camping les Ribières, Avenue de Sainte-Germain.
GPS: n46,01894 e0,67570.⬆

⬛free, May-Sep €5 ⛽🚰Ch.🚿WC included. **Surface:** metalled.
📅 01/01-31/12 ● service: 16/09-14/05
Distance: 🛒750m.

Tourist information Confolens:
ℹ 📅 Wed, Sa.

⬛S Couhé 20D2

Place du Marché. **GPS**: n46,29906 e0,17882.⬆

25 ⬛free ⛽🚰ChWC free. **Location:** Urban, simple, central, quiet.
Surface: asphalted. 📅 01/01-31/12
Distance: 🛒200m ⊗200m 🍽200m.

⬛S Coulon 🌿♨〰 20C2

Parking d'Autremont, Rue André Cramois.
GPS: n46,32102 w0,59063.⬆➡

80 ⬛€8,50 ⛽🚰Ch.🚿WC included. 🖥✏ **Location:** Urban, comfortable. **Surface:** grassy/gravel. 📅 01/04-30/11
Distance: 🛒350m ⊗350m 🍽350m 🚲on the spot 🏃on the spot.

⬛S Coulonges-sur-l'Autize 20C1

Avenue de la Gare. **GPS**: n46,48011 w0,59393.⬆

2 ⬛free ⛽🚰Ch.🚿WC free. **Location:** Urban, simple, noisy.
Surface: asphalted. 📅 01/01-31/12
Distance: 🛒450m ⊗350m 🍽350m.
Remarks: Max. 24h, picnic area.

⬛S Criteuil la Magdeleine 20C3

Le Bourg. **GPS**: n45,53788 w0,21597.⬆➡

3 ⬛free ⛽🚰Ch.🚿WC free. **Location:** Rural, simple, quiet.
Distance: 🛒on the spot.

⬛S Dolus-d'Oléron 20B3

Route du Stade. **GPS**: n45,91137 w1,25255.⬆

40 ⬛€6 ⛽€4/100liter 🔌€4/1h. **Location:** Rural, simple.
Surface: grassy. 📅 01/01-31/12
Distance: 🛒500m 🍽1,2km Hypermarché.
Remarks: Coins at tourist info.

⬛S Dompierre-sur-Charente 〰 20C3

Camping Municipal du Pré St Jean, Rue de Saintonge.
GPS: n45,70099 w0,49438.

5 ⬛free ⛽€4 🚰Ch. **Location:** Rural, simple, isolated.
Surface: gravel/metalled. 📅 15/06-15/09
Distance: 🛒on the spot 🛒300m ⊗100m 🍽100m.
Remarks: Coins at the bakery and campsite.

⬛S Echillais 20B3

Place de la Carrière. **GPS**: n45,89753 w0,95545.⬆

15 ⬛€5,10 ⛽€3 🚰Ch. **Location:** Rural, simple.
Surface: asphalted.
Remarks: Access via rue de l'église.

⬛S Fouras 20B2

Plage Nord, Avenue du Cadoret. **GPS**: n45,99194 w1,08694.

15 ⬛€7 ⛽€1/50liter. 🖥 **Location:** Urban, simple.
Surface: metalled. 📅 01/01-31/12
Distance: 🛒on the spot ⊗on the spot 🍽on the spot.
Remarks: In front of campsite Cadoret, Fun golf, max. 48h, coins at campsite and tourist info.

⬛S Fouras 20B2

Prairie du Casino, Dir pointe de la Fumée. **GPS**: n45,99583 w1,10611.

30 ⬛€6 ⛽liter. **Location:** Rural, simple. **Surface:** metalled.
📅 01/01-31/12
Distance: 🛒on the spot ⊗on the spot 🍽on the spot.
Remarks: Max. 48h.

⬛S Gencay 20D2

Place du Champs de Foire. **GPS**: n46,37315 e0,40638.⬆➡

10 ⬛free ⛽€2 🚰Ch🔌€2 WC. **Location:** Urban, simple, noisy.
Surface: grassy/metalled. 📅 01/01-31/12
Distance: 🛒200m ⊗200m 🍽200m.
Remarks: Coins at the shops.

⬛S Genté 20C3

Rue de l'Eglise. **GPS**: n45,62861 w0,315.⬆➡

6 ⬛free ⛽🚰Ch.🚿(6x)WC free. **Surface:** asphalted.
📅 01/01-31/12
Distance: 🛒on the spot ⊗350m 🍽on the spot.

⬛S Hiers-Brouage 20B3

D3. **GPS**: n45,86250 w1,07667.

20 ⬛free. **Location:** Rural. **Surface:** grassy/gravel.
📅 01/01-31/12
Distance: 🛒250m ⊗250m 🍽250m.
Remarks: Arrival >20h, departure <9h.

S Hiers-Brouage 20B3
Rue Palissy, D3. **GPS:** n45,85284 w1,07745.
€4 Ch . **Surface:** metalled. 01/01-31/12

S Jonzac 23C1
Place du 8 Mai 1945. **GPS:** n45,44800 w0,433.

18 free €4,20/100liter Ch €4,20/h. **Location:** Urban, simple, central. **Surface:** asphalted. 01/01-31/12
Distance: 500m 200m 200m on the spot.
Remarks: Max. 24h, coins at tourist info.

Jonzac 23C1
Chez M. Alex Beurg, Chez Marchand. **GPS:** n45,44121 w0,40427. .
3 free. **Location:** Rural, simple, isolated, quiet. **Surface:** grassy.
01/01-31/12
Remarks: Max. 24h.

S La Brée-les-Bains 20B2
Rue de la Baudette. **GPS:** n46,00810 w1,35764.

50 free Ch. **Location:** Rural, simple, quiet.
Surface: asphalted. 01/01-31/12
Remarks: Coins at tourist info.

S La Couronne 20D3
Rue du Champs de Foire. **GPS:** n45,60619 e0,10015.

free Ch WC free. **Location:** Simple, central.
Surface: asphalted. 01/01-31/12 Wed-morning, Sa-morning market
Distance: on the spot on the spot on the spot on the spot.

S La Mothe-Saint-Héray 20D2
Rue du Pont l'Abbé. **GPS:** n46,35971 w0,11775.

4 free €1/50liter Ch WC. **Location:** Rural, comfortable.
Surface: gravel. 01/01-31/12
Distance: 500m 200m 200m.

S La Roche-Posay 20E1
Super U, ZA Les Chaumettes. **GPS:** n46,79361 e0,79750.

free Ch free. **Location:** Simple, noisy. **Surface:** asphalted.
01/01-31/12
Distance: 1,5km on the spot.

S La Rochefoucauld 20D3
Aire camping-car, Rue des Flots, Rivières. **GPS:** n45,74505 e0,38085.

+20 Ch WC . 01/01-31/12
Distance: 1km.
Remarks: Beside river Tardoire, next to campsite, Château de La Rochefoucauld 1,3km.

S La Rochelle 20B2
Esplanade des Parc, Chemin des Remparts.
GPS: n46,16620 w1,1544.

24 free. **Location:** Urban. **Surface:** asphalted. 01/01-31/12
Distance: 250m 100m 250m 50m.

S La Rochelle 20B2
Vieux Port, Avenue Jean Moulin. **GPS:** n46,15250 w1,13944.

50 €10,50/24h Ch. **Surface:** asphalted. 01/01-31/12
Distance: 1,5km free.
Remarks: Pay at reception, shuttle bus to city centre.

La Rochelle 20B2
Quai du Lazaret. **GPS:** n46,14213 w1,16773.

40 free. **Location:** Urban, simple. **Surface:** asphalted.
01/10-30-06

Tourist information La Rochelle:
M La Maison Henri II, Rue de Augustins. Archeological museum.
15/5-30/9 Sa-Fr 10-19h Sa-Su 14-19h.
Aquarium, Port des Minimes. Sea aquarium. 01/07-31/08 9-23h, 01/09-30/06 10-19/20h.

S La Tremblade 20B3
85 Rue Marcel Gaillardon. **GPS:** n45,78268 w1,15228. .

49 €10/24h Ch ,16Amp included. **Location:** Rural, comfortable, central, quiet. **Surface:** gravel/metalled.
01/01-31/12
Distance: 2,2km on the spot 500m on the spot.
Remarks: Max. 72h, baker every morning.

Le Bois-Plage-en-Ré 20B2
Parking Municipal, Avenue du Pas des Boeufs.
GPS: n46,17708 w1,38613.
15 free. **Location:** Simple. **Surface:** gravel/sand.
Distance: 150m.

S Le Bois-Plage-en-Ré 20B2
Aire Camping-Car Campéole, Avenue du Pas des Boeufs.
GPS: n46,17741 w1,38674.

35 €8,60-€12,80 €3/time Ch €2/12h.
Location: Rural, simple. **Surface:** gravel/metalled.
01/01-31/12
Distance: 150m.
Remarks: Payment also possible at campsite.

S Le Château d'Oléron 20B3
Boulevard Philippe Daste. **GPS:** n45,89641 w1,20236. .

90 €10 Ch WC included. **Location:** Rural, comfortable. **Surface:** grassy.
Distance: on the spot.
Remarks: Former campsite.

S Le Grand Village Plage 20B3
Allée des Pins. **GPS:** n45,86222 w1,24111. .

8 €6 €4/100liter Ch €4. **Location:** Rural, simple.
Surface: asphalted. 01/01-31/12
Remarks: 01/04-30/09 max. 24h.

S Les Mathes/La Palmyre 20B3
Aire de la Garenne, Rue de la Garenne, Les Mathes.
GPS: n45,71433 w1,14752.

FR

20 ⌗ € 8/24h ⌐€4/100liter ⌐ChWC. 🅿 **Location:** Rural, simple, isolated. **Surface:** metalled. 🅾 01/01-31/12
Distance: 🚰400m.
Remarks: Coins at town hall Mo-Fri 9-18h and tourist info La Palmyre daily 9-19h in July/Aug.

Les Mathes/La Palmyre 🅂
Aire du Corsaire, Avenue de lAtlantique. **GPS:** n45,69193 w1,18896. ⬆.

90 ⌗ € 8/24h ⌐€4/100liter ⌐Ch ▪€2/1h 🚿.🅿 📐
Location: Simple, central, quiet. **Surface:** asphalted.
🅾 01/01-31/12
Distance: 🚶1km 🏊200m 🚲200m 🚣 on the spot.
Remarks: Max. 7 days.

Les Mathes/La Palmyre 🅂
Boulevard de la Plage, La Palmyre. **GPS:** n45,68287 w1,17942. ⬆.

50 ⌗ € 8/24h. 🅿 **Location:** Urban, simple, central, quiet.
Surface: asphalted. 🅾 01/01-31/12 ⊡ 01/07-31/08
Distance: 🚶1,2km 🏊100m 🚲200m 🚣 on the spot.

Tourist information Les Mathes/La Palmyre:
☺ Zoo de la Palmyre. Zoo, 1600 animals, 14Ha. 🅾 01/04-30/09 9-20.30h, 01/10-31/03 9-12h, 14-18h.

Les Portes-en-Ré 🅂
Parking de la Patache, Route du Fier. **GPS:** n46,22925 w1,48315. ⬆.

10 ⌗ € 10/24h ⌐ChWCfree. 🅿 **Location:** Rural, simple.
Surface: metalled. 🅾 01/01-31/12
Distance: 🏊on the spot 🚲3,5km.
Remarks: Max. 24h, payment only with coins.

Lezay 🅂 20D2
Rue de Gâte Bourse. **GPS:** n46,26500 w0,01139. ⬆.

15 ⌗free ⌐Chfree. **Location:** Urban, simple. **Surface:** asphalted.

🅾 01/01-31/12
Distance: ⊗200m 🚰200m.

Lizant 🅂 20D2
D107. **GPS:** n46,08614 e0,27834.
8 ⌗free ⌐Ch 🚿WC. **Surface:** gravel.
Distance: ⊗100m 🚰on the spot.
Remarks: Playground.

Londigny 🅂 20D2
Place de l'Eglise. **GPS:** n46,08333 e0,13472.

5 ⌗free ⌐Ch 🚿WCfree. **Location:** Isolated, quiet.
Surface: gravel. 🅾 01/01-31/12
Remarks: Max. 48h.

Loudun 🅂 17D3
Place de la Porte Saint Nicolas. **GPS:** n47,01357 e0,07833. ⬆➡.

3 ⌗free ⌐€2/10minutes ⌐Ch ▪€2/55minutes. **Location:** Urban, simple, noisy. **Surface:** asphalted.
🅾 01/01-31/12
Distance: 🚶500m ⊗500m 🚰100m, bakery 10m.
Remarks: Max 3,5t.

Lussac-les-Châteaux 🅂 20E2
GPS: n46,40250 e0,72583. ⬆.

20 ⌗free ⌐ChWCfree. **Location:** Urban, simple, central.
Surface: metalled. 🅾 01/01-31/12 ⊡ Wed, market
Distance: 🚶200m ⊗200m 🚰200m.

Marennes 🅂 20B3
1 Avenue William Bertrand. **GPS:** n45,82140 w1,13828. ⬆.

5 ⌗free. **Location:** Rural, simple. **Surface:** metalled.
🅾 01/01-31/12
Distance: 🏊on the spot.
Remarks: Max. 6,5m.

Mauléon 🅂 17C3
Rue de la Bachelette. **GPS:** n46,91904 w0,75267. ⬆➡.

---

4 ⌗free ⌐Chfree. **Location:** Rural, simple, quiet.
Surface: asphalted. 🅾 01/01-31/12
Distance: 🚶500m ⊗500m 🚰500m.
Remarks: Next to swimming pool.

Mauzé-sur-le-Mignon 🅂 20C2
Le Port, Rue du Port. **GPS:** n46,19989 w0,67952. ⬆.

10 ⌗free ⌐€4 ⌐Ch 🚿WC. **Location:** Rural. **Surface:** gravel.
🅾 01/01-31/12
Distance: 🚶1km 🏊on the spot.
Remarks: Coins at campsite and shops.

Ménigoute 🅂 20D1
Rue des Vignes. **GPS:** n46,49790 w0,05795. ⬆.

4 ⌗free ⌐Chfree. **Location:** Urban, simple, quiet.
Surface: gravel.
Distance: 🚰on the spot.

Meschers-sur-Gironde ⚓🅂 20B3
Port de Plaisance, Route des Salines. **GPS:** n45,55614 w0,9451. ⬆.

10 ⌗ € 7/24h ⌐€2/100liter ⌐Ch 🚿(8x) ⊡€1,50 ▪€2/2 📶.🅿
Location: Rural, comfortable, isolated, quiet. **Surface:** asphalted.
🅾 01/01-31/12
Distance: 🚶1km 🏊100m ⊗100m 🚰1km.

Messé 🅂 20D2
D114. **GPS:** n46,26306 e0,11203. ⬆.

20 ⌗free ⌐ChWCfree. **Location:** Rural, isolated, quiet.
Surface: gravel. 🅾 01/01-31/12
Distance: 🚲on the spot 🚰10km.

Montendre 🅂 23C1
Place de la Paix. **GPS:** n45,28627 w0,41116. ⬆.

FR

15 ⌂free ⌁⬜ChWCfree. **Location:** Urban, simple, central, quiet. **Surface:** asphalted. ⬜ 01/01-31/12 ⬤ Thu 6-14h **Distance:** ⬜100m ⊗500m ⬜500m.

Montguyon 23C1

Plaine des Sports, Rue de Vassiac. **GPS:** n45,21796 w0,18368.⬆

15 ⌂free ⌁⬜ChWCfree. **Location:** Urban, simple, central, quiet. **Surface:** gravel. ⬜ 01/01-31/12 **Distance:** ⬜500m ⊗500m ⬜500m 🚲on the spot. **Remarks:** Max. 72h.

Montils 20C3

Le Vignolet, D233. **GPS:** n45,65285 w0,50576.⬆

20 ⌂free ⌁⬜Ch⬜free. **Location:** Rural, simple, isolated. **Surface:** gravel/metalled. ⬜ 01/01-31/12 **Distance:** ⬜300m.

Montmorillon 20E2

Rue Léon Dardant. **GPS:** n46,42326 e0,86788.⬆

10 ⌂free ⌁€2/10minutes ⬜Ch🚿€2 ⬜. **Location:** Urban, simple, central, quiet. **Surface:** asphalted. ⬜ 01/01-31/12 **Distance:** ⬜500m ⊗500m ⬜2km. **Remarks:** Along theGartempe river, max. 24h.

Mortagne-sur-Gironde 20C3

Le Port de Mortagne, Quai des Pêcheurs. **GPS:** n45,47472 w0,79778.⬆

50 ⌂€8 ⌁⬜Ch🚿WC⬜againstpayment ⬜included. ⬜ **Location:** Rural, simple, isolated, quiet. **Surface:** grassy. ⬜ 01/01-31/12 **Distance:** ⬜750m ⊗200m ⬜750m 🚲on the spot. **Remarks:** In front of Capitainerie.

Moulismes 20E2

RN147. **GPS:** n46,33306 e0,81000.⬆.

50 ⌂free ⌁€3 ⬜Ch⬜WC. **Location:** Rural, simple, quiet. **Surface:** grassy/metalled. ⬜ 01/01-31/12 **Distance:** ⬜400m ⬜on the spot ⬜on the spot ⬜400m. **Remarks:** At small lake (plan d'eau).

Nersac 20D3

Rue d'Epagnac. **GPS:** n45,62599 e0,05015.⬆➡.

7 ⌂free ⌁⬜Ch🚿(4x)free. **Surface:** asphalted. ⬜ 01/01-31/12 **Distance:** ⬜on the spot ⊗100m ⬜100m 🚌100m. **Remarks:** Max. 48h.

Nieuíl-l'Espoir 20E2

Allée du champ de foire. **GPS:** n46,48505 e0,45417.⬆➡.

10 ⌂free ⌁€2 ⬜Ch⬜€2. **Location:** Rural, comfortable, quiet. **Surface:** grassy/metalled. ⬜ 01/01-31/12 **Distance:** ⬜200m ⬜150m 🚲on the spot 🧍on the spot. **Remarks:** At Base de Loisirs, coins at the shops.

Nieulle-sur-Seudre 20B3

Place de la Mairie. **GPS:** n45,75275 w1,00209.⬆

4 ⌂free ⌁€4/100liter ⬜Ch⬜againstpayment. **Location:** Urban, simple, central, quiet. **Surface:** asphalted. ⬜ 01/01-31/12 **Distance:** ⬜on the spot. **Remarks:** Coins at town hall.

Niort 20C2

Aire des camping-cars du Pré Leroy, Rue de Bessac. **GPS:** n46,32917 w0,46444.⬆➡.

14 ⌂€7,70 ⌁⬜Ch⬜included. ⬜ **Location:** Urban, comfortable, quiet. **Surface:** metalled. ⬜ 01/01-31/12 **Distance:** ⬜1,2km ⊗150m ⬜300m.

Tourist information Niort:
⬜ ⬜ Tue, Sa.
⬜ Marais Poitevin. Swamp area, possibility of making boat trips.

Pamproux 20D2

Rue de la Cueille. **GPS:** n46,39625 w0,05874.⬆➡.

3 ⌂free ⌁€2/20minutes ⬜Ch⬜€2/20minutes. **Location:** Rural, simple, quiet. **Surface:** asphalted. ⬜ 01/01-31/12 **Distance:** ⬜100m ⬜5,2km ⬜100m.

Parthenay 20D1

Aire base de loisirs Bois Vert, Rue de Boisseau 14. **GPS:** n46,64088 w0,26689.⬆➡.

8 ⌂€9,00 ⌁⬜Ch🚿included ⬜€3 ⬜€2 ⬜€4/day. **Location:** Urban. **Surface:** gravel. ⬜ 05/-4-31/10 **Distance:** ⬜2,5km ⬜on the spot ⊗nearby ⬜2km 🚌100m. **Remarks:** Along the Thouet river, check in at campsite.

Tourist information Parthenay:
⬜ Les Halles. Weekly market in the halls and streets. ⬜ Wed.

Pons 20C3

Camping municipal Le Paradis, Avenue du Poitou. **GPS:** n45,57765 w0,55536.⬆.

5 ⌂free ⌁€6/time ⬜Ch⬜€6/h. **Location:** Urban, simple. **Surface:** asphalted. **Distance:** ⬜300m.

Port-des-Barques 20B2

Pré des Mays, Avenue des Sports. **GPS:** n45,94722 w1,09.⬆➡.

30 ⌂€ 6,20/24h ⌁€2/10minutes ⬜Chfree 🚿€2/55minutes ⬜ ⬜ **Location:** Rural, simple. **Surface:** metalled. ⬜ 15/03-15/11 **Remarks:** In front of stadium.

Rivedoux-Plage 20B2

125, Av Gustave Perreau. **GPS:** n46,15889 w1,27139.⬆.

17 ⌁€ 14-€ 17 ⌁€4 ⌁Ch⌁. **Location:** Urban, simple.
Surface: asphalted. ◻ 01/01-31/12
Distance: ⌁100m ⌁Plage Nord.
Remarks: Next to campsite Le Platin, to be paid at campsite.

⌁S Rochefort 20B2
Rue de la Fosse aux Mâts. **GPS:** n45,92735 w0,95467.⌁⌁.

25 ⌁€ 6/24h ⌁⌁Chincluded. ⌁⌁ **Location:** Urban, simple.
Surface: asphalted. ◻ 01/01-31/112

⌁ Rochefort 20B2
Avenue Marcel Dassault. **GPS:** n45,94661 w0,96002.⌁.

15 ⌁€ 6. ⌁⌁ **Location:** Urban, simple. **Surface:** asphalted.
◻ 01/01-31/12
Distance: ⌁1km.

⌁ Rochefort 20B2
Pont Transbordeur, Chemin de Charente.
GPS: n45,91792 w0,96388.⌁.

5 ⌁free. **Location:** Urban, simple. **Surface:** grassy/gravel.
◻ 01/01-31/12

⌁ Rochefort 20B2
Rue de la Vieille Forme. **GPS:** n45,94448 w0,95554.⌁.
10 ⌁€ 6. ⌁⌁ **Location:** Simple. **Surface:** gravel.
Remarks: Near marina.

S Rochefort 20B2
Port de Plaisance, Quai Lemoigne de Sérigny.
GPS: n45,94444 w0,95556.⌁.
⌁⌁Chfree.
◻ 01/01-31/12

Tourist information Rochefort:
⌁ Corderie Royale. Old royal rope-walk.
⌁ ⌁ Tue, Thu, Sa.

⌁S Romagne 20D2
Rue du Vigneau. **GPS:** n46,26884 e0,30373.⌁⌁.

6 ⌁free. ⌁⌁ChWCfree. **Location:** Rural, comfortable, quiet.
Surface: gravel. ◻ 15/03-31/10
Distance: ⌁250m ⌁250m.

⌁S Rouillac 20D3
Super U, Rue de Genac. **GPS:** n45,77650 w0,06133.⌁⌁.

8 ⌁free ⌁€3 ⌁Ch⌁. **Surface:** gravel. ◻ 01/01-31/12
Distance: ⌁500m ⌁500m ⌁50m.
Remarks: Coins available at supermarket.

⌁S Roullet-Saint-Estèphe 20D3
Aire de camping-car Roullet, D210. **GPS:** n45,58086 e0,04461.⌁.
20 ⌁free ⌁⌁Chfree. **Location:** Rural. **Surface:** gravel.
◻ 01/01-31/12
Distance: ⌁300m ⌁150m ⌁350m.

⌁S Roumazières-Loubert 20E3
Aire de Détente de Ronmatiéres, RN141.
GPS: n45,88275 e0,57287.⌁⌁.

3 ⌁free ⌁⌁Ch⌁WCfree. **Surface:** asphalted.
◻ 01/01-31/12
Distance: ⌁500m ⌁100m ⌁300m.

⌁S Royan 20B3
Camping-Car Park Royan, Rue Bel-air. **GPS:** n45,62834 w1,01204.⌁.

28 ⌁€ 9,60 ⌁⌁Ch⌁⌁included. ⌁⌁ **Location:** Urban,
comfortable, central, quiet. **Surface:** gravel/metalled.
◻ 01/01-31/12
Distance: ⌁500m ⌁500m ⌁500m.

⌁S Ruffec 20D2
SARL Remy Frères Camping-Cars, D26. **GPS:** n46,03316 e0,18366.

10 ⌁free ⌁⌁Chfree. **Surface:** asphalted.
Distance: ⌁1km.

Remarks: At motorhome dealer.

⌁S Saint Césaire ⌁ ⌁ 20C3
Parking Paléosite, Rue de Groies. **GPS:** n45,75406 w0,50751.⌁⌁.

20 ⌁free ⌁⌁Chfree. **Location:** Rural, simple, isolated, quiet.
Surface: asphalted/metalled. ◻ 01/01-31/12
Distance: ⌁on the spot ⌁500m ⌁100m ⌁on the spot.

Tourist information Saint Césaire:
⌁ Paléosite, Route de la Montée Verte. Interactive park, in the foot-
steps of the Neanderthals. ⌁ 10.30-18.30, Jul-Aug 10-20 ◻ January.

⌁S Saint Laurant de la Prée ⌁ 20B2
La Cabane, Route de l'Océan. **GPS:** n45,99043 w1,04942.⌁.

10 ⌁€ 7 ⌁⌁Chincluded. ⌁ **Location:** Rural, simple.
Surface: gravel. ◻ 01/01-31/12

⌁S Saint-Agnant 20B3
Place de Verdun. **GPS:** n45,86635 w0,9641.⌁.

10 ⌁free ⌁⌁Chfree. **Location:** Rural, simple. **Surface:** asphalted.
◻ 01/01-31/12
Remarks: Next to town hall.

⌁S Saint-Amand-sur-Sèvre ⌁⌁ 20C1
Boulevard de Maumusson. **GPS:** n46,86903 w0,8.⌁.

5 ⌁free ⌁⌁Chfree. **Location:** Rural, simple, quiet.
Surface: grasstiles. ◻ 01/01-31/12
Distance: ⌁500m ⌁500m ⌁500m.

⌁⌁S Saint-Amand-sur-Sèvre ⌁⌁ 20C1
Le Moulin Chaligny. **GPS:** n46,88493 w0,82342.⌁.

10 ⌁€ 10 ⌁⌁Ch⌁WCincluded. **Location:** Rural, isolated, quiet.
Surface: grassy. ◻ 01/01-31/12
Distance: ⌁3km ⌁3km ⌁3km ⌁on the spot ⌁on the spot.

Saint-Clément-des-Baleines 20B2

Rue de la Forêt. **GPS:** n46,22756 w1,54644.⬆.

30 €11/night, € 18/2 nights stay Ch €4/1h free.
Location: Rural, simple. **Surface:** metalled.
01/01-31/12
Distance: 250m 500m.
Remarks: Next to campsite, payment only with coins.

Saint-Denis-d'Oléron 20B2

Aire du Moulin, Route des Huttes. **GPS:** n46,02750 w1,38306.⬆.

150 €9 Ch WC included. **Location:** Rural, simple.
Surface: grassy. 01/01-31/12
Distance: 1km.
Remarks: Max. 4 nights.

Saint-Genis-de-Saintonge 20C3

Rue Fanny. **GPS:** n45,48330 w0,56569.⬆➡.

20 €6/24h 10minutes Ch (20x)included4h.
Location: Urban, comfortable, central, quiet. **Surface:** asphalted.
01/01-31/12
Distance: 400m.
Remarks: Behind cinema, max. 72h.

Saint-Georges-de-Didonne 20B3

Parking Maudet, Rue du Docteur Maudet.
GPS: n45,60408 w0,99964.⬆.

19 €6/24h Chincluded. **Location:** Urban, simple,
central, quiet. **Surface:** asphalted.
01/01-31/12
Distance: 400m 500m.
Remarks: Max. 72h.

Saint-Georges-de-Didonne 20B3

Front de Mer, Boulevard de la Côte de Beauté.
GPS: n45,59557 w0,99163.⬆.

20 €6/24h. **Location:** Urban, simple, quiet.
Surface: gravel/metalled. 01/01-31/12
Distance: 500m on the spot 350m on the spot.
Remarks: Beach parking, max. 72h.

Saint-Georges-de-Didonne 20B3

Parking Gillet, Rue du Professeur Langevin.
GPS: n45,60324 w0,9921.⬆.

13 €6/24h. **Location:** Urban, simple, central, quiet.
Surface: asphalted. 01/01-31/12
Distance: on the spot 800m on the spot on the spot.
Remarks: Max. 72h.

Saint-Georges-de-Didonne 20B3

Parking Miramar, Rue du Port. **GPS:** n45,60031 w1,007.⬆.

15 €6/24h. **Location:** Urban. **Surface:** gravel/metalled.
01/01-31/12
Distance: 1km 100m on the spot 200m 1km.
Remarks: Max. 72h.

Saint-Germain-de-Marencennes 20C2

Rue du Moulin Neuf. **GPS:** n46,07882 w0,78283.⬆.
10 €6 Ch WC included. **Location:** Simple, quiet.
Surface: asphalted. 15/03-15/11
Distance: 500m.

Saint-Hilaire-la-Palud 20C2

Place de la Marie. **GPS:** n46,26444 w0,71306.⬆.

10 free. **Surface:** asphalted. 01/01-31/12
Distance: on the spot on the spot on the spot.
Remarks: Parking in front of town hall, max. 2 nights.

Saint-Jean-d'Angély 20C3

Base de Plein Air, Avenue de Marennes, D18.
GPS: n45,94537 w0,53735.⬆.

10 free Chfree. **Surface:** gravel. 01/01-31/12
Distance: 1km 100m 100m 200m 1km.
Remarks: Max. 2 nights.

Saint-Martin-de-Ré 20B2

Rue de Rempart. **GPS:** n46,19925 w1,36514.⬆➡.

17 € 11 Chincluded. **Location:** Rural. **Surface:** gravel.
01/01-31/12
Distance: 500m 700m 500m 500m.
Remarks: 01/04-30/09 max. 72h.

Saint-Pierre-d'Oléron 20B2

Avenue des Pins, La Cotinière. **GPS:** n45,92393 w1,3427.⬆.

10 €9 €4/time Ch. **Location:** Rural, simple.
Surface: grassy/gravel.
Remarks: In front of campsite municipal, pay at reception.

Saint-Porchaire 20C3

Place du Champ de Foire. **GPS:** n45,82063 w0,78215.⬆.

10 free ChWC free. **Location:** Urban, simple, central, quiet.
Surface: gravel. 01/01-31/12
Distance: 400m 200m 1km.
Remarks: Max. 48h.

Saint-Trojan-les-Bains 20B3

Parking de la Liberté, Rue Marie Curie. **GPS:** n45,84371 w1,20899.⬆.

9 free €4. **Location:** Urban, simple. **Surface:** asphalted
01/01-31/12
Distance: 200m on the spot.
Remarks: Max. 72h.

Saint-Trojan-les-Bains 20B3

Parking Patoizeau, Boulevard de la plage. **GPS:** n45,84100 w1,20491.

10 🛏free. **Location:** Rural, simple. **Surface:** asphalted.
◻ 01/01-31/12
Distance: 🚶600m ⚓100m.
Remarks: In front of fire-station, max. 72h.

Tourist information Saint-Trojan-les-Bains:
🛈 Bureau Municipal de Tourisme, Carrefour du Port, www.st-trojan-les-bains.fr. Seaside resort on the island of Oléron, well-known for the mimosa and oyster culture.
🎪 place de Filles de la Sagesse. Food and drugs market. ◻ Thu + Sa-morning, summer daily.
🎪 Marche Nocturne, rue de la République. Evening market. ◻ Thu from 17h.

| △ S | Saint-Yrieix-sur-Charente | 20D3 |

Camping du Plan d'eau, Rue du Plan d'Eau, Impasse des Ooyères.
GPS: n45,69176 e0,14517. ⬆➡

14 🛏 €7,20, Jul/Aug €9,25 🚰🔌Chfree 🚿€3,65.
Location: Comfortable, luxurious. **Surface:** asphalted.◻ 01/04-31/10
Distance: 🚶2km ⚓1km 🛒1km ⊗1km 🛒3km 🚆1km.

| S | Saintes | 20C3 |

Aire camping-cars Avenue de Saintonge, Chemin de la Prairie.
GPS: n45,74047 w0,62696. ⬆➡

12 🛏 €5/24h 🚰🔌Ch 💧Service€5 📶 🧺 🚐 **Location:** Urban, simple, central. **Surface:** asphalted.
◻ 01/01-31/12
Distance: 🚶1km ⚓200m 🛒Leclerc 100m.
Remarks: Max. 7 days.

Tourist information Saintes:
👁 Les Arènes. Roman anfiteatro.
🎪 Place 11 November. ◻ Tue + Fri morning.
🎪 Grande Foire. Large regional market. ◻ 1st Mon of the month.

| S | Saujon ♈ | 20B3 |

Route des Ecluses. **GPS:** n45,67503 w0,932. ⬆

14 🛏 €4/24h 🚰€2/100liter 🔌Ch💧€2/1h. 🚐 **Location:** Urban, simple, central, quiet. **Surface:** asphalted.
◻ 01/01-31/12
Distance: 🚶900m.
Remarks: Max. 6 days, coins at town hall.

| S | Sauzé-Vaussais | 20D2 |

Place des Halles. **GPS:** n46,13540 e0,10660.

🛏free 🚰🔌Ch💧WCfree. **Surface:** asphalted. ◻ 01/01-31/12
🔘 water: Nov-March
Distance: 🚶on the spot ⊗on the spot 🛒on the spot.

| S | Segonzac 🌿 | 20C3 |

Place Blanche. **GPS:** n45,61456 w0,22113. ⬆➡

4 🛏free 🚰🔌Ch 🚿(4x)WCfree. **Surface:** gravel.
◻ 01/01-31/12
Distance: 🚶500m, Cognac 8km ⊗500m 🛒500m.

| S | Segonzac 🌿 | 20C3 |

Cognac Forgeron, Chez Richon. **GPS:** n45,62545 w0,17514. ⬆
20 🛏free 🚰🔌Ch🚿. **Location:** Rural. **Surface:** grassy.
◻ 01/01-31/12
Distance: 🚶500m.

| S | Soubise | 20B3 |

Aire camping-car, Le Port/rue Colbert. **GPS:** n45,92833 w1,00666. ⬆

17 🛏 €7 🚰🔌Ch 🚿WC⬛included. **Location:** Rural, simple.
Surface: grassy/metalled.
◻ 01/01-31/12
Distance: 🚶on the spot ⊗50m.
Remarks: Along river, max. 24h, incl. showers and warm water.

| S | Thouars 🌿 | 17D3 |

Rue Felix Gellusseau. **GPS:** n46,97614 w0,21151. ⬆➡

10 🛏free 🚰🔌ChWCfree. **Location:** Urban, simple, quiet.
Surface: sand. ◻ 01/01-31/12
Distance: 🚶200m ⊗200m 🛒200m.

Tourist information Thouars:
🎪 ◻ Tue, Fri.

| S | Thurageau | 20D1 |

Fam. Turpeau, Agressais. **GPS:** n46,78388 e0,25644. ⬆

---

5 🛏free 🚰🔌Chfree. **Location:** Rural, simple, quiet.
Surface: gravel. ◻ 01/01-31/12
Distance: 🚶2,5km.
Remarks: Goat farm, farm products.

| S | Tonnay-Charente | 20B3 |

Quai des Capucins. **GPS:** n45,93921 w0,88171. ➡

15 🛏free 🚰🔌Chfree. **Location:** Urban, simple. **Surface:** gravel.
◻ 01/01-31/12
Distance: 🚶1km 🛒500m.

| S | Touvre | 20D3 |

Route de Pontil. **GPS:** n45,66085 e0,25834. ⬆
7 🛏free 🚰🔌Ch. **Surface:** gravel. ◻ 01/01-31/12

| S | Vasles 🌿 ♨ | 20D1 |

Mouton Village, Rue de la Cité. **GPS:** n46,57329 w0,02309. ⬆➡

10 🛏free 🚰🔌ChWCfree. **Location:** Rural, simple, quiet.
Surface: gravel. ◻ 01/01-31/12
Distance: 🚶400m 🛒400m.

| S | Vicq-sur-Gartempe | 20E1 |

25, Route de la Roche Posay. **GPS:** n46,72414 e0,86189. ⬆➡

10 🛏free 🚰🔌ChWCfree. **Location:** Rural, simple, quiet.
Surface: gravel. ◻ 01/01-31/12
Distance: 🚶500m.

Limousin

| S | Allassac | 23F1 |

Avenue du Saillant. **GPS:** n45,25897 e1,47358. ⬆

4 🛏free 🚰🔌Ch 🚿(2x)free. **Surface:** gravel/sand.
◻ 01/01-31/12

FR

Distance: 500m 5km 500m 500m.
Remarks: Parking station.

⬦⬦ **Aubusson** 20G3
Parking Champ de Foire, Rue des Fusilles, D988.
GPS: n45,95694 e2,17528.

10 free Ch free WC. **Surface:** asphalted.
01/01-31/12
Distance: 500m 500m 500m.

Auriat 20F3
Etang d'Auriat. GPS: n45,87790 e1,64277.
free Ch free. **Location:** Rural, simple, isolated, quiet.
Surface: metalled. 01/01-31/12
Distance: on the spot on the spot.
Remarks: At small lake.

Ayen 23F1
Route de la Noix, Ayen Bas. **GPS:** n45,24964 e1,32343.

20 free Ch free. **Surface:** grassy/gravel. 01/01-31/12
Distance: 300m.
Remarks: Nearby D39, campsite and sports grounds.

Beaumont du Lac 20G3
GPS: n45,78640 e1,87077.

20 free. **Surface:** gravel. 01/01-31/12
Distance: 5km on the spot on the spot 100m.
Remarks: At lake Vassivière.

Bellac 20E2
Aire d'accueil camping-car rives du Vincou, Rue des Tanneries.
GPS: n46,11513 e1,05242.
3 free Ch free. **Surface:** asphalted. 01/01-31/12
Distance: 1km.
Remarks: Service 100m.

Bellac 20E2
Le Champ de foire, Rue des Doctrinaires. **GPS:** n46,12085 e1,05018.
free. **Surface:** asphalted.
Distance: on the spot on the spot on the spot.
Remarks: >3,5t not allowed.

Bellac 20E2
Parking de la Mairie, Place de la République.
GPS: n46,12155 e1,04604.
4 free. **Surface:** asphalted. 01/01-31/12
Distance: 300m.

Bessines-sur-Gartempe 20F2
Rue d'Ingolsheim. **GPS:** n46,10979 e1,37008.

10 free €2 Ch €2. **Surface:** asphalted.
Distance: on the spot 900m 100m.

Bort-les-Orgues 23H1
Rue de la Fontaine Grande. **GPS:** n45,39913 e2,49710.

10 free Ch free. **Surface:** asphalted. 01/01-31/12
Distance: 200m river 200m 200m.

Bosmoreau-les-Mines 20F3
Le bourg. **GPS:** n46,00068 e1,75882.
3 free Ch free. **Location:** Rural. **Surface:** gravel.
01/01-31/12
Distance: 500m.

Bourganeuf 20F3
Place de l'Etang, Avenue du Dr Butaud. **GPS:** n45,95444 e1,75750.

10 free Ch free. **Surface:** gravel. 01/01-31/12 tue-
evening, wed-morning (market)
Distance: on the spot on the spot on the spot.
Remarks: Max. 48h.

Bujaleuf 20F3
Route du Champ de Foire. **GPS:** n45,79747 e1,63141.

5 free Ch free. **Surface:** gravel. 01/01-31/12
Distance: 500m 500m.
Remarks: Max. 24h.

Bussière-Poitevine 20E2
Croix de l'Hosanne, Rue du Quatriéme Zouave.
GPS: n46,23670 e0,90173.

Ch WC. **Surface:** gravel. 01/01-31/12
Distance: 450m.
Remarks: Coins at the shops.

Chalus 20E3
Aire des Energies, Avenue Jean Jaurès. **GPS:** n45,66095 e0,98798.
free €2 Ch €2. **Surface:** asphalted.
Distance: 1,2km on the spot.
Remarks: Behind petrol station.

Chamberet 20F3
Route de St Dulcet. **GPS:** n45,57961 e1,72051.
6 free Ch free. **Surface:** gravel. 01/01-31/12
Distance: 900m.
Remarks: Next to football ground.

Chambon-sur-Voueize 20H2
Rue du Stade. **GPS:** n46,18579 e2,43426.

4 free €2 Ch €2. **Surface:** asphalted. 01/01-31/12
service 01/11-31/03
Distance: 500m 500m 200m.
Remarks: Near camping municipal.

Châtelus-le-Marcheix 20F3
Rue du Tursaud. **GPS:** n45,99894 e1,60339.

8 free €2 Ch €2. **Surface:** asphalted. 01/01-31/12
Distance: 300m 300m 300m.
Remarks: Next to camping municipal.

Chénérailles 20G2
Route d'Aubusson, lotissement Marlaud, D990.
GPS: n46,11058 e2,17753.

5 free €2 Ch €2. **Surface:** asphalted. 01/01-31/12
Distance: 200m 50m.
Remarks: Coins available at restaurant le Coq d'Or (50m).

Collonges-la-Rouge 23F2
Parking le Marchadial. GPS: n45,05833 e1,65889.

20 €5/24h Ch WC included. **Surface:** gravel.
01/01-31/12
Distance: 500m 500m 500m.

Concèze 23F1
D56E. **GPS:** n45,35472 e1,34583.

3 ⛺free 🚰♨Chfree. **Surface:** gravel. 🅿 01/01-31/12
Distance: 🍴on the spot.

🏕S **Cressat** 20G2

D990, rue de Laprade. **GPS:** n46,13956 e2,11015. ⬆➡.

5 ⛺free 🚰€3 ♨Ch🔌€3. **Surface:** asphalted. 🅿 01/01-31/12
Distance: 🍴100m ⛲500m.
Remarks: At fish lake, coins at superette 'la Montagne' (500m) and town hall.

🏕S **Cussac** 20E3

Jardin de la Palène, Rue du 8 Mai 1945. **GPS:** n45,70519 e0,84936. ⬆.
4 ⛺free 🚰♨Ch✏. **Surface:** grassy/gravel. 🅿 01/04-31/10
Distance: 🍴200m ⊗200m ⛲100m.
Remarks: Coins at town hall, bar and restaurant.

🏕S **Dampniat** 23F1

Stade, Le Mas. **GPS:** n45,16262 e1,63728. ⬆.
⛺free 🚰€2/10minutes ♨Ch✏€2/55minutes. **Location:** Rural, simple. **Surface:** gravel.
Distance: 🍴850m.
Remarks: At sports centre.

©S **Donzenac** 23F1

Village de Vacance La Rivière, Rue de la Riviere.
GPS: n45,21897 e1,51829. ⬆➡.

10 ⛺free 🚰♨Ch✏€4/night,peak season WCfree. **Surface:** gravel.
🅿 01/01-31/12
Distance: 🍴4km ⚓1,3km ⊗4m ⛲4km.
Remarks: Max. 48h.

🏕S **Egletons** 23G1

Parking Espace Ventadour, Rue Henri Dignac.
GPS: n45,40406 e2,04791. ⬆.

20 ⛺free 🚰♨Chfree. **Surface:** gravel. 🅿 01/01-31/12 ◨ Service: winter
Distance: 🍴300m ⚓3,5km ⊗300m ⛲300m.

🏕S **Felletin** 20G3

Parking Lagrange, Avenue Joffre. **GPS:** n45,88308 e2,17667. ⬆➡.

10 ⛺free 🚰♨ChWCfree. **Surface:** gravel. 🅿 01/01-31/12
Distance: 🍴on the spot.

🏕S **Gouzon** 20G2

Place du champ de foire, Rue d'Alcantera.
GPS: n46,19139 e2,24028. ⬆➡.

6 ⛺free 🚰♨Chfree. **Surface:** sand. 🅿 01/01-31/12
Distance: 🍴300m ⊗300m ⛲300m.

🏕S **Jarnages** 20G2

Route des Promenctes, D65. **GPS:** n46,18417 e2,08098. ⬆➡.

6 ⛺free 🚰€2 ♨Ch🔌€2. **Surface:** asphalted. 🅿 01/01-31/12
Distance: 🍴500m ⊗500m ⛲500m.
Remarks: At tennis-courts.

🏕S **Javerdat** 20E3

Le Bourg. **GPS:** n45,95249 e0,98582. ⬆.

4 ⛺free 🚰€2 ♨Ch🔌€2 WC. **Surface:** gravel.
🅿 01/01-31/12
Distance: ⊗100m.
Remarks: Coins at Auberge Limousine (100m).

🏕S **La Courtine** 20G3

Rue Impasse J Bayle. **GPS:** n45,70591 e2,25890. ⬆.
10 ⛺free 🚰♨Ch🔌. **Surface:** asphalted. 🅿 01/01-31/12
Distance: 🍴1km ⚓100m.

🏕S **Les Salles-Lavaugyon** 20E3

Le Tilleul, Route de St Mathieu. **GPS:** n45,73998 e0,70100. ⬆➡.

6 ⛺€4 🚰♨✏ included. **Surface:** grassy. 🅿 01/01-31/12

©S **Liginiac** 23G1

Le Maury-Liginiac. **GPS:** n45,39158 e2,30387. ➡.

⛺free 🚰♨Chfree. **Surface:** gravel. 🅿 01/01-31/12
Distance: 🍴Liginiac 4,5km ⚓Sandy beach ⊗on the spot.
Remarks: At lake Neuvic. Follow restaurant Le Maury.

🏕S **Meuzac** 23F1

Étang de la Roche, D243. **GPS:** n45,54933 e1,43869. ⬆➡.

15 ⛺free 🚰♨ChWCfree. **Location:** Rural. **Surface:** gravel.
🅿 01/01-31/12
Distance: 🍴100m ⚓5km ⚓on the spot ⊗on the spot ⛲100m.

🏕S **Meymac** 23G1

Parking Lac de Sechemailles, Le Montbazet.
GPS: n45,52500 e2,12761. ⬆➡.

20 ⛺free 🚰€2,60 ♨Ch🔌€2,60. **Surface:** gravel.
🅿 01/01-31/12
Distance: 🍴2km ⚓500m ⊗500m.
Remarks: Coins available at Office du Tourisme and bar.

©S **Meymac** 23G1

Boulevard de la Garenne. **GPS:** n45,53973 e2,15381. ⬆.
30 ⛺free 🚰€2 ♨Ch✏€2. **Surface:** gravel. 🅿 20/04-02/11
Remarks: Coins at campsite and tourist info.

🏕S **Montboucher** 20F3

GPS: n45,95152 e1,68069. ⬆➡.

5 ⛺free 🚰♨ChWCfree. **Surface:** grassy/gravel.
🅿 01/01-31/12

🏕S **Nieul** 20F3

19 Mars 1962, D28. **GPS:** n45,92564 e1,17236. ⬆.

15 ⛺free 🚰♨ChWCfree. **Surface:** asphalted. 🅿 01/04-31/10
Distance: 🍴400m ⊗400m ⛲400m.

FR

S Objat 23F1

Parc Aquatique Espace Loisirs, Avenue Jules Ferry.
GPS: n45,27110 e1,41147.

20 € 5 €2/50liter Ch included WC €2
Surface: grassy/metalled.
01/01-31/12
Distance: 500m 500m.
Remarks: Max. 7 days, baker on site: Tue-Sa, free electricity 72h, swimming pool 200m, entrance code available at tourist info.

S Oradour-sur-Glane 20E3

Aire camping-car, Rue du Stade. **GPS**: n45,93570 e1,02471.

20 free €2 Ch €2 WC. **Surface:** grassy/metalled.
01/01-31/12
Distance: nearby.
Remarks: Playground.

Tourist information Oradour-sur-Glane:
Office de Tourisme, Place du Champ de Foire. Martyre town, was attacked by 200 SS-soldiers on 10 June 1944. They assassinated the population. Afterwards the village was burned down. In commemoration a wall was built round the the city after the war.
T free.

S Pageas 20E3

GPS: n45,67758 e1,00224.

20 free €3 Ch WC. **Surface:** grassy/gravel.
01/01-31/12
Distance: 100m on the spot on the spot on the spot.
Remarks: Near N21.

S Peyrat-le-Château 20F3

Auphelle. **GPS**: n45,80750 e1,84111.

100 € 4,20, Jul/Aug € 5,20 €2,50/100liter €6,80/4h.
Surface: grassy. 12/04-07/11
Distance: Lac de Vassivière 300m.
Remarks: In front of campsite, bread-service in summer period.

S Peyrat-le-Château 20F3

Parking Pré de l'Age. **GPS**: n45,81468 e1,77085.

20 free €2 Ch. **Surface:** gravel. 01/04-31/10
Distance: on the spot on the spot Terra Aventura.
Remarks: Coins at tourist info and town hall.

Tourist information Peyrat-le-Château:
Office de Tourisme, 1, Rue du Lac, www.peyrat-tourisme.com. Tourist town close water sports lake, Lac de Vassivière, marked cycle and hiking routes. Sa-Su 15-17h. T free.

S Sadroc 23F1

Place du Château. **GPS**: n45,28325 e1,54854.

6 free Ch free. **Surface:** asphalted. 01/01-31/12
Distance: on the spot 5,2km 50m.
Remarks: Max. 24h.

S Saint-Junien-la-Bregère 20F3

Rue du Chevalier de Châteauneuf. **GPS**: n45,88236 e1,75282.

3 free Chfree. **Surface:** asphalted. 01/01-31/12

S Saint-Laurent 20G2

Rue des Cerisiers. **GPS**: n46,16639 e1,96167.

4 free Ch free. **Surface:** metalled. 01/01-31/12
Distance: on the spot on the spot.

S Saint-Laurent-sur-Gorre 20E3

Les Chênes, Allée des Primevères. **GPS**: n45,76528 e0,95639.

20 € 6 Ch €2/24h WC included. **Surface:** grassy.
01/01-31/12
Distance: 300m 20m 20m 300m 300m.
Remarks: Motorhome washing place.

S Saint-Merd-les-Oussines 20G3

D109 > Tarnac. **GPS**: n45,63500 e2,03719.

6 free €2 Ch. **Location:** Rural, simple, isolated, quiet.
Surface: grassy/gravel. 01/01-31/12
Distance: 400m.
Remarks: Coins at Auberge du Mont-Chauvet.

S Saint-Privat 23G1

Rue des Chanaux. **GPS**: n45,14544 e2,09891.
10 €2 Ch. **Surface:** grassy/metalled. 01/01-31/12
Distance: 200m 200m 200m.

S Saint-Yrieix-la-Perche 23F1

Parking J.P Fabrègue, Avenue de Lattre de Tassigny, D901.
GPS: n45,51271 e1,20646.

5 free €3,50 Ch. **Surface:** asphalted. 01/01-31/12
Distance: 300m 300m 300m.
Remarks: Coins at tourist info, bar and maison de la presse.

S Saint-Yrieix-la-Perche 23F1

Ferme du Poumier, Lieu-dit Poumier, Marcognac.
GPS: n45,52065 e1,26853.

4 €3 €3 Ch. **Location:** Rural, isolated, quiet.
Surface: gravel. 01/01-31/12
Distance: St.Yrieix 5km.

S Servières-le-Château 23G1

Centre touristique du lac de Feyt. **GPS**: n45,14415 e2,03665.

15 free, 29/03-27/09 € 5 €2/100liter Ch €2/1h.
Location: Rural, isolated, quiet. **Surface:** grassy/metalled.
01/01-31/12
Distance: Sandy beach on the spot.

S Soubrebost 20G3

La Martinèche, D13. **GPS**: n45,98489 e1,85317.
3 free Chfree. **Location:** Isolated, quiet. **Surface:** asphalted.
01/01-31/12

S Treignac 23F1

Les rivières, Route du lac, D940. **GPS**: n45,54341 e1,79950.

FR

25 ⛺free 🚰🔧ChWCfree. **Surface:** grassy/gravel. 🔲 service: frost
Distance: 🚶2km 🏊on the spot.
Remarks: Along river.

Tourist information Treignac:
ℹ️ Office de Tourisme, 1, Place de la République. Free itinerary city tour along all curiosities, available at OT.

Turenne 🌿⛪ 23F2

Aire camping-cars, Avenue du Sénateur Labrousse, D8.
GPS: n45,05391 e1,57988. ⬆️➡️.

10 ⛺free 🚰€2 🔧Ch🔲€2 WC. **Surface:** gravel. 🔲 01/01-31/12
Distance: 🚶on the spot ⊗100m 🛒100m.
Remarks: Behind tourist info, coins at tourist info and supermarket, narrow road, not suitable for motorhomes +7m.

Tourist information Turenne:
⛪ Tour de Cesar.
🔲 Easter-Oct daily, winter Su.

Ussel 23G1

Aire du lac de Ponty. GPS: n45,54762 e2,28330. ⬆️.

15 ⛺free 🚰€2 🔧Ch🔲€2 WC. **Surface:** grassy/gravel.
🔲 01/01-31/12
Distance: 🚶Ussel 3km 🏊8,5km.
Remarks: At lake, in front of entrance campsite.

Uzerche 23F1

Place de la Petite Gare, Rue Paul Langevin.
GPS: n45,42477 e1,56696. ⬆️➡️.

20 ⛺free 🚰🔧ChWCfree. **Surface:** asphalted.
🔲 01/01-31/12
Distance: 🚶300m 🏊4,4km 🏞️little stream.

Vigeois 23F1

D7, route de Brive. **GPS:** n45,36717 e1,53392. ⬆️➡️.

12 ⛺free 🚰€3 🔧Ch🔲€3. **Surface:** grassy/gravel.
🔲 01/04-31/10
Distance: 🚶2km 🏊7,2km 🏖️beach 150m.
Remarks: Coins at town hall and bars in the village.

Auvergne

Aigueperse 🌿 21A3

Place du Foirail, Rue de la Porte aux Boeufs. **GPS:** n46,02634 e3,20313. ⬆️.

15 ⛺free 🚰€2/10minutes 🔧Ch🔲€2/1h. **Location:** Urban, simple, central, quiet. **Surface:** asphalted.
🔲 01/01-31/12 🔲 17/08-28/08
Distance: 🚶on the spot ⊗nearby 🛒nearby.
Remarks: Market square.

Aiguilhe 24B2

Avenue de Bonneville. **GPS:** n45,05077 e3,88318. ⬆️.
6 ⛺free. **Surface:** asphalted. 🔲 01/01-31/12
Distance: 🛒350m.
Remarks: Max. 24h.

Allanche 🏔️ 23H1

Aire de la Gare, Chemin de la Roche Marchal.
GPS: n45,23000 e2,93139. ⬆️.

25 ⛺free 🚰€2 🔧Ch. **Location:** Rural, simple, quiet.
Surface: gravel/sand. 🔲 01/05-30/09, parking 01/01-31/12
Distance: 🚶300m ⊗300m 🛒300m.
Remarks: Altitude 1000m, coins at camping, tourist info and town hall, accessed via Allanche centre.

Archignat 20H2

Rue des Chalets. **GPS:** n46,37336 e2,42408. ⬆️.
5 ⛺€5 + € 0,20/pp tourist tax 🚰€2 🔧Ch🔧€3 WC.
Location: Quiet. **Surface:** grassy/gravel.
Distance: 🚶on the spot.

Arlanc 24A1

Loumans. **GPS:** n45,41233 e3,71782. ⬆️➡️.

+10 ⛺free 🚰🔧Chfree 📶. **Location:** Rural, simple, quiet.
Surface: asphalted/grassy. 🔲 01/04-31/10
Distance: 🚶500m 🏊on the spot 🛒on the spot ⊗100m 🚶1km 🚶on the spot.
Remarks: At swimming pool and small lake.

Arnac (Cantal) 23G2

Aire camping-cars, RD61. **GPS:** n45,06056 e2,23389. ⬆️.

2 ⛺free 🚰€2/100liter 🔧Ch🔲€2/1h. **Location:** Rural, simple, quiet. **Surface:** grassy/gravel. 🔲 01/01-31/12
Distance: 🚶50m 🛒150m 🚶150m.

Aubusson-d'Auvergne 🌳❄️ 21A3

Base de Loisirs-lac d'Aubusson. GPS: n45,75377 e3,61079. ⬆️.

50 ⛺€6 🚰🔧ChWC📶free. **Location:** Rural, simple, isolated, quiet. **Surface:** metalled. 🔲 01/01-31/12
Distance: 🏊on the spot 🛒on the spot ⊗200m 🚶8km 🚶on the spot.

Aurec-sur-Loire 24B1

Rue des Cheminots. **GPS:** n45,37164 e4,19919. ⬆️.
⛺free 🚰🔧Ch. **Surface:** asphalted. 🔲 01/01-31/12
Distance: 🚶450m ⊗450m.
Remarks: At station.

Aurillac 🏛️⛲ 23G2

Place du Champ de Foire, Cours d'Angoulême.
GPS: n44,92944 e2,44963. ⬆️➡️.

10 ⛺free 🚰€3,50 🔧Ch🔲€3,50. **Location:** Urban, simple, noisy.
Surface: asphalted.
🔲 01/01-31/12 🔲 service: 31/10-01/05
Distance: 🚶on the spot ⊗100m 🛒100m.
Remarks: Max. 24h, coins at tourist info.

Tourist information Aurillac:
☀️ European street theatre and festival. 🔲 3rd week Aug.

Aydat 🌊 20H3

Aire camping-cars. GPS: n45,66025 e2,97778. ⬆️➡️.

41 ⛺€ 9/24h 🚰🔧Ch🔧(28x)WC included. 🚐🧹
Location: Rural, comfortable, quiet. **Surface:** grassy.
🔲 01/01-31/12
Distance: 🚶200m 🏊on the spot 🛒on the spot ⊗on the spot 🛒250m.
Remarks: Former campsite, max. 8,20m.

Beaulieu 24B2

Zone d'Activité la Gerle. **GPS:** n45,12597 e3,94608. ⬆️➡️.

15 ⌂free ⚡🅢Ch🚿(2x)free. **Location:** Rural, simple, quiet. **Surface:** gravel. 🅾 01/04-31/10 **Distance:** 🏊400m.

Beaulon 〰️ 21A1

Écluse de Beaulon, La Curesse. **GPS:** n46,60443 e3,65840. ⬆️➡️

+10 ⌂free ⚡🅢Ch🚿(4x)free. **Location:** Rural, simple, isolated, quiet. **Surface:** gravel. 🅾 01/01-31/12 **Distance:** 🏊1,2km ⛵Canal 🚣on the spot ❌1,2km 🍺1,2km 🚲on the spot 🚶on the spot.

Bellerive-sur-Allier 21A2

Riv'Air Camp, Rue Claude Decloitre. **GPS:** n46,11514 e3,43114. ⬆️

50 ⌂€10 ⚡🅢Ch🚿(50x)WC🚽included 🔌🚿 **Location:** Urban, comfortable, isolated. **Surface:** metalled. 🅾 01/01-31/12 **Distance:** 🏊2,5km ⛵17km ⛵on the spot 🚣on the spot ❌on the spot 🍺800m. **Remarks:** Along the Allier river.

Billy 21A2

Rue de la Fontaine. **GPS:** n46,23586 e3,43044. ⬆️⬆️

⌂free ⚡🅢Chfree. **Surface:** asphalted. 🅾 01/01-31/12 **Distance:** 🏊on the spot. **Remarks:** Max. 48h.

Blesle ⛰️ 24A1

Route du Babory, D8. **GPS:** n45,31716 e3,17583. ⬆️ 6 ⌂free **Surface:** gravel. 🅾 01/01-31/12 **Distance:** 🏊300m ❌300m 🍺300m.

Blesle ⛰️ 24A1

Hôtel-Restaurant Le Scorpion, D909. **GPS:** n45,31219 e3,18677. ⬆️

25 ⌂€12,50 ⚡🅢Ch🚿(8x)WC🚿included. **Location:** Rural, comfortable, quiet. **Surface:** grassy. 🅾 01/01-31/12

Distance: ⛵5,8km ❌on the spot.

Brioude 〰️⛰️ 24A1

Parking des Remparts, Avenue de Lamothe, D588. **GPS:** n45,29444 e3,38778. ⬆️➡️

30 ⌂free ⚡€2 🅢Ch🚌€2. **Location:** Urban, simple, central, quiet. **Surface:** asphalted. 🅾 01/01-31/12 **Distance:** 🏊100m ❌100m 🍺100m. **Remarks:** Coins at tourist info(100m).

Tourist information Brioude 👁️ L'aquarium-la Maison du Saumon et de la Rivière, Place de la Résistance. Museum about the salmon. 🅾 01/04-30/11.

Buxières-les-Mines 20H2

Le Boucher
Buxières-les-Mines

■ **Electricity at each pitch**
■ **Bread-service**
■ **Use swimming pool included**

www.camping-leboucher.com
margabolmer@orange.fr

Le Boucher. GPS: n46,45464 e2,96791. ⬆️➡️ 6 ⌂€9,90 ⚡€2 🅢Ch🚌🚿(6x)€2,60,12Amp WC🚿🔌€5/3,50 🚿included. **Location:** Rural, comfortable, isolated. **Surface:** grassy. 🅾 01/01-31/12 **Distance:** 🏊2km ⛵12km ⛵5km 🚣2km ❌5km 🍺2km.

Calvinet 23G2

Aire de Calvinet, Terrain de sport. **GPS:** n44,71023 e2,35914. ⬆️➡️

6 ⌂free ⚡€2 🅢Ch🚌€2. **Location:** Rural, simple, quiet. **Surface:** gravel. 🅾 01/01-31/12 🔘 service 01/11-31/03 **Distance:** 🏊1,5km ❌1,5km 🍺1,5km. **Remarks:** Nearby sports ground.

Cassaniouze 23G2

Aire camping-cars, Le Bourg. **GPS:** n44,69347 e2,38233. ⬆️➡️

6 ⌂free ⚡€2/80liter 🅢Ch🚌€2/1h 🚿€1. **Location:** Rural, simple, quiet. **Surface:** gravel. 🅾 01/01-31/12 🔘 service 01/11-31/03 **Distance:** 🏊600m ❌600m 🍺600m.

Cayrols 23G2

Aire camping-cars, La Devèze, D51. **GPS:** n44,83000 e2,23278. ⬆️➡️

10 ⌂free ⚡€3,80 🅢Ch🚌€3,80 WC. **Location:** Rural, comfortable, quiet. **Surface:** metalled. 🅾 01/01-31/12 🔘 service 01/11-31/03 **Distance:** 🏊100m 🍺200m. **Remarks:** Max. 1 week, coins at the shops in the village and petrol station.

Chambon-sur-Lac ⛰️⛰️❄️ 23H1

Camping Les Bombes, La Vergne. **GPS:** n45,56991 e2,90176. ⬆️➡️

30 ⌂€7 ⚡€3 🅢Ch🚲 **Location:** Rural, simple, quiet. **Surface:** grassy/gravel. 🅾 01/01-31/12 🔘 service: 15/09-01/05 **Distance:** 🏊500m 🍺200m 🚣1km ❌500m 🍺500m bakery 🚲on the spot 🚶on the spot. **Remarks:** Pay and coins at campsite.

Champeix 24A1

Champeix, Route de Montaigut, D996. **GPS:** n45,58845 e3,11568. ⬆️➡️

20 ⌂free ⚡€2 🅢Ch. **Location:** Rural, simple, isolated, quiet. **Surface:** grassy/gravel. 🅾 01/04-31/10 **Distance:** 🏊1,3km ❌1,3km 🍺500m.

Chanaleilles ⛰️ 24A2

Le Bourg. **GPS:** n44,85971 e3,49083. ⬆️

5 ⌂free ⚡🅢Ch. **Location:** Rural, comfortable, isolated, quiet. **Surface:** grassy/gravel. **Distance:** 🏊500m ❌375m.

Charbonnières-les-Varennes 20H3

Route de Saint-Georges, Paugnat. **GPS:** n45,88457 e2,97993. ⬆️

10 ⌂free ⚡€2/10minutes 🅢Ch€2/55minutes. **Location:** Rural, comfortable, quiet.

FR

Surface: grassy.
■ 01/01-31/12
Distance: 500m ⬛ bakery 500m 🚶 on the spot.
Remarks: Coins at the shops in the village, trail to volcano crater.

⬚S Chaspuzac 24A2
Rue du Vol à Voile. **GPS:** n45,07491 e3,76131. ➡.

6 ⬚free ⛽€2 ⬛Ch. **Location:** Rural, simple, quiet.
Surface: asphalted.
Distance: ⊗50m.
Remarks: View on airport.

⬚S Chastreix ⛰❄
Parking Station de Ski, Chastreix Sancy. **GPS:** n45,53507 e2,77695. ⬆.

14 ⬚free ⛽⬛Ch ⬛€9,(winter) WC ⬛€2,(winter). **Location:** Rural, simple, quiet. **Surface:** metalled.
■ 01/01-31/12
Distance: Chastreix 6km 🎿 on the spot.
Remarks: Check in between 9-17h.

⬚S Château-sur-Allier 20H1
Domaine Fessebois. **GPS:** n46,76379 e3,02714. ⬆.
4 ⬚free ⛽€3 ⬛Ch. **Location:** Rural, simple, isolated, quiet.
Surface: gravel. ■ 01/01-31/12
Remarks: Picnic area.

⬚S Châtel-Guyon ♨ 20H3
Place de la Musique Nationale. **GPS:** n45,92324 e3,06590. ⬆➡.

7 ⬚€5/day ⛽€2 ⬛ChWC. **Location:** Urban, comfortable, central, quiet. **Surface:** asphalted. ■ 01/01-31/12
Distance: nearby ⊗400m 400m on the spot.
Remarks: Check in at police station, coins at tourist info.

⬚ Châtel-Guyon ♨ 20H3
Parking des Roches, Chemin de Bussane.
GPS: n45,91789 e3,06545. ⬆.

10 ⬚free. **Location:** Urban, simple, quiet. **Surface:** asphalted.
■ 01/01-31/12
Distance: 500m ⊗600m 600m.

⬚ Châtel-Guyon ♨ 20H3
Pré Morand, Avenue de Russie. **GPS:** n45,91713 e3,05724.
⬚free. **Surface:** gravel. ■ 01/01-31/12
Remarks: Next to spa resort.

⬚S Chaudes-Aigues ♨ 23H2
Parking Beauredon, Avenue Georges Pompidou, D921.
GPS: n44,84972 e3,00306. ⬆➡.

10 ⬚free ⛽€2 ⬛Ch ⬛€2/55minutes. **Location:** Urban, simple.
Surface: gravel. ■ 15/04-15/10
Distance: 100m ⊗300m 300m.

Tourist information Chaudes-Aigues:
ℹ Office de Tourisme, 1, avenue Georges Pompidou, www.chaude-saigues.com. Small town with warm thermal sources (82ºC).

⬚S Chevagnes 21A1
Route Nationale. **GPS:** n46,61028 e3,55219. ⬆.
4 ⬚free ⛽€2 ⬛Ch ⬛€2. **Location:** Comfortable, isolated, quiet.
Surface: gravel. ■ 01/01-31/12
Distance: on the spot ⊗200m.

⬚S Chomelix 🌳 24B1
Centre Multi Activités Les Marches d'Auvergne, Route d'Estables, D135. **GPS:** n45,26219 e3,82573. ⬆.

6 ⬚free ⛽€4 ⬛Ch. **Location:** Rural, simple, quiet. **Surface:** gravel.
■ 01/01-31/12
Distance: on the spot ⊗on the spot 🚲 mountainbike trail 🚶 on the spot.

⬚S Clermont Ferrand 21A3
P&R Les Pistes, Rue de la Fontaine de la Ratte.
GPS: n45,79810 e3,11222. ⬆.

6 ⬚€5 ⛽⬛Chfree. 🚌 **Location:** Urban. **Surface:** asphalted.
■ 01/01-31/12
Distance: historical centre 3km 50m.
Remarks: Nearby Michelin museum, check in at parking attendant.

⬚S Coltines 23H2
D40. **GPS:** n45,09612 e2,98555. ➡.

5 ⬚free ⛽€2/100liter ⬛Ch ⬛€2. **Location:** Rural, simple.
Surface: gravel.
● water: 15/10-15/04
Distance: 400m ⊗400m 400m.
Remarks: Coins at Epicerie-Presse, Centre Chantarisa and town hall.

⬚S Condat 23H1
Parking au Pont, D678. **GPS:** n45,33889 e2,76250. ⬆.

4 ⬚free ⛽Service €2,50 ⬛Ch. **Location:** Simple.
Surface: asphalted. ■ 01/01-31/12 ● service: 01/10-01/05
Distance: 50m 10m 50m.
Remarks: Coins at campsite La Borie Basse (500m).

⬚S Coubon 24B2
Route du Plan d'Eau. **GPS:** n44,99735 e3,91742. ⬆.

5 ⬚free ⛽€2,50 ⬛ChWC. **Surface:** metalled. ■ 01/01-31/12
Remarks: Along river.

⬚S Cournon d'Auvergne 21A3
Les Pres des Laveuses, Rue de Laveuses. **GPS:** n45,73994 e3,22225.
10 ⬚€5 ⛽€2,30 ⬛Chfree. **Location:** Rural, simple. **Surface:** gravel.
■ 01/01-31/12
Distance: ⛵on the spot on the spot ⊗on the spot.

⬚S Crandelles 23G2
Aire camping-cars, Lac des Genevrières. **GPS:** n44,95877 e2,34289.

10 ⬚free ⛽€3,50 ⬛Ch. **Location:** Comfortable, central, quiet.
Surface: gravel. ■ 01/01-31/12 ● service: 01/11-01/04
Distance: 300m ⛵50m 50m ⊗50m 300m.

⬚S Craponne-sur-Arzon 24B1
Avenue de la Gare. **GPS:** n45,33360 e3,85057. ⬆.

+20 ⬚free ⛽€2 ⬛Ch ⬛€2/1h. **Location:** Urban, simple, quiet.
Surface: asphalted/gravel. ■ 01/01-31/12
Distance: 150m ⊗150m on the spot.

⬚S Diou 21B2
Camping du Gué de Loire, Chemin de la Procession.
GPS: n46,53523 e3,74401. ⬆.
6 ⬚free, 15/06-30/09 €5 ⬛Ch. **Surface:** grassy.
■ 01/01-31/12

⬚S Drugeac 23G1
Aire de campingcars, La Gare SNCF. **GPS:** n45,16694 e2,38667. ⬆➡.

4 🛏free 🚰€2/100liter 🗑Ch 🚽€2/1h. **Location:** Rural, simple, quiet. **Surface:** asphalted.
🅿 01/01-31/12 🅿 service: 01/11-01/05
Distance: 🚉100m ⊗100m 🛒100m.
Remarks: At former station, now start Vélorail.

Ebreuil — 20H2
Parking du Stade, D915. **GPS:** n46,10954 e3,07606.⬆.

10 🛏free. **Location:** Simple. **Surface:** gravel. 🅿 01/01-31/12
Distance: 🏖6,5km.
Remarks: In front of campsite municipal, service 500m.

Ebreuil — 20H2
Chemin des Nières. **GPS:** n46,11083 e3,08111.⬆.
🚰🗑Chfree. 🅿 01/01-31/12
Remarks: Overnight stay on Parking du Stade.

Estivareilles — 20H2
Salle Polyvalente, Rue de la République.
GPS: n46,42471 e2,61529.⬆➡.

20 🛏free 🚰🗑Chfree. **Location:** Urban, simple. **Surface:** gravel.
🅿 01/01-31/12
Distance: 🚉on the spot 🏖9km ⊗200m 🛒bakery 200m.

Jaligny-sur-Besbre — 21A2
Rue de la Chaume. **GPS:** n46,38155 e3,59147.⬆➡.

5 🛏free 🚰🗑Ch 🚿(5x)free. **Location:** Rural, simple, quiet.
Surface: gravel. 🅿 01/01-31/12
Distance: 🚉200m 🏊on the spot 🏖on the spot ⊗250m 🛒250m.
Remarks: Along the Besbre river.

La Bourboule — 23H1
Plateau de Charlannes. **GPS:** n45,57811 e2,73513.⬆.

10 🛏free. **Location:** Rural, simple, quiet. **Surface:** asphalted.

🅿 01/01-31/12
Distance: 🚉6,5km ⊗Snackbar 🛒on the spot 🏃on the spot.
Remarks: Parking at funicular railway.

La Chapelle-Laurent ❄ — 24A1
Aire camping-cars, D10. **GPS:** n45,18028 e3,24389.⬆.

5 🛏free 🚰🗑Chfree. **Location:** Rural, simple. **Surface:** grassy.
🅿 parking 01/01-31/12, service 01/04-15/11
Distance: 🚉50m 🏖nearby ⊗100m 🛒100m.

La Roche-Blanche — 21A3
Les Trolières, La Pigné Sud, Route des Fours à Chaux.
GPS: n45,71567 e3,14790.⬆.

100 🛏€6 🚰€2/100liter 🗑Ch 🚿(4x)€6/6h. 🧺 **Location:** Rural,
simple, isolated, quiet. **Surface:** grassy.
🅿 01/03-30/11
Distance: 🏖1,1km.
Remarks: Max. 48h.

La Tour-d'Auvergne — 23H1
Route de Bagnols. **GPS:** n45,53290 e2,68213.⬆.

25 🛏free 🚰€2/100liter 🗑Ch 🚽€2. **Location:** Simple, quiet.
Surface: metalled. 🅿 01/01-31/12
Distance: 🏖on the spot ⊗650m 🛒650m bakery.

Lacapelle-Viescamp — 23G2
Aire camping-cars, D18. **GPS:** n44,92167 e2,26361.⬆.

5 🛏free 🚰€3/100liter 🗑Ch 🚽€3/1h. **Location:** Rural, simple.
Surface: metalled. 🅿 01/01-31/12
Distance: 🚉100m ⊗100m 🛒on the spot.
Remarks: Coins available at the shop.

Lapalisse ❄❄❄ — 21A2
Place Jean Moulin, RN7 dir Roanne. **GPS:** n46,25000 e3,63500.➡.

---

50 🛏free 🚰€2 🗑Ch 🚿€2 WC. **Location:** Urban, simple, central,
quiet. **Surface:** asphalted. 🅿 01/01-31/12
Distance: 🚉300m 🛒on the spot ⊗on the spot 🛒on the spot.

Laprugne — 21A3
Domaine La Bourbonnaise, D477. **GPS:** n45,98661 e3,74569.
🛏€8 🚰🗑Ch 🚿. **Surface:** asphalted. 🅿 01/01-31/12
Distance: ⊗on the spot.

Lavaudieu — 24A1
Le Bourg. **GPS:** n45,26297 e3,45606.⬆.

+10 🛏free. **Location:** Simple, isolated, quiet. **Surface:** grassy/gravel.
🅿 01/01-31/12
Distance: 🚉200m 🛒on the spot ⊗on the spot 🏃on the spot.

Le Breuil-sur-Couze — 24A1
Allée de Treize Vents. **GPS:** n45,46867 e3,26121.⬆➡.

8 🛏free 🚰🗑Chfree. **Location:** Urban, simple. **Surface:** gravel.
🅿 01/01-31/12
Distance: 🏖900m 🛒700m bakery, supermarket.
Remarks: Along railwayline.

Le Cheix-sur-Morge — 21A3
D425. **GPS:** n45,95138 e3,17812.⬆➡.

6 🛏free 🚰🗑Chfree. **Location:** Rural, simple, isolated, quiet.
Surface: gravel. 🅿 01/01-31/12
Distance: 🚉500m.
Remarks: Max. 48h.

Le Donjon — 21B2
Place du Champ de Foire, Rue Georges Gallay.
GPS: n46,34940 e3,79473.⬆.

🛏free. **Location:** Simple, central, quiet. **Surface:** gravel.
🅿 01/01-31/12
Distance: 🚉100m 🛒50m.
Remarks: Tuesday market.

Le Monastier-sur-Gazeille — 24B2
Rue Augustin Ollier. **GPS:** n44,93720 e3,99250.⬆➡.

10 🛏free. **Location:** Rural, simple. **Surface:** grassy.
◻ 01/03-31/10
Distance: 🚮300m ⊗300m 🛢300m.

| **S** | Le Monastier-sur-Gazeille | 24B2 |

Le Moulin de Savin. **GPS:** n44,93680 e3,98600.⬆➡.
🚰🗑Ch.
Remarks: Next to campsite.

| **S** | Le Puy-en-Velay | 24B2 |

Avenue Charles Dupuy. **GPS:** n45,04358 e3,89240.⬆➡.

12 🛏€ 8, € 2/3h. 🅿 **Location:** Urban, simple, central, noisy.
Surface: asphalted. ◻ 01/01-31/12
Distance: 🚮500m.
Remarks: Behind bus terminal, max. 24h.

| **S** | Le Puy-en-Velay | 24B2 |

Boulevard de Cluny. GPS: n45,04963 e3,88976.⬆.
🗑€2 🗑Ch.

| **S** | Le Vernet | 24A2 |

Le Bourg. **GPS:** n45,03560 e3,66952.⬆.

10 🛏€ 2 🗑€2/80liter 🗑Ch🔌€2/10minutes.🚿 **Location:** Rural,
simple, isolated, quiet. **Surface:** grassy/sand.
◻ 01/01-31/12
Distance: 🚮50m 🧍on the spot.

| **©S** | Les Ancizes-Comps | 20H3 |

Camping de Comps les Fads, Le Moulin. **GPS:** n45,93986 e2,79985.⬆.
🛏€ 8,40, 2 pers.incl 🚰🗑Ch🗑€2. **Surface:** grassy.
◻ 01/01-31/12

| **S** | Les Estables | 24B2 |

Le Bourg. **GPS:** n44,90231 e4,15679.⬆.

8 🛏free 🚰🗑Chfree 📶. **Location:** Rural, simple.
Surface: asphalted. ◻ 01/01-31/12
Distance: 🚮50m ⊗50m 🛶on the spot.
Remarks: Free wifi, code at tourist info.

| **S** | Lezoux | 21A3 |

Parking Musée départemental de la Céramique, Rue de la République. **GPS:** n45,82686 e3,38459.⬆➡.

30 🛏free 🚰🗑ChWCfree. **Location:** Comfortable, central, quiet.
Surface: gravel.
◻ 01/01-31/12 ◉ water: 01/11-31/03
Distance: 🚮500m 🚲3,5km ⊗500m 🛢500m.

| **S** | Lurcy-Lévis 〰 | 20H1 |

Plan d'eau des Sézeaux, Rue de Fontgroix.
GPS: n46,73797 e2,93863.⬆➡.

6 🛏free 🗑€3/100liter 🗑Ch🔌€3/55minutes WC. **Location:** Rural,
comfortable, quiet. **Surface:** grassy/gravel.
◻ 01/01-31/12
Distance: 🚮800m 🏊Small lake 🛶on the spot ⊗800m 🛢800m.
Remarks: Coins at cafe, in front of the church.

| **S** | Mandailles-Saint-Julien 🏔 | 23H2 |

Aire de camping-cars, Le Mas, D17. **GPS:** n45,06916 e2,65611.➡.

5 🛏free 🗑€3,50 🗑Ch. **Location:** Rural, simple, quiet.
Surface: metalled. ◻ 01/01-31/12 ◉ service: 30/09-01/05
Distance: 🚮200m ⊗200m 🛢200m 🧍on the spot.
Remarks: Max. 24h, coins at restaurants.

| **S** | Manzat | 20H3 |

Place du 14 Juillet. **GPS:** n45,96180 e2,93883.⬆.

20 🛏free 🚰🗑Chfree. **Location:** Rural, simple, quiet.
Surface: unpaved. ◻ 01/01-31/12
Distance: 🚮on the spot 🚲5,6km ⊗250m 🛢200m.
Remarks: In front of police station.

| **S** | Marcolès | 23G2 |

Aire camping-cars, Terrain de sport. **GPS:** n44,78028 e2,35389.⬆.

5 🛏€ 2 🚰🗑Chfree 🚿. **Location:** Rural, simple, quiet.
Surface: gravel. ◻ 01/01-31/12 ◉ service 01/11-31/03
Distance: 🚮100m ⊗100m 🛢100m.

Remarks: Artists village.

| **S** | Massiac | 24A1 |

Rue Jacques Chaban Delmas. **GPS:** n45,25360 e3,19395.⬆.

5 🛏free 🚰🗑Chfree. **Surface:** asphalted.
Distance: 🚮350m ⊗400m 🛢400m.

| **S** | Massiac | 24A1 |

Rue Jacques Chaban Delmas. **GPS:** n45,25267 e3,19433.⬆➡.

🛏free. **Location:** Rural. **Surface:** grassy. ◻ 01/01-31/12
Distance: 🚮400m 🚲1,4km 🏊on the spot ⊗400m 🛢400m 🚍200m.

| **S** | Mauriac 〰 | 23G1 |

Aire de campingcars, Rue du Val Saint Jean.
GPS: n45,21863 e2,32183.⬆➡.

10 🛏free 🗑€2/100liter 🗑Ch🔌€2/1h 📇. **Location:** Rural, simple,
quiet. **Surface:** metalled. ◻ 01/01-31/12
Distance: 🚮1km 🏊beach 300m ⊗1,2km 🛢1,2km.

| **S** | Maurs | 23G2 |

Maurs La Jolie, Route de Quezac. **GPS:** n44,71442 e2,19615.⬆➡.

5 🛏free 🗑€2/100liter 🗑Ch🔌€2/1h. **Location:** Urban, simple,
central, quiet. **Surface:** asphalted.
◻ 01/01-31/12
Distance: 🚮300m ⊗300m 🛢300m 🧍300m.
Remarks: Coins at Papetterie and tourist office.

| **S** | Messeix | 20H3 |

Place des Pins. **GPS:** n45,61576 e2,55621.⬆➡.

6 🛏free 🗑€2/10minutes 🗑Ch🔌€2/55minutes. **Location:** Urban,
simple, quiet. **Surface:** asphalted.
◻ 01/01-31/12
Distance: 🚮500m 🚲18km 🛢1,7km 🚍on the spot.

Remarks: Coins at the shops.

Montluçon 20H2
Route de l'Etang de Sault, Prémilhat. **GPS:** n46,33469 e2,55855.

8 ⓢfree ⌐€6/150liter ⓒCh (6x)€2,50/10h **Location:** Rural, comfortable. **Surface:** gravel. 01/01-31/12
Distance: 5km Montluçon 2,6km 150m 150m 500m.
Remarks: Max. 72h.

Montluçon 20H2
Place de la Fraternité, Rue des Marais. **GPS:** n46,35535 e2,58686.

15 ⓢfree ⌐€5/150liter ⓒCh €2,50/10minutes WC.
Location: Urban, simple, noisy.
Surface: asphalted.
01/01-31/12 water: Nov-March
Distance: on the spot A71 16km on the spot on the spot on the spot.
Remarks: Thu-morning closed because of market (6-15h).

Montmurat 23G2
Aire camping-cars, Le Bourg, D345. **GPS:** n44,62811 e2,19804.

10 ⓢfree ⌐€1 ⓒCh. **Location:** Rural, simple, isolated, quiet.
Surface: gravel. 01/01-31/12
Distance: on the spot.

Montoldre 21A2
D21. **GPS:** n46,33272 e3,44727.

+10 ⓢfree ⌐€2/100liter ⓒCh. **Location:** Rural, simple, quiet.
Surface: asphalted. 01/01-31/12
Distance: centre on the spot.
Remarks: In front of town hall.

Montpeyroux 21A3
D797C, Rue De l'Hume. **GPS:** n45,62373 e3,19911.

+10 ⓢfree ⌐€2,50 ⓒCh €2,50/1h. **Location:** Rural, simple, quiet. **Surface:** gravel.
Distance: 100m 200m 200m.
Remarks: Coins at the shops in the village.

Tourist information Montpeyroux:
Small town with wine-cellar Cave de Montpeyroux. Mo/Sa 8.30-12.30h, 14-18/19h, Su 10.30-12h, 16-19h.

Montsalvy 23G2
Aire camping-cars, Route de Junhac. **GPS:** n44,70778 e2,49667.

21 ⓢfree ⌐€2 ⓒCh €2 WC€1. **Location:** Rural, comfortable, quiet. **Surface:** asphalted. 01/01-31/12
Distance: 400m 400m 400m.

Moulins 21A2
Flot Bleu Park, Chemin de Halage. **GPS:** n46,55852 e3,32491.

92 ⓢ€0,10/h ⌐€2 ⓒCh€2 €2/20minutes (12x)€ 2/4h. **Location:** Urban, comfortable, central, quiet.
Surface: grassy/metalled. 01/01-31/12
Distance: city centre 1km 100m 300m on the spot.

Murat 23H2
Place du 19 mars. **GPS:** n45,10917 e2,86917.

8 ⓢfree ⌐€2 ⓒCh €2 WC. **Surface:** asphalted.
01/05-31/10
Remarks: Marked pitches in the back of de parking.

Murat 23H2
Avenue d'Olonne-sur-mer. **GPS:** n45,10757 e2,85975.

ⓢfree. **Location:** Urban, simple. **Surface:** concrete.
01/01-31/12
Remarks: At sports park.

Murat 23H2
Parking du Stade, Rue du Stade. **GPS:** n45,10861 e2,87027.

ⓢfree. **Surface:** asphalted. 01/01-31/12
Tourist information Murat:
Fri-morning.

Murat-le-Quaire 20H3
Les Rives du Lac, Route de la Banne d'Ordanche.
GPS: n45,60274 e2,73797.

37 ⓢ€9/24h ⌐Ch (8x)WCincluded €1. **Location:** Rural, comfortable, quiet. **Surface:** grassy/metalled. 01/01-31/12
Distance: 1,2km 12km 100m 100m day pass available on the spot on the spot 100m 5km.
Remarks: Bread-service.

Naucelles 23G2
Aire camping-cars, Rue du Terrou. **GPS:** n44,95694 e2,41757.

5 ⓢfree ⌐€3,50/100liter ⓒCh €3,50/1h. **Location:** Urban, simple, quiet. **Surface:** asphalted. 01/01-31/12
Distance: Spar 300m.
Remarks: Coins at supermarket in the village.

Néris-les-Bains 20H2
Camping du Lac, Avenue Marrx Dormoy, D155.
GPS: n46,28673 e2,65235.

6 ⓢ€7 ⌐ⓒCh (6x)WCincluded €1,50/h. **Location:** Urban, comfortable. **Surface:** gravel. 01/03-31/10
Distance: 500m 12km bakery 500m.
Remarks: Max. 3 nights, to be paid at campsite.

Neussargues-Moissac 23H1
Allée des Peupliers. **GPS:** n45,13438 e2,98130.

5 ⓢfree ⌐€2/100liter ⓒCh €2/2h. **Location:** Rural, comfortable, quiet. **Surface:** gravel. 01/01-31/12 water disconnected in winter

Distance: 🚰300m ⊗50m ⚡300m.

Orcines 20H3
Route du Puy de Dôme, D68. **GPS:** n45,76958 e2,98624.
🚽free 🚰⚡Chfree. **Location:** Rural, isolated. **Surface:** asphalted.
🔲 01/01-31/12 ◉ Service: winter

Orcines 20H3
D941. **GPS:** n45,80394 e2,98726.

10 🚽free. **Location:** Simple, noisy. **Surface:** metalled. 🔲 01/01-31/12
🚶on the spot.

Orcines 20H3
D941B dir Orcines Vulcania. **GPS:** n45,78765 e3,00947. ⬆️.

🚰€2/100liter ⚡Ch⚡€2/1h. **Location:** Simple, noisy.
🔲 01/01-31/12

Paray-le-Frésil 21A1
Le Bourg. **GPS:** n46,65472 e3,61294. ⬆️.
3 🚽free 🚰€2 ⚡Ch⚡€2/55minutes. **Location:** Quiet.
Surface: sand. 🔲 01/01-31/12 🛝on the spot 🚶on the spot.
Remarks: Service only by credit card.

Périgny 21A2
Rue de l'Église. **GPS:** n46,25306 e3,55307.
8 🚽free ⚡ChWC. **Location:** Rural, simple, isolated, quiet.
Surface: gravel. 🔲 01/01-31/12

Pierrefort 23H2
Côte de Chabridet. **GPS:** n44,92172 e2,84199. ⬆️➡️.

20 🚽free 🚰€2/100liter ⚡Ch⚡€2. **Location:** Simple.
Surface: gravel. 🔲 01/01-31/12
Distance: 🚰100m ⊗200m ⚡200m.

Pleaux 23G1
Parc des Auzerals, Place d'Empeyssine.
GPS: n45,13556 e2,22833. ⬆️➡️.

30 🚽free 🚰⚡ChWCfree. **Location:** Urban, simple, central, quiet.
Surface: asphalted/gravel. 🔲 01/01-31/12
Distance: 🚰on the spot ⊗100m ⚡100m.

Pradelles 24B2
Aire de la Salaison, N88. **GPS:** n44,77540 e3,88752. ⬆️➡️.

20 🚽free 🚰⚡Ch (8x)€2 📶free. **Location:** Rural, comfortable,
noisy. **Surface:** grassy. 🔲 01/01-31/12
Distance: 🚰1km ⚡on the spot.
Remarks: Regional products and bread.

Prunet 23G2
Aire camping-cars, Le Bourg. **GPS:** n44,82049 e2,46398. ➡️.

3 🚽free 🚰⚡Ch⚡free. **Location:** Rural, simple, quiet.
Surface: gravel. 🔲 01/01-31/12 ◉ service 01/11-31/03
Distance: 🚰300m ⊗300m.

Randan 21A3
Rue du Puy de Dôme. **GPS:** n46,01630 e3,35075. ⬆️➡️.

5 🚽free 🚰€2/15minutes ⚡Ch⚡€2/15minutes. **Location:** Urban,
simple, quiet. **Surface:** gravel.
🔲 01/01-31/12
Distance: 🚰500m ⊗500m ⚡200m.
Remarks: Coins at Maison de la Presse, Rue de Commerce.

Raucoules 24B1
Raucoules, Le Bourg. **GPS:** n45,18640 e4,29750. ⬆️➡️.

4 🚽free 🚰€2 ⚡Ch (4x)€2. **Location:** Rural, comfortable, central,
quiet. **Surface:** asphalted. 🔲 01/01-31/12
Distance: 🚰200m ⊗300m.
Remarks: Coins available at the shops.

Retournac 24B1
Rue de la Loire. **GPS:** n45,20328 e4,04501. ⬆️➡️.

20 🚽free 🚰⚡Chfree. **Location:** Rural, simple, isolated, quiet.
Surface: gravel. 🔲 01/01-31/12 ◉ Service: winter
Distance: 🚰city centre 1km 🏊on the spot 🚣on the spot ⊗650m
🚶on the spot.
Remarks: Along Loire river.

Riom 21A3
Route d'Ennezat, D224. **GPS:** n45,89455 e3,12477. ⬆️➡️.

4 🚽free 🚰€2/15minutes ⚡Ch⚡€2/15minutes. **Location:** Urban,
simple, central, noisy. **Surface:** gravel.
🔲 01/01-31/12
Distance: 🚰700m 🚲2,5km ⊗nearby ⚡nearby.

Riom-es-Montagnes 23H1
Rue du Champ de Foire. **GPS:** n45,28444 e2,65389. ⬆️➡️.

🚰€2/100liter ⚡Ch⚡€2/1h. **Location:** Simple. **Surface:** metalled.
🔲 01/01-31/12
Distance: 🚰on the spot ⊗100m ⚡100m.
Remarks: Overnight stay on Parking de la Piscine, GPS N 45,27902 E
2,66403.

Ruynes-en-Margeride 24A2
GPS: n45,00111 e3,22389. ➡️.

6 🚽free 🚰€2/10minutes ⚡Ch⚡€2/55minutes.
Surface: asphalted. 🔲 01/01-31/12
Distance: 🚰50m ⊗50m ⚡50m.

Saint-Bonnet-le-Froid 24C1
Chemin de Brard. **GPS:** n45,14136 e4,43454. ⬆️.
6 🚽€5 🚰⚡Ch included. **Surface:** gravel. 🔲 01/03-15/11
Distance: 🚰150m ⊗150m ⚡150m.
Remarks: Access via D105.

Saint-Bonnet-Tronçais 20H1
Parking du Stade, Route de Tronçais, D39.
GPS: n46,66001 e2,69717. ⬆️.
10 🚽free 🚰€5 ⚡Ch. **Surface:** gravel. 🔲 01/01-31/12 ◉ water
disconnected in winter
Distance: 🚰300m.
Remarks: Coins at the bakery and campsite.

Saint-Bonnet-Tronçais 20H1
Rue de l'Étang. **GPS:** n46,65896 e2,69228. ⬆️➡️.
10 🚽free. **Location:** Simple, central. **Surface:** gravel.
🔲 01/01-31/12
Distance: 🚰on the spot 🚲27km ⚡Lake 450m ⚡bakery 200m.

Saint-Christophe-sur-Dolaison 24B2
Le Bourg. **GPS:** n44,99811 e3,82147. ⬆️.

6 🚽free 🚰€2 ⚡Ch⚡€2. **Location:** Rural, simple.
Surface: asphalted.

FR

Distance: 🚶100m ⊗150m.

Saint-Éloy-les-Mines ⬛S 20H2

Rue du Puy-de-Dôme, RN144. **GPS:** n46,15559 e2,83615. ⬆➡

30 🅿free 🚰€2 🔌Ch 🚽€2. **Location:** Rural, simple.
Surface: metalled. 🅾 01/01-31/12
Distance: 🏊on the spot ⊗700m 🛒400m Carrefour Market.
Remarks: Max. 48h.

Saint-Flour ⬛S 23H2

Cours Chazerat. **GPS:** n45,03389 e3,08750. ⬆

20 🅿free 🚰€2 🔌Ch. **Location:** Urban, simple. **Surface:** metalled.
🅾 01/01-31/12
Distance: 🚶on the spot 🚲4,6km ⊗50m 🛒50m.
Remarks: Higher part of the city.

Saint-Flour ⬛S 23H2

Place de l'Ander, ville basse. **GPS:** n45,03556 e3,09750. ⬆

8 🅿free 🚰€2 🔌Ch 🚽€4. **Location:** Urban, simple.
Surface: asphalted. 🅾 01/01-31/12
Distance: 🚶300m 🚲4km ⊗300m 🛒300m.
Remarks: Near campsite, lower part of the city.

Tourist information Saint-Flour:
ℹ Office de Tourisme, 17bis, place d'Armes, www.saint-flour.com. City with car-free historical centre, Vieux Saint Flour.

Saint-Georges ⬛S 24A2

GPS: n45,03167 e3,13500. ⬆

20 🅿free 🚰€2 🔌Ch 🚽€2 WC. **Location:** Highway.
Surface: asphalted. 🅾 01/01-31/12
Distance: 🚶3km 🚲1km ⊗200m 🛒on the spot.
Remarks: At petrol station Esso.

Saint-Gérand-de-Vaux ⬛S 21A2

Etang du Moulin, Les Gaillards. **GPS:** n46,38416 e3,39972.

30 🅿free 🚰€2/100liter 🔌Ch 🚽€2/1h. **Location:** Quiet.
Surface: grassy. 🅾 01/01-31/12
Distance: ⊗on the spot.

Saint-Just 📷S 24A2

GPS: n44,88972 e3,20889. ⬆

10 🅿€8 🚰€2/100liter 🔌Ch 🚽€2/55minutes WC 🚿.
Location: Comfortable, quiet. **Surface:** grassy. 🅾 01/01-31/12
Distance: 🚶50m 🚲6,2km ⊗100m 🛒100m.
Remarks: Incl. use camp-site facilities.

Saint-Mamet-la-Salvetat ⬛S 23G2

Aire camping-cars, D20. **GPS:** n44,85714 e2,30981. ⬆➡

3 🅿free 🚰€2/100liter 🔌Ch 🚽€2/1h WC. **Location:** Rural, simple,
quiet. **Surface:** asphalted. 🅾 01/01-31/12
Distance: ⊗500m 🛒350m.
Remarks: Coins at the shops and town hall.

Saint-Marcel-en-Murat ⬛S 20H2

D243. **GPS:** n46,32184 e3,00837. ⬆

10 🅿free 🚰€2/100liter 🔌Ch 🚽€2/1h. **Location:** Rural, simple.
Surface: gravel. 🅾 01/01-31/12
Distance: 🚲3,5km exit 11 A71 ⊗nearby.
Remarks: Coins at town hall and restaurant.

Saint-Paul-des-Landes ⬛S 23G2

Aire camping-cars, Rue du Moinac. **GPS:** n44,94250 e2,31694. ⬆➡

3 🅿free 🚰€3,50 🔌Ch 🚽€3,50. **Location:** Rural, simple, central,
quiet. **Surface:** asphalted. 🅾 01/01-31/12
Distance: 🚶50m ⊗200m 🛒50m.
Remarks: Coins at petrol station.

Saint-Pourçain-sur-Sioule 🌿🏊 ⬛S 21A2

Aire Camping-car de la Moutte, Rue de la Moutte.
GPS: n46,31262 e3,29656. ⬆➡

73 🅿free 🚰€2 🔌Ch 🚿(8x)€2/4h. **Location:** Urban, comfortable,
central, quiet. **Surface:** grassy.
🅾 01/01-31/12
Distance: 🚶800m 🚲on the spot ⊗on the spot 🛒on the spot.
Remarks: Along the Sioule river.

Saint-Rémy-de-Blot ⬛S 20H3

Place du Bourg. **GPS:** n46,07722 e2,93139. ⬆

7 🅿free WC. **Location:** Rural, simple, isolated, quiet.
Surface: grasstiles. 🅾 01/01-31/12
Distance: ⊗on the spot.

Saint-Romain-Lachalm ⬛S 24B1

Rulière. **GPS:** n45,26399 e4,33576. ⬆
4 🅿free 🚰 🔌Ch 🚿(4x)€2/4h. **Surface:** asphalted.
Distance: 🚶100m 🛒bakery 200m.
Remarks: Coins at the shops and town hall.

Saint-Sauves-d'Auvergne 🏔 ⬛S 20H3

Domaine de Lavaux, D82. **GPS:** n45,61688 e2,68975. ⬆➡

50 🅿€8 🚰🔌Ch 🚿(10x)€4/day WCincluded 🚽€1,25 🚿€5. 🚲
Location: Rural, comfortable, isolated, quiet. **Surface:** grassy.
🅾 15/05-30/09
Distance: 🚶1km 🚶on the spot.

Salers 🌿 ⬛S 23H1

Le Mouriol, Route du Puy Mary. **GPS:** n45,14718 e2,49900. ⬆

15 🅿€3,70 + €0,50 tourist tax 🚰€2,10 🔌Ch 🚽€1,50,on camp site.
Location: Rural. **Surface:** gravel.
Distance: 🚶1,2km ⊗50m.
Remarks: Next to camping municipal, coins at campsite and tourist info.

Salers 🌿 ⬛ 23H1

D680. **GPS:** n45,14010 e2,49478.
12 🅿€3. 🅿 **Location:** Rural. **Surface:** asphalted/metalled.
Distance: 🚶500m.
Remarks: Max. 24h, no camping activities.

Salers 🌿 ⬛ 23H1

Rue Notre-Dame. **GPS:** n45,13898 e2,49583.
6 🅿€3. 🅿 **Surface:** asphalted. 🅾 01/01-31/12

Distance: 🚰250m.
Remarks: Max. 24h, no camping activities.

🔲🆂 **Sansac-de-Marmiesse** 23G2
Aire camping-cars, Rue de la Vidalie. **GPS:** n44,88389 e2,34639.⬆️➡️

3 🗓free 🚰€3,50 🗑Ch€3,50. **Location:** Urban, simple, central.
Surface: asphalted.
⬛ 01/01-31/12 🔘 service: 01/10-30/04
Distance: 🚰on the spot ⊗200m 🛒on the spot.
Remarks: Coins at the bakery.

🔲🆂 **Saugues** 24A2
Place du Brieul. **GPS:** n44,95940 e3,54395.⬆️

10 🗓free 🚰🗑Chfree. **Location:** Simple. **Surface:** asphalted.
Distance: 🚰on the spot 🛒bakery 200m.

🔲🆂 **Sauret-Besserve** 20H3
D523. **GPS:** n45,99389 e2,81001.

4 🗓free 🚰€2 🗑Ch€2. **Location:** Rural, simple, isolated.
⬛ 01/01-31/12
Remarks: Near church, june 2012 during inspection service out of order.

🔲🆂 **Ségur-les-Villas** 23H1
Aire de camping-cars, Le Bourg. **GPS:** n45,22311 e2,81818.⬆️➡️

10 🗓free 🚰€3/100liter 🗑Ch🚽€3/1h. **Location:** Rural, simple,
quiet. **Surface:** grassy. ⬛ 01/05-31/10
Distance: 🚰200m ⊗300m 🛒200m.
Remarks: Nearby football ground, coins at the shops in the village.

🔲🆂 **Solignat** 24A1
Route des Dauphins d'Auvergne, D32. **GPS:** n45,51701 e3,17074.⬆️

+50 🗓free 🚰€2/100liter 🗑Ch🚽€2/1h. **Location:** Rural, simple,
quiet. **Surface:** grassy. ⬛ 01/01-31/12
Distance: 🚰100m.

🔲🆂 **St Anthème** 🏔 24B1
Rambaud. **GPS:** n45,52354 e3,91464.⬆️➡️

30 🗓€3 🗑Chincluded. **Location:** Rural, simple, central, quiet.
Surface: grassy/gravel.
⬛ 01/01-31/12 🔘 Water when frosty
Distance: 🚰200m ⊘beach 250m ⊗200m 🚶on the spot.
Remarks: Next to campsite Rambaud, water disconnected.

🔲🆂 **Super Besse** 🎿🏔❄ 23H1
Ronde de Vassivière. **GPS:** n45,50644 e2,85342.⬆️➡️

172 🗓€ 5,60/24h, € 37,80/8 days 🚰€1/20minutes 🗑Ch🚿(100x)€
2,40/4h 🗑🚽. **Location:** Comfortable, quiet. **Surface:** asphalted.
⬛ 01/01-31/12
Distance: 🚰300m ⊗300m 🚶on the spot 🚲300m.
Remarks: On ring-road around the lake, P5, P7 and P10, no camping
activities.

🔲🆂 **Super Lioran** 🏔🌲❄ 23H2
Aire de Laveissière, Parking Font d'Alagnon.
GPS: n45,08856 e2,73819.⬆️

25 🗓free. **Location:** Rural, simple, quiet. **Surface:** asphalted.
⬛ 01/01-31/12
Distance: ⊗200m 🛒200m 🚶50m 🚲30m 🚴30m.

🔲🆂 **Talizat** 23H2
Place du 19 mars 1962. **GPS:** n45,11417 e3,04583.

3 🗓free 🚰€2 🗑Ch🚽€2. **Location:** Rural, simple, quiet.
Surface: asphalted. ⬛ 01/01-31/12
Distance: 🚰on the spot ⊗100m 🛒100m.
Remarks: Behind town hall.

🔲🆂 **Thiel-sur-Acolin** 21A2
Rue de la Motte. **GPS:** n46,52269 e3,58776.⬆️
11 🗓free 🚰€2 🗑Ch🚿€2. **Location:** Rural, isolated, quiet.
Surface: gravel. ⬛ 01/01-31/12
Distance: 🚰650m.
Remarks: Service only by credit card.

🔲🆂 **Thiers** 21A3
Base de loisirs Iloa, D44 > Dorat. **GPS:** n45,87070 e3,48311.⬆️

🔲🆂 **St Anthème** 🏔 24B1
Rambaud. **GPS:** n45,52354 e3,91464.⬆️➡️

10 🗓free 🚰🗑free. **Location:** Rural, simple, isolated, quiet.
Surface: metalled. ⬛ 01/01-31/12
Distance: 🚵2,6km.

🔲🆂 **Thiézac** 🎎 23H2
Aire de camping-car La Sapinière, D59.
GPS: n45,01583 e2,66278.⬆️➡️

8 🗓free 🚰€2 🗑Ch🚽€2. **Location:** Rural, simple, quiet.
Surface: asphalted. ⬛ 01/01-31/12
Distance: 🚰50m ⊗100m 🛒100m.
Remarks: Max. 24h, coins at petrol station.

🔲🆂 **Tiranges** 24B1
Accueil Camping Car, La Nerceyre. **GPS:** n45,30702 e3,99107.⬆️➡️

10 🗓free 🚰€2 🗑Ch. **Location:** Rural, simple, quiet.
Surface: asphalted. ⬛ 01/01-31/12
Distance: 🚰400m.

🔲🆂 **Tourzel-Ronzières** 24A1
Aire camping-car, Chemin du Clos, D23. **GPS:** n45,52989 e3,13504.⬆️

15 🗓free 🚰🗑Ch🚽WCfree. **Location:** Rural, simple, isolated,
quiet. **Surface:** grassy/gravel. ⬛ 01/01-31/12
Distance: 🚰500m ⊗500m.

🔲🆂 **Treteau** 🌾 21A2
Rue du Rosier, D21. **GPS:** n46,36800 e3,51758.⬆️➡️

+10 🗓€3,50/night 🚰€2 🗑Ch🚽€2 WC. 🔘 **Location:** Rural,
simple, quiet. **Surface:** grassy/metalled. ⬛ 01/03-31/10
Distance: 🚰500m ⊘on the spot 🎫day pass available ⊗100m 🛒on
the spot.
Remarks: At small lake.

🔲🆂 **Valette** 🏔 23H1
Aire camping-cars, D678. **GPS:** n45,27000 e2,60222.⬆️➡️

FR

5 free €2 Ch €2. **Location:** Rural, comfortable, quiet.
Surface: gravel. 01/01-31/12 service: 01/11-01/05
Distance: 50m 100m 150m.

Valuéjols 23H2

Place de 19 Mars 1962, D34. **GPS:** n45,05333 e2,92944.

12 free €3 ChWC. **Location:** Rural, simple.
Surface: asphalted. 01/01-31/12
Distance: 400m 400m 400m on the spot.

Varennes-sur-Allier 21A2

Place Hôtel de Ville, Rue de Beaupuy. **GPS:** n46,31288 e3,40476.

30 free €2/100liter Ch €2/h WC. **Location:** Urban, simple,
central, noisy. **Surface:** metalled.
01/01-31/12
Distance: on the spot on the spot on the spot.
Remarks: Coins at town hall.

Velzic 23H2

Lavernière, Rue de Fracort. **GPS:** n45,00166 e2,54638.

5 free €3,50 Ch. **Location:** Rural, simple, isolated.
Surface: asphalted. 01/01-31/12 service: 31/10-01/04
Distance: 1km 1km 1km on the spot.
Remarks: Coins at épicerie Pas de Peyrols.

Vézac 23H2

Aire de camping-cars, Route de Cavanière.
GPS: n44,89059 e2,51779.

8 free €3,50 Ch. **Location:** Rural, simple. **Surface:** asphalted.
01/01-31/12
Distance: 100m 50m 700m.
Remarks: At golf court, coins at bar/tabac, 50m.

Vic-sur-Cère 23H2

Aire de camping-cars, Avenue des Tilleuls.
GPS: n44,98194 e2,63111.

10 free €2 Ch €2. **Location:** Rural, comfortable, quiet.
Surface: asphalted. 01/01-31/12
Distance: 200m 200m 150m.
Remarks: Coins at tourist info, Avenue Mercier.

Vieillevie 23G2

Aire de Vieillevie, Le Bourg. **GPS:** n44,64432 e2,41773.

5 free €2 Ch €2. **Location:** Rural, comfortable, quiet.
Surface: gravel. 01/01-31/12
Distance: 50m 100m 50m 50m.

Villefranche-d'Allier 20H2

Avenue du 8 Mai 1945. **GPS:** n46,39565 e2,85672.

4 free €2/10minutes Ch (4x)€2/2h. **Surface:** asphalted.
01/01-31/12
Distance: 150m 12km 150m 150m.
Remarks: Coins available at the shops.

Viverols 24B1

Camping Le Pradoux, Le Ruisseau. **GPS:** n45,43123 e3,88279.

6 free €2 Ch €2. **Surface:** gravel. 01/04-31/10

Vorey-sur-Arzon 24B1

Chemin de Félines. **GPS:** n45,18667 e3,90489.

5 €2 €3 Ch. **Surface:** gravel. service: 01/04-31/10
Distance: 200m on the spot 200m 200m on the spot
on the spot.
Remarks: Along river Arzon, coins and code wifi available at campsite.

Ytrac 23G2

Aire camping-cars, Impasse Jean de la Fontaine.
GPS: n44,91510 e2,36368.

3 free €3,50 Ch €3,50. **Location:** Rural, simple, central.
Surface: asphalted. 01/01-31/12
Distance: 150m 100m 150m.
Remarks: Coins at shops and tourist office.

Rhône Alpes

Aiguebelle 24E1

Pré de foire. **GPS:** n45,54289 e6,30635.

18 free €2/100liter Ch. **Surface:** asphalted/grassy.
01/01-31/12 Thu-morning closed because of market
Distance: on the spot 6,1km.

Tourist information Aiguebelle:
Tue-morning.

Aix-les-Bains 21E3

Avenue du Grand Port. **GPS:** n45,70504 e5,88810.

16 free free WC. **Location:** Urban, simple, noisy. **Surface:** gravel.
01/01-31/12
Distance: city centre 2km 2km Lake 100m 150m bread
service 500m on the spot.
Remarks: Max. 48h, market Wednesday and Saturday.

Alba-la-Romaine 24C3

Bragigous. **GPS:** n44,55329 e4,59741.

free €2 Ch. **Location:** Rural, quiet. **Surface:** grassy/gravel.
01/01-31/12
Distance: on the spot 200m 200m.
Remarks: Service to be paid at retirement home.

Albertville 21F3

Parking Conflans, Montée Adolphe Hugues, Conflans.
GPS: n45,67389 e6,39694.
6 free €3,50 Ch. **Surface:** asphalted.
Distance: 10 min walking.

Tourist information Albertville:
Quai des Allobroges. Thu 6-18h.

Allevard 24E1

Place du David. **GPS:** n45,38838 e6,07110.
+10 €4 ChWC free. **Location:** Rural. **Surface:** unpaved.

FR

▣ 01/01-31/12
Distance: 🛒500m ⊗300m.
Remarks: Max. 48h.

| 🅿🅂 | **Alpe d'Huez** | 24E2 |

Parking de Brandes. GPS: n45,08654 e6,07916. ⬆➡.

75 ⦿ € 10/day + € 0,40/pp tourist tax 🚰🅔Ch🅔WC. 🚮 ✎
Surface: asphalted.
Distance: 🛒1km 🎿on the spot.
Remarks: First buy a parking ticket at
Palais des Sports et des Congrès.

| 🅂 | **Alpe d'Huez** | 24E2 |

Parking l'Eclose, Rue du 93me Ram. **GPS:** n45,08796 e6,07019. ⬆➡.
25 ⦿€ 10/day + € 0,20/pp tourist tax 🚰🅔Ch🅔WC included.
Surface: asphalted.
▣ 01/12-01/04, 11/07-31/08
Distance: 🛒200m ⊗200m 🛒200m 🎿on the spot.
Remarks: First buy a parking ticket at Palais des Sports et des Congrès.

| 🅂 | **Ambierle** | 21B2 |

Complexe sportif, Rue Sainte Claude. **GPS:** n46,10663 e3,89384. ⬆➡.

3 ⦿free 🚰🅔Chfree. **Location:** Rural, simple, quiet.
Surface: asphalted.
Distance: 🛒on the spot ⊗200m 🛒300m.
Remarks: At sports park.

| 🅂 | **Amplepuis** | 21B3 |

Rue Paul de la Goutte. **GPS:** n45,97027 e4,33085. ⬆.
⦿free 🚰🅔Chfree. **Surface:** asphalted.
Distance: 🛒on the spot ⊗50m 🛒100m 🚂on the spot.
Remarks: Behind gymnasium.

| 🅂 | **Annecy** | 21E3 |

Parking de Colmyr, Rue des Marquisats, N1508.
GPS: n45,89070 e6,13915. ⬆➡.

14 ⦿free 🚰🅔Chfree. **Location:** Urban, simple, central, quiet.
Surface: asphalted.
▣ 01/01-31/12
Distance: 🛒700m 🛒100m 🛒on the spot ⊗700m 🛒700m.
Remarks: Max. 24h, market days Tuesday, Friday, Sunday.

Tourist information Annecy:
ℹ Office de Tourisme, Bonlieu, 1 rue Jean Jaurès, www.lac-annecy.com. Located on lake of the same name and surrounded by mountain peaks. The old city centre exists of covered lanes, canals and bridges. ⛺ Place de Romains. ▣ Tue 7-19h.

| 🅂 | **Anthy-sur-Léman** | 21F2 |

Rue du Lac. **GPS:** n46,35889 e6,42192.

5 ⦿free. **Surface:** gravel.
Distance: 🛒700m 🏊50m ⊗on the spot.
Remarks: Max. 48h, max. 7m.

| 🅂 | **Arçon** | 21B3 |

Le Bourg. **GPS:** n46,00977 e3,88793. ⬆➡.

3 ⦿free 🚰🅔Chfree. **Location:** Rural, simple, quiet.
▣ 01/01-31/12
Distance: 🛒on the spot ⊗50m.

| 🅂 | **Arlebosc** | 24C2 |

Place du Marché aux Fruits. **GPS:** n45,03683 e4,65238. ⬆.

10 ⦿free 🚰🅔Chfree. **Location:** Rural, simple. **Surface:** gravel.
▣ 01/01-31/12
Distance: 🛒on the spot 🛒bakery 150m 🚶on the spot.

| 🅂 | **Aubignas** | 24C3 |

Aire camping-cars. GPS: n44,58732 e4,63177.

10 ⦿voluntary contribution € 2 🚰€2/100liter 🅔ChWC.
Surface: gravel.
Distance: 🛒300m.
Remarks: Beautiful view.

| 🅂 | **Balazuc** | 24B3 |

Parking Champsgelly, La Croisette. **GPS:** n44,50601 e4,37366. ⬆➡.

⦿free. **Location:** Rural. **Surface:** gravel. ▣ 01/01-31/12
Distance: 🛒1km.

| 🅂 | **Banne** | 24B3 |

Quartier l'Eglise, D251. **GPS:** n44,36539 e4,15691. ⬆.

25 ⦿free 🚰€2/60liter 🅔Ch🛒€2/1h 🛶2.
Surface: gravel/metalled. ▣ 01/01-31/12
Distance: 🛒500m.
Remarks: Behind church, beautiful view.

| 🅂 | **Barjac** | 24B3 |

Rue Pierre Andre Benoit. **GPS:** n44,30589 e4,34343. ⬆.

20 ⦿free 🚰🅔Ch🛒€3,water 10min + electricity 55min.
Location: Simple.
▣ 01/01-31/12
Distance: 🛒100m ⊗100m 🛒on the spot.
Remarks: Coins at tourist info and town hall, friday market.

| 🅂 | **Beausemblant** | 24C1 |

Aire camping-cars, D122. **GPS:** n45,21826 e4,83282. ⬆➡.

6 ⦿free 🚰🅔Chfree. **Location:** Simple. **Surface:** gravel.
Distance: 🛒100m ⊗100m 🚶on the spot.
Remarks: Max. 48h.

| 🅂 | **Belleville** | 21C2 |

Ancienne Avenue du Port. **GPS:** n46,10626 e4,75470. ⬆.

8 ⦿free 🚰🅔Chfree. **Surface:** asphalted. ▣ 01/01-31/12
Distance: 🛒centre 500m 🛣A6 900m ⊗500m 🛒500m.

| 🅂 | **Belley** | 21D3 |

Route de Saint-Germain, D41. **GPS:** n45,75535 e5,67790. ⬆.

20 ⦿free 🚰€2 🅔Ch🛒€2. **Location:** Urban, simple, central, quiet.
Surface: asphalted. ▣ 01/01-31/12
Distance: 🛒city centre 1km ⊗1km 🛒1km 🚂1km.
Remarks: Near sports park, service only with 1-euro coins.

| 🅂 | **Belmont-de-la-Loire** | 21B2 |

Place de l'Église. **GPS:** n46,16543 e4,34634. ⬆.

FR

2 ⌁free 🚰 🗑Ch♻2 WCfree. **Location:** Rural, simple, quiet.
Surface: metalled. ◻ 03/03-19/07, 01/08-31/10
Distance: 🚶50m ⊗100m 🚆100m ⎯ on the spot.

⏚S Berrias-et-Casteljau 🌿🏕 24B3
Place du 7 juillet, Les Borels. **GPS:** n44,39956 e4,21332.⬆

⌁free 🚰🗑Ch♻€3. **Surface:** gravel. ◻ 01/01-31/12
Distance: 🚶Berias-et-Casteljau 3,5km.

⏚S Bibost 21C3
D91. **GPS:** n45,79500 e4,55144.⬆
⌁free 🚰🗑Ch♻free. **Location:** Rural, quiet. **Surface:** gravel.
◻ 01/01-31/12
Remarks: Beautiful view.

⏚S Boën 21B3
Boulevard Moizieux. **GPS:** n45,74401 e4,00263.⬆

⌁free 🚰🗑Chfree. **Surface:** gravel. ◻ 01/01-31/12
Distance: 🚶200m ⊗200m 🚆300m.

⏚S Boulieu-lès-Annonay 🌿 24C1
Chemin du Lavoir. **GPS:** n45,26928 e4,66963.⬆➡

6 ⌁free 🚰🗑ChWCfree. **Location:** Rural, comfortable, quiet.
Surface: gravel.
Distance: 🚶400m ⊗400m 🚆400m.
Remarks: Voluntary contribution, market on Sunday.

⏚S Bourg-en-Bresse 🌿🍽 21D2
Parking V.L./Bus, Boulevard de Brou. **GPS:** n46,19854 e5,23766.⬆

10 ⌁free WC100m. **Location:** Urban, simple, central, noisy.
Surface: asphalted. ◉ Wed, Sa
Distance: 🚶on the spot ⊘6km ⊗100m 🚆200m ⎯on the spot
♻ on the spot.

⏚S Bourg-Saint-Andéol 24C3
Chemin de la Barrière. **GPS:** n44,37520 e4,64327.⬆

30 ⌁free 🚰🗑Ch♻free. **Surface:** asphalted. ◻ 01/01-31/12
Distance: 🚶750m 🚆50m Lidl.
Remarks: Along railwayline, max. 48h.

⏚S Bourg-Saint-Maurice 🏔🌲❄ 24F1
Arc1600. **GPS:** n45,59523 e6,78951.
20 ⌁🚰€2 🗑Ch⎯€2. ◻ 01/01-31/12
Distance: 🚶Bourg St.Maurice 15km.

ⒸS Bourget-du-Lac 🏔🌲 21E3
International au l'Île de Cygnes. **GPS:** n45,65250 e5,86378.⬆➡

32 ⌁🚰€ 5,90-10,65 🚰🗑ChWC♻📶included. 🚐🛏 **Location:** Rural,
comfortable, quiet. **Surface:** metalled. ◻ 01/01-31/12 ◉ service:
01/12-01/03
Distance: 🚶500m ⊘500m ⛱beach 300m ⎯100m ⊗on the spot
🚆on the spot ⎯100m ♻on the spot 🚶on the spot.

⏚S Bourgneuf 24E1
Aire camping-cars, D925. **GPS:** n45,55257 e6,21091.⬆

30 ⌁free 🚰€2 🗑Ch. ◻ 01/01-31/12
Distance: ⊘5km ⊗Brasserie/Pizzeria 🥖bakery.
Remarks: Coins available at Pizzeria/Tabac.

⏚S Bouvante 🏔❄ 24D2
Font d'Urle, Font d'Urle. **GPS:** n44,89789 e5,32195.⬆

10 ⌁free 🚰€2/100liter 🗑Ch♻(5x)€7/24h WC♻€
2/time. **Location:** Simple, quiet. **Surface:** gravel.
◻ 01/01-31/12, service: 01/06-31/08
Distance: 🚆on the spot 🚶nordic walking 🎿on the spot.
Remarks: Altitude 1550m, coins at riding school.

⏚S Chalmazel 🌿❄ 21B3
Le Bourg Le Pont d'Ouest. **GPS:** n45,70149 e3,85459.⬆

---

8 ⌁free 🚰€2 🗑Ch♻€2/4h. **Location:** Comfortable.
Surface: metalled. ◻ 01/01-31/12
Distance: 🚶1km ⛱on the spot ⊗50m 🚆50m ⎯on the spot 🚶on
the spot 🎣2km.
Remarks: Along river.

⏚S Chambéry 🌿🏔🌲❄ 24E1
Rue Costa de Beauregard. **GPS:** n45,56289 e5,93302.⬆
6 ⌁free 🚰🗑Chfree.
Location: Urban. **Surface:** asphalted.
Distance: 🚶500m ⊘1,2km ⊗500m 🚆500m.
Remarks: Water closed during wintertime.

Tourist information Chambéry:
👁 Vieux Cité. Historical centre with old mansions.
👁 Château des Ducs de Savoie. Complex of buildings, 13-14th century.

⏚S Chamonix-Mont-Blanc 🌿🏔🌲❄ 21F3
Parking Grépon, Aiguille du Midi, D1506. **GPS:** n45,91578 e6,86970.⬆

50 ⌁🚰€ 12,50/24h 🚰🗑ChWCfree. 🚐 **Surface:** asphalted.
◻ 01/01-31/12, service only during summer period
Distance: 🚶1km ⊗350m 🚆600m.

Tourist information Chamonix-Mont-Blanc:
🚠 Aiguille du Midi. Telpher carrier from Chamonix (1036 m.) To Aiguille
de Midi (3842m).
🚠 Montenvers et mer de Glace. Tramline from Montenvers to the ice
lake, a glacier of 7 km long and 1.2 km broad.

⏚S Chamrousse ❄ 24E2
Place des Niverolles, Rue de la Cembraie. **GPS:** n45,12666 e5,87356.

12 ⌁🚰€8 🚰🗑Ch♻included. **Surface:** asphalted. ◻ 01/01-31/12
Distance: 🚶400m ⊗400m 🎿400m.
Remarks: Max. 24h.

🍽S Charix 🌿🌲🌊 21D2
Auberge du Lac Genin. **GPS:** n46,21981 e5,69556.⬆

20 ⌁🚰€ 5 + € 0,20/pp tourist tax, guests free 🚰🗑Chfree.🚿
Location: Rural, simple, isolated, quiet.
Surface: gravel.
Distance: 🚶4,7km ⛱lake ⎯on the spot ⊗on the spot ♻on the
spot 🚶on the spot.

⏚S Charlieu 🌿🌊 21B2
Place d'Eningen. **GPS:** n46,16031 e4,17813.⬆

FR

5 🚐 free 🚰 Ch WC free. **Location:** Rural. **Surface:** gravel/metalled.
📅 01/01-31/12
Distance: 🏘 historical centre 500m 🍴 500m 🍞 500m.
Remarks: In front of police station.

🚐 S Charols 24C3

Aire municipale, D9. **GPS**: n44,59160 e4,95441.

10 🚐 free 🚰 🚽 free. **Surface:** asphalted. 📅 01/01-31/12
Distance: 🏘 200m 🍴 200m 🍞 50m.

🚐 S Chichilianne 24D2

Passière. **GPS**: n44,81226 e5,57532.[↑].

🚐 free 🚰 €3 🚽 Ch. **Surface:** grassy. 📅 01/01-31/12 ⊙ water disconnected in winter
Distance: 🏘 on the spot 🍴 on the spot.
Remarks: Coins at town hall or Maison du Parc.

🚐 S Clansayes 24C3

Aire de Toronne, Quartier Toronne RD133.
GPS: n44,36975 e4,79901.[↑].

25 🚐 € 10, Jul/Aug € 13 🚰 🚽 Ch 🔌 €4/day WC 🚿 €4/time 📶.
🐕 **Location:** Rural, comfortable, luxurious, isolated, quiet.
Surface: grassy/gravel. 📅 01/01-31/12
Distance: 🏘 2km 🎣 10km 🍴 buvette-menu rapide-restauration 🍞 3km.
Remarks: Bread-service.

🚐 S Colombier-le-Jeune 24C2

Place de la Marie, Le Bourg. **GPS**: n45,01106 e4,70132.[↑].

🚐 free 🚰 🚽 Ch free. **Location:** Rural. **Surface:** metalled.
📅 01/01-31/12 ⊙ water disconnected in winter
Distance: 🏘 on the spot 🍴 on the spot 🍞 on the spot 🚶 on the spot.

🚐 S Cornas 24C2

Impasse de Iris, Grande Rue, D86. **GPS**: n44,96024 e4,84722.[↑].

5 🚐 free 🚰 🚽 Ch free. **Location:** Simple. **Surface:** gravel.
📅 01/01-31/12
Distance: 🏘 200m 🍴 200m 🍞 bakery 200m.
Remarks: Max. 48h, several 'Caves' with wine tasting.

🚐 S Coucouron 24B2

Les Eygades. **GPS**: n44,80168 e3,96148.[↑].

30 🚐 01/05-30/09 € 7/day 🚰 🚽 Ch 🪙 included. 🐕 **Location:** Rural, simple. **Surface:** gravel. 📅 01/01-31/12
Distance: 🏘 1km 🎣 on the spot 🍴 on the spot 🍞 1km 🚶 on the spot.
Remarks: At Lac de Coucouron, max. 7 days, outside season free stay on campsite municipal (no facilities).

🚐 S Cours-la-Ville 21B2

La Rivière. **GPS**: n46,10399 e4,32315.[↑].

10 🚐 free 🚰 🚽 Ch free. **Location:** Rural, simple.
Surface: grassy/gravel. 📅 01/01-31/12
Distance: 🏘 300m 🍴 on the spot 🚌 on the spot 🚶 on the spot.
Remarks: Along the river Trambouze, to be reached from northern direction, Boulevard Pierre de Coubertin.

🚐 Courtenay 21D3

Etang de Salette. **GPS**: n45,72417 e5,37124.[↑].

7 🚐 free. **Location:** Rural, isolated, quiet. **Surface:** gravel.
Distance: 🏘 1km 🍴 Pizzeria 🍞 bread service 1,2km 🚶 on the spot.

🚐 S Crémieu 21D3

Rue du 19 mars 1962. **GPS**: n45,72549 e5,24670.[↑].

12 🚐 free 🚰 🚽 Ch free. **Location:** Urban, simple, central.
Surface: asphalted. 📅 01/01-31/12
Distance: 🏘 300m 🍴 250m 🍞 300m 🚌 100m.

🚐 S Crest 24C2

Place du Champ de Mars, Avenue Agirond. **GPS**: n44,72600 e5,02100.[↑].

17 🚐 free 🚰 🚽 Ch 🪙 €5,10min. water + 1h electricity 📶 free.
Location: Urban, simple. **Surface:** asphalted. 📅 01/01-31/12
Distance: 🏘 200m 🍴 pizzeria 🍞 bakery 50m.

🚐 S De Saint-Victor 24B1

Base Nautique du lac de Grangent. **GPS**: n45,44787 e4,25626.[↑][→].

10 🚐 free 🚰 🚽 Ch free 🔌 (4x)€2,60/4h WC. **Location:** Rural, comfortable. **Surface:** asphalted. 📅 01/01-31/12
Distance: 🏖 on the spot 🎣 on the spot 🍴 on the spot.
Remarks: Max. 72h, coins at the shops in the village.

🚐 S Die 24D2

Aire de Meyrosse, Avenue du Maréchal Leclerc, D238.
GPS: n44,75103 e5,37385.[↑].

30 🚐 € 5/24h 🚰 🚽 Ch WC free. **Surface:** grassy/gravel.
📅 01/01-31/12
Distance: 🏘 300m 🍴 300m 🍞 1km.
Remarks: Max. 1 night, pay at Police Municpale.

🚐 S Donzère 24C3

Aire de respos. **GPS**: n44,44060 e4,71899.[↑][→].

🚐 free 🚰 🚽 Ch WC free. **Surface:** asphalted. 📅 01/01-31/12
Distance: 🏘 500m ⛽ 7km.
Remarks: Near RN7.

🚐 S Eyzin-Pinet 24C1

Rue du Stade. **GPS**: n45,47463 e4,99965.[↑].

6 🚐 free 🚰 🚽 Ch free. **Location:** Rural, simple, central, quiet.
Surface: gravel. 📅 01/01-31/12
Distance: 🏘 50m 🍴 50m 🍞 20m 🚲 on the spot 🚶 on the spot.

FR

⬛S Faverges 🏕️🍴🏖️ 21E3

Route d'Annecy, D2508. **GPS:** n45,74943 e6,28626. ⬆️➡️.

20 🚰free 🚽🔌Chfree. **Location:** Rural, simple, noisy.
Surface: gravel. ⬛ 01/01-31/12 🔘 Service: winter
Distance: 🛒800m ⊗800m 📍on the spot 🎿100m 🏊100m.
Remarks: Max. 48h, market Wednesday.

⬛S Flaine 21F3

Parking P1. GPS: n46,00377 e6,69083.

25 🚰€5. **Surface:** gravel. ⬛ 01/01-31/12
Distance: 🎿on the spot.
Remarks: Parking at skipistes.

⬛S Fontanes 24C1

Hameau Chantemerle. **GPS:** n45,54681 e4,44027. ⬆️.

3 🚰free 🚽🔌Chfree. **Location:** Rural, simple, quiet.
Surface: asphalted. ⬛ 01/01-31/12
Distance: 🛒500m 🚲13km 🚶400m.
Remarks: At tennis-courts, inclining pitches.

⬛S Gervans 24C2

Place des Amandiers, Rue de l'école. **GPS:** n45,10932 e4,83031. ⬆️➡️.

4 🚰free 🚽🔌Chfree. **Location:** Simple. **Surface:** gravel.
Distance: 🛒on the spot 🍴on the spot 🚶on the spot.
Remarks: Max. 24h, no camping activities.

⬛S Grane 24C2

Domaine Distaise, D104. **GPS:** n44,75564 e4,86768. ⬆️➡️.

15 🚰€2/pp 🚽📶. **Surface:** grassy. ⬛ 01/01-31/12

⬛S Gresse-en-Vercors 24D2

D8D, La Ville. **GPS:** n44,89184 e5,54766.

🚰free 🚽🔌Ch. **Surface:** gravel.
Distance: 🛒on the spot.
Remarks: Max. 24h, service on campsite.

⬛S Hauteluce 🏕️🏔️❄️ 21F3

Parking de la Fôret, Tetras, D123. **GPS:** n45,74633 e6,53441.

5 🚰free 🚽€2 🔌Ch🔲€2. **Surface:** gravel. ⬛ 01/01-31/12
Distance: 🛒3km ⊗3km 🍴3km.

⬛S Hauteluce 🏕️🏔️❄️ 21F3

Parking Du Col des Saisies, D218b. **GPS:** n45,76297 e6,53382. ⬆️➡️.

40 🚰€8 🚽€2 🔌Ch🔲€2 WC. **Surface:** asphalted. ⬛ 01/01-31/12
Distance: 🛒500m ⊗on the spot 🍴500m 🎿200m 🏊200m.

⬛S Hauterives ⚓ 24C1

D538. **GPS:** n45,25497 e5,03022.

🚰free, 01/04-31/10 €5/24h 🚽€2/50liter 🔌Chincluded WCfree.
Location: Rural, simple. **Surface:** gravel.
Distance: 🛒250m ⊗250m.
Tourist information Hauterives:
👁 Palais Idéal du Facteur Cheval.

⬛S Illiat 🌊 21C2

GPS: n46,18495 e4,88802. ⬆️.

4 🚰free 🚽🔌ChWCfree. **Location:** Rural, simple, quiet.
Surface: gravel. ⬛ 01/01-31/12
Distance: 🛒650m 🏊on the spot 🚣on the spot ⊗650m 🚲on the spot 🚶on the spot.
Remarks: At small lake.

⬛S Izernore 🌿 21D2

Rue de l'Oignin. **GPS:** n46,21847 e5,55041. ⬆️.

---

15 🚰free 🚽🔌Chfree.
Location: Rural, simple, central, quiet.
⬛ 01/01-31/12
Distance: 🛒on the spot 🚲6km 🍴500m 🍴500m 🚲500m 🚶500m.
Remarks: On the foot of the Monts Berthiand.

⬛S Joux 🍴🌿 21B3

Salle des Fêtes, La Noirie, D79. **GPS:** n45,88869 e4,37587. ⬆️.

10 🚰free 🚽🔌Chfree. **Location:** Rural. **Surface:** asphalted.
⬛ 01/01-31/12 🔘 water disconnected in winter
Distance: 🛒200m 🚲3,2km 🍴200m 🍴200m.
Remarks: Nearby castle garden.

⬛S La Balme de Sillingy 🌳 21E3

Aire de Camping-cars Domaine du Tornet, D508.
GPS: n45,97124 e6,03135. ⬆️.

30 🚰€5 🚽🔌Chfree. 🚲 **Location:** Rural, simple, central, quiet.
Surface: gravel. ⬛ 01/04-31/10
Distance: 🎣100m (fishing permit available) ⊗100m 🚶on the spot.
Remarks: Recreation park, max. 48h.

⬛ La Clusaz 21F3

Route des Confins. **GPS:** n45,92298 e6,48380.
🚰free. **Surface:** asphalted. ⬛ 01/01-31/12
Remarks: Parking at pistes.

⬛S La Féclaz 🌿🏕️🌳❄️ 21E3

Aire Camping-cars de la Féclaz, D206a. **GPS:** n45,64210 e5,98411. ⬆️.

40 🚰€4 🚽€1,50 🔌Ch🔲€1,50 📶. **Surface:** asphalted.
⬛ 01/01-31/12
Distance: 🛒on the spot ⊗on the spot 🍴on the spot 📍300m.

⬛S Lablachère 24B3

La Ferme Théâtre, D104, Notre Dame. **GPS:** n44,45481 e4,22004. ⬆️.

FR

20 🛏 € 5/24h, guests free ⟨water⟩€2 ⟨electric⟩€3/12h. **Location:** Rural.
Surface: gravel.
🗓 01/01-31/12
Distance: 🛒1km ⊗150m.
Remarks: Max. 24h, theater, regional products.

Lachamp-Raphaël 24B2
D122, Le Village. **GPS:** n44,81133 e4,28860. ⬆.

5 🛏 free ⟨water⟩€2 Ch. **Location:** Rural, simple, quiet. **Surface:** gravel.
🗓 01/01-31/12
Distance: 🛒300m ⊗300m 🍞Bread 300m 🚶departure Nordic.
Remarks: Altitude 1330m, 2013: during inspection service out of order, coins at bar/hotel, beautiful view.

Lalouvesc 24C2
Vallon d'Or, Sainte Agathe. **GPS:** n45,11947 e4,53384. ⬆.

3 🛏 free WC. **Location:** Simple, central. **Surface:** asphalted.
🗓 01/01-31/12
Distance: 🛒on the spot ⊗100m 🛒100m.

Lalouvesc 24C2
La Fontaine. **GPS:** n45,12149 e4,53393. ⬆.

⟨water⟩€2/15minutes Ch ⟨electric⟩€2.
🗓 15/05-15/10
Remarks: Coins at petrol station and camping municipal.

Lamastre 24C2
Parking Pont de Tain, Place Pradon. **GPS:** n44,98672 e4,58001. ⬆.

20 🛏 free ⟨water⟩€4,40/100liter Ch ⟨electric⟩€2,20/1h ⟨waste⟩. **Location:** Simple.
Surface: asphalted. 🗓 01/01-31/12
Distance: 🛒on the spot ⊗on the spot 🛒on the spot.

Lamure-sur-Azergues 21C3
Place de la gare. **GPS:** n46,06120 e4,49185. ⬆➡.

10 🛏 free ⟨water⟩€2 Ch ⟨electric⟩€2 WC. **Location:** Rural, simple.
Surface: asphalted.
🗓 01/01-31/12
Distance: 🛒on the spot ⊗100m 🛒100m 🚂train/bus 🚶on the spot.
Remarks: Near train station.

Lans-en-Vercors 24D2
Route de l'Aigle. **GPS:** n45,12570 e5,59002. ⬆➡.

30 🛏 free ⟨water⟩Ch WC free. **Location:** Rural, simple. **Surface:** gravel.
🗓 01/01-31/12
Distance: 🛒500m 🛒on the spot.
Remarks: Large parking, tuesday and Saturday market.

Lathuile 21E3
Les Jardin du Tailleter, 190 route de la Porte, Bout du lac, N 508.
GPS: n45,79480 e6,20796. ⬆➡.

24 🛏 € 8 ⟨water⟩Ch included ⟨electric⟩(24x)€2 ⟨wifi⟩. **Location:** Rural,
simple. **Surface:** grassy. 🗓 01/06-31/08
Distance: ⛱Lake of Annecy 750m.
Remarks: Max. 24h.

Le Bessat 24C1
Croix de Chaubouret. **GPS:** n45,36812 e4,52768. ⬆.

4 🛏 free ⟨water⟩€2,50/20minutes Ch ⟨electric⟩(4x)€2,50/6h. **Location:** Rural.
Surface: asphalted.
🗓 01/01-31/12
Distance: 🛒1km ⊗100m 🚵mountainbike trail 🚶on the spot 🛒on the spot.
Remarks: Altitude 1200m, coins at Chalet des Alpes and the shops.

Le Cheylard 24C2
Super U, Chemin du pre-jalla, ZI la Palisse.
GPS: n44,91143 e4,44162. ⬆.

20 🛏 free ⟨water⟩€2 Ch ⟨electric⟩€2. **Location:** Simple, noisy.
Surface: asphalted. 🗓 01/01-31/12
Distance: ⊗on the spot 🛒on the spot.
Remarks: Max. 24h.

Le Cheylas 24E1
Avenue de la Libération. **GPS:** n45,37170 e5,99014.
🛏 free ⟨water⟩Ch WC free. **Surface:** asphalted/metalled.
Distance: 🛒on the spot 🛒nearby.

Le Grand Bornand 21F3
Route de La Broderie. **GPS:** n45,94144 e6,43636.

10 🛏 free. **Surface:** metalled. 🗓 01/01-31/12
Distance: 🛒600m 🛒on the spot.
Remarks: Max. 48h.

Le Lac d'Issarlès 24B2
D16. **GPS:** n44,81948 e4,06156. ⬆.

16 🛏 € 8,50 + € 0,25/pp tourist tax ⟨water⟩Ch ⟨electric⟩ WC included.
Location: Central. **Surface:** metalled.
🗓 01/05-31/10
Distance: 🛒100m ⊗100m 🛒100m.
Remarks: Attention: this town is not Issarlès!.

Le Reposoir 21F3
Route Departementale D204. **GPS:** n46,01010 e6,53648.

10 🛏 free ⟨water⟩Ch free WC. **Surface:** metalled.
Distance: 🛒150m 🚶on the spot.

Le Teil 24C3
Alleé Paul Avon. **GPS:** n44,55138 e4,68972. ⬆.

6 🛏 free ⟨water⟩Ch free.
Location: Noisy. **Surface:** grassy/metalled.
Distance: ⛱on the spot ⊗on the spot 🛒500m.
Remarks: Nearby D86.

Tourist information Le Teil:
🏠 🗓 Thu morning.

Les Carroz-Arâches 21F3
Télécabine Les Cluses. **GPS:** n46,02500 e6,64361.

🛏 free ⟨water⟩Ch ⟨electric⟩free. 🗓 01/06-30/11
Distance: 🛒500m ⊗500m.
Remarks: Parking funicular railway.

FR

Les Deux-Alpes — 24E2

Avenue de la Muzelle, D213. **GPS:** n45,02394 e6,12120. ⬆.
€7 Ch included. **Surface:** asphalted. ● winter
Remarks: Beautiful view.

Les Gets 🚠🏔❄ — 21F2

Route du Front de Neige. **GPS:** n46,14992 e6,65673. ⬆.

25 € 0,90/pp tourist tax, winter € 17 Ch.
Surface: gravel. ● 01/01-31/12
Distance: 1km on the spot.
Remarks: Max. 7 days, bus to centre every 30 minutes.
Tourist information Les Gets:
Week market. ● Thu-morning.

Les Granges-Gontardes — 24C3

Domaine de la Tour d'Elyssas, Quartier Combe d'Elissas.
GPS: n44,41811 e4,75465.

15 free Ch free. **Surface:** gravel. ● 01/01-31/12
Distance: 9km.
Remarks: At wine-grower.

Les Houches — 21F3

Aire d'accueil camping-car Mont Blanc, 500 route du Pont.
GPS: n45,89257 e6,81706. ⬆➡.
22 € 15 Ch included. **Location:** Comfortable, isolated,
quiet. **Surface:** gravel. ● 01/04-30/11
Distance: 2,5km 1km 500m.

Les Karellis — 24F1

GPS: n45,22778 e6,40639.
free. ● 01/01-31/12
Remarks: Mountain station nearby St.Jean-de-Maurienne.

Les Menuires 🚠🏔❄ — 24F1

Les Bruyères, Dir Val Thorens. **GPS:** n45,32557 e6,53414. ⬆➡.
70 € 10/24h + € 0,20/pp tourist tax Ch (7x)€2/4h WC.
Surface: asphalted. ● 01/01-31/12
Distance: on the spot on the spot on the spot.
Remarks: Near the pistes.

Les Noës — 21B3

Le Bourg, D47. **GPS:** n46,04083 e3,85206. ⬆.

3 free Ch free. **Location:** Rural, simple, quiet.
Surface: gravel. ● 01/01-31/12
Distance: on the spot 50m.

Les Sauvages — 21B3

D121. **GPS:** n45,92083 e4,37711. ⬆➡.

free Ch free. **Location:** Rural, simple, quiet. **Surface:** gravel.
● 01/01-31/12
Distance: on the spot 100m 100m on the spot.

Mâcot-la-Plagne 🏔❄ — 24F1

GPS: n45,50677 e6,68652. ⬆.
46 free, Winter € 10 €2 Ch €4/8h. **Surface:** asphalted.
● 01/01-31/12
Distance: on the spot.

Marsanne — 24C3

Avenue de Bailliecourt, D57. **GPS:** n44,64568 e4,87175. ⬆.

10 free Ch free.
Location: Rural, quiet. **Surface:** grassy.
Distance: 300m 300m nearby.
Remarks: Max. 48h, medieval village.

Megève — 21F3

Chemin des Ânes. **GPS:** n45,86401 e6,62010.
free. ● 01/01-31/12
Remarks: In front of parking Télécabine du Jaillet.

Meyras — 24B2

Aire camping-cars, Grande rue, D26. **GPS:** n44,67939 e4,26847. ⬆.

15 €4 €3 Ch €3. **Surface:** asphalted. ● 01/04-31/10
Distance: 200m 200m nearby.
Remarks: Max. 48h, coins at the shops in the village.

Mijoux 🌼🚠🏔🌲❄ — 21E2

D50, Route de la Combe-en-Haut. **GPS:** n46,36963 e6,00247. ⬆➡.

20 free €3,50 Ch €3,50. **Surface:** gravel. ● Service:
winter
Distance: 500m 500m 500m on the spot on the spot.
Remarks: Coins at town hall and supermarket.

Mirabel-aux-Baronnies — 24D3

Aire camping-cars, Chemin des Grottes. **GPS:** n44,31260 e5,09968. ⬆.

free Ch free. **Location:** Rural, simple, quiet. **Surface:** gravel.
● 01/01-31/12
Distance: on the spot 100m 100m on the spot.

Montalieu-Vercieu — 21D3

Chamboud. **GPS:** n45,82776 e5,42100. ⬆.

6+10 voluntary contribution Ch free. **Location:** Rural.
Surface: grassy/metalled. ● 01/01-31/12
Distance: 200m.

6 free Ch WC campsite. **Location:** Rural, simple, isolated,
quiet. **Surface:** asphalted.
Distance: 2km 2km 2km 1,5km.
Remarks: Next to campsite/Base de Loisirs de la Vallée Bleue, max. 2
nights.

Montbrison-sur-Lez — 24C3

Place Publique. GPS: n44,43663 e5,01779. ⬆.

6 free free. **Surface:** metalled. ● 01/01-31/12
Distance: 100m 100m 100m.

Montbrison-sur-Lez — 24C3

GPS: n44,42751 e5,02438. ⬆.

€2/60liter Ch €2. **Location:** Isolated.
Remarks: Coins at bar and garage.

Montbrun-les-Bains 🌼🍃 — 27D1

Toscan. **GPS:** n44,17247 e5,43881. ⬆➡.

10 free. **Location:** Rural, quiet. **Surface:** grassy.
● 01/01-31/12
Distance: 500m 300m 400m on the spot 400m Tour de
la Citadelle.

Montbrun-les-Bains 🌼🍃 — 27D1

Condamine. **GPS:** n44,17413 e5,44071. ⬆.
€2 Ch €2.

Montélimar   24C3

Domaine du Bois de Laud, Chemin du Bois de Laud.
GPS: n44,56522 e4,75691.

17 €4,30 Chincluded. Location: Urban.
Surface: grassy/metalled. 01/01-31/12
Distance: 500m 100m.
Remarks: Near centre commercial Leclerc, max. 48h.

Morillon   21F3

GPS: n46,08289 e6,67968.
10 free ChWCfree. **Surface:** asphalted.
Distance: 200m 100m 300m 100m.

Nantua   21D2

D74. **GPS:** n46,15497 e5,59656.

13 €7 + €0,20/pp tourist tax Chfree WC.
Location: Urban, comfortable, central. **Surface:** gravel.
01/04-30/09
Distance: 700m 7km on the spot on the spot 150m
150m on the spot on the spot.
Remarks: At Nantua lake.

Noirétable   21B3

Aire d'accueil de camping-cars, Lieu-dit La Roche.
GPS: n45,80674 e3,77133.

7 free €3 Ch €1/2h. **Location:** Simple, quiet.
Surface: metalled. 01/01-31/12
Distance: 800m 100m 100m 100m 800m on the
spot on the spot.
Remarks: Next to campsite (50m), coins at campsite.

Nyons   24D3

Promenade la Digue. **GPS:** n44,35778 e5,13861.

20 €9/24h ChWCincluded. **Surface:** gravel.
01/01-31/12
Distance: 250m 250m 250m 250m.
Remarks: Next to Parc loisirs aquatique, max. 48h.

Nyons   24D3

Domaine Rocheville, D 538. **GPS:** n44,36850 e5,11775.

6 €6, 2 pers.incl €4/100liter Ch €3,50
WC included,summer free. **Surface:** grassy.

Tourist information Nyons:
Pavillon du Tourisme, Place de la Libération. Important Olive-city in
the Provence.
Musée de l'Olivier. Museum about the olive-tree and production of
olive oil. daily 01/11-28/02 Su.
Centre-ville. Regional market. Thu-morning.

Orgnac l'Aven   24B3

Le Fez, D217. **GPS:** n44,30419 e4,43240.

5 free Chfree. **Location:** Rural. **Surface:** gravel.
01/01-31/12
Distance: 200m 10m 300m.
Remarks: Caves of Aven d'Orgnac 2km.

Panissières   21B3

Aire camping-cars, Allée des Acacias. **GPS:** n45,78835 e4,34355.

4 €6,50 Ch included4 WC use sanitary €3,30/pp.
Location: Rural, simple, quiet. **Surface:** metalled. 01/01-31/12
Service: winter
Distance: 300m 300m 300m.
Remarks: Use sanitary € 2,40/pp per day.

Planfoy   24C1

Chemin du Vignolet. **GPS:** n45,37445 e4,44910.

10 free €2,50/15minutes Ch (8x)€2,50/6h.
Location: Rural, comfortable, quiet. **Surface:** asphalted.
01/01-31/12
Distance: 1,3km 7km 1,3km on the spot.
Remarks: Coins at the shops in the village.

Pont-de-Veyle   21C2

D933, Rue de la Poste. **GPS:** n46,26437 e4,88697.

20 free . **Location:** Urban, simple, central, noisy.
Surface: gravel.
Distance: on the spot 3,5km on the spot on the spot
50m 150m.

Pontcharra-sur-Turdine   21C3

Place A. Schweitzer. **GPS:** n45,87405 e4,49133.

4 free ChWCfree. **Location:** Urban. 01/01-31/12
Distance: 50m on the spot 50m 50m on the spot.

Pouilly-sous-Charlieu   21B2

Place du Marché, Rue de la République. **GPS:** n46,14335 e4,10832.
free ChWCfree. **Surface:** asphalted. Su-morning
(market)
Distance: on the spot.

Pouilly-sous-Charlieu   21B2

Rue de la Berge. **GPS:** n46,14699 e4,10075.
4 free. **Surface:** gravel. 01/01-31/12
Remarks: Parking at the Loire river.

Prapoutel-les-Sept-Laux   24E1

D281. **GPS:** n45,25769 e5,99785.

free WC. **Surface:** metalled. 01/01-31/12
Distance: 50m.
Remarks: Parking at pistes.

Privas   24C2

Avenue de la gare. **GPS:** n44,73134 e4,59309.

10 free Ch. **Location:** Urban. **Surface:** gravel/metalled.
01/01-31/12
Distance: centre 750m.

Puy-Saint-Martin   24C3

Aire de camping-car. **GPS:** n44,62753 e4,97492.

FR

13 ⬛free ⛽🍽Ch.
Location: Rural, comfortable. **Surface:** grassy.
Distance: 🚶on the spot 🚰50m 🛒bakery 300m.
Remarks: Former campsite, max. 48h, voluntary contribution.

🏕S Renaison 🌳⛵🏖👫 21B3
GPS: n46,04757 e3,92124.⬆➡.

5 ⬛free ⛽🍽Chfree. **Location:** Rural, simple, quiet.
Surface: grassy/gravel. ☐ 01/01-31/12
Distance: 🚶400m 🎣on the spot 🛒700m.
Remarks: Along river.

🏕S Renaison 🌳⛵🏖👫 21B3
Auberge du Barrage, La Tâche, D41 dir les Barrages.
GPS: n46,04519 e3,87272.

12 ⬛€ 4, free with a meal ⛽🍽Ch💳€4,guests free 🐟.
Surface: grassy. ☐ 15/03-01/11 ☐ Mon, Tue (except Jul/Aug)
Distance: 🚶Renaison ± 4km 🏊100m ⊗on the spot 🛒4km.
Remarks: Construction work during inspection June 2013.

🏕S Reventin-Vaugris 24C1
Rue Mouret. **GPS:** n45,46821 e4,84239.⬆.

10 ⬛free ⛽WC. **Location:** Rural, simple, central, quiet.
Surface: gravel/metalled. ☐ 01/01-31/12
Distance: 🚶on the spot 🏊6km ⊗20m 🛒bakery 10m.

🏕S Roanne 🌳⛵🍽 21B3
Port de Plaisance, Allée Amiral Vermeilleux du Vignaux.
GPS: n46,03750 e4,08306.⬆➡.

10 ⬛€ 6 ⛽€2/15minutes 🍽€2 Ch€2 💳€2,10 ⚡€2/8kWh WC
🧺🚌 **Location:** Urban, comfortable, quiet. **Surface:** gravel.
☐ 01/01-31/12
Distance: 🚶500m 🏊500m ⊗2km 🛒2km 🚎on the spot 🚲on the

spot 🚶on the spot.
Remarks: Max. 6 days.

🏕 Romans-sur-Isère 🍲 🐟 24C2
Avenue Gambetta. **GPS:** n45,04521 e5,05879.⬆.

4 ⬛free. **Location:** Urban, simple. **Surface:** metalled.
☐ 01/01-31/12
Distance: 🚶centre 700m.
Remarks: Parking in front of Marques Avenue, max. 48h.

🏕S Saillans 🐟 24D2
Parking Gite Rural, Montmartel. **GPS:** n44,69549 e5,19350.⬆➡.

20 ⬛free ⛽€2 🍽Ch.
Location: Rural, simple. **Surface:** gravel.
Distance: 🚶300m.
Remarks: Along the Drôme river, closed when high water.

🏕S Saint-Agrève 👫 24B2
Coussac. **GPS:** n45,01042 e4,39339.⬆.

⬛free ⛽€3 🍽Ch💳€3,water 10min + electricity 50min WC.
Location: Simple. **Surface:** asphalted. ☐ 01/01-31/12
Distance: 🚶500m ⊗500m 🛒500m.
Remarks: Coins at tourist info.

🍽S Saint-Agrève 👫 24B2
Le Lac de Véron, Pré de Gardy, D120. **GPS:** n44,99981 e4,40164.⬆.

5 ⬛€ 5/24h ⚓on demand 🍽free. **Location:** Rural, comfortable,
quiet. **Surface:** unpaved. ☐ 01/04-31/10
Distance: 🚶village 1km 🎣on the spot ⊗on the spot 🚲on the spot
🚶on the spot.
Remarks: At fish lake.

🏕S Saint-Alban-Auriolles 24B3
Rue Marius Perbost. **GPS:** n44,42693 e4,30096.⬆.

⬛free ⛽€3 🍽Ch💳€3. **Surface:** gravel.
Distance: 🚶300m ⊗€3.

🏕S Saint-André-d'Apchon 21B3
La Prébande. **GPS:** n46,03385 e3,92705.⬆.

3 ⬛free ⛽🍽Chfree. **Location:** Rural, simple, quiet.
Surface: gravel. ☐ 01/01-31/12
Distance: 🚶300m ⊗100m.

🏕S Saint-Bonnet-le-Château 🌳⛵🏖👫 24B1
Esplanade de la Boule. **GPS:** n45,42514 e4,06436.⬆.

50 ⬛free ⛽🍽ChWCfree. **Location:** Simple. **Surface:** metalled.
☐ Fri
Distance: 🚶200m 🎣1km ⊗200m 🛒200m.

Tourist information Saint-Bonnet-le-Château:
Ⓜ Musée de la Pétanque et des Boules, Esplanade de la Boule. All
about the beloved French national sport. ☐ 01/04-31/10.
Ⓜ Musée International Pétanque et Boules, Boulevard des Chauchères.
🍽 ☐ Fri.

👁S Saint-Désirat 24C1
Musée de l'Alambic ,Distillerie Jean Gauthier, D291.
GPS: n45,25856 e4,79261.⬆.

⬛free ⛽⚡WCfree. **Location:** Simple. **Surface:** asphalted.
Distance: 🚶300m ⊗300m.
Remarks: Max. 1 night.

🏕S Saint-Donat-sur-l'Herbasse 24C2
Route de St.Bardoux. **GPS:** n45,11902 e4,98284.➡.

⬛free ⛽🍽Chfree. **Location:** Simple. ☐ 01/01-31/12
Distance: 🚶400m ⊗400m 🛒1km.
Remarks: In front of gymnasium, max. 1 night.

🏕S Saint-Étienne-la-Varenne 21C3
Le Bourg. **GPS:** n46,07731 e4,63024.⬆.

4 ⬛free ⬛🔧Ch 🔧free. **Location:** Rural, simple, quiet.
Surface: gravel/metalled. 🅾 01/01-31/12
Distance: 🚰on the spot ⊗50m on the spot 🚶on the spot.
Remarks: Next to church.

⬛S Saint-Félicien 🍴 | 24C2

Place du Pré Lacour. **GPS:** n45,08453 e4,62848.

6 ⬛free ⬛€2 🔧Ch. **Location:** Urban, simple.
Surface: asphalted/gravel. 🅾 01/01-31/12
Distance: 🚰on the spot ⊗on the spot 🍺on the spot.
Remarks: Max. 24h.

⬛S Saint-Forgeux | 21C3

Le Tram. **GPS:** n45,85733 e4,47566.

⬛free ⬛🔧Ch 🔧free WC. **Location:** Rural, simple, quiet.
Surface: metalled. 🅾 01/01-31/12
Distance: 🚰300m ⊗300m 🍺300m 🚶on the spot.

⬛S Saint-Genest-de-Beauzon | 24B3

Domaine la Pize, La Pize. **GPS:** n44,43759 e4,19431.

⬛€ 10 ⬛🔧ChWCincluded 📶. **Location:** Rural, isolated, quiet.
Surface: unpaved. 🅾 01/01-31/12
Distance: 🚰1,6km.

⬛S Saint-Georges-d'Espéranche | 24C1

Chemin des Platières. **GPS:** n45,55560 e5,07478. ⬆➡.

14 ⬛free ⬛🔧Chfree. **Location:** Rural, simple, central, quiet.
Surface: metalled. 🅾 01/01-31/12
Distance: 🚰on the spot ⊗100m 🍺500m.
Remarks: Max. 48h.

⬛S Saint-Germain-Lespinasse | 21B2

Place du 8 mai 1945. **GPS:** n46,10510 e3,96229. ⬆➡.

2 ⬛free ⬛🔧Chfree. **Location:** Rural, simple, quiet.
Surface: gravel.
Distance: 🚰200m ⊗50m 🚌50m.

⬛S Saint-Gervais-les-Bains ⛰ | 21F3

77, impasse Cascade. **GPS:** n45,88864 e6,71287. ⬆.

20 ⬛free ⬛€2 🔧Ch €2. **Surface:** asphalted.
Distance: 🚰200m ⊗200m 🍺200m 🏂300m.
Remarks: Parking skating rink.

⬛S Saint-Haon-le-Châtel 🍂 | 21B3

Fondanges, Route de la Croix du Sud, D39.
GPS: n46,06362 e3,91313. ⬆➡.

3 ⬛free ⬛🔧Chfree. **Location:** Rural, quiet. **Surface:** metalled.
🅾 01/01-31/12
Distance: 🚰400m ⊗400m 🍺400m 🅿400m.

⬛S Saint-Jean-d'Ardières | 21C2

Domaine de Grande Ferrière, 831 route des Rochons.
GPS: n46,12954 e4,71581.

5 ⬛free ⬛🔧Chfree 🔧€5/4night WC. **Location:** Rural, simple,
quiet. **Surface:** gravel.
Distance: 🚰3km 🚲6km 🏊5km 🛒500m ⊗3km 🍺3km.

⬛S Saint-Jean-de-Bournay | 24D1

Place du Marche. **GPS:** n45,50130 e5,13845. ⬆.

10 ⬛free ⬛free Ch. **Location:** Rural, simple, central, quiet.
Surface: asphalted. 🅾 01/01-31/12
Distance: 🚰on the spot ⊗100m 🍺100m.

⬛S Saint-Jean-de-Maurienne ⛰🏔❄ | 24E1

Rue Louis Sibue. **GPS:** n45,27995 e6,34776. ⬆.
10 ⬛free ⬛€2 🔧Ch €2 WC. **Surface:** asphalted.
🅾 01/01-31/12

Distance: 🚲2,5km ⊗100m.

⬛S Saint-Jean-en-Royans 🏔🍴 | 24D2

Rue de la Gare. **GPS:** n45,02028 e5,29032. ⬆➡.

3 ⬛free ⬛🔧Chfree. **Location:** Simple. **Surface:** gravel.
Distance: 🚰200m ⊗200m 🍺200m.

⬛S Saint-Just-d'Ardèche | 24C3

Domaine La Favette, D86, route des Gorges d'Ardèche.
GPS: n44,30134 e4,60649.

6 ⬛€5 ⬛€2 🔧Ch €2. 🅾 01/01-31/12
Remarks: At wine-grower, max. 24h.

Tourist information Saint-Just-d'Ardèche:
ℹ Good starting point to discover the Ardèche gorges.
🚶 🅾 Thu.

⬛S Saint-Just-en-Chevalet | 21B3

Boulevard de l'Astrée. **GPS:** n45,91411 e3,84727.

5 ⬛free ⬛🔧Chfree. 🚌 **Location:** Rural, simple. 🅾 01/01-31/12
⊙ Thu-morning
Distance: 🚰on the spot ⊗on the spot 🍺on the spot 🅿on the spot.

⬛S Saint-Martin-en-Haut 🍴 | 21C3

Etang du Kaiser, Lieu-dit-Jeangouttière. **GPS:** n45,64206 e4,53511. ⬆.

4 ⬛free ⬛🔧ChWC. **Location:** Rural, comfortable, quiet.
Surface: gravel.
🅾 01/01-31/12
Distance: 🚰St.Martin 4km 🛒on the spot 🚴on the spot 🚶on the spot.
Remarks: At small lake, max. 72h.

⬛S Saint-Paul-le-Jeune | 24B3

Rue Louis Roux, D901. **GPS:** n44,33999 e4,15322.

⬛free ⬛€2 🔧Ch €2. **Location:** Rural. **Surface:** grassy.

◻ 01/01-31/12
Distance: 🚰on the spot 🛒100m.
Remarks: Coins at the shops in the village.

Saint-Paul-Trois-Châteaux | 24C3
Parking Office de Tourisme, Le Courreau, Place Chausy.
GPS: n44,34786 e4,76995.

🚰free 🚰🔧Chfree WC. **Location:** Urban. **Surface:** asphalted.
Distance: 🚶50m ⊗50m.
Remarks: Max. 24h.

Tourist information Saint-Paul-Trois-Châteaux:
⚥ Marché. ◻ Tue-morning.
⚥ Marché aux truffes du Tricastin. ◻ Dec-Mar Su-morning.

Saint-Pierre-en-Faucigny | 21E3
Avenue de la Gare. **GPS:** n46,05884 e6,37450.⬆

4 🚰free 🚰🔧Ch🚐free. **Surface:** asphalted. ◻ 01/04-30/11
Distance: 🚶on the spot ⊗60m 🛒on the spot 🚌on the spot.
Remarks: Nearby railway station.

Saint-Rémèze | 24C3
Les Chais du Vivarais, D362. **GPS:** n44,39536 e4,50576.⬆

🚰free 🚰🔧Chfree. **Surface:** asphalted. ◻ 01/03-15/11
Distance: 🚶500m ⊗200m.
Remarks: Max. 48h.

Tourist information Saint-Rémèze:
👁 Grotte de la Madelaine. Caves. ◻ Apr-Oct 10-18h.
👁 Grotte de Marzal. Caves. ◻ Sa/Su/Holidays, 01/04-30/09 10.30-18h.
Ⓜ Musée de la lavande. Museum and distillery with lavender fields.
◻ 01/05-30/09 10-17h, Apr + Oct Sa-Su-holiday 10-17h.

Saint-Restitut | 24C3
Le Village. **GPS:** n44,33144 e4,79093.⬆

🚰free 🚰🔧Chfree. **Surface:** asphalted. ◻ 01/01-31/12
Distance: 🚶on the spot.

Saint-Romain-d'Ay | 24C1
Praperier, D6. **GPS:** n45,16430 e4,66339.⬆

4 🚰free 🚰€2/20minutes 🔧Ch 🚿(4x)€2/4h WC. **Location:** Simple.
Surface: asphalted. ◻ 01/01-31/12
Distance: 🚶550m ⊗100m.
Remarks: Coins at town hall and superette.

Saint-Romain-de-Lerps | 24C2
Le Village, D287. **GPS:** n44,98029 e4,79596.⬆

10 🚰free 🚰🔧Ch🚐€4,100 liter water + 1h electricity WC.
Location: Rural, simple, quiet. **Surface:** gravel. ◻ 01/01-31/12
◉ 01/10 and 01/04
Distance: 🚶100m ⊗100m 🛒bakery 100m.
Remarks: Less suitable for motorhomes >6,5m, coins at bakery, bar/resto 3duPic and town hall, panoramic view over the Rhône-valley 200m.

Saint-Symphorien-sur-Coise | 21C3
Bois des Pinasses. **GPS:** n45,62578 e4,45837.⬆

🚰free. **Location:** Rural, simple. **Surface:** gravel.
◻ 01/01-31/12
Distance: 🚶1km 🏊50m.
Remarks: Next to sports fields.

Saint-Symphorien-sur-Coise | 21C3
Rue des Rameaux. **GPS:** n45,63378 e4,45883.⬆

🚰🔧Chfree. **Location:** Simple. ◻ 01/01-31/12
Remarks: Free coins at Bar-Tabac and town hall.

Saint-Théoffrey | 24E2
Camping Ser-Sirant, Chemin du Lavoir. **GPS:** n45,00034 e5,77819.⬆
4 🚰€8-9,50 🚰€1,50 🔧Ch. **Location:** Rural. **Surface:** grassy.
Distance: 🏊beach Saint Théoffrey.
Remarks: At lake Laffrey, pay at reception campsite.

Saint-Thomé | 24C3
N107, Les Crottes. **GPS:** n44,50059 e4,63445.⬆

1 🚰free 🚰🔧Chfree. **Surface:** asphalted.

Samoëns | 21F3
Aire d'accueil camping-car de Vercland, Hameau de Vercland.
GPS: n46,07283 e6,69957.⬆➡

10 🚰free 🚰🔧Ch🚐€5. **Surface:** metalled. ◻ 01/01-31/12
◉ Service: winter
Distance: 🚶2km ⊗100m 🛒2km.

Samoëns | 21F3
Parking du Giffre. **GPS:** n46,07666 e6,71899.⬆

5 🚰€10 🚰🔧Ch🔌🧺. **Surface:** asphalted. ◻ 01/01-31/12
◉ Service: winter
Distance: 🚶100m ⊗100m 🛒100m 🚌Skibus to Samoëns 1600 🎿100m 🏊on the spot.
Remarks: Near campsite du Giffre, parking 150m.

Sassenage | 24D1
Rue Pierre de Coubertin. **GPS:** n45,21346 e5,66858.⬆
9 🚰free 🚰🔧Chfree. **Surface:** asphalted. ◻ 01/01-31/12 🚲on the spot 🚶on the spot.
Remarks: At sports grounds, max. 48h.

Serrières-en-Chautagne | 21E3
GPS: n45,87964 e5,84230.⬆

15 🚰free 🚰🔧ChWCfree. **Location:** Rural, central, quiet.
Surface: metalled. ◻ 01/01-31/12 ◉ Service: winter
Distance: 🚶on the spot 🚲1km 🏊beach 50m 🚣on the spot ⊗200m 🛒100m 🍴100m.
Remarks: At little mountain stream.

Seyssel | 21E3
Parking Base de Loisirs, Quai du Rhône. **GPS:** n45,95146 e5,83343.

4 🚰free 🚰🔧Chfree. **Location:** Rural, simple, central, quiet.

FR

Surface: gravel. ⬛ 01/01-31/12
Distance: 🔥800m ⛱on the spot 🎣on the spot ⊗500m 🛒800m ☂on the spot.
Remarks: At recreational lake and Rhone river.

🏕🅂 Seyssel 🌿🍽🏔🏖 21E3
Quai du Rhône. **GPS:** n45,95001 e5,83406.⬆.

12 🛏free. **Location:** Rural, simple, central, quiet. **Surface:** gravel.
⬛ 01/10-01/06
Distance: 🔥400m ⛱on the spot 🎣on the spot ⊗400m 🛒400m
🚮400m ☂on the spot.

🏕🅂 Sixt-Fer-à-Cheval 🏔 21F3
Route du Cirque du Fer à Cheval. **GPS:** n46,05698 e6,78048.⬆.

20 🛏free 🚰🍽Ch 🔌€4/12h. **Surface:** asphalted.
⬛ 01/01-31/12
Distance: 🔥500m ⛱on the spot 🛒500m.

🏕🅂 Suze-la-Rousse 24C3
Route de Bollène, D94. **GPS:** n44,28598 e4,83185.

🛏free 🚰free. **Surface:** grassy/gravel. ⬛ 01/01-31/12
Distance: 🔥850m on the spot ☂on the spot.
Remarks: At sports grounds.

🅂 Suze-la-Rousse 24C3
50 Impasse de la Zone Artisanale. **GPS:** n44,28965 e4,84783.

🚰🍽Chfree. ⬛ 01/01-31/12
Distance: 🔥1,5km.

🏕🅂 Thueyts 🌿🎣🏔🍽🏖 24B2
Chemin d'Echelle du Roi, via N102. **GPS:** n44,67274 e4,21917.⬆➡.

10 🛏free 🚰€2 🍽Ch €2/10minutes. **Location:** Rural, simple,
quiet. **Surface:** grassy/gravel. ⬛ 01/01-31/12
Distance: 🔥200m 🛒200m ☂on the spot.

Remarks: Near the Ardèche river and Pont du Diable, max. 24h.

🏕🅂 Tournon-sur-Rhône 🏖 24C2
Chemin de la Beaume/D86. **GPS:** n45,07337 e4,82150.⬆➡.

25 🛏€5 🚰🍽Chfree. **Location:** Urban, simple. **Surface:** asphalted.
⬛ 01/01-31/12
Distance: 🔥1km 🎣5km ⊗1km 🛒1km.

Tourist information Tournon-sur-Rhône:
⛺ ⬛ Wed, Sa.
🖊 Route Panoramique, place Jean Jaurès. Starting point touristic route.

🏕🅂 Treffort 🏔🍽 24D2
Plage de la Salette, D110b. **GPS:** n44,90732 e5,67208.⬆.

12 🛏€ 10/24h 🚰€2 🍽Ch 🔌€2 WC. 🚮 **Surface:** gravel.
⬛ 01/05-31/10
Distance: 🔥3km ⛱lake 🎣lake ⊗on the spot 🚴on the spot ☂on the spot.
Remarks: At lake Monteynard.

🏕🅂 Trévoux 🌿🎣🍽🏖🍦 21C3
Chemin du Camping. **GPS:** n45,94017 e4,76694.⬆.

4 🛏€5 🚰€2 🍽Ch. 🚮 **Location:** Urban, simple, central, quiet.
Surface: grassy/metalled. ⬛ 01/01-31/12
Distance: 🔥on the spot 🖊7km ⛱100m ⊗1km 🛒1km 🚮1km.
Remarks: Along river, at entrance campsite, pay at campsite or town hall.

🏕🅂 Ugine 21F3
Place du 8 Mai 1945. **GPS:** n45,74634 e6,41774.⬆.
🛏free 🚰€2 🔌€2. **Surface:** asphalted. ⬛ 01/01-31/12
Distance: 🔥50m ⊗50m 🛒50m.

Tourist information Ugine:
⛺ ⬛ Wed, Sa-morning.

🏕🅂 Val d'Isère 24F1
Le Pont Saint-Charles, Route du Col de l'Iseran, D902.
GPS: n45,45432 e6,97005.

50 🛏free 🚰free. **Surface:** gravel. ⬛ 01/01-31/12
Distance: 🖊on the spot.
Remarks: Parking at skipistes.

🏕🅂 Valloire 24F1
Camping-Car Park Les Verneys, Route du Galibier.
GPS: n45,14591 e6,42011.⬆.
30 🛏€ 12 🚰🍽Ch 🖊WC 🚿included. **Surface:** asphalted.

⬛ 01/01-31/12
Distance: ⊗on the spot 🖊250m.
Remarks: Free shuttle.

🏕🅂 Vallon-Pont-d'Arc 🎣🏔🏖 24B3
Chemin du Chastelas. **GPS:** n44,40537 e4,39683.⬆.

20 🛏€6/24h 🚰€2 🍽Ch 🔌€2 WC. 🚮 ⬛ 01/01-31/12
Distance: 🔥100m ⊗100m 🛒100m.
Remarks: Free shuttle to the Pont d'Arc, 2x per hour.

🏕🅂 Vallon-Pont-d'Arc 24B3
Domaine de l'Esquiras, Chemin du Fez. **GPS:** n44,41583 e4,37738.⬆.

5 🛏€ 8, peak season € 10 + € 0,60/pp tourist tax 🚰🍽Ch 🔌€3
WC 🚿free. **Surface:** gravel. ⬛ 12/04-21/09
Distance: 🔥800m.
Remarks: Use sanitary facilities + swimming pool € 4/pp.

Tourist information Vallon-Pont-d'Arc:
ℹ Office de Tourisme, 1, place de l'ancienne gare, www.vallon-pont-darc.com. Small tourist town with the well-known Pont d'Arc, a natural arc over the Ardèche river.
👁 Grotte des Huguenots. Former shelter of the Huguenots. ⬛ 15/06-31/08.
⛺ ⬛ Thu-morning.

🏕🅂 Valvignères 24C3
Le Colombier. **GPS:** n44,49904 e4,57672.

🛏€ 7,70, 2 pers.incl. 🚰🍽Chfree. ⬛ 27/03-30/09 ⬤ Service:
winter

🏕🅂 Vassieux-en-Vercors 🏔🍽❄☀ 24D2
Avenue du Mémorial, D76. **GPS:** n44,89703 e5,36927.⬆.

30 🛏free 🚰🍽Chfree. **Location:** Rural, simple. **Surface:** metalled.
⬤ service in winter
Distance: 🔥200m ⊗200m 🛒200m ☂on the spot 🖊7km Font D'Urle
☃on the spot.
Remarks: Next to football ground.

🏕🅂 Vaujany 🏔🍽❄ 24E1
Télécabine. **GPS:** n45,15694 e6,08011.⬆➡.

15 ⬛free 🚿🔌Chfree 💧€5. **Surface:** gravel.
⬛ 01/01-31/12
Distance: 🚰300m ⊗300m 🛒300m ⚕300m.
Remarks: Max. 24h, coins at tourist info (electricity).

| 🛁S | **Vienne** 🌼🍴 | 24C1 |

Place Joseph Muray et Jean Tardy, N7. **GPS:** n45,53860 e4,87271. ⬆➡.

10 ⬛free 🚿🔌Chfree. **Location:** Urban, simple, central, noisy.
Surface: asphalted. ◉ Wed-afternoon (market)
Distance: 🚰50m ⚒2km ⊗50m 🛒50m ⚕50m.

| 🛁 | **Villards-de-Lans** | 24D2 |

Chemin des Bartavelles. **GPS:** n45,06619 e5,55609. ⬆.

15 ⬛free. **Surface:** asphalted.
Distance: 🚰600m ⊗600m 🛒600m.
Remarks: Max. 48h.

| 🅿 | **Villars-les-Dombes** 🌼🍃 | 21C3 |

Parc des Oiseaux, RN83. **GPS:** n45,99126 e5,02582. ⬆➡.

100 ⬛free.
Location: Simple, quiet. **Surface:** asphalted/grassy.
⬛ 01/01-31/12 ◉ sundays, holidays, winter
Distance: 🚰2km ⚒1km 🛒1km ⊗2km ⚕2km ⚕on the spot.
Remarks: Parking bird park, max. 1 night, gate closed from 21-8h.
Tourist information Villars-les-Dombes:
😊 Parc des Oiseaux. Bird park, 23ha.
⬛ 8.30-19h, winter 8.30-17.30h. 🎫 € 10.

| 🛁 | **Villerest** 🍃 | 21B3 |

Aire camping-car du Grezelon, D18, Route de Seigne.
GPS: n45,98610 e4,04300.

15 ⬛€5 🚿€4 🔌Ch. 🛁 **Surface:** gravel. ⬛ 01/01-31/12
◉ service: 01/10-30/04

Distance: ⊗on the spot 🛒1km ⚕on the spot.
Remarks: At Lac du Villerest and barrage, max. 48h.

| 🛁S | **Violay** | 21B3 |

Place Giroud. **GPS:** n45,85268 e4,35564. ⬆➡.

2 ⬛free 🚿free 🔌Ch. **Location:** Rural, simple, quiet.
Surface: metalled. ⬛ 01/01-31/12
Distance: 🚰100m ⚒A89 9km ⊗200m 🛒150m.
Remarks: Beautiful view.

| 🛁S | **Virieu** 🏔🌳 | 24D1 |

Rue du May, D17. **GPS:** n45,48166 e5,47746. ⬆➡.

4 ⬛free 🚿🔌ChWCfree. **Location:** Rural, simple, central, quiet.
Surface: gravel.
Distance: 🚰on the spot ⊗200m 🛒200m ⚕on the spot.
Remarks: Picnic area at edge of the village.

| 🛁S | **Viviers** 🌼 | 24C3 |

Rue Valpeyrousse. **GPS:** n44,48225 e4,67999. ⬆.

26 ⬛€ 6,50 🚿🔌Ch ✏WC 🔌included. 🛁 **Location:** Rural,
luxurious, quiet. **Surface:** metalled. ⬛ 15/04-29/09
Distance: 🚰1km ⚕1km.
Remarks: Former campsite.

Tourist information Viviers:
🏕 ⬛ Tue.

| 🛁 | **Vogüé** 🌼 | 24B3 |

Chemin de Setras. **GPS:** n44,55163 e4,41308.

20 ⬛free. **Surface:** asphalted. ⬛ 01/01-31/12
Distance: 🚰50m ⚓Ardèche 200m.
Remarks: At cemetery.

Aquitaine

| 🛁S | **Accous** | 26B3 |

La Nabe, D339. **GPS:** n42,91028 w0,61939. ⬆➡.

20 ⬛€ 12 🔌Ch 💧WC ⬛📶included. 🛁 **Location:** Rural,
comfortable, isolated, quiet. **Surface:** gravel.
Distance: 🚰7km 🛒100m ⚕on the spot.

| 🛁S | **Aillas** | 23C3 |

À Bourg. **GPS:** n44,47514 w0,07318. ⬆.

5 ⬛free 🚿🔌Chfree. **Location:** Urban, simple, quiet.
Surface: gravel. ⬛ 01/01-31/12
Distance: 🚰200m ⊗100m.
Remarks: Next to sports fields.

| 🛁S | **Aire-sur-l'Adour** 🌳 | 26C1 |

Rue des Graviers. **GPS:** n43,70333 w0,25535. ⬆.

50 ⬛€ 3 🚿€1 🔌Ch. 🛁 **Location:** Simple, quiet. **Surface:** gravel.
⬛ 01/01-31/12 ◉ 3rd week Jun
Distance: 🚰200m ⚓on the spot 🚤on the spot.
Remarks: Near campsite, max. 72h.

| 🅿S | **Amou** 🌳 | 26B1 |

Stade de Sport, Promenade pour Piétons.
GPS: n43,58917 w0,74083. ⬆➡.

10 ⬛free 🚿🔌Ch ✏free. **Surface:** asphalted. ⬛ 01/01-31/12
Distance: 🚰1km ⚓on the spot 🚤on the spot ⊗1km 🛒1km.

| ⚓S | **Andernos-les-Bains** 🌼⚓🍴 | 23B2 |

Port Ostréicole, Avenue du Commandant Allègre.
GPS: n44,74477 w1,10969. ⬆➡.

60 ⬛€ 9,20 🚿€2,50/100liter 🔌Ch🛢€2,10 ✏🚰♻.
Location: Urban, comfortable, quiet. **Surface:** grassy/metalled.
⬛ 01/01-31/12
Distance: 🚰500m ⚓on the spot 🚤on the spot ⊗50m.
Remarks: In harbour, max. 48h.

FR

Anglet 26A1

Aire de camping-car de La Barre, Avenue de l'Adour, D405.
GPS: n43,52608 w1,51488.

50 € 6, Jul/Aug € 10 €3 Ch. Surface: grassy/metalled.
13/04-11/11
Distance: 1km 300m 50m 500m 500m 100m.
Remarks: Private property.

Anglet 26A1

Aire de camping-car des Corsaires, Boulevard des Plages.
GPS: n43,50696 w1,53373.

80 € 6, Jul/Aug € 10 Chincluded. Surface: asphalted.
01/01-31/12
Distance: 500m, Biarritz 2km 500m 500m 500m.
Remarks: Max. 24h, baker every morning.

Angoisse 23E1

Le Pont du Jour, L'Hépital, D704. **GPS**: n45,43296 e1,14413.

8 € 5 Chincluded €3 €3. Location: Rural, simple.
Surface: grassy.
Distance: 500m 1km 4,5km.

Arcachon 23B2

Boulevard Mestrézat, D650. **GPS**: n44,65142 w1,14864.

20 free. Chfree. **Location**: Urban, simple, noisy.
Surface: gravel. 01/01-31/12
Distance: 1km 50m.
Remarks: Max. 24h.

Arcachon 23B2

Avenue du Parc. **GPS**: n44,64868 w1,19672.
free. **Surface**: gravel.
01/01-31/12
Distance: on the spot on the spot.

Tourist information Arcachon:
place du XI Novembre. Covered market. 01/06-31/08 daily 7-13h.

Arette 26B2

Aire de camping car d'Arette, Place de la Mairie.
GPS: n43,09477 w0,71511.
10 free Ch. **Location**: Simple. **Surface**: asphalted.
01/01-31/12

Arzacq-Arraziguet 26C2

Aire de camping cars, Place du Marcadieu.
GPS: n43,53481 w0,41035.

10 free ChWCfree. **Surface**: asphalted. 01/01-31/12
Distance: on the spot 500m 500m 100m 100m.

Azerat 23E1

Le Bourg. **GPS**: n45,14954 e1,12496.

6 € 2 €3 Ch. **Location**: Urban, simple, quiet. **Surface**: gravel.
01/01-31/12
Distance: 50m 150m.
Remarks: Pay at town hall.

Azur 26A1

Camping-Car Park, Route du Lac. **GPS**: n43,78842 w1,3119.
31 € 12 Ch included. **Location**: Rural, quiet.
Surface: gravel. 01/01-31/12
Distance: 1,5km 150m 150m 200m on the spot on the spot.
Remarks: Wifi code: 403105.

Badefols-sur-Dordogne 23E2

Le Bourg. **GPS**: n44,84254 e0,79160.

10 free €2/100liter ChWCfree. **Location**: Rural, simple.
Surface: asphalted. 01/01-31/12 Sa market
Distance: on the spot bakery 50m.
Remarks: Coins at town hall.

Beaumont du Périgord 23E2

Avenue Rhinau, D660. **GPS**: n44,77469 e0,76559.

20 free Chfree. **Surface**: asphalted. 01/01-31/12
Distance: 800m.

Tourist information Beaumont du Périgord:
Bastide de Beaumont.

Bergerac 23D2

Parc Public de Pombonne, Avenue Marceau Feyry.
GPS: n44,87104 e0,50408.

6 free €2/100liter Ch. **Location**: Simple.
Surface: metalled.
Distance: city centre 3km 1km.
Remarks: Max. 24h.

Tourist information Bergerac:
Musée du Tabac, Maison Peyrarède, Place du Feu. History of tobacco.
Mo-Fri 10-12h, 14-18, Sa 10-12h, 14-17h, Su 14.30-17.30h, Nov-Mar Mo-Fr.
Église Notre Dame, Rue Saint Esprit. Wed, Sa 7-13h.

Bernos-Beaulac 23C3

La Grande Route, N524. **GPS**: n44,36949 w0,24257.

10 free €2 Ch. **Location**: Simple, quiet. **Surface**: metalled.
01/01-31/12 water: frost
Distance: river on the spot bakery 100m.
Remarks: Coins at petrol station.

Beynac-et-Cazenac 23E2

Le Parc, D703. **GPS**: n44,84466 e1,14560.

20 free. **Location**: Rural, simple. **Surface**: gravel.
01/01-31/12
Distance: historical centre 500m 500m.

Biarritz 26A2

Parking Milady, Avenue de la Milady, Biarritz-sud, D911dir Bidart.
GPS: n43,46536 w1,57162.

50 € 12 Ch included. **Surface**: asphalted. 01/01-31/12
Distance: 500m 300m 500m 500m.
Remarks: Baker every morning.

Tourist information Biarritz:
Rue des Halles. daily.

Biron 23E2

Route de Vergt de Biron. **GPS**: n44,63080 e0,87055.

10 � free ⌖ €2/100liter ⌑ Ch ⌑ €2/1h. **Location:** Simple.
Surface: grassy/metalled. ⬛ 01/01-31/12 ◉ service 01/11-31/03
Distance: 250m ⊗250m.
Remarks: Coins at grocery.

Biscarrosse ⬛S 23B3

Aire camping-cars, Rue des Viviers, Biscarrosse-plage.
GPS: n44,46027 w1,24627. ⬆.

180 ⌐ € 8, Jul/Aug € 15 ⌖ ⌑Ch ⌑ WC. ⌑ ⌑ **Location:** Simple,
quiet. **Surface:** forest soil.
⬛ 01/05-31/10
Distance: 2,5km ⌑400m ⊗Superette 100m ⌑50m ⌑ on the spot.
Remarks: Video surveillance.

Biscarrosse ⬛S 23B3

Biscarrosse Plage Sud, Chemin de Navarosse.
GPS: n44,43223 w1,16566. ⬆.

30 ⌐ € 8, Jul/Aug € 15 ⌖ ⌑Chfree ⌑ WC. ⌑ ⌑ ⌑.
Location: Simple. **Surface:** metalled. ⬛ 01/01-31/12
Distance: 4km ⌑50m ⊗100m ⌑50m ⌑ on the spot.
Remarks: Video surveillance.

Blanquefort ⬛ 23C2

Château Saint Ahon, Rue de Saint-Ahon.
GPS: n44,92663 w0,63217. ⬆⮕.

4 ⌐ € 3 ⌖free. ⌑ **Location:** Urban, simple, central, quiet.
Surface: gravel/metalled.
⬛ 01/01-31/12 ◉ Su/holidays
Distance: 300m ⌑ 12km ⊗300m ⌑ on the spot.
Remarks: Arrival < 19h, max. 48h.

Blasimon ⬛S 23C2

Rue Abbé Greciet. **GPS:** n44,74836 w0,07537. ⬆.

---

4 ⌐free ⌑ ⌑Chfree. **Location:** Urban, simple, quiet.
Surface: gravel. ⬛ 01/01-31/12
Distance: 100m ⊗100m ⌑100m.

Blasimon ⬛S 23C2

Château la Peyraude, Bleurette. **GPS:** n44,73463 w0,09942. ⬆⮕.

15 ⌐free ⌖ ⌑Ch ⌑ WC ⌑ ◉ ⌑free. **Location:** Rural, simple.
Surface: grassy. ⬛ 01/01-31/12
Distance: 3km.
Remarks: Arrival <22h, regional products.

Blaye ⬛S 23C1

Parking de la Citadelle, Rue Pierre Semard.
GPS: n45,12549 w0,66535. ⬆.

30 ⌐free. **Location:** Urban, simple, central, quiet.
Surface: gravel/metalled. ⬛ 01/01-31/12
Distance: 250m ⌑on the spot ⌑on the spot ⊗300m ⌑2km
⌑300m.

Blaye ⬛S 23C1

Château le Cône, Route des Cônes. **GPS:** n45,13742 w0,66507. ⬆⮕.

12 ⌐free ⌖ ⌑Ch ⌑ (4x). **Location:** Rural, comfortable, quiet.
Surface: asphalted/gravel. ⬛ 01/01-31/12
Distance: 2km ⌑on the spot ⊗on the spot.

Bouglon ⬛S 23D3

Le Clavier. **GPS:** n44,38599 e0,10271.

4 ⌐free ⌖ WC. **Location:** Simple, quiet. **Surface:** asphalted.
⬛ 01/01-31/12
Distance: 500m ⊗500m ⌑500m.
Remarks: Picnic area.

Bourdeilles ⬛S 23E1

Plaine de loisirs, Le Bourg. **GPS:** n45,32270 e0,58260. ⬆.

40+ ⌐ € 4,50 ⌖ €2/100liter ⌑Ch. ⌑ **Location:** Comfortable, quiet.
Surface: grassy. ⬛ 01/01-31/12
Distance: 500m ⌑on the spot ⌑on the spot ⊗200m ⌑200m.
Remarks: Coins at the shops.

Bourg-sur-Gironde ⬛S 23C1

Quai Jean Bart. **GPS:** n45,03794 w0,55699. ⬆.

10 ⌐free ⌖ €3. **Location:** Urban, simple, central. **Surface:** asphalted.
⬛ 01/01-31/12
Distance: on the spot ⌑On the river Gironde ⌑on the spot ⌑on
the spot.

Branne ⬛ 23C2

Route de Cabara. **GPS:** n44,83191 w0,18448. ⬆⮕.

3 ⌐free ⌖ €2/100liter ⌑Ch ⌑ €2/1h. **Location:** Urban, simple,
noisy.
Distance: on the spot ⌑on the spot ⊗500m ⌑500m.

Brantôme ⬛S 23E1

Chemin de Vert Galant. **GPS:** n45,36134 e0,64842. ⬆⮕.

50 ⌐ € 5,50 ⌖ €2/12minutes ⌑Ch. ⌑ ⌑ **Location:** Simple, quiet.
Surface: grassy. ⬛ 01/01-31/12
Distance: 200m ⊗100m ⌑300m.

Brantôme ⬛S 23E1

Aire Camping-cars Font Vendôme, Route de Nontron.
GPS: n45,37924 e0,64588. ⬆⮕.

4 ⌐ € 2 ⌖ €2 ⌑Ch ⌑ €1/night WC. **Location:** Simple.
Surface: asphalted. ⬛ 01/01-31/12
Distance: 3,5km ⊗1km ⌑1km.
Remarks: Money in envelope in mail box.

Tourist information Brantôme:
⌑ ⬛ Fri-morning.

Buzet-sur-Baïse ⬛S 23D3

Port de Buzet-Val d'Albret. **GPS:** n44,25799 e0,30569. ⬆.

20 ⌂€7 🚰€2 Ch 💧€2 WC€2 ⬚€2 €2/24h. 🚿
Location: Rural, comfortable. **Surface:** grassy. 🕐 01/01-31/12
Distance: 🚲6,5km 🚶on the spot ⊗350m 🛒350m 🏧on the spot 🚮on the spot.

S Cadillac 🌿⛲ 23C2
Avenue du Parc. **GPS:** n44,63871 w0,31721.⬆.

10 ⌂free 🚰 Chfree 💧€2/3h. **Location:** Urban, simple.
Surface: asphalted. 🕐 01/01-31/12
Distance: 🚶on the spot ⊗100m 🛒100m ⬚100m.
Remarks: Max. 3 nights, closed when frosty.

S Cancon 23E3
Rue des Écoles. **GPS:** n44,53638 e0,62562.⬆➡.

10 ⌂free 🚰 Ch 💧 WCfree. **Location:** Simple. **Surface:** metalled.
🕐 01/01-31/12
Distance: 🚶100m ⊗100m 🛒100m.

S Canéjan 23C2
Impasse de la Pinède. **GPS:** n44,75044 w0,64.⬆.

5 ⌂free 🚰€1/10minutes Ch 💧(4x)€0,25/h. **Location:** Urban,
comfortable, central, quiet. **Surface:** asphalted.
🕐 01/01-31/12
Distance: 🚶on the spot 🚲6,5km ⊗300m 🛒150m 🚌300m.
Remarks: Max. 72h.

S Capbreton 26A1
Plage l'Océanide, Parking des Ortolans, Allée des Ortolans.
GPS: n43,63578 w1,44681.➡.

135 ⌂€7-€11 🚰 Ch 💧(120x) WCincluded. 🚮
Surface: asphalted. 🕐 15/11-31/03
Distance: 🚶1,5km 🏖on the spot 🚲on the spot ⊗1,5km 🛒1,5km.
Remarks: Beach parking, 14/07-20/08: max. 2 nights.

S Capian 23C2
D13/Chemin de Lavergne. **GPS:** n44,71177 w0,33093.⬆.

25 ⌂free 🚰€2/10minutes Ch 💧€2/55minutes. **Location:** Rural,
simple, quiet. **Surface:** gravel.
🕐 01/01-31/12
Distance: 🚶500m.

S Carcans 🍴 23B1
Route de Bombannes, Maubuisson. **GPS:** n45,08545 w1,14866.⬆.

20 ⌂€6,10 🚰 Ch free 💧€2. 🚮 **Location:** Rural, simple, isolated,
quiet. **Surface:** asphalted/gravel. 🕐 01/07-31/08
Distance: 🚶2km 🏖400m ⊗2km 🛒2km 🚮on the spot 🚶‍on the
spot.

Tourist information Carcans:
ℹ Office de Tourisme, Maison de la Station, www.carcans-maubuisson.
com. Touristic town between the ocean and a wine region, 120km
signposted cycle routes.

S Casseneuil 🌿 23E3
Rue Grande, D225. **GPS:** n44,44667 e0,61861.⬆.

20 ⌂free 🚰 Ch free. **Location:** Rural, simple. **Surface:** asphalted.
🕐 01/01-31/12
Distance: 🚶100m 🏖on the spot 🚲on the spot ⊗100m 🛒800m.

S Castelculier 23E3
GPS: n44,17475 e0,69452.⬆.

5 ⌂free 🚰€2 Ch. **Location:** Urban, simple, quiet.
Surface: metalled. 🕐 01/01-31/12
Distance: 🚶200m.

S Casteljaloux 🌙 23D3
Ste Castel Chalets, D933. **GPS:** n44,29230 e0,07361.⬆.

20 ⌂€10, Jul/Aug €15, dog €3 🚰 Ch 💧 WC ⬚ 🚿included.

Location: Comfortable, quiet. **Surface:** gravel/sand.
🕐 01/10-31/10
Distance: 🚶2km 🏊Lac de Clarens.

S Casteljaloux 🌙 23D3
Impasse de la Fôret. **GPS:** n44,31068 e0,07933.⬆➡.

4 ⌂free 🚰 Chfree. **Location:** Simple, quiet. **Surface:** asphalted.
🕐 01/01-31/12
Distance: 🚶250m 🛒250m.
Remarks: Parking at swimming pool, max. 48h.

S Casteljaloux 🌙 23D3
La Taillade, Route de la Forge, La Réunion.
GPS: n44,26998 e0,08004.⬆.
3 ⌂€10 🚰 Ch 💧 🚿. **Location:** Rural, isolated, quiet.
Surface: forest soil.

S Caumont-sur-Garonne 🌊 23D3
Bourg de Caumont. **GPS:** n44,44202 e0,17887.⬆.

12 ⌂free 🚰€1 Ch ⬚€1/2h. **Location:** Rural, simple, quiet.
Surface: gravel. 🕐 01/01-31/12
Distance: 🚲8km 🚶on the spot 🛒200m.

S Château-l'Evêque 23E1
Place de la Fontaine. **GPS:** n45,24472 e0,68743.⬆.

8 ⌂free 🚰€2 Ch ⬚€2. **Location:** Urban. **Surface:** gravel.
🕐 01/03-31/10 🕐 summer: Su (flea market)
Distance: 🚶50m 🛒100m 🛒on the spot.
Remarks: Coins at shops in the village 08-21h.

S Civrac-en-Médoc 23B1
Route de Montignac, Montignac. **GPS:** n45,33619 w0,922.⬆.

5 ⌂free. **Location:** Rural, simple, isolated, quiet. **Surface:** gravel.
🕐 01/01-31/12
Distance: 🚶2km.

S Contis-Plage 23A3
Avenue du Phare. **GPS:** n44,09333 w1,31861.⬆.

FR

76 🛏€ 7, 01/06-01/09 € 11/24h, 01/12-28/02 free 🚰€2 🚽Ch 🚻 WC. 🏧 **Location:** Simple. **Surface:** gravel. ⏰ 01/01-31/12

Distance: ⚓200m 🚲 on the spot.
Remarks: Max. 72h.

🏕🅂 Créon 🌿 23C2

Vélo-centre, Boulevard Victor Hugo, D20.
GPS: n44,77663 w0,34806. ⬆️➡️.

5 🛏free 🚰€3 🚽Ch 🚻€3/4h. **Location:** Urban, simple.
Surface: asphalted. ⏰ 01/01-31/12 ⬛ tue-evening, wed-morning (market)
Distance: ⚓500m ✖500m 🚲 on the spot.

🏕🅂 Damazan 23D3

Gites La Vignerai, Route Cap de Bosc. **GPS:** n44,28130 e0,26285. ⬆️.

6 🛏€ 9 🚰€1/time 🚽Ch€1/time ⚡€1/day 🚻€5/time 📶.🏧
Location: Simple. ⏰ 01/01-31/12
Distance: ⚡500m ✖1km.

🏕🅂 Dax ♨ 26B1

Parking du Pont des Arènes, Boulevard des Sports.
GPS: n43,71427 w1,04931. ⬆️.

8 🛏free 🚰🚽free. **Location:** Simple, noisy. **Surface:** asphalted.
⏰ 01/01-31/12
Distance: ⚓on the spot.
Remarks: Max. 72h, saturday market in the halls.

Tourist information Dax:
ℹ️ Office de Tourisme, 11, cours Foch, www.dax.fr. Health resort with warm water sources and medicinal mud.

🏕🅂 Domme 🌿⛲ 23F2

Le Pradal. GPS: n44,80053 e1,22156. ⬆️➡️.

20 🛏free, overnight stay € 5 🚰€2/100liter 🚽Ch 🔌€2/1h. 🏧
🏧 **Location:** Simple, quiet. **Surface:** asphalted. ⏰ 01/01-31/12
⬛ Service: winter
Distance: ⚓500m ✖500m.

Tourist information Domme:
ℹ️ Office de Tourisme, Place de la Halle, www.ot-domme.com. Fortified city worth seeing, parking for motorhomes outside of the town, being indicated.

🏕🅂 Douchapt 23D1

Beauclair. GPS: n45,25145 e0,44335. ⬆️➡️.

🛏€ 5 🚰€2/100liter 🚽Ch 🔌€2/1h. **Location:** Rural, simple, isolated. **Surface:** metalled. ⏰ 01/01-31/12
Distance: ⚓1,5km ⚓Dronne river ✖1,5km.
Remarks: Pay and coins at Village Vacances Beauclair.

🏕🅂 Duras 🌿 23D2

Municipal du Château de Duras, Le Bourg.
GPS: n44,67755 e0,17854. ⬆️➡️.

5 🛏free, July-Aug € 2,60 + € 3,15/pp 🚰🚽Chfree ⚡€2,10. 🏧
Location: Rural, simple, quiet. **Surface:** grassy.
⏰ 01/01-31/12
Distance: ⚓350m ✖350m 🛒350m.

🏕 Eaux-Bonnes 26C3

Parking du Ley. GPS: n42,96304 w0,33933. ⬆️.

20 🛏free. **Surface:** asphalted. ⏰ 01/01-31/12
Distance: ⚓1,4km ⚓1,4km ✖1,4km 🛒1,4km.

🏕🅂 Espés Undurein 26B2

Etche Gochoki, D11. **GPS:** n43,26388 w0,88083. ⬆️.

6 🛏€ 8 🚰€2 🚽Ch ⚡€2. **Surface:** grassy/metalled.
⏰ 01/01-31/12
Distance: ⚓500m ✖500m 🛒400m.

🏕🅂 Excideuil 23E1

Rue Léon Barreau. **GPS:** n45,33614 e1,05269. ⬆️.

4 🛏free 🚰🚽Ch ⚡€3. **Location:** Urban, simple, noisy.
Surface: asphalted. ⏰ 01/01-31/12
Distance: ⚓on the spot ✖100m 🛒100m.

🏕🅂 Fontet 🌊 23D2

Base de Loisirs Fontet. GPS: n44,56118 w0,02282. ⬆️➡️.

20 🛏€ 9 🚰🚽Ch ⚡ WCincluded 📶€1. 🏧 **Location:** Rural, comfortable, quiet. **Surface:** grassy/gravel. ⏰ 01/01-31/12
Distance: ⚓on the spot 🛒bakery 500m, supermarket 4km.
Remarks: At lake, near marina.

🏕🅂 Fourques-sur-Garonne 🌊 23D3

Halte Nautique d Pont des Sables, Pont des Sables, D933.
GPS: n44,46081 e0,13932. ⬆️.

4 🛏free 🚰🚽Chfree. **Location:** Urban, simple. **Surface:** metalled.
⏰ 01/03-31/10
Distance: ⚓Fourques 2,5km 🚤3km ✖on the spot.

🏕🅂 Frontenac 23C2

D236. **GPS:** n44,73781 w0,16308. ➡️.

10 🛏free 🚰🚽 WC 📶free. **Location:** Rural, simple.
Surface: grassy/gravel. ⏰ 01/01-31/12
Distance: ⚓200m ✖200m 🛒bakery 200m 🚲 on the spot.
Remarks: Behind town hall, max. 48h.

🏕🅂 Fumel 🌿 23E3

Place Du Saulou, rue Massenet, D911. **GPS:** n44,49809 e0,97165. ⬆️➡️.

10 🛏free 🚰🚽ChWCfree. **Location:** Urban, simple.
Surface: asphalted. ⏰ 01/01-31/12
Distance: ⚓200m ✖200m.
Remarks: Château de Bonaguil 7km.

🏕🅂 Gastes ⛲🌊 23B3

Port de Gastes, Avenue du lac. **GPS:** n44,32880 w1,15068. ⬆️.

100 ⛺ € 2-4,50, 16/05-15/09 € 7 🚰🔌Ch💧WC⬜included. 🚐📷
Location: Comfortable. **Surface:** grassy. ⬛ 01/01-31/12 ⬤ service in winter
Distance: 🚶Parentis-en-Born 7km ⚓on the spot 🍴on the spot ⊗800m 🛒800m.
Remarks: Along lake, baker every morning.

Gastes 🍴 ⛱ 23B3

Camping Les Echasses, 193 rue de Bernadon. **GPS:** n44,31871 w1,13879.⬆

10 ⛺ € 5-8 🚰€3 🔌Ch💧included. **Location:** Simple.
Surface: grassy. ⬛ 01/01-31/12
Distance: ⚓Gastes Lac 2km 🚲on the spot.
Remarks: Max. 1 night, no camping activities.

Gornac 23C2

Aire Municipale, Esplanade Fongave. **GPS:** n44,66020 w0,18129.⬆

30 ⛺free 🚰🔌Chfree. **Location:** Rural, simple, quiet.
Surface: asphalted. ⬛ 01/01-31/12
Distance: ⊗200m 🛒200m.

Grayan-et-l'Hôpital 23B1

Route de l'Océan. **GPS:** n45,43332 w1,1437.⬆➡

10 ⛺free 🚰€2/100liter 🔌Ch💧€2. **Location:** Rural, simple, isolated, quiet. **Surface:** forest soil.
Distance: 🚶5km ⚓200m 🏊100m 🍴on the spot 🚲on the spot 🎿on the spot.
Remarks: Near campsite.

Grenade-sur-l'Adour 26C1

Place du 19 mars 1962. **GPS:** n43,77500 w0,43472.⬆

10 ⛺free 🚰🔌ChWCfree. **Location:** Simple.
Surface: asphalted/gravel.

Distance: 🚶100m ⊗100m 🛒100m.
Remarks: Next to cemetery, max. 24h.

Grézillac 23C2

Le Bourg. **GPS:** n44,81727 w0,21692.⬆➡
2 ⛺free. **Surface:** gravel. ⬛ 01/01-31/12

Hautefort 🌿⛱ 23E1

Route de Boisseuil. **GPS:** n45,26017 e1,14907.⬆

3 ⛺free 🚰🔌Ch🍴€2 WCfree. **Location:** Simple.
Surface: asphalted. ⬛ 01/01-31/12
Distance: 🚶50m ⊗100m 🛒Intermarché 1km.
Tourist information Hautefort:
⚔ Château Hautefort. Classified castle. ⬛ 01/04-30/09 daily, 01/10-31/03 afternoons.
⚘ ⬛ Wed-morning.

Hendaye 26A2

Gare des deux Jumeaux, Rue d'Ansoenia.
GPS: n43,37019 w1,7648.⬆➡

25 ⛺ € 10 🚰€2/100liter 🔌Ch🍴€2/1h. **Surface:** asphalted.
⬛ 01/01-31/12
Distance: 🚶on the spot ⚓800m ⊗450m 🛒450m 🍴on the spot.
Remarks: Railway-station Hendaye-plage, max. 72h.

Hostens 🍴 23C3

Rue Chantegrue. **GPS:** n44,49321 w0,62898.

4 ⛺free 🚰service€3 🔌Ch📷 ♻. **Location:** Simple, quiet.
⬛ 01/01-31/12
Distance: 🚶1km ⚓on the spot 🍴on the spot ⊗on camp site 🛒on camp site.
Remarks: Next to campsite Ariales, june 2012 during inspection service out of order.

Houeillès 23D3

Aire de Repos, Rue du 19 Mars 1962. **GPS:** n44,19611 e0,03250.

⛺free 🚰WC. **Location:** Simple, quiet. **Surface:** grassy/gravel.
⬛ 01/01-31/12
Distance: 🚶100m 🛒250m.
Remarks: Max. 24h.

Hourtin 🌿⛱🍴♻ 23B1

Aire de camping Car Hourtin, 108, Avenue du Lac.
GPS: n45,18083 w1,08056.⬆➡

90 ⛺ € 7,90, 01/04-30/09 € 10,50 🚰🔌Ch💧(40x)€2
WCincluded. 🚐♻ **Location:** Urban, comfortable, central, quiet.
Surface: gravel/metalled. ⬛ 01/01-31/12
Distance: 🚶50m ⊗50m 🛒50m.

Jumilhac-le-Grand 23E1

Boulevard du Pigeonnier, D78. **GPS:** n45,49219 e1,06092.⬆➡

2 ⛺free 🚰🔌Chfree. **Location:** Urban, simple. **Surface:** asphalted
⬛ 01/01-31/12
Distance: 🚶on the spot ⊗200m 🛒bakery 200m.
Remarks: Near Château de Jumilhac.

L'Hôpital-Saint-Blaise 26B2

Parking l'Église. **GPS:** n43,25088 w0,76925.⬆

5 ⛺free 🚰WC. **Surface:** asphalted. ⬛ 01/01-31/12
Distance: 🚶on the spot ⚓on the spot 🍴on the spot ⊗on the spot.

La Coquille 23E1

N21, Place de l'église. **GPS:** n45,54245 e0,97702.⬆

5 ⛺free 🚰🔌ChWCfree. **Location:** Urban, simple, central.
Surface: asphalted. ⬛ 01/01-31/12
Distance: 🚶100m ⊗200m 🛒200m.

La Pierre-Saint-Martin ⛰❄ 26B3

Aire de campingcar de la Pierre-Saint-Martin, Braça de Guilhers.
GPS: n42,97918 w0,7487.⬆

40 ⛺ € 10 🚰🔌Ch💧(winter). **Surface:** asphalted. ⬛ 01/01-31/12
Distance: 🚶300m ⊗300m 🎿150m.

La Réole 🌿⛱ 23D2

Les Justices, Avenue Gabriel-Chaigne. **GPS:** n44,58059 w0,03036.⬆➡

10 ⌁€4 ⛲🔌Ch free. 🚲 **Location:** Urban, simple, noisy.
Surface: grassy. 🅿 15/04-01/10
Distance: 🚶800m 🛒700m.
Remarks: Nearby Musée Automobile et Militaire.

♿S La Roche-Chalais 🌿 23D1
Halte Nautique, D730. **GPS:** n45,15701 e0,00419.⬆

4 ⌁free ⛲🔌Ch WC free.
Location: Rural, simple. **Surface:** metalled.
🅿 01/01-31/12
Distance: 🚶400m 🏊100m 🚤100m.
Remarks: Service at Intermarché, Av.d'Aquitaine, n45,14633 o0,00569.

♿S La Roque-Gageac 🌿⛵ 23E2
D703. **GPS:** n44,82428 e1,18376.⬆

20 ⌁€7 ⛲€2/10minutes 🔌Ch 🔋€2/1h. **Location:** Simple.
Surface: metalled. 🅿 01/01-31/12
Distance: 🚶200m 🏊100m 🚤100m ⊗200m 🛒200m.
Remarks: Along the Dordogne river, canoe rental.
Tourist information La Roque-Gageac:
ℹ www.cc-perigord-noir.fr. Small town worth seeing, in the Dordogne valley.

♿S La Teste-de-Buch 23B2
Aire de Camping Car du Lac de Cazaux, Rue Guynemer.
GPS: n44,53158 w1,16025.⬆
30 ⌁€ 12/24h ⛲🔌Ch 🔧included. 🔋 **Location:** Comfortable, quiet. **Surface:** gravel/metalled. 🅿 01/01-31/12
Distance: 🏊450m 🚤450m ⊗on the spot.

♿S Labastide-d'Armagnac 🌿 26C1
Les Embarrats. **GPS:** n43,97205 w0,18602.⬆

20 ⌁free ⛲🔌Ch free. **Location:** Rural, simple, quiet.
Surface: grassy.
Distance: 🚶300m.

♿S Labenne 26A1
Route Océane. **GPS:** n43,59616 w1,45492.⬆

---

50 ⌁€8 🔌Ch 🔧included. 🚲 **Surface:** metalled.
🅿 10/04-01/10
Distance: 🚶1km 🏊2km 🚤2km 🚤1km 🛒1km.
Remarks: Max. 48h, no camping activities.

♿S Lacanau ⛱ 23B1
Le Huga, Alleé des Sauviels. **GPS:** n45,00583 w1,16528.⬆➡

160 ⌁€ 13,80/24h ⛲🔌Ch 🔋included. 🔋 🧺 **Location:** Rural, comfortable, quiet. **Surface:** gravel/metalled. 🅿 01/01-31/12
Distance: 🚶2km 🚤2km ⊗100m 🛒2km 🚴on the spot 🚶on the spot.
Remarks: In front of heliport, max. 48h.

♿S Ladaux 23C2
Vignobles Lobre & Fils, Le Bos. **GPS:** n44,69677 w0,24393.⬆➡

5 ⌁free ⛲🔌Ch 🔧WC. **Location:** Rural, simple.
Surface: grassy/metalled. 🅿 01/01-31/12
Distance: 🚶300m.

♿S Lalinde 23E2
Avenue Général Leclerc. **GPS:** n44,83938 e0,74302.⬆➡

2 ⌁free ⛲🔌Ch free. **Location:** Simple. **Surface:** unpaved.
🅿 01/01-31/12
Distance: 🚶500m ⊗500m 🛒500m 🚌on the spot.
Remarks: Near train station.

♿S Lanouaille 23E1
Rue du Chemin Neuf. **GPS:** n45,39248 e1,14002.⬆

6 ⌁free ⛲🔌Ch 🔧WC free. **Location:** Simple, central, quiet.
Surface: asphalted. 🅿 01/01-31/12
Distance: 🚶50m ⊗100m 🛒100m 🚶on the spot.
Remarks: Max. 48h.

♿S Lanton 23B2
Allée Albert Pitres, Taussat. **GPS:** n44,71710 w1,06991.➡

8 ⌁free ⛲🔌Ch free. **Location:** Urban, simple, isolated.
Surface: asphalted. 🅿 01/01-31/12
Distance: 🚶2km 🏖sandy beach 100m ⊗100m 🛒4km.

♿S Laruns ⛱⛰❄ 26C3
Artouste Fabrèges. **GPS:** n42,87914 w0,39693.⬆

80 ⌁free ⛲€5/100liter 🔌Ch 🔧€5/1h WC.
Surface: asphalted/grassy. 🅿 01/01-31/12
Distance: 🚶200m 🏊on the spot 🚤on the spot ⊗on the spot 🛒on the spot 🎿1km.
Remarks: Coins at tourist info.

♿S Laruns ⛱⛰❄ 26C3
Avenue de la Gare. **GPS:** n42,98919 w0,42481.⬆

30 ⌁€6 ⛲🔌Ch 🔧WC. 🔋 🧺 **Surface:** asphalted.
🅿 01/01-31/12
Distance: 🚶450m 🏊450m 🛒450m 🚌400m.
Remarks: Max. 24h, coins at tourist info.

♿S Lauzun 23D2
Rue Saint-Colomb. **GPS:** n44,62762 e0,45979.⬆

2 ⌁free ⛲🔌WC free. **Surface:** gravel. 🅿 01/01-31/12
Distance: 🚶350m 🚤on the spot ⊗350m 🛒350m 🚶on the spot.
Remarks: At small lake, max. 48h.

♿S Lavardac 🌿 23D3
Rue de la Victoire - Place du Foirail. **GPS:** n44,17883 e0,29928.⬆

3 ⌁free ⛲🔌Ch free. **Location:** Simple. **Surface:** asphalted.
Distance: 🚶on the spot 🚲22km 🥖bakery 150m.

FR

Layrac — 23E3
Aire de Layrac, Rue du 19 Mars 1962. **GPS**: n44,13233 e0,65946.

4 free Ch WC free. **Location:** Urban, simple.
Surface: asphalted. 01/01-31/12
Distance: on the spot 150m 150m.

Layrac — 23E3
Le Moulin, D129. **GPS**: n44,13640 e0,66441.

max. 4 € 10/24h Ch WC included. **Location:** Simple, noisy. **Surface:** gravel. 01/01-31/12
Distance: on the spot.
Remarks: Call if no one is present, video surveillance.

Le Bugue — 23E2
Place Léopold Salme. **GPS**: n44,91679 e0,92775.

50 € 7,00 Ch WC free. **Location:** Simple.
Surface: grassy. 01/01-31/12 Service: winter
Distance: 200m 20m 100m Intermarché 100m.
Remarks: Along the river Vézère, tuesday and Saturday market.

Le Mas-d'Agenais — 23D3
Grande Garesse. **GPS**: n44,40656 e0,22030.

8 free Ch (8x)free. **Location:** Urban, comfortable.
Surface: gravel. 01/01-31/12
Distance: 600m 600m.

Le Porge — 23B2
Avenue de l'Océan. **GPS**: n44,89437 w1,2131.

10 free. **Location:** Rural, simple, isolated. **Surface:** forest soil.
01/01-31/12
Distance: Le Porge 10km on the spot on the spot on the spot on the spot.
Remarks: Max. 24h.

Le Porge — 23B2
Intermarché, D107. **GPS**: n44,87574 w1,07883.
€2/20minutes Ch. **Location:** Simple. 01/01-31/12
Distance: on the spot on the spot.

Le Temple-sur-Lot — 23D3
Avenue de Verdun. **GPS**: n44,38000 e0,52639.

4 free Ch WC free. **Location:** Urban, simple, quiet.
Surface: asphalted. 01/01-31/12
Distance: 100m 100m.

Le Verdon-sur-Mer — 20B3
Plage fluviale, Allée des Baïnes. **GPS**: n45,54633 w1,0541.

31+19 € 5/24h, 01/06-30/09 € 8/24h €2/100liter Ch . **Location:** Urban, comfortable, isolated, quiet.
Surface: gravel/metalled.
01/01-31/12
Distance: 50m 500m 2km on the spot.
Remarks: Coins at town hall, tourist info and the shops at the beach.

Lège-Cap-Ferret — 23B2
Route des Pastourelles, Avenue Charles de Gaulle, D106, Claouey.
GPS: n44,75127 w1,18033.

10 free Ch (2x)free. **Location:** Urban, simple, noisy.
Surface: forest soil. 01/01-31/12
Distance: on the spot 1km 600m 600m on the spot.
Remarks: Coins at camping municipal, day parking also allowed, overnight stay on motorhome stopovers.

Lège-Cap-Ferret — 23B2
Avenue Edouard Branly. **GPS**: n44,75203 w1,18809.

15 free.
Location: Rural, simple. **Surface:** forest soil.
01/01-31/12
Distance: 2km 600m 600m 600m 600m on the spot.
Remarks: Near campsite Les Embruns.

Lège-Cap-Ferret — 23B2
D106, Avenue de Bordeaux, L'Herbe. **GPS**: n44,68655 w1,2451.

15 free. **Location:** Rural, simple, quiet. **Surface:** asphalted/metalled.
01/01-31/12
Distance: 2km 1km 2km 2km.

Léguillac-de-l'Auche — 23E1
Glenon. **GPS**: n45,20319 e0,55876.
6 free €2 €3/24h . **Location:** Rural, isolated, quiet.
Surface: grassy.
Distance: 2km 2km 2km.

Lembras — 23D2
Aire de Caudeau, Impasse de l'Anguillère.
GPS: n44,88300 e0,52522.

free Ch free (10x)€4/12h. **Location:** Rural, comfortable, central. **Surface:** gravel. 01/01-31/12
Distance: 200m 200m 200m 2,5km.

Léon — 26A1
Aire camping-cars, Route de Puntaou. **GPS**: n43,88444 w1,31861.

80 € 10 Ch included. **Location:** Simple.
Surface: grassy/gravel. 01/01-31/12
Distance: 1km 250m 50m 50m 50m.
Remarks: Nearby lake.

Les Eyzies — 23E2
Parking de la Vézère, Promenade de la Vézère.
GPS: n44,93863 e1,00907.

25 € 5/night €2/100liter Ch. **Location:** Urban, comfortable, quiet. **Surface:** grassy/sand.
01/01-31/12
Distance: 200m 200m 200m.
Remarks: Along the river Vézère, summer max. 48h, parking fee being collected at 9AM.

Tourist information Les Eyzies:
- Le Village Troglodytique de la Madeleine, Turzac. Troglodyte-village.
- Le Village du Bournat, Le Bugue. Open air museum.
  01/04-31/10 10-17/18h.

Lescar — 26C2
Parking Jacques Monod, Chemin de Beneharnum.
GPS: n43,33062 w0,43458.
5 free. **Surface:** asphalted. 01/01-31/12
Distance: on the spot on the spot on the spot on the spot.
Remarks: Max. 48h.

FR

Lescar — 26C2

Place de l'Evêché. **GPS:** n43,33348 w0,43401.
3 ⑃free. **Surface:** metalled. ⬛ 01/01-31/12
Distance: 🚰on the spot ⊗150m 🧍on the spot.
Remarks: Near office de tourisme, max. 48h.

Limeuil — 23E2

D31. **GPS:** n44,88564 e0,89151.⬆.

10 ⑃free. **Location:** Rural, simple, isolated. **Surface:** grassy/gravel.
⬛ 01/01-31/12
Distance: ⌁400m 🐟400m ⊗750m.

Lit-et-Mixe — 23A3

Cap de l'Homy, 600, avenue Océan. **GPS:** n44,03730 w1,33419.⬆.

36 ⑃€ 10-18, 2 pers.incl 🚰🖥Ch 🧹 WC. **Location:** Simple, quiet.
Surface: forest soil. ⬛ 01/05-30/09
Distance: ⌁400m ⊗200m 🛒200m 🐾 on the spot.
Remarks: Next to camping municipal.

Marmande — 23D3

La Filhole, Rue de la Filhole. **GPS:** n44,49667 e0,16412.⬆.

30 ⑃€ 8 🚰🖥Ch🧹included. 🖥 **Location:** Rural, simple, quiet.
Surface: grassy. ⬛ 01/04-01/11
Distance: 🚰500m ⊗500m 🛒1km.

Marmande — 23D3

Place du Moulin. **GPS:** n44,49833 e0,16028.

2 ⑃free 🚰🖥Chfree. **Location:** Urban. **Surface:** asphalted.
⬛ 01/11-01/04
Distance: 🚰150m ⌁on the spot.
Remarks: Max. 48h.

Marquay — 23E2

D6. **GPS:** n44,94401 e1,13529.⬆.
⑃free 🚰🖥Ch 🧹. **Surface:** gravel.
Distance: ⊗100m.

Mensignac — 23E1

Combecouyere-Sud. **GPS:** n45,22309 e0,56553.
3 ⑃free 🚰€2 🖥Ch. **Location:** Rural. **Surface:** metalled.
⬛ 01/03-31/10

Messanges — 26A1

Plage principale, Avenue de la Plage. **GPS:** n43,81549 w1,40088.⬆.

10 ⑃free. **Location:** Simple. **Surface:** metalled/sand.
Distance: 🚰1,5km ⌁200m.
Remarks: Max. 48h.

Mimizan — 23B3

Hélistation Plage Sud, Rue des Lacs, Mimizan-Plage.
GPS: n44,20517 w1,29675.⬆➡.

85 ⑃€ 8, 01/06-30/09 € 13 🚰🖥Ch🧹included.🖥⬛
Location: Comfortable. **Surface:** asphalted.
⬛ 01/01-31/12
Distance: 🚰500m ⌁on the spot⊗500m 🛒200m.
Remarks: Parking at dune, no trailers allowed.

Mimizan — 23B3

Route du C.E.L.. **GPS:** n44,21375 w1,28239.⬆.

150 ⑃€ 6 🚰€3 🖥Ch. **Location:** Simple. **Surface:** grassy/gravel.
⬛ 01/06-31/09
Distance: ⌁beach 1,5km 🐾 on the spot.

Mimizan — 23B3

Camping du Lac, Avenue de Woolsack, Mimizan-lac.
GPS: n44,21956 w1,22972.⬆.

21 ⑃€ 11,20-17,80 + € 0,22/pp tourist tax, dog € 1,10-1,90 🚰€
2 🖥Ch🧹WC🖥⬛. **Location:** Comfortable. **Surface:** gravel.
⬛ 30/04-30/09

Moliets-et-Maa — 26A1

Avenue de l'Océan, Moliets-Plage. **GPS:** n43,85091 w1,38188.⬆.

120 ⑃€ 5, 01/04-31/08 € 11 🚰🖥Ch🧹WC.🖥⬛
Location: Comfortable, noisy. **Surface:** grassy/gravel.
Distance: 🚰200m ⌁750m ⊗200m 🛒200m.
Remarks: Shady.

Monbahus — 23D3

Rue du Moulin, Le Bourg. **GPS:** n44,54738 e0,53517.⬆➡.

3 ⑃free 🚰🖥Ch🧹(2x)free. **Location:** Rural, simple.
Surface: asphalted. ⬛ 01/01-31/12 ⬤ **Service:** winter
Distance: 🚰300m ⊗200m 🛒300m.
Remarks: Beautiful view, steep entrance road.

Monbazillac — 23D2

Château du Haut Pezaud, Les Pezauds. **GPS:** n44,78471 e0,48687.⬆.

10 ⑃free 🚰€1 🧹€1/night,winter€2 WCfree 🧹€1/pppd 📶€1/day.
Location: Rural, simple. **Surface:** grassy.
⬛ 01/01-31/12
Distance: ⊗table d'hôtes 🧍through the vineyards.
Remarks: Baker every morning, tasting of regional products.

Monbazillac — 23D2

Domaine La Lande, Route de Ribagnac, D13.
GPS: n44,78822 e0,49587.⬆.

10 ⑃free 🚰🖥ChWCfree. **Location:** Rural, simple. **Surface:** grassy.
⬛ 01/01-31/12
Distance: 🚰800m ⊗200m 🛒on the spot.
Remarks: Baker every morning, sale of wines.

Monflanquin — 23E3

Chemin de la Source, 3, Allée des Érables.
GPS: n44,52812 e0,75537.⬆.

⑃free 🚰🖥Chfree.
Location: Simple. **Surface:** gravel.
⬛ 01/01-31/12
Distance: 🚰1,5km 🚤Lac de Coulon 150m ⊗1,3km 🛒250m.
Remarks: Service 500m n44,52477 o0,75642.

Tourist information Monflanquin:
ℹ Office de Tourisme, Place des Arcades, www.monflanquin-tourisme.
com. Medieval town.

Monpazier — 23E2

La Duelle-nord. **GPS:** n44,68499 e0,89362.⬆➡.

10 ⬛free ⤒⬛Chfree. **Surface:** gravel. ◻ 01/01-31/12
Distance: ⬛300m ⊗400m ⬛500m.

⬛S **Monségur** 23D2

Place du 8 mai. **GPS:** n44,65060 e0,08363. ⬆➡.

4 ⬛free ⤒⬛WCfree. **Location:** Simple, noisy. **Surface:** gravel.
◻ 01/01-31/12
Distance: ⬛on the spot.
Remarks: Max. 48h. No access via La Bastide.

⬛S **Mont-de-Marsan** 26C1

Aire du Camping-Cars du Marsan, 541 avenue de Villeneuve.
GPS: n43,88992 w0,47559.⬆.
45 ⬛€5, 01/05-30/09 € 7 ⤒€1/5minutes ⬛Ch⬛€0,50/60minutes.
Location: Rural. **Surface:** asphalted/grassy.
Distance: ⬛2,3km ⬛500m.

⬛S **Montalivet-les-Bains** 23B1

Boulevard de Lattre de Tassigny, Montalivet-sud.
GPS: n45,37611 w1,15667.⬆.

30 ⬛€5 ⤒€1 ⬛Ch.⬛ **Location:** Urban, simple, quiet.
Surface: grassy/metalled. ◻ 01/05-30/09
Distance: ⬛on the spot ⭘100m ⊗400m ⬛400m.
Remarks: At sea, max. 48h, service at Aldi 1km.

Tourist information Montalivet-les-Bains:
⬛ ◻ Fri.

⬛S **Montcaret** 23D2

Le Chalet du Gourmet, D936. **GPS:** n44,85337 e0,03988.⬆.

16 ⬛€ 6,50 ⤒⬛Ch⬛included WC⬛€2 ◻€3.⬛ **Location:** Rural,
simple. **Surface:** gravel. ◻ 01/01-31/12
Distance: ⬛1,2km ⊗on the spot.
Remarks: Bread-service, fruit-vegetables-wine-regional products for
sale.

⬛S **Monteton** 23D2

D423. **GPS:** n44,62249 e0,25745.⬆➡.

25 ⬛free ⤒⬛Chfree. **Location:** Rural, simple. **Surface:** grassy.
◻ 01/01-31/12
Distance: ⬛on the spot ⊗150m.
Remarks: Beautiful view.

⬛S **Montignac** 23E1

P Vieux Quartiers, Rue des Sagnes. **GPS:** n45,06800 e1,16547.⬆➡.

35 ⬛€ 5/night ⤒⬛Ch⬛included. ⬛⬛ **Location:** Comfortable,
central. **Surface:** gravel. ◻ 01/01-31/12
Distance: ⬛200m ⭘200m ⬛200m.

⬛S **Montignac** 23E1

Ferme du Bois Bareirou, Les Baraques, Montignac-Lascaux.
GPS: n45,09053 e1,11143.⬆➡.

20 ⬛free ⤒€3 ⬛Ch⬛€3. **Location:** Rural, isolated, quiet.
Surface: grassy. ◻ 01/01-31/12
Distance: ⬛5km.
Remarks: Max. 3 days.

⬛S **Montpon-Ménestérol** 23D2

Chez Lou Cantou, 46 rue Gustave Eiffel, D730. **GPS:** n45,02101 e0,15997.
4 ⬛€ 10/24h ⤒€3/100liter ⬛Ch⬛€3.
◻ 01/04-31/10 ◻ frost

⬛S **Morcenx** 23B3

Chemin des Abattoirs. **GPS:** n44,03811 w0,90914.⬆.

⬛free ⤒⬛Chfree. **Location:** Simple.
Distance: ⬛500m ⬛8,8km.
Remarks: Along railwayline.

⬛S **Mugron** 26B1

Avenue des Martyrs de la Résistance, D32e.
GPS: n43,74846 w0,75063.⬆.

4 ⬛free ⤒⬛Ch⬛(4x)free. **Location:** Rural, simple.

Surface: gravel.
Distance: ⬛300m ⬛on the spot.
Remarks: Max. 24h.

⬛S **Nailhac** 23E1

Lorserie, D62E3. **GPS:** n45,23276 e1,14214. ⬆➡.

6 ⬛free ⤒⬛Chfree ⬛€3,50/24h. **Location:** Rural, simple.
Surface: metalled.
Distance: ⬛1,5km ⊗1,5km.

⬛ **Naujan-et-Postiac** 23C2

Lafuge. **GPS:** n44,78715 w0,17928. ⬆➡.

⬛free. **Location:** Rural, simple. **Surface:** gravel.
◻ 01/01-31/12
Distance: ⬛200m.

⬛S **Nérac** 23D3

Place du Foirail. **GPS:** n44,13435 e0,33655.⬆.

2 ⬛free ⤒⬛ChWC. **Location:** Simple. **Surface:** asphalted.
◻ 01/01-31/12
Distance: ⬛50m ⊗on the spot ⬛on the spot.

⬛S **Oloron-Sainte-Marie** 26B2

Parking Trivoli, Rue Adour Oloron. **GPS:** n43,18399 w0,60854.⬆➡.

7 ⬛free ⤒€4/55minutes ⬛Ch⬛€4/55minutes.
Surface: asphalted. ◻ 01/01-31/12
Distance: ⬛100m ⭘on the spot ⬛on the spot ⬛400m ⬛400m.
Remarks: Max. 48h, coins at tourist info.

⬛S **Ondres** 26A1

P3, Avenue de la Plage, Ondres-Plage. **GPS:** n43,57611 w1,48611.⬆.

41 ⬛€ 7, 01/07-31/08 € 9 ⤒⬛Ch⬛WCfree. ⬛⬛
Surface: asphalted. ◻ 15/04-01/11
Distance: ⬛3km ⭘on the spot ⬛on the spot ⊗on the spot ⬛on

FR

the spot ♨ on the spot.
Remarks: Max. 48h.

⬛S **Parentis-en-Born** (📷) 23B3
Site du Lac, Route des Campings. **GPS:** n44,34432 w1,09879. ⬆.

25 🏕€7 🚰🔌Ch 💧(4x)included. **Location:** Comfortable.
Surface: gravel. ◻ 01/01-31/12 ◉ service in winter
Distance: 🚶3km 🏊50m ⊗50m.

⬛ **Pau** 26C2
Place de Verdun, Rue Ambroise Bordelongue.
GPS: n43,29848 w0,37811. ⬆⬆.

20 🏕free. **Location:** Urban. **Surface:** asphalted. ◻ 01/01-31/12
Distance: 🚶on the spot ⊗on the spot 🚆200m.
Remarks: Max. 48h, free shuttle.

⬛S **Payzac** 23F1
Le Bourg. GPS: n45,40008 e1,21950. ⬆➡.

2 🏕free 🚰🔌Ch💧free. **Location:** Simple. **Surface:** asphalted.
◻ 01/01-31/12
Distance: 🚶on the spot ⊗on the spot 🚆on the spot 🧍on the spot.

⬛S **Pellegrue** 23D2
Le Touran, Rue du Lavoir. **GPS:** n44,74514 e0,07416. ⬆➡.

3 🏕free 🚰🔌Ch💧free. **Location:** Urban, simple.
Surface: metalled. ◻ 01/01-31/12
Distance: 🚶100m ⊗200m 🚆700m.

⬛S **Périgueux** 🍴 23E1
Espace des Prés, Rue des Prés. **GPS:** n45,18770 e0,73081. ⬆➡.

40 🏕€6 🔌Chincluded. 🔋💨 **Location:** Urban, comfortable,
central. **Surface:** asphalted. ◻ 01/01-31/12 ◉ water disconnected
in winter
Distance: 🚶800m 🚌on the spot.

Remarks: Max. 48h.

⬛S **Peyrehorade** 26B1
Des Gaves, Route de la Pêcherie. **GPS:** n43,54300 w1,1071. ⬆.
16 🏕€8 🔌Ch 💧€2,50 WC 🚽. **Surface:** grassy.
◻ 01/06-30/09
Distance: 🚶150m 🏊on the spot 🚣on the spot ⊗150m 🚆150m.
🚌200m.

⬛S **Peyrehorade** 26B1
Place Jean Bridart, Rue du Sablot, D817. **GPS:** n43,54300 w1,09994. ⬆.

10 🏕free 🚰🔌Chfree. **Surface:** metalled. ◻ 01/01-31/12
Distance: 🚶50m 🏊on the spot 🚣on the spot ⊗100m 🚆on the
spot.
Remarks: In front of supermarket Carrefour.

⬛S **Port-Sainte-Foy-et-Ponchapt** 23D2
Rue Jacques Jasmin. GPS: n44,84210 e0,20915. ⬆➡.

4 🏕free 🚰🔌Chfree. **Location:** Urban, simple, central, quiet.
Surface: asphalted. ◻ 01/01-31/12
Distance: 🚣on the spot ⊗600m 🚆600m.
Remarks: Along the Dordogne river, service 200m.

🦢 **Prats-de-Carlux** 23F2
Les Oies du Périgord Noir, D47B. **GPS:** n44,89936 e1,31503. ⬆.

4 🏕free. **Location:** Rural, simple, quiet. ◻ 01/01-31/12
Distance: 🚶3km ⊗3km 🚆3km.
Remarks: Max. 24h.

ⒸS **Ribérac** 23D1
Camping de la Dronne, 91 Rue des Etats Unis.
GPS: n45,25704 e0,34255. ⬆.

10 🏕free, 01/06-15/09 €5,60 🚰🔌Chfree. 🔋 **Location:** Urban,
simple. **Surface:** metalled. ◻ 01/01-31/12 ◉ Water when frosty
Distance: 🚶1,3km ⊗50m 🚆Leclerc 900m.

⬛S **Roquefort** 23C3
Allée de Nauton. GPS: n44,04754 w0,32255. ⬆.
6 🏕free 🚰🔌Ch. **Surface:** grassy/gravel. ◻ 01/01-31/12
Distance: 🚶1,7km 🚲5km.
Remarks: Next to camping municipal.

⬛S **Saint Estèphe** 20E3
Etang de Saint Estèphe, Route du Grand Etang.
GPS: n45,59458 e0,67437. ⬆➡.

10 🏕€5 🚰🔌Chincluded. 🚲 **Location:** Rural, comfortable.
Surface: forest soil. ◻ 01/01-31/12
Distance: 🚶700m 🏊lake 🚣on the spot ⊗on the spot 🚆3km,
bakery 800m.
Remarks: Max. 48h, summer: beach, bar, restaurant.

⬛S **Saint-Antoine-Cumond** 23D1
Le Bourg, D43. **GPS:** n45,25553 e0,19963. ⬆.

10 🏕free 🚰🔌ChWCfree. **Location:** Rural, simple.
Surface: asphalted/gravel. ◻ 01/01-31/12
Distance: 🚶on the spot.

⬛S **Saint-Caprais-de-Blaye** 23C1
Route de Saintes, RN137, Ferchaud. **GPS:** n45,29120 w0,5692. ⬆.

8 🏕free 🚰service€2 🔌ChWC 🚽free, cold shower.
Surface: asphalted. ◻ 01/01-31/12
Distance: 🚲6,4km ⊗on the spot 🚆on the spot.
Remarks: Tourist information and picnic tables available.

⬛S **Saint-Cyprien** 🌿🏛 23E2
Place Mackenheim, Rue du Priolat. **GPS:** n44,86828 e1,04435. ⬆➡.

8 🏕free 🚰€3/100liter 🔌Ch 💧(8x)€3/12h. **Location:** Simple.
Surface: asphalted.
◻ 01/01-31/12
Distance: 🚶50m 🚆bakery 50m, supermarket 100m.
Remarks: Max. 24h, coins at tourist info and restaurant La Sivade.
Tourist information Saint-Cyprien
⊗ Marché repas gourmand. 🍴 summer Thu-evening.

⬛S **Saint-Estèphe** 🍇 23C1
Rue du Littoral. GPS: n45,26544 w0,7582. ⬆.

5 🏕free 🚰🔌Ch💧Service€5. **Location:** Rural, simple, quiet.
Surface: gravel/metalled. ◻ 01/01-31/12

Distance: 🚲2 km 🏊on the spot 🛒on the spot ⊗on the spot 🚲on the spot.
Remarks: Free, coins available at restaurant.

🅢 Saint-Front-la-Rivière — 23E1

Chez Boutau, D83. **GPS:** n45,46645 e0,72419.⬆.

10 🆓free 🚰🗑Ch.(2x)free. **Location:** Rural, comfortable, isolated, quiet. **Surface:** metalled. 🅿 01/01-31/12
Remarks: Max. 72h, picnic area.

🅢 Saint-Hilaire-de-Lusignan — 23D3

D813. **GPS:** n44,22491 e0,51364.⬆.

3 🆓free 🚰€3/10minutes 🗑Ch. **Location:** Urban, simple, noisy.
Surface: gravel. 🅿 01/01-31/12
Distance: 🛒on the spot ⊗1km 🚇5km, bakery 500m.

🅢 Saint-Jean-de-Côle — 23E1

Le Bourg. **GPS:** n45,41984 e0,84048.⬆.

3 🆓free 🚰€2 🗑Ch 🛒€2. **Location:** Urban, simple, quiet.
Surface: metalled. 🅿 01/01-31/12
Distance: 🛒on the spot ⊗200m 🚇300m 🚌200m.
Remarks: At tennis-court, coins at tourist info.

🅢 Saint-Jean-de-Luz — 26A2

Avenue Pierre Larramendy, D810. **GPS:** n43,38527 w1,6629.⬆.

18 🆓free 🚰🗑Ch🛒free. **Surface:** asphalted.
Distance: 🛒200m 🚲2,2km 🏊300m 🛒300m ⊗100m 🚇100m.
Remarks: Max. 48h.

Tourist information Saint-Jean-de-Luz:
ℹ Office de Tourisme, Place du Maréchal Foch, www.saint-jean-de-luz.com. Tourist town with beautiful shops. The local speciality is chipirones, octopus cooked in its own ink.
🍴 Halles, Bd Victor Hugo. 🅿 morning.

🅢 Saint-Jean-Pied-de-Port 🌿🏊🎣 — 26A2

Parking du Lai Alai. **GPS:** n43,16519 w1,23208.⬆.

50 🆓€ 5,50/24h 🚰🗑Chfree.🛒
Surface: metalled.
🅿 01/01-31/12
Distance: 🛒350m 🏊350m 🛒350m ⊗350m 🚇350m 🏃on the spot.
Remarks: Nearby stadium, max. 48h.

Tourist information Saint-Jean-Pied-de-Port:
ℹ Office de Tourisme, 14, Place Charles de Gaulle, www.pyrenees-basques.com. Fortified city on the foot of the Roncesvallespass on the road to Santiago de Compostela.
🌿 Forêt d'Iraty. Nature reserve, hiking trails available at OT.

🅢 Saint-Laurent-Médoc — 23B1

Place du 8 mai 1945. **GPS:** n45,14903 w0,8215.⬆.

6 🆓free 🚰🗑Ch. **Location:** Urban, simple, comfortable.
Surface: gravel/metalled. 🅿 01/01-31/12
Distance: 🛒on the spot ⊗300m 🚇300m.

🅢 Saint-Leon-sur-l'Isle 🏊 — 23D1

Skate Park Bord de l'Isle, D41E2. **GPS:** n45,12002 e0,49628.

6 🆓free 🚰🗑Chfree. **Location:** Rural, simple.
Surface: metalled/sand. 🅿 01/01-31/12
Distance: 🛒2km 🚲5,3km 🛒on the spot ⊗2km 🚇2km.
Remarks: Service in village 750m, n45.11515 o0.5003400.

🅢 Saint-Léon-sur-Vézère 🌿🏊🎣 — 23E2

Le Bourg, C201. **GPS:** n45,01230 e1,08978.⬆.

15 🆓free, 01/04-15/11 € 6 🚰€2 🗑WC.🛒 **Location:** Rural, simple, quiet. **Surface:** grassy/gravel. 🅿 01/01-31/12
Distance: 🛒100m ⊗200m 🚇150m.
Remarks: Coins at tourist info.

🅢 Saint-Martial-d'Artenset — 23D2

Le Gaec du Petit Clos, Ferrachat. **GPS:** n44,99877 e0,22052.
🆓€ 5, € 10 service incl 🚰🗑Ch 🛒. **Location:** Comfortable, isolated, quiet.
Distance: 🛒2,5km 🚲9km ⊗2,5km.

🅢 Saint-Médard-de-Guizières — 23D2

Place du 14 Juillet. **GPS:** n45,01526 w0,05813.⬆.
3 🆓free 🚰🗑ChWCfree. **Surface:** asphalted. 🅿 01/01-31/12
Distance: 🛒on the spot ⊗300m.

🅢 Saint-Palais-sur-Mer — 26B2

Parking Place Ste. Elisabeth, Rue Gaztelu Zena.
GPS: n43,32944 w1,0325.⬆.

---

10 🆓free 🚰🗑ChWCfree. **Surface:** asphalted. 🅿 01/01-31/12
Distance: 🛒200m ⊗250m 🚇250m.

🅢 Saint-Paul-lès-Dax 🐑 — 26B1

Allée Salvador Allende. **GPS:** n43,73460 w1,07865.⬆➡.

8 🆓free 🚰🗑Chfree. **Location:** Simple. **Surface:** gravel/sand.
🅿 01/01-31/12
Distance: 🏊500m 🚇500m.
Remarks: Max. 72h, shady.

🅢 Saint-Pée-sur-Nivelle — 26A2

Flot bleu park St. Pée sur Nivelle, Promenade du Parlement de Navarre. **GPS:** n43,34945 w1,5215.⬆⬆➡.

50 🆓€ 9,50/24h 🚰€2,50/120liter 🗑Ch 🛒€2,50/4h. 📷🏊
Surface: asphalted. 🅿 01/01-31/12
Distance: 🛒3km 🏊on the spot ⊗500m 🚇500m Restaurant Aintzira Le Lac.
Remarks: Parking at lake, max. 48h, bread-service.

🅢 Saint-Pey-d'Armens 🏛 — 23C2

Château Gerbaud, Gerbaud. **GPS:** n44,85310 w0,10699.⬆.

40 🆓€ 5 🚰🗑Chincluded 🏊(8x)€3. **Location:** Rural, simple.
Surface: grassy. 🅿 01/01-31/12
Distance: ⊗1km 🚇bakery 1km, supermarket 2km.
Remarks: Max. 48h.

🅢 Saint-Romain-la-Virvée 🍴 — 23C2

Rue des Milonis. **GPS:** n44,96449 w0,40139.➡.

5 🆓free 🚰🗑Chfree. **Location:** Rural, comfortable, quiet.
Surface: asphalted. 🅿 01/01-31/12
Distance: 🛒on the spot 🚲10km ⊗250m.
Remarks: Next to sports fields.

FR

Saint-Saud-Lacoussière 20E3

Étang de la Gourgousse, Route du Grand Etang.
GPS: n45,55780 e0,82237.

free. **Location:** Rural, isolated, quiet.
Surface: forest soil.
Distance: Sandy beach on the spot on the spot.
Remarks: Max. 72h.

Saint-Saud-Lacoussière 20E3

Domaine Sous Chardonnièras, 4, Impasse Sous Chardonnièras.
GPS: n45,54053 e0,81909.

4 € 12,50 WC included. **Location:** Simple, quiet.
Surface: grassy. 01/01-31/12
Distance: 500m 2km 2km 500m 500m.

Saint-Sauveur 23E2

Le Bourg, D21. **GPS:** n44,86850 e0,58834.

3 free WC free. **Location:** Simple. **Surface:** asphalted.
01/01-31/12
Distance: 100m 100m 100m.

Saint-Savin 23C1

Aire de Civrac-de-Blaye, Parc de la Mairie, D36, Civrac-de-Blaye.
GPS: n45,11222 w0,44444.

1 free WC free. **Surface:** grassy. 01/01-31/12
Distance: 50m 100m.

Saint-Savin 23C1

Aire de St.Girons d'Aiguevives, St.Girons d'Aiguevives.
GPS: n45,13972 w0,5425.

2 free. **Surface:** grassy/gravel. 01/01-31/12
Distance: on the spot 4km 10km.
Remarks: Parking in front of church.

Saint-Savin 23C1

Aire des Lacs du Moulin Blanc, St.Christoly-de-Blaye.
GPS: n45,15167 w0,47583.

2 free WC free. **Surface:** gravel. 01/01-31/12
Distance: 800m 50m on the spot on the spot 3km.
Remarks: Parking at lake.

Saint-Savin 23C1

Aire des Lagunes, St.Mariens. **GPS:** n45,11790 w0,40243.

2 free WC free. **Surface:** asphalted. 01/01-31/12
Distance: on the spot 6km 6km 2km 3km.

Saint-Savin 23C1

Parking Centre Culturel. **GPS:** n45,13800 w0,4465.

2 free WC. **Surface:** gravel. 01/01-31/12
Distance: on the spot 3km 3km 150m 800m, bakery 50m.
Remarks: Max. 48h.

Saint-Savin 23C1

Aire de l'Église, Générac. **GPS:** n45,18000 w0,54.
2 free. 01/01-31/12
Distance: on the spot 6km 10km.

Saint-Savin 23C1

Aire de Marcenais, Marcenais. **GPS:** n45,05808 w0,33889.

2 free. 01/01-31/12
Distance: on the spot 6km 6km.
Remarks: Next to community centre.

Saint-Savin 23C1

Aire de Saugon, Saugon. **GPS:** n45,17795 w0,50243.
2 free. 01/01-31/12
Distance: on the spot 6km 6km 3km 6km.
Remarks: Behind town hall.

Saint-Savin 23C1

Aire de St. Vivien, RN137, St.Vivien-de-Blay. **GPS:** n45,09917 w0,51666.

2 free. 01/01-31/12
Distance: on the spot 3km 3km 3km 3km.
Remarks: Parking at church.

Saint-Savin 23C1

Aire du Dojo, Cézac. **GPS:** n45,09000 w0,41.

1 free. 01/01-31/12
Distance: on the spot 6km 6km 3km 3km.
Remarks: Nearby town hall.

Saint-Savin 23C1

Aire du Lac des Vergnes, Laruscade. **GPS:** n45,10000 w0,34.
2 free. 01/01-31/12
Distance: 200m on the spot 500m 2km.
Remarks: Parking at lake.

Saint-Savin 23C1

Aire Maison de la Forêt, Donnezac. **GPS:** n45,24000 w0,44.

2 free. 01/01-31/12
Distance: on the spot 6km 6km.
Remarks: Next to community centre.

Saint-Savin 23C1

Parking communal Aire de Cavignac, Rue de Paix, Cavignac.
GPS: n45,10019 w0,39192.

2 free. 01/01-31/12
Distance: on the spot 8km 50m 300m.

Saint-Savin 23C1

Parking communal Aire de Saint Yzan, Parking de la Gare, St.Yzan-de-Soudiac. **GPS:** n45,14006 w0,40996.
2 free. 01/01-31/12
Distance: on the spot 12km 800m 3km 3km on the spot.

Saint-Savin 23C1

Parking de Marsas, Rue Chaignaud, Marsas. **GPS:** n45,06770 w0,3849.
2 free. 01/01-31/12
Distance: on the spot 4km 4km.

Saint-Savin 23C1

Parking Maison des Jeunes, Cubnezais.
GPS: n45,07500 w0,40861.

FR

⌂free. **Surface:** asphalted. ▯ 01/01-31/12
Distance: 50m ✕3km 🛒3km.

Saint-Sylvestre-sur-Lot — 23E3
Place du Lot, Avenue Jean Moulin. **GPS:** n44,39621 e0,80499.⬆➡.

12 ⌂free 🚰⚡Chfree.
Location: Urban, simple. **Surface:** asphalted.
▯ 01/01-31/12
Distance: 150m, Penne d'Agenais centre 1,8km ✕100m 🛒50m.
Remarks: Service 100m.

Saint-Vincent-de-Cosse — 23E2
Ferme d'Enveaux. **GPS:** n44,82669 e1,09822.⬆➡.

50 ⌂guests free 🚰⚡Chfree. **Surface:** unpaved.
▯ 01/01-31/12
Distance: 🏊pebbled beach 50m ⬤on the spot ✕on the spot.
Remarks: Along the Dordogne river, max. 48h, key service at canoe rental.

Saint-Vincent-Jalmoutiers — 23D1
Le Bourg. **GPS:** n45,20055 e0,19091.⬆➡.

25 ⌂free 🚰⚡ChWCfree. **Location:** Rural, simple.
Surface: grassy/sand. ▯ 01/01-31/12
Distance: 350m 🛒350m.

Sainte-Alvère — 23E2
Rue de la Fontaine Saint Jean. **GPS:** n44,94500 e0,80499.⬆➡.

10 ⌂free 🚰€2,50/100liter ⚡Ch🔌€2,50/h. **Location:** Rural,
simple. **Surface:** gravel. ▯ 01/01-31/12
Distance: 500m ✕500m 🛒500m.
Remarks: At sports centre, coins in town hall.

Sainte-Colombe-en-Bruilhois — 23D3
Lieu-dit Bécade. **GPS:** n44,17889 e0,51692.⬆.

4 ⌂free 🚰⚡ChWCfree. **Location:** Rural, simple, quiet.
Surface: gravel. ▯ 01/01-31/12
Distance: on the spot ✕200m 🛒200m.

Sainte-Eulalie-en-Born — 23B3
Route du Port, D652. **GPS:** n44,30634 w1,18206.⬆.

40 ⌂€ 7, 01/04-31/10 € 4,50 🚰⚡Ch 🔌WC included 📶€3.
Location: Comfortable, quiet. **Surface:** grassy. ▯ 01/04-31/10
◉ service 01/11-01/03
Distance: 🏊50m ✕50m 🛒on the spot 🚲on the spot.
Remarks: At marina, to be paid at campsite.

Sainte-Livrade-sur-Lot — 23E3
Avenue René Bouchon. **GPS:** n44,39588 e0,59179.⬆➡.

8 ⌂free 🚰⚡Chfree. **Location:** Urban, simple. **Surface:** asphalted.
▯ 01/01-31/12
Distance: on the spot 🛒850m.
Remarks: At fire-station.

Sainte-Nathalène — 23F2
Les Ch'tis, Le Bourg, D47. **GPS:** n44,90409 e1,28765.⬆.

6 ⌂€ 10 🚰⚡Ch 🔌included. 🛁 **Location:** Rural, simple.
Surface: gravel. ▯ 01/01-31/12
Distance: Sarlat 7km ✕50m 🛒bread service 50m.
Remarks: Market Wednesday (July-August).

Salies-de-Béarn — 26B2
Aire Camping-car du Herre, Quartiér du Herre.
GPS: n43,47270 w0,9339.⬆➡.

24 ⌂€ 6,50 🚰⚡Ch 🔌included. 🛁 **Surface:** metalled.
▯ 01/01-31/12
Distance: 300m 🏊on the spot ⬤on the spot ✕300m 🛒300m.
◉300m.

Salignac-Eyvigues — 23F2
Rue des Ecoles. **GPS:** n44,97257 e1,32061.⬆.

10 ⌂free 🚰⚡Chfree. **Location:** Simple, quiet. **Surface:** grassy.
▯ 01/01-31/12
Distance: 300m ✕300m 🛒250m.

Salignac-Eyvigues — 23F2
Les Jardins du Manoir d'Eyrignac, Rte des Jardins du Manoir.
GPS: n44,93875 e1,31609.

40 ⌂free. **Location:** Rural. **Surface:** grassy/gravel.
Distance: Sarlat 13km ✕on the spot.

Sanguinet — 23B2
Aire du camping-car Les Bardets, 1131, Avenue de Losa.
GPS: n44,48408 w1,09153.⬆.

15 ⌂free, € 8 (01/05-18/09) 🚰⚡Chfree. **Location:** Simple, quiet.
Surface: metalled. ▯ 01/01-31/12
Distance: 800m 🏊on the spot ⬤on the spot ✕50m 🛒on the spot.
Remarks: At lake, max. 48h.

Sanguinet — 23B2
Parking du Pavillon, 459, Avenue de Losa.
GPS: n44,48579 w1,08479.⬆.

30 ⌂free, € 8 (15/6-15/9) 🚰WC. **Location:** Simple, quiet.
Surface: forest soil. ▯ 01/01-31/12
Distance: 🏊on the spot ✕Le Pavillon.
Remarks: Max. 48h.

Sare — 26A2
Place de Campingcars de Sare. **GPS:** n43,31307 w1,57679.⬆.

15 ⌂€ 6 🚰⚡Chincluded. **Location:** Quiet. **Surface:** metalled.
▯ 01/01-31/12

Distance: 300m 300m 300m on the spot on the spot.
Remarks: Max. 48h.
Tourist information Sare:
Office de Tourisme, Bourg, www.sare.fr. Typical Basque village in Labourd-region.
Le petit train de la Rhune, Col de Saint Ignace. The little train runs through the mountains in the Basque Country on the Franco-Spanish border. 15/03-15/11 from 9h.
Les Grottes de Sare. Caves, prehistoric park and museum. 01/02-31/12.

Sarlat-la-Canéda 23F2
Place Flandres Dunkerque. **GPS:** n44,89530 e1,21266.

50 € 7/24h, € 15/48h €2 Ch €2
Location: Urban, simple, noisy. **Surface:** asphalted.
01/01-31/12
Distance: 1km 100m bakery 50m.
Tourist information Sarlat-la-Canéda:
Centre ville. Centre of the French trade in foie grass. Sa-morning.

Sauvagnon 26C2
Champ de Foire, Rue du Béarn. **GPS:** n43,40361 w0,38635.

6 free Ch WC free. **Surface:** asphalted. 01/01-31/12
Distance: on the spot on the spot on the spot on the spot.

Sauvagnon 26C2
Rue du Béarn. **GPS:** n43,40310 w0,3876.
6 free. **Surface:** grasstiles. 01/01-31/12
Distance: on the spot.

Sauveterre de Guyenne 23C2
Boulevard de 11 Novembre. **GPS:** n44,69022 w0,08624.

4 free €1,50/90minutes Ch €1,50/90minutes.
Location: Urban, simple, noisy. **Surface:** metalled.
01/01-31/12
Distance: 350m 1000m, bakery 100m.
Remarks: Coins at tourist info, supermarket.

Savignac-Lédrier 23F1
Route de Juillac. **GPS:** n45,36401 e1,22066.

15 free Ch free. **Location:** Rural. **Surface:** gravel.
01/01-31/12
Distance: on the spot 100m.

Remarks: Coins at restaurant des Forges.

Seignosse 26A1
Aire camping-cars, D79. **GPS:** n43,69089 w1,42539.

110 € 12 Ch WC included. **Surface:** grassy/gravel.
01/01-31/12
Distance: 500m 500m 500m 500m 500m.
Remarks: Next to campsite municipal Hourn-Nao, video surveillance.

Sévignacq Méracq 26C2
Aire du gave d'Ossau, Quartier Raguette.
GPS: n43,10712 w0,419.

[photograph]

20 € 10 €3 Ch €2 WC. **Surface:** grassy/gravel.
01/02-30/11
Distance: 1km on the spot on the spot 1km 1km.

Soorts-Hossegor 26A1
Route des Lacs. **GPS:** n43,67279 w1,42087.
85 € 6/24h €2 Ch WC. **Location:** Rural, quiet.
Surface: gravel. 01/01-31/12
Distance: 550m.
Remarks: Max. 5 days.

Sorges 23E1
Aire de repos Grangearias, Le Bourg, N21.
GPS: n45,30570 e0,87238.

4 free Ch free. **Location:** Urban, simple. **Surface:** metalled.
01/01-31/12
Distance: 100m 200m 250m.
Remarks: Service 100m.

Soulac-sur-Mer 20B3
Boulevard de L'Amélie. **GPS:** n45,49938 w1,1373.

[photograph]

45 € 4, 15/06-15/09 € 8 €3,70/10minutes Ch €3,70/h.
Location: Urban, comfortable. **Surface:** gravel/metalled.
01/01-31/12
Distance: 2km 50m 2,5km 2,5km on the spot on the spot.

Sourzac 23D1
D6089. **GPS:** n45,05147 e0,39518.

8 free €2/100liter Ch WC. **Location:** Rural, central.
Surface: gravel/metalled. 01/01-31/12 water disconnected in winter
Distance: 600m 100m.
Remarks: Coins at petrol station.

Soustons 26A1
Parking du Lac Marin, Avenue de la Pêtre, Soustons Plage.
GPS: n43,77560 w1,41167.

80 01/10-31/04 € 6,50, 01/05-30/09 € 12,50
Ch WC included. **Location:** Simple.
Surface: gravel/metalled. 01/01-31/12
Distance: city centre 3km lake 50m, ocean 300m 50m 50m on the spot.
Remarks: Max. 72h.

Taussat 23B2
Allée Albert Pitres. **GPS:** n44,71719 w1,06986.
8 free free. **Location:** Simple. **Surface:** metalled.
Distance: 50m 300m 300m.

Terrasson-Lavilledieu 23F1
MCD Camping-cars, Rue Alphonse Daudet.
GPS: n45,13389 e1,30832.

25 € 6 €2 Ch €3. **Location:** Rural, comfortable, quiet.
Surface: grassy. 01/03-31/11
Distance: 1km 600m 600m.

Tocane-Saint-Apre 23D1
Pré Sec, D103. **GPS:** n45,25712 e0,49471.

8 free €2/100liter Ch €2/1h. **Location:** Rural, simple.
Surface: metalled. 01/01-31/12
Distance: 300m 100m 300m 300m.
Remarks: Coins at the shops in the village.

Tournon-d'Agenais 23E3
Base de Loisirs Camp Beau, Pont Roumio, Route de Libos, D102.
GPS: n44,40444 e0,99833.
15 free Ch free. **Location:** Rural, simple. **Surface:** metalled.
01/01-31/12
Distance: 500m.

Trémolat 23E2
D30. **GPS:** n44,87378 e0,83065.

5 🍽free 🚰€2/25minutes 🔧Ch. **Location:** Rural, simple.
Surface: asphalted. ◻ 01/01-31/12
Distance: 🛒300m ⊗300m 🍴300m 🚶on the spot.
Remarks: Coins at town hall.

Valeyrac 🌊〰️ 23B1
Port de Goulée, Route Castillonaise. **GPS:** n45,40500 w0,91028.

5 🍽free. **Location:** Rural, simple, isolated, quiet.
Surface: gravel/metalled. ◻ 01/01-31/12
Distance: 🛒50m 🛶on the spot 🚤on the spot ⊗20m 🚌on the spot 🚶on the spot.
Remarks: At harbour.

🅿️S Vanxains 23D1
Le Petit Verteillac, D708. **GPS:** n45,21204 e0,28399. ⬆️➡️

2 🍽free 🚰🔧Ch🚻WC. **Location:** Rural, simple.
Surface: asphalted. ◻ 01/01-31/12
Distance: 🛒400m 🍴700m.

🅿️S Vertheuil 23B1
Château Ferré, 3 rue des Aubépines. **GPS:** n45,26225 w0,82798. ⬆️➡️

4 🍽free 🚰🔧ChWC. **Location:** Rural, comfortable.
Surface: grassy/gravel. ◻ 01/01-31/12
Distance: 🛒2km 🏊8km 🍴2,5km.

🅿️S Veyrines-de-Domme 23E2
Boutique des Bois d'Envaux, Route des Milandes, 6-102 Le Falgueyrat.
GPS: n44,82090 e1,10394. ⬆️

30 🍽free. **Location:** Simple, isolated. **Surface:** grassy.
Distance: ⊗on the spot.
Remarks: Sale of foie gras and wine, monday evening marché gourmand.

🅿️S Vézac 23E2
Camping-Car Park, La Malartrie. **GPS:** n44,82440 e1,16950. ⬆️
15 🍽€9,60, Jun/Aug €12 🚰🔧Ch📶included. **Surface:** gravel.
◻ 01/01-31/12
Remarks: At Edersee.

🅿️S Vielle-Saint-Girons 👫 26A1
Lac de Léon, plage de Vielle. GPS: n43,90279 w1,30944. ⬆️

30 🍽€9-12 + €0,61/ppp tourist tax, dog €4,70 🚰🔧Ch🔧(30x)€
4,50/night WC🚻. **Location:** Simple. **Surface:** gravel/metalled.
◻ 01/04-30/09
Distance: 🛒100m 🏊300m ⊗50m 🍴100m.
Remarks: Max. 48h.

🅲S Vielle-Saint-Girons 👫 26A1
Les Tourterelles, Saint Girons-Plage. **GPS:** n43,95278 w1,35778. ⬆️

40 🍽€9, 01/07-31/08 €15,50 🚰€2,70/10liter 🔧Ch🔧55minutes
WC🚻. **Location:** Comfortable. **Surface:** gravel/metalled.
◻ 01/01-31/12 🔧 Service 01/10-26/04
Distance: 🏊300m ⊗500m 🍴500m.

🅿️S Vieux-Boucau-les-Bains 26A1
Aire camping-cars Village, Avenue des Pêcheurs.
GPS: n43,77971 w1,40041. ⬆️

150 🍽€6, 01/05-30/09 €12 🚰🔧Ch🔧included. 🚐🧺
Location: Comfortable. **Surface:** gravel/sand. ◻ 01/01-31/12
Distance: 🛒500m 🏊200m ⊗500m 🍴500m 🚲on the spot.
Remarks: >3,5t not allowed.

🅿️S Vieux-Boucau-les-Bains 26A1
Aire du Marensin Plage, Boulevard du Marensin.
GPS: n43,79485 w1,4051. ⬆️

35 🍽€12 🚰🔧Ch🔧🚐
Location: Simple, quiet. **Surface:** gravel.
◻ 05/01-30/09
Distance: 🛒1,5km 🏊Ocean 500m ⊗1,5km 🍴1,5km 🚲on the spot.
Remarks: >3,5t not allowed, max. 48h.

🅿️S Villeneuve-de-Marsan 26C1
Avenue du Stade 40. **GPS:** n43,88737 w0,30595. ⬆️➡️

7 🍽free 🚰🔧Ch🔧(2x)free,16Amp. **Location:** Rural.
Surface: asphalted. ◻ 01/01-31/12
Distance: 🛒400m ⊗500m 🍴400m.
Remarks: Max. 48h.

🅿️S Villeréal 23E2
Aire de Jeux, Boulevard Alphonse de Poitiers, D104.
GPS: n44,63798 e0,74065. ⬆️
🍽free 🚰🔧Ch. **Surface:** asphalted. ◻ 01/01-31/12
Distance: 🛒300m ⊗300m 🍴300m.

🅿️S Villeton 〰️ 23D3
D120. **GPS:** n44,36386 e0,27279. ⬆️

4 🍽free, 01/04-31/10 €5 + tourist tax 🚰€4 🔧Ch🚐€2/4h WC.
🚿 **Location:** Rural, comfortable. **Surface:** gravel. ◻ 01/01-31/12
◻ water disconnected in winter
Distance: 🚴10,5km 🏊on the spot 🚤on the spot ⊗on the spot
🍴500m.

🅿️S Vitrac 🌊🚣 23F2
Montfort, D703. **GPS:** n44,83558 e1,24852. ⬆️➡️

10 🍽free 🚰€3/100liter 🔧Ch🔧€3/1h WC. **Location:** Rural, simple.
Surface: grassy/gravel. ◻ 01/01-31/12
Distance: 🛒50m 🏊2km beach at Dordogne river ⊗200m.
Remarks: Coins available at restaurant Le Point Vue (200m).

Midi Pyrénées

🅿️S Adé 🌊🚣 26C2
Feerie-des-Eaux, 70 Avenue des Pyrénées, N21.
GPS: n43,12834 w0,0277. ⬆️➡️

27 🍽€10 🚰🔧Ch🔧included. 🚿 **Location:** Comfortable, noisy.
Surface: asphalted/grassy. ◻ Easter-31/10
Distance: 🛒Lourdes 2km 🚴1km ⊗500m 🍴200m.

🅿️S Agos-Vidalos 🏔️👫 26C3
Le Pibeste, Avenue du Lavedan. **GPS:** n43,03552 w0,07069. ⬆️➡️

FR

30 �▨ € 9,60, 01/07-31/08 €10,80 ⟞⬛Ch⟿⟩⟩included. |⬛ ⬙
Location: Rural, comfortable. **Surface:** grassy/gravel.
⬛ 01/01-31/12
Distance: 🛁on the spot ⬗10km ⊗on the spot ⬙3km ⬥on the spot 🚶on the spot.

| ⌕S | Albi | 26G1 |

Base de Loisirs Pratgraussals. **GPS:** n43,92951 e2,13480.⬆
20 �▨free ⟞⬛Chfree. **Surface:** asphalted. ⬛ 01/01-31/12
Distance: 🛁1km.

| ⌕S | Albi | 26G1 |

Les portes d'Albi. GPS: n43,91846 e2,10968.⬆
�. ⌨free ⟞⬛Ch. **Surface:** asphalted. ⬛ 01/01-31/12
Distance: ⊗on the spot ⬙on the spot ⬌on the spot.
Remarks: Parking supermarket.

| ⌕S | Albi | 26G1 |

Parking Cathédrale. GPS: n43,92750 e2,14111.⬆➡

9 ⌨free. **Surface:** asphalted.
Distance: 🛁50m ⊗50m ⬙100m.
Remarks: Parking nearby cathedral Sainte Cécile, max. 48h.

FR | S | Albi | 26G1 |

Rue Michelet. **GPS:** n43,94583 e2,15111.⬆➡
⟞⬛Ch⬛free. ⬛ 01/01-31/12

| ⌕S | Alblas | 23F3 |

Pech del Gal. **GPS:** n44,47480 e1,23275.⬆➡

10 ⌨free ⟞⬛Chfree. **Location:** Simple, isolated, noisy.
Surface: gravel.
Remarks: At weir.

| ⌕S | Alvignac | 23F2 |

Parc du Samayou, Route de Padirac. **GPS:** n44,82504 e1,69711.⬆

10 ⌨free ⟞⬛ChWC. **Surface:** asphalted.
Distance: 🛁100m ⊗200m ⬙200m.

| ⌕S | Anglès | 26H2 |

Route de Saint-Pons. **GPS:** n43,56553 e2,56544.⬆
4 ⌨free ⟞⬛Ch⟿. **Surface:** metalled.
Distance: 🛁500m.

| ⌕S | Aragnouet ❄☀ | 26D3 |

Piau Engaly. **GPS:** n42,78599 e0,15800.⬆➡

120 ⌨free, Winter € 15 ⟞⬛Ch⟿(120x) WC⟩⟩.
Location: Comfortable, isolated, quiet. **Surface:** asphalted.
⬛ 01/12-31/08
Distance: 🛁300m ⬙300m ⬥300m.
Remarks: Service only during winter period.

| ⌕ | Arfons | 26G2 |

Pierron-Les Escudiés. **GPS:** n43,43972 e2,19472.

4 ⌨€ 5. **Surface:** grassy. ⬛ 01/01-31/12
Distance: 🛁4km ⬌1km ⊗4km ⬥4km.

| ⌕ | Argelès-Gazost ❄☀🎿 | 26C3 |

Carrefour Market, Route du Stade. **GPS:** n43,00455 w0,08636.⬆

26 ⌨free ⟞⬛Ch. **Location:** Rural, comfortable, quiet.
Surface: asphalted. ⬛ 01/01-31/12
Distance: 🛁4km ⬙350m ⬥on the spot 🚶on the spot.

| ⌕S | Arreau ❄🏔 | 26D3 |

Chemin de Fregel. **GPS:** n42,90708 e0,35912.⬆

25 ⌨free, July-Aug € 2 ⟞⬛Chfree. 🚿 **Location:** Urban, simple, central. **Surface:** metalled. ⬛ 01/01-31/12
Distance: 🛁100m ⬗on the spot ⛱100m ⊗150m ⬙300m ⬌200m ⬥on the spot 🚶on the spot.

| ⌕S | Arrens-Marsous 🏔🏞❄ | 26C3 |

D918. **GPS:** n42,95806 w0,20722.⬆

10 ⌨free ⟞€2/100liter ⬛Ch⬛€2. **Location:** Rural, simple, isolated, quiet. **Surface:** asphalted. ⬛ 01/01-31/12
Distance: 🛁650m ⊗550m ⬙500m ⬥on the spot 🚶on the spot.

| ⌕S | Arvieu 🏞 | 23H3 |

GPS: n44,19246 e2,65916.⬆

---

11 ⌨€ 2 ⟞€2/80liter ⬛ChWC. **Surface:** gravel. ⬛ 01/04-31/10
Distance: 🛁100m ⬗on the spot ⊗on the spot ⬙on the spot.
Remarks: Coins at the shops and town hall.

| ⌕ | Aubrac | 23H3 |

D533. **GPS:** n44,62026 e2,98705.
10 ⌨free ⟞⬛ChWCfree. **Location:** Simple, quiet. **Surface:** gravel.
⬛ 01/01-31/12
Distance: 🛁50m ⊗on the spot ⬙on the spot 🚿on the spot 🏊on the spot.

| ⌯S | Auch ❄⛲☕🍽 | 26D1 |

Camping municipal, Rue des Cormorans.
GPS: n43,63654 e0,58854.⬆➡

3 ⌨€ 4 ⟞⬛Chfree ⬛€1,50. **Surface:** asphalted. ⬛ 01/01-31/12
Distance: 🛁15min ⊗15min ⬙15min.

| ⌕S | Auterive | 26F2 |

Grande Allée du Ramier. **GPS:** n43,35025 e1,47730.⬆

6 ⌨free ⟞⬛Chfree. **Surface:** asphalted. ⬛ 01/01-31/12
Remarks: At fire-station.

| ⌕ | Auterive | 26F2 |

Rue des Docteurs Basset. **GPS:** n43,35182 e1,47641.⬆
10 ⌨free. **Surface:** asphalted.
Distance: 🛁200m ⊗200m.
Remarks: Along river.

| ⌕S | Auzas | 26E2 |

La Grangère. **GPS:** n43,17016 e0,88690.⬆

10 ⌨€ 4 ⟞⬛Ch⟿(4x)included. **Surface:** asphalted.
Distance: ⛱on the spot.
Remarks: At lake.

| ⌕S | Ax-les-Thermes ⛱🏔☕❄🎿 | 26F3 |

A Bonascre, Rue des Chalets. **GPS:** n42,70340 e1,81657.⬆
40 ⌨free ⟞€2/100liter ⬛Ch⬗€6/24h. **Location:** Isolated, quiet. **Surface:** gravel. ⬛ 01/01-31/12

| ⌕S | Ax-les-Thermes ⛱🏔☕❄🎿 | 26F3 |

N20. **GPS:** n42,72565 e1,83154.⬆
25 ⌨€ 6 ⟞€ 100/liter ⬛included1h. |⬛ ⬙ **Location:** Simple, noisy.
Surface: asphalted.
Distance: 🛁1km.

Ax-les-Thermes 26F3
Parc d'Espagne. **GPS:** n42,71504 e1,84142. ⬆.

35 ⌂ € 5. **Surface:** asphalted. ◻ 01/01-31/12
Distance: 🚶500m ⊗500m ◉500m.

S Bagnères-de-Bigorre 26D3
Rue René Cassin. **GPS:** n43,07319 e0,15256. ⬆➡.

30 ⌂free 🚰Ch WC free. **Location:** Rural, simple, noisy.
Surface: gravel. ◻ 01/01-31/12
Distance: 🚶500m ⚡15km ⊗500m 🛒650m.

S Bagnères-de-Bigorre 26D3
Avenue de Belgique. **GPS:** n43,06917 e0,14889. ⬆.

10 ⌂free. **Location:** Urban, simple, central, noisy. **Surface:** asphalted.
◻ 01/01-31/12
Distance: 🚶200m ⚡15km ⊗200m 🛒200m 🚗on the spot 🚲on the spot 🚶on the spot.
Remarks: At station.

S Bagnères-de-Luchon 26D3
Lac de Badech, Rue Jean Mermoz. **GPS:** n42,79540 e0,59875. ⬆.

50 ⌂€ 4/24h 🚰Service€4 🗑Ch ▯. ▯ ⚡**Location:** Rural, simple,
quiet. **Surface:** asphalted.
◻ 01/01-31/12 ◉ service: 01/12-01/04
Distance: 🚶1km ⊗1km 🛒500m 🚲on the spot 🚶on the spot.
Remarks: Coins at tourist info.

S Baraqueville 23G3
Rue du Val de l'Enne. **GPS:** n44,27850 e2,43407. ⬆.

10 ⌂free 🚰€3 🗑Ch WC. **Surface:** asphalted. ◻ 01/01-31/12
◉ service 01/11-31/03
Distance: 🚶on the spot ⚡50m 🚲on the spot 🚶on the spot.
Remarks: Coins at the shops in the village, inclining pitches.

Barbotan-les-Thermes 26C1
Avenue des Thermes. **GPS:** n43,94884 w0,04344. ⬆➡.

6 ⌂free, night € 4,50. **Surface:** asphalted. ◻ 01/01-31/12
Distance: 🚶500m ⊗50m 🛒500m.

S Bardigues 26E1
GPS: n44,03869 e0,89271. ⬆➡.

4 ⌂free 🚰€2/100liter 🗑Ch. **Surface:** gravel. ◻ 01/01-31/12
Distance: 🚶150m ⚡8,6km ⊗150m 🛒150m.

Barèges 26D3
Le Tournabou, Route de Tourmalet, D918. **GPS:** n42,90329 e0,10151. ⬆.

15 ⌂free. **Location:** Rural, isolated, quiet. **Surface:** asphalted.
◻ 01/01 -31/12
Distance: 🚶2,5km ⊗on the spot 🛒3km 🚲on the spot 🚶on the spot
🏊on the spot 🎿on the spot.

S Bellas 23H3
D995. **GPS:** n44,31256 e3,12689.
10 ⌂€ 5 🚰free ⚡€3. **Location:** Rural, quiet.
Surface: grassy/metalled. ◻ 01/01-31/12 🚲on the spot 🚶on the
spot.

S Belmont sur Rance 26H1
Parking de la Mairie, Route de Lacaune. **GPS:** n43,81630 e2,75269. ⬆.

3 ⌂free 🚰Ch free. **Surface:** asphalted. ◻ 01/01-31/12
Distance: 🚶on the spot.

S Boisse Penchot 23G3
Rue du Chateau Bas. **GPS:** n44,59201 e2,20567. ⬆.

8 ⌂free 🚰€3/100liter 🗑Ch ▯€3/1h. **Surface:** asphalted.
◻ 01/01-31/12
Distance: 🚶100m 🏊on the spot 🚤on the spot ⊗on the spot 🛒on

the spot.

S Bonac Irazein 26E3
Lac Bonac. **GPS:** n42,87541 e0,97565. ⬆.

10 ⌂€ 6 🚰Ch ⚡included. 🚗 **Surface:** grassy/gravel.
◻ 01/03-30/11
Distance: 🏊on the spot.
Remarks: At artificial lake of Bonac.

S Bouillac 23G3
Aire de Bouillac, D840. **GPS:** n44,57333 e2,15750. ⬆.

6 ⌂free 🚰€3 🗑Ch. **Surface:** metalled. ◻ 01/03-30/11
Distance: 🚶on the spot 🏊on the spot ⊗on the spot 🛒600m.
Remarks: Max. 24h, coins at the shops.

S Broquies 26H1
Route de Mazies. **GPS:** n44,00498 e2,69371. ⬆.

30 ⌂free 🚰🗑Ch ⚡WC ▯. **Surface:** gravel. ◻ 01/04-30/11
Distance: 🚶50m ⊗on the spot 🛒on the spot.
Remarks: Coins at supermarket.

Cadours 26E1
Rue Malakoff. **GPS:** n43,72320 e1,04861. ⬆➡.

5 ⌂free 🚰🗑Ch free. **Location:** Rural. **Surface:** grassy.
◻ 01/01-31/12 ◉ tue-evening, wed-morning
Distance: 🚶1km ⊗1km.
Remarks: At football ground.

S Cahors 23F3
Parking Chartreux, Rue de la Chartreuse.
GPS: n44,44016 e1,44119. ⬆➡.

3 ⌂free 🚰🗑Ch free. **Surface:** gravel. ◻ 01/01-31/12
Distance: 🚶500m 🏊on the spot ⊗250m 🛒50m 🚗on the spot.
Remarks: Along river.

Cahors 23F3

Parking Saint George, Rue Saint George.
GPS: n44,43875 e1,44111.
20 free. **Surface:** asphalted. 01/01-31/12
Distance: 1,2km 15km 100m on the spot.
Remarks: Shuttle bus to city centre.
Tourist information Cahors:
Wed, Sa.

Cahuzac-sur-Vère 26G1

Place du Mercadial. **GPS:** n43,98194 e1,91111.

5 free ChWC. **Surface:** gravel.
Distance: 200m 200m.

Cajarc 23F3

Place de la Gare. **GPS:** n44,48458 e1,84573.

8 free €1 Ch. **Surface:** grassy. 01/01-31/12
Distance: 100m 200m 200m.

Camares 26H1

Base de loisirs des Zizines. **GPS:** n43,81654 e2,87988.

10 free ChWC free. **Surface:** gravel.
01/04-31/10
Distance: 100m on the spot on the spot.

Campagnac 23H3

La Sagne. **GPS:** n44,41885 e3,08875.

5 free, 13/06-13/09 € 3 Ch. **Surface:** metalled.
01/01-31/12
Distance: 400m 400m 400m.
Remarks: Coins at campsite and town hall.

Campan 26D3

Le Bourg. **GPS:** n43,01817 e0,17828.

5 free ChWC. **Location:** Rural, simple, quiet. **Surface:** gravel.
01/01-31/12
Distance: 100m on the spot 300m 200m.
Remarks: Max. 48h.

Campan 26D3

Serre Crampe, Payolle. **GPS:** n42,93711 e0,30259.

15 free ChWC free. **Location:** Rural, isolated, quiet.
Surface: gravel. 01/01-31/12
Distance: 5km 150m 150m 600m 6km on the spot
on the spot on the spot on the spot.
Remarks: Max. 48h, service 100m.

Campuac 23H3

GPS: n44,57027 e2,59162.
10 free ChWC free. **Surface:** gravel. 01/01-31/12
Distance: 100m on the spot.

Cardaillac 23G2

Le Pré del Prie. **GPS:** n44,67868 e1,99805.

12 free €2/100liter Ch €2/h. **Location:** Isolated, quiet.
Surface: gravel. 01/01-31/12
Distance: 100m on the spot 100m.
Remarks: Behind church.

Castanet 23G3

GPS: n44,27889 e2,28944.

4 € 5 Ch included. **Surface:** gravel. 01/01-31/12
Distance: on the spot on the spot.

Castelnau-de-Montmiral 26F1

Domaine Les Miquels. **GPS:** n43,96667 e1,80278.

6 € 10,50, 2 pers.incl Ch included. **Location:** Rural,
comfortable, isolated, quiet. **Surface:** grassy. 01/01-31/12

Distance: 2,5km on the spot 2,5km.

Castelnau-Durban 26F3

D117. **GPS:** n42,99994 e1,33976.

10 free €2 Ch €2 WC. **Surface:** metalled.
Remarks: Parking in front of church, max. 48h.

Castelsarrasin 26E1

Allée de la Source. **GPS:** n44,03861 e1,10221.

40 € 3/24h €2,50/100liter Ch €2,50/24h.
Surface: gravel. 01/01-31/12
Distance: 500m 500m 500m.

Castres 26G2

Parc de Gourjade, Avenue de Roquecourbe, D89.
GPS: n43,62049 e2,25357.

5 free. **Surface:** metalled.
Distance: 2km.
Remarks: Max. 24h.

Castres 26G2

Place Gerard Philipe, Chemin des Porches. **GPS:** n43,60168 e2,24939.

free. **Location:** Urban. **Surface:** asphalted. 01/01-31/12
Distance: 2km 2km 2km.
Remarks: Max 3,5t, free bus to centre.

Castres 26G2

Route de l'Industrie Z.I. de Melou. **GPS:** n43,59069 e2,20648.
Ch free. 01/01-31/12
Tourist information Castres:
Palais Episcopal. Episcopal palace.
Tue, Thu-Su.

Cauterets 26C3

Ancien Boulodrome, Avenue Charles Thierry.
GPS: n42,88628 w0,11522.

24 �€ 10 ⌐⌐▫Ch⌐included. ▫ **Location:** Rural, simple, quiet. **Surface:** asphalted. ▫ 01/01-31/12 **Distance:** ▫300m ⌐20km ⊗300m ▫350m ⌐on the spot ⌐on the spot ⌐on the spot.

▫S Cauterets ⌐⌐⌐⌐ 26C3
Place de la Patinoire, D920. **GPS:** n42,89361 w0,11256. ⌐⌐.

50 ⌐€ 10/24h ⌐⌐▫Ch⌐included. ▫ **Location:** Rural, comfortable, quiet. **Surface:** asphalted. ▫ 01/01-31/12 **Distance:** ▫300m ⌐20km ⊗300m ▫300m ⌐on the spot ⌐on the spot. **Remarks:** Max. 21 nights.

▫S Caylus 23F3
Base de loisirs Labarthe, D19. **GPS:** n44,23363 e1,77225. ⌐.

6 ⌐free ⌐⌐▫Chfree. **Surface:** grassy/gravel. ▫ 01/01-31/12 **Distance:** ▫200m ⊗200m ▫200m.

Tourist information Caylus:
▫ St.Antonin. Small town with the oldest town hall of France.

▫S Condom 26D1
Avenue des Mousquetaires. **GPS:** n43,94788 e0,36422. ⌐.
12 ⌐free ⌐⌐▫Ch. **Location:** Comfortable, isolated, quiet. **Surface:** metalled. **Distance:** ▫500m. **Remarks:** Max. 5 days.

▫S Condom 26D1
Ferme de Parette, Route de Nérac, RN930. **GPS:** n43,98802 e0,35046. ⌐⌐.

8 ⌐€ 8, 2 pers.incl ⌐⌐▫Ch⌐included ▫€4. **Location:** Comfortable, isolated, quiet. **Surface:** grassy. ▫ 01/01-31/12 **Distance:** ▫2km ⊗2km ▫2km.

Tourist information Condom:
▫ Musée de l'Armagnac. All about Armagnac.

▫S Cordes-sur-Ciel 26G1
Parking les Tuileries. **GPS:** n44,06453 e1,95802. ⌐⌐.

Distance: ▫50m ⌐on the spot ⌐on the spot ⊗50m ▫50m.

▫ Coupiac 26H1
Route de Martin. **GPS:** n43,95174 e2,58464. ⌐.
10 ⌐free ⌐⌐▫Chfree. **Surface:** grassy. ▫ 01/01-31/12 **Distance:** ▫500m ▫450m. **Remarks:** Max. 72h.

▫S Cransac ⌐ 23G3
Aire de Camping-car Cransac, Route de la Gare. **GPS:** n44,52278 e2,27444.

6 ⌐€ 6,80, 2 pers.incl ⌐⌐▫Chincluded. **Surface:** gravel. ▫ 12/03-25/11 **Distance:** ▫500m ⊗500m ▫500m. **Remarks:** Max. 48h.

▫S Donzac 23E3
Lac de Sources, D30. **GPS:** n44,11308 e0,82044. ⌐.

10 ⌐free ⌐⌐▫Chfree. **Location:** Rural. **Surface:** gravel. ▫ 01/01-31/12 **Distance:** ⌐on the spot. **Remarks:** Max. 48h.

▫S Douelle ⌐⌐ 23F3
Domaine Marcilhac, D8. **GPS:** n44,47927 e1,34947. ⌐⌐.

10 ⌐free ⌐⌐€2 ▫Ch. **Location:** Rural. **Surface:** gravel. ▫ 01/01-31/12 **Distance:** ▫1km ⊗1km ▫1km ⌐1km.

▫S Entraygues-sur-Truyère ⌐⌐⌐⌐ 23H2
Route de Villecomtal, D904. **GPS:** n44,64020 e2,56925. ⌐.

⌐free. **Surface:** grassy. ▫ 01/04-31/12

▫S Entraygues-sur-Truyère ⌐⌐⌐⌐ 23H2
Rue de la Grave. **GPS:** n44,64417 e2,56278.

5 ⌐free. **Surface:** gravel. ▫ 01/01-31/12 **Distance:** ▫50m ⊗150m ▫150m.

▫S Entraygues-sur-Truyère ⌐⌐⌐⌐ 23H2
Rue du 16 Août 1944. **GPS:** n44,64269 e2,56577.

⌐€3 ▫Ch⌐. **Remarks:** Coins at tourist info.

▫S Figeac 23G3
Parking le Foiral, Boulevard Colonel Teulié. **GPS:** n44,61089 e2,03674. ⌐.

5 ⌐free ⌐€2 ▫Ch⌐€2. **Location:** Central, noisy. **Surface:** asphalted. ▫ 01/01-31/12 **Distance:** ▫100m ⊗400m ▫100m ⌐100m.

Tourist information Figeac:
▫ Marché régional. Regional market. ▫ Sa-morning.

▫S Fleurance 26E1
Boulevard de Metz. **GPS:** n43,85164 e0,66184. ⌐⌐.

20 ⌐free ⌐€2 ▫Ch⌐€2. **Surface:** gravel. **Distance:** ▫200m ▫on the spot ⌐on the spot.

▫S Frejairolles 26G1
Le Grand Chêne, D81. **GPS:** n43,86043 e2,24799. ⌐.
5 ⌐€ 5, free for clients ⌐⌐▫Ch⌐included.

▫S Gaillac 26F1
Parking des Rives Thomas, Rue Claude Nougaro. **GPS:** n43,89951 e1,89494. ⌐⌐.

⌐free ⌐⌐▫Chfree. **Surface:** asphalted. ▫ 01/01-31/12

FR

Distance: 🚶200m ⊗200m 🚰200m.

⛺Ⓢ Gavarnie 🌿⛱🏔❄ `26C3`

Parking Holle, Route de la station des Espécières, D923. **GPS:** n42,73857 w0,01959. ⬆.

20 🏕free, July-Aug € 7 🚰Ch included. 🏠 **Location:** Rural, simple, isolated, quiet. **Surface:** metalled. ◻ 01/01-31/12 **Distance:** 🚶1,5km ⛱100m ⊗800m 🚰800m 🚶 on the spot 🎿100m 🚠1,5km.

⛺ Gavarnie 🌿⛱🏔❄ `26C3`

Parking du Cirque, Baretge. **GPS:** n42,73549 w0,0116. ⬆.

20 🏕€ 7. 🏠 **Location:** Rural, simple. **Surface:** asphalted. ◉ 01/07-31/08 **Distance:** 🚶200m ⛱200m ⊗200m 🚰200m 🚶 on the spot 🎿on the spot 🚠on the spot.

Tourist information Gavarnie:

👁 Cirque de Gavarnie. Can be reached with a donkey, a horse or by foot. A giant waterfalll, snow pillars and mountain slopes.

⛺ Gèdre 🏔❄ `26C3`

Aire de stationnement de Héas, D922. **GPS:** n42,74916 e0,08935. 🏕free. **Location:** Rural, simple, isolated, quiet. **Surface:** grassy. ◉ winter **Distance:** 🚶9km ⊗600m. **Remarks:** At Chapelle de Héas.

⛺ Gèdre 🏔❄ `26C3`

Place de la Bergère, Gedre Débat. **GPS:** n42,78860 e0,01967. ⬆.

12 🏕free. **Location:** Rural, simple. **Surface:** asphalted. ◻ 01/01-31/12 **Distance:** 🚶on the spot ⊗250m 🚰50m.

⛺ Gèdre 🏔❄ `26C3`

Auberge de la Munia, Héas, D922. **GPS:** n42,73643 e0,08631. 5 🏕€ 6. **Distance:** ⊗on the spot.

⛺Ⓢ Gignac `23F2`

Le Moulin, Place des Troubadours. **GPS:** n45,00624 e1,45687. ⬆.

10 🏕free 🚰Ch. **Surface:** metalled. ◻ 01/01-31/12 **Distance:** 🚶50m ⊗150m 🚰150m.

⛺Ⓢ Gimont 🌿⛱🐟🍴 `26E1`

Avenue de Cahuzac, RN124. **GPS:** n43,62987 e0,87009. ⬆.

12 🏕free 🚰Ch 🚿free. **Location:** Simple, noisy. **Surface:** gravel. ◻ 01/01-31/12 **Distance:** 🚶100m ⛱on the spot 🎣on the spot ⊗300m 🚰300m 🚌300m. **Remarks:** At lake, max. 48h, market Wednesday and Sunday.

⛺Ⓢ Gourdon 🌿⛱🍦🏔🌳 `23F2`

Esplanade du foirail. **GPS:** n44,73423 e1,38523. ⬆➡.

8 🏕€ 1/6h 🚰Ch 🔌(8x)included. **Location:** Comfortable, quiet. **Surface:** gravel. ◻ 01/01-31/12 **Distance:** 🚶200m ⊗100m 🚰200m 🚌on the spot.

⛺Ⓢ Gramat `23F2`

La Garenne, Avenue Paul Mezet. **GPS:** n44,77966 e1,72904. ⬆➡.

10 🏕free 🚰Ch 📧. **Surface:** gravel. ◻ 01/01-31/12 **Distance:** 🚶400m ⊗400m 🚰400m. **Remarks:** Max. 48h.

⛺Ⓢ Grenade-sur-Garonne `26F1`

Quai de Garonne. **GPS:** n43,77201 e1,29673. ⬆.

4 🏕free 🚰Ch. **Surface:** gravel. **Distance:** 🚶100m ⊗100m 🚰100m 🚌100m. **Remarks:** Service: Allées Alsace Lorraine (100m).

⛺Ⓢ La Bastide-de-Sérou `26F3`

Bargnac, D15. **GPS:** n43,00194 e1,44556. ⬆.

15 🏕€ 14,60, Jul/Aug € 18,60 🚰Ch 🚿WC 📶included. **Location:** Rural, isolated, quiet. **Surface:** asphalted/gravel. ◻ 11/04-03/11

⛺Ⓢ La Couvertoirade 🌿⛱🏔 `27A1`

GPS: n43,91012 e3,31276.

---

10 🏕€ 3 🚰€ 3/100liter WC. **Location:** Rural, isolated, quiet. **Surface:** gravel. ◻ 01/01-31/12 **Distance:** 🚶50m ⊗50m. **Remarks:** Large parking on edge from village.

Tourist information La Couvertoirade:

ℹ Citadelle de l'Ordre de Tempeliers. Fortified city in original state. Now many old craft industries are exercised. There is a toll-house at the entrance of the village, entrance fee is charged.

⛺Ⓢ Labastide-Murat `23F2`

Route de Gramat. **GPS:** n44,64944 e1,57061. ⬆. 🏕free 🚰Ch. **Location:** Rural, simple. **Surface:** asphalted. **Distance:** 🚶300m 🚰on the spot. **Remarks:** At supermarket Carrefour.

⛺Ⓢ Labruguiere 🍴🏔 `26G2`

Domaine d'en Laure, Avenue Arthur Batut. **GPS:** n43,53139 e2,25528. ⬆➡.

10 🏕free 🚰€ 2/10minutes 🚰Ch 📧€ 2/minutes. **Location:** Rural, simple, isolated, quiet. **Surface:** grassy. ◻ 01/01-31/12 **Distance:** 🚶2km ⛱on the spot 🎣on the spot ⊗1,3km 🚰1,3km.

⛺Ⓢ Lacapelle Marival `23G2`

Place de Larroque. **GPS:** n44,72806 e1,92944.

50 🏕free 🚰€ 2/100liter Ch 📧€ 2/h. **Surface:** asphalted. ◻ service 15/05-30/09 **Distance:** 🚶on the spot ⊗100m 🚰50m.

⛺Ⓢ Lacaune `26H1`

Rue de la Balme. **GPS:** n43,70795 e2,69010.

20 🏕free. **Surface:** gravel. ◻ 01/01-31/12 **Distance:** 🚶on the spot ⊗on the spot.

⛺Ⓢ Lacroix-Barrez `23H2`

Le Ventoux. **GPS:** n44,77793 e2,63086. ⬆. 10 🏕€ 2,50 + € 0,30 tourist tax 🚰Ch free. **Surface:** grassy. ◻ 01/01-31/12 ◉ service: 01/11-17/04 **Distance:** 🚶400m.

⛺Ⓢ Laguepie `23G3`

Quai de l'Aveyron. **GPS:** n44,14485 e1,97226. ⬆➡.

FR

6 free Ch free. **Surface:** asphalted. 01/01-31/12
Distance: 200m 200m on the spot.

Laguiole 23H2

Du Bouyssou, La Serre. **GPS**: n44,67199 e2,92451.
€ 8 €3. **Surface:** asphalted.
Distance: 7km on the spot.

Laguiole 23H2

Rue de Lavernhe. **GPS**: n44,68408 e2,85048.

10 free Ch free. **Surface:** gravel.
01/01-31/12, service: 17/04-15/10
Distance: on the spot.

Laguiole 23H2

La Montagnettte, Les Clauzades. **GPS**: n44,70457 e2,84037.
5 free €2.
Location: Simple, isolated, quiet. **Surface:** gravel.
Distance: 4km.

Laissac 23H3

Place du Foirail des Ovins, RN88. **GPS**: n44,38590 e2,82160.

6 free Ch free. **Surface:** asphalted. 01/03-30/11
Distance: 500m 500m 500m.
Remarks: Max. 24h.

Lannemezan 26D2

L'Espace du Nébouzan, Chemin du Carrérot de Blazy.
GPS: n43,12779 e0,38085.

20 free Ch free. **Location:** Rural, comfortable.
Surface: gravel. 01/01-31/12
Distance: 450m 200m 250m.

Lanuéjouls 23G3

Aire Campingcar Lanuéjouls, Avenue du Rouergue, D1.
GPS: n44,42528 e2,16139.

14 € 5 Ch WC included. **Surface:** gravel.
01/01-31/12
Distance: 100m 100m 100m.

Latronquière 23G2

Place du Foirail. **GPS**: n44,79917 e2,07917.

4 free Ch WC free. **Surface:** asphalted.
01/01-31/12
Distance: 300m 3km 3km 300m 300m.

Lauzerte 23E3

1, Place du Foirail. **GPS**: n44,25432 e1,13666.

10 free Ch WC free. **Surface:** asphalted. 01/01-31/12
tue-evening, wed-morning
Distance: 500m on the spot on the spot.

Lauzerte 23E3

D2, Vignals. **GPS**: n44,26750 e1,14083.

20 free Ch WC free. **Surface:** grassy/gravel.
01/01-31/12
Distance: Lauzerte 2km on the spot 2km.
Tourist information Lauzerte:
Wed-morning.

Le Fossat 26F2

Aire des Lallières, Place de la Mairie. **GPS**: n43,17201 e1,41170.

21 € 12 Ch WC included. **Location:** Luxurious.
Surface: gravel. 01/03-30/11

Le Garric 26G1

Cap Découverte. **GPS**: n44,01361 e2,13778.

18 € 8 Ch included. **Surface:** asphalted. 01/01-31/12
Distance: 300m.

Le Houga 26D1

Ferme aux Cerfs, Route de Mont de Marsan, D6.
GPS: n43,78430 e0,20997.

15 € 3 Ch free. **Surface:** grassy. 01/01-31/12
Distance: 2,5km on the spot.

Le Ségur 26G1

Place de Marie. **GPS**: n44,10889 e2,05861.

3 free Ch WC free. **Surface:** metalled. 01/01-31/12
Distance: 50m 100m 100m.

Les Cabannes 26F3

Quartier la Bexane. **GPS**: n42,78493 e1,68301.

30 € 4/24h €2/100liter Ch WC. **Surface:** asphalted.
Distance: 300m 300m.

Lisle sur Tarn 26F1

Aire de Bellevue, Rue des Aulnes. **GPS**: n43,86167 e1,81833.

12 free Ch. **Location:** Comfortable, isolated, quiet.
Surface: sand. 01/01-31/12
Distance: 1,5km on the spot on the spot 1,5km 1,5km.

Lombez 26E2

Route de Toulouse, D632. **GPS**: n43,47417 e0,91592.

FR

20 ⌕free ⛽💧WCfree. **Surface:** gravel.
Distance: 🚶200m ⊗150m 🛒200m.

| 📷S | **Loudenvielle** 🏔🏖❄ | 26D3 |

Aire de campingcar Les Seguettes, Chemin du Hourgade.
GPS: n42,80163 e0,41088.

30 ⌕free, 01/07-15/09 € 3 ⛽€2/100liter 💧Ch🚽€2/h. ♨
Location: Rural, quiet. **Surface:** gravel.
🕐 01/01-31/12
Distance: 🚶700m ⊗700m 🛒800m.
Remarks: At lake, coins at Tourist Info and Maison de la Presse.

| 📷S | **Loudenvielle** 🏔🏖❄ | 26D3 |

La Ribère, D25 Génos. **GPS:** n42,79963 e0,40813.↑
6 ⌕free, 01/07-15/09 € 3. ♨ **Location:** Rural, simple, quiet.
Surface: gravel. 🕐 01/01 - 31/12
Distance: 🚶500m 🚲on the spot ⊗on the spot 🛒500m 🏍on the
spot 🚶on the spot.

| 📷S | **Lourdes** | 26C2 |

Le Vieux Berger, Route de Julos. **GPS:** n43,10451 w0,0332.↑→

27 ⌕€ 11, May-Jun € 13, Jul-Sep € 14 ⛽💧Ch 💧WC🚽🔌€
3/3 🛜included. 🍽🛒 **Location:** Rural, luxurious, noisy.
Surface: grassy/gravel. 🕐 01/01-31/12
Distance: 🚶1km 🚲2km ⊗700m 🛒700m 🚌100m 🚶on the spot.
Remarks: Next to campsite.

Tourist information Lourdes:
ℹ️ Office de Tourisme, Place Peyramale, www.lourdes-infotourisme.
com. Lively place of pilgrimage.
✝ Basilique St.Pius X. Underground basilica, of the largest sanctuaries
in the world, there is place for 25,000 people.

| 📷S | **Luzech** | 23F3 |

Les Berges de Caïx, D9. **GPS:** n44,49068 e1,29506.↑

15 ⌕€ 8,50 + € 0,22/pp tourist tax ⛽💧Ch 💧WCincluded 🔌€2.
Surface: gravel. 🕐 01/01-31/12
Distance: 🚶2km.
Remarks: Along Lot river.

| 📷S | **L'Hospitalet-près-l'Andorre** 🏔 | 31B1 |

N22. **GPS:** n42,58823 e1,79833.

5 ⌕free ⛽€2 💧Ch ✂€6. **Surface:** asphalted.
Distance: ⊗100m.

| 📷S | **Marbre** 🏔🐄 | 26D3 |

Lac de Payolle, D918, Campan > Col de Aspin.
GPS: n42,93528 e0,29222.↑🚶.

⌕free. **Location:** Rural, simple, isolated.
Surface: grassy/gravel.
Distance: 🚶5km 🚲50m 🚌50m ⊗700m 🛒5km 🏍on the spot
🚶on the spot.

| 📷S | **Martel** 🌿🎣 | 23F2 |

La Fontanelle, Avenue de Nassogne. **GPS:** n44,93505 e1,60656.↑→

12 ⌕free ⛽💧Ch. **Surface:** gravel. 🕐 01/01-31/12
Distance: 🚶250m ⊗250m 🛒250m.

| 📷 | **Martel** 🌿🎣 | 23F2 |

Parking Monti. **GPS:** n44,93957 e1,60827.↑
12 ⌕free. **Surface:** asphalted. 🕐 01/01-31/12
Distance: 🚶400m ⊗400m 🛒400m.

| 📷S | **Mazamet** | 26G2 |

D118. **GPS:** n43,46278 e2,34609.↑→
⌕free ⛽💧Chfree. **Location:** Rural, isolated, quiet.
Surface: grassy/gravel. 🕐 01/01-31/12
Distance: 🚶8km 🚲on the spot 🚌on the spot ⊗on the spot.

| 📷S | **Mazamet** | 26G2 |

Rue Galibert-Ferret, Champ de la Ville. **GPS:** n43,49089 e2,37918.↑

10 ⌕free ⛽💧Chfree. **Location:** Urban. **Surface:** asphalted.
🕐 01/01-31/12 🛒 Fri-Sa market
Distance: 🚶on the spot ⊗on the spot.
Remarks: At townhall, max. 24h.

| 📷S | **Mazères-sur-Salat** | 26E3 |

Rue de Vieux Ruisseau. **GPS:** n43,13457 e0,97633.↑

15 ⌕free ⛽💧Ch🚻free. **Surface:** metalled. 🕐 01/01-31/12
Distance: ✂4,5km 🚣river.

| 📷S | **Miélan** | 26D2 |

Rue du Cubet. **GPS:** n43,43319 e0,30900.→

6 ⌕free ⛽💧Chfree. **Location:** Rural, simple. **Surface:** gravel.
🕐 01/01-31/12
Distance: 🚶350m ⊗350m 🛒350m.

| 📷S | **Millau** 🏔🏖🏖 | 26H1 |

Rue de la Saunerie 19. **GPS:** n44,09610 e3,08577.↑→

44 ⌕€ 9,60, 01/07-31/08 € 12 ⛽💧Ch 🛜included. 🍽🛒
Location: Comfortable. **Surface:** gravel. 🕐 01/01-31/12
Distance: 🚶500m.
Remarks: Motorhomes <7.5m, entrance code night: parknight, video
surveillance.

Tourist information Millau:
ℹ️ Office de Tourisme, 1, Place du Beffroi, www.ot-millau.fr. City tourist
in the Valley of the Tarn and the Dourbie. Important for the leather
trade.
✂ Vieux Millau. Historical hiking route, info at Office de Tourisme.

| 📷S | **Mirandol-Bourgnounce** | 23G3 |

Place de Foirail. **GPS:** n44,14167 e2,16667.↑

8 ⌕free ⛽💧ChWCfree. **Surface:** asphalted. 🕐 01/01-31/12
Distance: 🚶on the spot ⊗on the spot 🛒50m.

| 📷S | **Mirepoix** | 26F3 |

Parking des Capitouls, Alée des Soupirs. **GPS:** n43,08491 e1,87399.↑

20 ⌕free ⛽💧ChWCfree. 🕐 01/01-31/12
Remarks: Next to community centre.

Tourist information Mirepoix:
🐄 Cattle market. 🕐 winter 2nd, 4th Mo of the month.

FR

⚐ ☐ Thu, Sa.

Moissac 26E1
Promenade Sancert. **GPS:** n44,10011 e1,08540.

4⛺free ⚡€2/4h. **Location:** Urban, simple. **Surface:** metalled.
☐ 01/01-31/12
Distance: ⊗100m 🚰100m.
Remarks: Coins at tourist info.

Mont Roc 26G1
Salle de Fêtes. **GPS:** n43,80330 e2,37192.⬆

8⛺free 🚰€2 🚽Ch🔌€2 WC. **Surface:** metalled.
☐ 01/01-31/12
Distance: 🚶50m ⊗on the spot 🚰on the spot.

Montauban 26F1
Mr. Lacaze, aire camping-car, 225, route de Corbarieu, D21.
GPS: n43,99188 e1,35196.⬆

15⛺€6 🚰€1 🚽Ch ⚡€2 WC🚽€1. **Surface:** gravel.
☐ 01/01-31/12
Distance: 🚶Montauban 3km 🚰1km.
Remarks: Max 3,5t.

Montauban 26F1
Port Canal, Rue des Oules. **GPS:** n44,00744 e1,34105.⬆
10⛺€6 🚰🚽Ch ⚡. **Location:** Comfortable, quiet.
Surface: grassy/gravel. ☐ 01/01-31/12
Distance: 🚶2,5km.
Remarks: At the canal.

Montauban 26F1
La Ferme des Pibouls, Route de Saint-Antonin.
GPS: n44,03658 e1,40499.⬆
12⛺free 🚰🚽Ch.
Surface: grassy.
Distance: 🚶5km.

Tourist information Montauban:
ℹ Office de Tourisme, 2, rue du Collège, officetourisme.montauban.
com. City of roses.
⚐ ☐ Sa.

Montcuq 23E3
Route de Cahors, D653. **GPS:** n44,34082 e1,20242.

15⛺free 🚰€2 🚽Ch ⚡€2. **Surface:** gravel.
☐ 01/01-31/12

Distance: 🚶250m ⊗250m 🚰250m.
Remarks: Coins at Tourist Info and petrol station.

Monteils 23G3
D47. **GPS:** n44,26694 e1,99667.⬆

4⛺free 🚰🚽Chfree. **Surface:** grassy/gravel. ☐ 01/01-31/12
Distance: 🚶100m ⊗100m 🚰50m.

Montézic 23H2
Les Prades Sud. GPS: n44,71054 e2,64413.⬆

4⛺free 🚰🚽Ch. **Surface:** asphalted. ☐ 01/03-31/10
Distance: 🚶500m ⊗on the spot 🚰on the spot.

Montréal (Gers) 26D1
Stade André Daubin, D29. **GPS:** n43,95375 e0,19730.⬆

⛺free 🚰🚽Chfree. **Surface:** gravel. ☐ 01/01-31/12
Distance: 🚶200m ⊗500m 🚰500m.
Remarks: Parking at rugby ground.

Tourist information Montréal (Gers):
ℹ Office de Tourisme, place de l'Hôtel de Ville, www.montrealdugers.
com/. Fortified city with ramparts, square with arcades and picturesque
alleys.

Montréjeau 26D3
Grande Halle, Place de Verdun. **GPS:** n43,08448 e0,57112.⬆

4⛺free. **Location:** Urban, simple, central, noisy. **Surface:** asphalted.
☐ 01/01-31/12
Distance: 🚶100m 🚰400m ⚐on the spot.

Mur de Barrez 23H2
Parc de la Corette, Place du Foirail. **GPS:** n44,84842 e2,65980.⬆

6⛺free 🚰🚽Ch. **Surface:** asphalted. ☐ 01/04-15/11
Distance: 🚶100m ⊗on the spot 🚰50m.

Remarks: Max. 72h.

Nages 26H2
Aire de camping car du Lac, Lac du Laouzas, D162.
GPS: n43,64694 e2,78194.⬆

22⛺€7 🚰🚽Ch🔌included. **Location:** Isolated, quiet.
Surface: grassy/gravel. ☐ 31/03-01/11
Distance: ⚓on the spot.
Remarks: Nearby base nautique.

Najac 23G3
GPS: n44,22167 e1,96778.⬆➡

10⛺free 🚰€2 🚽Ch🔌. **Surface:** asphalted. ☐ 01/01-31/12
Distance: 🚶1,8km ⚓on the spot ➤on the spot 🚰1,8km ⚐on the
spot ⚐on the spot.

Naucelle 23G3
Place du Ségala. **GPS:** n44,19723 e2,34175.⬆

4⛺free 🚰🚽Chfree. **Surface:** asphalted. ☐ 01/01-31/12
Distance: 🚶on the spot ⚓500m ➤500m.

Naussac 23G3
Aire de Loisirs de Peyrelevade. GPS: n44,52167 e2,07944.⬆➡

10⛺€4 🚰🚽Ch ⚡WCincluded. **Surface:** gravel.
☐ 01/01-31/12
Remarks: Recreation area.

Oust 26E3
Aire camping-car, Foute d'Aulus les Bains.
GPS: n42,87167 e1,21833.➡

10⛺€14,50, 2 pers.incl. 🚰🚽Ch ⚡WC🚽. **Surface:** gravel.
☐ 01/01-31/12
Remarks: Next to campsite Les 4 Saisons, arrival >14h departure <12h.

FR

Peyragudes 🏔️❄️ 26D3

Parking de Balestas, Culas. **GPS:** n42,79629 e0,44015. ⬆️.

25 🛏️free 🚰€2/100liter 🔌€2/1h. **Location:** Rural, simple, isolated, quiet. **Surface:** gravel. 🅿️ 01/01-31/12
Distance: 🚶10km ⊗150m ⚡850m 🚶on the spot 🚲on the spot 🏊 on the spot.
Remarks: Coins at Maison de Peyragudes.

Peyrusse le Roc 23G3

D87. **GPS:** n44,49500 e2,13972. ⬆️➡️.

8 🛏️free 🚰🚽Chfree. **Surface:** sand. 🅿️ 01/01-31/12
Distance: 🚶500m ⊗500m ⚡500m.

Pierrefitte-Nestalas 🏔️🌳📷 26C3

Chemin de la Portere. **GPS:** n42,96048 w0,07638. ⬆️➡️.

15 🛏️free 🚰€1/50liter 🚽ChWC. **Location:** Rural, isolated, quiet.
Surface: asphalted. 🅿️ 01/01-31/12
Distance: 🚶200m 🏊10km ⊗200m ⚡200m 🚴 on the spot 🚶on the spot.
Remarks: Max. 8 days.

Pinsac 23F2

Parking Salle des Fêtes, D43. **GPS:** n44,85500 e1,51222.

5 🛏️free 🚰€2 🚽Ch. **Surface:** gravel. 🅿️ 01/01-31/12
Distance: 🚶on the spot 🏊9,5km ⚡700m.

Pont-de-Salars 23H3

Place de la Rivière. **GPS:** n44,27822 e2,72853. ⬆️.

5 🛏️free 🚰€3 🚽ChWC. **Surface:** asphalted. 🅿️ 16/04-15/11
Distance: 🚶100m 🏊1km 🚲1km ⊗on the spot ⚡100m.
Remarks: Along river, max. 3 days.

Prayssac 🌳 23E3

Avenue Maréchal Bessières. **GPS:** n44,50352 e1,19197. ⬆️.

15 🛏️free 🚰🚽ChWC. **Surface:** grassy/gravel. 🅿️ 01/01-31/12

Preignan 26D1

Rue Emile Zola. **GPS:** n43,71243 e0,63378. ➡️.

20 🛏️free 🚰🚽Chfree. **Surface:** gravel.
Distance: 🚶1km.
Remarks: At sports park.

Puy l'Eveque 23E3

Place de la Gendarmerie. **GPS:** n44,50699 e1,13560. ⬆️.

4 🛏️free 🚰🚽ChWCfree. **Surface:** gravel. 🅿️ 01/01-31/12
🅿️ 05/08-14/08
Distance: 🚶250m ⊗300m ⚡300m.
Remarks: In front of town hall, max. 24h, upper city.

Puylaurens 26G2

Rue Albert Thorel. **GPS:** n43,56861 e2,01194. ⬆️➡️.

17 🛏️free 🚰🚽Chfree 📶. **Surface:** gravel. 🅿️ 01/01-31/12
Distance: 🚶700m ⊗700m ⚡400m.
Remarks: Max. 48h, wifi at supermarket.

Requista 🏔️ 26H1

Place François Fablé. **GPS:** n44,03465 e2,53599. ⬆️.

6 🛏️free 🚰🚽free. **Surface:** gravel. 🅿️ 01/01-31/12
Distance: 🚶200m.

Revel 26G2

Roy des Eaux, Chemin de la Pergue. **GPS:** n43,45286 e2,01233. ⬆️➡️.
28 🛏️€ 7, 01/06-31/08 € 9, tourist tax excl 🚰🚽Ch 🚿included. 🚐
🧺 **Surface:** gravel. 🅿️ 01/01-31/12
Distance: 🚶1km 🏊1km ⚡1km.

Remarks: Max. 7 nights.

Rignac 23G3

Hameau du Lac, La Peyrade. **GPS:** n44,40456 e2,28958. ⬆️➡️.

12 🛏️free, June-Aug € 5 🚰🚽Ch. **Surface:** grassy. 🅿️ 01/01-31/12
Distance: 🚶600m ⊗600m ⚡600m.

Rivières 🌊 26G1

Aire de Salta, La Courtade Haute. **GPS:** n43,91072 e1,98889. ⬆️.
6 🛏️€ 9,50, € 15 service incl 🚰🚽Ch🚿📶. **Location:** Rural,
luxurious. **Surface:** grassy/gravel. 🅿️ 01/06-30/09
Distance: 🚶200m.
Remarks: Along the Tarn river.

Rocamadour 23F2

Le Château, D673. **GPS:** n44,80000 e1,61528. ⬆️.

30 🛏️free. **Surface:** gravel. 🅿️ 15/06-15/09
Distance: ⊗100m.

Rodez 23H3

Route du Gué de Salelles. **GPS:** n44,35731 e2,59374. ⬆️.

6 🛏️free 🚰🚽Chfree. **Surface:** asphalted. 🅿️ 01/01-31/12
Distance: 🚶1km.
Remarks: Max. 72h.

Roquecor 🌳 23E3

Place du Foirail. **GPS:** n44,32346 e0,94496. ⬆️.

6 🛏️free 🚰🚽Chfree. **Surface:** asphalted. 🅿️ 01/01-31/12
Distance: 🚶250m ⊗300m ⚡250m.
Remarks: Max. 48h.

Roquefort-sur-Soulzon 26H1

D23. **GPS:** n43,98120 e2,98163. ⬆️.

🛏️free 🚰🚽ChWCfree. **Surface:** asphalted.

FR

◻ 01/01-31/12
Distance: 🚲100m.
Remarks: Parking behind tourist info, water closed during wintertime.

♿S Saint-Antoine 26E1
GPS: n44,03587 e0,84209. ⬆➡.

10 free 🚰♻Chfree. **Location:** Rural, simple, quiet.
Surface: asphalted.
Distance: 🚲200m ⛵4,3km 🛒200m.

♿S Saint-Antonin-Noble-Val 23F3
Chemin de Roumégous. **GPS:** n44,15222 e1,75139. ⬆➡.

15 free 🚰♻Chfree. **Surface:** asphalted. **◻** 01/01-31/12
Distance: 🚲200m ⊗300m 🛒100m.

♿S Saint-Bertrand-de-Comminges 💥⛱🏔🌳 26D3
Parking Cathédrale, D26a. **GPS:** n43,02944 e0,57221. ⬆.

25 free 🚰WC. **Location:** Rural, quiet. **Surface:** asphalted/grassy.
◻ 01/01-31/12
Distance: 🚲200m ⊗200m 🛒3km 🚲 on the spot 🚶 on the spot.

♿S Saint-Céré 23G2
Rue du Stade. **GPS:** n44,86139 e1,88583. ⬆.

3 free 🚰♻Chfree. **Location:** Simple, central. **Surface:** asphalted.
◻ 01/01-31/12
Distance: 🚲200m ⊗200m 🛒150m.
Remarks: Behind stadium, nearby cemetery.

♿S Saint-Cirq-Lapopie 💥⛱🏔🌳 23F3
Porte Roques, D662. **GPS:** n44,47055 e1,68050. ⬆.

40 free €7,50 🚰€2/100liter ♻Ch🛒€2 WC♻€2. 🛥
Location: Isolated, quiet. **Surface:** grassy/gravel. **◻** 01/01-31/12
Distance: 🚲1,5km 🛒 on the spot ⊗50m.
Remarks: Along Lot river, near campsite, max. 48h.

Tourist information Saint-Cirq-Lapopie:
ℹ Village, entirely under preservation order, has been built on a rock above the river Lot.
⛰ Grotte de Pech-Merle, Cabrerets. Temple cave, monument from the Paleolithicum with images of mammoth, horses and bizons.

♿S Saint-Clar 26E1
Aire de repos, Avenue de la Garlepe. **GPS:** n43,89111 e0,77250. ⬆.

10 free 🚰♻ChWC♻free. **Location:** Comfortable, isolated, quiet.
Surface: grassy/gravel. **◻** 01/01-31/12
Distance: 🚲500m ⊗250m.

♿S Saint-Félix-Lauragais 26F2
Lac de Lenclas, D622. **GPS:** n43,42667 e1,89806.

10 free 🚰♻ChWC. **Location:** Simple, isolated, quiet.
Surface: gravel. **◻** 01/01-31/12
Distance: 🛒100m ⊗100m.
Remarks: Max. 24h.

♿S Saint-Geniez-d'Olt ⛱♻ 23H3
Avenue de la gare. **GPS:** n44,46305 e2,97563. ⬆.

10 free 🚰WCfree. **Surface:** gravel. **◻** 01/01-31/12
Distance: 🚲on the spot ⛵on the spot 🛒on the spot ⊗on the spot
🛒on the spot.
Remarks: Max. 24h.

♿S Saint-Géry ♻ 23F3
Domaine du Porche, D662. **GPS:** n44,47818 e1,58091. ⬆.
15 €5,50 🚰€2/100liter ♻Ch🛒€2/1h. **Surface:** gravel.
◻ 01/01-31/12
Distance: ⊗100m 🛒100m.
Remarks: Market on Sunday.

♿S Saint-Girons 26E3
Rue Aristide Berges. **GPS:** n42,98865 e1,13852. ⬆.

7 free 🚰€2/150liter ♻Ch🛒€2/15minutes. **Surface:** asphalted.
Distance: 🚲100m.
Remarks: Max. 48h.

♿S Saint-Jean-et-Saint-Paul 26H1
Saint Jean d'Alcas. **GPS:** n43,92646 e3,00887. ⬆➡.
10 free 🚰♻ChWCfree. **Surface:** gravel. **◻** 01/01-31/12
Distance: 🚲on the spot.

♿S Saint-Just-sur-Viaur 26G1
Parking La Fabrie, D532. **GPS:** n44,12402 e2,37588. ⬆.

---

5 free 🚰♻ChWCfree. **Location:** Isolated, quiet. **Surface:** gravel.
◻ 01/04-30/11
Distance: 🚲10km ⛵on the spot 🛒on the spot.

♿S Saint-Lary-Soulan ⛱🏔❄ 26D3
Parking du Stade, Route de Vieille Aure. **GPS:** n42,82248 e0,32329. ⬆.

44 €6/night 🚰€2/100liter ♻Ch🛒€2/h. ♿ **Location:** Rural,
simple, noisy. **Surface:** asphalted.
◻ 01/01-31/12
Distance: 🚲500m ⊗500m 🛒500m 🚲on the spot 🚶on the spot.
Remarks: Parking behind stadium.

♿S Saint-Mamet 🏔❄ 26D3
Rue Pierre Baysse, D27. **GPS:** n42,78399 e0,60393. ➡.

7 €5 🚰♻Chfree. **Location:** Rural, quiet. **Surface:** asphalted.
◻ 01/01-31/12
Distance: 🚲200m ⊗850m 🛒150m.
Remarks: Next to cemetery, max. 3 nights, to be paid at town hall.

♿S Saint-Martory 26E2
Place Nationale, D52E, D117. **GPS:** n43,14141 e0,93033.

7 free 🚰♻ChWCfree. **Surface:** asphalted. ◉ Thu (market)
Distance: ⛵3km.
Remarks: Along river, max. 1 night.

♿S Saint-Maurice-en-Quercy 23G2
Place de l'église. **GPS:** n44,74306 e1,94722.

10 free. **Location:** Simple, quiet. **Surface:** gravel.
◻ 01/01-31/12

♿S Saint-Nicolas-de-la-Grave 26E1
Rue de la Calle. **GPS:** n44,06379 e1,02471. ➡.

free 🚰♻Chfree. **Surface:** asphalted/gravel. **◻** 01/01-31/12
Distance: 🚲100m ⛵50m ⊗100m.

FR

Saint-Puy 26D1
Grande Rue, D654. **GPS:** n43,87611 e0,46250. ⬆.

3 🛏free 🚰🔌Ch WC free. **Surface:** gravel. ⏹ 01/01-31/12
Distance: 🚰20m ⊗50m 🚰20m.

Saint-Thomas 26E2
Ferme Le Gros, D58. **GPS:** n43,50190 e1,07451. ⬆➡.
10 🛏€3 🚰🔌Ch 🔌included. **Location:** Rural.
Surface: grassy/gravel.
Distance: 🚰2km.

Sainte-Croix-Volvestre 26E3
Lenclos. **GPS:** n43,12673 e1,17094. ⬆➡.

🛏free 🚰🔌Ch free. **Location:** Simple, isolated, quiet.
Surface: grassy/gravel. ⏹ 01/01-31/12
Remarks: At football ground.

Sainte-Eulalie-d'Olt 23H3
La Grave. **GPS:** n44,46466 e2,94974. ⬆.

10 🛏€7, 15/05-15/09 € 8 🚰🔌Ch 🔌WC included. 🗑
Location: Rural, quiet. **Surface:** gravel. ⏹ 01/01-31/12
Distance: 🚰300m 🏊on the spot ⊗250m 🚰350m.
Remarks: Along Lot river, next to campsite.

Sainte-Geneviève-sur-Argence 23H2
Rue de l'Argence. **GPS:** n44,80194 e2,76222. ⬆.

30 🛏free 🚰€2 🔌Ch 🔌. **Surface:** gravel. ⏹ 01/01-31/12
Distance: 🚰300m 🏊500m 🚲500m ⊗300m 🚰300m.

Sainte-Marie-de-Campan 26D3
Place du 19 Mars 1962, D918. **GPS:** n42,98234 e0,22821. ⬆.

5 🛏free 🔌Ch free. **Location:** Rural, simple, quiet.
Surface: asphalted. ⏹ 01/01-31/12

Distance: 🚰100m ⊗250m 🚰200m 🚲on the spot 🚶on the spot.
Remarks: Max. 48h.

Samatan 26E2
Les Rivages Base de Loisirs, Avenue de Lombez, D39.
GPS: n43,48791 e0,92616. ➡.

10 🛏€3 + € 0,20/pp tourist tax 🚰🔌Ch 🔌 WC included.
Surface: asphalted. ⏹ 01/01-31/12
Distance: 🚰500m 🏊on the spot 🚲on the spot ⊗250m 🚰250m
🚗250m.

Sarrant 26E1
Route de Solomiac. **GPS:** n43,77532 e0,92822. ➡.

100 🛏free 🚰🔌Ch free. **Surface:** grassy/gravel.
⏹ 01/01-31/12
Distance: 🚰150m 🚰150m.
Remarks: In front of football stadium.

Sauveterre-de-Comminges 26D3
Hameau de Bruncan, D9. **GPS:** n43,03391 e0,66711. ⬆➡.

5 🛏€6 🚰🔌Ch 🔌WC included. 🚲 **Location:** Rural, simple, quiet.
Surface: grassy/gravel. ⏹ 01/01-31/12
Distance: 🚰on the spot ⊗on the spot 🚲10km 🚲on the spot 🚶on
the spot.
Remarks: Check in at bar, service passerby € 3.

Sauveterre-de-Rouergue 23G3
Le Sardou, D997. **GPS:** n44,21613 e2,31700. ⬆.
11 🛏free 🚰🔌Ch 🔌€2 WC 🚰1,50. **Surface:** grassy.
⏹ 01/05-31/10
Distance: 🚰500m ⊗500m 🚰500m.
Remarks: Coins at tourist info.

Ségur 23H3
GPS: n44,29087 e2,83503. ⬆.
5 🛏free 🚰🔌Ch 🔌WC 🚰€2. **Surface:** asphalted.
⏹ 01/01-31/12
Distance: 🚰500m 🚰on the spot.
Remarks: Covered picnic area with electricity.

Senergues 23G3
La Ferme des Autruches, La Besse. **GPS:** n44,58861 e2,48361. ⬆.
5 🛏free, voluntary contribution 🚰🔌Ch free. **Surface:** grassy/gravel.
⏹ 01/03-30/11
Distance: 🚰2km.

Serres-sur-Arget 26F3
GPS: n42,96990 e1,51972.

🛏€5 🚰🔌Ch 🔌included. **Location:** Isolated, quiet.
Surface: metalled. ⏹ 01/01-31/12
Remarks: Next to community centre.

Souillac 23F2
Parking de Baillot, Chemin de Baillot. **GPS:** n44,89139 e1,47667. ⬆➡.

20 🛏free 🚰€3 🔌Ch 🔌€3 🗑. **Surface:** asphalted.
⏹ 01/01-31/12
Distance: 🚰400m 🚲4,5km ⊗400m 🚰500m.

Tourist information Souillac:
ℹ Bd Louis-Jean Malvy. Monastery-city, 12th century, between the
regions Périgord and Quercy.

Soulom 26C3
Place des Fêtes, D921. **GPS:** n42,95611 w0,0725. ⬆.

15 🛏free 🚰free. **Location:** Rural, simple, noisy. **Surface:** asphalted.
⏹ 01/01-31/12
Distance: 🚰200m 🏊500m ⊗200m 🚰200m.

Sousceyrac 23G2
Place des Condamines. **GPS:** n44,87255 e2,03649. ⬆.

10 🛏free 🚰🔌Ch 🔌WC free. **Location:** Simple, central, noisy.
Surface: asphalted. ⏹ 01/01-31/12
Distance: 🚰on the spot 🚲on the spot ⊗on the spot 🚰100m.
Remarks: In front of town hall, max. 1 night.

Tarbes 26D2
Aire de Service Camping-car Ambulance Didier, Avenue de la
Libération. **GPS:** n43,24284 e0,06790. ⬆➡.

30 🛏€10 🚰🔌Ch included 🔌€2/night. 🚲 **Location:** Quiet.
Surface: asphalted. ⏹ 01/01-31/12
Distance: 🚰1 km 🚲1 km ⊗800m 🚰1 km.
Remarks: Service only: water € 2, water + electricity € 5, video

FR

surveillance.

Thémines 23F2
Place de L'église. **GPS**: n44,74083 e1,82972.

3 free Ch free. **Surface**: asphalted. 01/01-31/12
Distance: on the spot 100m 100m.
Remarks: Near church.

Therondels 23H2
La Cazournie. **GPS**: n44,89833 e2,75937.
10 free Ch free. **Surface**: grassy. 01/04-15/11
Distance: on the spot 100m 100m.

Vabre 26G1
Route de Castres. **GPS**: n43,69401 e2,42595.

free Ch free. **Surface**: asphalted.
Distance: 500m 500m on the spot on the spot.
Remarks: Tenniscourt, swimming pool (summer).

Vabres-l'Abbaye 26H1
Le Coustel, Rue de la Vigne. **GPS**: n43,94575 e2,83957.
15 free Ch free. **Surface**: gravel. 01/04-30/10
Distance: 50m on the spot on the spot.

Valderiés 26G1
Place de Mairie, D91. **GPS**: n44,01167 e2,23333.

5 free Ch WC free. **Surface**: asphalted. 01/01-31/12
Distance: on the spot on the spot on the spot.
Remarks: Weighbridge.

Valence (Tarn-et-Garonne) 23E3
Aire de camping-car à Valence d'Agen, D953EC.
GPS: n44,10547 e0,88608.
€ 4 Ch. **Surface**: asphalted.
Distance: 600m.

Valence (Tarn-et-Garonne) 23E3
M. Cadot, aire privée, 341, Route des Charretiers, Valence-sud.
GPS: n44,09803 e0,89043.
8 € 8 Ch included. **Location**: Rural, comfortable, isolated, quiet. **Surface**: gravel. 01/01-31/12
Distance: 1,2km 1,2km 1,2km.

Valence-sur-Baïse 26D1
Route d'Auch, D930. **GPS**: n43,87272 e0,38787.

7 free Ch WC free. **Location**: Simple, noisy. **Surface**: gravel.

01/01-31/12
Distance: 500m 500m 500m on the spot.

Vénerque 26F2
Allée du Duc de Ventadour. **GPS**: n43,43356 e1,44021.

10 free Ch free. **Surface**: gravel/metalled.
Distance: on the spot.

Vers 23F3
Halte Nautique. **GPS**: n44,48551 e1,55503.

20 € 5 Ch WC free. **Surface**: grassy.
01/05-30/09
Distance: 100m 100m 200m 100m on the spot on the spot.

Vic-en-Bigorre 26D2
Rue du Stade, Avenue de Pau D6. **GPS**: n43,38472 e0,04917.

4 free Ch free. **Location**: Rural, noisy. **Surface**: gravel.
01/01-31/12
Distance: 500m 300m 50m 50m.

Vicdessos 26F3
GPS: n42,76891 e1,50257.

20 € 6 Ch included. **Surface**: metalled.
01/01-31/12
Distance: on the spot.

Villecomtal-sur-Arros 26D2
Rue de la Fontaine. **GPS**: n43,40286 e0,19852.

15 free € 1,50/100liter Ch € 1,50/h. **Location**: Rural, simple, quiet. **Surface**: gravel. 01/01-31/12
Distance: on the spot 100m 200m 50m.
Remarks: Coins at townhall and bakery.

Villefranche-de-Rouergue 23G3
Parking des Ruelles, Traverse des Ruelles.
GPS: n44,35111 e2,03333.

3 free. **Location**: Urban. **Surface**: asphalted. 01/01-31/12
Distance: 100m 100m 100m.

Villefranche-de-Rouergue 23G3
Quai du Temple. **GPS**: n44,34937 e2,03917.

2 free. **Location**: Urban. **Surface**: asphalted. 01/01-31/12
Distance: 300m 200m 300m.
Remarks: At quay in front of the old bridge.

Tourist information Villefranche-de-Rouergue:
place Notre Dame. Thu.

Villeneuve (Aveyron) 23G3
Place du sol de la Dime. **GPS**: n44,43855 e2,03269.

13 € 5 Ch WC free. **Surface**: asphalted. 12/04-01/11
Distance: 100m 100m 100m.

Andorra

Pas de la Casa 31B1
Avinguda del Consell General. **GPS**: n42,54468 e1,73525.
20-8h € 2,10. **Surface**: metalled.

Sant-Julia-de-Lòria 31B1
Carretera de la Rabassa. **GPS**: n42,46573 e1,49462.

4 € 0,50/h, 20.00-08.00 free Ch (4x)included.
Surface: asphalted. 01/01-31/12
Distance: 1km.

Languedoc Roussillon

Agde 27A2
Les Peupliers. **GPS**: n43,29846 e3,45194.

FR

30 ⌷€ 8, Jul/Aug € 10 ⚡🔌Ch (30x)€2 📶.
Surface: gravel/metalled. ⬛ 03/04-14/11
Distance: 🚰2km ⚓1,7km 🛒on the spot.
Tourist information Agde:
✝ Cathédrale Ste Étienne. Romanesque fortified cathedral, 12th century.

| 📷Ⓢ | Aigues-Mortes 🌿⛵ | 27B2 |

Les Poissons d'Argent Aigues Mortes

- ■ **Medieval town**
- ■ **Restaurant with regional specialties**
- ■ **Bread-service**

www.lespoissonsdargent.com
contact@lespoissonsdargent.com

Les Poissons d'Argent, CD62. **GPS:** n43,56476 e4,16289.⬆
120 ⌷€ 10 ⚡🔌Chincluded 🔌(32x)€3/24h,5Amp 📶.
Location: Simple. **Surface:** gravel.
⬛ 01/03-31/10
Distance: 🚰3km ⚓3km 🛒on the spot ⊗on the spot 🛒1,5km Lidl 🏊500m 🚶500m.
Remarks: At fish lake, fishing permit incl, bread-service.

| 📷Ⓢ | Aigues-Mortes 🌿⛵ | 27B2 |

Rue du Port. **GPS:** n43,56631 e4,18575.⬆

50 ⌷€ 16 ⚡🔌Chfree. 🅿**Location:** Simple. **Surface:** metalled.
⬛ 01/01-31/12
Distance: 🚰600m.
Remarks: Max. 24h.
Tourist information Aigues-Mortes:
ℹ Office de Tourisme, Place Saint Louis, www.ot-aiguesmortes.fr. Medieval fortress, 13th century, in the swamp of the Camargue, tourist attraction. 🚂 free.
👁 La Tour Carbonnière, Place Saint Louis. Tower, guard-post for the defence of the city.

| 📷 | Aiguèze 🌿 | 24C3 |

GPS: n44,30530 e4,55250.⬆

+20 ⌷free. **Location:** Rural, simple, quiet. **Surface:** grassy/gravel.
⬛ 01/01-31/12
Distance: 🚰300m ⊗300m.

| 📷Ⓢ | Alès 🌿⛵🍴🏛🌊 | 27B1 |

Place du camping-car, Avenue Jules Guesde.
GPS: n44,12013 e4,08207. ⬆➡

6 ⌷free ⚡🔌Chfree. **Location:** Urban, comfortable, central, noisy.
Surface: asphalted. ⬛ 01/01-31/12
Distance: 🚰on the spot ⚓on the spot 🛒on the spot ⊗400m 🛒600m 🏊on the spot 🚶routes available at tourist office.

| 📷Ⓢ | Amélie-les-Bains-Palalda ♈ | 31C1 |

Carrer de l'Oreneta. **GPS:** n42,48063 e2,67951.⬆

40 ⌷€ 7 ⚡🔌Chincluded.🚿 **Surface:** gravel. ⬛ 01/01-31/12
Distance: 🚰2km 🛒500m.
Remarks: Behind hotel du Lion D'Or, max. 7 days.

| ⒸⓈ | Amélie-les-Bains-Palalda ♈ | 31C1 |

Camping Amélie, Avenue Beau Soleil, D115.
GPS: n42,47894 e2,67414.⬆

8 ⌷€ 6 ⚡🔌€4.🚿 **Location:** Simple, noisy. **Surface:** grassy/gravel.
⬛ 01/01-31/12
Distance: 🚰on the spot ⊗1km 🛒1km.
Remarks: Max. 48h, coins at campsite.

| 📷Ⓢ | Anduze 🌿⛵🍴🌊 | 27B1 |

Place de la Gare. **GPS:** n44,05000 e3,98444.

20 ⌷free 🔌Ch. **Location:** Urban, simple, central, quiet.
Surface: asphalted. ⬛ 01/01-31/12
Distance: 🚰on the spot ⊗300m 🛒400m 🏊on the spot 🚶on the spot.
Remarks: Max. 48h.

| ⒸⓈ | Anduze 🌿⛵🍴🌊 | 27B1 |

Camping l'Arche. GPS: n44,06889 e3,97282. ⬆➡

5 ⌷€ 12/night ⚡🔌Ch 📶WC included,sanitary at campsite.

Location: Rural, simple, isolated, quiet. **Surface:** asphalted.
⬛ 01/04-30/09
Distance: 🚰3km ⚓on the spot ⊗on the spot 🛒100m 🏊on the spot 🚶on the spot.

Tourist information Anduze:
👁 Bamboisserie de Prafrance. Bamboo garden laid out in 1835, with a large variety of bamboo species. ⬛ 01/03-15/11
🚂 Train Touristique. Tourist train from Anduze to St. Jean-du-Gard.
🚂 € 6,50.

| 📷Ⓢ | Aniane 🌿 | 27A2 |

Le Pont du Diable. GPS: n43,70270 e3,55988.⬆

⌷€ 5/day, € 18/24h ⚡€3 🔌Ch 🚿 **Location:** Rural, isolated.
Surface: gravel.
⬛ 01/01-31/12
Distance: 🏍9km.
Remarks: Max. 48h, Pont du Diable 600m, St.Guilhem-le-Désert 4km, free shuttlebus Mai-Sept: weekend (11-19h), July-Aug daily (10-23h).

| 📷Ⓢ | Aniane 🌿 | 27A2 |

Lotissement du Camp de Sauve. **GPS:** n43,68652 e3,58254.⬆➡

15 ⌷free. **Surface:** gravel. ⬛ 01/01-31/12
Distance: 🚰300m 🛒nearby ⊗300m 🛒300m.

| 📷Ⓢ | Arre 🏛🍴🌊 | 27A1 |

D999. **GPS:** n43,96771 e3,52139.⬆➡

6 ⌷free ⚡€2/100liter 🔌Ch 🛁€2/1h WC. **Location:** Rural, simple, central, quiet. **Surface:** metalled.
⬛ 01/01-31/12
Distance: 🚰on the spot ⚓on the spot 🛒on the spot ⊗on the spot 🛒bakery 200m 🚶on the spot.

| 📷Ⓢ | Avèze | 27A1 |

Aire du pont vieux, D999. **GPS:** n43,97517 e3,59899. ⬆➡

4 ⌷free ⚡stay 🔌Chfree 🛁€2/1h.
Surface: metalled.
⬛ 01/01-31/12
Distance: 🚰500m ⚓500m 🛒500m ⊗500m 🛒500m 🚶on the spot.
Remarks: Next to campsite municipal.

| 📷Ⓢ | Bagnols-sur-Cèze | 27C1 |

Av. de l Europe, D8086. **GPS:** n44,16820 e4,61958.⬆

20 ⏚free 🚰⏚Chfree. **Surface:** gravel.
Distance: 🚶200m ⊗200m 🛒200m.
Remarks: Max. 24h.

🅂 | **Balaruc-les-Bains** 🏊⛱⛲ | 27A2
Avenue des Hespérides 335. **GPS:** n43,44499 e3,67564.⬆️.

12 ⏚€ 8,50 🚰⏚Ch.🚿 **Location:** Rural, quiet. **Surface:** unpaved.
🅾️ 01/01-31/12
Distance: 🚶on the spot.

🅄🅂 | **Balaruc-les-Bains** 🏊⛱⛲ | 27A2
Thermes Hespérides, Avenue des Hespérides.
GPS: n43,44574 e3,67770.⬆️➡️.

6 ⏚€7 🚰⏚Ch⛽55minutes WCincluded 📶.🚿 **Location:** Simple,
quiet. **Surface:** asphalted. 🅾️ 01/01-31/12
Distance: 🚶1km.
Remarks: Free bus to centre.

🅂 | **Beaucaire** | 27C1
Les Marguilliers, Chemin des Marguilliers.
GPS: n43,81667 e4,64107.⬆️.

9 ⏚€ 12/24h 🚰⏚Ch🚿included. **Surface:** gravel.
🅾️ 01/01-31/12
Distance: 🚶500m 🏊500m ⊗500m 🛒500m.

🅂 | **Beaucaire** | 27C1
Quai de la Paix. **GPS:** n43,80615 e4,63739.⬆️.

10 ⏚free 🚰€2/100liter ⏚Ch➕€2/1h. **Location:** Urban, simple.
Surface: asphalted. 🅾️ 01/01-31/12 🅾️ water disconnected in winter
Distance: 🚶300m ⊗300m 🛒bakery 300m.
Remarks: Coins at tourist info.

🅂 | **Bédarieux** 🏊⛰⛲ | 26H2
Avenue Jean Moulin. **GPS:** n43,61071 e3,15329.⬆️➡️.

10 ⏚free 🚰⏚Chfree. **Location:** Urban, simple, central, quiet.
Surface: grassy. 🅾️ 01/01-31/12
Distance: 🚶on the spot 🏊on the spot ⛽on the spot ⊗800m.
Remarks: Along the Orb river.

🅂 | **Bélesta** 🌿⛰ | 26H3
Rue des Loisirs. **GPS:** n42,71560 e2,60786.⬆️➡️.

10 ⏚€ 5 🚰€2/20minutes ⏚📶(8x)€2/4h.🚿 **Location:** Rural,
simple, quiet. **Surface:** grassy/gravel. 🅾️ 01/04-31/10
Distance: 🚶100m 🎣on the spot.

⚓🅂 | **Bellegarde** 🌊 | 27C1
Port de plaisance, Las Courrejos Est. **GPS:** n43,74422 e4,51890.⬆️.

⏚free 🚰€2 ⏚Ch➕€2/1h. **Location:** Rural, simple.
Surface: gravel/sand. 🅾️ 01/01-31/12
Distance: 🚶city centre 1,5km.
Remarks: Near marina, max. 48h, coins at harbourmaster.

🅂 | **Belpech** | 26F2
Stade municipal, Rue du Stade. **GPS:** n43,19864 e1,74472.

15 ⏚free 🚰⏚Ch🔌free WC. **Surface:** grassy.
🅾️ 01/01-31/12
Distance: 🚶1km ⊗1km 🛒1km.
Remarks: At football ground.

🅂 | **Bréau-et-Salagosse** | 27A1
Le Rieumage, D272. **GPS:** n43,99338 e3,56716.⬆️.
6 ⏚€2 ⏚Chincluded. **Location:** Rural, isolated, quiet.
Surface: gravel.

🅂 | **Carcassonne** 🌿⛱⛲ | 26G2
Parking Cité, P2, Chemin de Montlegun. **GPS:** n43,20534 e2,37189.⬆️.

30 ⏚€ 5/6h, overnight stay free 🚰⏚Chfree. 🚌 **Location:** Urban,
simple, noisy. **Surface:** gravel.

Distance: 🚶1km 🚤5km.
Remarks: Free shuttle to centre.

🄿 | **Carcassonne** 🌿⛱⛲ | 26G2
Place Gaston-Jourdanne. **GPS:** n43,21000 e2,36028.

20 ⏚free. **Surface:** asphalted/metalled. 🅾️ 15/06-15/09
Distance: 🚶900m.

Tourist information Carcassonne:
ℹ️ Office de Tourisme, 15, Boulevard Camille Pelletan, www.
carcassonne-tourisme.com. Medieval fortified city, museum city with
many curiosities.
🛒 The new city has a modern shopping centre.

🅂 | **Carnon** | 27B2
Avenue Grassion Cibrand, Carnon-plage. **GPS:** n43,55097 e3,99417.⬆️.

15 ⏚€ 11,50, 01/07-31/08 € 13 🚰⏚Ch🚿 WC 🔌included,on
campsite 🔌€5. 🚿🍽 **Location:** Rural. **Surface:** asphalted.
🅾️ 01/04-15/10. **Distance:** 🚶1km 🏊80m 🛒50m.
Remarks: Next to campsite Les Saladelles.

🅂 | **Casteil** 🍴⛲ | 31B1
D116. **GPS:** n42,53324 e2,39230.⬆️.

5 ⏚free. **Location:** Rural, simple, isolated, quiet. **Surface:** forest soil.
🅾️ 01/04-31/10
Distance: 🚶1km 🏊on the spot ⛽on the spot.

🅂 | **Castelnaudary** 🌿⛱ | 26G2
Camping-Car Park Castelnaudary, Passage des Lavandières.
GPS: n43,31427 e1,94899.⬆️.

14 ⏚€ 8,40, 01/07-31/08 € 9,60 🚰⏚Ch📶(8x)📶included.
🚿🍽 **Location:** Urban, comfortable. **Surface:** grassy/gravel.
🅾️ 01/01-31/12
Distance: 🚶on the spot ⊗on the spot 🛒on the spot.
Remarks: At Canal du Midi.

🅂 | **Chusclan** | 27C1
Cave Chusclan, Route d'Orsan, D138. **GPS:** n44,14552 e4,67762.⬆️➡️.

40 🛏free 🚰⚡Chfree. **Surface:** gravel. ⬛ 01/01-31/12
Distance: ⊗500m 🛒500m.

🅢 **Clermont-l'Hérault** 🎣🏊🏔🚣 **27A2**
Aire de stationnement camping-car, Lac du Salagou.
GPS: n43,64677 e3,38915. ⬆➡.

8 🛏€ 5-7 🚰€2/100liter ⚡Ch 🧹(6x). **Location:** Rural, simple,
isolated, quiet. **Surface:** gravel. ⬛ 01/01-31/12
Distance: 🚲7km 🏊on the spot ⛵on the spot ⊗on the spot 🛒7km
🚴on the spot 🚶on the spot.
Remarks: Coins at campsite.

🅢 **Collioure** 〰🏖🏔🚣 **31C1**
Route de Madeloc. **GPS:** n42,52566 e3,06861. ⬆.

12 + 80 🛏€ 15/24h 🚰⚡Ch🧹(12x)WCincluded. 📷
Location: Comfortable, quiet. **Surface:** asphalted. ⬛ 01/05-31/10
Distance: 🚲2km 🏊2,3km ⊗2km 🛒2km.
Remarks: Monitored parking, may-Sep free shuttle to Collioure.

🅢 **Comps** **27C1**
Place des Arènes. **GPS:** n43,85402 e4,60724. ⬆.

50 🛏€ 5 🚰€2/110liter ⚡Ch📷€2/50minutes WC 🧹🔌
Location: Rural. **Surface:** grassy/gravel. ⬛ 01/01-31/12
Distance: 🚲50m 🏊on the spot ⛵on the spot 🚌50m 🚴on the spot
🚶on the spot.

Comps **27C1**
GPS: n43,85390 e4,60912.

30 🛏€ 5. 🔌 **Location:** Rural. **Surface:** unpaved.
⬛ 01/01-31/12
Remarks: Along river.

🅢 **Cuxac-Cabardès** **26G2**
La Cabasse. **GPS:** n43,36126 e2,30185. ⬆➡.

8 🛏€5 🚰€2 ⚡Ch🔌€3. **Location:** Isolated, quiet.
Surface: metalled.

🅢 **Duilhac-sous-Peyrepertuse** **26G3**
Route du château. **GPS:** n42,86160 e2,56527. ⬆.

25 🛏free 🚰⚡ChWCfree. **Location:** Rural, simple, quiet.
Surface: asphalted. ⬛ 01/04-31/10
Distance: 🚲200m ⊗200m.

🅢 **Espéraza** 🏔 **26G3**
Promenade François Mitterand. **GPS:** n42,93370 e2,21589. ⬆.

20 🛏free 🚰⚡Chfree. **Location:** Rural, simple, quiet.
Surface: grassy.
Distance: 🚲500m 🏊on the spot ⛵on the spot ⊗500m.

🅢 **Fanjeaux** 〰 **26G2**
Chemin des Fontanelles. **GPS:** n43,18611 e2,03222. ⬆➡.

15 🛏free 🚰⚡Chfree. **Location:** Rural, simple.
Surface: grassy/gravel. ⬛ 01/01-31/12
Distance: 🚲100m ⊗100m 🛒100m.
Remarks: Next to maison de retraite (home for the elderly), max. 48h.

🅢 **Félines-Termenès** **26H3**
Av. de Termenes, dir Mouthoumet. **GPS:** n42,98691 e2,61285. ⬆.

3 🛏free 🚰⚡Ch🔌free. **Location:** Rural, simple, quiet.
Surface: gravel. ⬛ 01/01-31/12
Distance: 🚲50m.
Remarks: Closed when frosty.
Tourist information Félines-Termenès:
👁 Cité Médiéval, Villerouge Termenes. Medieval village and castle
from 12-14th century. ⬛ 01/07-30/09.

🅢 **Fitou** **26H3**
Aragon, Route Nationale 9, Les Cabanes de Fitou.
GPS: n42,89275 e2,99672. ⬆.

15 🛏€ 5/12h, € 7/24h 🚰⚡Ch🔌€2,50 📶included.
Location: Rural. **Surface:** gravel. ⬛ 01/01-31/12
Distance: ✈A9 6,5km ⊗on the spot 🛒500m.
Remarks: Video surveillance.

🅢 **Fleury-d'Aude** 🎣🚣 **27A2**
Base de Loisirs Étang de Pissevache, Saint-Pierre-la-Mer.
GPS: n43,18972 e3,19694. ⬆.

100 🛏€ 6,50 🚰€2 ⚡Ch🔌€2/4h 🧹📷🔌 **Surface:** unpaved.
⬛ 01/01-31/12
Distance: 🏊sandy beach 300m.
Remarks: Parking directly behind the beach, next to tennis park and
small surf lake, follow Base de Loisirs.

🅢 **Fleury-d'Aude** 🎣🚣 **27A2**
Les-Cabanes-de-Fleury. **GPS:** n43,21529 e3,23315. ⬆.

100 🛏€ 6,50 🚰€2 ⚡Ch🔌 **Surface:** metalled/sand.
⬛ 01/01-31/12
Distance: 🚲on the spot 🏊on the spot ⊗200m.
Remarks: Next to campsite municipal Rive d'Aude, coins at capitainerie
(1km).

🅢 **Florac** 〰🎣🏔🚣 **24A3**
D16. **GPS:** n44,32582 e3,59032. ⬆➡.

23 🛏free 🚰€2/100liter ⚡Ch📷€2/1h WCfree. **Location:** Rural,
comfortable, central, quiet. **Surface:** asphalted.
⬛ 01/01-31/12
Distance: 🚲150m 🏊300m 🚌300m 🛒150m 🛒150m 🚴mountain-
bike trail 🚶on the spot.
Remarks: Nearby cemetery.

🅢 **Florensac** **27A2**
Domaine de Veyrac, Route de Bessan, D28.
GPS: n43,36221 e3,47671. ⬆➡.

FR

10 🛏 € 7 🚰.
Location: Simple, isolated, quiet. **Surface:** gravel.
Distance: 🚲5km 🛒3,6km.

| 🛏 S | **Fraïsse-sur-Agout** 🛫🍴🌲 | 26H2 |

Allée des Tilleuls. **GPS:** n43,60583 e2,79778. ⬆➡.

15 🛏 € 7 🚰⚡Ch 🚿(1x)included. **Surface:** asphalted/grassy.
🔲 01/01-31/12
Distance: 🚲400m 🏊20m 🛒20m ⊗400m.
Remarks: At the edge of village, on the Agout river.

| 🛏 S | **Génolhac** 🌲🌳 | 24B3 |

Les Taillades, Place du 19 Mars 1962, D906.
GPS: n44,35388 e3,94844. ⬆➡.

10 🛏 free 🚰⚡Ch free. **Location:** Rural, simple, isolated, quiet.
Surface: metalled. 🔲 01/01-31/12
Distance: 🚲200m ⊗800m 🧍on the spot.

| 🛏 S | **Gruissan** 🛫🌊 | 26H3 |

Aire des 4 Vents, Avenue des quatre vents.
GPS: n43,10444 e3,09944. ⬆⬆➡.

80 🛏free, 01/03-30/11 € 8,50 🚰⚡Ch 🚿 WC 🗑 included. 🚙
Surface: gravel. 🔲 01/01-31/12
Distance: 🚲on the spot 🏊on the spot 🛒on the spot ⊗on the spot 🧍on the spot.

| 🛏 S | **Gruissan** 🛫🌊 | 26H3 |

Aire des Châlets, Avenue de la Jetée, Gruissan-plage.
GPS: n43,09583 e3,11111. ⬆➡.

80 🛏free, 01/03-30/11 € 8,50 🚰⚡Ch 🚿included. **Surface:** gravel.
🔲 01/03-30/11
Distance: 🚲2km 🏊on the spot 🛒on the spot ⊗2km 🧍2km.

| 🛏 S | **Gruissan** 🛫🌊 | 26H3 |

Étang de Mateille, Gruissan dir Narbonne-Plage, base de voile, D332.
GPS: n43,12083 e3,11417. ⬆.

150 🛏 € 8,50-10 🚰⚡Ch 🚿(24x)€1 WC 🗑.
Surface: grassy/metalled.
🔲 01/07-31/08
Distance: 🚲4km 🏊on the spot 🛒on the spot ⊗800m 🧍Lidl 2km.
Tourist information Gruissan:
👁 L'Hospitalet. Probably the largest wine-cellar of the world.
👁 Vieux Port. Old fishing-port.

| 🛏 S | **Ispagnac** 🌿🏔 | 24A3 |

Le Pavillon, D907. **GPS:** n44,37077 e3,53687. ⬆➡.

6 🛏free 🚰⚡Ch 🗑€2 WC free. **Location:** Rural, simple, central,
quiet. **Surface:** asphalted/gravel. 🔲 01/04-31/10
Distance: 🚲100m 🏊river 200m 🛒100m 🧍100m 🚶on the spot.

| 🛏 S | **La Canourgue** 🌿🏔 | 24A3 |

Avenue du Lot, D998. **GPS:** n44,43325 e3,20775. ⬆.

10 🛏free 🚰⚡Ch free. **Location:** Rural, simple, isolated, quiet.
Surface: metalled. 🔲 01/01-31/12 🔵 Jul/Aug: tue
Distance: 🚲500m 🚴1,3km ⊗600m 🧍600m 🚶600m.
Remarks: Max. 24h.

| 🛏 S | **La Grande Motte** 🛫🌊 | 27B2 |

Aire camping-car Les Cigales, Avenue de la Petite Motte.
GPS: n43,56789 e4,07404. ⬆⬆.

50 🛏 € 11, May-Sep € 16 🚰⚡Ch WC 🗑. 🚙 🛏 **Location:** Rural.
Surface: gravel. 🔲 01/01-31/12
Distance: 🚲2km 🏊1,2km 🛒2km 🧍2km.

| 🛏 S | **La Palme** | 26H3 |

Les Salins de La Palme, Route de Port la Nouvelle.
GPS: n42,98033 e3,01858. ⬆.
49 🛏 € 12 🚰⚡Ch 🚿(49x) 🛏 **Location:** Rural, comfortable,
isolated, quiet. **Surface:** grassy. 🔲 01/01-31/12
Distance: 🚲2,5km 🏊2km 🛒on the spot.

| 🛏 S | **Lagrasse** 🌿🏔🌳 | 26H3 |

Parking de la Promenade, P2, Les Condamines.
GPS: n43,09273 e2,62004. ⬆.

40 🛏 € 3, 01/06-30/09 € 5 🚰⚡Ch WC free. 🚙 **Location:** Rural,
simple, quiet. **Surface:** grassy/gravel. 🔲 01/01-31/12
Distance: 🚲on the spot 🏊on the spot 🛒on the spot ⊗on the spot 🧍on the spot.

| 🛏 S | **Langogne** 🛫🌊 | 24B2 |

Base Nautique l'Espace Bleu. **GPS:** n44,73598 e3,83489. ⬆➡.

50 🛏 € 12 🚰⚡Ch 🚿(1x) 📻included. 🚙 🛏 **Location:** Rural,
simple, quiet. **Surface:** unpaved. 🔲 01/01-31/12
Distance: 🚲2km 🏊beach 1km 🛒on the spot ⊗2km 🧍2km.
Remarks: At lake Naussac, max. 48h.

| 🛏 S | **Langogne** 🛫🌊 | 24B2 |

Centre Polyvalente. **GPS:** n44,72281 e3,85419. ⬆.

10 🛏free 🚰⚡€2/100liter ⚡Ch. **Location:** Central, quiet.
Surface: asphalted. 🔲 01/01-31/12
Distance: 🚲on the spot ⊗300m 🧍300m 🚶on the spot.
Remarks: Coins at tourist info.

| 🛏 S | **Lapradelle Puilaurens** | 26G3 |

D117. **GPS:** n42,81003 e2,30854. ⬆.

6 🛏free 🚰⚡Ch free. **Location:** Rural, simple, quiet.
Surface: metalled. 🔲 01/01-31/12
Distance: 🚲on the spot ⊗on the spot 🧍on the spot.
Remarks: At fire-station.

| 🛏 S | **Latour-Bas-Elne** | 31C1 |

Aire de Latour Bas Elne, Route de la Mer.
GPS: n42,60017 e3,00667. ⬆➡.

40 🛏 € 10, € 14 Jun-Aug, trailer € 4 🚰⚡Ch 🚿included 📻€3/2day.
🚙 **Location:** Comfortable. **Surface:** grassy. 🔲 01/01-31/12
Distance: 🏊3km.
Remarks: Baker at 9am, monitored parking.

FR

Latour-de-Carol 31B1

Village Club Yravals, 2 Rue de Saneja. **GPS**: n42,45829 e1,89460.

5 € 10, 2 pers.incl, extra pers € 1 Ch WC included €2/day. **Surface:** grassy. 01/04-31/10
Distance: 2km.

Laudun-l'Ardoise 27C1

Place des Arènes. **GPS**: n44,10791 e4,65556.

3 free €4 Ch. **Location:** Simple, central, noisy.
Surface: asphalted. 01/01-31/12
Distance: 300m 300m 300m.

Laudun-l'Ardoise 27C1

Route d'Avignon, N580. **GPS**: n44,09527 e4,70164.

free Ch free. **Location:** Simple, central. **Surface:** asphalted.
 01/01-31/12
Distance: 5,5km.
Remarks: Behind police station, at tennis-court.

Laudun-l'Ardoise 27C1

Vignerons de Laudun, Avenue du Général de Gaulle.
GPS: n44,10388 e4,66362.

10 free Ch. **Surface:** grassy/gravel.
Distance: 750m 300m 750m.
Remarks: Max. 3 days.

Le Barcarès 26H3

Barcares le Port, Quai des Tourettes. **GPS**: n42,80165 e3,03277.
49 € 9,60, Jul/Aug € 12 Ch (16x) included.
 01/01-31/12
Distance: 1,5km 2km on the spot on the spot 1,5km.

Le Bosc 27A1

Parc Activités Méridienne. **GPS**: n43,68932 e3,35328.

10 free €2/100liter Ch €2/1h. **Location:** Highway, simple, isolated. **Surface:** asphalted. 01/01-31/12
Distance: 400m on the spot Intermarché 50m.

Le Boulou 31C1

Chemin du Moulin Nou. **GPS**: n42,52719 e2,83704.

21 free €2 Ch WC. **Location:** Rural, simple, comfortable.
Surface: asphalted. 01/01-31/12
Distance: 300m 1km 300m 300m.
Remarks: In front of cemetery, max. 24h.

Le Cap d'Agde 27A2

Rue du Gouverneur. **GPS**: n43,28600 e3,51739.

30 € 5 02/11-26/03, € 10 27/03-02/11 €2/25 Ch included. **Location:** Rural, simple, central.
Surface: asphalted/metalled. 01/01-31/12
Distance: on the spot 500m 500m 500m.
Remarks: Nearby Camping La Clape, video surveillance.

Le Caylar 27A1

Domaine des Templiers, Route de la Couvertoirade, D609.
GPS: n43,86944 e3,31466.

30 € 3 €2,10/100liter Ch €2,10/15minutes (9x)€
2,10/4h. **Location:** Comfortable, isolated, quiet. **Surface:** gravel.
 01/04-31/10
Distance: 600m 500m on the spot.

Le Grau du Roi 27B2

Parking de la plage, Rue du Commandant Marceau.
GPS: n43,54061 e4,13349.

40 € 8,80, June-Aug € 12,50 €2/100liter Ch €2/55minutes.
 Surface: asphalted. 01/01-31/12
Distance: centre 550m sandy beach 20m on the spot on

---

the spot.
Remarks: Beach parking, video surveillance.

Le Malzieu-Ville 24A2

Place Foirail. **GPS**: n44,85506 e3,33385.

6 free Ch WC free. **Location:** Rural, simple, comfortable, central, quiet. **Surface:** asphalted.
 01/01-31/12
Distance: on the spot 10km on the spot 200m 200m
on the spot.

Le Monastir 24A3

Place de la Gare. **GPS**: n44,50896 e3,25162.

4 free Ch WC free. **Location:** Rural, simple, isolated, quiet.
Surface: asphalted. 01/01-31/12
Distance: 1km 1,5km 1km.
Remarks: 2013: during inspection service out of order, coins at petrol station (200m), picnic area.

Le Ségala 26F2

Esplanade du Canal. **GPS**: n43,34089 e1,83544.

10 free WC. **Location:** Rural, simple, quiet. **Surface:** gravel.
 01/01-31/12
Distance: on the spot 1km on the spot on the spot on
the spot on the spot.
Remarks: No camping activities.

Les Angles 31B1

Pla del Mir. GPS: n42,56321 e2,06780.

100 free €3,50 Ch WC. **Location:** Rural, simple, quiet.
Surface: asphalted. 01/01-31/12
Distance: 2,6km on the spot.

Les Mages 24B3

Serre Marine, D904, St. Ambroix/Alés. **GPS**: n44,23442 e4,16967.

7 ⬛free ⬛ Chfree. **Location:** Rural, simple, isolated, noisy.
Surface: metalled. ⬛ 01/01-31/12
Distance: 700m ⊗700m ⬛800m.
Remarks: Picnic area.

Leucate 26H3

Aire camping-car, Chemin du Mouret, Leucate Plage.
GPS: n42,90022 e3,05272.⬆.

100 ⬛€ 7,20/24h ⬛€2 ⬛Ch ⬛ ⬛ ⬛ **Location:** Rural, simple.
Surface: asphalted/gravel. ⬛ 01/01-31/12
Distance: 300m ⬛on the spot ⬛on the spot.
Remarks: Beach parking, baker on site (20/03-31/10).

Leucate 26H3

Chemin des Coussoules, La Franqui. **GPS:** n42,94329 e3,02917.⬆.

70 ⬛€ 6 ⬛Chon camp site€5.
Surface: unpaved. 4
⬛ 01/02-30/11
Distance: 2km ⬛on the spot ⬛on the spot ⊗2km ⬛2km.
Remarks: Next to campsite Coussoules, check in at reception campsite.

Leucate 26H3

Le Goulet, D627. **GPS:** n42,91145 e3,01946.⬆.

150 ⬛€ 10,20-13,80 ⬛€2 ⬛Ch ⬛€2. ⬛ ⬛ **Location:** Rural,
simple. **Surface:** unpaved.
⬛ 01/01-31/12
Distance: centre Leucate 850m ⬛on the spot ⬛on the spot.
Remarks: Terraces, at lake of Leucate, baker on site (20/03-31/10).

Limoux 26G3

Parking, Rue Louis Braille. **GPS:** n43,05741 e2,21490.⬆➡.

30 ⬛free ⬛ Chfree. **Location:** Urban, simple, quiet.
Surface: metalled. ⬛ 01/01-31/12

Distance: 200m ⬛on the spot ⊗200m.

Lodève 27A2

Baie des Vailhés, Celles. **GPS:** n43,67087 e3,35565.
⬛ 5, 01/07-31/08 € 8 + tourist tax € 0,20/pp.

Tourist information Lodève:
⬛ Maison de Tourisme, 7, Place de la République, www.lodeve.com.
Old city to the gate of the Mediteranean.

Lunas 27A1

Base de Loisirs Prade, D35. **GPS:** n43,70555 e3,18555.⬆➡.

75 ⬛free ⬛Chfree. **Location:** Urban, simple, isolated, quiet.
Surface: grassy. ⬛ 01/01-31/12
Distance: 900m ⬛on the spot ⬛on the spot ⊗200m ⬛700m
⬛200m.

Marseillan-Plage 27A2

Rue des Goélands. **GPS:** n43,31902 e3,54864.⬆➡.

122 ⬛€ 4-6-10/24h ⬛€2/10minutes ⬛Ch ⬛ ⬛ ⬛
Location: Comfortable, quiet. **Surface:** gravel. ⬛ 01/01-31/12
Distance: on the spot ⬛sandy beach 600m ⊗on the spot ⬛on
the spot.

Marvéjols 24A3

Boulevard Aurelle de Paladines, Le Pré de Suzon.
GPS: n44,55406 e3,28753.⬆.

10 ⬛free ⬛ ⬛ChWCfree.**Location:** Central.
Surface: asphalted.
Distance: on the spot ⬛7,5km ⊗on the spot ⬛on the spot.

Tourist information Marvéjols:
⬛ Maison de Tourisme, Porte du Soubeyran, www.ville-marvejols.fr.
Old fortress city, gates with battlements and towers.

Matemale 31B1

GPS: n42,57964 e2,10227.⬆.

10 ⬛free ⬛€1 ⬛ChWC. **Location:** Rural, simple, isolated, quiet.
Surface: asphalted. ⬛ 01/01-31/12
Distance: 3km ⬛on the spot ⬛on the spot ⊗300m.
Remarks: Parking at lake.

Matemale 31B1

Rue de la Truite. **GPS:** n42,56559 e2,10433.⬆.

10 ⬛free. **Location:** Rural, simple, isolated, quiet. **Surface:** gravel.
⬛ 01/01-31/12
Distance: 1,5km ⬛20m ⊗1,5km ⬛1,5km.
Remarks: Parking at lake.

Mende 24A3

Rue du Faubourg Montbel. **GPS:** n44,52063 e3,49660.⬆.

23 ⬛free ⬛€2/10minutes ⬛Chfree ⬛€2/55minutes.
Location: Urban, comfortable, central, quiet. **Surface:** asphalted.
⬛ 01/01-31/12
Distance: ⬛on the spot ⬛on the spot ⊗200m ⬛400m ⬛on the
spot ⬛on the spot.
Remarks: Along Lot river, max. 4 days.

Mèze 27A2

Complexe sportif des Sesquiers, Route de Villeveyrac.
GPS: n43,44135 e3,59436.⬆.

6 ⬛free ⬛ ⬛Chfree. **Location:** Simple, noisy.
Surface: gravel.
Distance: 2,5km ⬛10km.

Mont-Louis 31B1

Parking des Remparts. **GPS:** n42,50765 e2,12273.⬆.

20 ⬛€ 5 ⬛included. ⬛ **Location:** Urban, simple, quiet.
Surface: asphalted.
Distance: 200m ⊗200m ⬛200m.
Remarks: Parking at city wall.

Montagnac 27A2

D613. **GPS:** n43,47520 e3,49129.⬆➡.

3 ⬛free ⬛ ⬛Chfree. **Surface:** gravel.
Distance: 1km ⊗1km ⬛1km.

Montcalm 27B2

Le Caveau du Chêne, Route d'Aigues Mortes, D58.
GPS: n43,57322 e4,30505.⬆.

40 free for clients. **Location:** Rural, isolated, quiet. **Surface:** grassy.
◯ 01/01-31/12

Montferrand 26F2

Col de Naurouze, Route du Ségala, N113> D218.
GPS: n43,35238 e1,82390.⬆.

20 free. **Location:** Rural, simple, quiet. **Surface:** gravel.
◯ 01/01-31/12
Distance: 2km ⊗on the spot 2km on the spot on the spot.

Montpellier 27B2

Parking Joffre, Rue d'Argencour. **GPS:** n43,61316 e3,88608.
€ 1/h. **Surface:** asphalted. ◯ 01/01-31/12
Distance: 4km.
Remarks: Overnight stay possible. Via avenue Jean Mermoz.

Tourist information Montpellier:
◉ Corum. Opera-complex.
◉ Place de la Comédie. Square with many cafés.

Monze 26G3

La Bretonne. GPS: n43,15475 e2,45867.⬆.

2 free. **Location:** Rural, simple, isolated, quiet. **Surface:** asphalted.
◯ 01/01-31/12
Distance: 50m ⊗500m.
Remarks: Max. 48h.

Mourèze 27A2

D8. **GPS:** n43,61728 e3,36111.⬆.

6 € 6 ChWCincluded. **Location:** Simple, isolated, quiet.
Surface: gravel. ◯ 01/01-31/12
Distance: on the spot ⊗300m on the spot.

Murviel-lès-Béziers 26H2

Route de Réals, D36. **GPS:** n43,43953 e3,13420.⬆.

12 € 3 Ch (6x)WCincluded. **Location:** Rural, comfortable, isolated, quiet. **Surface:** unpaved.
◯ 15/04-15/10
Distance: 700m 10km ⊗700m 1,7km on the spot.
Remarks: Max. 7 nights, entrance code available at tourist info, GPS n43.43365, e3.14834.

Narbonne 26H3

Parking du Parc des Sports, Avenue de la Mer.
GPS: n43,18017 e3,02294.⬆.

36 € 9/day €2 Ch €2.
Surface: asphalted.
◯ 01/01-31/12
Distance: on the spot 2,3km Carrefour.
Remarks: Free bus to centre every 30 minutes.

Tourist information Narbonne:
◉ Autorail Touristique du Minervois. Train tourist from Narbonne to Bize. ◯ 01/07-17/09.
✘ Palais des Archevêques. Palace, 11th century, with cathedral.
⚓ Thu, Su.

Nîmes 27B1

Domaine de Fontbespierre, 3359, route d'Anduze.
GPS: n43,87142 e4,27746.⬆.

50 € 10 €2 Ch €2/day WC. **Location:** Rural.
Surface: grassy. ◯ 01/01-31/12
Distance: 6km ⊗6km 6km.
Remarks: Terrain with video surveillance.

Octon 27A2

Avenue de la Molière. **GPS:** n43,65390 e3,30378.⬆.

8 free. **Location:** Simple, quiet.
Surface: asphalted.
Distance: 50m ⊗50m 50m Lac du Salagou Lac du Salagou.
Remarks: Parking behind 'Clamery', Lac du Salagou.

Ouveillan 26H2

Place Cave Coopératieve. **GPS:** n43,29204 e2,97080.⬆.

7 free Chfree. **Surface:** gravel/metalled.
◯ 01/01-31/12
Distance: 2km ⊗2km 2km.

Palavas-les-Flots 27B2

D62E2. **GPS:** n43,53281 e3,92654.⬆.

23 € 11-19 Ch included. **Surface:** asphalted.
◯ 01/01-31/12
Distance: centre 600m sandy beach 800m.

Palavas-les-Flots 27B2

Port Fluvial, Base Paul Riquet, Avenue de Lattre Tassigny.
GPS: n43,53091 e3,92316.⬆.

200 € 11, Jul-Aug € 19 + € 0,22/pp tourist tax, extra charge >8m and trailer €3 Ch €2 WC included. **Surface:** asphalted.
◯ 01/01-31/12
Distance: 1km ⊗1km 1km.

Peyriac-de-Mer 26H3

Rue des Étangs. **GPS:** n43,09372 e2,96205.⬆.

20 € 5 ChWC. **Location:** Rural, simple, simple.
Surface: grassy/metalled. ◯ 01/01-31/12
Distance: 1km on the spot ⊗1km 1km on the spot on the spot.
Remarks: Next to rugby ground.

Pezens 26G2

Place de la Liberté, D6113. **GPS:** n43,25528 e2,26361.⬆.

5 free free. **Location:** Urban, simple, noisy. **Surface:** gravel.
◯ 01/01-31/12
Distance: 50m ⊗50m 50m.

Port Vendres 31C1

Plage des Tamarins, Route de la Jetée. **GPS:** n42,51778 e3,11375.⬆.

30 🛏 € 5,50, Jul/Aug € 9 ⛽€2/100liter 🚰Ch included WC.
Location: Rural, simple. **Surface:** gravel. 🅿 01/01-31/12
Distance: 🛒1,3km 🏖100m on the spot.

🅂 **Port-la-Nouvelle** ⚓ 〰 26H3
Chemin des Vignes. **GPS:** n43,01366 e3,04077. ⬆➡.

30 🛏free, May-Jun, Sep € 4, Jul/Aug € 7 ⛽€2/15minutes 🚰Ch 🚽€
2/15minutes 🔌included, on camp site 🧺 🚿 **Location:** Rural, simple.
Surface: grassy/gravel.
Distance: 🛒2km 🚲8,6km 🏖2km ⊗2km 🍴1km Huit-à-huit,
Passage de l'Abbé Gavanon.

🅂 **Port-la-Nouvelle** ⚓ 〰 26H3
Parking Super U, Avenue du Général de Gaulle.
GPS: n43,01609 e3,04933.
🛏free ⛽€2/10minutes 🚰Ch free 🚿€2/55minutes 🔌against
payment. **Surface:** asphalted. 🅿 01/01-31/12, 19.30-08.30h
Distance: 🛒1km 🏖1km ⊗1km 🍴on the spot.

🅂 **Portiragnes** ⚓ 〰 27A2
Avenue de la Grande Maïre. **GPS:** n43,27558 e3,35156. ⬆.

± 15 🛏free. **Location:** Rural, simple, quiet. **Surface:** unpaved.
🅿 01/01-31/12
Distance: 🏖sandy beach 200m.
Remarks: Max. 2 days.

🅂 **Quillan** 26G3
Parking Joseph Courjétaire, D117. **GPS:** n42,87366 e2,18266. ⬆.

10 🛏free ⛽€3,10 🚰Ch WC. **Location:** Urban, simple, quiet.
Surface: asphalted. 🅿 01/01-31/12
Distance: 🛒on the spot 🏖on the spot ➤on the spot ⊗on the spot
🍴on the spot.
Remarks: Nearby railwayline, coins available at Office du Tourisme and bar.

🅂 **Remoulins** 〰 27C1
N86. **GPS:** n43,93789 e4,55851.

10 🛏free ⛽€5/20minutes 🚰Ch. **Location:** Urban.
Surface: asphalted.
Distance: 🛒100m ⊗100m 🍴100m.
Remarks: Parking nearby river, service on the other side of the bridge:
Route du Pont du Gare.

Tourist information Remoulins:
⌂ Pont du Gard. Roman aqueduct.

🅂 **Rennes-les-Bains** 〰 26G3
Plateau Sport Nature, Route des Corbières.
GPS: n42,91479 e2,31814. ⬆.

7 🛏€ 5/24h ⛽€ 5/24h 🚰Ch free. **Location:** Rural, simple, quiet.
Surface: asphalted. 🅿 01/01-31/12
Distance: 🛒500m 🏖100m.

🅂 **Rieutort-de-Randon** 24A3
Lac de Charpal. **GPS:** n44,62491 e3,56046. ⬆.

10 🛏free. **Location:** Rural, isolated, quiet. **Surface:** unpaved.
🅿 01/01-31/12
Distance: 🛒8km 🚲18km 🏖on the spot ➤on the spot ⊗on the spot
🎣on the spot.
Remarks: At lake Charpal.

🅂 **Routier** 26G3
Sous la Serre. **GPS:** n43,10813 e2,12362. ⬆➡.

7 🛏free ⛽🚰Ch free. **Location:** Rural, simple, quiet.
Surface: grassy/gravel. 🅿 01/01-31/12 🔘 water disconnected in
winter
Distance: 🛒on the spot.

Tourist information Routier:
ℹ Corbières. Region is known for its wines and the Cathar citadels, the
castle of Queribus in Cucugan is one of the last bastions of the Cathars.

🅂 **Saillagousse** ⛰ ♨ 31B1
Rue des Sports. **GPS:** n42,45764 e2,03766. ⬆.

7 🛏free ⛽€4 🚰Ch WC. **Location:** Urban, simple, quiet.
Surface: asphalted. 🅿 01/01-31/12
Distance: 🛒on the spot ⊗on the spot 🍴on the spot.
Remarks: Coins at tourist info and town hall.

🅂 **Saint-André** 31C1
Parking de Taxo. GPS: n42,55248 e2,97303. ⬆➡.

6 🛏€ 2,30 ⛽€2 🚰Ch 🚽€2. **Surface:** asphalted. 🅿 01/01-31/12
Distance: 🛒on the spot.
Remarks: Max. 3 nights, coins at tourist info.

🅂 **Saint-Chély-d'Apcher** ♨ 24A2
Parking du Péchaud, Boulevard G. d'Apcher, N9.
GPS: n44,80084 e3,27296. ⬆➡.

2 🛏free ⛽€2/100liter 🚰Ch 🚽€2/10minutes. **Location:** Simple,
central, quiet. **Surface:** asphalted.
🅿 01/01-31/12
Distance: 🛒200m 🚲2,5km ⊗200m 🍴200m 🚌on the spot.
Remarks: Coins at tourist info.

🅂 **Saint-Couat-d'Aude** 26H2
La Bellevue. **GPS:** n43,21429 e2,63052.
🛏€5 ⛽€3 🚰Ch 🚿€3 WC. **Location:** Comfortable, isolated,
quiet.

🅂 **Saint-Cyprien** ⚓ 〰 31C1
Aire du Théâtre de la Mer, Quai Arthur Rimbaud.
GPS: n42,61776 e3,03512. ⬆.

49 🛏€ 12,50/24h 15/10-31/03 € 10,15/24h ⛽🚰Ch 🚽included. 🚐
🧺 **Location:** Comfortable. **Surface:** asphalted. 🅿 01/01-31/12
🔘 service 15/10-31/03
Distance: 🛒450m marina ⊗300m.

🅂 **Saint-Gilles** 27B2
Quai du Canal. **GPS:** n43,67154 e4,43281. ⬆⬆.

FR

⌁free. **Location:** Rural. **Surface:** asphalted. ▣ 01/01-31/12
Distance: ⟲500m ⊗200m ⟰500m.
Tourist information Saint-Gilles:
✝ Abbay St.Gilles. Abbey with underground church.

🅂 **Saint-Jean-du-Gard** 🏊🏕👥🏕 27B1
Av. de la Resistance. **GPS:** n44,10210 e3,88347. ⬆.

20 ⌁free 🚐🔌Ch WC free. **Location:** Urban, simple.
Surface: metalled. ▣ 01/01-31/12
Distance: ⟲on the spot ⟰100m ⟿100m ⊗50m ⟰300m 🚶on the spot.
Remarks: 2013: during inspection service out of order, tourist train.

🅂 **Saint-Laurent-de-Cerdans** ⛰ 31B1
Parking Halle Polyvalente, Place du Syndicat.
GPS: n42,38336 e2,61572. ⬆➡.

15 ⌁free 🚐🔌Ch WC free. **Location:** Urban, simple, quiet.
Surface: gravel. ▣ 01/01-31/12
Distance: ⟲500m ⊗100m ⟰500m 🚶on the spot.
Remarks: Max. 48h.

🅂 **Saint-Mamert-du-Gard** 27B1
Rue des Fraisses. **GPS:** n43,88965 e4,19039. ⬆.

6 ⌁free. **Location:** Simple. **Surface:** asphalted. ▣ 01/01-31/12
Distance: ⟲400m.

🅂 **Saint-Mamert-du-Gard** 27B1
Route du Stade. **GPS:** n43,88491 e4,19054.
🚐🔌Ch free. ▣ 01/01-31/12

🅂 **Saint-Marsal** ⛰ 31B1
GPS: n42,53755 e2,62242. ⬆.

25 ⌁€ 3 🚐free. 🏊 **Location:** Rural, simple. **Surface:** asphalted.

▣ 01/01-31/12
Distance: ⟲on the spot.

🅂 **Saint-Martin-de-Londres** 27A1
Rue des Sapeurs. **GPS:** n43,79046 e3,73470. ⬆➡.

6 ⌁€ 4 🚐🔌💧 included. **Location:** Simple. ▣ 01/01-31/12
Distance: ⟲150m ⊗on the spot.

🅂 **Saint-Mathieu-de-Tréviers** 27B1
D17. **GPS:** n43,76206 e3,86016. ⬆➡.

8 ⌁€ 5 🚐🔌Ch 💧 included. **Surface:** gravel. ▣ 01/01-31/12
Distance: ⟲1km.
Remarks: Check in at gymnasium.

🅂 **Saint-Thibéry** 27A2
Domaine de la Vière, Chemin de la Vière.
GPS: n43,38301 e3,40137. ⬆➡.

26 ⌁€ 10 🚐🔌Ch 💧 WC 🔊 included. 🏊 **Location:** Rural, comfortable, isolated. **Surface:** unpaved. ▣ 01/01-31/12
Distance: ⟲2km 🚗 A9 3km ⟰14km ⟿3km ⟰4km.
Remarks: During the weekend possible inconvenience of motocross.

🅂 **Salasc** 27A2
Route de la Gloriette, D148. **GPS:** n43,61746 e3,31709.
2 ⌁free. ▣ 01/01-31/12
Distance: ⟲300m ⊗300m.

🅂 **Salles-sur-l'Hers** 26F2
Allée des Platanes. **GPS:** n43,29194 e1,78844. ⬆.

10 ⌁free 🚐🔌Ch ⬛free. **Location:** Rural, simple, isolated, quiet.
Surface: gravel. ▣ 01/01-31/12
Distance: ⟲on the spot ⊗100m ⟰100m.
Remarks: At football ground.

🅂 **Sauve** 🏊🏕⛰ 27B1
D999. **GPS:** n43,94017 e3,95218. ⬆➡.

5 ⌁free 🚰🔌Ch free. **Location:** Urban, simple, central, noisy.
Surface: metalled. ▣ 01/01-31/12
Distance: ⟲50m ⊗50m 🚶on the spot.

🏕🅂 **Sérignan-Plage** ⛱🌊 27A2
Parking Mini-Golf, Avenue de la Plage. **GPS:** n43,26892 e3,33629. ⬆.

20 ⌁€ 13, Jul/Aug € 17 🚐🔌Ch 💧WC included 📷€
4. **Location:** Rural, comfortable, quiet. **Surface:** unpaved.
▣ 01/01-31/12
Distance: ⟰150m ⊗on the spot ⟰150m.
Remarks: Behind restaurant, bread-service, swimming pool.

🅂 **Sète** 🏕🍦🌊 27A2
Parking Les 3 Digues. **GPS:** n43,36663 e3,61523. ⬆.

30 ⌁free 🚐€2/10 🔌Ch ⬛. **Location:** Rural, simple.
Surface: gravel.
▣ 01/01-31/12
Distance: ⟰50m 🐾on the spot 🚶on the spot.
Remarks: Beach parking, 01/06-30/09 no dogs allowed on the beach.

🅂 **Sommières** 🏛 27B1
Chemin de la Princesse. **GPS:** n43,78701 e4,08717. ⬆.

25 ⌁free 🚐€3 🔌Ch. **Location:** Simple. **Surface:** gravel.
Distance: ⟲500m ⟿100m ⊗300m.
Remarks: In front of campsite municipal.

🅂🅂 **Thues-entre-Valls** ⛰🌲 31B1
Gorges de la Carança. **GPS:** n42,52346 e2,22517. ⬆.

25 ⌁€ 9/24h 🚐🔌Ch 🔊included. 🖥 **Location:** Simple, isolated, quiet. **Surface:** grassy/gravel. ▣ 01/01-31/12 ❄ frost
Distance: ⟲2km ⟰on the spot ⟿on the spot 🚶on the spot.

ⓈS Trouillas 31C1

Les Oliviers de la Canterrane, Solt de las Moles, D612.
GPS: n42,61399 e2,81599.⬆➡.

20 🅕free 🔌Chfree. **Location:** Rural, isolated, quiet.
Surface: gravel. 🅾 01/01-31/12
Distance: 🚶500m 🚊4km 🏊on the spot.

ⓈS Vailhan 27A2

Parking de l'Eglise. GPS: n43,55527 e3,29882.⬆➡.

6 🅕€5 🔌Chincluded. **Surface:** gravel. 🅾 01/01-31/12
Distance: 🚶1km 🚊200m 🛒50m.

ⓈS Vallabrègues 27C1

Route d'Aramon, D183A. **GPS:** n43,85763 e4,62639.⬆.

5 🅕free 🔌€2 🔌Ch🔌€2. **Location:** Rural. **Surface:** gravel.
🅾 01/01-31/12 🅾 high water
Distance: 🚶500m.
Remarks: At lake and along the Rhone river.

ⓈS Valleraugue 27A1

Avenue de l'Aigoual, D986. **GPS:** n44,08054 e3,63613.⬆.
6 🅕free 🔌€2 🔌Ch. **Surface:** asphalted. 🅾 01/01-31/12
Distance: 🚶450m.

ⓈS Valras-Plage 27A2

Avenue du Casino. **GPS:** n43,24230 e3,28162.⬆.

30 🅕free 🔌€2 🔌Ch. **Surface:** asphalted/metalled. 🅾 01/10-30/06
🅾 summer
Distance: 🚶on the spot 🚊200m 🎣on the spot 🛒on the spot 🏊on the spot.
Remarks: Behind casino/disco, service: Boulevard Pierre Giraud 200m, no camping activities.

ⓈS Valras-Plage 27A2

Boulevard de la Recanette. **GPS:** n43,25310 e3,29623.⬆.
20 🅕€12 🔌Ch🔌(9x)included. **Surface:** gravel.
Distance: 🚶800m 🚊800m 🛒800m.

ⓈS Vernet-les-Bains 31B1

Chemin de la Laiterie. **GPS:** n42,54268 e2,39092.⬆.

7 🅕free 🔌€2,50/20minutes 🔌Ch🔌€2,50/20minutes.
Location: Rural, simple, quiet. **Surface:** gravel.
Distance: 🚶600m 🚊on the spot 🛒600m.
Remarks: Coins at tourist info and town hall.

ⓈS Villasavary 26G2

Camping-Car Park des Collines, Zone du Pradel.
GPS: n43,21881 e2,03242.⬆.

11 🅕€ 8,40, 01/07-31/08 € 9,60 🔌🔌Ch🔌🛰included. 🅿 ⬛
Location: Rural, comfortable, isolated, quiet. **Surface:** asphalted.
🅾 01/01-31/12
Distance: 🚶650m 🚲10km 🏊on the spot.
Remarks: Video surveillance.

ⓈS Villeneuve-lès-Maguelone 27B2

Avenue René Poitevin. **GPS:** n43,52980 e3,86584.⬆➡.

26 🅕€ 9, 26/04-30/09 € 14/24h 🔌🔌Ch🔌included. 🅿 ⬛
Location: Rural. **Surface:** asphalted. 🅾 01/01-31/12
Distance: 🚶500m 🚲8km 🚊2,5km 🛒500m 🎣250m 🏍50m 🏊on the spot.
Remarks: 26/04-30/09: also cash payment at office de tourisme (200m).

ⓈS Villeneuve-Minervois 26G2

Avenue du Jeu de Mail. **GPS:** n43,31516 e2,46432.⬆.

20 🅕free 🔌🔌ChWC. **Surface:** asphalted/metalled.
🅾 01/01-31/12
Distance: 🚶on the spot 🛒on the spot 🏊on the spot.
Remarks: In front of town hall, max. 48h.

Provence-Alpes-Côte d'Azur

ⓈS Allos 🏔❄ 24F3

Les Prés. **GPS:** n44,24289 e6,62220.⬆.

30 🅕€6 🔌🔌Ch🔌(9x)included WC. 🅿 ⬛ **Surface:** asphalted.
🅾 01/01-31/12
Distance: 🚶500m 🚊200m 🏊500m 🚮500m 🎣200m 🏊200m.
Remarks: Max. 72h.

ⓈS Allos 🏔❄ 24F3

Parking de la Cluite. GPS: n44,24677 e6,66918.⬆.

6 🅕free. **Location:** Isolated, quiet. **Surface:** gravel.
Distance: 🚶Allos 6,5km.
Remarks: Isolated parking, jul/Aug shuttle bus to Lac d'Allos.

ⓈS Allos 🏔❄ 24F3

La Foux d'Allos. **GPS:** n44,29583 e6,56944.⬆➡.

5 🅕free 🔌🔌ChWCfree. **Surface:** asphalted.
Distance: 🚶1km 🏊100m 🎣100m 🚌Skibus 50m 🏊50m.

ⓈS Annot 🏔 27F1

Chemin de la Colle Basse. **GPS:** n43,96351 e6,66386.⬆➡.

20 🅕free 🔌🔌Chfree. **Surface:** grassy/gravel. 🅾 01/01-31/12
Distance: 🚶400m 🛒400m 🏊400m.

ⓈS Arles 🏛 27C2

Place Lamartine. **GPS:** n43,68151 e4,63046.⬆.

6 🅕free 🔌🔌Chfree. **Location:** Urban. **Surface:** asphalted. 🅾 Wed 5-15h, market
Distance: 🚶50m 🚊on the spot 🎣on the spot 🛒50m 🏊100m.
Tourist information Arles:

FR

ℹ Office de Tourisme, Boulevard des Lices, www.tourisme.ville-arles.fr. City on the border of the nature reserve Camargue with Roman ruin. The painter Van Gogh lived in Arles, 1888-89.
✝ Église St.Trophine. Romanesque and Gothic construction.
⌒ Palais Constantin. Large Roman imperial palace of which only the baths are left.

Avignon 🌿⛲🍰 27C1
Chemin de l'Ile Piot. **GPS:** n43,95167 e4,79361.⬆.

20 free. **Surface:** asphalted. ☐ 01/01-31/12
Distance: 🚶800m ⊗800m 🚰800m on the spot.
Remarks: Max. 24h, free bus to centre every ten minutes.
Tourist information Avignon
ℹ Office de Tourisme, 41, cours Jean Jaurès, www.ot-avignon.fr. Roman city dominated by the Palais du Papes. ☐ 01/04-31/08, 01/10-31/10 9-17h, 01/09-30/09 9-20h, 01/11-31/03 9-12.45h, 14-18h.
👁 Place d'Horloge. Cosy square in the old centre of the city.
👁 Pont Saint Bénézet. Known as the Pont d'Avignon, bridge over the river Rhône.
🏰 Petit Palais. Former residence of the archbishop.

Bagnols-en-Fôret 27F2
Parc de Notre-Dame Les Merles, 1 chemin des Meules, D47.
GPS: n43,53590 e6,68893.⬆➡.

15 €5 🚰€4 📶. **Location:** Rural, comfortable, isolated, quiet.
Surface: grassy. ☐ 01/01-31/12
Distance: 🚶1km ⊗1km 🚰1km on the spot.

Banon 🍴 27D1
Espace de la Grand Fontaine, Rue de la Grande Fontaine.
GPS: n44,03982 e5,63006.⬆.

± 15 €3/24h 🚰Chfree WC. **Location:** Rural, simple.
Surface: gravel/metalled.
Distance: 🚶250m ⊗250m 🚰100m on the spot 🚶 on the spot.
Remarks: Max. 7 days, tuesday morning market.

Barcelonnette 🏔 24F3
Parking du Bouquet, Chemin des Alpages.
GPS: n44,38222 e6,65778.⬆➡.

15 €6 🚰€2/100liter 🔌Ch📶€2/1h 🧹. **Location:** Isolated, quiet.
Surface: grassy. ☐ 01/01-31/12
Distance: 🚶500m ⊿200m ⊗500m 🚰500m.

Barcelonnette 🏔 24F3
GPS: n44,38717 e6,64626.⬆.
3 free. **Location:** Simple. **Surface:** asphalted. ☐ 01/01-31/12
Distance: 🚶500m ⊗500m 🚰600m.
Remarks: Max. 48h.

Bédoin 🍴 27D1
Chemin des Sablières. **GPS:** n44,12472 e5,17167.⬆➡.

€3 🚰€2/10minutes,only 2-euro coins 🔌Chfree 🧹€ 2/55minutes,only 2-euro coins. **Location:** Rural, simple, quiet.
Surface: grassy/metalled.
☐ 01/01-31/12
Distance: 🚶600m ⊗600m 🚰600m 🚠Mont-Ventoux 🚶 on the spot.
Remarks: Next to campsite La Pinède, max. 3 nights.

Bollène 24C3
Centre Leclerc, Route de Saint Paul Trois Châteaux, D26.
GPS: n44,32222 e4,74306.⬆.

free 🚰Chfree. ☐ 01/01-31/12
Distance: ✈4,3km.
Remarks: Service only during opening hours shop.
Tourist information Bollène:
👁 Village Troglodyte. Cave dwelling village. ☐ 01/04-31/10 9.30-19h, 01/11-31/03 Sa-Su, holidays 14-18h ☐ 01/12-31/01.

Briançon 🌿🏔 24F2
Parc des Sports, Rue Jean Moulin. **GPS:** n44,89028 e6,62883.⬆.
4 free 🚰€2/100liter 🔌Ch🔌€2.
Surface: asphalted.
Distance: 🚰1km.
Remarks: At sports park, max. 24h.
Tourist information Briançon:
ℹ Office de Tourisme, 1, place du Temple, www.ot-briancon.fr. Highest city of Europe, fortress is now a tourist centre, in winter as winter sports resort and in summer parapente, rafting and biking.
🌿 Parc des Écrins. Nature reserve.

Caille 🏔 27F1
Aire de Caille, Chemin de la Plaine. **GPS:** n43,77893 e6,73331.⬆➡.

3 free 🚰€4/15minutes 🔌Ch🔌€2/15minutes. **Location:** Simple, quiet. **Surface:** asphalted.
☐ 01/01-31/12
Distance: 🚶50m ⊗50m 🚰100m 🚶 on the spot 🚵10km 🚣150m.

Carpentras 🏛 27C1
Parking de Coubertin, Avenue de Coubertin.
GPS: n44,04398 e5,05372.⬆.

8 free 🚰🔌Chfree. **Location:** Urban, simple. **Surface:** asphalted.
Distance: 🚶1,5km.
Remarks: At sports centre P.de Coubertin, max. 24h.
Tourist information Carpentras:
👁 Hôtel Dieu. Former hospital, 18th century.
🌳 Centre-ville.
☐ Fri-morning.

Carro 🌊 27C2
Quai Jean Verandy. **GPS:** n43,32931 e5,04076.

70 € 6,30, 01/04-30/06 € 8,40, 01/07-31/08 € 10,50 🚰Ch🧹 included. **Location:** Comfortable, central, quiet. **Surface:** gravel.
☐ 01/01-31/12
Distance: 🚶on the spot ⊿on the spot 🚣on the spot ⊗200m 🚰200m.
Remarks: Max. 72h, fish sales from 08h.

Carry-le-Rouet 27D2
Avenue Pierre Sémard. **GPS:** n43,33829 e5,15921.⬆.

4 free. **Location:** Simple, noisy. **Surface:** asphalted.
☐ 01/01-31/12
Distance: 🚶1km ⊿1km 🚰500m.
Remarks: Nearby police station, max. 48h.

Castellane 🌳🏔🌊 27F1
Ancienne Route de Grasse. **GPS:** n43,84630 e6,51484.⬆.

28 €6 🚰🔌Ch🧹 included. **Surface:** asphalted.
Distance: 🚶100m 🚣on the spot.
Remarks: Directly at the river, near Pont du Roc.
Tourist information Castellane:
🌳 ☐ Sa-morning.

Cavalière 27F3
Avenue du Cap Nègre, D559. **GPS:** n43,15228 e6,43078.⬆.

50 ⌆ € 16-18 ⌂ ⌆Ch 🚿⌐ 📶included. **Surface:** sand.
Distance: 🚶50m 🏊50m ⊗50m ⌶200m.

Château-Arnoux-Saint-Auban ⌆S 27E1
Avenue Gén. de Gaulle, N85. **GPS:** n44,09543 e6,01022. ⬆➡.

+10 ⌆free ⌂ ⌆Chfree. **Location:** Urban, central, noisy.
Surface: asphalted.
Distance: 🚶on the spot ⌶2,3km.
Remarks: Max. 48h, service 50m.

Chorges ⌆S 24E3
Place du champ de foire. **GPS:** n44,54600 e6,28008. ⬆.

10 ⌆free ⌂ ⌆free. **Surface:** gravel. ◻ 01/01-31/12
Distance: 🚶400m ⊗400m ⌶1km.
Remarks: Max. 12h.

Tourist information Chorges:
ℹ Lac de Serre Ponçon, Serre Ponçon. Clear blue artificial lake, many water sports.

Colmars-les-Alpes ⌆S 24F3
GPS: n44,17943 e6,62695. ⬆➡.

10 ⌆free ⌂ €2 ⌆Ch ⌐ **Surface:** asphalted. ◻ 01/01-31/12
Distance: 🚶300m 🏊50m ⊗50m ⌶300m.
Remarks: Tuesday market.

Comps-sur-Artuby ⌆S 27F1
La Grange du Roux, D955. **GPS:** n43,70652 e6,50678. ⬆.

10 ⌆free ⌂ €3 ⌆ChWC. **Location:** Rural, comfortable, isolated, quiet. **Surface:** gravel. ◻ 01/01-31/12
Distance: 🚶350m ⊗pizzeria/crêperie 50m ⌶350m.
Remarks: Coins at the shops.

Cuges-les-Pins ⌆S 27E2
Le Jardin de la Ville. GPS: n43,28150 e5,70558. ⬆➡.

10 ⌆€3 ⌂ €1,50 ⌆Ch. **Location:** Rural, comfortable, isolated, quiet.
Surface: grassy/gravel. ◻ 01/01-31/12
Distance: 🚶500m ⊗500m ⌶500m.
Remarks: Monitored parking.

Tourist information Cuges-les-Pins:
Ⓜ Musée Légion Etrangères, Aubagne. Museum about the French Foreign Legion.

Dauphin ⌆ 27E1
Route de la Rencontre. **GPS:** n43,90028 e5,78417. ⬆.

4 ⌆free. **Location:** Rural, simple, quiet.
Surface: metalled.
Distance: 🚶300m ⊗300m ♨ on the spot 🚶 on the spot.
Remarks: Near Salle des Fêtes.

Digne-les-Bains ⌆⌆S 27E1
Le Vallon des Sources, Avenue des Thermes.
GPS: n44,07998 e6,26091. ⬆.

25 ⌆free ⌂ €2 ⌆Ch. ◻ 01/01-31/12
Distance: 🚶2,5km ⊗750m ⌶2km 🚌100m.
Remarks: Coins available at pay-desk of theTherme.

Ensuès-la-Redonne ⌆ 27D2
Avenue de la Côte Bleue. **GPS:** n43,35530 e5,18915.

20 ⌆ ⌂ ⌆Chfree. **Location:** Isolated, noisy. **Surface:** gravel.
◻ 01/01-31/12
Distance: 🚶1,2km ⌆3km ⊗1km ⌶1km 🚌100m.

Esparron de Verdon ⌆⌆⌆ 27E1
D82. **GPS:** n43,74233 e5,97366. ⬆.

7 ⌆free ⌂. **Location:** Rural, simple.

Distance: 🚶500m 🏊500m ⊗500m ⌶500m 🚶on the spot.

Fayence ⌆ 27F2
Allée des Jardins. **GPS:** n43,62308 e6,68982. ⬆➡.

2 ⌆free ⌂ €4 ⌆Ch. **Location:** Simple, central, noisy.
Surface: asphalted.
Distance: 🚶750m ⊗750m ⌶300m.
Remarks: At tennis-court and swimming pool, max. 48h.

Fontaine-de-Vaucluse ⌆S 27D1
Camping-Car Park, Route de Cavaillon. **GPS:** n43,92024 e5,12452. ⬆.

⌆€ 12 ⌂ ⌆Ch 🚿(2x) 📶included. ⌶ ⌐ **Location:** Rural, comfortable, quiet. **Surface:** gravel/metalled. ◻ 01/01-31/12
Distance: 🚶500m ⊗500m ♨ on the spot 🚶 on the spot.

Fontvieille ⌆S 27C1
Parking du Moulin de Daudet, Allée des Pins.
GPS: n43,72000 e4,71200. ⬆.

⌆€5 ⌂ €2 ⌆Ch. ⌶ ⌐ **Location:** Rural, comfortable, quiet.
Surface: gravel.
Distance: 🚶800m ⊗800m.

Gap ⌆S 24E3
Parking Dumont, Avenue Commandant Dumont, N85.
GPS: n44,56544 e6,08447. ⬆➡.

3 ⌆free ⌂ €3 ⌆Ch 🔌€3 ⌐ **Surface:** asphalted
Distance: 🚶500m ⊗on the spot ⌶on the spot.
Remarks: Stay overnight allowed at other pitches.

Gémenos ⌆S 27D2
Cours Sudre. **GPS:** n43,29772 e5,62953. ⬆➡.

3 ⌆free ⌂ ⌆ChWCfree. **Location:** Central, quiet.
Surface: metalled. ◻ 01/01-31/12
Distance: 🚶100m ⊗100m ⌶100m 🚌50m.

FR

Remarks: Near office de tourisme, max. 24h.

Gigondas 27C1

Domaine des Florets, Route des Dentelles, D80.
GPS: n44,16220 e5,01725.

3 free free. **Location:** Rural, simple, quiet. **Surface:** gravel.
01/01-31/12
Distance: 1,7km 500m on the spot Des Dentelles.
Remarks: Check in at tasting room.

Gordes 27D1

D2. **GPS:** n43,90056 e5,19306.

20 free. **Location:** Rural, simple. **Surface:** gravel.
01/01-31/12
Distance: 2km 2km 2km.

Greasque 27D2

Musée de la Mine, Route de Puits Hely d'Oissel.
GPS: n43,43281 e5,53439.

15 free Ch free. **Surface:** gravel. 16/01-20/12
Distance: 600m.

Gréoux-les-Bains 27E1

Aire Camping-car, Chemin de la Barque.
GPS: n43,75562 e5,88862.

80 €9/24h Ch WC included. **Location:** Urban,
simple, noisy. **Surface:** gravel. 01/01-31/12
Distance: 150m 150m 150m on the spot.
Remarks: Max 3,5t, max. 30 days.

Grimaud 27F2

Saint Pons Les Mûres, D98. **GPS:** n43,28000 e6,57806.

12 €15 Ch included €2,50 . **Location:** Simple, noisy.
Surface: asphalted. 01/01-31/12

Distance: 800m 800m 200m 500m.
Remarks: Max. 72h.

Guillaumes 27F1

D2202. **GPS:** n44,08861 e6,85285.

10 free €2/100liter Ch €2/1h.
01/01-31/12
Distance: 50m on the spot on the spot 50m 50m.
Remarks: Coins at Bar-Tabac, tourist info, town hall.

Hyères 27E3

Les Etangs de Sauvebonne, 566 Route de Pierrefeu.
GPS: n43,16220 e6,12291.

20 €10 Ch included €3/day. **Location:** Rural, comfortable,
quiet. **Surface:** grassy. 01/01-31/12
Distance: on the spot on the spot.

Jausiers 24F3

Route de Jausiers-Barcelonette, D900. **GPS:** n44,41266 e6,72936.

3 free €3 Ch. **Surface:** metalled. 01/01-31/12
Distance: 600m 50m 100m 400m.

Jausiers 24F3

Pont de Barnuquel, Lotissement des Neiges. **GPS:** n44,41278 e6,72472.

20 free. **Surface:** unpaved. 01/01-31/12
Distance: 600m on the spot 100m 400m.
Remarks: Service 200m.

Jouques 27D2

Parking Saint Honorat, D11. **GPS:** n43,63176 e5,64414.
5 free Ch . **Surface:** asphalted.
Distance: 750m 750m 750m.

L'Isle-sur-la-Sorgue 27C1

Parking de la Gare, Avenue Julien Guigue.
GPS: n43,91768 e5,04686.
free. **Location:** Simple, noisy. **Surface:** gravel.
Distance: 500m 150m 700m on the spot.
Remarks: At station.

La Bréole 24E3

Bourg La Bréole. **GPS:** n44,45777 e6,29194.

6 free Ch WC free. **Location:** Simple, quiet.
Surface: asphalted. 01/01-31/12
Distance: on the spot 2km 2km Lac de Serre Ponçon 100m
100m.

La Crau 27E3

Espace Lavage Auto Grand Bleu, La Moutonne.
GPS: n43,12417 e6,07444.

3 free €4 Ch. **Location:** Simple, noisy. **Surface:** concrete.
01/01-31/12

La Londe-les-Maures 27E3

Rond-point Ducourneau, chemin du Pansard.
GPS: n43,13185 e6,23053.

4 free €3 Ch . **Location:** Simple, isolated, quiet.
Surface: asphalted.
01/01-31/12
Distance: 800m 3km 800m 800m.
Remarks: 03/07/2015 during inspection service out of order, max. 24h.

La Martre 27F1

Chemin de Fontvieillle. **GPS:** n43,77233 e6,60255.

3 €5 Ch included. **Location:** Comfortable, isolated, quiet.
Surface: grassy/gravel. 01/01-31/12
Distance: 300m 300m 300m.

La Motte 27F2

Chemin des Correns. **GPS:** n43,48860 e6,54212.

10 free €2 Ch. **Location:** Rural, simple, isolated, quiet.
Surface: gravel. 01/01-31/12
Distance: 800m 300m.
Remarks: At tennis-courts, max. 24h, coins at the shops.

FR

ⓈⓈ La Motte — 27F2
Moulin de Vallongues, Avenue Fréderique Mistral, D47.
GPS: n43,49630 e6,53134.⬆

10 ⓈΔfree 🚰🔌Chfree 🗑. **Location**: Isolated, quiet. **Surface**: gravel.
⬛ 01/01-31/12
Distance: 🚶600m ⊗600m 🛒4km.
Remarks: Max. 24h.

ⓈⓈ La Roche-des-Arnauds — 24E3
D994, Chemin des Digues. **GPS**: n44,56134 e5,95637.⬆

5 ⓈΔfree. **Surface**: asphalted. ⬛ 01/01-31/12
Distance: 🚶100m ⎯on the spot 🔌on the spot 🛒100m.
Remarks: Max. 24h.

ⓈⓈ La Salle-les-Alpes 🏔❄ — 24F2
Aire camping car Pontillas, Hameau de Bez.
GPS: n44,94805 e6,55564.⬆
20 Ⓢ€8 🚰🔌Ch ✏included. **Surface**: metalled.
Distance: 🚶400m ⎯400m 🔌400m 🎿20m.
Remarks: Pay at tourist office.

ⓈⓈ La Salle-les-Alpes ❄❄ — 24F2
Chemin de l'Oratoire, Villeneuve. **GPS**: n44,94417 e6,55583.⬆

15 ⓈΔ€8, winter €18 🚰🔌Ch ✏included. **Surface**: gravel.
⬛ 01/01-31/12
Distance: 🚶200m ⊗50m.
Remarks: Parking at skipistes.

Laragne-Montéglin — 24E3
Avenue de Provence, D1075. **GPS**: n44,31212 e5,82543.⬆

15 ⓈΔfree 🚰🔌Ch 📶free. **Surface**: asphalted. ⬛ 01/01-31/12
Distance: 🚶300m ⊗300m 🛒300m.

ⓈⓈ Laragne-Montéglin — 24E3
Intermarché, D1075. **GPS**: n44,30300 e5,83700.⬆

30 ⓈΔfree 🚰€2 🔌Ch. ⬛ 01/01-31/12
Distance: 🚶2km.

Le Lauzet-Ubay 🏔🌲❄ — 24F3
D900. **GPS**: n44,42833 e6,43389.⬆

10 ⓈΔfree. **Location**: Isolated, quiet. **Surface**: gravel.
⬛ 01/01-31/12
Distance: 🚶50m ⎯50m ⊗50m 🛒100m.
Remarks: At small lake.

ⓈⓈ Le Monêtier-les-Bains ❄ — 24F2
Aire camping car les Charmettes, Route des Bains.
GPS: n44,97602 e6,50933.⬆
40 ⓈΔ€4,80/day + tourist tax 🚰🔌Chfree. **Surface**: metalled.
⬛ 01/01-31/12
Distance: 🎿on the spot.
Remarks: Parking at skipistes.

ⓈⓈ Le Thoronet — 27E2
D17, boulevard du 17 aout 1944. **GPS**: n43,45097 e6,30411.⬆

2 ⓈΔfree 🚰€2 🔌Ch. **Location**: Rural, simple, central, noisy.
Surface: asphalted. ⬛ 01/01-31/12
Distance: 🚶on the spot 🛒50m.
Remarks: Max. 48h, coins at tourist info.

ⓈⓈ Les Issambres 🏖🌲 — 27F2
Chez Marcel, Plage La Gaillarde, N98. **GPS**: n43,36559 e6,71202.⬆

40 ⓈΔ€11, peak season €16 🚰🔌Chincluded ✏€3/day 🗑€0,50 ⬛€
5/5 📶. **Location**: Comfortable, isolated, quiet. **Surface**: gravel/sand.
⬛ 01/01-31/12
Distance: 🚶3km ⎯50m ⊗200m 🔌200m 🛒50m.

ⓈⓈ Les Salles-sur-Verdon — 27E1
L'Ermitage, D957. **GPS**: n43,77434 e6,21773.⬆

5 ⓈΔ€6, Jul/Aug €8 🚰🔌Ch ✏€5 📶included. **Location**: Rural,
simple. **Surface**: gravel/sand.
Distance: 🚶700m ⎯Lac de Ste Croix 1km ⊗on the spot 🔌on the
spot 🎿on the spot.
Remarks: Service passerby €5, swimming pool incl.

ⓈⓈ Malaucène 🏖🏔👥 — 24D3
Avenue Charles de Gaulle. **GPS**: n44,17792 e5,12970.⬆

ⓈΔ€3,50 🚰🔌Chfree. ✏ **Location**: Rural, simple, noisy.
Surface: asphalted/metalled.
⬛ 01/01-31/12
Distance: 🚶150m ⊗150m 🔌150m 🚴Mont-Ventoux 🎿on the spot.
Remarks: Between sports fields and gendarmerie.

Tourist information Malaucène:
🎪 Marché Provencal. ⬛ Wed-morning.

ⓈⓈ Malemort-du-Comtat — 27D1
Avenue Docteur Tondut, D5. **GPS**: n44,02175 e5,15714.⬆

ⓈΔfree 🚰🔌Chfree. **Location**: Rural, simple.
Surface: gravel.
Distance: 🚶200m 🔌on the spot.
Remarks: Near Salle des Fêtes.

ⓈⓈ Marseille — 27D2
Marlyparc, Chemin de Morgiou 120. **GPS**: n43,24085 e5,40693.⬆

40 ⓈΔ€12 🚰🔌Ch ✏included 📶. **Location**: Urban, simple, central,
quiet. **Surface**: metalled. ⬛ 01/01-31/12
Distance: 🚶7km Marseille ⎯3km 🛒1km.

Ⓢ Ménerbes 🌿🏖👥 — 27D1
Parking Longue Durée. **GPS**: n43,83193 e5,20828.⬆

ⓈΔfree. **Location**: Rural, simple. **Surface**: gravel.
Distance: 🚶250m 🔌100m 🎿on the spot.

ⓈⓈ Montgenèvre 🏖🏔❄ — 24F2
Aire des Marmottes. **GPS**: n44,93417 e6,73317.⬆➡

FR

250 ⌷€ 10 🚰⌷Ch🔌(80x)included. **Location:** Comfortable, isolated, quiet. **Surface:** metalled. ⬜ 01/01-31/12
Distance: 🚶500m ⊗500m 🍴on the spot.

⬛⬛ Moustiers-Sainte-Marie 🌿⛺🏞 **27E1**
P5, D952. **GPS:** n43,84361 e6,21874. ⬆➡.

⌷€ 8,50/night 🚰€2/10minutes ⌷Ch🔌€2/10minutes. ⬜🚐🎫
Location: Rural, simple. **Surface:** gravel.
Distance: 🚶10 min walking 🐕on the spot 🚶on the spot.
Remarks: Max. 2 nights.

⬛⬛ Névache **24F2**
D994G. **GPS:** n45,01666 e6,64261.

⌷free, 01/07-31/08 € 5 🚰⌷free. **Location:** Isolated.
Surface: grassy. ⬜ 01/01-31/12

⬛ Ollioules **27E3**
Route des Gorges, DN8. **GPS:** n43,13868 e5,85002.
8 ⌷€ 3. ⬜ 01/04-30/09
Distance: 🚶600m ⊗600m 🍴450m.
Remarks: Max. 48h.

⬛⬛ Oppède-le-Vieux 🌿⛺🏞 **27D1**
Parking Oppéde-le-Vieux. GPS: n43,83094 e5,15897. ⬆.

2 ⌷€ 5/day 🚰free WC.🔌 **Location:** Rural, simple.
Surface: gravel.
Distance: 🚶500m ⊗500m.
Tourist information Oppède-le-Vieux:
🥾 Hiking route through medieval top-hill village.

⬛⬛ Orcières-Merlette ⛺🏔❄ **24E2**
Camping-car Casse Blanche, Pra Palier, P2.
GPS: n44,69517 e6,32567. ⬆.
24 ⌷€ 10/24h 🚰⌷Ch🔌included. **Surface:** asphalted.
⬜ 01/01-31/12
Distance: 🚶on the spot 🚵on the spot.
Remarks: Summer pay at tourist office.

⬛⬛ Pélissanne **27D2**
Prouvenque, Chemin de la Prouvenque.
GPS: n43,62805 e5,15307. ⬆➡.

6 ⌷free 🚰⌷Chfree. **Location:** Urban, simple, quiet.
Surface: asphalted.
Distance: 🚶500m 🚲8km.
Remarks: Parking stadium.

⬛ Plan-de-la-Tour **27F2**
Parking Foch. GPS: n43,33787 e6,54532.

⌷free. **Location:** Simple, central, quiet.
Surface: gravel.
Distance: 🚶on the spot ⊗100m 🍴150m.
Remarks: Max. 48h.
Tourist information Plan-de-la-Tour:
🥾 Thu morning 6-12h.

⬛⬛ Port Saint-Louis-du-Rhône **27C2**
Av. de la 1 Dfl. **GPS:** n43,38424 e4,81909. ⬆➡.

50 ⌷€ 6,25 🚰⌷Chincluded. **Location:** Simple, isolated, quiet.
Surface: asphalted/gravel. ⬜ 01/01-31/12
Distance: 🚶1,5km 🏊2km 🚤on the spot ⊗1km 🍴1,5km.
Remarks: Max. 48h.

⬛⬛ Pra-Loup 🏔❄ **24F3**
Parking des Choupettes. GPS: n44,36806 e6,60611. ⬆.

50 ⌷free 🚰€3 ⌷Ch€3 WC. **Surface:** asphalted.
⬜ 01/01-31/12
Distance: 🚶400m ⊗400m 🍴400m 🚵50m.
Remarks: Parking at skipistes.

⬛ Puget Theniers 🏔 **27F1**
Aire de la Condamine, Route des Grandes Alpes.
GPS: n43,95306 e6,89944. ⬆➡.

10 ⌷€ 3,50 🚰⌷Ch🔌included. **Surface:** asphalted.
⬜ 01/01-31/12

Distance: 🚶300m 🏊20m ⊗300m 🍴300m.
⬛⬛ Puy-Saint-Vincent ⛺🏔❄ **24F2**
Clôt de Saint-Romain, D4. **GPS:** n44,83245 e6,48331. ⬆.
20 ⌷€ 6 🚰⌷included. ⬜ 18/12-25/04
Remarks: Altitude 1600m, max. 15 days, information at cableway.

⬛⬛ Puyvert **27D1**
Super U, D118. **GPS:** n43,74763 e5,33727. ⬆.

5 ⌷free 🚰⌷Ch🔌(2x)free ⬜€4/time. **Location:** Rural.
Surface: asphalted. ⬜ 01/01-31/12
Distance: 🚶1,5km 🍴on the spot.
Remarks: Parking near Super-U.

⬛⬛ Quinson 🏞 **27E1**
Les Prés du Verdon, Allée des Prés du Verdon.
GPS: n43,69801 e6,03911. ⬆.

5 ⌷free ⌷Chfree. **Location:** Rural, simple, quiet.
Surface: gravel/sand. ⬜ 01/01-31/12
Distance: 🏊100m 🚤100m ⊗300m 🍴500m 🚶on the spot.
Remarks: Near the prehistoric museum of the gorges du Verdon.

⬛⬛ Ramatuelle **27F2**
Parking de Tamaris, Plage de Pamplonne, Route des Tamaris.
GPS: n43,23893 e6,66149. ⬆.

60 ⌷€ 5/day, € 5/night, 1/7-31/8 € 9day, € 9/night, dog € 1 🚰
Ch🔌(20x)€7/day. 🔌 **Location:** Rural. **Surface:** gravel.
Distance: 🏊on the spot ⊗on the spot 🍴on the spot.
Remarks: Beach parking.

⬛⬛ Ramatuelle **27F2**
Parking Municipal, Plage de Pamplonne, Route de Bonne-Terrasse.
GPS: n43,21126 e6,66217. ⬆➡.

130 ⌷€ 8,20, 02/11-10/03 € 5,10 🚰⌷ChWC🔌📶🔌
Location: Rural. **Surface:** gravel. ⬜ 01/04-31/10
Distance: 🏊200m ⊗200m 🍴2km.
Remarks: Beach parking, max. 48h, bread-service.
Tourist information Ramatuelle:
🥾 La place de l'Ormeau. Provencal Market. ⬜ Thu, Su.

⬛⬛ Riez 🏛 **27E1**
P de l'Auvestre, Chemin du Relais. **GPS:** n43,82180 e6,09197. ⬆➡.

30 ⌧ € 5/24h ⚡ Ch free. **Location:** Rural, comfortable, quiet.
Surface: gravel.
Distance: 500m ⊗500m 100m ♿ on the spot ⚹ on the spot.

⌧ € 6 + € 0,40/pp tourist tax ⚡ Ch WC included.
Location: Quiet. **Surface:** grassy. ◻ 01/01-31/12
Distance: 500m ⚓ on the spot.
Remarks: Service on the other side of the bridge.

10 ⌧ free ⚡ **Location:** Simple. **Surface:** gravel.
◻ 01/03-15/11
Distance: 200m ⊗200m ⚓ on the spot.
Remarks: Beautiful panorama.

Roussillon 27D1
Parking Saint Joseph, D149. **GPS:** n43,89660 e5,29593. ⬆➡

Saint-Étienne-de-Tinée 24F3
Camping du Plan d'Eau, Boulevard de la Digue.
GPS: n44,25847 e6,92307. ⬆
6 ⌧ € 10 ⚡€3 Ch 📶. **Location:** Comfortable, quiet.
Surface: gravel. ◻ 01/06-30/09
Remarks: At lake, in the village.

Saint-Paul-lès-Durance 27E2
Rue du Camping le Retour. **GPS:** n43,68700 e5,70588. ⬆➡

Saint-Laurent-du-Var 27G1
Route des Pugets. **GPS:** n43,68584 e7,18459. ⬆

20 ⌧ € 2/day, € 7/night. **Location:** Rural, comfortable.
Surface: gravel.
Distance: 800m ⊗800m ♿ on the spot ⚹ on the spot.
Remarks: Max. 48h, no camping activities.

Tourist information Roussillon:
⚑ Sentier des Ocres. Hiking trail, 45 min.

6 ⌧ free ⚡ Ch free. **Location:** Rural, simple, quiet.
Surface: gravel. ◻ 01/01-31/12
Distance: 500m ⚐ 4km ⊗500m ⛽700m.
Remarks: Max. 48h.

Sablet 24C3
Domaine du Parandou, D977. **GPS:** n44,19325 e4,99522. ⬆➡

7 ⌧ free ⚡ Ch free. **Location:** Isolated, noisy. **Surface:** asphalted.
◻ 01/01-31/12
Distance: 1,2km ⚐ 4,5km ⊗1,2km ⛽1,2km.
Remarks: Max. 7 days.

Saint-Tropez 27F2
Aire camping-car, Chemin Fontaine du pin, Chemin de la Moutte.
GPS: n43,26468 e6,67227. ⬆

Saint-Laurent-du-Var 27G1
Avenue Francis Teisseire. **GPS:** n43,66628 e7,19595. ⬆➡

5 ⌧ € 2 ⚡ Ch 🔧(2x)€3 WC included. **Location:** Rural, simple.
Surface: gravel. ◻ 01/01-31/12
Distance: 2km.

Saint-André-les-Alpes 27F1
Grand Rue. **GPS:** n43,96525 e6,50735. ⬆➡

15 ⌧ € 16 ⚡€2 Ch 🔧€2,50 WC €1. **Location:** Isolated.
Surface: grassy/sand. ◻ 01/01-31/12
Distance: 3km ⚓800m.

Tourist information Saint-Tropez:
🏛 La Citadelle, musée de la Marine. Navy museum.
⛲ Place des Lices. Week market. ◻ Wed + Sa morning.

5 ⌧ free. **Location:** Simple, central, noisy. **Surface:** asphalted.
◻ 01/01-31/12
Distance: city centre 2km ⚐ 200m ⚓600m ⊗500m ⛽500m
🚌500m.
Remarks: Max. 8M.

Saint-Véran 24F2
D5. **GPS:** n44,70447 e6,86091.
20 ⌧ € 2/day, € 5/night ⚡ Ch WC free. **Location:** Isolated, quiet.
Surface: metalled. ◻ 01/01-31/12
Distance: 100m ⊗100m ⛽200m 🎿 on the spot 🚠200m.

Saint-Mandrier-sur-Mer 27E3
Pin Roland, Impasse de la Mer. **GPS:** n43,07771 e5,90444. ⬆

Sainte-Croix-du-Verdon 27E1
Route du Lac. **GPS:** n43,76077 e6,15102. ⬆

30 ⌧ free ⚡€3/10minutes Ch. **Location:** Comfortable, quiet.
Surface: asphalted. ◻ 01/01-31/12
Distance: 250m ⊗100m ⛽250m.

Saint-Chamas 27C2
Avenue Marx Dormoy. **GPS:** n43,54636 e5,03246. ⬆
10 ⌧ free ⚡ Ch. **Location:** Urban, simple. **Surface:** gravel.
◻ 01/01-31/12
Distance: ⚓ on the spot ⊗on the spot.
Remarks: Near marina.

Saint-Crépin 24F2
D138. **GPS:** n44,70562 e6,60196.

6 ⌧ free ⚡ Ch free. **Surface:** asphalted. ◻ 01/01-31/12
Distance: ⚓500m ⊗500m.
Remarks: Max. 48h.

Saint-Martin-de-Crau 27C2
Place François Miterrand. **GPS:** n43,63859 e4,81454. ⬆
3 ⌧ free ⚡ Ch WC free. **Location:** Urban. **Surface:** metalled.
◻ 01/01-31/12
Distance: 400m ⊗400m ⛽1,5km.
Remarks: In front of town hall, max. 48h.

Saint-Michel-l'Observatoire 27E1
GPS: n43,90908 e5,71750. ⬆

20 ⌧ € 6,50/24h ⚡€2/10minutes Ch WC included.
Location: Rural, simple. **Surface:** asphalted.
Distance: 100m ⊗100m ♿ on the spot ⚹ on the spot.
Remarks: Max. 3 nights, water closed during wintertime.

Sainte-Maxime 27F2
D25, le Muy dir Ste.Maxime. **GPS:** n43,31730 e6,62999. ⬆

FR

50 🛏 € 10/24h, 01/10-31/03 € 5 🚰 🔧Chfree. **Location:** Comfortable, quiet. **Surface:** metalled. 🅿 01/01-31/12
Distance: 🚶city centre 1km 🏊1,2km ⊗McDonalds 50m 🛒Lidl 200m.
Remarks: Max. 48h.

Tourist information Sainte-Maxime:
🏕 🅿 Thu-morning.
🏕 Les Greniers du Golfe, Aire des Magnoti. Bric-a-brac. 🅿 Wed 08-18h.

| 🛏🚿S | **Salernes** | 27E2 |

Aire Municipal, Route des Quatre Chemins. **GPS:** n43,55923 e6,23381.
35 🛏free 🚰 🔧Chfree. **Surface:** grassy/gravel. 🅿 01/01-31/12
Distance: 🚶300m.
Remarks: Max. 24h.

| 🛏🚿S | **Salin-de-Giraud** | 27C2 |

Rue de la Bouvine. **GPS:** n43,41222 e4,73056. ⬆➡.

20 🛏free 🚰€2 🔧Ch🔧€0,80. **Location:** Simple, quiet.
Surface: gravel.
🅿 01/04-31/10
Distance: 🚶500m ⊗500m 🛒500m.
Remarks: At fire-station, coins at town hall, showers only in july/aug.

| 🛏🚿S | **Sarrians** | 27C1 |

Avenue de la Camargue. **GPS:** n44,07943 e4,97788. ⬆.

10 🛏€ 3/day 🚰 🔧Chfree 🔧. 🚿 **Location:** Rural, simple.
Surface: gravel. 🅿 01/01-31/12
Distance: 🚶800m 🛒500m.

| 🛏🚿S | **Sault** 🍴 | 27D1 |

P3, Route de Saint-Trinit. **GPS:** n44,09434 e5,41308. ⬆.

15 🛏free 🚰€2/10minutes 🔧Ch🔧stay. **Location:** Rural, simple.
Surface: gravel. 🅿 01/01-31/12
Distance: 🚶500m ⊗500m 🚲 on the spot 🚶4km chemin des Lavandes.

| 🛏🚿S | **Sausset-les-Pins** 🏖 | 27D2 |

Avenue Pierre Matraja. **GPS:** n43,33890 e5,10916. ⬆.

---

15 🛏free 🚰€4/100liter 🔧Ch 🔧€4/1h. **Location:** Simple, isolated, quiet. **Surface:** asphalted. 🅿 01/01-31/12
Distance: 🚶1,2km ⊗1,2km 🛒1,2km 🚂5m.
Remarks: At stadium, max. 72h.

| 🛏🚿S | **Savines-le-Lac** | 24F3 |

Parking du Barnafret, Av. du Faubourg, D954.
GPS: n44,52495 e6,40090. ⬆.

17 🛏€ 8 🚰€2/120liter 🔧Ch 🚿(20x). 🏠 **Location:** Comfortable, central. **Surface:** asphalted.
Distance: 🚶300m 🏊500m ⊗100m.

| 🛏🚿S | **Selonnet** | 24E3 |

Quartier de Boulangère. **GPS:** n44,36862 e6,31525. ⬆➡.

7 🛏free 🚰€2/10minutes 🔧Ch🔧€2/55minutes 📶.
Location: Rural. **Surface:** gravel. 🅿 01/01-31/12
Distance: 🚶300m ⊗300m 🛒300m.
Remarks: Coins at town hall, supermarket, bakery and Tabac, free wifi at town hall.

| 🛏🚿S | **Sénas** | 27D1 |

Avenue des Jardins. **GPS:** n43,74403 e5,08020. ➡.

6 🛏free 🚰€3/10minutes 🔧Ch. **Location:** Urban, simple.
Surface: asphalted. 🅿 01/01-31/12
Distance: 🚶200m 🏊1,5km ⊗200m 🛒200m.
Remarks: Coins at tourist info and maison de presse.

| 🛏🚿S | **Sillans-la-Cascade** | 27E2 |

Route de Salernes. **GPS:** n43,56692 e6,18277. ⬆⬆➡.
🛏free, July-Aug € 2 🚰€3 🔧Ch. 🅿 01/01-31/12
Distance: 🚶500m ⊗500m.
Remarks: Free entrance swimming pool.

| 🛏🚿S | **Sisteron** 🌿⛵🏖 | 24E3 |

Aire camping-cars, Avenue de la Libération.
GPS: n44,19105 e5,94542. ⬆.
12 🛏€2/12h 🚰€2/20minutes 🔧Ch🔧€2/4h.
Surface: asphalted. 🅿 01/01-31/12
Distance: 🚶800m.
Remarks: Along railwayline.

| 🛏🚿S | **Sisteron** 🌿🏖🏖 | 24E3 |

Parking Melchior Donnet, D4085. **GPS:** n44,20028 e5,94389. ⬆.

---

10 🛏free 🚰€2 🔧Ch 🔧€2/12h. **Surface:** asphalted.
🅿 01/01-31/12
Distance: 🚿4,5km.

| ⛵🚿S | **Six-Fours-les-Plages** ⛵ | 27E3 |

Port de la Coudoulière. **GPS:** n43,09750 e5,81194.

5 🛏€ 10 🚿WCincluded 🔧€2. **Location:** Central.
Surface: asphalted. 🅿 01/10-30/04
Distance: 🚶100m ⊗100m 🛒100m.

| S | **Six-Fours-les-Plages** ⛵ | 27E3 |

Promenade Gén. Charles de Gaulle. **GPS:** n43,11252 e5,81172. ⬆.
🚰€3 🔧Ch. 🅿 01/01-31/12
Remarks: Behind tourist info, 8-12, 14-19h.

| 🛏🚿S | **Sospel** ⛰ | 27G1 |

Stade E. Donato, D2566. **GPS:** n43,87876 e7,44213. ⬆.

4 🛏free 🚰 🔧Chfree. **Surface:** asphalted. 🅿 01/01-31/12
Distance: 🚶300m ⊗300m 🛒300m.

| 🛏🚿S | **Stes.Maries-de-la-Mer** | 27B2 |

Avenue d'Arles, D570. **GPS:** n43,45535 e4,42750. ⬆➡.

60 🛏€ 12 🚰 🔧ChWCincluded. **Location:** Simple, central, quiet.
Surface: asphalted. 🅿 01/01-31/12
Distance: 🚶200m 🏊beach 400m ⊗100m 🛒50m 📮100m.
Remarks: Max. 48h, service: 8.30-11.30h, 16-19.30h.

| 🛏🚿S | **Stes.Maries-de-la-Mer** | 27B2 |

Plage Ouest, Route d'Aigues-Mortes, D38.
GPS: n43,44991 e4,40407. ⬆.

50 🛏€ 12, >7.50m € 24 🚰 🔧Chincluded. **Location:** Isolated, quiet.
Surface: asphalted/gravel. 🅿 01/01-31/12
Distance: 🚶1,5km 🏊50m.
Remarks: Beach parking.

FR

⬛S Stes.Maries-de-la-Mer 27B2

Valée des Lys, Parking Plage Est, Avenue Cousteau.
GPS: n43,45364 e4,43695. ⬆➡.

150 🅿 € 12 ⛽ 🗑 Ch free. **Surface:** metalled. ⬛ 01/01-31/12
Distance: 🚶250m ⛱beach 50m ⊗100m 🛒250m.

©S Stes.Maries-de-la-Mer 27B2

Camping de la Brise. GPS: n43,45572 e4,43620. ⬆➡.

50 🅿 € 16 + tourist tax ⛽🗑Ch ✎ WC ▢▢ 📶included.
Location: Comfortable, central, quiet. **Surface:** grassy/gravel.
⬛ 16/12-11/11
Distance: 🚶850m ⛱direct access to sandy beach ⊗800m 🛒800m
🚲on the spot 🚶on the spot.
Remarks: Max. 48h.

P Stes.Maries-de-la-Mer 27B2

Parking du Large, Avenue du Docteur Cambon.
GPS: n43,45430 e4,43326. ⬆.

20 🅿 free. **Location:** Simple, central.
Surface: gravel.
Distance: 🚶250m ⊗700m ⊗250m 🛒250m.

P Stes.Maries-de-la-Mer 27B2

Route de Cacharel. **GPS:** n43,45684 e4,43305.

10 🅿 free. **Location:** Simple, isolated, quiet.
Distance: 🚶700m ⛱750m.

⬛S Thorenc 🏔🎡🍃 27F1

Lac de Thorenc, D2. **GPS:** n43,79921 e6,80802. ⬆.

10 🅿 free ⛽€5 🗑Ch ▦ WC. **Location:** Rural, simple, isolated, quiet.
Surface: metalled. ⬛ 01/01-31/12
Distance: 🚶750m ▸on the spot ⊗on the spot
🛒épicerie 750m 🚌on the spot.

Remarks: Along Lake Thorenc.

⬛S Trigance 27F1

Quartier Saint Roch. **GPS:** n43,76060 e6,44255. ⬆.

10 🅿 €5 ⛽🗑Ch ▦ free. **Location:** Isolated, quiet.
Surface: asphalted/gravel. ⬛ 01/01-31/12
Remarks: Max. 2 days.

⬛S Uvernet-Fours 🏔🎡❄ 24F3

Losissement Le Bachelard, D902. **GPS:** n44,36816 e6,62783. ⬆.

6 🅿 free ⛽€2 🗑Ch ▦ €2. **Location:** Isolated, quiet.
Surface: gravel/sand. ⬛ 01/01-31/12
Distance: 🚶900m.

⬛S Vaison-la-Romaine 🌿🏔 24D3

Aire camping-car, Avenue André Coudray.
GPS: n44,24650 e5,07392. ⬆➡.

25 🅿 € 8/24h ⛽🗑Ch free. 🚿 **Location:** Urban, comfortable.
Surface: gravel. ⬛ 01/01-31/12 ⬤ Tue-morning
Distance: 🚶800m.

Tourist information Vaison-la-Romaine:
👁 Le Pont Romain. Bridge from the Roman Empire.
⛰ Le Château. Ruins of the castle of the Counts of Toulouse.
🎪 ⬛ Tue.

⬛S Valberg ⛱🏔❄ 27F1

Le Lagopède, Route de Rouya. **GPS:** n44,09615 e6,93675. ⬆➡.

21 🅿 € 10 + € 0,20/pp tourist tax ⛽🗑Ch ✎ (21x) WC included.
Location: Comfortable, isolated, quiet. **Surface:** asphalted.
⬛ 01/01-31/12
Distance: 🚶500m ▸on the spot ⊗500m 🛒500m ⛷600m.

⬛S Valréas 24C3

Aire camping-car. GPS: n44,38713 e4,99245. ⬆➡.

5 🅿 free. **Location:** Simple. **Surface:** asphalted. ⬛ 01/01-31/12
Distance: 🚶400m ⊗250m.
Remarks: Behind tourist info, max 3,5t.

⬛S Valréas 24C3

Domaine du Lumian, Route de Montélimar, D941.
GPS: n44,39384 e4,96325. ⬆➡.

6 🅿 free ⛽🗑Ch ✎ free. **Surface:** gravel. ⬛ 01/01-31/12
Distance: 🚶2,5km.

⬛S Vauvenargues 27D2

Boulevard Moraliste. **GPS:** n43,55485 e5,59764. ⬆.
3 🅿 free. **Surface:** asphalted. ⬛ 01/01-31/12
Distance: 🚶300m ⊗on the spot 🛒300m.
Remarks: At cemetery.

⬛S Veynes 24E3

Base de Loisirs Les Iscles, Les Graviers, D994.
GPS: n44,51830 e5,79860. ⬆.
🅿 € 5,50 📶. **Location:** Rural, simple, quiet.
Surface: gravel.
Distance: ⛱on the spot ⊗on the spot.
Remarks: Wifi at restaurant.

⬛S Villeneuve 27E1

GPS: n43,89611 e5,86167. ⬆➡.

12 🅿 free ⛽🗑Ch free. **Location:** Rural, simple, quiet.
Surface: gravel. ⬛ 01/01-31/12 ⬤ service: 30/11-01/03
Distance: 🚶200m ✎ 5,5km 🚲on the spot 🚶on the spot.
Remarks: Max. 48h.

⬛S Vinon sur Verdon 27E1

Chemin du Plan. **GPS:** n43,72952 e5,80141. ⬆.

20 🅿 free ⛽€2/20minutes 🗑Ch included. **Location:** Rural, simple.
Surface: asphalted.
Distance: 🚶3km ⊗on the spot 🛒on the spot.
Remarks: Parking Carrefour Market, coins at petrol station.

⬛S Visan 24C3

Domaine de Lucena, 1600 chemin du Rastelet.
GPS: n44,31576 e4,98406. ⬆.
5 🅿 ⛽🗑Ch. **Location:** Isolated, quiet. **Surface:** gravel.
⬛ 01/01-31/12
Distance: 🚶4km.

FR

⬛S Visan 24C3

Domaine des Lauribert, D976. **GPS**: n44,34833 e4,97276. ⬆.

20 ⬛free 🚰🗑Ch 🔌(8x)€2 WC. **Surface:** unpaved.
⬛ 01/01-31/12

Remarks: At wine-grower, max. 72h.

Corsica

⬛S Barretalli 31G1

Marine de Giottani. **GPS**: n42,86593 e9,34370. ⬆.
10 ⬛€ 10 🚰🗑Ch included. **Location:** Rural, simple.
Surface: gravel/sand. ⬛ 01-01-31/12
Distance: 🏖150m ⊗150m.

⬛ Col de Bavella 🏔 31G1

Parking du Col, D268. **GPS**: n41,79567 e9,22470. ⬆.
15 ⬛€ 3,50. **Location:** Simple. **Surface:** gravel/sand.
⬛ 01/01-31/12
Distance: ⊗250m.

⬛ Galéria 🏖 31F1

D351. **GPS**: n42,41661 e8,65660.
20 ⬛€ 15. 🚿 **Location:** Rural, simple. **Surface:** gravel.
Distance: 🚤600m 🏖400m ⊗400m.

⬛S Ogliastro 🏖 31G1

Parking de la Plage, Marine d'Albo D80. **GPS**: n42,81041 e9,33592. ⬆.
10 ⬛€ 6 🚰service€2 🗑Ch. **Location:** Simple. **Surface:** gravel/sand.
⬛ 01/01-31/12
Distance: 🏖100m ⊗100m.
Remarks: Coins at the shops and restaurant.

⬛S Porto Vecchio 🏖 31G2

Parking de la Plage, Route de Palombaggia.
GPS: n41,55011 e9,30605. ⬆➡.
50 ⬛€ 13,50 🚰€2 🗑€5 Ch. 🚿 **Location:** Comfortable.
Surface: sand. ⬛ 01/6-01/10
Distance: 🏖200m ⊗200m.
Remarks: Bread-service.

⬛S Rogliano 31G1

Parking de Tollare, D153. **GPS**: n43,00733 e9,38831.
10 ⬛€ 10 🚰. **Location:** Simple. **Surface:** gravel.
⬛ 01/01-31/12
Distance: 🏖on the spot.

◪ United Kingdom

Capital: London
Government: Constitutional monarchy
Official Language: English
Population: 63,743,000 (2014)
Area: 244,820 km²

General information
Dialing code: 0044
General emergency: 112
Currency: Pound sterling (GBP),
£1 = € 1,35, € 1 = £0.74 (October 2015)

Regulations for overnight stays
Wild camping is forbidden in the UK. Motorway service stations allow overnight parking.

Additional public holidays 2016
March 17 St. Patricksday (Northern Ireland)
March 25 Good Friday
March 28 Easter monday
May 1 Labour Day
May 2 Early May Bank Holiday
May 29 Spring Bank Holiday
July 12 Orangemens' Day (Northern Ireland)
August 31 Summer Bank Holiday
October 31 Halloween
November 51 Guy Fawkes Day
December 26 Boxing Day

Time Zone
Winter (Standard Time) GMT+0
Summer (DST) GMT+1

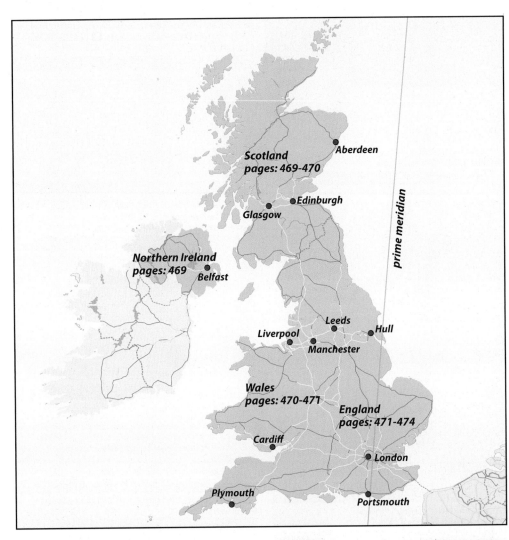

Scotland pages: 469-470
Aberdeen
Edinburgh
Glasgow
Northern Ireland pages: 469
Belfast
Leeds
Hull
Liverpool
Manchester
Wales pages: 470-471
England pages: 471-474
Cardiff
London
Plymouth
Portsmouth
prime meridian

GB

Northern Ireland

⛺🅂 Aghadowey   1B2
Golf Car Park, Brown Trout Golf and Country Inn, 209 Agivey Road, A54. **GPS**: n55,02413 w6,59985.
🆓free 🚰
Remarks: Max. 48h.

⛺ Antrim   1B2
The Ramble Inn, 236 Lisnevenagh Road. **GPS**: n54,76198 w6,24265.
🆓free.
Distance: 🚆Antrim 7km.

🅂 Ballinamallard   1B2
Ballinamallard Football Club, Ferney Park. **GPS**: n54,41474 w7,60092.

🆓free. **Surface:** gravel.
Distance: 🚆1,5km.
Tourist information Ballinamallard:
ℹ️ Ballinamallard River, Kilgortnaleague Bridge, A35 Enniskillen > Irvinestown. Wild Salmon and Trout River.

⛺ Ballymoney   1B2
Anglers' Rest, 139 Vow Road. **GPS**: n54,99087 w6,56672.
🆓free.
Distance: ⊗on the spot.
Tourist information Ballymoney:
👁 Leslie Hill Open Farm, 9, Macfin Road. Living history on the farm, picnic area, playground, Tea-room etc. 🕐 Easter-31/05: Su-Bank Holidays 14-18h, 01/06-30/06: Sa-Su 14-18h, 01/07-31/08: Mo-Sa 11-18h, Su 14-18h.

👁 Old Bushmills Distillery, Main Street, Bushmills. World's oldest licensed whiskey distillery. 🕐 Mo-Sa 9.30-17h, Su 12-17h ● Good Friday, 12/07, 25-26/12, 31/12-01/01.

🅂 Broughshane   1B2
Houston Mills, Buckna road. **GPS**: n54,89352 w6,20076.⬆️.

🆓free 🚰£1 🔵Ch 💧(4x)£1. **Location:** Central, noisy.
Surface: asphalted.
Distance: 🚆on the spot ⊗on the spot.
Remarks: Coins at supermarket.

⚓🅂 Carrickfergus   1B2
Carrickfergus Harbour Car Park, Rodgers Quay.
GPS: n54,71177 w5,8119.
🆓free 🚰£1 🔵Ch 💧£1.
Remarks: Coins at harbourmaster and tourist office.

🅂 Donaghadee   1B2
The Commons Parks, Millisle Road. **GPS**: n54,63475 w5,5312.⬆️.
🆓free 🚰£2/100liter 🔵 🔌£2/h. **Surface:** asphalted.
Distance: 🚆on the spot 🛁on the spot 🚐on the spot ⊗on the spot 🔌on the spot.
Remarks: Coins at petrol station.

⛺ Newtownards   1B2
Daft Eddys, Sketrick Island. **GPS**: n54,48812 w5,64807.

🆓free.
Distance: 🚆Newtownards 17km.
Tourist information Newtownards:
Ⓜ Somme Heritage Centre, 233 Bangor Road, Conlig, A21. The centre examines Ireland's role in the 1st World War.
🦆 Castle Espie Wildfowl And Wetlands Centre, 78 Ballydrain Road, Comber. 🕐 01/01-31/12 ● 23-25/12.

🅂 Portrush   1B2
Sandhill Drive. **GPS**: n55,20107 w6,65253.
10🆓 🚰£1,25/100liter 🔵Ch 💧£1,25/kWh. 🚿 ♨
Location: Simple, central. **Surface:** asphalted.
Distance: 🚆on the spot 🏖600m.

🅂 Whitehead   1B2
Bentra Golf Club, Slaughterford Road. **GPS**: n54,75908 w5,72012.⬆️.
🆓free 🚰£1 🔵Ch. **Surface:** asphalted.
Distance: 🚆1km 🏖1,5km 🏊150m.

Scotland

🅂 Aberdeen   1C1
Hazelhead Park, Hazledene Road. **GPS**: n57,13987 w2,17956.

◉ free. **Surface:** asphalted.
Distance: 200m ⊗400m 400m.

| 🅂 | Ballachulish | 1C1 |

Glencoe, A82 Ballachulish > Achallader. **GPS**: n56,63295 w4,82744.

£15.
Remarks: Parking ski-lifts.

| | Dufftown | 1C1 |

Castle Road. **GPS**: n57,45325 w3,12912.

+20 free. **Surface:** asphalted.
Distance: 400m ⊗400m 400m.

| | Dumfries | 1C2 |

P Long Stay, White Sands. **GPS**: n55,06722 w3,6125.

10 free. **Surface:** asphalted. 01/01-31/12
Distance: 100m on the spot ⊗on the spot 100m.

| 🅂 | Dunthulm | 1B1 |

Isle of Skye. **GPS**: n57,65020 w6,40459.
12 £12 ChWC. **Surface:** metalled.
Distance: on the spot.
Remarks: Nearby Dunthulm Castle.

| 🅂 | Easdale | 1B1 |

Souvenir shop, Ellenabeich, Isle of Seil. **GPS**: n56,29540 w5,6462.

10 £10 ChWC. **Surface:** metalled.
Distance: on the spot on the spot ⊗on the spot on the spot.

| | Fettercairn | 1C1 |

Car Park Bowling Club, Fettercairn, Laurencekirk.
GPS: n56,84971 w2,57306.
.

Tourist information Fettercairn:

◉ Fettercairn Distillery Visitor Centre Information, Distillery Road. One of Scotland's oldest malt whiskey distilleries. 01/05-30/09, Mon-Sa 10-14.30h. free.

| | Givran | 1B2 |

Harbour street- Henriettastreet. **GPS**: n55,24324 w4,85869.

50 free. **Surface:** asphalted. 01/01-31/12
Distance: 100m sandy beach 50m ⊗50m.

| | New Abbey | 1C2 |

Parking Sweetheart Abbey, A710, Main Street.
GPS: n54,98070 w3,61966.

6 free. **Surface:** metalled.

| | Oban | 1B1 |

Longsdale Car park, Longsdale Road. **GPS**: n56,41997 w5,46846.
± 10 free. **Location:** Simple, central. **Surface:** asphalted.
01/01-31/12
Distance: 400m 300m ⊗50m 400m.

| | Rhugarbh | 1B1 |

Parking Scottish Sea Life Sanctuary, A828 Rhugharb - Barcaldine.
GPS: n56,51731 w5,34679.

10 free. **Surface:** metalled.

Wales

| 🅂 | Abergynolwyn | 1C3 |

Riverside Guest House, Llanegryn Street.
GPS: n52,64584 w3,95856.

5 £10/night Chincluded £6/night.
Location: Rural, comfortable, central, quiet. **Surface:** grassy/metalled.
01/01-31/12
Remarks: Arrival <18h, narrow entrance (2.6m), Snowdonia National Park.

| 🅂 | Brecon | 1C3 |

The Watton Car Park, Heol Gouesnou. **GPS**: n51,94609 w3,38531.

---

25 £0.50/h, max. £2.50 8-18h, overnight stay free WC free,150m.
Location: Urban, simple, quiet. **Surface:** asphalted.
01/01-31/12
Distance: on the spot on the spot.
Remarks: 1 night per 7 nights.

| | Brecon | 1C3 |

Canal Road Car/Coach-Lorry Park, Canal Road.
GPS: n51,94486 w3,38993.

10 8-18h parking rate, overnight stay free.
Location: Urban, simple, central, quiet. **Surface:** asphalted.
01/01-31/12
Distance: 100m 100m.
Remarks: 1 night per 7 nights.

| 🅂 | Brecon | 1C3 |

The Promenade Car Park, Fenni-Fach Rd. **GPS**: n51,95089 w3,4036.

25 8-18h parking rate, overnight stay free. **Location:** Urban, simple, isolated, quiet. **Surface:** asphalted. 01/01-31/12
Distance: 600m on the spot 700m.
Remarks: 1 night per 7 nights.

| 🅂 | Builth Wells | 1C3 |

The Groe Car Park, The Strand. **GPS**: n52,14969 w3,40252.

20 8-18h parking rate, overnight stay free WC.
Location: Urban, simple, quiet. **Surface:** asphalted.
01/01-31/12
Distance: on the spot on the spot on the spot.
Remarks: 1 night per 7 nights.

| 🅂 | Builth Wells | 1C3 |

Smithfield Car Park, Brecon Rd. **GPS**: n52,14714 w3,40261.

50 8-18h parking rate, overnight stay free.

Location: Urban, simple, central. **Surface:** asphalted. ☐ 01/01-31/12
Distance: 🚶200m.
Remarks: 1 night per 7 nights.

| 🅂 | **Crickhowell** | 1C3 |

Beaufort Street Car Park, Greenhill Way. **GPS:** n51,85838 w3,13557.⬆.

8 🅿8-18h parking rate, overnight stay free. 🚐
Location: Urban, simple, central, quiet. **Surface:** asphalted.
☐ 01/01-31/12
Distance: 🚶50m.
Remarks: 1 night per 7 nights.

| 🅂 🅂 | **Hay-on-Wye** ✈ | 1C3 |

Oxford Road Car Park, Oxford Road. **GPS:** n52,07316 w3,12592.⬆.

25 🅿£0.50/h, max. £2.50 8-18h, overnight stay free WC free. 🚐
Location: Urban, simple, central, quiet. **Surface:** asphalted.
☐ 01/01-31/12
Distance: 🚶150m ⊗150m 🚊150m 🚌on the spot.
Remarks: 1 night per 7 nights.

| 🅂 🅂 | **Knighton** | 1C3 |

Bowling Green Lane Car Park, Bowling Green Lane.
GPS: n52,34324 w3,04553.⬆.

30 🅿£0.50/h, max. £2.50 8-18h, overnight stay free WC free. 🚐
Location: Rural, simple, central, quiet. **Surface:** asphalted.
☐ 01/01-31/12
Distance: 🚶200m 🚊300m 🚌on the spot.
Remarks: 1 night per 7 nights.

| 🅂 | **Llandrindod Wells** | 1C3 |

High Street Car Park, High Street. **GPS:** n52,24151 w3,38042.⬆.

30 🅿8-18h parking rate, overnight stay free. 🚐
Location: Urban, simple, central. **Surface:** asphalted. ☐ 01/01-31/12
Distance: 🚶150m 🚌on the spot.
Remarks: 1 night per 7 nights, max. 6m.

| 🅂 | **Llanidloes** | 1C3 |

Mount Street Car Park, Mount Lane. **GPS:** n52,44750 w3,53938.⬆.

12 🅿8-18h parking rate, overnight stay £5. 🚐
Location: Urban, simple, central, quiet. **Surface:** asphalted.
☐ 01/01-31/12
Distance: 🚶on the spot ⊗100m 🚊100m 🚌100m.
Remarks: 1 night per 7 nights.

| 🅂 | **Moelfre** | 1C2 |

Lligwy Bay. **GPS:** n53,35910 w4,26132.
🅿£10/night.
Remarks: Beach parking.

| 🍴 🅂 | **Nantgaredig** | 1B3 |

Railway Hotel, B4310. **GPS:** n51,86533 w4,18976.⬆.
5 🅿£5 WC. ☐ 01/01-31/12

| 🅂 | **Newton** | 1C3 |

Back Lane Car Park, Back Lane. **GPS:** n52,51534 w3,31735.⬆.

40 🅿8-18h parking rate, overnight stay £5 WC free. 🚐
Location: Urban, simple, central, quiet. **Surface:** asphalted.
☐ 01/01-31/12
Distance: 🚶150m ⊗on the spot 🚌on the spot.
Remarks: 1 night per 7 nights.

| 🅂 | **Newton** | 1C3 |

The Gravel Car Park, Heol Les Herbiers. **GPS:** n52,51421 w3,31167.⬆.

25 🅿8-18h parking rate, overnight stay £5. 🚐
Location: Urban, simple, central. **Surface:** asphalted. ☐ 01/01-31/12
Distance: 🚶250m ⊗50m 🚌250m.
Remarks: 1 night per 7 nights.

| 🅂 🅂 | **Presteigne** | 1C3 |

Hereford Street Car Park, Hereford Street.
GPS: n52,27245 w3,00488.⬆.

10 🅿8-18h parking rate, overnight stay free WC free. 🚐
Location: Urban, simple, central, quiet. **Surface:** asphalted.
☐ 01/01-31/12
Distance: 🚶100m 🚌on the spot.
Remarks: 1 night per 7 nights, max. 6m.

| 🅂 🅂 | **Welshpool** | 1C3 |

Berriew Street Car Park, Berriew Rd. **GPS:** n52,65875 w3,14806.⬆.

30 🅿8-18h parking rate, overnight stay £5 WC free. 🚐
Location: Urban, simple, central, quiet. **Surface:** asphalted.
☐ 01/01-31/12
Distance: 🚶200m 🚊500m.
Remarks: 1 night per 7 nights.

| 🅂 🅂 | **Welshpool** | 1C3 |

Church Street Car Park, Church Street. **GPS:** n52,66031 w3,1438.⬆.

25 🅿8-18h parking rate, overnight stay £5 WC free. 🚐
Location: Urban, simple, central, quiet. **Surface:** asphalted.
☐ 01/01-31/12
Distance: 🚶150m 🚊300m.
Remarks: 1 night per 7 nights.

England

| 🅂 | **Abingdon** | 1C3 |

Rye Farm Pay & Display car park, Bridge Street, A415.
GPS: n51,66746 w1,27799.⬆.

8 🅿£7.30/24h WC. 🚐 **Location:** Urban, simple. **Surface:** asphalted.
☐ 01/01-31/12
Distance: 🚶500m ⊗500m 🚌800m.
Remarks: Max. 24h, first call or mail, carparks@southandvale.gov.uk, 01235 547665.

| 🅂 | **Aldershot** | 1C3 |

Parsons Barracks Car park, Ordnance Road. **GPS:** n51,24979 w0,75731.
🅿£1. **Surface:** asphalted. ☐ 01/01-31/12

| 🅂 🅂 | **Ambleside** 🌿 | 1C2 |

Miller Field Motorhome Camping, Rothay Rd.
GPS: n54,42898 w2,96586.⬆.
50 🅿£10 🚿🍴Ch.🚽 **Location:** Rural, comfortable, quiet.
Surface: grassy.
Distance: 🚶200m 🚤Lake Windmere 800m 🚲on the spot
🚶on the spot.
Remarks: At Lake District National Park.

| 🅂 🅂 | **Appledore** ✈ | 1B3 |

Churchfields Car Park, The Quay. **GPS:** n51,05464 w4,19135.⬆.

25 🅿£5 18-10h, £3 day WC free. 🚐
Location: Urban, simple, quiet. **Surface:** asphalted. ☐ 01/01-31/12
Distance: 🚶150m 🚊50m ⊗200m.
Remarks: Max. 2 nights, min. 6m space between motorhomes.

Bakewell 🏌 | 1C2
Car Park, Asford Lane, Monsal Head. **GPS**: n53,24015 w1,72325.
£10.
Distance: ⊗on the spot.

Bideford ⚓ 〰 | 1B3
Riverbank (long stay) Car Park, Kingsley road.
GPS: n51,02086 w4,20386. ⬆

20 £5 18-10h, £3 day. 🚐 **Location:** Urban, simple, quiet.
Surface: asphalted. 📷 01/01-31/12
Distance: 1,5km ⚓50m ⊗500m 🚆1km 🚌500m.
Remarks: Max. 2 nights, min. 6m space between motorhomes.

Bourton-on-the-Water | 1C3
Bourton Rovers, Rissington Road. **GPS**: n51,87995 w1,7513. ⬆

5 £10 🚰 Ch WC 📶free, Password at the bar. 🚻
Location: Rural, simple, central, quiet. **Surface:** grassy.
📷 01/01-31/12
Distance: 500m ⊗500m 🚆500m.

Bourton-on-the-Water | 1C3
Bourton Vale Car & Coach Park, Station Rd.
GPS: n51,88512 w1,75471. ⬆

10 9-18h parking rate, overnight stay £8 WCfree. 🚐
Location: Urban, simple, central, quiet. **Surface:** asphalted.
📷 01/01-31/12
Distance: 200m ⊗on the spot 🚆on the spot.

Bury St Edmunds | 1D3
Ram Meadow Carpark Annexe, Cotton Lane.
GPS: n52,24775 e0,71893. ⬆

5 £2.20 8-18h, overnight stay free WCfree. 🚐
Location: Urban, simple, central, quiet. **Surface:** asphalted.
📷 01/01-31/12
Distance: 300m ⊗300m 🚌300m.
Remarks: Max. 1 night.

Canterbury | 1D3
Canterbury Coach Park, Kingsmead Road.
GPS: n51,28554 e1,08492. ⬆➡

12 £10/12h WCfree. 🚐
Location: Urban. **Surface:** asphalted. 📷 01/01-31/12
Distance: 650m ⊗650m

Canterbury | 1D3
New Dover Road Park&Ride, New Dover Road.
GPS: n51,26199 e1,10258. ⬆

24 £3 🚰 Chincluded WCfree. 🚐
Location: Rural, simple, isolated, quiet. **Surface:** asphalted.
📷 Acces Mo-Sa 6.30-20.30h, exit 24/24
Distance: ⊗Vintage Inn 🚌on the spot.
Remarks: Max. 24h, bus to city centre incl.

Cheltenham | 1C3
The Gloucester Old Spot, Tewkesbury Road, A4109.
GPS: n51,93325 w2,14881. ⬆

5 free, use of a meal obligated 🚰 WCincluded, during opening
hours. **Location:** Rural, simple, isolated. **Surface:** gravel/sand.
📷 01/01-31/12
Distance: 500m ⊗on the spot.

Chester 〰 | 1C2
Car Park, Little Roodee, Castle Road. **GPS**: n53,18447 w2,89245.
£5.80/day £1.50/night 🚰 WC.
Distance: 3,5km.
Remarks: Along the Dee river, gate closed from 22.30-6h.

Cirencester | 1C3
Old Cricklade Road lorry park, Cricklade Road.
GPS: n51,70760 w1,955. ⬆

20 £6.20. 🚐 **Location:** Urban, simple. **Surface:** asphalted.
📷 01/01-31/12
Distance: 1,5km ⊗50m 🚆150m.
Remarks: Near McDonalds.

Cirencester | 1C3
The Crown Inn, High Street, Cerny Wick. **GPS**: n51,66264 w1,88933. ⬆

5 £10 🚰 Ch 🚰 WCduring opening hours. 🚻
Location: Rural, simple. **Surface:** grassy/metalled.
📷 01/01-31/12
Distance: ⊗on the spot.

Crediton | 1C3
Thelbridge Cross Inn, Thelbridge. **GPS**: n50,89530 w3,72228.
6 £5. **Location:** Isolated, quiet. **Surface:** asphalted.
Distance: 14km ⊗on the spot.

Darlington | 1C2
Car Park, Chesnut Street. **GPS**: n54,52993 w1,54758.
£4/day £2/night. **Surface:** metalled.
Distance: 700m 4,7km.

Exeter | 1C3
Huntisbeare, Oak Road, Aylesbeare. **GPS**: n50,72816 w3,33599. ⬆

5 £12/night 🚰 Ch 🚰 WCincluded. 🚻 **Location:** Rural, simple,
isolated, quiet. **Surface:** metalled. 📷 01/01-31/12
Distance: 1,5km 🚆1,5km.
Remarks: Arrival <18h.

Great Missenden | 1C3
The Black Horse, Aylesbury Road. **GPS**: n51,71019 w0,71215.
5 guests free. **Surface:** metalled.
Distance: 800m ⊗on the spot.

Hayling Island | 1C3
West Beach Car Park, Sea Front. **GPS**: n50,78530 w1,0007. ⬆

40 8-22h parking rate, max. £6, overnight stay £10, 01/03-01/10 £20
🚰 free Ch WC 🚰At TI, 7 Sea-Front (600m). ⬆
Location: Rural, simple, quiet. **Surface:** grassy/gravel. 📷 01/01-31/12
Distance: 🌊on the spot ⊗on the spot 🚌600m.
Remarks: Max. 72h.

Holsworthy | 1B3
The Manor Car Park, Western Road. **GPS**: n50,81133 w4,35282. ⬆

12 £5 18-10h, £3 day. 🚐
Location: Urban, simple, quiet. **Surface:** asphalted. 📷 01/01-31/12
Distance: on the spot ⊗150m 🚆150m.
Remarks: Max. 2 nights.

Holy Island | 1C2
Lindisfarne Causeway. **GPS**: n55,67815 w1,87552.
5. **Surface:** metalled.

GB

Huntingdon 1C3

Wellsbridge Motorhomes Sales, Ramsey Forty Foot, Ramsey. **GPS:** n52,47540 w0,08834.⬆.

5 ⬛£5 ⚡ WC. 🚿 **Location:** Rural, simple, isolated, quiet. **Surface:** asphalted. 🗓 02/01-23/12
Distance: 🚐on the spot.

Ipswich 1D3

Burnt House Farm, Wash Lane, Witnesham. **GPS:** n52,11418 e1,20094.⬆➡.

5 ⬛£8 🔌🗑Ch ⚡WCincluded. 🚿 **Location:** Rural, comfortable, isolated, quiet. **Surface:** grassy/metalled. 🗓 01/01-31/12
Distance: 🚰2km ⊗2km.

Ipswich 1D3

Orwell Crossing Lorry Park, A14 Eastbound, Nacton. **GPS:** n52,02473 e1,22678.⬆.

20 ⬛£12. 🚿🎦 ♻
Location: Highway, simple, noisy. **Surface:** asphalted. 🗓 01/01-31/12
Distance: ⊗on the spot.

Ivybridge 1B3

Lee Mill Services, A38. **GPS:** n50,38493 w3,97041.⬆➡.
10 ⬛£8/night. 🚿 **Location:** Simple, noisy. **Surface:** asphalted.
🗓 01/01-31/12
Distance: ⊗on the spot 🍴500m.

Maidstone 1D3

Maidstone Services, M20. **GPS:** n51,26568 e0,61588.⬆.
8 ⬛£20 WC🗑📶against payment. 📷♻
Location: Highway, simple, noisy. **Surface:** asphalted. 🗓 01/01-31/12
Distance: ⚡200m ⊗on the spot.

Tourist information Maidstone:
Ⓜ Museum of Kent Life, Lock Lane, Sandling. History and traditions of Kent. 🗓 14/02-05/11, 10-17h.

Marazion 1B3

Car Park, Kings Road. **GPS:** n50,12415 w5,47587.⬆.

12 ⬛£10. 🚿
Location: Simple, quiet. **Surface:** metalled. 🗓 17-09h 🌙 9-17h
Distance: 🚰50m 🏖on the spot ⊗100m 🍴100m.
Remarks: Parking at sea, nearby Saint Michael's Mount, not suitable for big motorhomes. Follow Marazion Car Parkings.

Tourist information Marazion:

👁🏰 Saint Michael's Mount. Rocky island with medieval castle and church. 🗓 01/04-31/10.

Mevagissey ⚓ 1B3

Willow Car & Coach Park, Valley Road. **GPS:** n50,27155 w4,79044.⬆.

10 ⬛10-18h parking rate, overnight stay £7.50 🔌on demand. 🚿
Location: Urban, simple, central. **Surface:** metalled.
🗓 01/01-31/12
Distance: 🚰150m 🏖1km ⊗300m.

New Milton 1C3

New Lane Orchard, New Lane, Bashley. **GPS:** n50,77182 w1,6645.⬆.

5 ⬛£13 🔌🗑Chincluded 🚿 **Location:** Rural, comfortable, isolated, quiet. **Surface:** grassy/metalled. 🗓 01/01-31/12
Distance: 🚰400m ⊗6,5km 🚶on the spot 🧍New Forest.
Remarks: Arrival <18h.

Newnham on Severn 1C3

Elton Farm, Littledean Road, A4151. **GPS:** n51,82355 w2,44753.⬆.
5 ⬛£5 🔌🗑Ch. 🚿
Location: Rural, simple, isolated. **Surface:** grassy. 🗓 01/01-31/12
Distance: 🚶on the spot 🚐on the spot.

Newton Abbot 1C3

Sunnyside, Yvonne Bassett, Totnes Road, A381, Ipplepen. **GPS:** n50,48591 w3,63376.⬆.

5 ⬛£8,50,50/night 🔌🗑Ch ⚡£1,50/day WCincluded. 🚿
Location: Rural, simple, quiet. **Surface:** grassy/metalled.
🗓 01/01-31/12
Distance: 🚐100m.
Remarks: Arrival <18h.

Oldham 1C2

The Hawthorn, Roundthorn Road. **GPS:** n53,53352 w2,08637.
5 ⬛£9 ⚡£2,50/night WC🗑.
Distance: 🚰3km.

Pickering 1C2

Antiques Centre, Southgate. **GPS:** n54,24413 w0,78026.
5 ⬛£10 🔌Ch. **Location:** Simple. **Surface:** asphalted.
🗓 01/01-31/12
Distance: ⊗500m.

Praa Sands 1B3

Car Park, Castle Drive. **GPS:** n50,10375 w5,38888.
🗑against payment.

Rake 1C3

The Flying Bull, London Road. **GPS:** n51,04419 w0,85418.
⬛£5 🔌🗑WC🗑. **Location:** Rural, isolated, quiet. **Surface:** grassy.
🗓 01/01-31/12
Distance: 🚰3km ⊗on the spot.

Scarborough 1C2

South Moor Farm, Dalby Forest Drive. **GPS:** n54,30049 w0,61169.⬆.
5 ⬛£10 🔌🗑Ch. **Location:** Rural, simple. **Surface:** grassy.
🗓 01/01-31/12

Sewerby 1C2

The Ship Inn, Cliff Road. **GPS:** n54,10167 w0,16411.
5 ⬛£15 🔌Ch. **Surface:** unpaved.
Distance: ⊗on the spot.

St Austell 1B3

Edgemoor, Enniscaven, St.Dennis. **GPS:** n50,39636 w4,8676.⬆.

5 ⬛£5/night 🔌🗑ChWCincluded. 🚿 **Location:** Comfortable, quiet.
Surface: grassy/metalled. 🗓 01/01-31/12
Distance: 🚰St.Austell 14,5km 🐎on the spot 🧍on the spot.
Remarks: Arrival <18h.

St Ives 1C3

The Seven Wives, Ramsey road. **GPS:** n52,33193 w0,07634.⬆.

5 ⬛£5 🔌🗑Ch ⚡£6/night WC. 🚿 **Location:** Urban, simple, central. **Surface:** metalled. 🗓 01/01-31/12
Distance: 🚰1,4km ⊗on the spot.

St Jidgey 1B3

Halfway House Inn. **GPS:** n50,48949 w4,89943.
4 ⬛£10, guests free. **Location:** Rural, isolated, quiet.
Surface: grassy.
Distance: ⊗on the spot.

Stratford-upon-Avon 🎭 1C3

Stratford Marina Car Park, Bridgeway. **GPS:** n52,19280 w1,70154.⬆.

10 ⬛9-18h £8, overnight stay £15. 📶 ♻ **Location:** Urban, simple, central. **Surface:** asphalted. 🗓 01/01-31/12
Distance: 🚰200m ⊗200m 🚐200m.

Stratford-upon-Avon 🎭 1C3

The New Inn Hotel, Clifford Chambers. **GPS:** n52,16929 w1,7168.⬆.

5 ⬛£8 🔌 ⚡£4,80. 🚿 ♻
Location: Rural, simple. **Surface:** grassy. 🗓 01/01-31/12
Distance: ⊗on the spot 🚐on the spot.

Tourist information Stratford-upon-Avon:
🏠 Birthplace of William Shakespeare.

Tarrington 1C3

The Tarrington Arms, Ledbury road. **GPS:** n52,06473 w2,5604.

5 🕳free WCfree. **Location:** Rural, simple.
Surface: metalled.
Distance: 🚶200m ⊗on the spot.

| 🚐S | **Tenby** | 1B3 |

Carew Airfield & Pavilion, Sageston. **GPS:** n51,69362 w4,80973.⬆.

5 🕳£15-20/night 🚰🍽Ch 🔧 WCincluded. 🚿
Location: Comfortable, quiet. **Surface:** concrete. 🔲 01/01-31/12
Distance: 🏖150m ⛰8km ⊗500m 🛒1,5km 🚉1,5km.

| 🚐S | **Thaxted** | 1C3 |

Margaret Street Car Park, Margaret Street.
GPS: n51,95530 e0,34328.⬆.

2 🕳free WCfree. **Location:** Urban, simple, central, quiet.
Surface: concrete. 🔲 01/01-31/12
Distance: 🚶150m 🚌150m.
Remarks: Max. 48h in fortnight.

| 🚐S | **Tintagel** 🏖 | 1B3 |

King Arthur's Car Park, Fore Street. **GPS:** n50,66356 w4,75129.⬆.
50 🕳£3 10.00-16h, £3 16-10h WC. 🚐**Location:** Simple.
Surface: asphalted. 🔲 16-10h
Distance: 🚶on the spot ⊗on the spot 🚌100m.
Remarks: Opposite Tintagel Old Post Office.

| 🚐 | **Tintagel** 🏖 | 1B3 |

Mayfair Car Park, Fore Street. **GPS:** n50,66329 w4,75103.⬆.
50 🕳£2 8.00-20h, £3.50 20-08h. 🚐**Location:** Urban, simple, central.
Surface: asphalted/grassy. 🔲 01/01-31/12
Distance: 🚶on the spot ⊗100m.
Remarks: Next to King Arthur's Car Park.

| 🚐 | **Tintagel** 🏖 | 1B3 |

Sword in Stone Car Park, Bossine Rd. **GPS:** n50,66257 w4,74763.⬆.
20 🕳£2 10.00-20h, £3.50 20-10h. 🚐
Location: Urban, simple. **Surface:** asphalted. 🔲 01/01-31/12
Distance: 🚶150m ⊗250m.

Tourist information Tintagel:
👁 Tintagel Old Post Office, Fore Street. 600 year-old traditional Cornish Longhouse.
🏰 King Arthur's Castle, Castle Road. 🔲 10-17/18h 🔲 24-26/12, 01/01.

| 🚐 | **Torrington** | 1B3 |

Sydney House Car Park, South Street. **GPS:** n50,95121 w4,14438.⬆.

20 🕳£5 18-10h, £3 day. 🚐**Location:** Urban, simple, quiet.
Surface: asphalted. 🔲 01/01-31/12
Distance: 🚶300m ⊗250m 🛒250m.
Remarks: Max. 2 nights, min. 6m space between motorhomes.

| 🚐 | **Westward Ho!** 🏖 ≈ | 1B3 |

Main Car Park, Golf Links Rd. **GPS:** n51,04069 w4,23728.⬆.

8 🕳£5 18-10h, £7 day. 🚐**Location:** Urban, simple, central, quiet.
Surface: asphalted. 🔲 01/01-31/12
Distance: 🚶on the spot ⛱200m ⊗200m 🛒150m.
Remarks: Max. 5000kg, min. 6m space between motorhomes.

| 🍴S | **Whaplode St Catherines** | 1C3 |

The Bleu Bell Inn, Cranesgate S. **GPS:** n52,75956 w0,0155.⬆.
5 🕳£5, free with a meal 🚰🍽Ch 🔧(2x)£2,50/night.🚿
Location: Simple. 🔲 01/01-31/12 🔲 Mo
Distance: ⊗on the spot.

| 🚐 | **Winchester** | 1C3 |

Car Park, Worthy Lane, B3044. **GPS:** n51,06396 w1,31632.
🕳£4.
Remarks: Max. 24h.

| 🚐S | **Yeovil** | 1C3 |

Cartgate Truckstop and Picnic Area, A303/A3088 roundabout.
GPS: n50,96926 w2,74087.⬆.

20 🕳free WC 📶Password at the restaurant. **Location:** Highway, simple, noisy. **Surface:** asphalted/metalled. 🔲 01/01-31/12
Distance: 🚶15km ⊗on the spot.

🇬🇷 Greece

Capital: Athens
Government: Parliamentary democracy
Official Language: Greek
Population: 10,780,000 (2014)
Area: 131,990 km²

General information
Dialling code: 0030
General emergency: 112
Currency: Euro

Regulations for overnight stays
Wild camping and overnight parking is not officially allowed. Overnight parking places mentioned here are not official motorhome stopovers but tolerated areas.

Additional public holidays 2016
January 6 Epiphany
March 14 Ash Monday, 41 days before Easter
March 25 Independence Day
May 1-2 Orthodox Easter
May 1 Labor Day
August 15 Assumption of the Virgin Mary
October 28 National Holiday, Ochi day

Time Zone
Winter (Standard Time) GMT+2
Summer (DST) GMT+3

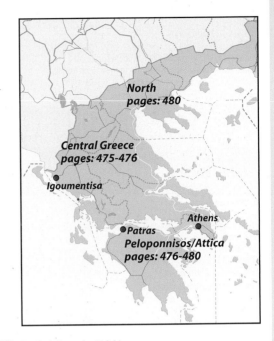

North
pages: 480

Central Greece
pages: 475-476

Igoumentisa

Patras
Peloponnisos/Attica
pages: 476-480

Athens

GR

Central Greece

Achillio 33G1
Epar. Od. Archilliou-Glifas. **GPS**: n39,00943 e22,95758.
Distance: 🚰on the spot ⛴on the spot ⊗on the spot.

Agios Nikolaos 33F2
GPS: n38,34959 e22,15661.
🛁. 🅿 01/10-30/04
Remarks: Parking at harbour.

Ammoudia 33E1
GPS: n39,23636 e20,48073.

🛁 🚰. **Surface:** gravel/sand.
Distance: 🚰on the spot ⛴50m ➤on the spot ⊗100m 🍴250m.
Remarks: At harbour.

Ammoudia 33E1
GPS: n39,23989 e20,48116.

🛁 🚰 🗑. **Surface:** sand.
Distance: 🚰on the spot ⛴on the spot ➤on the spot ⊗200m 🍴50m.
Remarks: Beach parking.

Arahova 33G2
GPS: n38,47948 e22,58164.
🛁. 🅿 01/01-31/12

Arillas 33E1
Restaurant Soukas, Aglias-Platarias. **GPS**: n39,35278 e20,28861.⬆.

🛁free for clients 🚰🗑WC🗑📶.
Location: Rural. **Surface:** grassy/sand. 🅿 01/05-01/10
Distance: ⛴on the spot ⊗on the spot.

Boukka 33F1
GPS: n38,93125 e21,14200.

🛁 🗑. **Surface:** sand.
Distance: ⛴on the spot ⊗100m.
Remarks: Next to sports fields, beach parking.

Corfu 33E1
Dionysus, Dassia. **GPS**: n39,66472 e19,84440.
🛁🚰Ch.🛁. 🅿 15/04-15/10

Corfu 33E1
Dolphin Camping, Sidari. **GPS**: n39,78890 e19,72354.
🛁🚰Ch. 🅿 15/04-31/10

Corfu 33E1
Karda Beach, Dassia. **GPS**: n39,68611 e19,83861.
🛁🚰🗑Ch.🛁. 🅿 01/04-15/10
Distance: ⛴on the spot.

Tourist information Corfu:
🛈 Esplanada, Kerkyra (Corfu). Meeting point for inhabitants and tourists.
⚔ Kerkyra (Corfu).
⚔ Frurion, Kerkyra (Corfu). Citadel, 1550.
💧 Aqualand, Corfu Water Park, Ag.Ioannis. Leisure pool park.

Delphi 33F2
Apollon. **GPS**: n38,48388 e22,47550.
🛁🚰🗑Ch. 🅿 01/01-31/12

Delphi 33F2
Delphi Camping. **GPS**: n38,47833 e22,47450.
🛁🚰🗑Ch. 🅿 20/03-30/11

Delphi 33F2
Chrissa. **GPS**: n38,47267 e22,46206.
🛁. 🅿 01/01-31/12

Tourist information Delphi:
🛈 Site of Delphi. Archeological site. 🅿 7.30-17.30h 🅿 holiday. 🎫 € 6.

Eratini 33F2
N48/E65 km 47. **GPS**: n38,33769 e22,19198.

🛁. **Surface:** grassy/sand.
Distance: ⛴on the spot 🚰on the spot.
Remarks: Beach parking, max 3,5t.

Eretria 33G2
Milos Camping. **GPS**: n38,39139 e23,77556.
🛁🚰🗑Ch.

Tourist information Erétria:
🛈 Seaside resort and archological site Antique Eretria.

Gliki 33E1
Taverne Panorama. **GPS**: n39,32726 e20,61568.

🛁guests free 🚰WC🗑. **Surface:** grassy.
Distance: 🚰500m 🍴500m.
Remarks: Along the Acheron river.

Hiliadou 33F2
GPS: n38,39408 e21,92096.

🛁 🚰🗑. **Surface:** gravel.
Distance: 🚰Nafpaktos 7km ⛴on the spot.
Remarks: Beach parking.

Igoumenítsa — 33E1
GPS: n39,51278 e20,25741.

Distance: on the spot 600m on the spot.
Remarks: Parking supermarket at the ring-road 6, dir Ioánnina.

Igoumenítsa — 33E1
GPS: n39,51540 e20,21087.

10.
Surface: sand.
Distance: on the spot 100m.
Remarks: Beach parking.
Tourist information Igoumenítsa:
Goumani (titani). Archeological site.

Ioánnina — 33E1
Sta Papagou 7. **GPS**: n39,67319 e20,85476.

10 € 8. **Surface**: metalled. 01/01-31/12
Distance: 100m 100m 100m.
Remarks: Monitored parking.

Ioánnina — 33E1
Limnopoula. GPS: n39,67770 e20,84280.

01/04-15/10
Tourist information Ioánnina:
Capital of Epirus, important city in the Turkish time.
Perama. Caves.
daily.

Itea — 33F2
Ayannis, Kirra. **GPS**: n38,42440 e22,45880.

Tourist information Itea:
Nautical Museum, Mouseio, 4, Galaxídi.

Krioneri — 33F2
GPS: n38,34397 e21,58823.

Surface: gravel. 01/01-31/12
Distance: on the spot on the spot 300m.

Levkas — 33F2
Vlycho. **GPS**: n38,68318 e20,69819.

Distance: on the spot.
Remarks: Parking on the quay.

Levkas — 33F2
Dessimi Beach, Vlicho, Lefkada (Levkas). **GPS**: n38,67250 e20,71100.
01/04-30/11

Levkas — 33F2
Poros Beach, Poros, Lefkada (Levkas). **GPS**: n39,64095 e20,69700.
01/05-30/09

Mesolóngi — 33F2
GPS: n38,36358 e21,42016.

01/01-31/12
Remarks: Parking in harbour.

Metéora — 33F1
Taverna Arsenis, East Street, Kalambaka. **GPS**: n39,69923 e21,64109.
8 guests free €5 WC 01/01-31/12

Metéora — 33F1
Meteora Garden, Kalambaka. **GPS**: n39,70869 e21,60915.
Ch. 01/01-31/12

Metéora — 33F1
Rizos International, Kalambaka. **GPS**: n39,69010 e21,64564.
Ch. 01/01-31/12

Metéora — 33F1
Vrachos Kastraki, Kastraki. **GPS**: n39,71338 e21,61588.
Ch.

01/01-31/12
Tourist information Metéora:
Important cultural inheritance, 24 monasteries built on enormous sandstone peaks, of which 6 can be visited. 7
9-13h, 15-17h. against payment.

Métsovo — 33F1
GPS: n39,76898 e21,17749.

Tourist information Métsovo:
Traditional mountain village.
Archotiko Tositsa.
Restored 18th century mansion, museum or folk art.
8.30-13h, 16-18h.
€ 2.

Nafpaktos — 33F2
Xiliadou, N48/E65 km 80,5.
GPS: n38,38139 e21,81661.

Surface: gravel/sand.
Distance: on the spot
on the spot nearby.
Remarks: Parking at the beach.
Tourist information Nafpaktos:
Old city with Venetian Castle and circular walled harbor.

Parga — 33E1
Enjoy Lichnos. GPS: n39,28358 e20,43340.
Ch. 01/05-15/10

Parga — 33E1
Valtos Camping.
GPS: n39,28556 e20,38972.

01/05-30/09
Tourist information Parga:
Lively bathing resort.
Necromanteion of Ephyra.
Oracle of death.

Perdika — 33E1
GPS: n39,38607 e20,27473.

free.
Distance: Perdika 7km on the spot.
Remarks: Beach parking.

Pilion — 33G1
Olizon, Milina. **GPS**: n39,16472 e23,21666.
Ch. 01/05-15/10

Pilion — 33G1
Sikia Fig Tree, Kato Gatzea. **GPS**: n39,31025 e23,10977.
Ch. 01/04-15/10
Tourist information Pilion:
Mythological peninsula, beautiful nature, authentic mountain villages and fishing towns.
Makrinitsa. Village worth seeing, car-free.
Miliés. Folk museum. 01/04-31/10 Tue-Su, 01/11-31/03 Wed-Su.
Archeological Museum, Athanasáki 1, Vólos. Tue-Su holiday.

Plataria — 33E1
Nautilos. GPS: n39,44389 e20,25806.
Ch. 01/04-20/10

Préveza — 33F1
Mitikas. GPS: n39,01719 e20,71555.

. **Surface**: asphalted/gravel.
Distance: Preveza 7km on the spot on the spot 500m.
Remarks: Parking at the beach.

Préveza — 33F1
GPS: n38,95008 e20,75498.

.
Tourist information Préveza:
Kassópi, Kassópi. Archeological site.
Nikopolis. Old Roman city.

Sivota — 33E1
Parking. GPS: n39,40924 e20,24061.
free. **Surface**: unpaved.
Distance: 200m harbour 200m 200m 200m.
Remarks: No beach.

Sivota — 33E1
Parking. GPS: n39,40772 e20,24270.
. **Surface**: unpaved.
Distance: 200m harbour 200m 200m 50m.
Remarks: No beach.

Vagia — 33G2
Restaurant Ynaiopio, Palaia Ethniki Odos Athinon-Lamias.
GPS: n38,34331 e23,19378.
free with a meal.

Vonitsa — 33F2
Agio Sotiriou. GPS: n38,93302 e20,91937.

. **Surface**: grassy.
Distance: Vonitsa 3km lake on the spot taverne 3km.

Vonitsa — 33F2
Marina. GPS: n38,92172 e20,88482.
5 free. **Location**: Simple. **Surface**: gravel.
Remarks: Near marina.

Peloponnisos/Attica

Agia Kyriaki — 33G3
GPS: n36,71883 e23,02305.

.
Remarks: At the beach.

Agios Andreas — 33G2
GPS: n37,37120 e22,78262.

WC free. **Surface**: gravel.
Distance: 3km on the spot on the spot on the spot.
Remarks: At harbour.

Agios Andreas 33G2

Camping Agios Andreas. **GPS**: n36,86664 e21,92087.⬆️
🚐 ⭕ 20/04-30/09
Distance: 🏖️on the spot.

Agios Fokas 33G3

GPS: n36,59565 e23,06108.

5🚐. **Surface:** sand.
Distance: 🚢Monemvasia 13km.
Remarks: Parking at pier.

Agios Kirlaki 33F3

Filiatra, Epar.Od.Filiatron. **GPS**: n37,11963 e21,57611.
🚐 ⭕ 01/01-31/12

Assini 33G2

Kastraki. **GPS**: n37,52861 e22,87556.
🚐 ⭕ 01/04-01/10

Athens 33G2

GPS: n37,96987 e23,72263.
🚐 ⭕ 01/01-31/12
Remarks: Parking of the Acropolis, guarding after authorization Probably only outside the main season.

Athens 33G2

Athens camping, Leoforis Athinon.
GPS: n38,00889 e23,67222.
🚐 € 26, 2 pers.incl 🔌💺Chincluded 🚿€4.
⭕ 01/01-31/12

Tourist information Athens:
👁️🚶🍽️ Monasteraki. Old district with Athenian flea market.
🕐 Su 8-14h.
👁️ Panathenaic Stadium. Stadium of the first Olympic Games in 1896.
👁️🍽️ Plaka. Old district around the Acropolis.
👁️ Tomb of the Unknown Soldier, Plateía Syntágmatos. Sunday 11h changing of the guard.
⛪ Acropolis. Archeological site.
⭕ 01/05-31/10 Mo-Fri 8-18.30h, Sa-Su 8.30-14.30h, 01/11-30/04 8.30-16.30h
⭕ 01/05, 28/10, holiday.

Bozas 33G3

GPS: n36,70437 e22,82144.

20🚐free for clients 🔌💺Ch.
Location: Isolated. **Surface:** sand. ⭕ 01/01-31/12
Distance: 🏖️on the spot ⊗on the spot.

Diakofto 33F2

GPS: n38,19747 e22,20167.

🚐. **Surface:** asphalted.
⭕ 01/01-31/12
Distance: 🏖️on the spot 🚤on the spot ⊗on the spot 🚊500m.
Remarks: Parking at harbour.

Tourist information Diakofto:
👁️ Rack railway, Kalavryta.

Train journey with rack-railway.

Dimitsána 33F2

Kefalari tou Ai-Yanni. **GPS**: n37,59058 e22,04286.
4🚐.
Remarks: Parking water museum.

Dimitsána 33F2

Taverna Koustenis, Eparchiaki Odos Kato Davias.
GPS: n37,58650 e22,04459.⬆️
5🚐free. **Location:** Rural, simple.
Surface: gravel.
Distance: 🚲9km ⊗on the spot.
Tourist information Dimitsána:
🌿 Loúsios-kloof. 5km long and 300m deep, marked trails.

Elefsina 33G2

GPS: n38,04235 e23,53942.
🚐 ⭕ 01/01-31/12
Remarks: Parking in front of the ruins in the city center.

Epidaurus 33G2

GPS: n37,59675 e23,07444.

🚐🚰WCfree.
Surface: gravel.
Remarks: Overnight stay on parking at the Ancient theater is generally tolerated.
Tourist information Epidaurus:
⛪ Ancient Epidaurus. Archeological site. ⭕ 8-19h.

Ermioni 33G2

Hydras Wave. **GPS**: n37,40583 e23,31556.
🚐. ⭕ 15/4-15/10

Galatas 33G2

Epar.Odos Ermionis. **GPS**: n37,49491 e23,45546.
20🚐.
Distance: 🚢on the spot ⊗on the spot.
Remarks: At the quay.

Gerolimenas 33G3

GPS: n36,48230 e22,39969.

3🚐. **Surface:** asphalted.
Distance: 🏖️on the spot 🚤on the spot ⊗50m 🧍on the spot.
Remarks: Parking at the beach.

Gialova Pylou 33F3

Navarino Beach. **GPS**: n36,94770 e21,70620.
🚐🔌💺Ch💠. ⭕ 01/04-31/10

Glifa Kyllini 33F2

Ionion. **GPS**: n37,83640 e21,13340.
🚐🔌💺Ch💠📶. ⭕ 01/01-31/12

Gythion 33G3

Valtaki beach, Valtaki. **GPS**: n36,78883 e22,58225.

🚐. **Surface:** sand.
Distance: 🏖️on the spot ⊗on the spot.

Remarks: At the beach, ± 5km from Gythion dir Skala.

Gythion 33G3

Gythion Bay. **GPS**: n36,72920 e22,55243.
🚐🚰💺Ch💠. ⭕ 01/01-31/12

Kakovatos 33F2

GPS: n37,45721 e21,63869.
🚐. **Surface:** metalled.
Remarks: Parking at the beach.

Kalo Nero 33F2

GPS: n37,29786 e21,69525.

10🚐free. **Surface:** gravel.
Distance: 🚢100m 🏖️Sandy beach ⊗100m.

Kalogria 33F2

Camper Stop Kalogria, Kalogria. **GPS**: n38,15986 e21,37162.⬆️

40🚐 € 10, 16/07-31/08 € 12 🔌💺Ch🚿(20x)€3/day
WC🔋🍽️included. **Surface:** unpaved.
⭕ 01/05-31/10
Distance: 🚢5km 🚲11km 🏖️500m 🌊300m ⊗50m 🚊on the spot
🚐on the spot 🚴on the spot 🧍on the spot.
Tourist information Kalogria:
🌿 Kotychi, Lapas. Visitors centre, swamp area.

Kamares 33G3

GPS: n36,68203 e22,52090.

🚐. **Surface:** sand.
Distance: 🏖️on the spot 🚤on the spot ⊗350m.

Kameras Irion 33G3

Poseidon. **GPS**: n36,68826 e22,51753.
🚐.

Karathona 33G2

GPS: n37,54389 e22,82278.

50🚐free.
Distance: 🏖️Sandy beach.

Karavostasi 33G3

Taverna O Faros, Karavostasi. **GPS**: n36,69733 e22,38073.⬆️➡️

GR

15 ⌁free 🚰. **Location:** Rural, simple. **Surface:** gravel.
Distance: ⌂on the spot ⊗on the spot.
Remarks: No beach.

Kastro 33F2

Killinis Beach. **GPS:** n37,87413 e21,10748.

⌁free. **Surface:** grassy/sand.
Distance: ⌁2km ⌂on the spot ⌁on the spot ⊗Beach taverne.
Remarks: Beach parking.
Tourist information Kastro:
🏰 Chlemoutsi. Medieval castle.

Kato Alissos 33F2

Kato Allissos. **GPS:** n38,14986 e21,57740.
⌁€ 19 🚰Ch⌁🔌📶♨ ▣ 01/04-20/10

Kifisiá 33G2

Dionissiotis. **GPS:** n38,10535 e23,81355.
⌁🚰ChWC. ▣ 01/01-31/12
Remarks: 18km north of Athens, route Athens dir Lamia.
Tourist information Kifisiá:
ℹ Holiday resort of the Athenian since the Roman time.
Ⓜ Goulándris, Levidou 13. History of nature.

Killini 33F2

Epar Od. Andravidas-Killinis. **GPS:** n37,92598 e21,16699.
⌁.
Distance: ⌁2km.
Remarks: Parking at the beach.

Kiveri 33G2

GPS: n37,52761 e22,73120.

10 ⌁free. **Surface:** gravel.
Distance: ⌁200m ⌂pebbled beach 50m ⊗100m.
Remarks: At harbour.

Kokkinia 33G3

GPS: n36,79762 e22,78485.

20 ⌁free 🚰. **Surface:** metalled.
Distance: ⌂Sandy beach ⊗400m.
Remarks: Beach parking.

Korfos 33G2

GPS: n37,76361 e23,13302.

⌁. **Surface:** gravel.
Remarks: At fishing port.

Korinthos 33G2

Afrodites Waters, Ancient Corinth. **GPS:** n37,91139 e22,87861. ⬆➡

20 ⌁€ 10 ⌁Ch ⌁WC ⌁included. ▣ 01/01-31/12
Distance: ⌁350m ⊗350m ⌁350m.

Korinthos 33G2

Ancient Corinth. **GPS:** n37,90750 e22,87806.

⌁.
Tourist information Korinthos:
ℹ Important trade centre.
👁 Korinth Canal. Canal, 23m wide.
🏰 Acrocorinth. Fortress.
🕐 8-19h.
🎫 free.
🏰 Ancient Korinthos. Archeological site.
▣ 01/04-31/10 8-19h, 01/11-31/03 8-17h
◉ 25/12-26/12, 01/01, 25/03, Easter, 01/05.

Koroni 33F3

GPS: n36,79729 e21,96002.

⌁.
Remarks: Parking at harbour.

Koroni 33F3

Camping Koroni. **GPS:** n36,81168 e21,93303.
Distance: ⌁600m ⌂on the spot ⊗on the spot.
Tourist information Koroni:
ℹ Port city with Venetian castle, 1206.

Kosmas 33G3

Epar.Od.Leonidiou-Kosma. **GPS:** n37,09180 e22,74043.

⌁. **Surface:** metalled.
Distance: ⌂on the spot ⊗on the spot ⌁on the spot.
Remarks: Behind church.

Kotronas 33G3

GPS: n36,61899 e22,49367.

⌁🚰free. **Surface:** concrete.
Distance: ⌂on the spot ⌁on the spot ⊗50m.
Remarks: Parking at pier.

Lambiri 33F2

Tsolis, Old National Road. **GPS:** n38,32083 e21,97194.
⌁. ▣ 15/04-30/09

Legrena 33G2

GPS: n37,66206 e23,99772.
⌁. ▣ 01/01-31/12

Marathon 33G2

Ramnous.
GPS: n38,13139 e24,00722.
⌁.
▣ 01/04-31/10
Tourist information Marathon:
ℹ www.marathon.gr. The name marathon, course of 41 km, comes from this town.

Mavroyouni/Gythion 33G3

Meltemi.
GPS: n36,72986 e22,55360.
⌁.
Tourist information Mavroyouni/Gythion:
ℹ Tourist Information Areópoli,
Vasiléos Pávlou 21
Máni. Peninsula.
👁 Pýrgos Diroú
Máni. Caves.

Monemvasia 33G3

GPS: n36,68875 e23,05076.
⌁. **Surface:** asphalted.
Distance: ⊗on the spot ⌁on the spot ⌁shuttle to old town.

Monemvasia 33G3

GPS: n36,68240 e23,03821.
⌁.
Remarks: Parking harbour.
Tourist information Monemvasía:
ℹ Fortified city,
lower town have been restored.
⛪ Agía Sofia.
Church 13th century.

Mycenae 33G2

Atreus. **GPS:** n37,71911 e22,74114.
⌁.
▣ 01/01-31/12
Tourist information Mycenae:
Ⓜ Archeological Museum, Argos.
🏰 Archeological site. ▣ 1/4-31/10 8-19h, 1/11-31/3 8-17h
◉ holiday.
🏰 Agora Argos, Argos. Archeological site. ▣ summer 8.30-15h.

Nafplio 33G2

GPS: n37,56823 e22,80170.

🛏free.
Surface: asphalted.
Distance: 🛒500m ⊗300m.
Remarks: Parking marina.

Tourist information Nafplio:
ℹ️ Tourist information, Ikostispémtis Martiou 2. First Greek capital.
Ⓜ️ Archeological Museum. ☐ Tue-Su 8.30-15h ● Mo.
✖ Palamídi. Citadel 18th century.

Neo Itylo — 33G3
Black Pirate. GPS: n36,69154 e22,38986. ⬆.

10 🛏free. **Surface:** grassy/gravel.
Distance: 🛒on the spot 🏖pebbled beach ⇤on the spot ⊗50m.

Olympia — 33F2
Alphios. GPS: n37,64360 e21,61930.
🛏. ☐ 01/04-31/10

Tourist information Olympia:
Ⓜ️ Archeological Museum. Important Greek archeological museum.
☐ Mo 11-19h, Tue-Su 8-19h.

Paralia Astros — 33G2
GPS: n37,44475 e22,74800.

🛏. **Surface:** gravel.
Distance: 🏖on the spot ⇤on the spot ⊗200m.
Remarks: At the beach.

Paralia Platanou — 33F2
GPS: n38,17104 e22,26828.

🛏. **Surface:** gravel.
Distance: 🏖on the spot.
Remarks: At the beach.

Paralia Rizomilos — 33F2
GPS: n38,21898 e22,14745.

🛏 🚰free. **Surface:** gravel.
Distance: 🏖on the spot ⇤on the spot ⊗on the spot
🛒mini market (summer).
Remarks: Not in front of hotel.

Pátra — 33F2
Golden Sunset, Old national Road km 19. **GPS:** n38,14389 e21,58778.
🛏. ☐ 01/04-15/10

Tourist information Pátra:
👁 Archaïa Klauss. First commercial producer of wine of Greece.

Perahóra — 33G2
Limni Vouliagmenis. **GPS:** n38,03188 e22,87293.

🛏.
Distance: 🏖on the spot ⊗on the spot.
Remarks: At the lake.

Petalidi — 33F3
GPS: n36,95871 e21,93418.
🛏 ⚓. **Surface:** asphalted.
Remarks: Nearby port.

Petalidi — 33F3
GPS: n36,95915 e21,92870.

🛏. **Surface:** asphalted.
Distance: ⊗on the spot.
Remarks: Parking in village, near the sea.

Pirgos Dhiroú — 33G3
Diros. **GPS:** n36,64206 e22,38357.

20 🛏. **Location:** Isolated. **Surface:** unpaved.
Distance: 🏖on the spot.

Porto Kagio — 33G3
Taverna Porto. GPS: n36,42811 e22,48697. ⬆.
max. 3 🛏guests free.
Surface: grassy.
Distance: 🏖on the spot ⇤on the spot ⊗on the spot 🛒mini market.

Pylos — 33F3
GPS: n36,91633 e21,69524.

🛏. **Surface:** concrete.
Distance: 🛒100m ⊗100m.
Remarks: Parking at pier.

Rafina — 33G2
GPS: n38,01835 e24,01227.
🛏. ☐ 01/01-31/12

Salandi — 33G2
GPS: n37,44748 e23,12474.

🛏. **Location:** Isolated. **Surface:** gravel.
Distance: 🛒Didyma 5km 🏖on the spot ⇤on the spot.
Remarks: At the beach.

Savalia — 33F2
Savalia Beach. **GPS:** n37,79685 e21,25578.

🛏. **Surface:** asphalted.
Distance: 🏖on the spot ⇤on the spot.

Skoutari — 33G3
GPS: n36,65921 e22,49962.

max. 3 🛏. **Surface:** concrete.
Distance: 🏖on the spot ⇤on the spot ⊗within walking distance.
Remarks: Near fishing-port.

Sounion — 33G2
Camping Bacchus. GPS: n37,67694 e24,04750.
🛏.
☐ 01/01-31/12

Tourist information Sounion:
Ⓜ️ Mineralogical Museum
Lavrió. Old mine shaft of the silvermines.
☐ Wed, Sa-Su.
⌒ Archeological site.

Tolo — 33G2
GPS: n37,51469 e22,85662.

⅃ ⌐WC. **Surface:** asphalted.
Distance: ↳500m ⌐100m ⌐on the spot ⊗200m.
Remarks: Near fishing-port.

Tyrchu · 33G2

Taverne Ostria. GPS: n37,31414 e22,82054.

3 ⅃guests free. **Surface:** gravel.
◻ 15/05-30/09
Distance: ↳Tyros 10km ⌐on the spot ⌐on the spot ⊗on the spot.
Remarks: At the beach, attention: via steep path.

Zacharo · 33F2

GPS: n37,51917 e21,60248.

⅃.
Distance: ⌐on the spot.

Zacharo · 33F2

Tholo Beach. GPS: n37,41160 e21,66830.
⅃. ◻ 01/04-31/10

Greece North

Ag.Mamas Moudania · 33G1

Ouzoni Beach. GPS: n40,21611 e23,31833.
⅃. ◻ 01/05-30/09

Akt Armenistis Sithonia · 33H1

Armenistis. GPS: n40,15222 e23,91361.
⅃. ◻ 01/05-15/09

Alexandroúpoli · 33H1

GPS: n40,84364 e25,87693.
⅃.
Remarks: Parking harbour.

Alexandroúpoli · 33H1

Apollonias. GPS: n40,84342 e25,86477.
⅃.
Surface: asphalted.
Remarks: Parking near stadium.

Tourist information Alexandroúpoli:
ℹ Tourist Information, Mákris. Large holiday resort, beautiful beach.

Gerakani · 33H1

Kouyoni. GPS: n40,26464 e23,46347.
⅃. ◻ 01/05-30/09

Kalamaria · 33G1

Zampetaz, Tessaloniki-Perea. **GPS:** n40,50289 e22,97053. ⬆.
10 ⅃free ⌐⬛Ch⚡⅃free.
Location: Simple. **Surface:** asphalted.
Distance: ↳10km ⬟3km ⌐on the spot.

Kastoriá · 33F1

GPS: n40,50461 e21,27977.
⅃against payment ⌐.
Remarks: Voluntary contribution.

Metamorphosi · 33H1

Sunny Bay. GPS: n40,22694 e23,58944.
⅃. ◻ 01/05-31/10

Moustheni · 33H1

Moystheni Station. GPS: n40,84413 e24,11506.
10 ⅃free ⌐⬛Ch⚡. **Surface:** asphalted.
Distance: ⬟100m ⊗on the spot ⬛mini market.
Remarks: Special part for motor homes, shop, restaurant, station 24/24.

Ouranoupoli · 33H1

Ouranoupoli. GPS: n40,33944 e23,97056.
⅃.

Paralia Epanomi · 33G1

Golden Beach. GPS: n40,40469 e22,89925.
10 ⅃€ 10 ⌐⚡€5.
Location: Rural, simple. **Surface:** grassy/sand.
Distance: ⌐on the spot ⊗on the spot.

Porto Lagos · 33H1

GPS: n41,00633 e25,12028.

5 ⅃free ⌐. **Surface:** asphalted.
Distance: ⊗on the spot.
Remarks: Parking at pier.

Vergina · 33G1

Parking, Aristotelos 25. **GPS:** n40,48506 e22,31978. ⬆➡.
25 ⅃€4 ⌐⚡€2.
Location: Urban, simple. **Surface:** asphalted.
Distance: ↳on the spot ⊗200m ⬛450m.

Croatia

Capital: Zagreb
Government: parliamentarian democracy
Official Language: Croatian
Population: 4,491,000 (2014)
Area: 56,594 km²

General information

Dialling code: 00385
General emergency: 112
Currency: Kuna, kn, 1 kuna = 100 lipa
1kn = € 0,13, € 1 = 7,64 kn (October 2015)
10kn = £ 0,95, £ 1 = 10,60 kn (October 2015)
Credit card are accepted almost everywhere.

Regulations for overnight stays

Wild camping is forbidden.

Additional public holidays 2016

January 6 Epiphany
May 1 Labor Day
May 26 Corpus Christi
June 22 Dan antifasisticke borbe, Anti-Fascist Resistance Day
June 25 Dan drzavnosti, National Holiday
August 5 Victorie Day and National Thanksgiving
August 15 Assumption of the Virgin Mary
October 8 Independence Day

Time Zone

Winter (Standard Time) GMT+1
Summer (DST) GMT+2

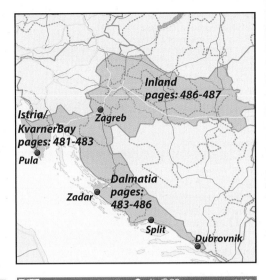

Istria/Kvarner Bay

Baderna — 36A2

Farm Pino, Katun 1. **GPS**: n45,22020 e13,72908.⬆️.

14 🛇€ 10 + € 3/pp 🚰🗑️Ch🚿(23x) WC Service€4 🗑️€2 🚿📷🚽
🏊 **Location:** Rural, isolated, quiet. **Surface:** grassy.
📅 01/01 - 31/12
Distance: 🚐2km ⊗6km 🏊2km 🚌400m 🚲on the spot
🚶on the spot.

Cres/Cres — 36A2

Kovačine, Melin I, 20. **GPS**: n44,96278 e14,39694.
🛇🚰🗑️Ch🚿WC🚿included. 📅 15/04-15/10
Distance: 🏊on the spot.

Tourist information Cres/Cres:
ℹ️ Turisticka zajednica, Riva Creskih Kapetana, www.tzg-cres.hr. Island can be reached with ferry service from Brestova, south of Rijeka and Valbiska, west Krk.

Cres/Martinščica — 36A3

Slatina. **GPS**: n44,82091 e14,34238.
🛇🚰🗑️Ch🚿WC🚿🗑️ 📅 15/04-31/10

Cres/Nerezine — 36A3

Baldarin, Punta Križa. **GPS**: n44,61680 e14,50834.
🛇🚰🗑️Ch🚿WC🚿included. 📅 15/04-01/10
Distance: 🚐3,5km 🏊on the spot.

Cres/Nerezine — 36A3

Lopari, Nerezine. **GPS**: n44,68253 e14,39846.
🛇 📅 15/04-30/09

Cres/Nerezine — 36A3

Preko Mosta, Osor 76, Nerezine. **GPS**: n44,69250 e14,39167.
🛇 📅 01/04-30/09

Cres/Nerezine — 36A3

Rapoća, Rapoća, Nerezine. **GPS**: n44,66357 e14,39756.
🛇 📅 01/05-30/09

Cres/Valun — 36A2

Zdovice, Valun bb. **GPS**: n44,90297 e14,36338.
🛇 📅 15/05-01/10

Crikvenica — 36A2

Kacjak, Kacjak BB. **GPS**: n45,16703 e14,70511.
🛇 📅 15/05-15/09

Fažana — 36A3

Ul.1.Maja. **GPS**: n44,92880 e13,80255.⬆️.

🛇200kn/€ 30 WC.🚽 **Location:** Urban, simple, central.
Surface: grassy/sand. 📅 01/01-31/12
Distance: 🚐100m 🏊on the spot ⊗100m 🚊100m 🚲on the spot
🚶on the spot.
Remarks: Max. 24h.

Fažana — 36A3

Bi Village, Dragonja 115. **GPS**: n44,91750 e13,81111.
🛇 📅 01/04-15/11

Fažana — 36A3

Pineta Fažana, Perojska cesta bb.
GPS: n44,93835 e13,79554.

🛇 22/04-30/09

Tourist information Fažana:
🌿 Nationaal Park Brijuni, Brijuni. Nature reserve, boat connection from Fažana. 📅 daily.

Grožnjan — 36A2

Parking bus. GPS: n45,38163 e13,72375.⬆️➡️.

20 🛇free. **Location:** Rural, simple, isolated, quiet. **Surface:** gravel.
📅 01/01-31/12
Distance: 🚐200m ⊗200m 🏊on the spot 🚲on the spot
🚶on the spot.
Remarks: Next to cemetery.

Ičići — 36A2

Opatija. **GPS**: n45,31083 e14,28472.
🛇 📅 01/04-01/10

Klenovica — 36A2

Klenovica, Zidinice BB. **GPS**: n45,09788 e14,84393.
🛇 📅 01/05-30/09
Distance: 🏊on the spot 🚐on the spot.

Koromačno — 36A2

Tunarica. **GPS**: n44,96917 e14,09889.
🛇 📅 20/05-05/09

Kraljevica — 36A2

Ostro. **GPS**: n45,27109 e14,56402.
🛇 📅 01/05-30/09

Krk/Baška — 36A2

Kamp Mali, Put Zablace 100. **GPS**: n44,96609 e14,74710.⬆️.

33 🛇€ 10-20 🚰🗑️Ch🚿(30x),10Amp WC 🗑️€5 🚿included.🚽
Location: Urban, comfortable, central, quiet. **Surface:** grasstiles.
📅 01/03-30/10
Distance: 🚐300m 🏊150m 🏊on the spot ⊗on the spot 🚊50m
🚲on the spot 🚶on the spot.

Krk/Baška — 36A2

Zablace, Emila Geitslicha 34, Baška. **GPS**: n44,96694 e14,74528.
🛇 📅 01/05-01/10

Krk/Klimno — 36A2

Slamni. **GPS**: n45,15351 e14,61770.
🛇
Remarks: Mini-camp.

Krk/Klimno — 36A2

Slamni, Klimno 8a. **GPS**: n45,15364 e14,61721.
🛇
Remarks: Mini-camp.

Krk/Krk — 36A2

Camper Stop Felix, Ulica Narodnog preporoda 51.
GPS: n45,02928 e14,58149.⬆️.

12 🛇€ 25 🚰🗑️Ch🚿(12x),16Amp WC 🗑️€5 🚿included.🚽
Location: Urban, comfortable, central, quiet. **Surface:** grassy/gravel.
📅 01/01-31/12
Distance: 🚐300m 🏊300m 🚐300m ⊗50m 🚊50m 🚐on the spot
🚲on the spot 🚶on the spot.

Krk/Krk — 36A2

Jezevac, Plavnička bb. **GPS**: n45,01877 e14,56684.
🛇from € 20,30 🚰🗑️Ch🚿WC🚿included. 📅 01/05-30/09

Krk/Krk — 36A2

Bor. **GPS**: n45,02250 e14,56194.
🛇 📅 01/01-31/12

Krk/Krk — 36A2

Marta, Škrbcici 29. **GPS**: n45,04930 e14,48940.
🛇
Remarks: Mini-camp.

Tourist information Krk/Krk:

HR

ℹ Tourist Information, Vela placa 1/1, www.krk.hr. Krk accessible via toll-bridge south-east from Rijeka.
☀ Jazz-festival, Kamplin. ▢ Aug.

△S Krk/Malinska 36A2
Glavotok, Glavokok 4. **GPS:** n45,09472 e14,44111.
🛏from € 20 🚰🔌Ch✂ WC included. ▢ 01/05-30/09
Distance: ⊿on the spot.

△ Krk/Malinska 36A2
Draga, Palih Boraca 4. **GPS:** n45,12052 e14,52494.
🛏
Remarks: Mini-camp.

△S Krk/Njivice 36A2
Njivice, Primorska bb. **GPS:** n45,16963 e14,54740.
🚰🔌Ch✂ WC included. ▢ 20/04-01/10

△ Krk/Omišalj 36A2
Pusca, Pušča bb. **GPS:** n45,23613 e14,55108.
🛏 ▢ 01/06-30/09

△ Krk/Pinezici 36A2
Amar, Njivine 8. **GPS:** n45,04351 e14,47985.
🛏
Remarks: Mini-camp.

△S Krk/Punat 36A2
Pila, Setalište Ivana Brusića. **GPS:** n45,01581 e14,62860.
250🛏from € 20 🚰🔌Ch✂ included. ▢ 15/04-30/09

△S Krk/Punat 36A2
Škrila, Stara Baška. **GPS:** n44,96611 e14,67389.
350🛏🚰🔌Ch✂ ▢ 01/05-30/09

△ Krk/Punat 36A2
Maslinik, Nikole Tesle 1.
GPS: n45,01809 e14,63478.
🛏
Remarks: Mini-camp.

Tourist information Krk/Punat:
✝ Otočić Košljun. Monastery.

△ Krk/Šilo 36A2
Tiha Šilo, Konjska bb. **GPS:** n45,14876 e14,67150.
🛏
Remarks: Mini-camp.

⎢S Labin 36A2
Kamp Tunarica, Koromačno. **GPS:** n44,96933 e14,09979. ⬆

50🛏€ 15, 01/07-31/08 € 19 🚰🔌Ch✂ (50x)€4/night,16Amp WC
🔌€5 included. 🚿 **Location:** Rural, simple, isolated, quiet.
Surface: forest soil. ▢ 01/05-30/09
Distance: ⛵15km ⊿on the spot ▸on the spot ⊗on the spot
🛒on the spot ⛟2km ⚶on the spot.

△ Labin 36A2
Marina. **GPS:** n45,03333 e14,15806.
🛏
▢ 15/04-30/09

Tourist information Labin:
Ⓜ Narodni muzej, N. Katunara 6. Ethnological museum. ▢ daily 10-13h, 17-19h.

△ Lošinj/Mali Lošinj 36A3
Kredo. **GPS:** n44,53444 e14,44751.

🛏 ▢ 01/01-31/12
Distance: ⛵2km ⊿on the spot.
Remarks: Mini-camp.

△S Lošinj/Mali Lošinj 36A3
Čikat. **GPS:** n44,53750 e14,45056.
940🛏from € 18,40 🚰🔌Ch✂ WC included. ▢ 15/04-15/10

△S Lošinj/Mali Lošinj 36A3
Poljana. **GPS:** n44,55556 e14,44167.
🛏from € 17,85 🚰🔌Ch✂ WC included. ▢ 01/05-30/09

Tourist information Lošinj/Mali Lošinj:
☀ Dolphins day, action day with possibility for adoption of a dolphin.
▢ 1st Sa Aug.

△S Medulin 36A3
Kazela. **GPS:** n44,80695 e13,95015.
🛏🚰🔌Ch✂ WC included. ▢ 01/04-15/10

△S Medulin 36A3
Medulin. **GPS:** n44,81417 e13,93194.
1500🛏🚰🔌Ch✂ WC included. ▢ 03/04-09/10

△ Medulin 36A3
Indie, Banjole. **GPS:** n44,82398 e13,85090.
🛏 ▢ 01/05-01/10

△ Medulin 36A3
Kranjski Kamp, Runke 52, Premantura. **GPS:** n44,80694 e13,91616.
🛏
Remarks: Mini-camp.

△ Medulin 36A3
Piškera, Indie 49, Banjole. **GPS:** n44,82332 e13,84855.
🛏
Remarks: Mini-camp.

△ Medulin 36A3
Pomer, Pomer. **GPS:** n44,82064 e13,90205.
🛏
Remarks: Mini-camp.

△ Medulin 36A3
Postolovic, Bumbište 10. **GPS:** n44,82037 e13,85749.
🛏
Remarks: Mini-camp.

△ Medulin 36A3
Runke, Premantura. **GPS:** n44,80742 e13,91632.
🛏 ▢ 01/05-30/09

△ Medulin 36A3
Širola, Rupice Bd. **GPS:** n44,82113 e13,85872.
🛏
Remarks: Mini-camp.

△ Medulin 36A3
Stupice, Premantura. **GPS:** n44,79779 e13,91354.
🛏 ▢ 01/05-25/09

△ Medulin 36A3
Tasalera, Premantura. **GPS:** n44,81425 e13,91275.

▢ 01/04-30/09

Tourist information Medulin:
ℹ Premantura. Most Southern place of Istria.
👁 Banjole. Fisherman's village with natural harbour.

△ Mošćenička Draga 36A2
Draga. **GPS:** n45,24023 e14,25021.
🛏
Remarks: Mini-camp.

△ Mošćenička Draga 36A2
Draga. **GPS:** n45,24000 e14,25028.
165🛏 ▢ 15/04-15/10

⎢S Motovun 36A2
Motovun Camping, Rizanske skupstine 1a.
GPS: n45,33446 e13,82523. ⬆ ➡

12🛏€ 15-25 + tourist tax € 1/pp 🚰🔌Ch✂ WC 📶included 📹
🚿 **Location:** Rural, comfortable. **Surface:** gravel.
▢ 01/01-31/12
Distance: ⛵50m ⊿on the spot ⊗50m 🛒50m ⛟100m
⚶on the spot ⚶on the spot.
Remarks: Free entrance swimming pool, discount longer stays.

△ Novi Vinodolski 36A2
Autocamp Sibinje, Sibinj. **GPS:** n45,04405 e14,87751.
Distance: ⊿on the spot ⊗50m 🛒50m.
Remarks: Mini-camp.

△ Novi Vinodolski 36A2
Punta. **GPS:** n45,11587 e14,84725.
🛏 ▢ 01/06-30/09
Distance: ⊿on the spot 🛒3km.
Remarks: Mini-camp.

△S Novigrad (Istria) 22H3
Mareda. **GPS:** n45,34149 e13,54610.
800🛏from € 17 🚰🔌Ch✂ WC included. ▢ 15/04-30/09

△S Novigrad (Istria) 22H3
Sirena. **GPS:** n45,31528 e13,57556.
🛏🚰🔌Ch✂ WC included. ▢ 01/04-30/09

Tourist information Novigrad (Istria):
✝ Hoofdstraat van de oude stad. Farmers market. ▢ daily.
☀ Feest van de beschermheilige Pelegrinus, Umag. ▢ 23/05.

⎢S Poreč 36A2
30. Travinja/Karla Huguesa. **GPS:** n45,22104 e13,60742. ⬆

28🛏150kn, winter free. **Location:** Urban, simple, central, noisy.
Surface: asphalted. ▢ 01/01 - 31/12
Distance: ⛵800m ⊿2km ▸2km ⊗400m 🛒2km ⛟500m
🚿on the spot ⚶on the spot.

△ Poreč 36A2
Bijela Uvala. **GPS:** n45,19139 e13,59667.
2000🛏from € 20 🚰🔌Ch✂ WC included. ▢ 01/04-15/10

△S Poreč 36A2
Laternacamp. **GPS:** n45,29639 e13,59444.
3000🛏from € 22,65 🚰🔌Ch✂ WC included. ▢ 01/04-15/10

△S Poreč 36A2
Puntica, Funtana. **GPS:** n45,17749 e13,60406.
250🛏 🔌Ch✂ ▢ 11/04-13/10

△S Poreč 36A2
Zelena Laguna. **GPS:** n45,19611 e13,58917.
1000🛏from € 20 🚰🔌Ch✂ WC included. ▢ 01/04-15/10

△ Poreč 36A2
Materada, Materada. **GPS:** n45,24628 e13,59600.
🛏
Remarks: Mini-camp.

Tourist information Poreč:
ℹ Turisticka zajednica, Zagrebacka 9, www.istra.com/porec. Old city, centre tourist and cultural.
👁 Decumanus. Roman main street with palazzi from the Venetian time.
Ⓜ Zavicajnog muzeja porestine. Native museum of Porec. ▢ daily 10-13h, 18-22h.
✝ Eufrazijeva bazilika. Basilica, 6th century, in the centre. ▢ daily 7-19h.

△ Pula 36A3
Puntižela. **GPS:** n44,89806 e13,80722.
🛏🚰🔌Ch✂ WC included. ▢ 01/05-31/10

△S Pula 36A3
Stoja. **GPS:** n44,86000 e13,81472.
750🛏🚰🔌Ch✂ WC included.
▢ 03/04-02/11

Tourist information Pula:
Ⓜ Arheoloski Muzej Istre, Carrarina 3. Archeological museum.
▢ winter Mo-Fri 9-14h, summer Mo-Sa 9-19h.
♫ Amfiteatar. Large anfiteatro from Roman time. ▢ daily 8-21h.
☀ Ljetni klasicni Festival, Amfitheatar. Opera festival. ▢ Aug.

△ Rab 36A3
Mel, Kampor 319. **GPS:** n44,79390 e14,70302.
🛏
Remarks: Mini-camp.

△ Rab 36A3
Planka, Kampor 326. **GPS:** n44,78049 e14,72048.

HR

🛏.
Remarks: Mini-camp.

| △ S | Rabac 🏖 | 36A2 |

Oliva. GPS: n45,07960 e14,14777.
300🛏 🚰🍴Ch 🔌WC🛁. ⏻ 15/03-30/09
Distance: 🏖on the spot.

| △ | Rijeka | 36A2 |

Preluk Katalinic, Preluk 1.
GPS: n45,35340 e14,33235.
🛏.
Remarks: Mini-camp.

Tourist information Rijeka:
👁 Tourist Information, Kastav 47, Kastav. Walled city with rich history.
Ⓜ Pomorski i povijesni muzej, Muzejski trg 1. Navy museum.
⏻ Mo-Fri 10-13h, 18-21h.
🏛 Velika trznica. Market opposite to Modello palace.
☀ Carnaval van Rijeka. ⏻ Feb.

| 🍇 S | Rovinj 🌊🏖🍦 | 36A2 |

Aleja Ruera Boskovica. GPS: n45,08898 e13,64537.⬆.

30🛏25kn/h 6-23h (± € 55), overnight stay free 🚰🍴ChWC included.
🏙 **Location:** Urban, simple, central, noisy. **Surface:** asphalted.
⏻ 01/01-31/12
Distance: 🏊1km 🏖300m 🎣300m ⊗300m 🍴1km 🚌300m
🚲on the spot 🚶on the spot.

| 🍇 S | Rovinj 🌊🏖🍦 | 36A2 |

Cesta za Valaltu-Lim. GPS: n45,10500 e13,64608.

15🛏€ 10 🚰🍴ChWC included.
Location: Quiet. **Surface:** grassy. ⏻ 01/05-31/08
Distance: 🏊1km 🏖500m 🍴1km 💧500m.

| ⒸS | Rovinj 🌊🏖🍦 | 36A2 |

Camping Polari. GPS: n45,06300 e13,67480.⬆➡.

40🛏€ 12-32 🚰🍴Ch 🔌WC included 🏖25kn 📶100kn 📷👜📹
Location: Rural, simple, quiet. **Surface:** grassy/metalled.
⏻ 22/04-04/10
Distance: 🏊3km 🏖on the spot 🎣on the spot ⊗on the spot 💧on the spot 🖥on the spot 🚌June/July/Aug 🚲on the spot 🚶on the spot.
Remarks: Camperstop max. 48h.

| △ S | Rovinj 🌊🏖🍦 | 36A2 |

Mon Paradiso, Uvala Veštar. **GPS:** n45,04947 e13,69000.
40🛏 🚰🍴Ch 🔌. ⏻ 01/06-30/09
Remarks: Mini-camp.

| △ S | Rovinj 🌊🏖🍦 | 36A2 |

Polari. GPS: n45,06258 e13,67477.
2150🛏 🚰🍴Ch 🔌WC included. ⏻ 01/04-30/09

| △ S | Rovinj 🌊🏖🍦 | 36A2 |

Porton Biondi. GPS: n45,09410 e13,64232.
🛏 🚰🍴Ch 🔌WC included. ⏻ 01/04-30/09

| △ S | Rovinj 🌊🏖🍦 | 36A2 |

Valdaliso. GPS: n45,10389 e13,62500.

400🛏 🚰🍴Ch 🔌WC included. ⏻ 20/04-15/10

| △ S | Rovinj 🌊🏖🍦 | 36A2 |

Vestar. GPS: n45,05389 e13,68639.
800🛏 🚰🍴Ch 🔌WC included. ⏻ 15/04-30/09

| △ | Rovinj 🌊🏖🍦 | 36A2 |

Ulika, Polari Bd. **GPS:** n45,06528 e13,67583.
🛏. ⏻ 01/04-01/10
Remarks: Mini-camp.

Tourist information Rovinj:
ℹ Turisticka zajednica, Budicin 12, www.istra.com/rovinj. City has been a cultural monument since 1963.
👁 Aquarium, Obala G. Paliage 5. ⏻ daily 9-21h.
🏛 Palazzo Califfi, Trg Marsala Tita 11. ⏻ Tue-Su 10.30-14h, summer 18-20h.
🛒 Market.
☀ Grisia, Grisia. Art festival. ⏻ 2nd week Aug.

| △ S | Savudrija 🏖🍦 | 22H3 |

Pineta. GPS: n45,48667 e13,49250.
🛏from € 16,50 🚰🍴Ch 🔌WC included. ⏻ 15/04-30/09

| △ | Savudrija 🏖🍦 | 22H3 |

Ravna Dolina. GPS: n45,49246 e13,50490.
🛏. ⏻ 01/05-30/09

| △ | Savudrija 🏖🍦 | 22H3 |

Veli Jože, Borozija. **GPS:** n45,49556 e13,50444.
🛏. ⏻ 01/04-30/09

| △ | Selce | 36A2 |

Selce. GPS: n45,15408 e14,72533.
🛏. ⏻ 01/04-31/10

| 🍇 S | Selina 🌊🏔🌲🍦 | 36A2 |

Camp Terre, 79. **GPS:** n45,15770 e13,76765.⬆➡.

10🛏100-125kn 🚰🍴Ch 🔌(14x),16Amp WC🛁€4 📶included.👜
Location: Rural, luxurious, isolated, quiet.
Surface: gravel.
⏻ 01/01-31/12
Distance: 🏊3km 🚤5km ⊗3km 💧3km 🚲on the spot 🚶on the spot.

| △ S | Umag 🏖🍦 | 22H3 |

Finida. GPS: n45,39278 e13,54194.
🛏 🚰🍴Ch 🔌WC included. ⏻ 15/04-30/09

| △ S | Umag 🏖🍦 | 22H3 |

Stella Maris. GPS: n45,45056 e13,52278.
400🛏 🚰🍴Ch 🔌WC included. ⏻ 15/04-15/10

| 🛖 S | Vižinada 🌲 | 36A2 |

Agroturizam Jadruhi, Jadruhi 11. **GPS:** n45,29978 e13,74819.⬆.

10🛏50kn 🚰🍴Ch 🔌(6x)included,16Amp WC🛁free.👜
Location: Rural, simple, isolated, quiet. **Surface:** gravel/metalled.
⏻ 01/01-31/12
Distance: 🏊4km 🚤6km ⊗on the spot 💧4km 🚌on the spot 🚲on the spot 🚶on the spot.
Remarks: Check in at restaurant.

| ⒸS | Vrsar 🏖🍦 | 36A2 |

Camperstop Valkanela, Fontana. **GPS:** n45,16501 e13,60804.⬆.

20🛏€ 12-32 🚰🍴Ch 🔌WC included 🖥📶100kn/24h 👜👜📹
Location: Urban, simple, central, quiet.
Surface: grassy.
⏻ 22/04-03/10
Distance: 🏊500m 🏖on the spot ⊗on the spot 💧on the spot 🍴1km 🚲on the spot 🚶on the spot.
Remarks: Camperstop, max. 48h, use camp-site facilities incl.

| 🛏 | Vrsar 🏖🍦 | 36A2 |

Dalmatinska ulica. GPS: n45,14706 e13,60422.⬆.

30🛏50kn/day.🏙 **Location:** Urban, simple, central, noisy.
Surface: asphalted. ⏻ 01/01-31/12
Distance: 🏊350m 🏖350m 🎣350m ⊗350m 💧350m 🚌350m 🚲on the spot 🚶on the spot.

| △ S | Vrsar 🏖🍦 | 36A2 |

Porto Sole. GPS: n45,14139 e13,60222.
800🛏 🚰🍴Ch 🔌WC included. ⏻ 15/04-30/09

Dalmatia

| △ | Babino Polje | 37B2 |

Marina, Ropa 11. **GPS:** n42,73543 e17,54650.
🛏.
Remarks: Mini-camp.

| △ | Babino Polje | 37B2 |

Mungos. GPS: n42,73885 e17,53441.
🛏 € 31.
Remarks: Mini-camp.

| △ | Baška Voda 🏖🍦 | 37A2 |

Basko Polje. GPS: n43,34878 e16,96478.
🛏. ⏻ 15/05-30/09

| △ | Bibinje 🏖🍦 | 36B3 |

Andela. GPS: n44,06889 e15,29464.
🛏.
Remarks: Mini-camp.

| △ | Bibinje 🏖🍦 | 36B3 |

Dido, Težački put. **GPS:** n44,05670 e15,29008.
🛏.
Remarks: Mini-camp.

| △ | Bibinje 🏖🍦 | 36B3 |

Kero, Punta Bibinje. **GPS:** n44,05730 e15,28918.
🛏.
Remarks: Mini-camp.

| △ | Bibinje 🏖🍦 | 36B3 |

Punta, Težački put. **GPS:** n44,05680 e15,29162.
🛏.
Remarks: Mini-camp.

| △ | Biograd na Moru 🌊🏖🍦 | 36B3 |

Dijana & Josip, Put Solina 26. **GPS:** n43,93422 e15,44828.
🛏.
Remarks: Mini-camp.

| △ | Biograd na Moru 🌊🏖🍦 | 36B3 |

Ljutic, Put Solina. **GPS:** n43,92654 e15,45353.
🛏.
Remarks: Mini-camp.

| △ | Biograd na Moru 🌊🏖🍦 | 36B3 |

Mia, Put Solina 47. **GPS:** n43,93441 e15,44803.
🛏.
Remarks: Mini-camp.

HR

Biograd na Moru 🌿⛺🐚 36B3
Soline, Put Kumenta. **GPS:** n43,92756 e15,45595.
🚿. ⏱ 01/05-30/09

Bol 37A2
Kito, Ante Radića 1. **GPS:** n43,26407 e16,64820.
⏱ 01/05-31/10

Drace-Pelješac 37B2
Plaža, Janjina. **GPS:** n42,92477 e17,43079.
🚿.
Remarks: Mini-camp.

Dubrovnik 🌿⛺🐚 37B2
Solitudo, Vatroslava Lisinskog 17. **GPS:** n42,66178 e18,07052.
🚿. ⏱ 01/04-31/10
Tourist information Dubrovnik:
👁 Aquarium, D. Jude 2. ⏱ Mo-Sa 9-13h.
👁 City Walls, Gundulićeva poljana 2. City wall surround the entire Old City. ⏱ 10-15h, 01/04-31/10 9-18.30h.
👁 Place Stradun. Main street with Onofrio-fountain and Sveti Frane monastery.
Ⓜ Dubrovacki Muzej, Pred Dvorom 3. History of the city. ⏱ Mo-Sa 9-14h.
Ⓜ Pomorski Muzej, Sveti Ivan. Shipping museum. ⏱ Tue-Sa 9-13h.
🎭 Zomerfestival. ⏱ 10/07-25/08.

Dugi Rat ⛺🏔🐚 37A1
Ivo, Duce Rogac. **GPS:** n43,44111 e16,65778.
🚿.
Remarks: Mini-camp.

Dugi Rat ⛺🏔🐚 37A1
Luka, Duce Rogac. **GPS:** n43,44164 e16,65347.
🚿.
Remarks: Mini-camp.

Dugi Rat ⛺🏔🐚 37A1
Orij, Orij, Duce Rogac. **GPS:** n43,44631 e16,63429.
🚿.
Remarks: Mini-camp.

Grebaštica 🐚 37A1
Ante&Toni, Brodarica. **GPS:** n43,63833 e15,95833.
🚿. ⏱ 01/05-01/10
Distance: 🏖100m 🏊on the spot.
Remarks: Mini-camp.

Grebaštica 🐚 37A1
Tomas, D8. **GPS:** n43,62986 e15,95443.
🚿.
Distance: 🏊on the spot.
Remarks: Mini-camp.

Kaštel Kambelovac 37A1
U Dragama, A. Starcevica 39. **GPS:** n43,55053 e16,37676.
🚿.
Remarks: Mini-camp.

Kaštel Štafilic 37A1
Koludrovac, Resnik Bb. **GPS:** n43,54281 e16,31844.
🚿.
Remarks: Mini-camp.

Kaštel Stari 37A1
Adria. **GPS:** n43,55143 e16,35349.
🚿.
Remarks: Mini-camp.

Kaštel Stari 37A1
Kamp- Biluš Josip. **GPS:** n43,55162 e16,34978.
🚿.
Remarks: Mini-camp.

Kolan 36B3
Sveti Duh. **GPS:** n44,51518 e14,95525.
🚿.
Remarks: Mini-camp.

Korčula 🌿⛺🐚 37A2
Kalac. **GPS:** n42,95056 e17,14500.
🚿. ⏱ 01/06-01/10

Korčula 🌿⛺🐚 37A2
Oskorušica, Oskorušica 27/ VI, Racišce. **GPS:** n42,96795 e17,07335.
🚿.
Remarks: Mini-camp.

Korčula 🌿⛺🐚 37A2
Vela Postrana, Lumbardra 142.
GPS: n42,92230 e17,17266.
🚿.
Remarks: Mini-camp.
Tourist information Korčula:

ℹ Turisticka zajednica, Obala Tudmana, www.korcula.net. City with historical centre, birth-place Marco Polo.
🕷 Marco Polo fest. ⏱ 09/07-11/07.
🎭 Zwaarddansfestival. ⏱ daily 04/07-23/08.

🍴Ⓢ Korenica 🌿⛺🐚 36B2
Bistro Marina, Zagrebačka 6. **GPS:** n44,74702 e15,70464. ⬆➡.

12 🚐guests free 🚰€2/100liter 🔌€2/night,10Amp WC 📶.
Location: Urban, simple, central, quiet. **Surface:** asphalted.
⏺ 06/01-30/01
Distance: 🏪100m ✏on the spot ⊗on the spot 🍴10m 🚆100m on the spot 🚶on the spot.
Remarks: Guests free.

⛺Ⓢ Kornati/Murter 🌿⛺🐚 36B3
Slanica, Jurija Dalmatinca 17. **GPS:** n43,81682 e15,57733.
🚐from € 14,30 🚰 🔌 WC included. ⏱ 01/05-15/10

Kornati/Murter 🌿⛺🐚 36B3
Jazina, Tisno. **GPS:** n43,80940 e15,62760.
🚿. ⏱ 01/05-30/09

Kornati/Murter 🌿⛺🐚 36B3
Jezera-Lovišča, Jezera. **GPS:** n43,79370 e15,62867.
🚿. ⏱ 15/04-15/10

Kornati/Murter 🌿⛺🐚 36B3
Kosirina, Betina. **GPS:** n43,79727 e15,61004.
🚿. ⏱ 01/05-30/09

Kornati/Murter 🌿⛺🐚 36B3
Plitka Vala, Betina. **GPS:** n43,80515 e15,61284.
🚿. ⏱ 15/04-15/10

Krvavica 🐚 37A2
Autocamp Krvavica. **GPS:** n43,32375 e16,98559.

Distance: 🏊100m.

Kucište 37A2
Palme. **GPS:** n42,97639 e17,12917.
🚿. ⏱ 01/06-01/10

Kucište 37A2
Plaža, Viganj 4, Od Gaja. **GPS:** n42,97935 e17,10400.
🚿.
Remarks: Mini-camp.

Lokva Rogoznica 37A2
Danijel, Ruskamen bb. **GPS:** n43,40973 e16,74529.
🚿.
Remarks: Mini-camp.

Lokva Rogoznica 37A2
Linda. **GPS:** n43,40817 e16,75485.
🚿.
Remarks: Mini-camp.

Lovište 37A2
Lupiš. **GPS:** n43,02790 e17,03012.
🚿.
Remarks: Mini-camp.

Lukoran 36B3
Novi Kamp, Punta 28. **GPS:** n44,10538 e15,15518.
🚿.
Remarks: Mini-camp.

Mlini 37B2
Kate, Tupina 1. **GPS:** n42,62472 e18,20806.
🚿.
Remarks: Mini-camp.

Mlini 37B2
Kupari, Kupari bb. **GPS:** n42,62462 e18,18833.
🚿. ⏱ 01/04-30/09
Remarks: Mini-camp.

Mlini 37B2
Matkovica, Srebreno 8. **GPS:** n42,62450 e18,19295.
🚿.
Remarks: Mini-camp.

Mlini 37B2
Paradiso Laguna, Za Gospom, Plat. **GPS:** n42,60759 e18,22838.
🚿.
Remarks: Mini-camp.

Mlini 37B2
Porto, Srebreno. **GPS:** n42,62433 e18,19107.
🚿.
Remarks: Mini-camp.

Mljet 37B2
Marina, Marina Matana,Ropa 11. **GPS:** n42,75260 e17,46000.
🚿.
Remarks: Mini-camp.

Mokalo 37B2
Adriatic. **GPS:** n42,97694 e17,22500.
🚿. ⏱ 01/04-31/10

Molunat 37B2
Adriatic II. **GPS:** n42,45327 e18,43582.
🚿.
Remarks: Mini-camp.

Molunat 37B2
Adriatic I, Višnjici 4, Đurinici. **GPS:** n42,45341 e18,43554.
🚿.
Remarks: Mini-camp.

Molunat 37B2
Monika, Molunat 10. **GPS:** n42,45284 e18,42871.
🚿.
Remarks: Mini-camp.

Nin 🌿⛺🐚 36B3
Dišpet, Put Ždrijaca 13. **GPS:** n44,24618 e15,18971.
🚿.
Remarks: Mini-camp.

Nin 🌿⛺🐚 36B3
Nin, Put Venere Anzotike 41. **GPS:** n44,24541 e15,17401.
🚿.
Remarks: Mini-camp.

Nin 🌿⛺🐚 36B3
Ninska Laguna, Put blata 10. **GPS:** n44,24639 e15,17389.
🚐€ 11 - € 18.
Remarks: Mini-camp.
Tourist information Nin:
Ⓜ Arheološka zbirka Nin, Trg Kraljevac 8. Archeological museum.
⏱ 01/10-31/5 8-14h, 01/06-30/09 8-22h.

Novigrad (Dalmatia) 36B3
Adria-Sol Mulic. **GPS:** n44,18472 e15,54944.

Remarks: Mini-camp.

Omiš 37A1
Galeb. **GPS:** n43,44061 e16,68128.
🚿.

Omiš 37A1
Lisičina, Lisičina 2. **GPS:** n43,44737 e16,69038.
🚿. ⏱ 01/01-31/12
Remarks: Mini-camp.

Opuzen 37B2
Rio, Put Zlatinovca 23. **GPS:** n43,02227 e17,55136.
🚿. ⏱ 01/05-01/10

Orašac 37B2
Pod Maslinom, Put prema moru b.b.. **GPS:** n42,69907 e18,00592.
🚿. ⏱ 01/05-30/09
Remarks: Mini-camp.

Pag 🌿⛺🐚 36B3
Košljun, Košljun B.B.. **GPS:** n44,39849 e15,07936.
🚿.
Remarks: Mini-camp.

Pag 🌿⛺🐚 36B3
Pere, Dinjiška. **GPS:** n44,35939 e15,18641.
🚿.
Remarks: Mini-camp.

Pag 🌿⛺🐚 36B3
Porat, Stjepana Radića bb., Povljana. **GPS:** n44,34551 e15,10869.
🚿.
Remarks: Mini-camp.

Pag 🌿⛺🐚 36B3
Simuni, V. Nazora b.b, Simuni. **GPS:** n44,43766 e15,05408.
🚿. ⏱ 04/04-01/10

⛺Ⓢ Pakoštane ⛺🐚 36B3
Kozarica. **GPS:** n43,90970 e15,49881.

HR

🏕from € 15,70 Ch WC included. ◻ 15/04-15/10

△ Pakoštane 36B3
Blaž. GPS: n43,90763 e15,50089.
Remarks: Mini-camp.

△ Pakoštane 36B3
Marin. GPS: n43,90445 e15,51750.
Remarks: Mini-camp.

△ Pakoštane 36B3
Nordsee. GPS: n43,90525 e15,51617.
◻ 01/04-03/10

△ Pakoštane 36B3
Oaza Mira, Dr. Franje Tuđmana bb, Drage. **GPS**: n43,88607 e15,53290.
Remarks: Mini-camp.

△ Pakoštane 36B3
Oaza, Drage. **GPS**: n43,87035 e15,55917.
◻ 01/04-15/10
Remarks: Mini-camp.

△ Pakoštane 36B3
Pakoštane. GPS: n43,91258 e15,49772.
Remarks: Mini-camp.

△ S Pelješac/Orebić 37B2
Ulica Bana Josipa Jelačića. **GPS**: n42,97499 e17,16929.
±10 🏕70kn Surface: grassy/gravel ◻ 01/01-31/12
Distance: pebbled beach ⊗500m.

△ S Pelješac/Orebić 37B2
Glavna Plaža. GPS: n42,97583 e17,18917.
🏕from € 15 Ch WC included. ◻ 15/05-01/10

△ S Pelješac/Orebić 37B2
Trstenica, Šetalište Kneza Domagoja 50. **GPS**: n42,98095 e17,19435.
Ch WC included.
Remarks: Mini-camp.

△ Pelješac/Orebić 37B2
Paradiso. GPS: n42,97475 e17,23497.
Remarks: Mini-camp.

△ Pelješac/Orebić 37B2
Paradiso, Obala Pomoraca 70 A. **GPS**: n42,96693 e17,24230.
Remarks: Mini-camp.

△ Pelješac/Orebić 37B2
Perna. GPS: n42,97638 e17,13272.
◻ 17/04-30/09

△ Pelješac/Trpanj 37B2
Divna. GPS: n43,00944 e17,26806.
Remarks: Mini-camp.

△ Pelješac/Trpanj 37B2
Vrila. GPS: n43,00360 e17,28467.
◻ 20/05-10/10

△ Petrcane 36B3
Pineta, Punta Radman 21. **GPS**: n44,18362 e15,16291.
Remarks: Mini-camp.

△ Podgora 37A2
Sutikla. GPS: n43,23590 e17,07833.
◻ 01/05-30/09

△ Podstrana 37A1
Car, Sv. Martin 180. **GPS**: n43,47479 e16,56624.
Remarks: Mini-camp.

△ Podstrana 37A1
Tamaris, Sv.Martin 114. **GPS**: n43,47551 e16,56383.
50 🏕from € 16,50. ◻ 01/01-31/12
Distance: on the spot.
Remarks: Mini-camp.
Tourist information Podstrana:
Sinjska alka, Sinj. Knight celebration. ◻ 5th August.

△ Posedarje 36B3
Bristi. GPS: n44,21231 e15,48038.
Remarks: Mini-camp.

△ Posedarje 36B3
Kristina. GPS: n44,00000 e15,47961.

Remarks: Mini-camp.

△ Povijana 36B3
Mali Dubrovnik, Kralja P. Svacica 1. **GPS**: n44,34931 e15,10060.
Remarks: Mini-camp.

△ Povijana 36B3
Porat, Ante Starcevica Bb. **GPS**: n44,34560 e15,10897.
Remarks: Mini-camp.

△ S Primošten 37A1
Zagrebacka ul.. **GPS**: n43,58854 e15,92632.
10 🏕€ 7/24h.
Distance: 200m 200m 200m 200m.

△ S Primošten 37A1
Adriatic, Huljerat b.b.. **GPS**: n43,60645 e15,92193.
🏕from € 24 Ch WC included ◻ 08/04-31/10

△ S Privlaka 36B3
Dalmacija, Ivana Pavla II 40. **GPS**: n44,25613 e15,12557.
Ch included. ◻ 01/05-15/10

△ Privlaka 36B3
Medanić, Put Brtalica 47. **GPS**: n44,24887 e15,13379.
Remarks: Mini-camp.

△ Ražanac 36B3
Kamp Miočić, Rtina I 139, Rtina. **GPS**: n44,29219 e15,30179.
Remarks: Mini-camp.

△ Ražanac 36B3
Kamp Odmoree, Rtina Stošići bb. **GPS**: n44,30040 e15,28881.
Remarks: Mini-camp.

△ Ražanac 36B3
Planik. GPS: n44,27778 e15,34472.
🏕€ 5,07-12, € 3,33-5,33/pp. ◻ 15/05-30/09
Remarks: Mini-camp.

△ Ražanac 36B3
Puntica. GPS: n44,28389 e15,34306.
🏕€ 12 -20.
Remarks: Mini-camp.

△ Rovanjska 36B3
Tamaris. GPS: n44,25037 e15,53735.
Remarks: Mini-camp.

△ S Senj 36A2
Kamp Škver, Filipa Vukasovica 5. **GPS**: n44,99385 e14,90012.

50 🏕69kn, Jun/Sep 89kn, Jul/Aug 106kn Ch 20kn, 16Amp WC 35kn included. **Location:** Urban, comfortable.
Surface: gravel/metalled. ◻ 01/04-01/10
Distance: 500m on the spot on the spot ⊗on the spot 150m 500m on the spot on the spot.
Remarks: Fishing permit available.

△ Senj 36A2
Bunica, Bunica 33. **GPS**: n45,02607 e14,88630.
Remarks: Mini-camp.

△ Senj 36A2
Ujca, M. Cihlar Nehajeva, 4. **GPS**: n44,96833 e14,92167.
◻ 01/05-01/10
Distance: on the spot.
Remarks: Mini-camp.

△ S Šibenik 36B3
Cikada, Konjevodci 63. **GPS**: n43,78200 e15,99116.
10 🏕€ 9-12 + € 0,50-1/pp tourist tax Ch € 2,50 WC.
Location: Rural. **Surface:** gravel. ◻ 01/05-31/10

△ Šibenik 36B3
Krka. GPS: n43,79463 e15,68120.

🏕free. ◻ 01/01-31/12
Remarks: 1km from Krka waterfalls.

△ S Šibenik 36B3
Solaris. GPS: n43,69917 e15,87795.
Ch ◻ 15/03-30/11

△ Šibenik 36B3
Solaris-Zablaće, Obala palih boraca 2a. **GPS**: n43,70524 e15,86850.
◻ 01/05-30/09
Tourist information Šibenik:
Internationaal kinderfestival. ◻ 22/06-06/07.
Nacionalni Park Krka, Krka. Nature reserve.

△ Slano 37B2
Baldo. GPS: n42,79683 e17,84989.
Remarks: Mini-camp.

△ Slano 37B2
Bambo. GPS: n42,77513 e17,88500.
Remarks: Mini-camp.

△ Slano 37B2
Banja, Put Od Banje. **GPS**: n42,77414 e17,88405.
Remarks: Mini-camp.

△ Slano 37B2
Rogac, Grgurici. **GPS**: n42,78229 e17,87536.
🏕€ 4-5 + € 2-2,50/pp. ◻ 01/04-31/10
Remarks: Mini-camp.

△ Slano 37B2
Sladenovici, Sladenovici 9. **GPS**: n42,78450 e17,86104.
Remarks: Mini-camp.

△ Slatine 37A1
Domic, Put Porta 71, Ciove. **GPS**: n43,49784 e16,34060.
Remarks: Mini-camp.

△ Split 37A1
Stobreč. GPS: n43,50401 e16,52644.

◻ 01/01-31/12
Distance: centre 7km on the spot.
Tourist information Split:
Ⓜ Arheoloski Muzej, Zrinjsko-Frankopanska 25. Findings from Roman time and Middle Ages. ◻ Tue-Fri 9-14h, Sa-Su 9-13h, 01/06-30/09 Tue-Fri 9-12, 13-20h, Sa-Su 9-13h.
Ⓜ Galerija Ivana Mestrovica, Setaliste I. Mestrovica 46. Gallery. ◻ Mo-Sa 10-18h, Su 10-14h.
Ⓜ Muzej Hrvatskih Arheoloskih Spomenika, S. Gunjace bb. Archeological findings. ◻ Mo-Sa 9-20h.
Dioklecijanova palača. Roman palace.

△ S Starigrad/Paklenica 36B3
Camp National Park, Paklenica. **GPS**: n44,28832 e15,44573.
Ch ◻ 15/03-15/10
Remarks: Mini-camp.

△ Starigrad/Paklenica 36B3
Jaz, Seline, Paklenica. **GPS**: n44,28323 e15,46028.
◻ 01/05-30/09
Remarks: Mini-camp.

HR

HR

Starigrad/Paklenica — 36B3
Marko, Paklenicka 7, Paklenica. **GPS**: n44,28851 e15,45261.
🏕. ⏺ 01/01-31/12
Remarks: Mini-camp.

Starigrad/Paklenica — 36B3
Pinus, Ive Senjanina 5, Paklenica. **GPS**: n44,30928 e15,42320.
🏕.
Remarks: Mini-camp.

Starigrad/Paklenica — 36B3
Pisak, Paklenica. **GPS**: n44,27285 e15,47806.
🏕.
Remarks: Mini-camp.

Starigrad/Paklenica — 36B3
Plantaža, Put Plantaže 2, Paklenica. **GPS**: n44,30056 e15,43211.
🏕.
Remarks: Mini-camp.

Starigrad/Paklenica — 36B3
Vesna, Paklenicka 103, Paklenica. **GPS**: n44,28610 e15,45243.
🏕. ⏺ 01/01-31/12
Remarks: Mini-camp.

Tourist information Starigrad/Paklenica:
ℹ Nacionalni park "Paklenica". Nature reserve, 150 km biking ad hiking trails, bird observation, tunnels and caves. 🎫 30kn/day.

Ston — 37B2
Prapratna. GPS: n42,81778 e17,67611.
🏕. ⏺ 01/06-30/09

Ston — 37B2
Vrela, Brijesta 10. **GPS**: n42,90397 e17,53266.
🏕.
Remarks: Mini-camp.

Sukošan — 36B3
Brajde. GPS: n44,04256 e15,30755.
🏕.
Remarks: Mini-camp.

Sukošan — 36B3
Kaj. GPS: n44,04278 e15,30655.
🏕.
Remarks: Mini-camp.

Sukošan — 36B3
Malenica, Vl. Milan Gašparović. **GPS**: n44,03658 e15,32790.
🏕.
Remarks: Mini-camp.

Sukošan — 36B3
Oliva. GPS: n44,04247 e15,30805.
🏕.
Remarks: Mini-camp.

Supetar — 37A2
Waterman Beach. GPS: n43,38076 e16,56439.
🏕. ⏺ 01/05-30/09

Sutivan — 37A2
Mlin, Brac. **GPS**: n43,38316 e16,47795.
Remarks: Mini-camp.

Sutivan — 37A2
Sutivan, Gorana Pavlova 12. **GPS**: n43,38523 e16,48460.
🏕. ⏺ 01/01-31/12

Sv. Filip I Jakov — 36B3
Djardin, Sveti Filip i Jakov bb. **GPS**: n43,96139 e15,42750.
🏕 from € 18 🚰🍴Ch🔌included. ⏺ 01/05-30/09

Sv. Filip I Jakov — 36B3
Filip, Put Primorja 10a. **GPS**: n43,96055 e15,42910.
🏕 from € 15,20 🚰🍴Ch🔌included.
Remarks: Mini-camp.

Sv. Filip I Jakov — 36B3
Ante, Turanj. **GPS**: n43,99637 e15,37915.
🏕.
Remarks: Mini-camp.

Sv. Filip I Jakov — 36B3
Antonio, Turanj. **GPS**: n43,97488 e15,39990.
🏕.
Remarks: Mini-camp.

Sv. Filip I Jakov — 36B3
Bepo, Turanj. **GPS**: n43,96562 e15,41254.
🏕.
Remarks: Mini-camp.

Sv. Filip I Jakov — 36B3
Bozo, Sv. Petar. **GPS**: n43,99688 e15,37838.

🏕.
Remarks: Mini-camp.

Sv. Filip I Jakov — 36B3
Jugo, Turanj. **GPS**: n43,96605 e15,41173.
🏕.
Remarks: Mini-camp.

Sv. Filip I Jakov — 36B3
Livada. GPS: n43,95976 e15,43108.
🏕.
Remarks: Mini-camp.

Sv. Filip I Jakov — 36B3
Maestral, Turanj 90. **GPS**: n43,96611 e15,41162.
🏕.
Remarks: Mini-camp.

Sv. Filip I Jakov — 36B3
Milan, Sv. Petar. **GPS**: n44,00205 e15,36859.
🏕.
Remarks: Mini-camp.

Sv. Filip I Jakov — 36B3
Moce, Put Primorja 8. **GPS**: n43,95968 e15,42915.
🏕.
Remarks: Mini-camp.

Sv. Filip I Jakov — 36B3
R & B, Turanj. **GPS**: n43,96592 e15,41196.
🏕.
Remarks: Mini-camp.

Sv. Filip I Jakov — 36B3
Rio, Put Primorja. **GPS**: n43,95583 e15,43500.
🏕.
Remarks: Mini-camp.

Sveti Petar na Moru — 36B3
Autocamp Martin. GPS: n44,00003 e15,36880. ⬆.
15🏕 € 14 🍴Ch🔌€3 WC🚿.
Surface: grassy/gravel. ⏺ 01/01-31/12
Distance: 🏖on the spot 🎣on the spot.

Tkon — 36B3
Adriana. GPS: n43,91734 e15,42596.
🏕.
Remarks: Mini-camp.

Tkon — 36B3
Brist. GPS: n43,92312 e15,41493.
🏕.
Remarks: Mini-camp.

Tribanj — 36B3
Camp CTT, D8. **GPS**: n44,34673 e15,32444.
7🏕. **Surface:** grassy/gravel. ⏺ 01/01-31/12
Distance: 🏖900m 🏖on the spot.
Remarks: Not suitable for motorhomes +7m.

Tribanj — 36B3
Ante, Krušcica. **GPS**: n44,34469 e15,32842.
🏕.
Remarks: Mini-camp.

Tribanj — 36B3
Punta Šibuljina, Šibuljina. **GPS**: n44,33631 e15,34627.
🏕.
Remarks: Mini-camp.

Trogir — 37A1
Vranjica Belvedere, Seget Vranjica. **GPS**: n43,51196 e16,19159.
🏕 from € 20 🚰🍴Ch🔌WC🚿.⏺ 15/04-15/10

Trogir — 37A1
Seget, Seget Donji. **GPS**: n43,51904 e16,22430.
50🏕 from € 21. ⏺ 01/03-31/10
Distance: 🏖800m 🏖on the spot.
Remarks: Mini-camp.

Tourist information Trogir:
ℹ Tourist Information, Ivana Pavla II Square, www.trogir-online.com. City with rich culture from Greek, Roman and Venetian time.
Ⓜ Town Museum, Fanfogna palace, Garagnin. History of the city.
⏺ 16/09-14/06 by request 8-14h, 15/06-15/09 9-21h.
Ⓜ Zbirka Kairos. Ecclesiastical art collection. ⏺ 15/6-15/9 8-13, 15-19h.
⚔ Fort Kamerlengo. ⏺ 15/6-15/9 9-20h.
✝ Katedrala St. Lawrence. Bell-tower of Cathedral of St. Lawrence, 47m. ⏺ 15/6-15/9 9-12, 16-19h. 🎫 5kn.

Vela Luka — 37A2
Mindel, Stani 193. **GPS**: n42,98369 e16,67060.
🏕. ⏺ 01/01-31/12

Viganj — 37A2
Antony Boy. GPS: n42,97889 e17,10752.
🏕. ⏺ 01/01-31/12

Vir — 36B3
Luka. GPS: n44,29610 e15,10605.
🏕.
Remarks: Mini-camp.

Vir — 36B3
Sapavac, Put Bunara 101. **GPS**: n44,29432 e15,07640.
🏕.
Remarks: Mini-camp.

Vodice — 36B3
Imperial, Vatroslava Lisinskog 2/I. **GPS**: n43,75287 e15,78992.
🏕 from € 22 🚰🍴Ch🔌 ⏺ 21/03-11/11

Vransko Jezero — 36B3
Crkvine. GPS: n43,93035 e15,51012.
🏕. ⏺ 15/04-15/10

Vrsi — 36B3
Mulic, Mulo. **GPS**: n44,26174 e15,21246.
🏕.
Remarks: Mini-camp.

Zaboric — 37A1
Jasenovo. GPS: n43,65116 e15,95025.
50🏕 from € 13 🚰🍴Ch🔌WC🚿. ⏺ 01/05-01/10
Distance: 🏖on the spot.
Remarks: Mini-camp.

Zadar — 36B3
Rosmari, Emanuela Vidovica 2. **GPS**: n44,13250 e15,20861.
20🏕 🚰🍴Ch🔌WC🚿.
Distance: 🏖on the spot 🏖on the spot.
Remarks: Mini-camp.

Zadar — 36B3
Borik, Radovana 7. **GPS**: n44,13528 e15,21528.
🏕. ⏺ 01/05-30/09

Tourist information Zadar:
👁 Trg Pet Bunara. Square of the five fountains.
Ⓜ Arheoloski Muzej, Simuna Kozicica Benje bb. Archeological findings.
⏺ Mo-Sa 9-13h, 18-20h.
✹ Muziekavonden in de St. Donatius van Zadar. ⏺ 01/07-15/08.

Zaostrog — 37B2
Uvala Borova, Mkarska. **GPS**: n43,13123 e17,28750.
🏕. ⏺ 01/05-30/09

Zaton — 36B3
Zaton. GPS: n44,23385 e15,16671.
🏕. ⏺ 01/05/30/09

Ždrelac — 36B3
Ruža. GPS: n44,00925 e15,28067.
🏕.
Remarks: Mini-camp.

Živogošče — 37A2
Dole. GPS: n43,17118 e17,19669.
🏕. ⏺ 01/05-30/09

Žrnovo — 37A2
Tri Žala, Uvala Tri Žala 808. **GPS**: n42,96407 e17,09104.
🏕.
Remarks: Mini-camp.

Žrnovo — 37A2
Vrbovica, Vrbovica bb. **GPS**: n42,95882 e17,11394.
🏕.
Remarks: Mini-camp.

Žuljana — 37B2
Vucina. GPS: n42,88257 e17,45135.
🏕.
Remarks: Mini-camp.

Inland

Kopačevo — 36D1
Family-Camperstop, Ferenca Kiša 7. **GPS**: n45,59832 e18,78467. ⬆.
20🏕🔌.⏺ 01/04-30/09

Koprivnica — 36C1
Cerine, Miroslava Krleze 81. **GPS**: n46,15361 e16,84250. ⬆.

11 ⌇first night 110kn, 75kn each additional night, 2 pers incl. + 7kn tourist tax ⌁🔌Ch⌁ ✎WC⌁included.
Location: Comfortable. **Surface:** grasstiles. ◘ 01/01-31/12
Distance: ⛱1,5km ⊗300m ⚲1km.
Remarks: Parking spa resort, wifi code at swimming pool.

| △ | Lipovac | 36D2 |

Spacva. GPS: n45,04593 e18,99682.
⌇. ◘ 01/05-01/10

| ⌇S | Plitviča 🌿⛱🏔🍴 | 36B2 |

Bear, Selište Drežničko 52. **GPS:** n44,94804 e15,63639.⬆➡.

30 ⌇130kn, 01/06-30/09 150kn, 01/07-31/08 170kn ⌁🔌Ch⌁ ✎
(30x),16Amp WC⌇🔲⌇included. 🚲 **Location:** Rural, comfortable, central, quiet. **Surface:** asphalted/gravel. ◘ 01/04-15/10
Distance: ⛱300m ⚓700m ⛟20km ⊗150m ⚲400m 🚌on the spot 🚴on the spot 🚶on the spot.
Remarks: Baker every morning, water falls Plitvica 5km.

| ⌇S | Plitviča 🌿⛱🏔🍴 | 36B2 |

Cvetkovic, Jezerce 28. **GPS:** n44,86338 e15,63967.⬆.

20 ⌇€ 10/pp ⌁🔌Ch⌁ ✎WC⌇⌇included. 🚲
Location: Rural, comfortable, central, quiet. **Surface:** grassy/gravel.
◘ 01/01-31/12
Distance: ⛱800m ⊗10km ⚲800m 🚌800m 🚴on the spot 🚶on the spot 🏊800m ⚓800m.
Remarks: Water falls Plitvica 2km.

| △ | Plitviča 🌿⛱🏔🍴 | 36B2 |

Korana. GPS: n44,99260 e15,64916.
⌇€ 6 + € 5/pp.

Tourist information Plitviča:
🌿 Nacionalni Park Plitviča Jezera, www.np-plitvicka-jezera.hr.
National park Plitvice lakes. ◘ 9-17h.

| △ | Racovica | 36B2 |

Turist, Grabovac 102. **GPS:** n44,97222 e15,64750.
⌇€ 23. ◘ 01/05-31/10

| ⌇S | Zagreb 🌿🍦 | 36B2 |

Camp-Zagreb, Jezerska 6. **GPS:** n45,80253 e15,82622.⬆.

50 ⌇€ 23-31 ⌁🔌Ch⌁ ✎WC⌇included.
Location: Urban, luxurious. **Surface:** metalled.
Distance: ⛱on the spot ⛟on the spot ⊗on the spot 🚴on the spot 🚶on the spot.

Remarks: Bus to Zagreb € 8/round trip.
Tourist information Zagreb:
ℹ www.zagreb-touristinfo.hr. Capital, surface 64133 km^2, inhabitants 885,000, 11 theaters and 22 museums.
Ⓜ Archeological Museum, 19 Nikola Subic Zrinski Square. ◘ Tue-Fri 10-17h, Sa-Su 10-13h.
Ⓜ Atelje Mestrovic, Mletacka 8. Former dwellinghouse of sculptor Ivan Mestrovic. ◘ Tue-Fri 10-18h, Sa-Su 10-13h.
Ⓜ Ethnographic Museum, Mazuranicev trg 14. ◘ Tue-Thu 10-18h, Fri-Su 10-13h.
Ⓜ Muzej Grada Zagreb, Opaticka 20. City museum. ◘ Tue-Fri 10-18h, Sa-Su 10-13h.
Ⓜ Tehnicki Muzej, Savska cesta 18. Technical museum. ◘ Tue-Fri 9-15h, Sa-Su 9-13h.
✳ Medjunarodna Smotra Folklora. International folk festival.
◘ 20/07/05-24/07/05.
✳ Zomerfestival van Zagreb. ◘ 01/07-15/08.
🌿 Park Prirode Kopacki Rit. Nature reserve, boat rental. ◘ daily 8-16h.

HR

Hungary

Capital: Budapest
Government: parliamentary constitutional republic
Official Language: Hungarian
Population 9,919,000 (2014)
Area: 93,024 Km²

General information
Dialling code: 0036
General emergency: 112
Currency: Forint (HUF)
€ 1 = 310 HUF, 100 HUF = € 0,30 (October 2015)
£ 1 = 433 HUF 100 HUF = £ 0,23 (October 2015)
Credit cards are accepted almost everywhere.

Regulations for overnight stays
Free overnight stay is not allowed.

Additional public holidays 2016
March 15 Revolution Memorial Day 1848
March 28 Easter Monday
August 20 Hungarian National Day
October 23 Revolution Memorial Day 1956
November 1 All Saints' Day

Time Zone
Winter (Standard Time) GMT+1
Summer (DST) GMT+2

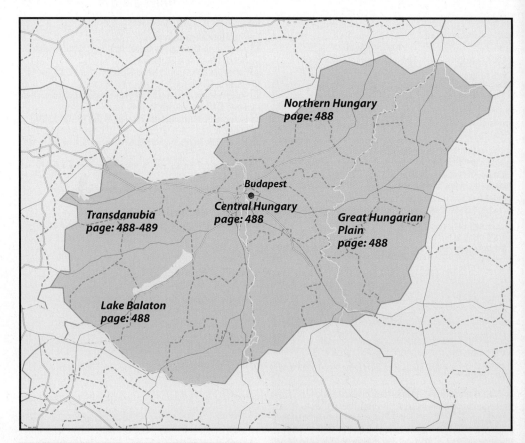

Northern Hungary page: 488

Budapest

Transdanubia page: 488-489

Central Hungary page: 488

Great Hungarian Plain page: 488

Lake Balaton page: 488

HU

Northern Hungary

△S | **Bekölce** | 35C3
Camping Bekölce, Béke út 252. **GPS**: n48,08260 e20,24904.
10 ⚡€ 15 ⌁▭Ch☀included. ◻ 01/01-31/12

△S | **Borsodbóta** | 35C2
Camping Amedi, Rákóczi út 181. **GPS**: n48,21329 e20,40569.
40 ⚡€ 12,50, 01/07-31/08 € 16,50 ⌁▭Chincluded ☀€ 4.
Surface: grassy. ◻ 01/05-30/09

△S | **Budapest** | 35C3
Ave Natura, Csermely u 3.
GPS: n47,51416 e18,97300.

12 ⚡€ 18,50 ⌁▭Ch☀(12x) € 3,80 WC ▯⌁included.
Surface: grassy/sand. ◻ 01/04-10/11
Distance: ◱5km ⊗100m ⚑2km ▭on the spot 🚲on the spot 🚶on the spot.

△S | **Hernádvécse** | 35C2
Zonnebloempaleis, Rákóczi út 96. **GPS**: n48,43360 e21,17230.
1 ⚡€ 10, 15/06-28/08 € 12 ⌁▭Ch☀included. **Location:** Rural.
Surface: grassy. ◻ 14/4-1/10
Distance: ⚑2km.

△S | **Pécs** | 36C1
Família Camping, Gyöngyösi utca 6. **GPS**: n46,08559 e18,26206.
15 ⚡€ 15 ⌁▭Ch☀included. **Location:** Rural. **Surface:** metalled.
◻ 01/05-30/09
Distance: ◱2,5km ⊗200m ⚑100m.

Great Hungarian Plain

△S | **Püspökladány** | 35C3
Árnyas Thermal Camping és Üdülőpark, Petőfi Sándor Ut 62.
GPS: n47,32192 e21,10273.
50 ⚡€ 15 ⌁▭Ch☀included. **Location:** Rural.
Surface: grassy/metalled. ◻ 01/05-30/09
Distance: ◱on the spot.

△S | **Szentkirály** | 35C3
Fantazia Tanya, Felsö Tanya 165. **GPS**: n46,94087 e19,93109.
20 ⚡€ 13 ⌁▭Chincluded ☀€ 4. **Location:** Rural. **Surface:** grassy.
◻ 01/04-01/11 🚶on the spot.

△S | **Zsana** | 36D1
Camping Oázis Tanya, L Körzet 15. **GPS**: n46,41438 e19,61111.
20 ⚡€ 16,20, 01/07-31/08 € 18 ⌁▭Ch☀€ 2,50 ⌁included.
Location: Rural. **Surface:** grassy. ◻ 15/04-30/09
Distance: ◱10km.

Central Hungary

▭S | **Csemő** | 35C3
Békés Föld, Bezzeg dülö. **GPS**: n47,13217 e19,73983.
4 ⚡€12,50 ⌁▭Ch☀included. **Surface:** grassy/sand.
◻ 01/01-31/12

Lake Balaton

▭S | **Balatonkeresztúr** | 36C1
Ady Endre utca 51. GPS: n46,70333 e17,37047.⬆.
8 ⚡€ 12 ⌁☀included. **Location:** Urban. **Surface:** grassy.
◻ 01/01-31/12
Distance: ◱lake Balaton 600m ⊗200m ⚑500m ☀500m.

△S | **Cserszegtomaj** | 36C1
Camping Panorama, Panoráma köz 1. **GPS**: n46,80667 e17,21306.
15 ⚡€ 16 ⌁▭Ch☀included. **Surface:** grassy. ◻ 01/04-31/10
Distance: ◱5km ◱5km ⊗2km ⚑2km.

△S | **Gyenesdiás** | 36C1
Wellnes-Park, Napfény utca 6. **GPS**: n46,76417 e17,30250.
⚡€ 15,80-18,80 ⌁▭Ch☀included. **Surface:** grassy.
◻ 01/04-15/10
Distance: ◱2km ◱lake Balaton 2km ⊗200m ⚑500m ▭2km.

△S | **Kisbárapáti** | 36C1
Camping Jó Napot, Ady Endre utca 46. **GPS**: n46,59827 e17,86750.
15 ⚡€ 15,50 ⌁▭Chincluded ☀€ 3,50. **Location:** Rural.
Surface: grassy. ◻ 15/04-15-09

△S | **Koppányszántó** | 36C1
Tranquil Pines, Dózsa György utca 334. **GPS**: n46,59027 e18,10344.

10 ⚡€ 11,50 ⌁▭Ch☀included ◉ € 5,50. **Location:** Rural.
Surface: metalled. ◻ 01/01-31/12
Distance: ◱1,5km.

▭S | **Somogyvár** | 36C1
Kimis Camp, Bartók Béla utca 58. **GPS**: n46,58275 e17,62398.
24 ⚡€ 9 ⌁▭Ch☀included ⌁ € 1. **Location:** Rural.
Surface: grassy. ◻ 01/05-30/09
Distance: ▭500m 🚶on the spot.

Transdanubia

▭S | **Bozsok** | 35B3
Nagy Vendégház, Rákoczi út 105. **GPS**: n47,32059 e16,48590.
5 ⚡€ 10 ⌁▭Ch☀included. **Surface:** grassy. ◻ 01/01-31/12
Distance: ⊗100m ⚑on the spot.
Remarks: Arrival >14h departure <12h.

△S | **Felsőszentmárton** | 36C1
Camping de-ommekeer, Szent Lhászló Utca 38.
GPS: n45,85261 e17,69925.
10 ⚡€ 15 ⌁▭Ch☀included. **Surface:** grassy. ◻ 01/04-30/09

△S | **Győr** | 35B3
Camping Pihenö, Mártírok útja. **GPS**: n47,72515 e17,71406.

35 ⚡€ 15,50 ⌁▭Ch☀included. **Surface:** grassy.
◻ 01/01-31/12
Distance: ◱7km ✈9km.

| ⚐S | **Halászi** | 35B3 |

Party Csárda, Duna sétány. **GPS**: n47,88586 e17,32201.
5 ⌁ € 12 ⚡ ⚡Chfree ⚡ € 2. **Surface**: gravel. ◻ 01/01-31/12
Distance: ⚡300m ⚡on the spot ⚡on the spot ⚡on the spot.

| ⚐S | **Lenti** | 36B1 |

Rudas, Béke utca 32. **GPS**: n46,62582 e16,53266.
6 ⌁ € 10 ⚡ ⚡Chincluded ⚡on demand. **Location**: Rural.
Surface: grassy. ◻ 01/01-31/12
Distance: ⚡800m ⚡800m ⚡500m ⚡700m ⚡600m.

| ⚠S | **Magyaregregy** | 36C1 |

Camping Máré Vára, Várvölgyi utca 2. **GPS**: n46,23361 e18,30833.
36 ⌁ € 17,50 ⚡ ⚡Ch ⚡included. **Location**: Rural. **Surface**: grassy.
◻ 15/04-30/09
Distance: ⚡500m ⚡on the spot ⚡1000m ⚡1000m ⚡on the spot
⚡on the spot.

| ⚐S | **Mosonmagyaróvár** | 35B3 |

Kocisi Joseph, Vízpart utca 59. **GPS**: n47,87335 e17,27851.
8 ⌁ € 13 ⚡ ⚡Ch ⚡included. **Surface**: grassy/metalled.
◻ 01/01-31/12
Distance: ⚡300m ⚡on the spot ⚡200m ⚡200m.

| ⚐S | **Mosonmagyaróvár** | 35B3 |

Thermalcamp, Gyümölcsös utca. **GPS**: n47,87715 e17,27948.
40 ⌁ € 27 ⚡ ⚡Ch ⚡ WC ⚡included. **Surface**: grassy.
◻ 01/01-31/12
Distance: ⚡on the spot ⚡on the spot ⚡on the spot ⚡on the spot.

| ⚐S | **Nagysáp** | 35B3 |

Granarium, Granárium domb 3. **GPS**: n47,68573 e18,60741.

7 ⌁ € 10 ⚡ ⚡Ch ⚡ WC ⚡included. **Surface**: gravel.
◻ 01/01-31/12
Distance: ⚡on the spot.

| ⚠S | **Patosfa** | 36C1 |

Camping Farkas, Petőfi utca 52-56. **GPS**: n46,12545 e17,65788.
⌁ € 19 ⚡ ⚡Ch ⚡included. **Location**: Rural. **Surface**: sand.
◻ 01/05-30-09

HU

▌▌Ireland

Capital: Dublin
Government: parliamentary constitutional republic
Official Language: Irish and English
Population 4,832,000 (2014)
Area: 69,825 Km²

General information

Dialling code: 0353
General emergency: 112
Currency: Euro
Credit cards are accepted almost everywhere.

Regulations for overnight stays

Free overnight stay is allowed with consent of the landowner, and up to 24 hours on regular parking spaces.

Additional public holidays 2016

March 17 Saint Patrick's Day
March 25 Good Friday
March 28 Easter Monday
May 2 Early Bank Holiday
June 6 June Bank Holiday
August 1 First Moday in August
October 31 October Bank Holiday
November 1 All Saints'Day

Time Zone

Winter (Standard Time) GMT+0
Summer (DST) GMT+1

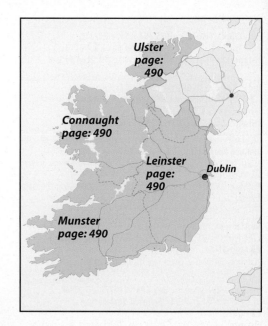

Ulster page: 490
Connaught page: 490
Leinster page: 490
Munster page: 490
Dublin

Ulster

Buncrana · 1B2
R238. **GPS**: n55,12828 w7,45782.
3 🛏free ⚡free ⚡€5. **Surface**: metalled. ⬛ 01/01-31/12

Donegal · 1B2
Parking 4 Port, Quaystreet. **GPS**: n54,65183 w8,1123.
4 🛏€ 2,70. **Location**: Urban. **Surface**: asphalted. ⬛ 01/01-31/12

Dunfanaghy · 1B2
N56. **GPS**: n55,18392 w7,97303.
10 🛏 ⚡🗨Ch. ⬛ 01/01-31/12

Connaught

Corraguan · 1A2
White Strand. **GPS**: n53,66904 w9,90211.
10 🛏free. **Location**: Rural. ⬛ 01/01-31/12

Galway · 1B2
Galway Harbour, Dockstreet. **GPS**: n53,27004 w9,04885.
15 🛏8-19h € 2/h, 19-8h € 4 ⚡⚡€3/10kWh. 🚐
Location: Urban. **Surface**: asphalted. ⬛ 01/01-31/12

Portumna · 1B2
Castle Avenue. **GPS**: n53,08388 w8,22038.
8 🛏free ⚡WCfree 🗑.
Location: Rural. **Surface**: asphalted. ⬛ 01/01-31/12

Templeboy · 1B2
Beach Bar, Aughris head. **GPS**: n54,26908 w8,75696.
10 🛏€ 20 ⚡🗨Ch⚡included.
Location: Rural. **Surface**: grassy. ⬛ 01/01-31/12

Leinster

Glenmalure · 1B2
Glenmalure lodge, Wicklow Way. **GPS**: n52,95743 w6,35405.
4 🛏. **Location**: Rural. **Surface**: metalled. ⬛ 01/01-31/12

Munster

Askeaton · 1A2
Askeaton Leisurecenter, The Quay. **GPS**: n52,60273 w8,97511.
4 🛏. **Location**: Urban. **Surface**: asphalted. ⬛ 01/01-31/12

Ballinskellig · 1A3
Cois Tra Lower. **GPS**: n51,82093 w10,27323.
10 🛏free. **Location**: Rural. **Surface**: asphalted. ⬛ 01/01-31/12

Castletownbere · 1A3
Berehaven Golf Club, Filane West. **GPS**: n51,65417 w9,86125.
10 🛏€ 18 ⚡included 🗨Ch⚡€2 WCfree 🗑.
Location: Rural. **Surface**: metalled. ⬛ 01/01-31/12

Cobh · 1B3
Whitepoint Moorings. **GPS**: n51,84716 w8,30735.
10 🛏free. **Location**: Urban. **Surface**: asphalted. ⬛ 01/01-31/12

Liscanor · 1A2
Cliffs of Moher. **GPS**: n52,97145 w9,42475.
🛏€ 6/pp. **Location**: Rural. **Surface**: metalled. ⬛ 01/01-31/12

Midleton · 1B3
Distillery Road Car Park. **GPS**: n51,91344 w8,16981.
6 🛏 ⚡€0,25 🗨€0,25 Ch€0,25.
Location: Urban. **Surface**: asphalted. ⬛ 01/01-31/12

▮▮ Italy

Capital: Rome
Government: parliamentarian republic
Official Language: Italian
Population: 61,680,000 (2014)
Area: 301,318 km²

General information

Dialling code: 0039
General emergency: 112
Currency: Euro
Credit cards are accepted almost everywhere.

Regulations for overnight stays

Wild camping is allowed with permission of municipality, police or property owner when no problems occur.

Additional public holidays 2016

January 6 Epiphany
April 25 Liberation Day
May 1 Labor Day
June 2 Festa della Republica, National Holiday
August 15 Assumption of the Virgin Mary
November 1 All Saints' Day
November 2 Armistice Day
December 8 Immaculate Conception

Time Zone

Winter (Standard Time) GMT+1
Summer (DST) GMT+2

Trentino South Tyrol pages: 500-504
Friuli Venezia Giulia pages: 512-514
Aosta Valley pages: 491-492
Lombardy pages: 504-508
Veneto pages: 508-512
Milaan
Piemonte pages: 492-500
Emilia-Romagna pages: 514-519
Liguria pages: 519-521
Florence
San Marino pages: 530
Marche pages: 530-536
Tuscany pages: 521-530
Umbria pages: 539-542
Abruzzo pages: 542-543
Rome
Lazio pages: 536-539
Molise pages: 543
Campania pages: 545-546
Puglia pages: 543-545
Bašilicata pages: 546
Sardinia pages: 547-548
Calabria pages: 546-547
Palermo
Sicily pages: 548-551

IT

Aosta Valley

⛶S Antey-Saint-André 🏔 21G3
Località Filey, SR46. **GPS:** n45,81246 e7,58898.⬆.
15 ⬙free ⛽Ch. **Surface:** metalled. ⬛ 01/01-31/12
Distance: 🚶850m.

⛶S Aosta 🏔 ❄ 21G3
Via Cadutti del Lavoro. **GPS:** n45,73600 e7,33035.

30 ⬙€ 12/24h ⛽€1/100liter ⬙€2 Ch. ⚡€1/kWh.
Location: Urban, noisy. **Surface:** asphalted.
⬛ 01/01-31/12 ⬛ Thu-morning closed because of market
Distance: 🚶on the spot ⛽4,5km 🛒200m.
Remarks: Parking closes at 22h.

⛶S Aymavilles 21G3
Strada Comunale del Moulins. **GPS:** n45,70125 e7,23960.⬆.
20 ⬙€ 8/24h ⛽. **Surface:** metalled. ⬛ 01/05-31/10
Distance: 🚶on the spot ⛽2km.

⛶S Bionaz 21G3
Area Attrezzata Bosco di Lexert. GPS: n45,87458 e7,42381.
⬙€ 10/night ⛽⛽Ch.
Remarks: Picnic area at small lake.

⛶S Brusson 🏔 21H3
Foyer du Ski, Rue Vollon. **GPS:** n45,76617 e7,71117.

50 ⬙€ 10/24h ⛽⛽Ch ✂included. **Surface:** grassy/metalled.
⬛ 01/01-31/12
Distance: 🏊on the spot.
Remarks: At lake.

⛶S Cervinia/Breuil 🏔 ❄ 21G3
GPS: n45,92614 e7,62026.
50 ⬙€ 7/24h ⛽. **Surface:** asphalted. ⬛ 01/01-31/12
Distance: 🚶1km ⛵Lago Blu 400m ⊗on the spot.
Remarks: Shuttle bus to city centre.

⛶S Champorcher 🏔 ❄ 21G3
Area pic-nic, Loc. Chardonney. **GPS:** n45,62153 e7,60654.⬆➡.
⬙free ⛽free. **Surface:** grassy/metalled.
Remarks: Nearby parking funicular railway.

⛶S Chatillon 21G3
Area Camper attrezzata Chatillon, Località Chopine.
GPS: n45,74889 e7,62388.⬆.
⬙€ 6/12h ⛽⛽Ch ✂. **Surface:** metalled. ⬛ 01/01-31/12
Distance: 🚶historical centre ⛽500m.

⛶S Cogne 21G3
Fraz. Lillaz. **GPS:** n45,59602 e7,38815.⬆.

38 ⬙€ 8,50, Jul-Aug and 24/12-6/1 € 10,50, tourist tax excl ⛽⛽Ch.
Surface: asphalted. ⬛ 01/01-31/12
Distance: 🚶100m 🛒on the spot ⊗100m 🍴100m 🚲on the spot
🚶1km.
Remarks: Altitude 1650m.

⛶S Cogne 🏔 21G3
Fraz. Revettaz. **GPS:** n45,60840 e7,35830.⬆.

120 ⬙€ 8, 1/7-31/8 + 24/12-6/1 € 10 ⛽⛽Ch ✂€2.
Surface: asphalted. ⬛ 01/01-31/12 ⬛ water disconnected in winter
Tourist information Cogne:
🌿 Parco Nacionale Gran Paradiso, Vall d'Aosta. Nature reserve, information centres: Dégioz, Rhêmes-Notre-Dame and Cogne.

⛶S Courmayeur 🏔 ❄ 21F3
Funivia Val Veny. GPS: n45,81428 e6,95612.⬆➡.
⬙free ⛽⛽. **Surface:** metalled. ⬛ 01/01-31/12
Distance: 🚶3km ⊗on the spot.

Gressoney ⛰️ ❄️ 21H3

P Weissmatten, Via Bildschocke, Saint Jean.
GPS: n45,76028 e7,83556. ⬆️.

🚐15/12-31/03 - 01/07-31/08 € 10/24h ⚡🔌. Surface: asphalted.
⬛ 01/01-31/12
Remarks: Parking funicular railway.

Gressoney ⛰️ ❄️ 21H3

Tschaval, La Trinité. GPS: n45,85657 e7,81362. ⬆️➡️.

36 🚐 € 12/24h, May-Oct € 10 ⚡🔌Ch 🔌€3 WC 🚿.
Surface: metalled. ⬛ 01/01-31/12, 24/24h
Distance: ⊗2 restaurants 🛒300m 🔌on the spot 🚌on the spot
🏊on the spot 🚲200m.

Hône ⛰️ 21H3

Via Raffort. GPS: n45,61169 e7,73262. ⬆️.
10 🚐 € 8 ⚡🔌Ch 🔌included. Surface: metalled.
⬛ 01/01-31/12
Distance: 🚶350m 🚲7km.
Remarks: Max. 48h.

La Thuile ⛰️ 🏕️ ❄️ 21F3

Area Azzura. GPS: n45,70823 e6,95335.

75 🚐 € 12/24h ⚡🔌Ch 🔌(45x)€3 🚿. Surface: metalled.
⬛ 01/01-31/12
Distance: 🚶500m 🏊500m 🚲100m.

Pont-Saint-Martin 21H3

Piazzale Palazzetto dello Sport. GPS: n45,60025 e7,79338.
🚐free. Surface: asphalted.
Distance: 🚲1km.

Rhemes Notre Dame 24G1

Loc. Chanavey. GPS: n45,57960 e7,12392.
🚐 € 5 ⚡🔌 🔌included. Surface: metalled.
Distance: 🏊on the spot.

Rhemes Notre Dame 24G1

Frazione Bruil. GPS: n45,57148 e7,11848.
20 🚐free. Surface: asphalted.

Saint-Denis ⛰️ 21G3

Strada Regionale del Col Saint Pantaléon, Loc. Plaù.
GPS: n45,77129 e7,56092.
10 🚐free ⚡🔌Ch 🔌free. Surface: grasstiles/grassy.
Distance: 🚲16km.

Saint-Oyen ⛰️ ❄️ 21G3

Rue de Flassin. GPS: n45,82133 e7,20822. ⬆️.
🚐 € 12/24h ⚡🔌Ch 🔌 WC included 🔌€1. ⬛ 01/01-31/12
Distance: 🚲22km ⊗on the spot 🚲on the spot.

Torgnon 21G3

Plan Prorion. GPS: n45,80397 e7,55490. ⬆️➡️.
25 🚐 € 8/24h ⚡🔌Ch 🔌. Surface: asphalted. ⬛ 01/01-31/12
Distance: 🏊50m.

Valgrisenche ⛰️ 21G3

Frazione Bonne. GPS: n45,61931 e7,05930.

20 🚐 € 10/24h ⚡🔌Ch 🔌€3. Surface: grassy/sand.
Remarks: At weir.

Valsavarenche ⛰️ 24G1

GPS: n45,59229 e7,20839. ⬆️.
🚐 € 5/12h ⚡🔌Ch. Surface: grasstiles. ⬛ 01/01-31/12
Distance: 🚶100m.
Remarks: Check in at town hall Tabaccheria or Bar Lo Fourquin, with registration number motorhome.

Verrès 21G3

Via Stazione. GPS: n45,66214 e7,69356. ⬆️.

6 🚐 € 5 ⚡🔌free. Surface: asphalted.
Distance: 🚶200m 🚲1,5km.

Piedmont

Acceglio 24F3

SP422. GPS: n44,47526 e6,98530. ⬆️.
🚐free. Location: Rural, isolated, quiet. Surface: grassy/gravel.
⬛ 01/01-31/12
Remarks: Max. 24h.

Acqui Terme 🌿 🏕️ ♨️ 25A2

Area comunale, SS456, Viale Einaudi. GPS: n44,66533 e8,47228. ⬆️.

150 🚐 € 8 ⚡🔌Ch 🔌(16x)included WC. 🚿
Location: Urban, comfortable, central, noisy.
Surface: grasstiles/metalled. ⬛ 01/01-31/12
Distance: 🚶1,5km 🚲25km ⊗50m 🚲250m.

Aglié 24H1

Via della Gula. GPS: n45,36662 e7,76381. ⬆️.

40 🚐free. Location: Urban, simple. Surface: metalled.
⬛ 01/01-31/12
Distance: 🚶on the spot.

Alba 🌿 🏕️ 24H2

Alba Village, Corso Piave 219, loc. San Cassiano.
GPS: n44,68537 e8,01019. ➡️.

20 🚐 € 8 + € 0,50/pp tourist tax ⚡€0,50/30liter 🔌Ch 🚿free 🧺.
Location: Urban, comfortable, central. Surface: grassy.
⬛ 01/01-31/12
Distance: 🚶2,5km 🚲1km ⊗on the spot 🛒100m 🚌on the spot.
Remarks: Nearby Hotel&Camping Alba Village, max. 48h, check in at reception, monitored parking.

Alessandria 25A2

Area comunale, Viale Teresa Michel. GPS: n44,92075 e8,62722. ⬆️.

25 🚐free ⚡🔌Ch. Location: Urban, simple. Surface: asphalted.
⬛ 01/01-31/12
Distance: 🚶2km 🚲2km ⊗on the spot 🛒500m 🚌on the spot.

Arona 22A3

Via Michelangelo Buonarotti. GPS: n45,76879 e8,54495.
20 🚐free. Surface: metalled. ⬛ 01/01-31/12
Distance: 🚶2km ⊗200m 🛒2km.

Asti 🌿 24H2

Piazza Campo del Palio. GPS: n44,89712 e8,21057. ⬆️.
>50 🚐free ⚡🔌. Location: Urban, simple, central, noisy.
Surface: asphalted. ⬛ 01/01-31/12 ⬤ Wed-Sa
Distance: 🚶on the spot ⊗on the spot 🛒on the spot.

Avigliana 🌿 ⛰️ ➡️ 24G2

Via Giovanni Suppo. GPS: n45,07304 e7,39004. ⬆️➡️.

8 🚐free ⚡🔌Ch free. Location: Urban, simple, quiet.
Surface: asphalted.
Distance: 🚶1km 🚲4,6km.
Remarks: Nearby sports complex.

Tourist information Avigliana:
🏕️ ⬛ Thu.

Barge 24G2

Via Carlo Alberto. GPS: n44,73108 e7,32000. ⬆️.

4 🚐free ⚡🔌Ch free. Location: Simple. Surface: asphalted.
Distance: 🚶800m 🚌on the spot.

Battifollo 24H3

Pian del Mondo, Via Crosa. GPS: n44,31994 e8,01858. ⬆️➡️.
30 🚐 € 10 ⚡🔌Ch 🔌 WC included 🚿. Location: Rural, comfortable. Surface: gravel. ⬛ 01/01-31/12
Distance: 🚶700m 🛒500m.

IT

Baveno | 22A3

Area Comunale, Piazza Umberto Giordano.
GPS: n45,91139 e8,50056.↑.

40 free € 12/24h ⚡ ChWC included. Surface: metalled.
01/01-31/12
Distance: 500m 2,8km Lago Maggiore 300m 300m.
Remarks: Behind railway station, max. 72h, no camping activities, weekend: noisy.

Bibiana | 24G2

Piazza 3° Alpini. **GPS**: n44,79581 e7,29366.→.

8 free ⚡ Ch. **Location:** Urban, simple.
Surface: metalled.
Distance: 500m 500m.

Biella | 24H1

Area Comunale, Piazzale Sandro Pertini. **GPS**: n45,55559 e8,06760.↑.

30 free ⚡ free. **Location:** Urban. **Surface:** asphalted.
01/01-31/12
Distance: on the spot 100m station 100m.
Remarks: Square next to station F.S San Paolo.

Bielmonte | 21H3

Piazzale 2, SS232. **GPS**: n45,66250 e8,08472.
8 € 3,50 ⚡ Ch included € 3,50.

Borgo San Dalmazzo | 24G3

P Area Camper, Strada Communale Del Cimitero.
GPS: n44,32889 e7,49167.↑→.

15 free ⚡ Ch free. **Location:** Urban, simple, quiet.
Surface: asphalted. 01/01-31/12
Distance: 100m.
Remarks: At sports park.

Borgosesia | 21H3

Piazza Valentino milanaccio, Via Varallo.
GPS: n45,72005 e8,27408.↑.

✈ ☐ Su.

8 free ⚡ Ch free. **Location:** Urban. **Surface:** asphalted.
01/01-31/12 Jun
Distance: 300m.
Remarks: Market Saturday.

Candelo | 24H1

Area Comunale, Via C. Pavese/Via F. Bianco.
GPS: n45,54244 e8,11524.↑.

10 free ⚡ Ch free. **Location:** Urban, quiet. **Surface:** gravel.
01/01-31/12
Distance: 400m 400m 100m.
Remarks: Nearby sports center.

Candelo | 24H1

Area Ricetto, Via Mulino. **GPS**: n45,54624 e8,11573.↑.

25 free ⚡ Ch free. **Location:** Comfortable.
Surface: metalled. 01/01-31/12
Distance: 400m 400m.

Canelli | 24H2

Piazza Unione Europea. **GPS**: n44,72039 e8,29369.↑.

15 free ⚡ Ch free. **Location:** Urban, simple, noisy.
Surface: asphalted. 01/01-31/12
Distance: 500m on the spot on the spot.

Cannobio | 22A2

Area Comunale, Via Al Fiume / Via San Rocco.
GPS: n46,06179 e8,69242.↑→.

20 € 15/24h ⚡ ChWC free. **Location:** Rural.
Surface: grasstiles. 01/01-31/12
Distance: 500m on the spot 500m 300m.
Remarks: Along river, max. 3 days.
Tourist information Cannobio:

Carcoforo | 21H3

Le Giare, SP11, Loc. Tetto Minocco. **GPS**: n45,90769 e8,05130.↑.

100 € 10/day, € 15/weekend, € 40/week ⚡ Ch free (16x) € 1,50
WC € 1. **Surface:** grassy. 01/03-30/09
Distance: on the spot 50m 300m.
Remarks: Along the Egua river.

Casale Monferrato | 25A1

Palazzetto dello Sport Paolo Ferraris, Via Visconti.
GPS: n45,12556 e8,46194.↑.

15 free ⚡ in shopping centre. **Location:** Rural.
Surface: asphalted. 01/01-31/12
Distance: 1,5km 3,6km 200m 200m.
Remarks: At sports centre.

Casale Monferrato | 25A1

Parcheggio Castello, Piazza Castello. **GPS**: n45,13722 e8,44806.↑.

>10 free. **Location:** Urban, simple, central, noisy.
Surface: asphalted. Tue, Fri 6-16h (market)
Distance: 200m 4km 100m 250m on the spot on the spot.

Casaleggio Boiro | 25A2

Via Castello. **GPS**: n44,63354 e8,73254.↑→.

8 free ⚡ Ch free (6x) included. **Location:** Rural, comfortable, quiet. **Surface:** gravel. 01/01-31/12
Distance: 250m 10km 150m 250m.

Castelletto Stura | 24G3

Via Cuneo. **GPS**: n44,44194 e7,63444.↑.

20 free ⚡ free. **Location:** Rural, simple.
Surface: gravel.

Remarks: Nearby sports park.

Castiglione Falletto · 24H2
Area comunale, Piazzale Muntelier. **GPS:** n44,62379 e7,97486. ⬆.

10 🛏free 🚰Chfree 📶. **Location:** Rural, comfortable, quiet.
Surface: metalled. 🔲 01/01-31/12
Distance: 🚶100m ⊗100m 🛒100m.

Castiglione Tinella · 24H2
Camperstop Ai Ciuvin, Agriturismo, Strada Manzotti 3.
GPS: n44,73357 e8,18140. ⬆.

12 🛏€ 20 🚰Ch 🧺WC. **Location:** Rural, comfortable, isolated,
quiet. **Surface:** grassy. 🔲 01/01-31/12
Distance: 🚶15km ⌁20km ⊗on the spot 🛒15km.
Remarks: Max. 48h.

Cavour · 24G2
Via Vigone. **GPS:** n44,78766 e7,37660. ⬆.

18 🛏€ 5/24h 🚰Chfree. **Surface:** metalled.
Distance: 🚶400m ⊗100m.

Ceresole Reale · 24G1
Borgata Chiapili Inferiore, SP50. **GPS:** n45,45142 e7,18587. ⬆.
🛏€ 8 🚰€4 🚰Ch 🚰€3. **Surface:** unpaved.
Distance: 🚶4km ⊗Ristorante Lo Sciatore 🛒2km.
Remarks: Along the Orco river, national Park 'Gran Paradiso'.

Ceresole Reale · 24G1
Borgota Villa, SP50. **GPS:** n45,44053 e7,21066.

40 🛏free 🚰WCfree.
Surface: grassy/gravel.
Distance: 🚶Ceresole Reale 2km ⌁on the spot ⊗200m.
Remarks: At lake, national park 'Gran Paradiso', altitude 1350m.

Cesana Torinese · 24F2
Area Sosta Camper Casa Cesana, Viale Sen. Bouvier.
GPS: n44,94782 e6,79516. ⬆.

12 🛏€ 10/24h 🚰Chincluded 🔌(12x)€3/day,6Amp.
Location: Simple. **Surface:** asphalted. 🔲 01/06-01/11
Distance: 🚶300m ⊗50m 🍴100m.
Remarks: Check in at hotel.

Cherasco · 24H2
Parking Area Camper, Piazza Giovanni Paolo II.
GPS: n44,64946 e7,85529. ⬆.

9 🛏free 🚰Chfree 🔌(8x)against payment WC.
Location: Rural, simple, quiet. **Surface:** asphalted.
🔲 01/01-31/12
Distance: 🚶400m ⌁3,7km ⊗200m 🛒300m.
Remarks: Max. 48h.

Chianocco · 24G1
Area Camper Giraude. **GPS:** n45,14110 e7,16592. ⬆➡.

20 🛏€ 3-6 🚰Ch WCincluded. **Location:** Rural, simple.
Surface: grassy/gravel. 🔲 01/04-31/10
Distance: 🚶1km.

Chiaverano · 24H1
Area Camper Lago Sirio, Strada Provinciale 75.
GPS: n45,48585 e7,88815. ⬆.

🛏€ 10 🚰Ch 🔌€2 WC. **Surface:** grassy. 🔲 01/01-31/12
Distance: ⌁on the spot 🛒on the spot ⊗on the spot 🏃on the spot.

Chieri · 24H2
Piazza Quarini, via Bernardo Vittone. **GPS:** n45,00391 e7,82744.

12 🛏free 🚰Chfree. **Surface:** asphalted. 🔲 01/01-31/12
Distance: 🚶on the spot 🚆200m > Turin.
Remarks: Behind Barracks, tuesday market.

Chieri · 24H2
Strada San Silvestro. **GPS:** n45,01460 e7,83214. ⬆.

10 🛏free 🚰Chfree. **Location:** Urban, simple.
Surface: asphalted.
Distance: 🚶on the spot ⊗50m 🛒50m.

Chiusa di Pesio · 24H3
Via Provinciale (SP42). **GPS:** n44,27233 e7,66361.

8 🛏€ 4 🚰Ch.
Distance: ⌁on the spot ⊗300m 🛒700m 🚲on the spot
🏃on the spot.

Chiusa di San Michele · 24G2
Via Pragallo. **GPS:** n45,10294 e7,33034. ⬆➡.

5 🛏€ 8 🚰 🔌included. **Location:** Simple, comfortable.
Surface: gravel.
🔲 01/04-31/10
Distance: ⌁8km ⊗600m.
Remarks: Max. 48h, to be paid at Uffici Comunali, Piazza Bauchiero 2.

Chivasso · 24H1
Piazza Libertini, Via Gerbido. **GPS:** n45,18514 e7,89296. ⬆.

20 🛏free 🚰€2 🛒. **Location:** Urban, simple.
Surface: asphalted.
Distance: 🚶300m 🛒Carrefour 100m.
Remarks: Parking swimming pool.

Collegno · 24G2
Collegno Area Sosta Camper, Corso Pastrengo.
GPS: n45,08070 e7,58313. ⬆.

30 🛏free 🚰€0,50 🛒€0,50 Ch€1 🔌€1/4h.
Location: Quiet. **Surface:** asphalted.
Distance: ⌁4km 🚆on the spot.
Remarks: Coins at Autolavaggio Il Draghetto, video surveillance.

Cortemilia 24H3

Strada San Roco. **GPS**: n44,57848 e8,18567.
10 free Chfree. **Location**: Simple. **Surface**: gravel.
Distance: 500m 500m.
Remarks: Max. 48h.

Cravagliana 21H3

Pian delle Fate, Loc. Brugarolo, SP di Valle Mastallone.
GPS: n45,85223 e8,22473.

30 € 14/24h Ch (4x)WC included. **Surface**: grassy.
15/03-15/10
Distance: on the spot on the spot.

Crissolo 24G2

Via Ruata. **GPS**: n44,69771 e7,15931.

20 € 5 ChWC included. **Location**: Urban, simple, quiet.
Surface: asphalted.
Distance: on the spot on the spot.

Cuceglio 24H1

Area Camper Erbaluce, Via Porta Pia 69/71. **GPS**: n45,34724 e7,81168.

10 € 12 (10x) included.
Location: Rural, comfortable. **Surface**: gravel.

Donato 24H1

Area Camper Fabrizio de André, Via S. Pertini, SP405.
GPS: n45,52774 e7,90944.

6 € 3/night WC free. **Location**: Rural. **Surface**: grasstiles.
01/01-31/12
Distance: 300m 300m.
Remarks: Pay at Tabaccheria in the village.

Entracque 24G3

Area C'era una Volta, SS22. **GPS**: n44,25151 e7,38975.

18 € 15 Ch (16x)WC €5/day €1 included.
Location: Rural. **Surface**: unpaved. 01/01-31/12
Distance: 1km river-beach 500m 500m on the spot 1km
> Cuneo on the spot on the spot 1km.

Entracque 24G3

Parcheggio Camper Real Park, Ponterosso.
GPS: n44,26111 e7,37750.

66 € 6 Ch included. **Location**: Rural.
Surface: grassy/gravel.
Distance: 3km on the spot on the spot 6km.
Remarks: Recreation park, max. 2 days.

Entracque 24G3

Via del Mulino. **GPS**: n44,23389 e7,39723.

60 € 12/24h, € 20/48h (50x)included €2.
Location: Rural, simple. **Surface**: gravel.
Distance: 300m.

Fenestrelle 24G2

Le Casermette. GPS: n45,03671 e7,05090.

20 free, fri-su € 5-10, Jun-Aug € 10 Ch included.
Surface: unpaved. 01/01-31/12

Fenestrelle 24G2

GPS: n45,03889 e7,04583.

9 free free. **Surface**: asphalted.
Remarks: Next to cemetery.

Frabosa Soprana 24H3

Grotta di Bossea, Loc.Bossea 10. **GPS**: n44,24077 e7,83939.
5 free Chfree WC. **Location**: Rural, simple, isolated.
Surface: asphalted. 01/01-31/12
Distance: 12km on the spot on the spot 12km on the

spot.
Remarks: Parking at the caves.

Garessio 24H3

Area Comunale, Str.Provinciale del Colle di San Bernardo (P582).
GPS: n44,19927 e8,02587.

30 free Chfree. **Location**: Rural, simple. **Surface**: asphalted.
01/01-31/12
Distance: 1km 22km 1km 1km.

Genola 24H3

Grosso Vacanze, Via Divisione Alpina Cuneense 2, SS20.
GPS: n44,59751 e7,65982.

free Ch. **Surface**: metalled. 01/01-31/12
Remarks: Motorhome dealer, accessory shop.

Giaveno 24G2

SP187, via Torino. **GPS**: n45,04154 e7,36096.

free free. **Surface**: asphalted.
Distance: 100m.

Grinzane Cavour 24H2

Piazza Ugo Genta, Via Bricco. **GPS**: n44,65515 e7,98936.

3 free Chfree. **Location**: Rural, simple, isolated, noisy.
Surface: asphalted. 01/01-31/12
Distance: 500m 500m 2km on the spot.

Ivrea 24H1

La Dora d'Ivrea, Via Dora Baltea. **GPS**: n45,46334 e7,87621.

10 € 5 Chincluded. **Location**: Comfortable.
Surface: asphalted. 01/01-31/12
Distance: 500m 4,5km Ipermercato 800m 350m.
Remarks: Beside river.

ⓈLocana 24G1
Via Nusiglie. **GPS:** n45,41361 e7,46278.
€ 5/24h ⛽💧€3/24h WC.

ⓈMacugnaga ⛰ 21H3
Pecetto, Di Iacchine Pierluigi Loc. Pecetto. **GPS:** n45,97015 e7,95352.⬆.

28 🅿 € 10, 2 nights € 15 ⛽🍴ChWCfree.♿
Location: Rural, simple, quiet. **Surface:** concrete.
▢ 01/05-30/11
Distance: 🚶1km ⊗100m 🛒500m 🚗100m 🏃on the spot.
Remarks: At ski-lift.

ⓈMadonna del Sasso 22A3
Area Comunale, Via Santuario, Fraz. Boleto.
GPS: n45,78974 e8,37222.⬆.

8 🅿free ⛽🍴Chfree. **Surface:** grasstiles. ▢ 01/01-31/12
Distance: 🚶200m 🛶Lago d'Orta 700m ⊗100m 🛒50m.
Remarks: Narrow entrance, view at Lago d'Orta.

Maglione ⚜🏕 24H1
SP78, Via Cigliano. **GPS:** n45,34338 e8,01456.⬆.

20 🅿free. **Location:** Rural, simple, quiet. **Surface:** grassy.
Distance: 🚶on the spot ⊗50m.
Remarks: Art city.

ⓈMarsaglia 24H3
Via della Stazione, SP115. **GPS:** n44,45228 e7,97929.
18 🅿 € 13 ⛽Ch💧 WC. **Surface:** asphalted/grassy.
▢ 01/01-31/12
Distance: 🚶on the spot.
Remarks: Inspection june 2013: closed because of renovation.

ⓈMelle 24G3
SP8. **GPS:** n44,56245 e7,31739.⬆.

22 🅿 € 3, 01/06-01/10 € 5 ⛽🍴ChWCincluded.♿
Location: Comfortable. **Surface:** metalled. ▢ 01/01-31/12
Distance: ⊗250m.

ⓈMirabello Monferrato 25A2
SS31. **GPS:** n45,03016 e8,52946.⬆.

---

8 🅿free ⛽€2🍴Ch€1. **Location:** Simple, isolated, quiet.
Surface: asphalted. ▢ 01/01-31/12
Distance: 🚶900m ✈10km ⊗800m 🛒50m 🚗50m.

ⓈMombarcaro 24H3
SP103. **GPS:** n44,46900 e8,08352.
8 🅿€5 ⛽🍴Ch💧included. **Location:** Rural, comfortable.
Surface: metalled. ▢ 01/01-31/12
Distance: ⊗500m.

ⓈMombaruzzo 25A2
Club Agrisportivo Mombaruzzo, SP4. **GPS:** n44,77993 e8,45061.
🅿 € 10 ⛽🍴Ch💧€2 WC. ▢ 01/01-31/12
Distance: 🚶1,5km.

ⓈMondovì ⚜ 24H3
Piazza le Giardini. **GPS:** n44,39430 e7,82370.⬆➡.
🅿free ⛽🍴Chfree. **Location:** Simple, noisy. **Surface:** asphalted.
▢ 01/01-31/12
Distance: 🚶500m.
Remarks: Nearby bus station, parking under railway bridge.

ⓈMondovì ⚜ 24H3
Piazza Republica. **GPS:** n44,38964 e7,81930.⬆.
🅿free. **Location:** Urban, simple, central. **Surface:** asphalted.
▢ 01/01-31/12
Distance: 🚶400m ✈5km ⊗50m 🛒100m 🚗on the spot.
Remarks: Nearby the old station.

ⓈMondovì ⚜ 24H3
Mondovicino Outlet Center. **GPS:** n44,41889 e7,84966.⬆➡.
🅿free ⛽🍴Ch. **Location:** Simple. **Surface:** asphalted. ▢ 25/12, 01/01
Distance: 🚶4km ✈1,2km 🛒on the spot.
Remarks: Parking at Outlet Center and Centro Commercial.

ⓈMongrando 24H1
Area Comunale, Via dei Giovanni. **GPS:** n45,52543 e8,00595.⬆.

15 🅿 € 4/24h ⛽🍴Ch💧included.♿ **Location:** Urban, quiet.
Surface: grasstiles. ▢ 01/01-31/12
Distance: 🚶900m.
Remarks: At sports centre.

ⓈMontiglio Monferrato 24H2
Via Padre Carpignano. **GPS:** n45,06261 e8,10045.
25 🅿free ⛽💧.

ⓈNeive 24H2
Via Crocetta. **GPS:** n44,72753 e8,11332.⬆.

6 🅿 € 10 ⛽🍴Ch💧(6x)WC included. **Surface:** grassy/gravel.
Distance: 🚶100m ⊗100m.
Remarks: Check in at sport centre.

ⓈNiella Tanaro 24H3
Agriturismo i Fornelli, Via Fornello 1. **GPS:** n44,41418 e7,90988.⬆.

3 🅿€5 ⛽€3,50🍴Ch💧€2,50/24h WC.
Location: Rural, simple, isolated, quiet. **Surface:** grassy/gravel.
▢ 01/01-31/12
Distance: 🚶4km ✈2km ⊗1km 🛒10km.
Remarks: Farm products.

ⓈNizza Monferrato ⚜ 25A2
Parking Camper Piazzale S.Pertini, Piazzale Sandro Pertini.
GPS: n44,77140 e8,35346.⬆.

14 🅿€5 ⛽🍴Ch💧Service, electricity incl. €3.♿
Location: Urban, comfortable, central, quiet. **Surface:** grassy.
▢ 01/01-31/12
Distance: 🚶200m ✈20km ⊗500m 🛒500m.
Remarks: Gate closed, first call Motorhome Club Nicese between 9-20h.

ⓈNovi Ligure 25A2
Viale Pinan Cichero, zona stadio comunale. **GPS:** n44,77006 e8,78200.⬆.

25 🅿free ⛽🍴free. **Location:** Urban, simple, noisy.
Surface: asphalted. ▢ 01/01-31/12
Distance: 🚶1,5km ✈2km ⊗on the spot 🛒600m.
Remarks: Parking gymnasium.

ⓈOccimiano 25A2
Via Circonvallazione. **GPS:** n45,05834 e8,50940.⬆.

5 🅿€5 ⛽🍴Ch💧included. **Location:** Rural, comfortable.
Surface: asphalted. ▢ 01/01-31/12
Distance: 🚶250m ✈15km ⊗250m 🛒400m.
Remarks: To be paid at bar Concordia.

ⓈOggebbio 22A3
Fiesta, Via Martiri Oggebbiesi 6. **GPS:** n45,99680 e8,65304.⬆➡.

20 🅿 € 18/24h ⛽🍴Ch💧WCincluded 🔌€1 🚿€5,/24h.

IT

Location: Luxurious.
Surface: gravel.
🚐 01/06-31/12
Distance: ⚓on the spot ⊗700m.
Remarks: Attention: narrow road, view on Lago Maggiore.

Omegna 22A3
Lido di Omegna, Via Caduti di Bologna. **GPS:** n45,86340 e8,39840.⬆️.

25 🚐€ 8-15 🚽♨Ch✦€3. **Surface:** metalled. 🚐 01/01-31/12
Distance: 🏙️1,8km ⚓beach.
Remarks: Caution key electricity € 30.

Ormea 24H3
Via Orti della Rana. **GPS:** n44,14532 e7,90751.➡️.

10 🚐€ 10 🚽♨Ch. **Location:** Rural, comfortable, quiet.
Surface: grasstiles. 🚐 01/01-31/12
Distance: 🏙️1km ⊗500m 🍴1km.

Oropa 21H3
Area di Santuari, Via Santuario di Oropa.
GPS: n45,62864 e7,97530.⬆️➡️.

31 🚐€ 10, 01/05-30/09 € 15, 01/07-31/08 € 21 🚽♨Ch✦WC.
Location: Rural. **Surface:** metalled.
🚐 01/01-31/12 ☀️ snow
Distance: ⊗500m.

Orta San Giulio 22A3
Parco del Sacro Monte, Via Sacro Monte. **GPS:** n45,79732 e8,41204.⬆️.

8 🚐free. **Surface:** gravel. 🚐 01/01-31/12
Distance: 🏙️900m ⊗400m.
Remarks: Max. 48h.

Orta San Giulio 22A3
Via Panoramica. **GPS:** n45,79729 e8,41527.⬆️.

20 🚐€ 10/24h. 🚌 **Surface:** asphalted. 🚐 01/01-31/12
Distance: 🏙️500m ⚓Lago d'Orta 500m ⊗100m.

Ovada 25A2
Via Gramsci. **GPS:** n44,64084 e8,64920.➡️.

25 🚐free 🚽free. **Location:** Simple, central. **Surface:** metalled.
🚐 01/01-31/12
Distance: 🏙️300m 🚲3km ⊗100m 🍴500m.

Piatto 21H3
Area Comunale, Fraz. Malina. **GPS:** n45,58908 e8,13630.⬆️.

10 🚐free 🚽♨Ch. **Location:** Urban. **Surface:** asphalted.
🚐 01/01-31/12
Remarks: At sports park.

Pietraporzio 24G3
Area Camper Pontebernardo, Via Nazionale, SS21.
GPS: n44,34868 e7,01831.⬆️.

21 🚐€ 5/24h 🚽♨Ch. **Location:** Rural, comfortable.
Surface: gravel. 🚐 01/01-31/12
Distance: 🏙️100m.
Remarks: 3rd night free.

Pinerolo 24G2
Olimpico, Via Alpi Cozie. **GPS:** n44,88917 e7,35111.⬆️.

10 🚐free 🚽♨Ch✦(10x)against payment. **Location:** Urban,
simple. **Surface:** metalled. 🚐 01/03-01/11
Distance: 🏙️2km 🚲1,5km ⊗300m 🍴300m 🚗200m.
Remarks: Nearby sports park.

Pollone 21H3
Burcina di Pollone, Via Felice Piacenza.
GPS: n45,58548 e8,00521.⬆️➡️.

20 🚐€ 10/24h 🚽♨Ch✦WCincluded 🚰€2. 🚌 **Location:** Rural,

comfortable. **Surface:** grasstiles.
🚐 01/01-31/12
Distance: 🏙️600m ⊗on the spot.
Remarks: At parco Naturale Burcina.

Pombia 22A3
Safari Park, SS 32 km 23,4. **GPS:** n45,64167 e8,61740.
🚐free 🚽WC. **Surface:** asphalted.

Ponderano 24H1
Area Comunale, Strada Vicinale al Cimitero.
GPS: n45,53683 e8,04949.⬆️.

10 🚐free 🚽free. **Location:** Urban, simple. **Surface:** gravel.
🚐 01/01-31/12
Distance: 🏙️400m.
Remarks: Nearby sports park.

Pont Canavese 24G1
Via Roma. **GPS:** n45,42153 e7,60020.
12 🚐€ 7 🚽♨2 Ch✦€2. **Surface:** grassy. 🚐 01/01-31/12
Distance: ⚓on the spot.
Remarks: Max. 48h.

Pontechianale 24G3
Area Camper, Fraz Maddalena. **GPS:** n44,62158 e7,02776.
🚐€ 8/24h 🚽♨ **Surface:** grassy.

Pontechianale 24G3
Chianle, SP 251. **GPS:** n44,65055 e6,99280.
15 🚐free. **Location:** Simple, isolated. **Surface:** grassy/gravel.
Distance: 🏙️4km ⚓on the spot.

Pragelato 24F2
Villagio GoFree, SS23. **GPS:** n45,02187 e6,94914.

🚐€ 16-21, 4 pers.incl 🚽♨Ch✦€1,50 WC📶. 🚐 12/06/-13/09
Distance: 🚴on the spot 🥾on the spot 🚵on the spot ⛷️on the spot.
Remarks: Spa, ski, tennis, golf.

Prali ❄️ 24G2
Fraz.Ghigo. **GPS:** n44,89176 e7,04956.⬆️.

🚐free 🚽♨Chfree. **Surface:** grassy.
Distance: 🏙️300m ⚓on the spot.
Remarks: Altitude 1450m, along river.

Prarostino 24G2
Porto di Montagne, Via Piani. **GPS:** n44,86488 e7,26970.⬆️.

IT

15 ⫼ € 7 ⛽🗑Ch🚿 WC included. **Location:** Comfortable.
Surface: grassy/gravel. ⬛ 01/01-31/12 ❄ With snow
Distance: ⊗300m 🛒200m 🚲 on the spot.
Remarks: To be paid at bar.

🏕S　　Prato Nevoso 🏔❄　　24H3
Area Stalle Lunghe, Via Corona Boreale. **GPS:** n44,25200 e7,78192. ⬆.

⫼ € 15-20 ⛽🗑Ch🚿. **Surface:** asphalted. ⬛ 01/01-31/12
Distance: 🚶 on the spot ✈A6 33km ⊗on the spot 🛒50m
🚲 on the spot.

🏕S　　Prato Nevoso 🏔❄　　24H3
Piazza G. Dodero. **GPS:** n44,25200 e7,78192. ⬆➡.

10 ⫼ free. **Location:** Rural, simple, central. **Surface:** asphalted.
⬛ 01/01-31/12
Distance: 🚶 on the spot ⊗on the spot 🚲 on the spot 🚌 on the spot.

🍴S　　Rimasco　　21H3
Il Laghetto, Strada del Lago. **GPS:** n45,86109 e8,06450. ⬆.

20 ⫼ € 10/24h ⛽🗑Ch🚿 €2/day WC included 🗑. **Surface:** grassy.
⬛ 01/05-30/09 🍴 Restaurant: Tue
Distance: 🛶 on the spot ⊗on the spot.

🍴S　　Riva Valdobbia　　21H3
Area Lo Chalet, Fraz Gabbio. **GPS:** n45,83467 e7,95469. ⬆.

48 ⫼ € 13/24h ⛽🗑Ch🚿 €3 WC included 🗑.
Surface: grassy/metalled. ⬛ 01/04-31/10
Distance: 🛶 on the spot ⊗on the spot.
Remarks: Along river.

🏕S　　Roaschia 🏔🍴　　24G3
Area camper I Funtanil, Via Circonvallazione, SP 108.
GPS: n44,26758 e7,45860. ⬆.

15 ⫼ € 9 ⛽🗑Ch WC 🚿 included. **Location:** Rural, comfortable,

---

quiet. **Surface:** gravel.
Distance: 🚶 on the spot.

🏕S　　Romano Canavese　　24H1
Strada provinciale 56. **GPS:** n45,38644 e7,86177. ⬆.

10 ⫼ ⛽🗑. **Location:** Rural, simple.
Surface: grasstiles/metalled.
Distance: ✈2,2km.

🏕S　　Rosta　　24G2
Via Buttigliera Alta 2, Via Piave. **GPS:** n45,07106 e7,46333.

5 ⫼ free ⛽€2 Ch€2. **Location:** Urban. **Surface:** asphalted.
⬛ 01/01-31/12
Distance: 🛒 on the spot 🚆 train > Turin 19min.

🏕S　　Saluzzo 🌿　　24G2
Area Bodoni, Via Olivero Matteo. **GPS:** n44,63886 e7,49192. ⬆.

17 ⫼ free ⛽🗑 free. **Location:** Urban, simple. **Surface:** grasstiles.
⬛ 01/01-31/12
Distance: 🚶700m ⊗200m.
Remarks: Small pitches.

🏕S　　Saluzzo 🌿　　24G2
Via Cuneo 16. **GPS:** n44,63739 e7,49740. ⬆.

±10 ⫼ free ⛽🗑 free. **Location:** Urban. **Surface:** asphalted.
⬛ 01/01-31/12
Distance: 🚶1km.

🏕S　　San Damiano d'Asti 🌿　　24H2
Via Monsignor Franco. **GPS:** n44,82659 e8,05921. ⬆.

50 ⫼ free ⛽🗑Ch. **Location:** Rural, simple. **Surface:** gravel.
⬛ 01/01-31/12
Distance: 🚶1km ⊗1km 🛒1km.
Remarks: At cemetery.

🏕S　　San Damiano d'Asti 🌿　　24H2
Azienda Agricola Cascina Piana, Fraz S.Grato.
GPS: n44,85136 e8,07417.

25 ⫼ € 8-10 ⛽🗑Ch🚿 (8x)WC 🗑 included. **Location:** Rural,
comfortable, isolated, quiet. **Surface:** grassy. ⬛ 01/01-31/12
Distance: 🚶1,5km ⊗1,5km 🛒500m.
Remarks: Farm products.

🏕S　　Sanfront　　24G2
Via Montebracco, SP26. **GPS:** n44,64944 e7,32056. ⬆➡.

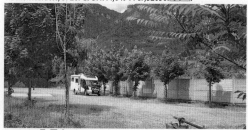

15 ⫼ free ⛽🗑Ch free.
Location: Urban, simple. **Surface:** unpaved.
Remarks: At sports park, max. 24h.

🏕S　　Santa Maria Maggiore ✈　　22A2
Area Verde Attrezzata, Via Alfredo Belcastro/via Pineta.
GPS: n46,13219 e8,45500. ⬆➡.

32 ⫼ € 15/24h ⛽🗑Ch🚿🚮 **Location:** Rural. **Surface:** gravel.
⬛ 01/01-31/12
Distance: ⊗200m 🚲 on the spot.
Remarks: Max. 48h.

🏕S　　Santa Maria Maggiore ✈　　22A2
Agriturismo Al Piano delle Lutte, Via Domodossola 57.
GPS: n46,13569 e8,44753.

3 ⫼ € 10/24h ⛽🗑Ch🚿 according consumption WC 🗑. 🚮
Location: Rural, simple. **Surface:** grassy/gravel.
⬛ 01/01-31/12
Distance: 🛒 on the spot.

🏕S　　Sant'Antonino di Susa　　24G2
Area Sosta Il Sentiero Dei Franchi, Borgo Cresto 16/1.
GPS: n45,09973 e7,27754. ⬆.

20 🛏 € 10 🚰🔌Ch 🚿€2. **Location:** Simple, comfortable, quiet.
Surface: grassy/gravel. 🅿 01/01-31/12
Distance: ⊗on the spot 🚶on the spot.
Remarks: Check in at restaurant.

⛺S Sestriere ⛰❄ 24F2
Lago Losetta, Strada Azzurri d'Italia. **GPS:** n44,96465 e6,88141.⬆.

60 🛏 € 15/24h 🚰🔌Ch 🚿📶included. **Surface:** unpaved.
🅿 01/01-31/12
Distance: 🚶800m 🚌Shuttle bus to ski-piste.

⛺S Sommariva Perno 24H2
Area comunale, Loc.Piano, SP0. **GPS:** n44,75126 e7,89667.⬆➡.

10 🛏free 🚰🔌Chfree. **Location:** Rural, simple, noisy.
Surface: gravel. 01/01-31/12
Distance: 🚶500m 🚲13km ⊗250m 🍴250m.

⛺S Susa ⛱ 24G1
Piazza Repubblica. **GPS:** n45,13861 e7,05389.⬆.

12 🛏free 🚰🔌Chfree 🚿€1. **Location:** Urban, simple, central.
Surface: asphalted. 🅿 01/01-31/12
Distance: 🚶300m ⊗500m 🍴800m.

⛺S Tagliolo Monferrato 25A2
Str. del Varo. **GPS:** n44,63760 e8,67029.
21 🛏 € 5/24h 🚰🔌Ch. **Location:** Rural, simple, quiet.
Surface: grassy/gravel.
🅿 01/01-31/12
Distance: 🚶250m 🚲2km ⊗200m 🍴400m.
Remarks: Max. 72h, keycard barrier at Bar/Tabac, caution € 10.

⛺S Torino ⛱🍴 24H2
Corso Casale 327. **GPS:** n45,08084 e7,72993.⬆➡.

🛏free 🚰🔌free. **Location:** Urban, noisy.
Surface: asphalted.
Distance: 🚶800m ⊗100m 🚌150m.

⛺S Torino ⛱🍴 24H2
Corso Giovanni Agnelli. **GPS:** n45,02888 e7,63924.⬆.

57 🛏 € 10 🚰🔌Chincluded 🚿€0,50 WC 🗑€1 📶.🚮
Location: Urban, comfortable. **Surface:** grasstiles.
🅿 01/01-31/12
Distance: 🚶4km 🚲4km ⊗100m 🍴100m 🚌on the spot.
Remarks: Max. 5 days, monitored parking 24/24.

⛺S Torino ⛱🍴 24H2
Parco Ruffini, Corso Lione/Corso Carlo Piaggia, Turin (Torino).
GPS: n45,05686 e7,63166.⬆.

20 🛏free 🚰🔌Chfree. **Location:** Urban, simple, noisy.
Surface: asphalted.
Distance: 🚶city centre 5km ⊗on the spot.

Tourist information Turin (Torino):
Ⓜ Mole Antonelliana. National Film museum.
Ⓜ Museo Nazionale dell'Automobile, Corso Unità d'Italia 40. Museum of motor-cars. 🅿 Tue-Sa, 10-18.30h, Su 10-20.30h ⬤ Mo.
Ⓜ Palazzo Madame. Historical art.
♜ Palazzo Reale. Royal palace.
✝ Cathedral, 1498.
✝ Basilica di Superga. Baroque basilica.

⛺S Usseaux ⛱🌳🎡 24G2
Magic Forest, Strada Comunale dell'inverso 1.
GPS: n45,04170 e6,98518.⬆.

100 🛏 € 15 🚰🔌Ch 🚿 WC 🗑€1 ⬤€5 📶included. **Location:** Rural, comfortable. **Surface:** grassy. 🅿 01/06-01/09

⛺S Usseaux ⛱🌳🎡 24G2
Area sosta Usseaux, Fraz. Fraisse-Pourrières. **GPS:** n45,04146 e6,98500.
🛏 € 15 🚰🔌ChWC 🚿. **Surface:** grassy.

⛺S Usseaux ⛱🌳🎡 24G2
Lago di Laux, Via Lago 7. **GPS:** n45,04166 e7,02222.➡.

100 🛏 € 15/24h 🚰€3 🔌€3 Ch 🚿(54x)€2,50/24h. **Location:** Rural, simple, isolated, quiet. **Surface:** grassy.
🅿 01/06-31/09
Distance: 🚶500m 🚲200m ⊗on the spot 🍴5km.
Remarks: Pay at restaurant.

⛺S Valdieri ⛰🐾 24G3
Centro Alpino S.Anna, Loc. S. Anna. **GPS:** n44,24513 e7,32548.⬆➡.

40 🛏 € 12 🚰🔌Ch 🚿included. **Location:** Rural.
Surface: grassy/gravel.
Distance: 🚶100m ⚓on the spot ⊗100m.
Remarks: Narrow entrance (bridge).

⛺S Valdieri ⛰🐾 24G3
Parco Alpi Marittime, Terme di Valdieri. **GPS:** n44,20546 e7,26840.

🛏 € 10 🚰🔌Ch 🚿. **Surface:** gravel. 🅿 01/01-31/12

⛺S Valle Mosso 21H3
Piazza Alpini d'Italia. **GPS:** n45,63316 e8,14629.⬆.

3 🛏free 🚰🔌Chfree. **Location:** Urban. **Surface:** asphalted.
🅿 01/01-31/12
Distance: 🚶on the spot 🛒Conad 20m 🚌50m.

⛺S Varallo 21H3
Area Comunale, Via Sant'Antonio. **GPS:** n45,81797 e8,24857.⬆.

8 🛏 € 10/24h 🚰🔌Ch 🚿included. **Location:** Urban, quiet.
Surface: gravel/sand. 🅿 01/01-31/12
Distance: 🚶500m 🍴500m.
Remarks: To be paid at town hall.

⛺S Venaria Reale 24G1
Relax and Go, Via Scodeggio 15. **GPS:** n45,14108 e7,62404.➡.

15 🛏 € 18-20 🚰🔌Chincluded 🚿€2/day. **Location:** Simple.
Surface: grassy.
Distance: 🚲2km ⊗500m 🍴500m 🚌bus GTT, tram 72>Turin.

⛺S Venasca 24G3
SP8, Via Provinciale. **GPS:** n44,56620 e7,39328.⬆➡.

20 🛏free 🚰🔌Chfree. **Location:** Rural, simple, noisy.
Surface: asphalted.
Distance: 🚶600m.

Verbania 22A3

Area Zone Arena, Via San Bernardino. **GPS:** n45,93143 e8,57106. 🔼.
13 🛏 € 10/24h 🔧 included. 🚿 **Location:** Simple. **Surface:** asphalted.
🅿 01/01-31/12
Distance: 🚶600m 🏊50m ⊗100m 🛒250m.

Vercelli 25A1

Via Trento, c/o piazzale Pala-hockey. **GPS:** n45,33417 e8,41861. 🔼.

10 🛏free 🚰🔌free. **Location:** Urban, simple. **Surface:** asphalted.
🅿 01/01-31/12
Distance: 🚶1,5km 🚲6km ⊗50m 🛒1,5km 🚌on the spot.
Tourist information Vercelli:
✝ Basilica di Sant'Andrea. Basilica, part of abbey.

Vergne 24H3

Piazza della Vite e del dell Vina. **GPS:** n44,61298 e7,92064. 🔼.
6 🛏free 🚰🔌Chfree. **Location:** Simple. **Surface:** metalled.
Distance: 🚶on the spot ⊗on the spot.

Vernante 24G3

E74. **GPS:** n44,24489 e7,53219. 🔼.

20 🛏 € 5 🚰free. **Location:** Urban, simple. **Surface:** asphalted.
Distance: 🚶200m ⊗200m 🛒300m 🚴on the spot.

Vialfrè 24H1

Via Luigi Emanuel, SP55. **GPS:** n45,38298 e7,81754. 🔼.

7 🛏free 🚰🔌Chfree. **Location:** Rural, simple.
Surface: grasstiles.
Distance: 🚶on the spot 🚲6km ⊗300m 🛒300m.

Vidracco 24H1

Damanhur Crea, Via Baldissero 21. **GPS:** n45,42884 e7,75327. 🔼.

30 🛏 € 8/24h 🚰🔌Ch 🚿(24x)WC included.
Location: Simple, quiet. **Surface:** asphalted.
Distance: ⊗cafetaria 🛒on the spot.
Tourist information Vidracco:
👁 Damanhur Crea, Via Baldissero 21. Extraordinary Italian artistic and spritual community.

Villar Focchiardo 24G2

Area Camper Villar Focchiardo, Via Fratta, SS24.
GPS: n45,11336 e7,22408. 🔼➡.

54 🛏 € 5-10, weekend € 15 🚰🔌Chfree. 🚿 **Location:** Rural, simple, comfortable, quiet. **Surface:** grassy. 🅿 01/01-31/12 🅿 camper service: 01/11-31/03
Distance: 🚲4,5km.

Villar Pellice 24G2

Parco Flissia, Via Cave del Fin. **GPS:** n44,80472 e7,15083. 🔼.

20 🛏 € 6 🚰🔌ChWCfree. **Location:** Rural, simple, isolated.
Surface: grassy. 🅿 01/04-01/10
Distance: 🚶500m 🏊on the spot 🎣fishing permit obligatory 🛒agriturismo.
Remarks: Service passerby € 3.

Vinadio 24G3

Area di Sosta Communale, Bagni di Vinadio, Fraz. Strapesi.
GPS: n44,28747 e7,07534. 🔼🔼.

30 🛏 € 11/24h 🚰🔌Ch free. **Location:** Rural, simple.
Surface: grassy/gravel.
Distance: 🚶300m, Vinadio 10km 🏊on the spot 🎿on the spot.
Remarks: Altitude 1350m, parking at the spa resort of Strapeis.

Vinadio 24G3

Piazza d'Armi, SS21. **GPS:** n44,30667 e7,17083. 🔼.

🛏1/6-31/8 € 5 🚰 🔌Chfree. **Surface:** asphalted.
Distance: 🚶400m.

Volpedo 25B2

Lungo Curone Matteotti. **GPS:** n44,88512 e8,98707. 🔼➡.

6 🛏free 🚰🔌Chfree. **Surface:** grassy/gravel.
Distance: 🚶600m.
Remarks: At sports park.

Zubiena 24H1

Prà Gros Agriturismo, SS338, Casale Montino.
GPS: n45,49812 e7,98934. 🔼.

6 🛏 🚰🔌. **Location:** Rural. **Surface:** gravel/metalled.
Distance: ⊗on the spot.

Trentino South Tyrol

Andalo 22D2

Via Rindole, 6, Loc. Rindole. **GPS:** n46,16113 e11,00647.

80 🛏 € 15 🚰🔌Ch 🔧€5. **Surface:** asphalted. 🅿 summer
Distance: 🚶200m ⊗on the spot.
Remarks: Service passerby € 5, beautiful view.

Arco 22D3

Piazzale Carmellini, Viale Paolina Caproni.
GPS: n45,92232 e10,89032. 🔼.

14 🛏 € 1,50/4h, max. € 10/24h. **Surface:** asphalted.
🅿 01/01-31/12
Distance: 🚶200m ⊗200m.
Remarks: Max. 72h.

Arco 22D3

Viale Rovereto. **GPS:** n45,91820 e10,89225. 🔼.
🚰🔌Chfree. 🅿 water disconnected in winter

Barbiano 22E1

Kollmann Stop, Frazione Colma, SS12. **GPS:** n46,58728 e11,52401. 🔼.

IT

15 🛏 € 10, in envelope in mail box 🚰🔌Ch 🛁 included.
Location: Simple, noisy. **Surface:** gravel. 🗓 01/01-31/12
Distance: 🚶300m 🚲9km ⊗300m 🚉300m 🚌on the spot
🚲 on the spot.
Remarks: Along through road, max. 48h.

Baselga di Pine 22E2

Ice Rink Piné, Via Dello Stadio. **GPS:** n46,12617 e11,25382.⬆

10 🛏 free. **Surface:** metalled.

Bolzano/Bozen 22E1

Parking Fiera Messe, Via Bruno Buozzi. **GPS:** n46,47417 e11,32617.⬆

30 🛏 free 🚰🔌Chfree. **Location:** Urban, simple, noisy.
Surface: asphalted. 🗓 01/01-31/12
Distance: 🚶centre 4km 🚲1,1km ⊗on the spot 🚉4km 🚌on the spot.
Remarks: Along railwayline.

Bolzano/Bozen 22E1

Via Maso della Pieve. **GPS:** n46,47327 e11,33693.⬆

8 🛏 € 0,70/h mo-fr 8-19h, sa 8-13, overnight stay free 🚰🔌Ch.🛢
Location: Urban, simple, noisy. **Surface:** asphalted.
🗓 01/01-31/12
Distance: 🚶city centre 3km 🚉100m 🚌on the spot.

Borgo Valsugana 22E2

Via Tommaso Temanza. **GPS:** n46,05444 e11,46361.

18 🛏 € 10/24h 🚰🔌Ch 🛁 included. **Surface:** metalled.
Distance: 🚶100m ⛵20m 🚣20m ⊗100m 🚉100m.
Remarks: Max. 48h, service passerby € 5.

Braies 22F1

P2, Lago di Braies, Fraz. San Vito. **GPS:** n46,70265 e12,08520.➡

25 🛏 € 5-15 🛢€0,50. 🚲 **Location:** Rural, simple, quiet.
Surface: gravel. 🗓 30/05-31/10
Distance: 🚶Braies 5km ⛵Lago di Braies 250m ⊗250m 🚉5km
🚲 on the spot 🏃 on the spot.

Brentonico 22D3

Via al Dosset. **GPS:** n45,81540 e10,95581.⬆➡

11 🛏 € 7 🚰€2 🔌Ch 🛁€3. **Surface:** asphalted. 🗓 01/01-31/12
Distance: 🚶400m 🚲10km ⊗250m 🚉300m.

Brunico/Bruneck 22F1

P2, Piazza Mercato di Stegona. **GPS:** n46,79558 e11,93006.⬆

>25 🛏 free. **Location:** Urban, simple, noisy. **Surface:** gravel.
🗓 01/01-31/12
Distance: 🚶800m ⊗500m 🚉500m 🚌on the spot 🚲on the spot
🏃 on the spot.

Tourist information Brunico/Bruneck:
ℹ️ Associazione Turistica, Via Europa,24. Fortified city, 14th century.
Ⓜ Regional museum.
☀ Annual fair. 🗓 last week Oct.

Caldes 22D2

Rafting Val di Sole, Loc. Contrè. **GPS:** n46,36139 e10,94528.

30 🛏 € 10, Jul € 13, Aug € 15 🚰🔌🛁€6. **Surface:** asphalted.
🗓 01/04-30/09
Distance: 🚶2km ⊗200m 🚉2km.

Caldonazzo 22E2

Via al Lago. **GPS:** n46,00501 e11,26307.⬆

30 🛏 € 8/6-22h (01/04-30/9), € 10/night. **Surface:** grassy/sand.
🗓 01/01-31/12
Distance: ⛵50m ⊗300m.
Remarks: Payment only with coins.

Cavalese 22E2

P Fondovalle, SP232. **GPS:** n46,28438 e11,47256.⬆

50 🛏 € 10 🚰. **Location:** Simple. **Surface:** grasstiles/metalled.
🗓 01/01-31/12

Chiusa 22E1

Gamp, Via Gries 10. **GPS:** n46,64128 e11,57244.➡

20 🛏 € 14,50-16/24h 2 pers. + 2 children incl, dog € 2 🚰🔌Ch
included. **Location:** Rural, simple. **Surface:** grassy.
🗓 01/01-31/12
Distance: 🚶300m 🚲800m ⊗on the spot 🚉mini market 🚌100m
🚲 on the spot 🏃 on the spot.

Corvara in Badia 22F1

P Corvara, Strada Planac SS244. **GPS:** n46,54105 e11,88388.⬆

10 🛏 free. **Location:** Rural, simple, isolated. **Surface:** gravel.
🗓 01/01-31/12
Distance: 🚶3,5km 🚉3,5km.

Dimaro 22D2

Camper Solander, Loc. Rovina. **GPS:** n46,32488 e10,86215.⬆

10 🛏 € 20/24h, € 10/night 🚰🔌Ch 🛁 WC 🛢 included.
Surface: gravel. 🗓 01/01-31/12
Distance: 🚶500m ⊗on the spot.
Remarks: Near campsite Dolomiti.

Dimaro 22D2

Hotel Belvedere, SS239. **GPS:** n46,29734 e10,86765.
🛏 € 15/24h 🚰🔌Ch 🛁 included. **Surface:** asphalted.
🗓 01/01-31/12

Eppan 22E1

Camper Stop Eppan, Sillnegg 2. **GPS:** n46,44871 e11,26418.⬆
27 🛏 € 18/24h 🚰🔌Ch 🛁 WC 🛢 included. **Location:** Comfortable,
luxurious, quiet. **Surface:** gravel.
Distance: 🚶800m ⊗pizzeria 200m 🚉800m 🚌100m 🚲 on the spot
🏃 on the spot.

Folgaria 22E3

Area Sosta Bucaneve, Via Negheli 87. **GPS:** n45,91849 e11,19255.⬆
25 🛏 € 8. **Surface:** grassy/metalled. 🗓 01/01-31/12
Distance: 🚶300m 🚲mountainbike trail 🏄100m.
Remarks: Golf court, shuttle bus.

IT

⌂S Folgaria ❄🏕🏔🎪❄ 22E3
Osteria Carador, Via Neghelli 58. **GPS:** n45,91748 e11,19094. ⬆
🏕€ 8/24h 🚰€5. **Surface:** gravel/sand. ⬛ 01/01-31/12
Distance: ⊗on the spot 🚲on the spot.
Remarks: Golf court.

S Folgaria ❄🏕🏔🎪❄ 22E3
SS3501. **GPS:** n45,91397 e11,17081. ⬆
🚰€1 🍳Ch.

S Gargazzone ❄🏔🎪 22E1
Weisshof-Törgelle-Keller, Landstrasse 65 SS38.
GPS: n46,58500 e11,20528. ⬆.

10 🏕€ 10 🚰🍳Ch 🚰€2/24h WC🍳€1. **Location:** Rural, simple, quiet. **Surface:** grassy/gravel. ⬛ 01/01-31/12
Distance: 🚶2km 🏊1,5km ⊗500m 🛒2km 🚐on the spot 🚿on the spot 🧍on the spot.
Remarks: Reservation for Christmas holidays, tel.: +39 (0)473 292448.
Tourist information Gargazzone:
ℹ Consorzio Turistico, Via Maria Trost, 5, Merano, www.meranerland.com. Place with medicinal sources.
M🏛 Castel Tirolo, 4km N. de Merano. Regional museum. ⬛ 01/03-31/12.
🛍 Merano. ⬛ Tue, Fri.
🎉 Festa della Città, Merano. ⬛ 1st weekend Aug.

⌂S Glorenza 22D1
Glurms Camping im Park, > SS41. **GPS:** n46,67067 e10,54520. ⬆➡

40 🏕€ 12 🚰🍳Ch 🚰€2 WC🍳. **Surface:** grassy.
Distance: 🚶500m 🏊on the spot.
Remarks: Along the Adige river.

⌂S La Villa in Badia 🏔❄ 22F1
Odlina, Strada Ninz, 49. **GPS:** n46,58889 e11,90028. ➡

45 🏕summer € 25, winter € 30 🚰🍳Ch 🚰WC🍳included ⬛€5 📶€3. 🅿 **Location:** Rural, luxurious, quiet. **Surface:** metalled. ⬛ 01/01-31/12
Distance: 🚶400m ⊗150m 🛒150m 🚐on the spot 🚿on the spot 🧍on the spot 🚲300m.
Remarks: Reservation for Christmas holidays: info@odina.it, use of sauna against payment.

⌂S Lago 22E2
Via Tresselume. **GPS:** n46,28291 e11,52557.

30 🏕free 🚰€1 🍳€2 Ch€1 🍳(12x)€2/8h. 🅿 **Location:** Rural, simple. **Surface:** metalled. ⬛ 01/01-31/12
Distance: 🚶200m ⊗200m.

⌂S Lavarone 🏕🏔🎪❄ 22E2
Prà Grando, Via Padova. **GPS:** n45,93602 e11,27099.

40 🏕€ 14 May/June/July, € 15 Aug, € 18 Dec-April 🚰🍳Ch🚰 included. **Surface:** grassy/gravel. ⬛ 01/05-30/09, 01/12-31/03
Distance: 🚶300m 🚲32km 🏊Lago di Lavarone 1km 🛒1km ⊗300m 🛒300m 🚐300m 🚴1km 🚲1km.

⌂S Lavarone 🏕🏔🎪❄ 22E2
SS 349, Loc Moar. **GPS:** n45,94575 e11,26397. ⬆

10 🏕€ 0,40/h 🚰€0,50 🍳Ch. 🅿
Location: Simple. **Surface:** metalled.
Distance: 🚶800m 🏊Lago di Lavarone 1,9km ⊗500m.

⌂S Levico Terme ❄🏕🏔🎪❄♨ 22E2
Area Sosta Camper Valsugana, Loc Pleina.
GPS: n46,00691 e11,28706. ⬆➡

50 🏕€ 25 🚰Ch WC. **Surface:** grassy. ⬛ 01/01-31/12
Distance: 🚶1,3km 🏊200m, Lido di Levico 1,1km ⊗50m 🛒50m 🚐on the spot.
Remarks: Max. 3 nights, check in at reception campsite.

⌂⌂S Levico Terme ❄🏕🏔🎪❄♨ 22E2
Area 47, SP1. **GPS:** n46,00415 e11,28880.
24 🏕€ 15, 01/06-30/09 € 25 🚰🍳Ch 📶included.
Distance: 🚶1,3km ⊗on the spot.
Remarks: Including access to swimming pool and private beach.

⌂⌂S Moena 🏔❄ 22E2
Bar Il Giardino, SS 48 Forno di Moena. **GPS:** n46,35238 e11,63149. ➡

50 🏕€ 10-12 🚰🍳Ch included 🚰€4/24h.
Location: Rural, comfortable, central. **Surface:** grassy/metalled. ⬛ 01/01-31/12
Distance: 🚶3,5km ⊗500m 🛒2km 🚐300m 🚐on the spot 🧍on the spot 🚲on the spot.
Remarks: Max. 48h, skibus comes at parking.

⌂S Molveno 22D2
Area attrezzata per camper Lago di Molveno, Via Lungolago, 25, Loc. Ischia. **GPS:** n46,14018 e10,96011. ⬆➡

50 🏕€ 12-28 🚰🍳Ch🚰included. **Surface:** metalled. ⬛ 01/01-31/12
Distance: 🚶800m 🏊200m ⊗200m 🛒100m.

⌂S Molveno 22D2
Via Lungolago,Loc. Ischia. **GPS:** n46,14165 e10,95727. ⬆

20 🏕€ 9-22 🚰🍳Ch🚰included. **Surface:** metalled. ⬛ 01/01-31/12
Distance: 🚶1km 🏊400m ⊗200m 🛒100m.

⌂S Pergine Valsugana ❄ 22E2
Soleando Camperparking, Via al lago 23/A. **GPS:** n46,05184 e11,22494.

10 🏕€12/day 🚰🍳Ch. **Surface:** gravel.
Distance: 🚶600m 🏊Lago di Caldonazzo 1km ⊗300m 🛒300m 🚐100m 🚲on the spot.
Tourist information Pergine Valsugana:
ℹ www.apt.trento.it. City at the foot of the Dolomites with historical centre.
M Palazzo Pretorio, Trento. Ecclesiastical museum.

⌂S Predazzo 🏔❄ 22E2
Latemar 2200, SS48, dir Moena. **GPS:** n46,32582 e11,59970. ⬆

50 🏕free, peak season € 7-10/24h 🚰🍳Ch included. 🅿
Location: Rural, simple, noisy. **Surface:** asphalted/gravel. ⬛ 01/01-31/12
Distance: 🚶2,5km 🛒2,5km 🚐on the spot 🧍on the spot 🚲on the spot 🚠on the spot.
Remarks: Parking ski-lifts.

⌂S Rabbi 22D2
Area camper Plan, Loc. Plan, Bagni di Rabbi.
GPS: n46,40619 e10,82629. ⬆➡

105 🏕€ 14-21, 2 pers.incl. 🚰🍳Ch 🚰WC included 🍳against

payment ▣. **Surface:** metalled. ▣ 01/06-30/09
Distance: 🚂600m.
Remarks: Former campsite, max. 48h.

Racines 🏔   19E3

Sportzone Ratschings, Belprato, Stanghe.
GPS: n46,88254 e11,38383. ⬆.

20 🅿free. **Location:** Rural, simple. **Surface:** gravel.
▣ 01/01-31/12
Distance: 🚂400m ⌁ 5km ⊗400m 🍴400m 🚌400m
🚶Gilfenklammroute.

Riva del Garda 🌿 ◳   22D3

Via Monte Brione. **GPS:** n45,87986 e10,85872. ⬆.

41 🅿€ 0,50/h, max. € 24/48h 🚰🅲h ✎ included.
Surface: grasstiles. ▣ 01/11-07/12
Distance: 🚂1,5km ⛱200m.
Remarks: Max. 48h.

Tourist information Riva del Garda:
Ⓜ Museo Civico, Piazza Battisti.

Rovereto 🌿   22E3

Area Camper Quercia, Via Palestrina. **GPS:** n45,90232 e11,03704. ⬆➡.
15 🅿€ 8/12h, € 16/24h 🚰🅲h ✎ WC▣. **Surface:** metalled.
▣ 01/01-31/12
Distance: 🚂1,5km ⌁2km.
Remarks: Caution € 5, bicycle rental.

Tourist information Rovereto:
Ⓜ Castello di Rovereto. War museum. ▣ Tue-Su ▣ 01/01-28/02.
🏰 Castel Beseno. ▣ Tue-Su.

San Candido 🏔 ❄   22F1

Area di Sosta Camper, Via Prato alla Drava, 1/A.
GPS: n46,73924 e12,36559. ➡.

90 🅿€ 15 🚰🅲h ✎WCincluded ▣€2. 🚴 **Location:** Rural,
comfortable, quiet. **Surface:** gravel. ▣ 01/01-31/12
Distance: 🚂6km ⊗on the spot 🍴500m 🚌on the spot 🚲on the spot
🚶on the spot 🚲2km ⛱500m.
Remarks: Bicycle rental, shuttle bus San Candido and skipistes € 1/pp.

San Guiseppe al Lago ◳   22E2

Posteggio Camper Lago di Caldero, San Guiseppe 18.
GPS: n46,39038 e11,25663. ➡.

35 🅿€ 15/night 🚰🅲h ✎WC▣. 🚴 **Location:** Rural, comfortable,

---

quiet. **Surface:** gravel. ▣ 13/03-15/11
Distance: 🚂5km Caldero ⛱Private beach ⊗50m 🍴Nearby campsite.
Remarks: Next to campsite, max. 4 days.

San Martino di Castrozza 🏔 ❄   22F2

Area camper Tognola, Loc.Tognola. **GPS:** n46,25373 e11,80158. ⬆.

80 🅿€ 12 🚰▣included 🅲h ▣€ 1/80minutes. 🚗 ▣ 01/01-31/12
Location: Rural, comfortable, quiet. **Surface:** gravel. ▣ 01/01-31/12
Distance: 🚂1,5km ⊗500m 🚌on the spot 🚶on the spot
🚲on the spot.
Remarks: Next to ski-lift, free shuttle.

San Vigilio di Marebbe 🏔 ❄   22F1

Restaurant Pizzeria Rittenkeller, Ras-Costa 2.
GPS: n46,70630 e11,92920. ➡.

120 🅿01/04-30/11 € 20, 01/12-31/03 € 25 🚰🅲h ✎included.
Location: Rural, simple, quiet. **Surface:** gravel.
▣ 01/01-31/12
Distance: 🚂600m ⌁500m ⊗on the spot 🍴600m 🚌600m
🚲on the spot ⛱600m.
Remarks: Next to ski-lift, reservation for Christmas holidays:
info@ritterkeller.it.

Santa Cristina Valgardena 🏔   22E1

P1 Monte Pana, Strada Pana. **GPS:** n46,55174 e11,71624. ⬆.

50 🅿free, peak season € 4/day. 🚐 **Location:** Simple, isolated, quiet.
Surface: gravel. ▣ 01/01-31/12
Distance: 🚂2,5km 🍴2,5km.
Remarks: Altitude 1650m, max. 7 days, narrow entrance.

Selva di Val Gardena 🏔 ❄   22F1

Piz Sella, Strada Plan de Gralba. **GPS:** n46,53204 e11,77230. ⬆.

15 🅿free, Winter € 6/day, € 6 night. **Location:** Rural, simple.
Surface: gravel. ▣ 01/01-31/12
Distance: 🚂4km ⊗150m 🚶on the spot 🚲on the spot.
Remarks: Inclining pitches.

Sesto/Sexten ⚓ ❄ 🍴   22F1

Caravanpark Sexten, SS52 St Josefstrasse 54.
GPS: n46,66741 e12,39996. ➡.

36 🅿€ 23-29 🚰🅲h ✎WCincluded ▣€4 🔌€2.
Location: Rural, luxurious, quiet. **Surface:** grasstiles.
▣ 01/01-31/12
Distance: 🚂3km ⊗on the spot 🍴on the spot 🚌on the spot
🚲on the spot 🚶on the spot 🚲900m ⛱on the spot.
Remarks: Sauna and spa.

Silandro 🏔   22D1

Via Ospedale, Silandro/Schlanders. **GPS:** n46,62721 e10,78185.

🅿free. **Surface:** grasstiles.
Distance: 🚂500m ⊗500m.

Smarano 🏔 🏔 🍴   22E2

Area Sosta Ostaria del Filò, Viale Merlonga 48/a.
GPS: n46,34962 e11,10956. ⬆.

43 🅿€ 10-13-15 🚰🅲h ✎WC▣. **Surface:** grassy.
▣ 01/01-31/12
Distance: 🚂1km ⊗on the spot.
Remarks: Check in at restaurant.

Solda 🏔   22D1

GPS: n46,51448 e10,59578.
25 🅿free. **Location:** Simple. **Surface:** gravel. ▣ 01/01-31/12
Distance: 🚂1km ⊗100m 🚶on the spot 🚲on the spot.

Tirolo 🏔   22E1

Via principale. **GPS:** n46,68636 e11,15904. ⬆.

15 🅿€ 10,50/night 🚰WC. 🚴 **Location:** Rural, simple, quiet.
Surface: asphalted. ▣ 01/01-31/12
Distance: 🚂200m ⊗50m 🍴200m 🚌50m 🚲on the spot
🚶on the spot.

Tirolo 🏔 ❄ 🍴   22E1

Schneeburghof, Monte Benedetto 26. **GPS:** n46,67789 e11,16495.

IT

20 🛏 € 23 🚰🔌Ch 🔧 included. **Location:** Comfortable.
Surface: grassy.
Distance: 🏊 on the spot.

| 🍴S | Tonadico 🏔❄ | 22F2 |

Lanterna Verde, Via Zocchet 10. **GPS:** n46,18216 e11,84318. ➡️

45 🛏 € 15 🚰🔌Ch 🔧 included WC. **Location:** Rural, comfortable, quiet. **Surface:** grasstiles. 🅾 01/01-31/12
Distance: 🚰 1km ⊗100m 🚰 1km 🚌 on the spot 🚲 on the spot 🚶 on the spot 🚴 15km 🎿 15km.
Remarks: Max. 48h, check in at restaurant.

| 🛏S | Trento | 22E2 |

P Zuffo, Loc. Vela. **GPS:** n46,07650 e11,11050. ⬆️➡️

20 🛏 € 5 🚰 €1 🔌Ch. **Surface:** asphalted. 🅾 01/01-31/12
Distance: 🚰 1,8km 🚲 150m 🚌 200m.

| 🛏S | Trento | 22E2 |

Camper Trento Park, Via Brennero, 181. **GPS:** n46,09438 e11,11335.
200 🛏 € 12/24h 🚰🔌Ch 🔧 included 🚿€1 📶. **Surface:** asphalted.
🅾 01/01-31/12
Distance: 🚰 city centre 3km 🚲 2km ⊗400m 🚌 400m bus 3-11-17 > centre.
Remarks: Inspection 2015: closed because of renovation.

| 🛏S | Trento | 22E2 |

Parking Trentino, Via Santi Cosma e Damiano 64.
GPS: n46,07674 e11,10411. ⬆️

20 🛏 € 15 🚰🔌Ch 🔧 included. **Location:** Urban.
Surface: grasstiles. 🅾 01/01-31/12
Distance: 🚰 1,8km 🚲 300m ⊗300m 🚌 bus > centre 15 min.
Remarks: Call for entrance code: 3389004343 Mr. Pisetta.

| 🛏 | Trento | 22E2 |

P3 Giardino Botanico Fondo Viote, SP85. **GPS:** n46,02445 e11,03973.

100 🛏 € 4-10/10h, overnight stay free. **Location:** Rural, simple, isolated, quiet. **Surface:** asphalted. 🅾 01/01-31/12
Distance: 🚰 18km Trento 🏊 150m 🚌 on the spot 🚲 on the spot 🚶 on the spot 🚴 on the spot.
Remarks: Max. 48h.

| 🛏S | Tres 🏔🌲 | 22E2 |

A Monte del Paese, SP della Predaia. **GPS:** n46,32040 e11,10202. ⬆️

15 🛏 € 10/24h 🚰🔌Ch 🔧WC included. **Surface:** gravel.
🅾 01/01-31/12
Distance: 🚰 800m.

| 🍴 | Vezzano | 22D2 |

Vecchio Mulino, SS45bis. **GPS:** n46,07684 e11,01980. ⬆️
10 🛏. **Location:** Rural, simple. **Surface:** grassy.
🅾 25/04-10/11
Distance: ⊗ on the spot.

Lombardy

| 🛏S | Alzano Lombardo | 22C3 |

Via Europa. GPS: n45,73690 e9,72007. ⬆️➡️

3 🛏 🚰🚿. **Surface:** asphalted. 🅾 Sa 6-15h market
Remarks: At sports park.

| 🛏S | Biassono | 22B3 |

Via al Parco/Via della Sciavatera. GPS: n45,63102 e9,28865. ⬆️➡️

10 🛏 free 🚰🔌Ch free. **Location:** Rural, simple, isolated.
Surface: asphalted. 🅾 01/01-31/12
Distance: 🚰 500m 🛒 Centro Commerciale Vilasanta 4km 🚂 train > Milan 500m.

| 🛏S | Borgofranco sul Po | 25E1 |

Via Filipo Turati. GPS: n45,04775 e11,20524. ⬆️➡️

4 🛏 free 🚰🔌Ch free. **Location:** Simple, quiet. **Surface:** grassy.
🅾 01/01-31/12 🅾 water: frost
Distance: 🚰 600m 🏊 1km ⊗200m 🛒 300m 🚴 200m 🚶 200m.

| 🛏S | Bormio 🌺🏔❄🚴 | 22C1 |

Bormio 2000, Via Battaglion Morbegno. **GPS:** n46,46260 e10,37190. ⬆️

🛏 € 8/24h 🚰🔌Ch included. **Surface:** sand. 🅾 01/01-31/12

Distance: 🚰 500m ⊗500m 🏍 on the spot.
Remarks: Parking funicular railway, service passerby € 5.

Tourist information Bormio:
ℹ️ Ufficio Informazioni e di Accoglienza Turistica, Via Roma, 131/b. Alps city, large winter sport area, also summer skiing.
🌿 Parco Nazionale dello Stelvio. Region with 50 glacier lakes and high mountain peaks. Access around Bormio.

| 🛏 | Campione | 22D3 |

Area Camper Campione del Garda, Via Verdi.
GPS: n45,75651 e10,74985. ⬆️

30 🛏 € 15/24h 🚰. **Surface:** unpaved. 🅾 01/04-31/10
Distance: 🚰 500m 🏊 on the spot ⊗200m.

| 🛏S | Capo di Ponte | 22C2 |

Concarena, Via Santo Stefano. **GPS:** n46,02447 e10,34325. ⬆️➡️

12 🛏 € 8/24h, 1/10-28/2 free 🚰🔌Ch 🔧WC included.
Surface: asphalted. 🅾 01/01-31/12
Distance: 🚰 300m ⊗300m 🛒 300m.

| 🛏S | Certosa di Pavia 🏛 | 25B1 |

Parking Certosa, Via di Vittorio, SP27. **GPS:** n45,25735 e9,14161. ⬆️

20 🛏 € 4/night, € 5/day 🚰🔌ChWC free. 🚐
Location: Simple. **Surface:** grassy/gravel.
🅾 01/01-31/12 🅾 water disconnected in winter
Distance: 🚰 1km ⊗200m 🚌 on the spot 🚶 on the spot.
Remarks: Monastery Certosa di Pavia 450m.

| 🛏S | Certosa di Pavia 🏛 | 25B1 |

Località Certosa Monumento. GPS: n45,25574 e9,14632. ⬆️

🛏 € 4/night, € 4/day 🚰🔌ChWC free. **Surface:** sand.
🅾 01/01-31/12
Distance: ⊗500m.
Remarks: Monastery Certosa di Pavia 80m.

| 🛏S | Chiavenna | 22B2 |

Piazzale Leonardo da Vinci, Via A. Moro, SS36.
GPS: n46,31424 e9,39631. ⬆️➡️

IT

🚐free 🚰🚽Chfree. **Surface:** asphalted.
Distance: 🏙800m 🛒200m.

[S] Chiesa in Valmalenco 22C2

Loc. Vassalini. **GPS**: n46,27020 e9,85670.[↑].

🚐free 🚰€3 🚽. **Surface:** gravel.
Distance: 🏙1km 🥾200m.

[S] Clusone 22C3

Busgarina, Via Vago 6, loc Fiorine. **GPS**: n45,87312 e9,91642.[↑].

80🚐€ 13 🚰🚽Ch🔌(33x)€2 🚿€1/7minutes. ☐ 01/01-31/12
Distance: 🚲on the spot.

[S] Clusone 22C3

Viale Vittorio Emanuele. **GPS**: n45,88926 e9,95812.[↑].

5🚐free 🚰🚽Chfree. **Surface:** asphalted. ☐ 01/01-31/12
Distance: 🏙600m 🛒on the spot.
Remarks: Max. 48h.

[S] Colico 22B2

L'Ontano, Via Montecchio Nord. **GPS**: n46,14213 e9,37452.[↑][→].

25🚐€ 15/24h 🚰🚽Ch🔌WC🚿€1/3minutes. **Surface:** metalled.
☐ 01/02-31/12
Distance: 🏙500m ⛱on the spot 🍴on the spot.
Remarks: View on Lake Como.

[S] Cremona 25C1

Piazzale della Croce Rossa, Via Mantova.
GPS: n45,13744 e10,03464.[↑].

🚐free 🚰🚽Chfree. **Location:** Simple. **Surface:** asphalted.
☐ 01/01-31/12
Distance: 🏙on the spot 🎣3km 🍴on the spot 🛒200m
🚌on the spot.
Remarks: Nearby stadium.

[🍴][S] Desenzano del Garda 22D3

Pit-Stop La Spiaggia, Via Valtenesi, 19. **GPS**: n45,48783 e10,52468.[↑].

100🚐€ 10/24h 🚰🚽Chincluded. **Surface:** unpaved.
☐ 01/01-31/12
Distance: ⛱200m 🍴Pizzeria Stella Del Garda 🚌10m.

[🍴][S] Esine 22C3

Parco e Ristorante Le Fontanelle, Via Toroselle 12, SS42.
GPS: n45,90302 e10,21820.

15🚐 🚰🚽Ch. **Surface:** grassy. ☐ 01/01-31/12
Distance: 🏙4km 🍴on the spot.

[S] Gandino 22C3

Via Giovanni Pascoli. **GPS**: n45,81286 e9,90538.[↑][→].

2🚐free 🚰🚽Chfree. **Surface:** metalled. ☐ 01/01-31/12
Distance: 🏙historical centre 250m.
Remarks: Max. 48h.

[S] Gavirate 22A3

Via Cavour. **GPS**: n45,83913 e8,72105.[↑][→].

30🚐€ 8/day 🚰€2 🚽Ch€1 🔌€1/12h. 🚿
Location: Rural, simple, quiet. **Surface:** grasstiles.
☐ 01/01-31/12
Distance: 🏙200m ⛱10m 🍴on the spot 🚲on the spot 🥾on the spot.
Remarks: At lake of Varese, friday market.

[S] Germignaga 22A3

Via A. Bodmer. **GPS**: n45,99630 e8,72421.[↑].

6🚐€ 1,50/h, € 15/24h 🚰€1 🚽Ch🔌€3 WC. 🚿
Location: Simple, central, quiet. **Surface:** asphalted.
☐ 01/01-31/12
Distance: 🏙500m ⛱on the spot 🚲on the spot 🍴500m 🛒500m.
Remarks: Max. 48h, key electricity at pay-desk.

[🚐] Iseo 22C3

Viale Europa. **GPS**: n45,65396 e10,04449.

🚐free. **Surface:** unpaved. ☐ 01/01-31/12
Distance: 🏙1km ⛱250m 🍴600m.

Tourist information Iseo:
[i] I.A.T. (Ufficio Informazioni e di Accoglienza Turistica), Lungolago Marconi, 2. Old fishermen's village.
⛱ Week market. ☐ Fri.

[S] Lecco 22B3

Via Arturo Toscanini, Loc. Bione di Lecco. **GPS**: n45,83136 e9,40779.[↑].

12🚐free 🚰🚽Chfree. **Surface:** asphalted. ☐ 01/01-31/12
Distance: 🏙2,8km.
Remarks: At lake Garlate, cycle routes.

[S] Livigno ⛰❄ 22C1

Aquafresca, Via Palipert 374. **GPS**: n46,50713 e10,11952.[↑].
🚐 🚰🚽Ch🔌WC🚿. ☐ 01/01-31/12
Distance: 🥾on the spot ⛷on the spot.
Remarks: Free shuttle.

[S] Livigno ⛰❄ 22C1

Stella Alpina, Via Palipert 570. **GPS**: n46,50515 e10,11958.[↑].

28🚐€ 15 🚰🚽Ch🔌€3 WC🚿🧺📶. **Surface:** gravel.
☐ 01/01-31/12
Distance: 🏙400m 🚌Free bus 🥾on the spot.
Remarks: Free shuttle to ski-lifts.

[S] Livigno ⛰❄ 22C1

Trepalle, SS301. **GPS**: n46,52655 e10,17578.[↑].

IT

50 ⌐⌐ € 10 ⌐⌐ Ch free. **Surface:** asphalted.
Distance: 🏃Livigno 6,6km ⊗200m 🚌bus to Livigno every 40 minutes 🏃on the spot.
Remarks: Altitude 2000m.

Tourist information Livigno:
👁 Latteria di Livigno, Via Pemonte 911. Discover the secrets of dairy products from Livigno. On Wednesday the possibility of preparing meals, costs € 7, from 14h. ⌚ summer Mo-Fr 8-20h.

| 🗑S | **Lodrino** | 22C3 |

Via Kennedy, Localité Dade. **GPS:** n45,71450 e10,28107.⬆.

3 ⌐⌐free ⌐⌐Ch 🧹free. **Surface:** asphalted. ⌚ 01/01-31/12
Distance: 🏃500m.

| 🗑S | **Luino** | 22A3 |

Via Gorizia. **GPS:** n45,97255 e8,75275.⬆➡.

16 ⌐⌐€ 9 Ch. **Location:** Rural, isolated, quiet.
Surface: asphalted/grassy. ⌚ 01/01-31/12
Distance: 🏃3km ⊗on the spot 🏊3km.
Remarks: At sports grounds.

| 🗑S | **Maccagno** | 22A2 |

Via Virgilio Parisi. **GPS:** n46,04010 e8,73545.⬆➡.

18 ⌐⌐free ⌐free. **Location:** Rural, simple, central, quiet.
Surface: gravel.
Distance: 🏃300m 🏊200m 🚣200m ⊗300m 🏊300m 🚌300m 🚴on the spot 🏃on the spot.
Remarks: At sports centre, max. 72h, friday market.

| 🗑S | **Magnacavallo** | 25E1 |

Via Salvador Allende. **GPS:** n45,00587 e11,17906.⬆➡.

4 ⌐⌐free ⌐⌐Ch free. **Location:** Simple. **Surface:** asphalted.
⌚ 01/01-31/12

Distance: 🏃200m ⊗200m 🚣200m 🏍50m.
Remarks: At sports park.

| 🗑S | **Mandello del Lario** | 22B3 |

Area Cima, Via Giulio Cesare. **GPS:** n45,91830 e9,31589.➡.

12 ⌐⌐€10 ⌐⌐Ch. **Surface:** asphalted. ⌚ 01/01-31/12
Distance: 🏃800m 🏊Lago di Lecco 400m.

| 🗑S | **Mantova** 🍽 | 25D1 |

Parco Paganini, Via Fiera 11, Grazie di Curtatone.
GPS: n45,15333 e10,69111.⬆➡.

108 ⌐⌐€ 12 ⌐⌐Ch 🧹WC included. 🚐 **Location:** Simple, central.
Surface: asphalted/grassy. ⌚ 01/03-13/11
Distance: 🏃300m, Mantova 6km ⊗300m 🚣4km, bakery 300m.

| 🗑S | **Mantova** 🍽 | 25D1 |

Sparafucile, Via Legnago 1/a. **GPS:** n45,16336 e10,81244.⬆➡.

54 ⌐⌐€ 10/12-12h, € 15/24h ⌐⌐Ch 🧹WC included. 🚐
Location: Comfortable, luxurious, quiet. **Surface:** grassy/metalled.
⌚ 01/01-31/12
Distance: 🏃1km 🚣4km ⊗500m 🚣500m 🏊on the spot 🏃on the spot.
Remarks: Thursday market.

| 🗑S | **Mantova** 🍽 | 25D1 |

Anconetta. **GPS:** n45,15322 e10,79864.⬆.

⌐⌐free. **Location:** Urban, simple. **Surface:** asphalted.
⌚ 01/01-31/12
Distance: 🏃centre 800m 🏊on the spot.
Remarks: Marina.

| 🗑S | **Menaggio** | 22B2 |

Via Armando Diaz 12. **GPS:** n46,02454 e9,23900.
20 ⌐⌐free. ⌚ 01/01-31/12
Distance: 🏃550m 🏊on the spot 🚌on the spot.

| 🗑S | **Merate** | 22B3 |

Via Papa Giovanni Paolo I, loc. Sartirana. **GPS:** n45,71326 e9,41865.⬆.

10 ⌐⌐€ 5,50 ⌐⌐Ch. **Surface:** grasstiles.
Remarks: Max. 72h.

| 🗑S | **Milano** | 25B1 |

Ripamonti SNC, Via Ripamonti 481, Milan (Milano).
GPS: n45,40914 e9,20937.

30 ⌐⌐€ 20/24h ⌐⌐Ch 🧹€5 WC included. **Surface:** asphalted.
Distance: ⌚on the spot 🚌Milan 40min.
Remarks: Monitored parking.

| 🗑 | **Milano** | 25B1 |

Camper Village Linate Parking, Viale Enrico Forlanini, 123, Milan (Milano). **GPS:** n45,46245 e9,27024.⬆.
⌐⌐€ 20/24h. **Location:** Urban. **Surface:** metalled.
⌚ 01/01-31/12
Distance: 🏃centre 7km 🚌N 74 > centre.

| 🗑S | **Milano** | 25B1 |

Agriturismo Cascina Gaggioli, Via Selvanesco 25, Milan (Milano).
GPS: n45,41785 e9,19578.⬆.
8 ⌐⌐€ 20 ⌐⌐🧹WC. **Surface:** metalled.
Distance: 🏃6km 🏊500m 🚌250m.

Tourist information Milan (Milano):
Ⓜ Castello Sforzesco.
✝ Duomo. History of Gothic architecture. ⌚ Tue-Su.
⛪ Via Fauché. ⌚ Tue, Sa.
⛪ Mercatone del Naviglio Grande, Naviglio Grande. Antiques market, 400 stalls. ⌚ last Su of the month.
🏛 Galleria.

| 🗑S | **Moglia** | 25E2 |

Via Tazio Nuvolari. **GPS:** n44,93639 e10,91582.⬆.

14 ⌐⌐free ⌐⌐Ch free. **Surface:** asphalted. ⌚ 01/01-31/12
Distance: 🏃300m 🛣A22 7km ⊗300m.
Remarks: At swimming pool.

| 🗑S | **Monte Marenzo** | 22B3 |

Via Papa Gionvanni. **GPS:** n45,77639 e9,45222.⬆.

6 ⌐⌐free ⌐⌐free. **Surface:** gravel. ⌚ 01/01-31/12
Distance: 🏃300m.

| 🗑S | **Monzambano** | 25D1 |

Area attrezzata camper Comunale di Monzambano, Via Degli Alpini n. 9. **GPS:** n45,38916 e10,69277.⬆➡.

IT

140 �€ 12/24h ⛽💧♻ (24x)☐included 📶€1/12h. **Surface:** gravel.
☐ 01/01-31/12
Distance: ⊗100m 🚉300m, bakery 100m.
Remarks: Max. 48h.

Morbegno 🌿🏔❄ 22B2
Area Sosta Camper Morbegno, Via del Foss.
GPS: n46,14419 e9,57500. ⬆
22 ⌂€ 10 ⛽💧Ch♻ 📶included. **Location:** Rural.
Surface: grasstiles.
☐ 01/01-31/12
Distance: 🚶historical centre 500m ⊗100m 🚌Skibus 🏍on the spot.

Niardo 22C2
Area di sosta Mr. Sanders, Località Crist.
GPS: n45,97690 e10,31959. ⬆

20 ⌂€ 10 ⛽💧Ch♻€2 WC☐. **Surface:** metalled.
☐ 01/01-31/12
Distance: 🚶Niardo 1,3km 🏊on the spot ⊗on the spot.
Remarks: Bread-service.

Nova Milanese 🧺 22B3
Via G. Brodolini. **GPS:** n45,58298 e9,19668. ⬆➡

4 ⌂free ⛽💧free. **Location:** Urban, simple. **Surface:** asphalted.
☐ 01/01-31/12
Distance: 🚶500m 🚲1,6km ⊗200m.
Remarks: Video surveillance.

Novate Mezzola 🌊 22B2
Via al Lido. **GPS:** n46,21083 e9,45000. ⬆➡

25 ⌂free. **Surface:** grassy/gravel. ☐ 01/01-31/12
Distance: 🚶800m 🏊40m 🚉800m 🏍on the spot.
Remarks: At lake Mezzola, signposted cycle routes.

Olginate 22B3
Via Cesare Cantù. **GPS:** n45,79523 e9,41610. ⬆

---

46 ⌂€ 8/12h ⛽💧Ch♻. **Surface:** metalled.
☐ 01/01-31/12 ☐ Thu>16h-Fri<16h (market)
Distance: 🚶200m 🏊on the spot.
Remarks: At Olginate lake.

Pizzighettone 🏛 25C1
Via De Gasperi. **GPS:** n45,18538 e9,79402. ⬆➡

4 ⌂free ⛽💧Chfree. **Location:** Simple. **Surface:** gravel.
☐ 01/01-31/12
Distance: 🚶400m ⊗300m 🚉Lidl 100m.

Rovetta 22C3
Campo sportivo, Via Papa Giovanni XIII. **GPS:** n45,88892 e9,98224. ⬆

⌂free ⛽💧Ch. **Surface:** asphalted.
Distance: 🚶400m.
Remarks: Parking at gymnasium.

Ruino 🌿🏕🏔🍴 25B2
Agriturismo Adriana Tarantani, Loc. Tre Venti.
GPS: n44,92833 e9,26311. ⬆

6 ⌂free with a meal ⛽💧Ch♻. **Location:** Rural, simple.
Surface: grassy/gravel. ☐ 01/01-31/12
Distance: 🚶1km ⊗on the spot 🚉1km 🏍100m.

Sabbioneta 🏛 25D2
Via Piccola Atene. **GPS:** n44,99459 e10,48849. ⬆➡

15 ⌂free ⛽💧Chfree. **Location:** Simple, quiet. **Surface:** metalled.
☐ 01/01-31/12
Distance: 🚶200m ⊗400m 🚉500m.

San Benedetto Po 🌿 25E1
Via Cardinal Ruffini. **GPS:** n45,04292 e10,93432. ⬆
4 ⌂free ⛽💧Chfree. **Surface:** asphalted. ☐ 01/01-31/12
Distance: 🚶500m 🏍on the spot.

Santa Caterina Valfurva 22D2
Baita de Naségn, Via Forni, loc. Nassegno.
GPS: n46,40917 e10,50833. ⬆➡

⌂€ 12 ⛽💧Ch♻€3. **Surface:** grassy.
Distance: 🚶500m 🚲on the spot 🏊on the spot.

Saronno 22B3
Via E.H.Griegh. **GPS:** n45,61265 e9,04274. ⬆

2 ⌂free ⛽💧€1/100liter 💧Ch. **Location:** Simple, simple.
Surface: asphalted. ☐ 01/01-31/12
Distance: 🚶1,5km 🚲3,5km ⊗500m 🚉200m.

Saronno 22B3
Via Dalmazia 11. **GPS:** n45,62446 e9,02469. ⬆

2 ⌂free. **Location:** Urban, central. **Surface:** concrete.
☐ 01/01-31/12
Distance: 🚶on the spot 🚲2km ⊗1km 🚉1km.
Remarks: Max. 24h.

Sartirana Lomellina 25A1
Via Cavour. **GPS:** n45,11337 e8,66936. ⬆➡⬆

3 ⌂free ⛽💧€2/100liter 💧Ch. **Location:** Simple. **Surface:** asphalted.
☐ 01/01-31/12 ☐ Sa-morning market
Distance: 🚶100m ⊗200m 🚉100m 🏍on the spot.

Sirmione 🌿 22D3
Camper Park Sirmione, Via Cantarane. **GPS:** n45,46083 e10,63333. ⬆

150 ⌂€ 20/24h, € 11/20.30-9.30h ⛽💧Ch♻€3 📶included.
Surface: gravel. ☐ 15/03-31/10
Distance: 🚶1,5km 🏊Lake Garda ⊗100m 🚉1km 🚌100m.

Sirmione 🌿 22D3
Piazzale Montebaldo. **GPS:** n45,48694 e10,61028. ⬆➡

21 from € 2,50 1/2h till-€ 21/24h ChWC. **Surface:** asphalted.
01/01-31/12
Distance: 200m on the spot 50m 200m.

S Sondrio 22C2

Area Sportiva, Via Vanoni. **GPS:** n46,16064 e9,86957.

6 free Chfree. **Surface:** asphalted.
Distance: 600m.
Remarks: Parking sports park.

S Stezzano 22B3

Via Pietro Mascagni. **GPS:** n45,65594 e9,65301.

free Chfree. **Surface:** asphalted.

S Sulzano 22C3

Parking Gerolo, Via Tassano 14. **GPS:** n45,63546 e10,07665.

25 € 15/24h, € 10/night ChWC. **Surface:** grassy.
01/01-31/12
Distance: 300m Lago Iseo 400m 300m.

S Ternate 22A3

Via Roma. **GPS:** n45,78006 e8,69780.

8 free Ch (4x)free. **Location:** Simple, central, quiet.
Surface: unpaved. 01/01-31/12
Distance: 200m on the spot on the spot 100m 200m on the spot on the spot.
Remarks: At Comabbio lake.

S Tirano 22C2

Area Camper Tirano, Via Polveriera/Via Sala Piero.
GPS: n46,21361 e10,15722.

20 € 10/24h Ch included. **Location:** Comfortable.
Surface: metalled.
Distance: 1km station 800m.

Tourist information Tirano:
Bernina Express. The highest-altitude trans-Alpine line in Europe, with one of the steepest gradients in the world between Tirano (It) and Chur (Ch). UNESCO's List of World Heritage. T ± € 100/pp return ticket (Tirano-Chur), ± € 45/pp return ticket (Tirano-Pontresina).

S Torbole 22D3

Tr@ns.it, Via Al Cor. **GPS:** n45,87264 e10,87260.

120 € 20-33 Ch WC included. **Surface:** grassy.
01/01-31/12
Distance: on the spot on the spot on the spot on the spot.
Remarks: Along Lake Garda.

S Toscolano Maderno 22D3

Area Sosta Maderno, Via Promontorio.
GPS: n45,63487 e10,61103.

25 € 25 Ch WC included. **Surface:** grassy.
01/01-31/12
Distance: 500m.

S Treviglio 22B3

Via al Malgari. **GPS:** n45,53142 e9,59710.

4 free Chfree. **Surface:** metalled. 01/01-31/12
Distance: 700m 400m.
Remarks: At sports park.

S Varzi 25B2

Strada Circonvallazione. **GPS:** n44,82172 e9,19727.

30 free, summer € 5 ChWCfree. **Location:** Simple, central.
Surface: asphalted/metalled. 01/01-31/12
Distance: 200m 50m 50m.
Remarks: Along the Staffora river, friday market.

Veneto

S Arquà Polesine 25F1

Ostello Canalbianco, SS 16, n15. **GPS:** n44,99665 e11,76243.
12 € 10 Ch WC.
Distance: on the spot.

Asiago 22E3

P Verdi Mosele, SS349, Via Giuseppe Verdi.
GPS: n45,87129 e11,50026.

20 € 1/h, € 4/day. **Surface:** asphalted. 01/01-31/12
Distance: 300m 500m.

S Asolo 22F3

Area Camper Communale, Via Forestuzzo.
GPS: n45,79637 e11,91283.

13 € 7/24h Ch (14x)included.
Surface: grassy/sand.
01/01-31/12
Distance: 400m 400m 400m.
Remarks: Access 8-19.30h, barbecue place, picnic area.

S Auronzo di Cadore 22F1

Taiarezze, SR48, Via Reaneloc. **GPS:** n46,56217 e12,41640.

30 € 8, 20/07-31/08 and 24/12-06/01 € 12 Chincluded.
Location: Rural, simple, quiet. **Surface:** asphalted.
01/01-31/12
Distance: 1,5km on the spot on the spot on the spot on the spot on the spot on the spot 1,6km 1,6km.
Remarks: Max. 48h, payment only with coins.

S Barbarano Vicentino 25E1

Viale Vittorio Veneto 66. **GPS:** n45,40725 e11,54654.

3 free free. **Surface:** asphalted. 01/01-31/12
Distance: 200m 200m 200m.

S Bardolino 22D3

Via Gardesana dell'Acqua. **GPS:** n45,56115 e10,71412.

80 ⌁ € 15 ⌂⌁Ch included. ⌂ **Location:** Rural, simple, quiet.
Surface: concrete. ☐ 01/01-31/12
Distance: ⌁2km ⌁on the spot ⌁on the spot ⊗on the spot
⌁Lidl 2km ⌁on the spot ⌁on the spot ⌁on the spot.
Tourist information Bardolino:
ℹ️ I.A.T. (Ufficio Informazioni e di Accoglienza Turistica), Piazzale Aldo Moro.

⌁S Bassano del Grappa 22F3
Parcheggio Gerosa, Via Alcide de Gasperi.
GPS: n45,75831 e11,73091.⬆️➡️.

20 ⌁ € 12/24h ⌂⌁Ch included. **Surface:** asphalted.
☐ 01/01-31/12
Distance: ⌁300m ⊗300m ⌁300m ⌁on the spot.
Remarks: Max. 48h.

⌁ Bassano del Grappa 22F3
Prato Santo Caterina, Via Chini 6. **GPS:** n45,76009 e11,73413.
⌁free.
Distance: ⌁on the spot.

⌁S Belluno 🌿⛱🧺🍽⌁ 22F2
Rio Cavalli, Via Sagrogna 74. **GPS:** n46,15646 e12,26136.⬆️.

20 ⌁ € 10, electricity included € 15 ⌂⌁⌁€5 📶.
Location: Comfortable, central, quiet. **Surface:** grassy/sand.
☐ 01/01-31/12 **Distance:** ⌁3km ⌁6km ⌁on the spot ⊗on the spot ⌁3km ⌁on the spot.

⌁S Belluno 🌿⛱🧺🍽⌁ 22F2
Viale dei Dendrofori, loc. Lambioi. GPS: n46,13712 e12,21371.⬆️➡️.

12 ⌁8-18 € 0,80/h, overnight stay free ⌂⌁Ch free.
Location: Simple, central, noisy. **Surface:** grasstiles/metalled.
☐ 01/01-31/12
Distance: ⌁100m ⊗100m ⌁100m.
Remarks: Nearby swimming pool and skating rink.

⌁S Bibione 22H3
Strada Brussa. GPS: n45,62458 e12,95866.⬆️.

100 ⌁ € 7/day, overnight stay free ⌂WC ⌁.
Location: Rural, simple, isolated, quiet. **Surface:** grassy.
☐ 25/04-30/09
Distance: ⌁sandy beach 250m.
Remarks: Guarded during the day, dog permitted on the beach.

⌁S Borghetto di Valeggio sul Mincio 🌿 25D1
Camper parking Visconteo, Strada provinciale 55.
GPS: n45,35537 e10,72017.⬆️.
60 ⌁ € 10/24h ⌂⌁€3 ⌁Ch ⌁€1/12h. **Location:** Rural, comfortable.
Surface: gravel.
Distance: ⌁on the spot ⌁Lake Garda 13km ⊗250m ⌁on the spot ⌁on the spot.
Remarks: Borghetto 200m.

⌁S Caorle ⛱⌁ 22G3
Area di sosta Ai Parchi, Via Traghete. **GPS:** n45,60490 e12,88500.⬆️.

65 ⌁ € 11-16/24h ⌂⌁Ch ⌁(60x)€4/kWh WC ⌁€1/3minutes 📶.
Location: Comfortable, isolated, noisy. **Surface:** gravel.
☐ 01/01-31/12
Distance: ⌁historical centre 1,1km ⌁500m ⊗300m ⌁300m ⌁350m ⌁150m.
Remarks: Max. 72h, monitored parking, Luna Park 150m, Parco Acquatico 150m.

⌁S Castelguglielmo 25E1
Via Alessandro Volta. GPS: n45,02246 e11,53518.⬆️➡️.

10 ⌁free ⌂⌁Ch free. **Surface:** metalled.
Distance: ⌁500m ⌁500m.

⌁S Cavallino-Treporti ⌁⌁ 22G3
Spiaggia di Cà Ballarin, Via Gabrielle Berton.
GPS: n45,45998 e12,51659.⬆️.

4 ⌁free. **Location:** Simple, central, quiet. **Surface:** sand.
☐ 01/05-31/10
Distance: ⌁1km ⌁on the spot ⌁on the spot ⊗on the spot ⌁1km ⌁300m.
Remarks: Beach parking.
Tourist information Cavallino-Treporti:
⌁ Week market. ☐ Tue-Thu morning.

⌁S Chioggia 25G1
2 Palme, Lungomare Adriatica. **GPS:** n45,22122 e12,29624.⬆️.

100 ⌁ € 12, peak season € 20, Su/holidays € 15 ⌂⌁Ch ⌁(100x)
WC included ⌁€0,50. ⌁ **Location:** Urban, simple, central.
Surface: grassy/gravel. ☐ 01/01-31/12
Distance: ⌁centre 1,8km ⌁200m.
Remarks: Chioggia: little Venice.

⌁S Colà di Lazise ♈ 22D3
Villa dei Cedri, Via Possoi. **GPS:** n45,46777 e10,74972.⬆️.

200 ⌁ € 1/h, 5 hours min ⌂⌁Ch ⌁📶 included. ⌂
Location: Rural. **Surface:** grasstiles. ☐ 01/01-31/12
Remarks: Parco Termale 300m.

⌁S Conegliano ⌁ 22F2
Area de Sosta Campeggio Club Conegliano, Via Don Bosco, SS13.
GPS: n45,87799 e12,30111.⬆️➡️.

30 ⌁ € 12/24h ⌂⌁Ch ⌁(16x)included WC ⌁. **Location:** Simple,
central, quiet. **Surface:** grassy.
☐ 01/01-31/12
Distance: ⌁2km ⊗nearby ⌁on the spot.

⌁S Domegge di Cadore Belluno ⌁⌁❄♈ 22F1
Camping Cologna, Vallesella di Cadore. **GPS:** n46,44605 e12,40658.⬆️.

30 ⌁ € 10 ⌂⌁Ch. **Location:** Rural, simple, quiet. **Surface:** grassy.
☐ 01/05-20/10
Distance: ⌁1km ⌁At the lake ⌁on the spot ⊗on the spot ⌁1km ⌁1km ⌁on the spot ⌁on the spot.
Remarks: Max. 24h, narrow entrance.

⌁S Feltre 22F2
Area Camper Vincheto, Via Casonetto 158C.
GPS: n46,03124 e11,95911.⬆️.
12 ⌁ € 15 ⌂⌁Ch included ⌁€3. **Surface:** grassy/metalled.
☐ 01/01-31/12

⌁S Feltre 22F2
Piazale Pra del Vescovo, Viale A. Gaggia.
GPS: n46,02013 e11,90792.⬆️.

IT

15 ⌷free 🚐 🔧Chfree. **Surface:** metalled. ⬛ 01/01-31/12
Distance: 🚲500m ⊗500m 🛒500m 500m.
Remarks: Max. 48h.

Ferrara di Monte Baldo 22D3
Via Chiesa. **GPS:** n45,67794 e10,85491.⬆.

16 ⌷free 🚐 🔧Ch (16x). **Location:** Rural, simple, isolated, quiet.
Surface: gravel. ⬛ 01/01-31/12
Distance: 🚲300m ⊗300m 🛒300m on the spot 🚶on the spot.

Garda 22D3
P Centro, SS249. **GPS:** n45,57501 e10,71019.

20 ⌷€ 13/24h 🚐WC. **Surface:** metalled. ⬛ 01/01-31/12
Distance: 🚲200m ⊗on the spot 🛒on the spot.

Garda 22D3
Via Preite. **GPS:** n45,57620 e10,71404.⬆➡.
30 ⌷€ 15/24h 🚐 🔧Ch. **Surface:** metalled.
⬛ service: Easter-31/10
Distance: 🚲300m 🏊Lake Garda 300m.

Lazise 22D3
Parking Lazise Dardo, Via San Martino, SP31.
GPS: n45,50623 e10,73584.

15 ⌷€ 17/24h. **Surface:** asphalted. ⬛ 01/01-31/12
Distance: 🚲200m 🚤5,8km⊗200m 🛒200m 200m.

Lido di Jesolo 22G3
Area camping Albatros, Via Correr 102/A.
GPS: n45,52477 e12,68995.⬆.

131 ⌷€ 9-17 🚐 🔧Ch 🔧WC ⌷included. **Location:** Comfortable,
isolated, quiet. **Surface:** grassy. ⬛ 01/03-31/10
Distance: 🚲500m 🏊700m ⊗100m 🛒100m 🖥100m 100m.

Lido di Jesolo 22G3
Boscopineta, Via Vettor Pisani. **GPS:** n45,52278 e12,69178.⬆.

250 ⌷€ 10-20 🚐 🔧Ch 🔧WC ⌷. **Location:** Comfortable, central.
Surface: grassy. ⬛ 01/01-31/12
Distance: 🏊400m.

Lido di Jesolo 22G3
Camping Park dei Dogi, Viale Oriente. **GPS:** n45,52146 e12,68828.⬆.

200 ⌷€ 14-26, 4 pers.incl. 🚐 🔧Ch 🔧WCincluded ⌷€0,50 🖥 📶
Location: Comfortable, central, quiet. **Surface:** grassy.
⬛ 01/01-31/12
Distance: 🚲200m 🏊sandy beach 200m ⊗40m 🛒40m 20m.

Lido di Jesolo 22G3
Jesolo Camper Don Bosco, Via Oriente/via G.Don Bosco.
GPS: n45,52188 e12,68943.⬆➡.

250 ⌷€ 10-20 🚐 🔧Ch 🔧€3/kWh WC ⌷€1 🖥€5.
Surface: grassy/gravel. ⬛ 01/01-31/12
Distance: 🚲within walking distance 🏊100m ⊗on the spot 🛒100m
on the spot.
Remarks: Bus to Venice stops in front of motorhome parking.

Lido di Jesolo 22G3
Parcheggio Mare d'Oriente, Viale Oriente, Lido di Jesolo est.
GPS: n45,52083 e12,68556.⬆.

⌷€ 10/24h, € 13/Sunday, Aug 🚐 🔧Ch 🔧included 🖥.
Location: Simple, central, quiet. **Surface:** grassy.
⬛ summer
Distance: 🚲100m 🏊100m ⊗on the spot 🛒on the spot on the
spot.
Remarks: Servicepoint at Don Bosco, incl.

Livinallongo del Col di Lana 22F1
Sportbar del Ghiaccio, Via Piagn,6 Arabba.
GPS: n46,49678 e11,87692.⬆.

50 ⌷€ 10/24h, Jul-Aug-Dec € 14 🚐 🔧Ch 🔧(17x)€3/24h WC ⌷€3.
Location: Rural, comfortable, quiet. **Surface:** grassy/gravel.
⬛ 01/01-31/12
Distance: 🚲on the spot ⊗on the spot 🛒200m 200m 🐟on the
spot 🚶on the spot 🎣200m.
Remarks: At the skating rink, check in at bar.

Malcesine 22D3
Camping Lombardi, Via Navene, loc. Campagnola.
GPS: n45,78429 e10,82187.⬆.

20 ⌷€ 17/24h, 28/06-01/09 € 20/24h 🚐€1 🔧Ch 🔧WC ⌷€1.
Surface: unpaved. ⬛ 01/04-31/10
Distance: 🚲3km 🏊Lake Garda 500m.
Remarks: Max. 48h.

Marghera 22F3
Parcheggio Terminal Service, Via dei Petroli 1/3 angolo via della
Libertà. **GPS:** n45,46806 e12,26589.

⌷€ 10/24h. **Location:** Simple, central, quiet.
⬛ 01/01-31/12
Distance: > Venice.
Remarks: Monitored parking.

Mirano 22F3
Camper Club Mirano, Via viasana, 4. **GPS:** n45,49322 e12,08968.⬆.

⌷€ 12/24h 🚐 🔧Ch.
Location: Comfortable.
Surface: grasstiles.
Distance: 🚲historical centre 1,5km 🚤8km 300m Padua-Venice.
Remarks: For entrance email: camperclubmirano@libero.it of phone
3479831010.

Misurina 22F1
Piazzale Loita, Via Monte Piana. **GPS:** n46,58839 e12,25737.➡.

50 🛏 € 14 ⚡🔌 Chincluded. 🚿 **Location:** Rural, simple, simple, central, noisy. **Surface:** gravel.
🅿 01/01-31/12
Distance: 🚰300m ⛱500m ⊗50m 🛒300m 🚌on the spot
♨on the spot 🧍on the spot 🏊3km.
Remarks: Max. 48h.

Misurina 🏔🚡⛰🚣❄ 22F1
P camper Rifugio Auronzo, Rifugio Auronzo.
GPS: n46,61267 e12,29342. ➡.

40 🛏 € 33 toll road incl., extra night € 15. 🚿 **Location:** Rural, simple, isolated. **Surface:** gravel. 🅿 01/05-30/10
Distance: 🚰Misurina 12km ⊗on the spot 🛒12km 🛒on the spot
🧍Tre Cime di Lavadero 🏊15km.
Remarks: Beautiful view.

Montagnana 🏵 25E1
Via Circonvallazione. **GPS:** n45,23528 e11,46639. ⬆➡.

20 🛏free ⚡🔌ChWCfree. **Surface:** asphalted. 🅿 01/01-31/12
Distance: 🚰200m ⊗200m 🛒200m.
Remarks: At sports centre.

Padova 🏵 25F1
P1, Piazza della Pace Ytzhak Rabbin, Via cinquantottesimo Fanteria, Padua (Padova). **GPS:** n45,39686 e11,87673. ⬆.
🛏8-20h € 10, 20-8h € 10, 18-10h € 20.
Surface: asphalted.
🅿 01/01-31/12
Distance: 🚰on the spot 🛒6km ⊗on the spot 🛒on the spot
🛒on the spot.

Tourist information Padua (Padova):
👁 Caffe Pedrocchi, Via Oberdan. Café, meeting point for students.
👁 Capella degli Scrovegni. Chapel.

Peschiera del Garda 🏝S 25D1
Area camper Peschiera, Via Milano. **GPS:** n45,43995 e10,68474. ⬆.
100 🛏 € 12-15/24h ⚡🔌Ch 🚿included WC 🚽€1 📶🚗
Surface: gravel. 🅿 01/01-31/12
Distance: 🚰500m ⊗400m.
Remarks: Monday-morning market.

Peschiera del Garda 🏝S 25D1
P4, Via Milano 67. **GPS:** n45,44141 e10,67892. ⬆.

33 🛏 € 15/24h ⚡🔌Chfree. **Surface:** gravel. 🅿 01/01-31/12

Distance: 🛒5km ⛱Lake Garda 300m ⊗100m 🛒nearby.
Remarks: Parking nearby campsite Bella Italia.
Tourist information Peschiera del Garda:
ℹ Tourist town at Lake Garda.
🎯 🅿 Mo-morning.

Porto Tolle 🚣 25G2
Via strada del Mare, loc. Barricata, SP38. **GPS:** n44,84997 e12,46342. ⬆.

50 🛏 € 3,50. 🚿 **Location:** Rural, quiet. **Surface:** grassy/sand.
Distance: ⛱50m.
Remarks: Beach parking.

Punta Sabbioni 🏖🚣 22G3
Parking Dante Alighieri, Dante Alighieri 26.
GPS: n45,44132 e12,42131. ⬆.

36 🛏 € 17-20 + € 3/pp ⚡🔌Ch 🚿€3 WC 🚽🖥€3.
Location: Simple, central, quiet.
Surface: grassy.
🅿 01/01-31/12
Distance: 🚰on the spot ⛱1,5km 🛥700m 🛒free shuttle to beach.
Remarks: Arrival <22h, monitored parking, ferry boat to Venice 500m.

Punta Sabbioni 🏖🚣 22G3
Agricamping da Scarpa, Via Pealto 17. **GPS:** n45,44279 e12,44055.

15 🛏 € 14-16 + € 5/pp ⚡🔌Ch 🚿 WCincluded 📹🚿.
Surface: grassy.
🅿 01/01-31/12
Distance: 🏊500m ⊗on the spot 🛥500m ferry Venice 1,5km.

Recoaro Terme 🏔⛰🌲❄ 22E3
Area Communale, Via Della Restistenza.
GPS: n45,70430 e11,22902. ⬆➡.

16 🛏 € 5/24h ⚡€0,10/10liter 🔌Ch 🚿(16x)€0,50/2h,6Amp.
🅿 01/01-31/12
Distance: 🚰on the spot ⊗on the spot 🛥on the spot 🛒on the spot
🏊on the spot.

Santo Stefano di Cadore ⛰🌲 22G1
Albergo Gasperina, Loc. Cima Canale, Val Visdende.
GPS: n46,60835 e12,63053. ⬆➡.

49 🛏 € 11/24h, Aug € 12 ⚡🔌Ch 🚿(49x)€3/day WCincluded 🚽€2.
Surface: gravel. 🅿 25/04-01/10
Distance: 🚰12km 🛒300m ⊗on the spot 🛥6km 🚴on the spot
🧍on the spot.
Remarks: Check in at restaurant, bread-service, 10% discount at restaurant.

Sappada ⛰❄ 22G1
Area Camper, Borgata Palù. **GPS:** n46,56254 e12,67991. ⬆➡.

60 🛏 € 10/24h ⚡🔌Ch 🚿(24x)included. 🚿
Location: Rural, simple, quiet. **Surface:** gravel. 🅿 01/01-31/12
Distance: 🚰1,1km ⊗500m 🛥1km 🚴on the spot 🧍on the spot
🏊100m.
Remarks: Keycard at townhall, caution € 5.

Schio 🏔⛰🌲❄ 22E3
Parking Palasport, Viale dell'Industria. **GPS:** n45,71389 e11,37599. ⬆.

4 🛏free ⚡🔌Chfree. **Surface:** asphalted. 🅿 01/01-31/12
Distance: 🚰1km ⊗1km 🛥1km 🏊on the spot 🚲on the spot.

Sernaglia della Battaglia 22F3
Area attrezzata Le Grave, Via Passo Barca, Falzè di Piave.
GPS: n45,85676 e12,16566. ⬆➡.

26 🛏 € 5/12h, € 8/24h ⚡🔌Chincluded 🚿€2/24h.
Location: Simple. **Surface:** grassy. 🅿 01/01-31/12
Distance: 🚰150m ⊗on the spot 🛥100m 🛒150m 🛒300m.

Soave 🏵🚣 25E1
Via Invalidi del Lavoro. **GPS:** n45,42340 e11,24541. ⬆➡.

8 🛏 € 5 ⚡🔌Ch 🚿(8x)free,16Amp. 🚿
Surface: grasstiles.
🅿 01/01-31/12
Distance: 🚰200m 🛒3km 🛒on the spot ⊗200m 🛥200m 🛒300m.

Torre di Mosto 22G3

Agriturismo La Via Antiga, Via S. Martino 13.
GPS: n45,64389 e12,67056.

8 € 15/day Ch (5x)included. **Location:** Simple, isolated, quiet. **Surface:** grassy/gravel. 01/03-30/09
Distance: 7km.

Treviso 22F3

Parking ex Foro Boario, Via Castello d'Amore.
GPS: n45,67014 e12,25733.

13 free Chfree. **Surface:** metalled. 01/01-31/12
Distance: 500m 11,5km 500m 500m 200m.
Remarks: Max. 48h.

Treviso 22F3

Via Giovanni Boccaccio. **GPS:** n45,66769 e12,26361.

40 free Chfree. **Location:** Simple, central, noisy.
Surface: asphalted. 01/01-31/12
Distance: 1km 500m 500m 300m.
Remarks: Along railwayline.

Tourist information Treviso:
Sile. Fish-market on island.

Venezia 22G3

Parcheggio Al Tronchetto, Venice (Venezia).
GPS: n45,44146 e12,30514.

€ 21/0-12h, 12-24h € 16 Ch. **Location:** Urban, simple, central, quiet. **Surface:** asphalted.
01/01-31/12
Distance: 2km on the spot ferry Venice.

Venezia 22G3

Parco di San Giuliano, Via San Giuliano, Venice (Venezia).
GPS: n45,46742 e12,27916.

100 € 10/24h €3 Ch WC. **Location:** Simple, central, quiet. **Surface:** grassy. 01/01-31/12
Distance: ferry Venice 100m.
Remarks: Inspection 2015: closed because of renovation.

Tourist information Venice (Venezia):
A.P.T. (Azienda di Promozione Turistica), www.turismovenezia.it. Historical city consits of 117 islands, 150 canals and 400 bridges.

Verona 25E1

Area sosta camper Porta Palio, Via dalla Bona.
GPS: n45,43354 e10,97879.

37 € 5/4h, € 10/24h Chincluded. **Surface:** asphalted.
01/01-31/12
Distance: 500m Pizza (ordering service) bus 62 > centre.

Verona 25E1

Agricamping Corte Finiletto, Strada Bresciana, 41.
GPS: n45,44651 e10,91917.

€ 18, 2 pers.incl Ch €2 WC. **Surface:** grassy/gravel.

Tourist information Verona:
Arena. Large anfiteatro, in July/August opera performances.
Via Capella. Known for the love drama of Romeo and Juliet.
Piazza dellen Erbe. daily.

Vicenza 22E3

Park Interscambio CentroBus, Via Bassano, Zona sud-est.
GPS: n45,54321 e11,55886.

40 € 10/24h WCincluded. **Surface:** asphalted.
01/01-31/12 during event
Distance: 2km on the spot Free bus to centre, every 15 min.
Remarks: At stadium.

Vicenza 22E3

Park Interscambio CentroBus, Viale Cricoli, Zona nord.
GPS: n45,56418 e11,54903.

18 € 8,40/24h Ch WCincluded.
Surface: asphalted.
01/01-31/12
Distance: 1,6km on the spot on the spot Free bus to centre.

Tourist information Vicenza:
Quartiere delle Barche. District with palaces in Venetian style.

Friuli Venezia Giulia

Andreis 22G2

SP20. **GPS:** n46,19880 e12,61157.

€ 5/day . **Location:** Simple. **Surface:** grassy/gravel.
Distance: little stream.

Barcis 22G2

Loc. Portuz, SS251. **GPS:** n46,19055 e12,56507.

20 € 12/24h Ch . **Location:** Comfortable, isolated, quiet.
Surface: grasstiles/metalled. 01/01-31/12
Distance: 400m on the spot 500m 500m.
Remarks: At the lake of Barcis.

Corno di Rosazzo 22H2

Via dei Pini. **GPS:** n45,98955 e13,43917.

8 free . **Location:** Rural, simple, quiet. **Surface:** asphalted.
01/01-31/12
Distance: 300m.

Dolegna del Collio 22H2

Frazione Vencò. **GPS:** n46,00370 e13,47700.

free Ch . **Surface:** asphalted.
Distance: Dolegna del Collio 4km.
Remarks: 50m from border with Slovenia, picnic area.

Forni di Sopra 🏔🌲❄ 22G1
Santa Viela, SS52. **GPS**: n46,42500 e12,57036. ⬆.

20 🅿 € 7-9 🚰♻Chfree. 🚲 **Location**: Rural, simple, noisy.
Surface: asphalted. ⭕ 01/01-31/12
Distance: 🚶800m ⊗on the spot 🛒800m 🚲400m ⛷on the spot
🏃on the spot 🎿on the spot ⛸on the spot.
Remarks: No camping activities.

Gemona del Friuli 22H2
Piazzale Mons. Battista Monai. GPS: n46,27585 e13,13728. ⬆.
🅿free 🚰♻Chfree. **Location**: Simple, central, noisy.
Surface: asphalted.
Distance: 🚶on the spot ⛵3,3km.

Gorizia ✈ 22H2
Viale Oriani. GPS: n45,94554 e13,61603. ⬆.

30 🅿free 🚰♻Chfree. **Location**: Simple, quiet. **Surface**: asphalted.
⭕ 01/01-31/12
Distance: 🚶centre 500m.

Gradisca d'Isonzo 22H2
Viale Trieste. GPS: n45,88577 e13,49582. ⬆.

3 🅿free 🚰♻Chfree. **Location**: Central.
Surface: asphalted.
Distance: 🚶on the spot ⛵2,3km ⊗on the spot 🛒on the spot.
Remarks: Max. 48h.

Grado 22H3
Viala Italia. GPS: n45,68218 e13,41230. ⬆➡.

40 🅿 € 12 🚰♻Ch🏊included. 🍴 **Location**: Simple.
Surface: asphalted. ⭕ 01/01-31/12
Distance: 🚶1km ⛵24km 🏖600m.

Montereale Valcellina 22G2
Via dell'Omo. GPS: n46,15168 e12,66122. ⬆➡.

15 🅿free 🚰♻Ch. **Location**: Urban. **Surface**: asphalted.
⭕ 01/01-31/12
Distance: 🚶500m 🛒300m.

Pordenone 22G2
Agip, SS13, Pordenone. **GPS**: n45,97236 e12,64332. ⬆.

8 🅿 € 3/24h 🚰♻Ch. **Location**: Urban, simple, isolated, quiet.
Surface: asphalted. ⭕ 01/01-31/12
Distance: 🚶1km ⛵3km ⊗200m 🛒200m.
Remarks: To be paid at petrol station.

San Daniele del Friuli 🏔 22G2
Via Udine, SP16. GPS: n46,15610 e13,01368. ⬆.

20 🅿free 🚰♻Chfree. **Location**: Comfortable, central, quiet.
Surface: grasstiles. ⭕ 01/01-31/12
Distance: 🚶300m ⊗on the spot 🛒300m 🚲200m.
Remarks: Parking sports park.

San Vito al Tagliamento 22G2
Area di sosta San Vito al Tagliamento, Via Pulet.
GPS: n45,91224 e12,86590. ⬆➡.

12 🅿 € 5/12h, € 8/24h, € 15/48h 🚰 € 1 ♻Ch🚲.
Location: Rural, simple, isolated, quiet. **Surface**: asphalted.
⭕ 01/01-31/12
Distance: 🚶500m ⛵15km ⊗500m 🛒500m 🚲500m.
Remarks: Gate can be opened manually.

Sauris 🏔 22G1
Prosciuttificio Wolf Sauris, Sauris di Sotto 88.
GPS: n46,46756 e12,70833. ⬆.
10 🅿free 🚰♻free WC 🚲. **Location**: Rural, simple, quiet.
Surface: asphalted.
Distance: 🚶on the spot ⊗150m 🏃on the spot.

Tarcento 22H2
Plein-air Torre, Via Sotto Colle Verzan. **GPS**: n46,21496 e13,22503. ⬆.

10 🅿free 🚰♻Ch🚲free.
Location: Simple, quiet.
Surface: grasstiles.
Distance: 🚶200m ⊗200m 🛒200m.
Remarks: Nearby sports center, max. 72h, no camping activities.

Tarvisio ⛰🏔❄ 22H1
Parcheggio P3, Via Armando Diaz. **GPS**: n46,50426 e13,57157. ⬆➡.

25 🅿 € 0,60/h 🚰♻Ch.🍴 **Location**: Urban, simple, central.
Surface: metalled.
Distance: 🚶on the spot ⊗100m 🛒100m.

Trieste 🌊⛱🍦 36A2
Via Von Bruck, Torre del Lloyd. GPS: n45,63710 e13,76990. ⬆➡.

50 🅿 € 4 🚰♻Chfree. **Location**: Highway, simple, noisy.
Surface: asphalted. ⭕ 01/01-31/12
Distance: 🚶3km 🚌shuttle to centre.
Remarks: Max. 72h, pitches under motorway.

Trieste 🌊⛱🍦 36A2
Piazzale 11 settembre 2001, Viale Miramare.
GPS: n45,68250 e13,75138.

20 🅿free. **Location**: Urban, simple, quiet.
Surface: metalled.
Distance: 🚶on the spot.
Remarks: In front of porticciolo di Barcola, quiet at night, crowdy during the day.

Trieste 🌊⛱🍦 36A2
Via Ottaviano Augusto. GPS: n45,64599 e13,75654.

🅿free. **Location**: Urban. **Surface**: asphalted. ⭕ 01/01-31/12
Distance: 🚶centre 500m ⊗100m 🚌on the spot.
Remarks: In opposite of Piazza Unitá d'Italia.

IT

Tourist information Trieste:
Grotta del Giganta. Caves. ☐ Tue-Su, 01/07-31/08 Mo-Su.

⛺Ⓢ Udine 22H2
Via Chiusaforte. **GPS:** n46,08115 e13,22317.⬆.
50 ⛺free ☞ 🅼Chfree. **Surface:** grasstiles. ☐ 01/01-31/12
Distance: 🚶city centre 2km ⚓3,5km 🚋line 1 > centre.

⛺Ⓢ Zoppola 22G2
Via Manteghe. **GPS:** n45,96502 e12,78019.⬆▶.

2 ⛺free ☞ 🅼Chfree. **Location:** Rural, isolated, quiet.
Surface: metalled. ☐ 01/01-31/12
Distance: 🚶centre 800m.
Remarks: At gymnasium.

Emilia-Romagna

⛺Ⓢ Anita 25F2
Agriturismo Prato Pozzo, Via Rotta Martinella 34/a.
GPS: n44,54892 e12,13322.⬆▶.

20 ⛺€ 5 + € 5/pp, guests free ☞ 🅼Ch ✎(12x)€2,50/day WC
⍾included 🔌. **Location:** Rural, comfortable, isolated, quiet.
Surface: grassy/metalled. ☐ 01/01-31/12
Distance: 🚶1km ⛱500m ⛽500m ⊗on the spot 🍽1km 🚏1km.

⛺Ⓢ Argenta 25F2
Area Golf Club, Via Poderi. **GPS:** n44,63027 e11,81112.⬆.
5 ⛺€ 5 ☞ 🅼Ch ✎included. **Surface:** gravel/metalled.
☐ 01/01-31/12
Distance: 🚶3km.
Remarks: Key at Golf Club.

⛺Ⓢ Argenta 25F2
Via Galassi. **GPS:** n44,61265 e11,83972.⬆▶.

10 ⛺free ☞ 🅼free. **Surface:** metalled. ☐ 01/01-31/12
Distance: 🚶200m ⊗200m 🍽200m 🚏200m.
Remarks: At tennis-courts.

⛺ Bagno di Romagna 🏕🚻 32C1
Via Lungo Savio 1. **GPS:** n43,84108 e11,96532.

10 ⛺free. **Surface:** metalled. ☐ 01/01-31/12
Distance: 🚶500m ⚓1km ⊗500m 🍽500m.
Remarks: Parking swimming pool.

Tourist information Bagno di Romagna:
🏕 Week market. ☐ Fri 7.30-12.30h.

⛺Ⓢ Bellaria-Igea Marina 🏕🌊 25G3
Parking delle Robinie, Via Pinzon 258, Igea Marina, Zona sud.
GPS: n44,12783 e12,48873.

106 ⛺€ 10-12, Apr-Sept € 14,00-16,50 ☞ 🅼Ch ✎€2,50/
day ⍾€1/time. **Location:** Rural, comfortable, central, quiet.
Surface: grassy/gravel. ☐ 15/03-05/10, 08-23h
Distance: ⛱10m ⊗200m 🍽100m 🚏50m.

⛺Ⓢ Bellaria-Igea Marina 🏕🌊 25G3
Mare d'Inverno, Via Murri, 13. **GPS:** n44,11639 e12,49972.⬆.

45 ⛺€ 8, peak season € 10, holidays + € 2 ☞ 🅼Ch ✎€2,50/day
⍾€1/time. **Location:** Rural, comfortable, quiet. **Surface:** grassy.
☐ Easter-30/09
Distance: 🚶800m ⛱200m ⊗800m 🍽1,5km, bakery 800m
🚏100m.

⛺Ⓢ Bellaria-Igea Marina 🏕🌊 25G3
Area di sosta Rio Pircio, Via Benivieni 4, Igea Marina.
GPS: n44,12688 e12,48849.

68 ⛺€ 10-18/24h ☞ 🅼Ch ✎€2/day WC€1/time ⍾hot shower €1.
Location: Rural, comfortable, central, quiet. **Surface:** grassy.
☐ 01/01-31/12
Distance: ⛱100m ⊗200m 🍽250m.

⛺Ⓢ Bellaria-Igea Marina 🏕🌊 25G3
L'Adriatico Parking, Via Benivieni, 12. **GPS:** n44,12644 e12,48740.

60 ⛺€ 10-16/24h ☞ 🅼Ch ✎€2,50/day ⍾€1/time ⍾against
payment 📶€1/24h,€5/week. **Location:** Rural, comfortable, quiet.
Surface: grassy. ☐ Easter-Oct
Distance: ⛱250m.

⛺Ⓢ Berceto 25C3
Via P. Salas. **GPS:** n44,51123 e9,98589.⬆▶.

20 ⛺€ 7 ☞ 🅼Ch ✎WC included.
Surface: asphalted.
☐ 01/01-31/12
Distance: 🚶200m ⚓4km ⊗200m 🍽200m 🚲on the spot
🚶on the spot.
Remarks: Caution € 20, key at kiosk in front of restaurant Rina.

⛺Ⓢ Bertinoro 🏕🚻♨ 25G3
Via Superga, SP 83, Loc. Fratta Terme. **GPS:** n44,13749 e12,10313.⬆▶.

⛺free ☞ 🅼Chfree. **Surface:** asphalted. ☐ 01/01-31/12
Distance: 🚶1km ⊗1km 🍽1km 🚏300m.
Remarks: Near spa resort and sports centre.

⛺Ⓢ Bomporto 25E2
Piazza dello Sport, Via Verdi. **GPS:** n44,72886 e11,03585.

10 ⛺free ☞ 🅼free. **Location:** Urban, simple.
Surface: metalled.
Distance: 🚶500m 🍽500m.
Remarks: Parking at sports park.

⛺Ⓢ Brisighella 🏕🚻 25F3
Piazzale Donatori di Sangue. **GPS:** n44,22168 e11,77883.⬆▶.

18 ⛺€ 8 ☞ 🅼Chfree ✎€2/12h. **Surface:** asphalted.
☐ 01/01-31/12
Distance: 🚶1km ⊗1km 🍽1km 🚏500m.

⛺Ⓢ Carpi 25D2
Piazzale delle Piscine. **GPS:** n44,78444 e10,86817.⬆.

⛺free ☞ 🅼Chfree. **Surface:** metalled.
Distance: 🚶300m ⊗50m 🍽on the spot.
Remarks: Parking swimming pool.

⛺Ⓢ Casal Borsetti 25G2
Area Sosta Camper Mare e Parco, Via Ortolani.
GPS: n44,55000 e12,27997.⬆▶.

IT

238 � € 9, 01/06-01/09 € 11 🚰🗑Ch included. 🚿€3/24h WC🗑.
Location: Rural, comfortable, central, quiet. **Surface:** grassy/metalled.
🔲 01/01-31/12
Distance: 🏊150m ⊗150m.

🏕S Casola Valsenio 🏔🌳 25F3
Via don Milani/Via Antonio Gramsci. **GPS:** n44,22597 e11,62953. ⬆➡.

3 ⌂free 🚰free. **Surface:** asphalted. 🔲 01/01-31/12
Distance: 🏪300m ⊗500m 🛢500m.
Remarks: At swimming pool.

🏕S Casola Valsenio 🏔🌳 25F3
Viale Domenico Neri. **GPS:** n44,22483 e11,62392. ⬆.
4 ⌂free 🚰free. **Surface:** asphalted. 🔲 01/01-31/12
Distance: 🏪100m ⊗500m 🛢100m.

🏕S Castel San Pietro Terme ♨ 25F3
Via Oriani. **GPS:** n44,39725 e11,59197. ⬆➡.

8 ⌂free 🚰€1 🗑Ch WC€0,20. **Surface:** asphalted. 🔲 01/01-31/12
Distance: 🏪300m 🚲4,2km 🛥200m ⊗250m 🛢250m 🚌250m.
Remarks: Nearby hospital.

🏕S Castellarano 🛁 25D2
Parco Don Reverberi, Via Don Reverberi.
GPS: n44,50777 e10,73419. ⬆➡.

5 ⌂free 🚰🗑Ch free. **Location:** Rural, simple. **Surface:** asphalted.
🔲 01/01-31/12
Distance: 🏪500m 🏊500m ⛴500m ⊗500m 🛢500m.

🏕S Castelnovo ne' Monti 🏔 25D3
Impianti Sportivi, Zona PEP, Via Fratelli Cervi, SS63.
GPS: n44,43277 e10,41133. ⬆.

4 ⌂free 🚰🗑Ch free. **Location:** Simple, quiet. **Surface:** asphalted.
🔲 01/01-31/12

Distance: 🏪500m 🚶on the spot.

🏕S Cervia ♨ 25G3
Via Aldo Ascione, Cervia-nord. **GPS:** n44,28151 e12,32459. ⬆.

50 ⌂free 🚰🗑Ch free. **Location:** Simple, isolated, noisy.
Surface: asphalted. 🔲 01/01-31/12
Distance: 🏪3km 🏊3km ⊗1,3km.

🏕S Cervia ♨ 25G3
Viale Tritone, Fraz. Pinarella. **GPS:** n44,23984 e12,35883. ⬆.

40 ⌂free 🚰🗑Ch free. **Location:** Urban, simple, noisy.
Surface: asphalted/metalled. 🔲 01/01-31/12
Distance: 🏪750m 🏊900m on the spot.

♨S Cervia ♨ 25G3
Terme di Cervia, Viale C. Forlanini, Cervia-nord.
GPS: n44,27335 e12,32964. ⬆.

50 ⌂€ 8/24h 🚿€2. **Location:** Rural, quiet. **Surface:** grassy/gravel.
🔲 01/04-30/11
Distance: 🏪3km 🏊3km ⊗50m.
Remarks: Parking spa resort.
Tourist information Cervia:
🚶 Week market. 🔲 Thu.

🏕S Cesena 25G3
Zona Ippodromo, Via G. Ambrosini. **GPS:** n44,14549 e12,22865.
⌂free 🚰€1 🗑€2 Ch. **Location:** Urban. **Surface:** grasstiles.
Distance: 🏪500m.

🏕S Cesena 25G3
Agriturismo Macin, Via San Mauro 5280. **GPS:** n44,13592 e12,16953. ⬆.

4 ⌂€ 5, free for clients 🚰🗑Ch 🚿WC 📶 included.
Surface: grassy/metalled. 🔲 01/01-31/12
Distance: 🏪5km 🚲8,4km ⊗5km 🛢5km.

🏕S Cesenatico 🛁🏖 25G3
Piazzale della Rocca. **GPS:** n44,19855 e12,39086. ⬆.

35 ⌂free 🚰🗑Ch free. **Location:** Simple. **Surface:** metalled.
🔲 01/01-31/12
Distance: 🏪500m 🏊2km ⊗200m 🛢500m 🚌200m.

🏕S Cesenatico 🛁🏖 25G3
Via Mazzini, zona Ponente. **GPS:** n44,21408 e12,38008. ⬆.

21 ⌂€ 12/24h 🚰🗑Ch 🚿included. **Location:** Rural, simple.
Surface: grassy/gravel. 🔲 01/01-31/12
Distance: 🏪centre 3,5km 🏊800m.
Remarks: At entrance campsite Cesenatico, max. 48h.

🏕S Civitella di Romagna 25F3
Agriturismo Acero Rosseo, Via Seggio.
GPS: n44,00200 e11,97539. ⬆➡.

20 ⌂guests free 🚰free 🚿. **Surface:** grassy.
🔲 01/01-31/12
Distance: 🏪5km ⊗on the spot 🛢5km.

🏕S Collecchio 25C2
Via Spezia. **GPS:** n44,75178 e10,22265. ⬆➡.

8 ⌂free 🚰🗑Ch. **Location:** Simple. **Surface:** asphalted.
🔲 01/01-31/12
Distance: 🛢500m.

🏕S Comacchio 🛁 25F2
Area di sosta Cavallari, Via Villaggio San Carlo 9.
GPS: n44,70297 e12,16862. ⬆.

90 ⌂€ 13 🚰🗑Ch Service € 4 🚿included WC 🗑€2/time.
Location: Rural, luxurious, quiet. **Surface:** grassy. 🔲 01/01-31/12
Distance: 🏪1km.

🏕 Comacchio 🛁 25F2
Via Fattibello. **GPS:** n44,69095 e12,18447. ⬆➡.

13 �️free. **Location:** Rural, central, quiet. **Surface:** asphalted.
🅾 01/01-31/12
Distance: 🚂300m.

Conselice 25F2
Agriturismo Massari, Via Coronella 110, Chiesanuova di Conselice.
GPS: n44,53167 e11,81856. ⬆➡.

10 �️€ 9/pp, guests free 🚰🗑Ch 🧹WC⬜🔲📶included 📷.
Surface: metalled.
🅾 01/01-31/12
Distance: 🚂1,5km 🛒200m ⊗on the spot ⛽1,5km.

Cusercoli 25F3
Agriturismo Ca'Bionda, Via San Giovanni 41.
GPS: n44,04153 e11,97544. ⬆➡.

20 �️free 🚰🗑Ch 🧹free WC. **Surface:** metalled.
🅾 01/01-28/02 in case of snow
Distance: 🚂3,5km ⊗on the spot ⛽3,5km.
Remarks: Last 3km narrow road, swimming pool.

Faenza 25F3
Via Proventa. **GPS:** n44,31272 e11,89289. ⬆➡.

2 �️free 🚰🗑Chfree. **Surface:** asphalted. 🅾 01/01-31/12
Distance: 🚂4km ⊗2km.

Faenza 25F3
Agriturismo Trerè, Via Casale 19. **GPS:** n44,29968 e11,80368. ⬆➡.

5 �️€ 8 + € 5/pp, guests free 🚰🗑Ch 🧹€ 2 WC⬜.
Surface: metalled. 🅾 01/01-31/12
Distance: 🚂7km ⊿on the spot 🛒200m ⊗on the spot.
Remarks: Dog € 1, swimming pool € 5.

Farini 25B2
Viale dei Sassi Neri. **GPS:** n44,70994 e9,56611. ⬆➡.

---

50 �️free 🚰🗑Chfree. **Surface:** grassy/gravel. 🅾 01/01-31/12
Distance: 🚂400m ⊿on the spot.

Ferrara 25F2
Via Rampari di San Paolo. **GPS:** n44,83544 e11,61090. ⬆➡.
30 �️€ 6/24h 🚰€ 1/100liter 🗑€ 2 Ch€ 1 🧹€ 5/2h 📶.
Location: Central, noisy. **Surface:** metalled.
🅾 01/01-31/12
Distance: 🚂800m 🚲6,5km ⊗250m ⛽500m 🚃50m.

Tourist information Ferrara:
Ⓜ Museo della Cattedrale. 🎁 gift.
✠ Castello Estence.
✠ Palazzo Scifanoia.
🏛 🅾 Mo, Fri.

Fontanellato 25C2
Via Caduti di Cefalonia. **GPS:** n44,88195 e10,17762. ⬆.

30 �️free 🚰🗑free. **Location:** Simple, quiet. **Surface:** asphalted.
🅾 01/01-31/12
Distance: 🚂centre 500m 🚲5,4km ⛽500m.
Remarks: At cemetery.

Fontanellato 25C2
Via Nazionale Emilia. **GPS:** n44,87797 e10,16987. ⬆➡.

20 �️free 🚰🗑Ch 🧹(16x)WCfree. **Surface:** asphalted.
🅾 01/01-31/12
Distance: 🚂300m 🚲6km ⊗200m ⛽500m.

Forlimpopoli 25G3
Via De Gasperi. **GPS:** n44,19044 e12,12608.

�️free. **Surface:** asphalted. 🅾 01/01-31/12
Distance: 🚂100m ⊗100m ⛽100m 🔲100m.
Remarks: Nearby railway station.

Forlimpopoli 25G3
Palazzetto dello Sport, Via del Tulipano. **GPS:** n44,18534 e12,11960.
🚰🗑Chfree.

Gropparello 25C2
Via D. Aligieri. **GPS:** n44,83521 e9,73051. ⬆➡.

�️€ 10 🚰🗑free. 🔲 **Location:** Rural, simple, quiet.
Surface: asphalted. 🅾 01/01-31/12
Distance: 🚂100m ⊗500m.
Remarks: Castello di Gropparello 300m.

Guastalla 25D2
Piazzale Ugo Foscolo. **GPS:** n44,92364 e10,65148. ⬆.

�️free 🚰🗑free 🧹(6x)€ 3. **Surface:** asphalted. 🅾 01/01-31/12
Distance: 🚂historical centre 300m ⊿1,5km ⊗600m 🔲100m.
Remarks: Cycle route along the Po river.

Imola 25F3
Via Pirandello. **GPS:** n44,34628 e11,70922.

30 �️free 🚰🗑free. **Surface:** grassy/sand. 🅾 01/01-31/12
Distance: 🚂700m 🛒50m ⊗80m ⛽50m supermercato Famila.
Remarks: In front of the Ferrari Circuit.

Tourist information Imola:
🏛 Piazza Gramsci. 🅾 Mo-Thu, Sa 8-12.30h.

Lagosanto 25F2
Ristorante Il Varano, Via Valle Oppio 6, Marozzo di Lagosanto.
GPS: n44,78167 e12,12533. ⬆.

36 �️€ 15, guests free 🚰🗑Ch 🧹(36x)WC⬜ 📷.
Location: Rural, comfortable, quiet. **Surface:** gravel.
🅾 01/01-31/12
Distance: 🚂3km ⊿12km ⊗on the spot ⛽500m.

Langhirano 25D2
Salumificio La Perla, Quinzano. **GPS:** n44,58748 e10,23783. ⬆.

50 �️free 🚰🗑.
Location: Rural, simple, quiet. **Surface:** gravel.
🅾 01/01-31/12
Distance: 🚂3km ⊗on the spot ⛽3km 🚶on the spot.

Remarks: Producer Parma ham.

Langhirano 🌿 🏛 25D2

La Fazenda, Cascinapiano di Langhirano. **GPS:** n44,63322 e10,27410.⬆

50 🛒 € 10, guests € 5 🚰🔌🚿 WC included. **Location:** Simple, quiet. **Surface:** grassy/gravel. ⭕ 01/01-31/12 **Distance:** 🛒1km 🍴on the spot ⊗on the spot 🛒500m.

Lido di Dante 🏖 25G3

Via Marabina 208. **GPS:** n44,38867 e12,31364.

30 🛒 € 6 🚰🔌Ch included. **Surface:** grassy. ⭕ 01/04-30/09 **Distance:** 🛒100m 🏊100m ⊗50m 🛒200m 🛒50m.

Maranello 25E2

Area Camper Maranello, Via Fondo Val Tiepido 77, Torre Maina. **GPS:** n44,50008 e10,87384.⬆

10 🛒 € 5 🚰🔌Ch 🚿 WC 🧺 📶. **Location:** Rural, comfortable, quiet. **Surface:** unpaved. ⭕ 01/01-31/12 **Distance:** ⊗on the spot 🚌shuttle Bologna-Modena 🚲on the spot. **Remarks:** Entrance code available at bar.

Marzaglia 25D2

Area di sosta Marzaglia, Strada Pomposiana 305. **GPS:** n44,63514 e10,80733.⬆➡

130 🛒 € 8 -15 🚰🔌Ch 🚿(100x)€ 2/day WC 🗑 against payment 📶included. **Location:** Rural, comfortable, quiet. **Surface:** grassy.

⭕ 01/03-01/11 **Distance:** ⊗400m 🛒1km. **Remarks:** Free bicycles available.

Mesola 25G2

Via Beatrice d'Este. **GPS:** n44,92331 e12,23469.⬆

6 🛒free 🚰🔌Ch free. **Location:** Rural, simple. **Surface:** asphalted. ⭕ 01/01-31/12 **Distance:** 🛒400m ⊗400m 🛒150m. **Remarks:** Parking sports park.

Mesola 25G2

Agriturismo Ca'Laura, SP 27, Bosco Mesola. **GPS:** n44,87122 e12,24444.⬆

6 🛒 € 15 🚰🔌Ch 🚿 WC 🧺. **Location:** Luxurious, quiet. **Surface:** metalled. ⭕ 01/01-31/12 **Distance:** 🏊10km ⊗on the spot 🛒1km 🛒1km. **Remarks:** Swimming pool, training golf course.

Mirandola 25E2

Via Luigi Galvani. **GPS:** n44,89812 e11,06199.⬆ 10 🛒free 🚰🔌Ch free. **Location:** Simple, quiet. **Surface:** gravel. **Distance:** 🛒500m ⊗1km 🛒1km 🛒500m. **Remarks:** At cemetery.

Misano Adriatico 25G3

Centro Caravan Misano, Via Taveleto 53. **GPS:** n43,96694 e12,67306.

12 🛒 € 18 🚰🔌Ch 🚿(12x)€ 2,6Amp WC 🗑€ 0,50 🔌 📶included. **Location:** Luxurious, quiet. **Surface:** grassy. ⭕ 01/01-31/12 **Distance:** 🛒500m ⊗5km 🏊2km ⊗500m 🛒500m. **Remarks:** Caution key € 10, video surveillance.

Modena 🌿 25E2

Camper Club Mutina, Strada Collegarola 76/A, zona Vaciglio. **GPS:** n44,61361 e10,94444.⬆

32 🛒 € 15/24h 🚰🔌Ch 🚿 WC 📶included. **Location:** Rural, comfortable, luxurious, quiet. **Surface:** asphalted. ⭕ 01/01-31/12 **Distance:** 🛒600m ⊗3km 🛒600m 🧍on the spot.

Modena 🌿 25E2

Ristorante Pizzeria Taverna Napoleone, Via San Lorenzo 44. **GPS:** n44,57567 e10,96415.

10 🛒free 🚰🔌free. **Location:** Rural. **Surface:** metalled. ⭕ 01/01-31/12 **Distance:** 🛒5km ⊗2,8km ⊗pizzeria 🛒5km. **Remarks:** 10% discount at restaurant.

Tourist information Modena:
Ⓜ Galleria Ferrari, Via Dino Ferrari 43, Maranello. Museum of motor-cars.

Monticelli d'Ongina 25C1

Piazza Resistenza. **GPS:** n45,09050 e9,93537.⬆➡

10 🛒free 🚰🔌Ch free. **Location:** Simple, quiet. **Surface:** asphalted. ⭕ 01/01-31/12 **Distance:** 🛒centre 300m ⊗6,2km ⊗300m 🛒300m.

Parma 🌿🏛🎪 25D2

Area Camper Parma, Largo XXIV Agosto 1942, n° 21/a. **GPS:** n44,80931 e10,28495.⬆➡

26 🛒 € 20 🚰🔌Ch 🚿 WC 🧺€ 1. **Location:** Comfortable. **Surface:** grasstiles. ⭕ 01/01-31/12 **Distance:** 🛒centre 3,5km ⊗7km 🛒Lidl 100m 🛒100m. **Remarks:** Monitored parking, arrival <22h, motorhome washing place 50m.

Tourist information Parma:
👁 Palazzo Pilotta. ⭕ morning. 🎪 Via Verdi. Week market. ⭕ Wed-Sa 7-14h.

Pavullo nel Frignano 🏔👥 25D3

Via Degli Abeti. **GPS:** n44,34294 e10,83309.⬆

12 🛒free 🚰🔌Ch free. **Location:** Comfortable, quiet. **Surface:** gravel/sand. **Distance:** 🛒700m ⊗600m 🛒600m 🛒600m. **Remarks:** Picnic area.

Porto Corsini 🏖 25G2

Pro Loco, Via G. Guizzetti. **GPS:** n44,49620 e12,27950.⬆➡

IT

155 ☐ 01/04-30/09 € 9, 01/06-30/09 € 11 ⚡🔧Ch 💧€3/day WC.
Location: Rural, comfortable, quiet. **Surface:** grassy.
🗓 01/04-30/09
Distance: 🚶500m 🏊200m 🚲300m ⊗300m ⛽300m.

⬛S Portomaggiore 🌿 25F2
Via Giuseppe Mazzini. **GPS:** n44,69584 e11,81389.⬆.

10 ☐free ⚡free. **Surface:** asphalted. 🗓 01/01-31/12
Distance: 🚶500m ⊗500m ⛽500m.
Remarks: Nearby cemetery.

Tourist information Portomaggiore:
🦅 Valli di Comacchio. Nature reserve, in winter whereabouts birds.

⬛ Premilcuore 25F3
Parcheggio Fluviale, Loc. Fontanalba. **GPS:** n43,97618 e11,77615.

☐€ 1. **Surface:** metalled. 🗓 01/01-31/12
Distance: 🚶500m 🚲20m ⊗500m ⛽50m.
Remarks: Along river.

⬛S Ravenna 🌿🏛⛲ 25G3
Parking Bus-Camper, Via E.Ferrari. Loc.Classe.
GPS: n44,37849 e12,23461.⬆➡.

30 ☐free ⚡☐free. **Location:** Urban, simple. **Surface:** grasstiles.
🗓 01/01-31/12
Distance: 🚶Ravenna centre 6km.
Remarks: Nearby basilica.

⬛S Ravenna 🌿🏛⛲ 25G3
Piazza della Resistenza. **GPS:** n44,41433 e12,18852.⬆.

10 ☐€ 0,50/h, € 2,50/24h ⚡🔧Chfree. 🚐 **Location:** Urban, simple,
central. **Surface:** grasstiles. 🗓 01/01-31/12
Distance: 🚶historical centre 500m 🏊5km ⊗150m ⛽500m.
⛽50m.

Remarks: Max. 24h.

⬛S Ravenna 🌿🏛⛲ 25G3
Via Pomposa. **GPS:** n44,43002 e12,20827.⬆.

10 ☐free ⚡🔧Chfree. **Surface:** asphalted. 🗓 01/01-31/12
Distance: 🚶city centre 2km ⛽100m on the spot.

⬛S Ravenna 🌿🏛⛲ 25G3
Via Teodorico. **GPS:** n44,42317 e12,20981.

10 ☐free ⚡🔧Chfree. **Location:** Urban, simple, quiet.
Surface: asphalted. 🗓 01/01-31/12
Distance: 🚶500m ⊗on the spot.
Remarks: In front of the Mausoleum.

⬛ Ravenna 🌿🏛⛲ 25G3
Via Brancaleone/circonvallazione S. Gaetanino.
GPS: n44,42339 e12,20478.⬆.

25 ☐free. **Location:** Urban, simple, noisy. **Surface:** metalled.
🗓 01/01-31/12
Distance: 🚶200m 🏊5km 🚲100m ⊗200m ⛽200m 🚌10m.
Remarks: Next to Rocca Brancaleone.

◉S Ravenna 🌿🏛⛲ 25G3
Area Camper Atrezzata, Eurolandia, SS16.
GPS: n44,33533 e12,26949.⬆.

68 ☐€ 10/day, € 15/2 days ⚡🔧Chincluded. 🚐
Location: Rural, simple. **Surface:** gravel. 🗓 01/01-31/12

😊S Ravenna 🌿🏛⛲ 25G3
Parco Divertimenti Mirabilandia, SS16, via Romea Sud 463.
GPS: n44,33290 e12,26966.⬆.

400 ☐€ 15 ⚡🔧free. **Location:** Rural, simple, noisy. **Surface:** gravel.
Distance: 🚶Ravenna centre 10km ⊗McDonalds.

Remarks: Max. 48h.
Tourist information Ravenna:
ℹ U.I.A.T. (Ufficio Informazioni e di Accoglienza Turistica), Via Salara,
8/12, www.turismo.ravenna.it. City of the mosaics, historical city with
many curiosities.
🏛 Piazza Garibaldi. Antiques market. ⬛ 3rd weekend of the month.
🎡 Parco Divertimenti Mirabilandia, SS16, via Romea Sud 463. Amusement park. 🗓 01/04-15/09.

⬛S Reggio nell'Emilia 25D2
Parking Ex Foro Boario, Via XX Settembre.
GPS: n44,70941 e10,62463.⬆➡.

200 ☐free ⚡🔧Chfree. **Location:** Urban, simple.
Surface: grasstiles.
🗓 01/01-31/12
Distance: 🚶1km 🚲3,7km ⊗100m ⛽500m 🚌Free bus to centre.

⬛S Riccione 🏛🏖 25G3
Piazza 1° Maggio. **GPS:** n44,00392 e12,65115.⬆➡.

10 ☐free ⚡€4 🔧Ch. **Location:** Urban, simple, central, quiet.
Surface: asphalted.
🗓 01/01-31/12 ◉ Service: winter
Distance: 🚶100m 🏊500m ⊗500m 🏛100m 🚌50m.

⬛S Rimini 🌿🏛🏖 25G3
Park Settebello, Viale Roma 86. **GPS:** n44,06068 e12,57572.⬆➡.

300 ☐€ 10/24h ⚡€2 🔧€2 🔌(80x)€3/day.
Location: Urban, simple, central, noisy. **Surface:** metalled.
🗓 01/01-31/12
Distance: 🚶200m 🏊500m.
Remarks: Next to cinema Settebello.

⬛S Rimini 🌿🏛🏖 25G3
Sostaverde La Valletta, Via Della Lama 47, SS 16.
GPS: n44,09889 e12,49867.⬆➡.

150 ☐€ 10/24h ⚡🔌€3 WC included. **Location:** Rural, noisy.
Surface: grassy/gravel. 🗓 01/04-30/09
Distance: 🚶Rimini 11km 🚲3,8km 🏊2km ⊗800m ⛽800m.
Remarks: Shuttle bus to beach.

⬛S Rimini 🌿🏛🏖 25G3
P30 Chiabrera, Via Chiabrera. **GPS:** n44,04803 e12,59548.⬆.
☐01/05-30/09 € 12,10. **Location:** Urban, simple, central, noisy.
Surface: asphalted.

IT

Tourist information Rimini:
⊗ Casa Zanni, Via Casale, 205, Villa Verucchio. Restaurant with authentic Italian cuisine.

🅂 Ro 🏞 25F1

Mulino sul Po. GPS: n44,95498 e11,75668. ⬆.

4 🆓free 🚰💧 (4x)free. **Location:** Rural, simple.
Surface: metalled.
Distance: 🚰1km ⊗ on the spot 🚶 on the spot.
Remarks: Along the Po river.

🅂 Rocca San Casciano 🎭 25F3

GPS: n44,06173 e11,84604. ⬆.
4 🆓free 🚰€1/100liter 💧Ch€1/4h. **Location:** Rural.
Surface: metalled. 🅾 01/01-31/12
Distance: 🚰300m ⊗100m.

🅂 Rubiera 25D2

Via della Chiusa. GPS: n44,64229 e10,77765. ⬆➡.

🆓free 🚰💧Ch. **Location:** Simple, quiet. **Surface:** asphalted.
🅾 01/01-31/12
Remarks: At sports park.

🅂 Sala Baganza 25C2

Via Vittorio Emanuele, 42. GPS: n44,70856 e10,23070. ⬆.

2 🆓free 🚰💧Ch 💧(4x)free. **Location:** Rural, simple, quiet.
Surface: asphalted. 🅾 01/01-31/12
Distance: 🚰500m 🚲15km 💧500m.

🅂 Salsomaggiore Terme ♨ 25C2

Via Antonio Gramsci. GPS: n44,82005 e9,98981. ⬆.

20 🆓free 🚰💧free. **Location:** Urban, simple, quiet. **Surface:** gravel.
🅾 01/01-31/12
Distance: 🚰800m.
Remarks: Parking next to station.

🅂 San Piero in Bagno 32C1

Via G.Mazzini. GPS: n43,86353 e11,97692. ⬆.

---

5 🆓free. **Surface:** asphalted. 🅾 01/01-31/12
Distance: 🚰500m 🚲1km ⊗500m 💧500m 🚗200m.

🅂 Santa Sofia 🏔🎭 32C1

Piazzale K. Marx. GPS: n43,94165 e11,90930. ⬆.

🆓free 🚰💧Chfree. **Surface:** asphalted. 🅾 01/01-31/12
Distance: 🚰200m.

Tourist information Santa Sofia:
🥾 Foreste Casentinesi. National nature reserve.

🅂 Serramazzoni 🏔🏕🏔🎭❄ 25D3

Piazza Olimpico. GPS: n44,42223 e10,79402. ⬆➡.

20 🆓free 🚰💧Chfree. **Location:** Urban. **Surface:** asphalted.
🅾 01/01-31/12
Distance: 🚰300m ⊗100m 💧300m 🚲300m 🚶300m 🎿800m.

🚻🅂 Serramazzoni 🏔🏕🏔🎭❄ 25D3

**Via Giardini Nord, Montagnana di Serramazzoni.
GPS:** n44,47250 e10,82005. ⬆.

15 🆓free 🚰💧. **Location:** Rural, simple, quiet. **Surface:** gravel.
🅾 01/01-31/12
Distance: 🚰8km Maranello 💧8km.
Remarks: Maranello: Ferrari factory and museum.

🅂 Soragna 🏔 25C2

Via Matteotti / via Gramsci. GPS: n44,92988 e10,12566. ⬆.

10 🆓free 🚰💧Chfree. **Location:** Urban, simple, quiet.
Surface: asphalted. 🅾 01/01-31/12
Distance: 🚰120m ⊗200m 💧200m.

🅂 Suviana 25E3

Via Lungo Lago. GPS: n44,12039 e11,04592.

---

60 🆓Free, hollidays € 9. 🚲 **Location:** Rural, simple, quiet.
Surface: asphalted.
Distance: 🏊on the spot 🚣on the spot ⊗on the spot.
Remarks: At lake Suviana.

🅂 Terenzo 🏔🏔🎭 25C2

Loc. Bardone. GPS: n44,62528 e10,10083. ⬆.

10 🆓€ 13 🚰💧Ch 💧WC included. 🚲 **Location:** Rural,
comfortable, quiet. **Surface:** metalled. 🅾 01/01-31/12
Distance: 🚰200m 🚲12km 💧12km ⊗on the spot.

🅂 Tredozio 🏔🎭 25F3

Area Le Volte, Via Salvo D'Acquisto. GPS: n44,07431 e11,73228. ⬆➡.

40 🆓€5 🚰💧Ch 💧€2,50. **Surface:** metalled. 🅾 01/01-31/12
Distance: 🚰1,5km ⊗200m camping 💧1,5km.
Remarks: Next to campsite Le Volte, max. 48h, discount at restaurant/
swimming-pool.

🅂 Tresigallo 25F2

Fraz. Finale di Rero. GPS: n44,81643 e11,90050.
🆓free 🚰💧.
Remarks: Nearby sports park.

🅂 Vergato 25E3

SS 64, Bologna-Pistoia. GPS: n44,28952 e11,11270. ⬆.

25 🆓free 🚰💧Chfree. **Location:** Rural, simple. **Surface:** asphalted.
🅾 01/01-31/12
Distance: 🚰400m ⊗400m 💧500m 🚗500m.

🅂 Vezzano Sul Crostolo 🎭 25D2

Area Sosta Camper Matildica, SS63. GPS: n44,58960 e10,53608.
10 🆓 🚰💧Ch 💧 **Surface:** asphalted. 🅾 01/01-31/12
Distance: 🚰1,5km ⊗on the spot 🚲on the spot 🚶on the spot.
Remarks: Eco Parco di Vezzano, keycard at Bar Sport, Via Roma, SS63,
n44,59963, o10,54542.

Liguria

🅂 Borghetto Santo Spirito 27H1

Via Tevere. GPS: n44,11548 e8,23758. ⬆➡.

150 🛥 € 10/24h, Jul-Aug-Dec € 13 🚰 🔌Ch🔌(50x)€3/day,16Amp.
Surface: gravel.
Distance: 🚶1,1km 🚲2,5km ⛵400m.
Remarks: Along the river Varatella.

🏛️S **Castelnuovo Magra** **25C3**

Agriturismo Cascina dei Peri, Via Montefrancio 71.
GPS: n44,10355 e10,00734.⬆️➡️.

6 🛥 € 8,50/pp, children free 🚰 🔌Ch 🔌€3 WC included 🔌€5 🗑️.
Surface: grassy/gravel. 🅿️ 01/01-31/12
Distance: 🚲2,4km.
Remarks: Dinner € 20/pp wine incl. (to order <16h), selling of wine and olive oil, swimming pool from june.

🏛️S **Cengio** **24H3**

Area Attrezzata Cengio Isole, Via Isole.
GPS: n44,39083 e8,20194.⬆️➡️.

🛥free 🚰 🔌Chfree. **Surface:** asphalted.
Distance: 🚶600m ⛵on the spot. ⊗on the spot.
Remarks: Nearby sports park.

🏛️S **Cervo** **27H1**

Camper Cervo, Via Steria. **GPS:** n43,92833 e8,10527.⬆️➡️.

130 🛥 € 12-15/day 🚰 🔌Chincluded 🔌€3/24h. **Surface:** gravel.
🅿️ 01/01-31/12
Distance: 🚲2,5km.

🏛️S **Diano Marina** **27H1**

Oasi Park, Via Sori 5. **GPS:** n43,90667 e8,07083.⬆️➡️.

300 🛥 € 8-15/day 🚰 🔌Ch 🔌€3 WC 🔌€1 🗑️.
Surface: grassy/gravel. 🅿️ 01/01-31/12
Distance: 🚶600m 🚲6,8km ⛵800m ⊗600m 🚶600m 🚉600m
🚵mountainbike trail.

Remarks: Beachshuttle with bar/restaurant.

🏛️S **Diano Marina** **27H1**

Il bowling di Diano, Via Diano S. Pietro, 71 - Diano Castello.
GPS: n43,91683 e8,07576.⬆️.

🛥 € 18/day 🚰 🔌Ch 🔌€4. **Surface:** unpaved.
🅿️ 01/01-31/12
Distance: 🚶1km 🚲5,5km ⛵1,2km on the spot 🗑️50m.
Remarks: Narrow entrance, swimming pool, bar, bowling.

🏛️S **Diano Marina** **27H1**

Al Roseto, Via Case Parse, San siro, Diano Castello.
GPS: n43,91983 e8,07733.⬆️.

🛥 € 12-15 🚰 🔌Ch 🔌WC 🔌€2 🗑️. 🅿️ 01/01-31/12
Distance: 🚲5,5km.
Remarks: At Floriculturist, shuttle bus to beach.

🏛️S **Finale Ligure** **25A3**

Area Caprazoppa, Via Aurelia, SS1. **GPS:** n44,16549 e8,33750.⬆️.

40 🛥 € 18/24h 🚰 🔌Chincluded. **Surface:** gravel/sand.
🅿️ 01/01-31/12
Distance: 🚶500m 🚲4km ⛵700m.

🏛️S **Imperia** **27H1**

Francy Park, Via dei Giardini. **GPS:** n43,86917 e8,00010.⬆️.

32 🛥 € 10, 01/06-30/09 € 13. 🏪 **Surface:** metalled.
🅿️ 01/01-31/12
Distance: 🚶centre 4km ⛵sea 150m ⊗150m.

🏛️S **La Spezia** **25C3**

Viale San Bartolomeo. **GPS:** n44,10417 e9,85917.

100 🛥 € 5 🚰free. **Surface:** grassy. 🅿️ 8-20h
12.30-13.30h
Distance: 🚶4km.

Remarks: Monitored parking.
Tourist information La Spezia:
ℹ️ Lerici. Former fishing village, nowadays holiday resort.
ℹ️ Cinque Terre. Protected coast area.
🏰 Castello di Lerici, Lerici. 🅿️ 01/04-31/10.
🎪 Lerici. 🅿️ Sa-morning.

🏛️S **Levanto** **25C3**

SP556, Loc. Moltedi. **GPS:** n44,17476 e9,61836.⬆️➡️.

16 🛥 € 12/12h, € 15/24h, € 20/36h 🚰 🔌Chfree.
🅿️ 01/01-31/12
Distance: 🚶500m ⛵1km 🚉train 100m.
Remarks: Behind railway station, well situated for visiting the Cinque Terre by train.

🏛️S **Loano** 🌿 **24H3**

La Sosta, Via delle Fornaci, 31. **GPS:** n44,13115 e8,24111.⬆️.
41 🛥 € 15 🚰 🔌Ch 🔌WC 🗑️included. 🏪 **Surface:** gravel.
🅿️ 01/01-31/12
Distance: ⛵2km ⊗400m.
Remarks: Shuttle bus.

Tourist information Loano:
👁️ Grotta di Santa Lucia, Toirano. Stalactites and stalagmites.
👁️ Grotta della Basura, Toirano. Man and beast from the stone age.

🏛️S **Pietra Ligure** **25A3**

Area Camper, Via Crispi 43. **GPS:** n44,15484 e8,28397.⬆️➡️.

53 🛥 € 13/24h, 01/06-30/09 € 16/24h 🚰 🔌Ch 🔌(53x)included WC 🔌€0,70. **Surface:** gravel.
Distance: ⛵200m.

🏛️S **Portovenere** 🌿 **32A1**

Via Olivo, Loc. Cavo. **GPS:** n44,05961 e9,84843.⬆️.

20 🛥 € 1,85/h 8-20h, overnight stay free 🚰 🔌Ch. 🏪
Surface: metalled. 🅿️ 01/01-31/12
Distance: 🚶2km ⛵750m 🚶600m 🚉50m.

🏛️S **San Lorenzo al Mare** **27H1**

Area Camper Il Pozzo, Via Gaetano Salvemini.
GPS: n43,85512 e7,96083.⬆️➡️.

30 🛥 € 15-23 🚰 🔌Ch 🔌WC 🔌€4 🗑️included.
Location: Luxurious. **Surface:** gravel.
Distance: 🚶400m ⛵600m ⊗400m.
Remarks: Max. 7m.

San Rocco 25B3

Viale Franco Molfino, Camogli. **GPS**: n44,33472 e9,16084.

9 € 9/8-20h. **Surface**: asphalted.
Distance: 150m on the spot.
Remarks: Marked hiking trails in Parco di Portofino (45min-2h).

Santo Stefano al Mare 27H1

Camper Village, Strada Porsani. **GPS**: n43,84378 e7,90824.

60 € 12-30/24h Ch €3 WC. **Surface**: gravel.
Distance: 10km 800m on the spot.
Remarks: Free shuttle, swimming pool.

Santo Stefano al Mare 27H1

Marina degli Aregai, Via Gianni Cozzi. **GPS**: n43,83723 e7,90581.

± 30 € 1,50/h, € 5-10/day. **Surface**: asphalted.
Distance: on the spot Sandy beach on the spot on the spot.

Torriglia 25B3

Area Comunale Piscina, Via degli Alpini. **GPS**: n44,51667 e9,16000.

10 free Ch free. **Surface**: grasstiles.
Distance: 200m.
Remarks: Next to swimming pool, market Saturday.

Tuscany

Alberese 32B2

Parco Naturale della Maremma, Via del Bersagliere.
GPS: n42,66944 e11,10416.

50 free. **Location**: Rural. **Surface**: gravel/sand.
01/04-30/09
Distance: 100m 7km on the spot on the spot on the spot.

Albinia 32B2

Ai Delfini, Via Aurelia km153. **GPS**: n42,50882 e11,19552.

24 € 1/h, Aug € 1,50/h 4 pers. incl. + tourist tax Ch
WC included €1 €5 1h incl., €10/15 days
Location: Comfortable, quiet. **Surface**: grassy/sand.
24/04-31/10
Distance: 2km 50m on the spot 2km.

Anghiari 32C1

Via Campo della Fiera. **GPS**: n43,53904 e12,05291.

8 free Ch free. **Location**: Simple, quiet. **Surface**: asphalted.
01/01-31/12
Distance: on the spot on the spot on the spot.

Anghiari 32C1

Agriturismo Val della Pieve, Via della Fossa 8.
GPS: n43,53657 e12,05131.

10 € 15/24h, Jul/Aug € 20 Ch WC €3 included.
Location: Comfortable, isolated, quiet. **Surface**: gravel.
01/01-31/12
Distance: 300m 300m 300m 300m.
Remarks: Swimming pool € 3/pppd.

Anghiari 32C1

Agriturismo La Taverna dei Sorci, San Lorenzo.
GPS: n43,51467 e12,07799.

20 free free. **Location**: Simple, quiet. **Surface**: metalled.
01/01-31/12
Distance: 3km on the spot.

Arcidosso 32B2

Parco Faunistico Monte Amiata, Località Poderi.
GPS: n42,83740 e11,52922.

15 free Ch. **Location**: Rural, simple, central, quiet.
Surface: grassy. 01/01-31/12
Distance: 10km.
Remarks: Nature reserve.

Arezzo 32C1

Via Da Palestrina/via Tarlati (centro-nord). **GPS**: n43,47213 e11,88773.

30 € 0,80/h, € 8/24h Ch free.
Location: Simple, quiet. **Surface**: asphalted. 01/01-31/12
Distance: historical centre 1km.
Remarks: Escalator to city centre.

Arezzo 32C1

P Tarlati, Via Guido Tarlati. **GPS**: n43,47237 e11,88362.

50 free. **Location**: Urban, simple, central. **Surface**: grasstiles.
01/01-31/12
Distance: city centre 1km 500m 300m.

Tourist information Arezzo:
Week market.

Barberino di Mugello 25E3

SS65, Fraz. Monte di Fó. **GPS**: n44,07613 e11,28062.

30 free Ch free. **Location**: Simple, quiet. **Surface**: metalled.
01/01-31/12
Distance: 4km 150m (camping) 150m (camping).
Remarks: In front of campsite Il Sergente.

Barga 25D3

Area San Cristoforo, Via Hayange. **GPS**: n44,07234 e10,48131.

€ 10/24h Ch (10x) WC 200m.
Distance: centro storico within walking distance.

Bibbiena 32C1

La Collina delle Stelle, Loc. Casanova 63.
GPS: n43,71669 e11,85173.

IT

8 ⌁€ 15, 01/05-30/09 € 20 2 pers. incl., extra pers. € 4 🚐🍽Ch🔧€2/day WC 🚿🗑€5,ironing services€5 📶included. **Location:** Comfortable, quiet. **Surface:** gravel. 🔌 15/03-01/11, Christmas
Distance: 🛁7km ⊗on the spot.🚌on the spot.
Remarks: Swimming pool € 5/pp (free with a meal).

🖼S Borgo a Mozzano 32A1
Via I° Maggio, SP2. **GPS:** n43,97612 e10,54113.⬆.

4 ⌁free 🚐🍽Ch 🔧(4x)free. **Surface:** gravel.
Distance: 🛁200m Serchio river.
Remarks: At tourist office.

🖼S Borgo San Lorenzo 32B1
Via Caduti di Montelungo. **GPS:** n43,95112 e11,38518.⬆.

10 ⌁ 🚐🍽Chfree. **Location:** Simple. **Surface:** asphalted.
🔌 01/01-31/12 🔲 Fri
Distance: 🛁500m ⊗500m 🚌300m.
Remarks: Friday market.

🖼 Buonconvento 🌿 32B2
Viale della Liberta. **GPS:** n43,13854 e11,48109.⬆.

⌁free. **Location:** Simple. **Surface:** unpaved.
Distance: 🛁50m ⊗50m.
Remarks: At the city walls.

S Buonconvento 🌿 32B2
Viale Ferruccio Parri. **GPS:** n43,13065 e11,48349.⬆➡.

🚐€1🍽Ch. 🔌 01/01-31/12

🖼S Calci 32A1
Via Brogiotti. **GPS:** n43,72769 e10,51722.⬆.

6 ⌁€ 8/24h 🚐🍽Ch 🔧included. **Surface:** asphalted.
🔌 01/01-31/12
Distance: 🛁100m 🚌200m.
Remarks: At sports park, payment only with coins.

🖼S Campiglia Marittima 32B2
Parcheggio La Pieve, Via di Venturina. **GPS:** n43,05672 e10,61439.⬆.

4 ⌁free 🚐🍽Chfree. **Location:** Rural. **Surface:** asphalted.
Distance: 🛁350m ⊗450m 🚌500m.
Remarks: In front of cemetery, near gymnasium.

🖼S Capalbio 32B3
Via della Torba. **GPS:** n42,40753 e11,31566.
⌁€ 6. **Surface:** sand.
Distance: ⊗150m ⊗on the spot.
Remarks: Beach parking.

🖼S Capraia e Limite 32B1
Via delle Ginestre, zona industriale, loc. Capraia Fiorentina.
GPS: n43,73660 e11,00442.⬆.
⌁free 🚐🍽Chfree. **Surface:** metalled.

🖼S Casola in Lunigiana 25C3
Area La Linea del Drago. GPS: n44,19916 e10,17333.⬆➡.

20 ⌁€ 7 + € 5/pp 🚐🍽Ch 🔧WC 🗑📶included.
Surface: grassy. 🔌 01/01-31/12
Distance: ⊗on the spot.
Remarks: At little stream with swimming area.

🖼S Castagneto Carducci 32A2
Camperesort, Via Aurelia 373/B. **GPS:** n43,15630 e10,56097.⬆.

50 ⌁€ 10 + € 7/pp, 16/09-14/06 € 5/pp 🚐🍽Ch 🔧WC 🗑€0,50 🔌€3 📶included. **Location:** Luxurious. **Surface:** grassy/gravel.
🔌 01/01-31/12
Distance: ⊗1,2km ⊗on the spot. **Remarks:** Swimming pool incl.

🖼S Castagneto Carducci 32A2
Via del Seggio, Marina di Castagneto. **GPS:** n43,18401 e10,54841.⬆.

30 ⌁€ 10/24h 🚐🍽Chfree. **Surface:** unpaved.
Distance: 🛁2km ⊗500m ⊗2,5km 🚌2,5km.

🖼S Castagneto Carducci 32A2
Viale delle Palme, Marina di Castagneto. **GPS:** n43,19323 e10,54152.⬆.

20 ⌁€ 10/24h 🚐🍽Ch. **Surface:** unpaved.
Distance: ⊗100m.
Remarks: Max. 48h, dogs beach.

🖼S Castel del Piano 🌿⛵🏔 32B2
Via Po. **GPS:** n42,88872 e11,53733.➡.

30 ⌁free 🚐🍽Chfree. **Location:** Rural, simple. **Surface:** asphalted.
🔌 01/01-31/12
Distance: 🛁500m.

🖼S Castelfiorentino 32B1
Ara Comunale, Via Che Guevara, circonvallazione Ovest.
GPS: n43,60885 e10,96365.⬆.

5 ⌁free 🚐🍽free. **Location:** Simple, isolated.
Surface: asphalted.
Distance: 🛁1,5km ⊗1,5km 🚌1,5km.

🖼S Castellina in Chianti 32B1
La Strada del Chianti, SR222. **GPS:** n43,47330 e11,28760.⬆➡.

15 ⌁€ 10/24h, 01/11-31/03 free 🚐€0,20/10liter 🍽Ch 🔧(8x) included WC€0,50. 📷 **Location:** Rural, comfortable.
Surface: asphalted. 🔌 01/01-31/12
Distance: 🛁200m.

Tourist information Castellina in Chianti:
🏛 Via IV Novembre. Week market. 🔲 Sa-morning.

🖼S Castelnuovo di Garfagnana 25D3
Via Valmaira. **GPS:** n44,11447 e10,40304.⬆.

☕free ⚡🔧Chfree. **Surface:** metalled. ⭕ 01/01-31/12
Distance: 🚶1km.
Remarks: At sports park.

| 🅱S | **Castelnuovo di Val de Cecina** | 32B2 |

Via della Fonte, Sasso Pisano. **GPS:** n43,16748 e10,86586.⬆.

10 ☕free ⚡€2 🔧Ch 🔌€3/12h. **Location:** Rural.
Surface: metalled. ⭕ 01/01-31/12
Distance: 🚶100m ⊗200m.

| 🅱S | **Castiglion Fiorentino** | 32C1 |

Piazza Garibaldi, viale Marconi. **GPS:** n43,34465 e11,92278.⬆.

20 ☕free ⚡🔧Chfree WC. **Location:** Rural, simple.
Surface: asphalted. ⭕ 01/01-31/12 ⚫ Fri-morning market
Distance: 🚶on the spot ⊗on the spot.

| 🅱S | **Castiglione della Pescaia** 🌊⛱🏖 | 32B2 |

Paduline, Via Andromeda. **GPS:** n42,76888 e10,89079.⬆➡.

120 ☕€12-15 ⚡€2 🔧€3. 🔌 **Location:** Rural, simple.
Surface: gravel. ⭕ 01/05-30/09
Distance: 🚶1km.
Remarks: Market Saturday.

| 🅱S | **Castiglione della Pescaia** 🌊⛱🏖 | 32B2 |

Rocchette Serignano, Via Rio Palma, Rocchette.
GPS: n42,77970 e10,79955.⬆➡.

120 ☕€20/day ⚡€3 🔧Ch 🔌(18x) 💧€1. 🔌 **Location:** Rural,
comfortable. **Surface:** gravel. ⭕ 01/04-15/09
Distance: 🚶Castiglione della Pescaia 7km 🏖200m ⊗200m.
Remarks: Beach parking, unguarded.

| ⛽ | **Castiglione della Pescaia** 🌊⛱🏖 | 32B2 |

Via Ponte Giorgini. **GPS:** n42,76515 e10,88545.⬆➡.

5 ☕€ 1,50h, € 10/24h. 🚏 **Location:** Urban, simple.
Surface: asphalted. ⭕ 01/01-31/12
Distance: 🚶on the spot.
Remarks: Market Saturday.

| 🅱S | **Castiglione d'Orcia** 🌊🏖 | 32C2 |

Area Pro Loco, Viale Marconi. **GPS:** n43,00292 e11,61552.⬆.

5 ☕free ⚡🔧free. **Location:** Rural, simple. **Surface:** gravel/sand.
⭕ 01/01-31/12
Distance: 🚶200m 🚶on the spot.

Tourist information Castiglione d'Orcia:
♟ Rocco d'Orcia. Medieval citadel.

| 🅱S | **Certaldo** | 32B1 |

Area Comunale, Piazza dei Macelli. **GPS:** n43,54629 e11,04611.⬆➡.

10 ☕free ⚡🔧Chfree. **Location:** Rural. **Surface:** metalled.
⭕ 01/01-31/12
Distance: 🚶medieval centre 150m (elevator) ⊗150m 🍴250m.

| 🅱S | **Chifenti** | 32A1 |

Area sosta Chifenti, SS12. **GPS:** n44,00492 e10,56337.
10 ☕free ⚡🔧Chfree. **Surface:** asphalted/gravel.
⭕ 01/01-31/12
Distance: 🚶500M.

| 🅱S | **Chiusdino** | 32B2 |

Abbazia San Galgano, SS441. **GPS:** n43,15283 e11,15137.⬆.

15 ☕€ 1,50/h, € 10/8-20h, overnight stay free 🔌(9x)free.
Location: Rural, isolated, quiet. **Surface:** grasstiles.
⭕ 01/01-31/12
Distance: 🚶12km ⊗300m.
Remarks: Abbey of San Galgano 300m.

| 🅱S | **Chiusi** | 32C2 |

Via Torri del Fornello. **GPS:** n43,01461 e11,94972.⬆.

5 ☕free ⚡🔧free. **Surface:** asphalted.
Distance: 🚶100m 🚲4,5km.
Remarks: Next to school.

| 🅱S | **Chiusi** | 32C2 |

Loc. Sbarchino. **GPS:** n43,05049 e11,95756.⬆.
10 ☕free. ⭕ 01/01-31/12
Distance: ⊗Pesce d'Oro on the spot 🚶on the spot.

| 🅱S | **Cutigliano** | 25D3 |

Via di Risorgimento/Sp37. **GPS:** n44,09877 e10,75450.
14 ☕€ 1,50/h, € 15/24h ⚡🔧Ch 🔌included. 🚏
Surface: metalled.
Remarks: Max. 48h.

| 🅱S | **Dicomano** 🌊🏞 | 32B1 |

SS67, Tosco Romagnola. **GPS:** n43,89407 e11,53715.⬆.

4 ☕free ⚡🔧Chfree. **Location:** Simple. **Surface:** asphalted.
⭕ 01/01-31/12
Distance: 🚶1km ⊗200m.

| 🅱S | **Equi Terme** 🌊🏖 | 25C3 |

Via della Stazione. **GPS:** n44,17009 e10,15513.⬆➡.

40 ☕€ 10/night ⚡🔧Ch 🔌included. **Surface:** gravel.
Distance: ⊗100m.
Remarks: Near spa resort (100m), caves (500m) and marble quarry.

| 🅱S | **Firenze** 🌊🏖🍴 | 32B1 |

FiPark, Viale Europa, Fraz. Bagno a Ripoli, Florence (Firenze).
GPS: n43,75554 e11,30609.⬆.

40 ☕7-19h € 2/h, 19-7h € 1/h, € 15/24h ⚡🔧Ch. 🚏
Location: Simple. **Surface:** metalled. ⭕ 01/01-31/12
Distance: 🚌bus 23/33 > centre.

| 🅱S | **Firenze** 🌊🏖🍴 | 32B1 |

Area sociale 'Flog', Via M Mercati 24/b, zona Careggi, Florence (Firenze).
GPS: n43,79491 e11,24835.⬆.

IT

25 ⏏️€ 15/24h 🚰€3 Ch. **Location:** Simple. **Surface:** gravel.
🅿️ 01/01-31/12
Distance: 🚶city centre 2km ⊗Pizzeria 🚌centre : bus 4, 6-24h.

🅂 Firenze 32B1

Florence Park Scandicci, Via di Scandicci 241, Florence (Firenze).
GPS: n43,76267 e11,20875.⬆️.

25 ⏏️€ 15 🚰Ch 📶included. **Location:** Urban, comfortable,
central, quiet. **Surface:** metalled. 🅿️ 01/01-31/12
Distance: 🚶4km 🚲5km 150m.
Remarks: Video surveillance.

🅂 Firenze 32B1

Gelsomino SCAF, Via del Gelsomino 11, Florence (Firenze).
GPS: n43,75173 e11,24388.⬆️.

150 ⏏️€ 15/24h 🚰Ch 🚿included. 🍴
Surface: grasstiles.
🅿️ 01/01-31/12
Distance: 🚶2km 🚌bus 37 > centre.

Tourist information Florence (Firenze):
ℹ️ U.I.A.T. (Ufficio Informazioni e di Accoglienza Turistica), Piazza
Stazione, 4, www.firenze.turismo.toscana.it. Renaissance city with
many curiosities.
👁️ Ponte Vechio. Famous bridge with jeweller's shops.
✝️ Cappella Brancacci, Santa Maria del Carmine. Renovated frescoes.
🛍️ The Mall, le griffe, Via Europa 8, Leccio Reggello. Factory outlet.

Firenzuola 25E3

Area Picnic, Loc. Badia a Moscheta. **GPS:** n44,07586 e11,42030.➡️.

10 ⏏️free. **Location:** Simple, isolated, quiet.
Surface: gravel.
🅿️ 01/01-31/12
Distance: 🚶Firenzuola 8km ⊗500m agriturismo Badia di Moscheta.

🅂 Firenzuola 25E3

Loc. Pieve di Camaggiore. **GPS:** n44,14594 e11,45361.⬆️.

50 ⏏️free 🚰ChWC. **Location:** Simple, quiet. **Surface:** grasstiles.
🅿️ 01/01-31/12
Distance: 🚶Firenzuola 10km 🚣river 100m 🛒1km.
Remarks: Playground.

🅂 Fivizzano 25C3

Agriturismo Ristorante Al Vecchio Tino, Loc. Germalla 1, Monte dei
Bianchi. **GPS:** n44,17155 e10,13325.
6 ⏏️€ 12 🚰Ch 🚿included. **Surface:** gravel. 🅿️ 01/01-31/12

🅂 Foiano della Chiana 32C1

Outlet Village Valdichiana, Via Enzo Ferrari 5, loc. Farniole.
GPS: n43,22489 e11,80291.⬆️.

10 ⏏️free. **Location:** Simple. **Surface:** asphalted. 🅿️ 01/01-31/12
Distance: ⊗on the spot 🛒on the spot.
Remarks: Motorhome parking at Outlet.

🅂 Follonica 32B2

Eucalyptus Camper Park, Via Sanzio. **GPS:** n42,92804 e10,77569.

40 ⏏️€ 10 🚰€4 Ch 🚿included 🗑️€1.🚿
Distance: 🏖️beach 1,8km 🚲1km 🛒1km.

Fonteblanda 32B2

Talamone Wind Beach Parking, Strada Provinciale Talamone.
GPS: n42,56334 e11,15659.⬆️➡️.

150 ⏏️free, June-Sep € 15. **Location:** Rural, simple, isolated.
Surface: gravel. 🅿️ 01/01-31/12
Distance: 🚶1,5km 🏖️on the spot 🚲on the spot ⊗1,5km 🛒1,5km.
Remarks: Beach parking, shuttle bus to village.

🅂 Gaiole in Chianti 32B1

Via Michelangelo Buonarroti. **GPS:** n43,46434 e11,43440.⬆️➡️.

⏏️free 🚰Ch free. **Location:** Rural, simple. **Surface:** metalled.
🅿️ 01/01-31/12

Remarks: At footballstadium.

🅂 Gallicano 25D3

Via dei Cipressi. **GPS:** n44,05827 e10,44565.⬆️➡️.

4 ⏏️free 🚰Ch 🚿(2x)free. **Surface:** metalled.
🅿️ 01/01-31/12
Distance: 🚶500m.
Remarks: Grotta del Vento.

🅂 Greve in Chianti 32B1

Monte S. Michele, Via Montebeni. **GPS:** n43,59066 e11,31355.⬆️➡️.

17 ⏏️free 🚰free. **Location:** Rural, comfortable, quiet.
Surface: metalled. 🅿️ 01/01-31/12
Distance: 🚶500m 🛒500m.

Tourist information Greve in Chianti:
⛺ 🅂 Sa-morning.

🅂 Isola dElba 32A2

Area Camper Cavo, San Bennato, Cavo, Elba (Isle) (Isola dElba).
GPS: n42,85459 e10,42267.⬆️.
50 ⏏️€ 18/24h 🚰Ch 🚿€2 🗑️€1. **Surface:** gravel.
🅿️ 01/04-30/10
Distance: 🚶600m 🏖️400m.

🅂 Isola dElba 32A2

Loc. Bocchetto, Porto Azzurro. **GPS:** n42,77114 e10,39985.
60 ⏏️free, peak season € 10/24h 🚰Ch free.
Surface: asphalted.
Distance: 🚶city centre 1km.
Remarks: Nearby cemetery.

🅂 Isola dElba 32A2

Sighello, area La Pila, Marina di Campo. **GPS:** n42,75905 e10,23645.⬆️.
20 ⏏️€ 15 🚰Ch 🚿€3. **Surface:** unpaved. 🅿️ 01/05-30/09
Distance: 🏖️1,5km.
Remarks: At sports park.

🅂 Larciano 32B1

Residence Poggetto, Via Stradella 1489.
GPS: n43,83319 e10,88042.⬆️.

25 ⏏️€ 15/24h, free with a meal 🚰Ch 🚿. **Surface:** grassy/gravel.
🅿️ 01/01-31/12
Distance: 🚶1km ⊗1km.

Livorno 32A1

Piazza Ordoardo Borrani, Viale d'Antignano.
GPS: n43,50465 e10,32144.⬆️.

524

IT

50 ⌇free. **Location:** Rural.
Surface: asphalted.
Distance: 400m Antignano 100m 300m.
Tourist information Livorno:
ℹ Ufficio Informazioni, Piazza del Municipio. Medieval port city.

| 🔲S | Lucca | 32A1 |

Il Serchio, Via del Tiro a Segno 704, loc. Sant'Anna.
GPS: n43,85000 e10,48583.

66 ⌇€ 25/24h, dog € 1 Ch (66x)WC €4,50 included.
Surface: grasstiles. 01/03-31/01
Distance: 1km 2km 500m on the spot 2km on the spot.
Remarks: Waste dump € 2/day, shuttle € 1/pp, swimming pool € 5/pp.

| 🔲S | Lucca | 32A1 |

Area Sosta Lucca, Viale Gaetano Luporini.
GPS: n43,84028 e10,48878.

65 ⌇€ 10/24h, peak season € 14/24h, € 3/h Ch included.
Surface: asphalted.
Distance: 5 min walking 2km.
Tourist information Lucca:
👁 Casa di Puccini, Via di Poggio. Birth place of the composer. Tue-Su.
Wed, Sa, 3rd Su of the month antiques market.

| 🔲S | Lucignano | 32C1 |

SP19. **GPS:** n43,27664 e11,74512.

20 ⌇free Ch (9x)free. **Location:** Rural, simple.
Surface: grassy. 01/01-31/12
Distance: 500m.
Remarks: At the edge of village.

| 🔲S | Marina di Cecina | 32A1 |

Parcheggio Aqua Park, Marina di Cecina.
GPS: n43,30070 e10,49948.

100 ⌇01/03-15/11 € 8 Ch. **Location:** Rural. **Surface:** metalled.
01/01-31/12
Distance: 2km 1km 200m 200m.

| 🔲S | Marina di Cecina | 32A1 |

Via della Cecinella. **GPS:** n43,29278 e10,50785.

30 ⌇1/3-15/11 € 8/24h Ch. **Location:** Rural, simple, quiet.
Surface: asphalted. 01/01-31/12
Distance: 2km 300m 2km 2km.

| 🔲S | Marina di Grosseto | 32B2 |

Oasi di Maremma, SP158 delle Collacchie Km 34,4.
GPS: n42,72611 e10,99055.

50 ⌇€ 16, peak season € 20, 4 pers.incl Ch (100x)€2 WC €1 €4. **Location:** Comfortable, quiet. **Surface:** grassy.
01/04-30/09
Distance: 1km 1km 1km 1km on the spot.
Remarks: Water at each pitch, shuttle € 1/pp.

| 🔲S | Marina di Grosseto | 32B2 |

Area di sosta l'Oasi, S332 > dir San Vincenzo d'Elba.
GPS: n42,73466 e10,97483.

50 ⌇€ 12, Jun € 15, Jul/Aug € 20 Ch €2 WC €2. **Location:** Rural, comfortable. **Surface:** grassy. Easter-30/09
Distance: Marina 1,5km 1,1km 400m nearby.

| 🔲S | Marina di Grosseto | 32B2 |

Via Costiera, SP158. **GPS:** n42,73722 e10,96388.

50 ⌇free. **Location:** Rural, simple. **Surface:** gravel.
01/01-31/12
Distance: 2km 400m.

| P | Marina di Grosseto | 32B2 |

Via Grossetana. **GPS:** n42,71552 e10,98646.

8 ⌇free. **Location:** Urban. **Surface:** sand.
Distance: 400m 400m on the spot.
Remarks: At harbour.
Tourist information Marina di Grosseto:
🌿 Parco Naturale della Maremma. Nature reserve. Wed, Sa, Su 9h 01/06-30/09 guided walk 7h, 16h.

| 🔲S | Marina di Pisa | 32A1 |

Parcheggio Camper Pisamo, Viale Gabriela d'Annunzio.
GPS: n43,67908 e10,27830.
130 ⌇€ 15/24h Ch. **Surface:** sand. 01/01-31/12
Distance: sea 1km.

| 🔲S | Marradi | 25F3 |

Area sosta Marradi, Via San Benedetto. **GPS:** n44,07347 e11,61166.

30 ⌇free 100liter Ch 8kWh,Service€5. **Location:** Simple, quiet. **Surface:** asphalted. 01/01-31/12
Distance: 50m on the spot 100m 200m.
Remarks: Caution key service € 7.

| 🔲S | Massa Marittima | 32B2 |

Viale del Risorgimento. **GPS:** n43,04530 e10,89050.

7 ⌇free Chfree. **Surface:** asphalted.
01/01-31/12
Distance: historical centre 650m 600m 500m on the spot.

| 🔲S | Montalcino | 32B2 |

Geen, Via Osticcio. **GPS:** n43,04913 e11,48749.

30 ⌇€ 5/24h Chfree. **Location:** Rural, comfortable, quiet.
Surface: asphalted/metalled. 01/01-31/12
Distance: 700m 700m 700m.

| 🔲S | Monte San Savino | 32C1 |

Via del Casalino. **GPS:** n43,33177 e11,72204.

20 free ⚡ Ch free. **Location:** Rural, simple. **Surface:** gravel.
⊡ 01/01-31/12
Distance: on the spot ⚓ 4,2km ✕ 200m.
Remarks: Steep ramp.

Montecatini Terme ♈ 32B1
Piazza Pietro Leopoldo, SS 436. **GPS:** n43,88286 e10,76386.
40 free. **Surface:** asphalted. ⊡ 01/01-31/12 ◉ Thu (market)
Distance: ⚓ 3km ✕ 500m 500m.
Remarks: In front of stadium, tuesday market.

Montepulciano 🌿 32C2
P5, Piazza Pietro Nenni. **GPS:** n43,09577 e11,78684. ⬆️➡️

32 € 10/24h ⚡ free. Ⓘ **Location:** Rural, simple.
Surface: asphalted. ⊡ 01/01-31/12 ◉ Thu-morning closed because
of market **Distance:** 200m ✕ 100m 400m.

Monteriggioni 🌿 32B1
Strada di Monteriggioni. **GPS:** n43,38801 e11,22511. ⬆️

12 € 1/h 8-20h, max. € 5, overnight stay free. Ⓘ **Location:** Rural,
comfortable. **Surface:** gravel. ⊡ 01/01-31/12
Distance: 300m 1,4km ✕ 300m ⚓ on the spot.

Monteroni d'Arbia 32B1
Via San Giusto. **GPS:** n43,23048 e11,42371. ⬆️➡️

free ⚡ Ch free. **Location:** Rural, simple. **Surface:** sand.
⊡ 01/01-31/12
Distance: 50m.
Remarks: P centre.

Montespertoli 32B1
Molino del Ponte, Via Volterrana Nord. **GPS:** n43,65606 e11,08445. ⬆️

5 free ⚡ €1/100liter Ch. **Location:** Rural. **Surface:** metalled.
⊡ 01/01-31/12

Distance: Montespertoli 2,3km ✕ on the spot 400m.

Montevarchi 32B1
Via B. Latini. **GPS:** n43,53052 e11,56784. ⬆️

free ⚡ free. **Location:** Urban, simple.
Surface: asphalted.
Distance: ⚓ 7km Coop.
Remarks: Nearby stadium.

Montopoli in Val d'Arno 32B1
Piazza Amerigo Vespucci, Via di Masoria. **GPS:** n43,67333 e10,75222. ⬆️

31 free ⚡ Ch free. **Surface:** metalled. ⊡ 01/01-31/12
Distance: within walking distance.

Orbetello ◀ 32B3
Lanino Parco Sosta, Loc. Santa Liberata.
GPS: n42,43346 e11,15959. ⬆️➡️

50 € 10/motorhome, € 8/pp, € 5/child ⚡ Ch (40x)included
WC. **Location:** Rural. **Surface:** grassy/gravel.
⊡ 01/01-31/12
Distance: Orbetello 5km 50m ✕ 200m alimentari.
Remarks: Max. 72h.

Palazzuolo sul Senio 🌿 25F3
Parcheggio Casone, Via Casone. **GPS:** n44,11073 e11,54968. ⬆️➡️

free ⚡ Ch free. **Location:** Simple. **Surface:** asphalted
⊡ 01/01-31/12
Distance: 100m ✕ 100m 100m.
Remarks: Narrow entrance.

Palazzuolo sul Senio 🌿 25F3
Via Francesco Pagliazzi. **GPS:** n44,11551 e11,55000. ⬆️

6 free. **Location:** Isolated. **Surface:** metalled.
⊡ 01/01-31/12

Distance: on the spot.
Remarks: Next to cemetery, upper part of the parking.

Peccioli 32B1
Parco Preistorico, Via Cappuccini. **GPS:** n43,55694 e10,71889. ⬆️

15 free, after 2 days € 5/day ⚡ WC. **Location:** Rural, simple.
Surface: gravel. ⊡ 01/01-31/12
Distance: 500m ✕ 500m 2km.
Remarks: Picnic area, playground.

Tourist information Peccioli:
◉ Parco Preistorico, Via Cappuccini. ⊡ 01/01-31/12.

Pienza 🌿 32C2
Via Mencattelli e Foro Boario. **GPS:** n43,07799 e11,68087. ⬆️➡️

8-20h: € 1,50/1h, € 5/4h, € 10/8h, overnight stay free ⚡ Ch
included WC. **Location:** Rural, simple. **Surface:** asphalted.
⊡ 01/01-31/12 ◉ Fri-morning market
Distance: 100m.

Pieve Santo Stefano 32C1
Grey camper, Via della Verna. **GPS:** n43,67058 e12,03729. ⬆️➡️

20 € 10 ⚡ Ch WC included €1. **Location:** Simple, noisy.
Surface: metalled. ⊡ 01/01-31/12
Distance: on the spot 1,7km.
Remarks: Nearby viaduct E45.

Piombino ◀ 32A2
Camperoasi, Loc. Mortelliccio, Riotorto.
GPS: n42,95416 e10,66638. ⬆️➡️

93 € 20, Apr-Jun, Sep € 30, Jul/Aug € 40 ⚡ Ch WC included
€0,50 **Location:** Comfortable. **Surface:** grasstiles/grassy.
⊡ 01/01-31/12 ◉ 01/10-31/03 Mo-Thu
Distance: 200m 50m 50m.
Remarks: Water/drainage at each pitch, 10% discount on presentation
of the guide 2012, reception open: 9.30-12.30 14-19.30.

Piombino ◀ 32A2
Carbonifera 1, Loc. Torre Mozza. **GPS:** n42,94750 e10,69277. ⬆️➡️

± 75 🚐 € 2/h, € 18/24h 🚰 ⤓ Ch included. 🚌
Surface: grassy/gravel.
Distance: 🏖 50m.
Remarks: Beach parking, no camping activities.

🚐 [S] Piombino 32A2

Parcheggio Caldanelle, Loc. Caldanelle. **GPS:** n43,00216 e10,52816. [↑]

150 🚐 € 2/h, € 17/8-20h, overnight stay free 🚰 ⤓ Ch.
Location: Isolated, quiet. **Surface:** grassy. ■ 01/01-31/12
Distance: 🏘 Piombino 9km 🏖 1,5km.
Remarks: Beach parking, camper service 8-20h, no camping activities, shuttle bus.

🚐 [S] Piombino 32A2

Perelli 1-3, Loc. Perelli. **GPS:** n42,95527 e10,61944. [↑]

50 🚐 € 2/h, € 16/8-20h, overnight stay free 🚰 ⤓ Ch free. 🚌
Location: Quiet. **Surface:** grassy/sand. ■ 01/06-30/09
Distance: 🏖 Sandy beach 🍴 Perelli 1.
Remarks: Beach parking, service: Perelli 3, no camping activities, dogs beach.

🚐 [S] Piombino 32A2

Via della Pace. **GPS:** n42,93777 e10,52194. [↑]

15 🚐 free 🚰 €0,10/10liter ⤓ Ch. **Location:** Urban, noisy.
Surface: metalled. ■ 01/01-31/12
Distance: 🏘 500m 🏖 1km 🍴 700m 🛒 800m.

🚐 [S] Pisa 32A1

Parcheggio camper, Via di Pratale 78. **GPS:** n43,72106 e10,42066. [↑]

100 🚐 € 12/night, € 1/h, € 5/6h 🚰 €3 ⤓ Ch 🔌. **Location:** Quiet.
Surface: asphalted.
Distance: 🏘 800m ✎ 7km 🛒 on the spot.
Remarks: Monitored parking.

🚐 [S] Pistoia 32B1

Via Marino Marini/via della Quiete. **GPS:** n43,94389 e10,91556. [↑][→].
50 🚐 free 🚰 ⤓. **Surface:** asphalted.
Distance: 🏘 city centre 1km ✎ 6km 🚌 on the spot.
Remarks: At sports park.

🍇 [S] Pistoia 32B1

Agricamper Podere Campofossato. **GPS:** n43,99503 e10,89520.
8 🚐 € 20 🚰 ⤓ Ch 🔌 included.
Distance: 🚌 50m.
Remarks: Regional products.

🚐 [S] Poggibonsi 32B1

Via Fortezza Medicea, loc. Vallone. **GPS:** n43,46203 e11,14593. [↑][→].

± 15 🚐 free 🚰 €0,10/10liter ⤓ Ch 🔌 (6x) €1/12h. **Location:** Rural.
Surface: gravel. ■ 01/01-31/12
Distance: 🏘 centre 500m 🍴 400m 🛒 500m.

Tourist information Poggibonsi:
[i] Monteriggioni. Walled small town.

🚐 [S] Pontassieve 32B1

Viale Hanoi/viale Lisbona. **GPS:** n43,77355 e11,42764. [↑].

🚐 free 🚰 ⤓ Ch free. **Location:** Simple. **Surface:** asphalted.
■ 01/01-31/12
Distance: 🏘 500m.

🚐 [S] Poppi 32C1

La Crocina, Viale dei Pini. **GPS:** n43,71982 e11,76529. [↑][→].

12 🚐 free 🚰 ⤓ Ch free 🔌 €3/5h. **Location:** Simple, quiet.
Surface: asphalted. ■ 01/01-31/12
Distance: 🏘 historical centre 500m 🍴 300m.

🚐 [S] Porto Ercole 32B3

Le Miniere, SP di Porto Ercole. **GPS:** n42,41749 e11,20386. [↑][→].

130 🚐 € 20-25, Aug € 30 🚰 ⤓ Ch 🔌 WC 🚿 €0,50 🧺 €5 📶 included.
🐕 **Location:** Comfortable, noisy. **Surface:** grassy.
■ Easter-30/09
Distance: 🏘 Porto Ercole 2km 🏖 800m 🍴 800m 🛒 2km.
Remarks: Bread-service, borrow cycles for free, free shuttle to beach every 30 minutes.

🚐 [S] Porto Ercole 32B3

Parking Da Renzo, SC della Feniglia. **GPS:** n42,41527 e11,20777. [↑][→].

150 🚐 € 18 🚰 ⤓ Ch 🔌 €3 WC 🚿 📶 included 🧺 🐕
Location: Rural, comfortable, quiet. **Surface:** grassy.
■ Easter-01/10
Distance: 🏘 Porto Ercole 3km 🏖 beach 1km 🍴 800m 🚲 on the spot.
Remarks: No camping activities, bike/car rental, beach shuttle (August).

🚐 [S] Pratovecchio 32C1

Via Uffenheim. **GPS:** n43,78666 e11,71952. [↑][→].

12 🚐 free 🚰 ⤓ Ch 🔌 free. **Location:** Simple, quiet.
Surface: asphalted. ■ 01/01-31/12
Distance: 🏘 50m 🍴 100m 🛒 100m.
Remarks: Along river, follow signs instead of GPS.

🚐 [S] Radda in Chianti 32B1

Viale 20 Settembre. **GPS:** n43,48643 e11,37543. [↑][→].

6 🚐 € 12/24h 🚰 ⤓ WC free. 🚌 **Location:** Rural, simple.
Surface: metalled. ■ 01/01-31/12
Distance: 🏘 200m (stairs).

🚐 [S] Radicofani 32C2

Via della Mossa. **GPS:** n42,89427 e11,77598. [↑].

5 🚐 free 🚰 ⤓ Ch free. **Location:** Rural, simple.
Surface: grassy/gravel. ■ 01/01-31/12
Distance: 🏘 400m.

🚐 [S] Radicondoli 32B1

Il Pianetto. **GPS:** n43,25888 e11,04250. [↑][→].

🚐 € 1/1h, >1 hour € 0,50/h 🚰 ⤓ Ch 🔌 (16x). **Surface:** unpaved.
■ 01/01-31/12
Distance: 🏘 medieval centre 300m 🍴 300m 🛒 2km.

IT

Rapolano Terme 32C1

Villa dei Boschi, Loc. Villa dei Boschi 50, Fraz San Gimignanello, SP10.
GPS: n43,22829 e11,65429.

20 € 15, free with a meal WC included.
Location: Rural, simple. **Surface**: grassy. 01/01-31/12
Distance: on the spot.

Rapolano Terme 32C1

Area di sosta Le Terme, Via Trieste. **GPS**: n43,29243 e11,60752.

64 € 5/6h, € 8/12h, € 12/24h Ch WC included €2.
Location: Rural, comfortable. **Surface**: gravel/metalled.
01/01-31/12
Distance: 500m 50m 200m.
Remarks: Terme Antica Querciolaia 50m.

Rosignano Marittimo 32A1

Molino a Fuoco, Via dei Cavalleggeri Antica, Vada.
GPS: n43,32816 e10,46005.

70 1/4-15/9 € 10 Ch. **Surface**: grassy/gravel.
Distance: 400m 500m 400m 400m.
Remarks: Max. 72h.

Rosignano Marittimo 32A1

Il Fortullino, Loc. Castiglioncello. **GPS**: n43,42889 e10,39750.

150 € 15/night, Jul-Aug € 20 Ch included.
Surface: unpaved. 01/04-30/09
Distance: Castiglioncello 4km, Livorno 20km, Pisa 40km 150m
Pizzeria 100m 5km.

Rosignano Marittimo 32A1

SP39, Via Aurelia, Loc Caletta. **GPS**: n43,39900 e10,42807.

18 € 8 free. **Surface**: metalled.
Distance: on the spot 300m 100m.

Remarks: Along busy road, max. 48h.

Rosignano Marittimo 32A1

Parcheggio del Lillatro, Via Fratelli Gigli, loc Lillatro.
GPS: n43,38380 e10,43206.

40 € 9. **Location**: Simple, isolated, quiet. **Surface**: sand.
Easter-31/10
Distance: 50m 50m.

Rosignano Marittimo 32A1

Sportiva Vada, Via Mare Mediterraneo, Vada.
GPS: n43,35208 e10,45183.

75 € 10/day. **Location**: Rural, quiet. **Surface**: unpaved.
01/04-01/10
Distance: 400m 200m 200m 400m.

San Casciano dei Bagni 32C2

Via Della Pineta. **GPS**: n42,86530 e11,87383.

15 free. **Location**: Rural, simple. **Surface**: gravel/sand.
01/01-31/12
Distance: 500m.

San Casciano dei Bagni 32C2

Piazzale del Ponte. **GPS**: n42,87024 e11,87742.

15 € 6/12h, € 12/24h Ch. **Surface**: asphalted.
01/01-31/12
Distance: 100m.
Remarks: Near spa resort.

San Casciano in Val di Pesa 32B1

Parco Il Poggione. **GPS**: n43,65395 e11,18768.

5 € 8 free.

San Gimignano 32B1

Area di Sosta Santa Chiara, Via di Castel San Gimignano, Loc. Fprmace.
GPS: n43,45572 e11,03476.

30 € 22/24h €2 Ch WC included.
Location: Rural, luxurious. **Surface**: gravel. 01/01-31/12
Distance: 3km osteria/bar 1,5km shuttle.
Remarks: Free shuttle bus to San Gimignano, tenniscourt.

San Gimignano 32B1

Park Santa Lucia, Loc. Santa Lucia. **GPS**: n43,45205 e11,05586.

± 30 € 1/h, € 15/24h Ch (14x) included.
Location: Rural, simple. **Surface**: gravel.
Distance: 3km Citybus Linea 1.
Remarks: Next to swimming pool, 24/24 video surveillance, shuttle bus
to city centre.

San Miniato Basso 32B1

Piazza G. Impastato, Via Pestalozzi/Via G. Pizzigoni, zona industriale.
GPS: n43,69417 e10,83638.

€ 0,50/h free. **Surface**: asphalted. 01/01-31/12
Distance: 800m 50m Superal.

San Miniato Basso 32B1

Area Camper Il Salice, Via Pier delle Vigne 28/A, ioc. La Catena.
GPS: n43,68434 e10,82224.

20 € 15/24h Ch WC. **Surface**: gravel.
01/01-31/12
Distance: 1km on the spot.
Remarks: Max. 3 days, shuttle bus to city centre.

San Piero a Sieve 32B1

GPS: n43,96260 e11,32732.

20 free Ch free. **Location**: Simple, quiet. **Surface**: metalled.

IT

🔲 01/01-31/12
Distance: 🚶500m ⊗250m.

| ♿ S | **San Quirico d'Orcia** 🌿 ☂ | 32C2 |

Via delle Scuole. **GPS:** n43,05607 e11,60682. ⬆➡.

30 🚐 € 10/24h 🚰 🗑 free. 🚿 **Location:** Rural, simple.
Surface: asphalted. 🔲 01/01-31/12
Distance: 🚶200m.
Remarks: Picnic area, playground.

| ☂ | **San Quirico d'Orcia** 🌿 ☂ | 32C2 |

Strada di Bagno Vignoni, Bagno Vignoni.
GPS: n43,02904 e11,62450. ⬆➡.

± 20 🚐 free. **Location:** Rural, simple, quiet.
Surface: unpaved.
🔲 01/01-31/12
Distance: ⊗350m.
Remarks: Parco dei Mulini: natural hot springs, free entrance, 400m.

| ♿ S | **San Romano in Garfagnana** | 25D3 |

Via Campo Sportivo/via Prà di Lago. **GPS:** n44,17243 e10,34199. ⬆➡.

15 🚐 free 🚰 🗑 Ch free. **Surface:** grassy.
🔲 01/01-31/12
Remarks: At sports park, Parco Avventura Selva del Buffardello 100m.

| ♿ S | **San Vincenzo** | 32A2 |

Via Biserno. **GPS:** n43,08790 e10,54134. ⬆.

90 🚐 € 10/24h 🚰 🗑 free. 🚿 **Surface:** sand. 🔲 01/01-31/12
Distance: 🚶1km ⌇beach 200m ⊗50m 🛒50m.
Remarks: Beach parking, no camping activities.

| ♿ S | **Sansepolcro** 🌿 ☂ | 32C1 |

Viale Alessandro Volta. **GPS:** n43,56976 e12,13727. ⬆.

20 🚐 free 🚰 🗑 Ch free. **Location:** Urban, simple. **Surface:** asphalted.

🔲 01/01-31/12
Distance: 🚶200m.

| 🍴 S | **Sansepolcro** 🌿 ☂ | 32C1 |

Podere Violino, Via del Tevere 1150, Gricignano.
GPS: n43,55539 e12,12312. ⬆➡.

8 🚐 € 6 + € 5/pp 🚰 🗑 Ch 🚿 WC 🔌 included.
Location: Comfortable, isolated, quiet. **Surface:** grassy.
🔲 01/03-31/12
Distance: 🚶2km ⌇river ⊗on the spot 🛒500m.
Remarks: Restaurant closed on Sunday, swimming pool available.

| ♿ S | **Santa Fiora** | 32C2 |

Strada di San Rocco. **GPS:** n42,83531 e11,58397. ⬆➡.

20 🚐 free 🚰 🗑 Ch free. 🚿(6x) € 1/2h. **Location:** Rural, simple.
Surface: gravel/sand. 🔲 01/01-31/12
Distance: 🚶450m.

| ♿ S | **Saturnia** ☂ | 32B2 |

L'Alveare dei Pinzi, Strada della Peschiera, Saturnia.
GPS: n42,65597 e11,50368. ⬆➡.

400 🚐 € 14/24h 🚰 🗑 Ch 🚿(120x) € 2 WC 🔌 € 0,50 🗑 € 6 🔌 included
📷 🚿 **Location:** Rural, comfortable, quiet. **Surface:** gravel.
🔲 01/01-31/12
Distance: 🚶Saturnia 3km ⌇1,5km.
Remarks: Panoramic view, free shuttle to spa resort and Saturnia, bar/snack/fruit, terme di Saturnia (sulfur baths) 1,7km, Cascate del Mulino (water fall, free entry) 2,5km, friday market.

| ♿ S | **Saturnia** ☂ | 32B2 |

La Quercia, Via Aurina 15. **GPS:** n42,66667 e11,50457. ⬆➡.

30 🚐 € 16/24h 🚰 🗑 Ch 🚿 WC 🔌 € 1 🔌 included. 🏧
Location: Rural, comfortable, central. **Surface:** gravel.
🔲 01/01-31/12
Distance: 🚶200m ⊗100m 🛒100m.
Remarks: Shuttle bus, terme di Saturnia (sulfur baths) 1,7km, Cascate del Mulino (water fall, free entry) 2,5km.

| 🍴 S | **Scarperia** 🍷 👭 | 25E3 |

Ranch Ricavo, Via di Galliano 21. **GPS:** n44,01189 e11,30681. ⬆.

20 🚐 € 10 🚰 🗑 Ch 🚿 WC included. **Location:** Simple, quiet.
Surface: grassy. 🔲 01/01-31/12
Distance: 🚶5km ⊗on the spot 🛒5km.

| ♿ S | **Sestino** | 32C1 |

Via Travicello. **GPS:** n43,71223 e12,30356. ⬆➡.

12 🚐 free 🚰 🗑 free. **Surface:** grasstiles.
Distance: 🚶2km.
Remarks: Nearby sports park.

| ♿ S | **Sesto Fiorentino** | 32B1 |

Area Antica Etruria, Via Ferruccio Parri. **GPS:** n43,84150 e11,17667. ⬆.

50 🚐 € 18/24h 🚰 🗑 Ch 🚿 WC 🔌 included 📷 📶 € 1,50/day 🚿
Location: Comfortable. **Surface:** asphalted. 🔲 01/01-31/12
Distance: ⚕1,5km 🚏400m ⊗400m 🚌30m > Florence.
Remarks: Monitored parking.

| ♿ S | **Sesto Fiorentino** | 32B1 |

Viale Ariosto. **GPS:** n43,83238 e11,18997. ⬆.

15 🚐 free. **Location:** Simple, quiet. **Surface:** asphalted.
🔲 01/01-31/12
Distance: 🚶500m ⚕3km ⊗200m 🛒500m 🚂train 100m.
Remarks: In front of Lidl supermarket, 20 mins to Florence by train.

| ♿ S | **Siena** 🌿 ☂ | 32B1 |

P1, Palasport, Via Achille Sclavo. **GPS:** n43,33323 e11,31739. ⬆.

75 🚐 € 20/motorhome (8.00-20.00h) 🚰 🗑 Ch WC free.
Location: Urban, simple. **Surface:** metalled. 🔲 01/01-31/12
Distance: 🚌on the spot.

| ♿ S | **Siena** 🌿 ☂ | 32B1 |

P2, Il Fagiolone, Via di Pescaia. **GPS:** n43,31456 e11,31760. ⬆.

IT

€ 20/motorhome (8-20h), overnight stay free WC free.
Location: Urban, simple, noisy. **Surface:** metalled.
01/01-31/12
Distance: on the spot.
Remarks: Along busy road.

| Siena | 32B1 |

Acqua Calda, Via Fausto Coppi. **GPS:** n43,33627 e11,29695.

free. **Location:** Urban, simple. **Surface:** asphalted.
01/01-31/12
Distance: 650m bus 10 centre Siena.

| Siena | 32B1 |

Via delle Province/via Napoli. **GPS:** n43,34168 e11,30512.

free. **Location:** Urban, simple, noisy. **Surface:** asphalted.
01/01-31/12
Distance: 200m McDonalds on the spot.

Tourist information Siena:
- Palazzo Publico. Gothic town hall from 1342.
- Torre del Mangia. Bell tower. daily.
- Duomo. Romanesque Gothic cathedral.
- La Lizza. Week market. Wed morning.
- Palio, Piazza del Campo. Famous historical horse race. 02/07, 16/08.

| Stia | 32C1 |

Parco comunale del Canto della Rana, Via Londa, SP556.
GPS: n43,80417 e11,70326.

12 free free. **Location:** Rural, simple, quiet. **Surface:** grassy.
01/01-31/12
Distance: medieval centre 200m 300m 300m.

| Torrita di Siena | 32C2 |

Via di Ciliano. **GPS:** n43,16475 e11,77173.

6 free Ch free. **Location:** Rural, comfortable, quiet.
Surface: grasstiles/metalled. 01/01-31/12
Distance: 400m 200m.

| Venturina | 32B2 |

Parco Termale Calidario, Via del Bottaccio.
GPS: n43,03666 e10,60000.

20 free €0,10/10liter Ch. **Location:** Quiet. **Surface:** metalled.
01/01-31/12
Distance: 800m 50m 800m.
Remarks: Thermal centre 50m.

| Viareggio | 32A1 |

Via Martiri di Belfiore. **GPS:** n43,88120 e10,25080.

44 € 15/24h Ch included.
Surface: asphalted.
01/01-31/12
Distance: 1km 2,5km.
Remarks: Check in at All Events Festival Puccini Viareggio, Viale Regina Margherita 1, 43,8673339 10,2431529, terrain with video surveillance.

| Vinci | 32B1 |

Via Girolamo Calvi. **GPS:** n43,78080 e10,92830.
12 free Ch free. **Surface:** metalled. 01/01-31/12
Distance: 300m.
Remarks: At sports park.

| Volterra | 32B1 |

Parking P3, Fonti Docciola, Viale Dei Filosofi.
GPS: n43,40306 e10,86417.

15 € 8/24h Ch free. **Location:** Urban.
Surface: gravel.
Distance: historical center 100m 200m 300m.

San Marino

| San Marino | 25G3 |

Camper Stop, Via del Serrone 94. **GPS:** n43,92057 e12,45056.
free. **Surface:** grassy.
Distance: city centre 3km on the spot.

| San Marino | 25G3 |

P13, Baldasserona, Borgo Maggiore. **GPS:** n43,94054 e12,44289.

50 free Ch. **Surface:** asphalted. 01/01-31/12
Remarks: Service 300m.

| San Marino | 25G3 |

Strada Genghe di Atto, Acquaviva. **GPS:** n43,94491 e12,42963.

5 free Ch WC free. **Surface:** asphalted.

| San Marino | 25G3 |

P10, Via Napoleone Boneparte. **GPS:** n43,93567 e12,44362.

20 € 8/24h. **Surface:** asphalted. 01/11-31/03
Remarks: Elevator to centre 50m.

Tourist information San Marino:
- Borgo Maggiore. Week market. Thu.

Marche

| Amandola | 32D2 |

Piazzale Sandro Pertini. **GPS:** n42,97085 e13,35488.
€ 8,50 Ch WC included. **Surface:** asphalted.
01/01-31/12
Distance: 850m.

| Ancona | 32D1 |

Via Sanzio Blasi, Loc. Posatore. **GPS:** n43,59964 e13,48530.

IT

30 ⛺€ 12-13 🚰⚡Ch🚿(24x)included.🚲
Location: Simple. **Surface:** asphalted/grassy. ⬛ 01/01-31/12
Distance: 🚶4,5km 🚌10m.
Remarks: Max. 72h, entrance between 8-22h.

Ancona 32D1
Centro Commerciale Auchan, Via Scataglini, Zona Industriale Baraccola, SS16, Ancona-sud. **GPS:** n43,55133 e13,51506.⬆➡.

25 ⛺free 🚰⚡free. **Location:** Simple. **Surface:** grasstiles.
⬛ 01/01-31/12
Distance: 🚶8km 🏖3,6km.

Tourist information Ancona:
ℹ Riviera del Conera. Touristic peninsula with beaches and several bathing resorts.

Apecchio 32C1
Via Isidoro Pazzaglia. **GPS:** n43,55938 e12,41969.⬆➡.
30 ⛺free 🚰⚡Ch🚿(6x)free. **Surface:** metalled.
⬛ 01/01-31/12
Distance: 🚶100m 🛒50m.

Tourist information Apecchio:
🎪 Week market. ⬛ Fri-morning.

Ascoli Piceno 32E2
Ex Seminario, Viale Alcide Gasperi. **GPS:** n42,85222 e13,58222.⬆➡.

20 ⛺€ 3/night,20/h, night € 3 🚰🚿. **Location:** Urban.
Surface: asphalted.
Distance: 🚶centre 500m ✴200m 🛒200m.
Remarks: Guarded parking.

Ascoli Piceno 32E2
Bed & Breakfast Chartaria, Via Adriatico.
GPS: n42,84792 e13,57306.⬆.
7 ⛺€ 15 🚰⚡€3. **Surface:** grassy.

Tourist information Ascoli Piceno:
ℹ City with many monumental bldg.
🎪 ⬛ Wed, Sa.

Camerino 32D1
Via Macario Muzio. **GPS:** n43,13677 e13,06718.⬆.

8 ⛺free 🚰⚡Chfree 🚿€1/4h WC. **Location:** Rural.
Surface: asphalted. ⬛ 01/01-31/12
Distance: 🚶centre 500m ✴350m.
Remarks: Beautiful view, escalator to city centre.

Carpegna 32C1
Via Aldo Moro. **GPS:** n43,78083 e12,34040.⬆.

10 ⛺free 🚰€1 ⚡Ch 🚿€0,60/h. **Surface:** concrete.
⬛ 01/01-31/12
Distance: 🚶300m 🛒300m.

Castelfidardo 32D1
Croce Verde, Via Lumumba/via Donato Bramonte.
GPS: n43,46603 e13,55563.⬆➡.

3 ⛺free 🚰⚡free. **Location:** Simple. **Surface:** asphalted.
⬛ 01/01-31/12
Distance: 🚶200m.
Remarks: Max. 48h.

Castelsantangelo sul Nera 32D2
Strada Provinciale 136. **GPS:** n42,89117 e13,15355.⬆.
8 ⛺free 🚰⚡Chfree. **Location:** Isolated, quiet. **Surface:** asphalted.
⬛ 01/01-31/12
Distance: 🚶200m.

Cerreto D'Esi 32D1
Via Dante Alighieri. **GPS:** n43,32714 e12,99114.➡.

10 ⛺free 🚰⚡. **Location:** Simple. **Surface:** metalled.
⬛ 01/01-31/12
Distance: 🛒500m.

Colmurano 32D1
Via Piero della Francesca, Contrada Peschiera.
GPS: n43,16260 e13,35828.⬆➡.

8 ⛺free 🚰⚡ChWCfree. **Surface:** asphalted. ⬛ 01/01-31/12
Distance: 🚶400m.
Remarks: Near sports park and historical centre.

Corinaldo 32D1
Viale Dante. **GPS:** n43,64703 e13,04910.⬆.

8 ⛺free 🚰⚡Chfree. **Location:** Simple. **Surface:** asphalted.
⬛ 01/01-31/12
Distance: 🚶400m 🛒50m.

Corinaldo 32D1
Ristorante Camping Colverde, Via per Montalboddo 52.
GPS: n43,63504 e13,09743.⬆➡.

10 ⛺€ 13, guests € 10 🚰⚡Ch🚿WC,on camp site 🚿included,on campsite.🚲 **Location:** Rural, simple. **Surface:** grassy.
⬛ 01/01-31/12
Distance: 🚶5km ✴on the spot.

Cossignano 32E2
Via Gallo. **GPS:** n42,98050 e13,69213.⬆.
6 ⛺€ 6 🚰€3 ⚡Ch🚿included. **Location:** Simple.
Surface: metalled. ⬛ 01/01-31/12
Distance: ✴500m.

Cupramontana 32D1
Verdicchio, SP 11. **GPS:** n43,43934 e13,11837.⬆➡.

10 ⛺free 🚰⚡free Ch🚿(10x). **Location:** Simple, noisy.
Surface: metalled. ⬛ 01/01-31/12
Distance: ✴100m 🛒500m.
Remarks: Beautiful view of Monte San Vicino.

Fabriano 32D1
Fraz. Poggio San Romualdo. **GPS:** n43,36473 e13,02534.⬆.

35 ⛺free 🚰⚡free. **Location:** Rural, simple, quiet. **Surface:** grassy.
⬛ 01/01-31/12
Distance: 🚶3,5km 🚶on the spot.

Fabriano 32D1
Via Bruno Buozzi. **GPS:** n43,34650 e12,91645.➡.

18 ⛺free 🚰€0,20/10liter ⚡Ch🚿(6x)€3/12h. **Location:** Simple.

Surface: grassy. ◻ 01/01-31/12
Distance: 🚉3km.
Remarks: Next to sports centre.

📷S Falerone 32D1

Ex-stazione FS di Piane di Falerone, Via Togliatti.
GPS: n43,09944 e13,49944.⬆️.

15 🏕free 🚰🚱Ch🧹free. **Surface:** metalled. ◉ 1st Su of the month
Distance: 🚉100m ⊗200m.
Remarks: Nearby the old station and theatre Romano.

📷S Fano 🌼⛵🏖 32D1

Lungomare Sassonia, Via Ruggeri. **GPS:** n43,84238 e13,03197.⬆️.

60 🏕€ 7-8,50 🚰🚱included 🧹(20x)€2/day WC🚿♨️€0,50/day.🚿
Surface: grassy/gravel. ◻ 01/01-31/12
Distance: 🚉1km 🚲2km ⚓50m ⊗50m 🛒600m.

📷S Fano 🌼⛵🏖 32D1

Area di Sosta Adriatico, SS16, Torrette di Fano.
GPS: n43,80789 e13,08198.⬆️.

30 🏕€ 13-20, Camperstop 18-9h€ 8-10 🚰🚱Ch🧹
(12x)WCincluded 🧹€0,50 ▯€3/time.🚿 **Location:** Comfortable.
Surface: grassy/gravel. ◻ 24/04-15/09
Distance: 🚉4km 🚲9km ⚓200m ⊗50m 🛒500m.
Remarks: Service passerby € 5.

📷S Fano 🌼⛵🏖 32D1

Viale Kennedy. GPS: n43,84557 e13,01133.➡️.

16-20 🏕free 🚰🚱Chfree. **Location:** Simple. **Surface:** asphalted.
◻ 01/01-31/12
Distance: 🚉200m 🚲2,7km ⚓800m.
Remarks: Nearby cemetery.

📷S Fano 🌼⛵🏖 32D1

Campo Nunzia, SS Adriactica Sud-Loc. Torrette di Fano.
GPS: n43,80444 e13,08472. ⬆️➡️.

28 🏕€ 10-15 🚰🚱Ch🧹€3/24h WC🧹€3. **Location:** Comfortable.
Surface: grassy/gravel. ◻ 24/04-01/09
Distance: 🚉7km 🚲10km ⚓150m.

🍴 Fano 🌼⛵🏖 32D1

BarRistorante La Tratta, Via Fratelli Zuccari 37.
GPS: n43,83589 e13,04182.⬆️.

14 🏕€ 6. 🚿 **Location:** Simple, quiet. **Surface:** grassy.
◻ 01/04-01/10
Distance: 🚉2,5km ⚓50m 🔌on the spot ⊗on the spot.
Remarks: P camper.

Tourist information Fano:
⛺ ◻ Wed, Sa.

📷S Fermo 32E1

Area Camper 2004, Lungomare Marina Palminese.
GPS: n43,15085 e13,81382.⬆️.

64 🏕€ 10, electricity included € 12 🚰🚱Ch🧹(32x)included 🧹hot
shower against payment. **Surface:** grassy. ◻ 01/04-30/09
Distance: 🚲2,5km ⚓on the spot.

📷S Fermo 32E1

Baia dei Gabbiani, Viale A. de Gasperi, Lido S. Tomasso.
GPS: n43,22158 e13,78113. ⬆️➡️.

50 🏕€ 13-15, Aug € 20 🚰🚱Ch🧹€0,50 ▯.
Surface: grassy/gravel. ◻ 01/04-30/09
Distance: 🚲6,6km ⚓Private beach.

📷S Fermo 32E1

Onda Verde, Via Usodimare, Lido di Fermo.
GPS: n43,20289 e13,78825. ⬆️➡️.

100 🏕€ 10-€ 18 (Aug) 🚰🚱Ch🧹2Amp WC🧹included.
Surface: grassy. ◻ 01/04-30/09

Distance: 🚉Fermo 10km 🚲5,4km ⚓10m ⊗10-500m 🛒200m.

📷S Fossombrone 32D1

Via Oberdan. **GPS:** n43,69301 e12,81835.

8 🏕free 🚰🚱Chfree. **Surface:** asphalted. ◻ 01/01-31/12
Distance: 🚉500m 🚲1,4km.

Tourist information Fossombrone:
⛺ Week market. ◻ Mo.

☀️S Genga 🌼⛰ 32D1

Frasassi, Fraz San Vittore. **GPS:** n43,40321 e12,97597.⬆️.

50 🏕free 🚰🚱WCfree. **Location:** Simple, quiet. **Surface:** gravel.
◻ 01/01-31/12
Distance: 🚉7km ⊗on the spot.
Remarks: Nearby pay-desk Gole di Frasassi, free shuttle to the caves.

📷S Gradara 🌼⛰ 25H3

Parking P1, Piazza Paolo e Francesca. **GPS:** n43,94083 e12,77083.⬆️.

14 🏕€ 10/24h 🚰🚱ChWCfree. 🚌 **Location:** Simple, central.
Surface: asphalted.
◻ 01/01-31/12
Distance: 🚉historical center 100m 🚲7,3km ⊗on the spot 🛒400m.
Remarks: Parking centre.

📷S Grottammare ⛰ 32E2

Sosta Camper 43° Parallelo, Via Carlo Alberto dalla Chiesa.
GPS: n42,96673 e13,87694.⬆️.
40 🏕€ 15 🚰🚱Ch🧹WC▯📶. **Surface:** asphalted.
Distance: 🚲2,7km ⚓500m ⊗500m 🛒100m 🔌on the spot.
Remarks: Behind centro commerciale Cityper, along railwayline.

🍴S Grottammare ⛰ 32E2

Briciola di Sole, Contr. Granaro 19. **GPS:** n42,98278 e13,84000.⬆️.

14 🏕€ 15, guests free 🚰🚱Ch🧹included.
Surface: gravel/metalled.
◻ 01/04-31/10
Distance: 🚲2,5km ⚓sea 5km ⊗on the spot 🛒2km.
Remarks: Restaurant with traditional kitchen, located on estate.

📷S Jesi 32D1

Via Zannoni. **GPS:** n43,51882 e13,24180. ⬆️➡️.

IT

10 ⬛free 🚰⬛free. **Location:** Simple, quiet. **Surface:** asphalted.
⬛ 01/01-31/12
Distance: 🚶500m centro storico.

Tourist information Jesi:
ℹ️ Area with many vineyards.
👁️ Grotte di Frasassi. Caves.

🏕️S Loreto 32D1

Area Camper Pro Loco, Via Maccari. **GPS:** n43,44125 e13,61491. ⬆️➡️

65 ⬛€ 12/24h 🚰⬛Chincluded ⚡(20x)€3/day WC⬛€1/time.♿
Location: Comfortable. **Surface:** grasstiles. ⬛ 01/01-31/12
Distance: 🚶150m ⛱️15km.
Remarks: Max. 48h.

🏕️S Loreto 32D1

Parking P1, Via Benedetto XXV. **GPS:** n43,44129 e13,60756.

6 ⬛€ 6/day, overnight stay free WC. 🚐 **Surface:** asphalted.
Distance: 🚶300m ⊗50m.
Remarks: Parking at city wall.

🏕️S Macerata 32D1

Stadio Helvia Recina, Via dei Velini. **GPS:** n43,30701 e13,43722. ⬆️

20 ⬛free 🚰€1/15minutes ⬛free. **Location:** Urban, simple.
Surface: asphalted. ⬛ 01/01-31/12
Distance: 🚶3,5km.

🏕️S Macerata Feltria 32C1

Loc. San Gasparre. **GPS:** n43,80098 e12,42886.

4 ⬛free 🚰⬛ChWC⬛free. **Surface:** metalled.
01/01-31/12
Distance: 🚶1km ⛱️on the spot ⊗Pizzeria.
Remarks: Along Aspa river.

Tourist information Macerata Feltria:

🌾 Week market. ⬛ Tue.

🏕️S Marina di Montemarciano 🌊 32D1

Lungomare Alfredo Cappellini. **GPS:** n43,65936 e13,32780.

40 ⬛€ 0,70/h 🚰⬛Ch⚡(32x)€2. 🚐 **Location:** Simple, noisy.
Surface: gravel. ⬛ 15/05-15/09
Distance: 🚶4km ⚓9km ⛱️pebbled beach 60m ⊗100m.
Remarks: To coast road and railwayline.

🏕️S Marotta 🌊 32D1

Area di Sosta Marotta, Lungomare Colombo 157, Mondolfo.
GPS: n43,76067 e13,15312. ⬆️

80 ⬛€ 8-11 🚰⬛Ch⚡(80x)€2/24h WC⬛included,cold.♿
Location: Simple. **Surface:** grassy. ⬛ 01/04-30/09
Distance: 🚶500m ⚓1,5km ⛱️50m ⊗on the spot.
Remarks: Between coast road and railwayline.

🏕️S Matelica 🌾🌊 32D1

Porte Capamante, Via Circonvallazione. **GPS:** n43,25917 e13,01083. ➡️

6-8 ⬛free ⬛free. **Location:** Simple. **Surface:** asphalted.
⬛ 01/01-31/12
Distance: 🚶200m ⊗200m ⛱️200m.

🍴S Matelica 🌾🌊 32D1

Country House Salomone, Località Salomone 437.
GPS: n43,29635 e13,00031. ⬆️➡️

20 ⬛€ 7, free with a meal 🚰⚡(16x)included WCat restaurant.♿
Location: Rural, simple. **Surface:** grassy/gravel.
⬛ 01/01-31/12
Distance: ⊗on the spot.

🏕️S Mergo 32D1

Area Sosta Comunale, Via Colli. **GPS:** n43,47394 e13,03598. ⬆️➡️

10 ⬛free 🚰⬛Chfree ⚡(8x). **Location:** Simple. **Surface:** concrete.

⬛ 01/01-31/12
Distance: 🚶300m.
Remarks: Nearby sports park.

🏕️S Mondavio 🌾 32D1

Borgo Gramsci. **GPS:** n43,67487 e12,96700. ⬆️

5 ⬛free 🚰⬛WCfree,50m. **Location:** Simple.
Surface: metalled.
⬛ 01/01-31/12
Distance: 🚶historical center 100m ⊗100m ⛱️200m.
Remarks: Nearby old town and medieval citadel Roveresca.

Tourist information Mondavio:
🌾 Week market. ⬛ Mo.

🏕️S Montalto delle Marche 🌾 32E2

Via Cuprense. **GPS:** n42,98726 e13,60870. ⬆️

6 ⬛free 🚰⬛free. **Surface:** metalled. ⬛ 01/01-31/12
Distance: 🚶100m.

🏕️S Monte San Giusto 32D1

Campo Sportivo, Via Magellano, Villa San Filippo.
GPS: n43,26343 e13,60070. ⬆️➡️

20 ⬛free 🚰⬛Chfree. **Surface:** asphalted. ⬛ 01/01-31/12
Distance: 🚶1km.
Remarks: Outlet center leather and shoes.

🏕️S Monte Vidon Corrado 32D1

Viale Trento e Trieste. **GPS:** n43,12205 e13,48381. ⬆️

4 ⬛free 🚰Chfree. **Surface:** metalled. ⬛ 01/01-31/12
Distance: 🚶200m ⊗200m.

🏕️S Montecosaro 32E1

Via Martiri della Libertà Ungherese. **GPS:** n43,31779 e13,63653.

IT

30 ⏻free ⚒🔲Chfree. **Surface:** concrete. 🔲 01/01-31/12
Distance: 🚶100m ⊗100m 🛒100m 🏖50m.

| | | Montefiore dell'Aso 🌿⛰ | 32E1 |

Piazza Pietro Nenni. **GPS:** n43,04992 e13,75021.

10 ⏻free ⚒🔲free. **Surface:** sand. 🔲 01/01-31/12
Distance: 🚶200m.

| | | Montefiore dell'Aso 🌿⛰ | 32E1 |

Agricamper Il Poggio del Belvedere, Contrada Aso no. 11.
GPS: n43,04611 e13,72500.⬆.

6 ⏻€8/pp ⚒🔲Ch ⚡WC 🔲included. **Surface:** metalled.
🔲 01/01-31/12

| | | Montelupone 🌿 | 32D1 |

Loc. San Firmano. **GPS:** n43,36383 e13,54950.⬆.

20 ⏻free ⚒🔲free. **Location:** Simple. **Surface:** asphalted.
Distance: 🚶500m.
Remarks: Parking sports park.

| | | Montelupone 🌿 | 32D1 |

Via Allesandro Manzoni. **GPS:** n43,34300 e13,57080.⬆.

10 ⏻free ⚒🔲free. **Location:** Simple. **Surface:** asphalted.
🔲 01/01-31/12
Remarks: Parking city park.

| | | Morro d'Alba | 32D1 |

Area Comunale, Via degli Orti. **GPS:** n43,60198 e13,21263.⬆➡.

10 ⏻free ⚒🔲free. **Location:** Simple, quiet. **Surface:** asphalted.
🔲 01/01-31/12
Distance: 🚶500m.
Remarks: Access with electronic card, Bar Pro Loco or town hall.

| | | Offida 🌿 | 32E2 |

Via Tommaso Castelli. **GPS:** n42,93689 e13,69180.⬆.

3 ⏻free ⚒🔲free. **Surface:** unpaved. 🔲 01/01-31/12
Remarks: At the city walls.

| | | Pedaso | 32E1 |

Via Martiri della Libertà. **GPS:** n43,09985 e13,84272.
⏻free. **Surface:** asphalted. 🔲 01/01-31/12
Distance: 🚶on the spot ⚓on the spot ⊗150m.
Remarks: Parking at the beach.

| | | Pesaro 🏖🌊 | 25H3 |

Via dell Aquedotto. **GPS:** n43,90842 e12,90097.⬆.

12 ⏻free ⚒🔲Chfree ⚡(12x)€1. **Surface:** asphalted.
Distance: 🚶1km 🚲7,5km.

| | | Pesaro 🏖🌊 | 25H3 |

Waterfront Parking, Via Calata Caio Duilio.
GPS: n43,92244 e12,90657.⬆.
20 ⏻€12. 🔲 01/01-31/12
Distance: ⚓on the spot.

Tourist information Pesaro:
⛺ Week market. 🔲 Tue.

| | | Petritoli | 32E1 |

Impianti Sportivi. GPS: n43,07306 e13,65139.⬆.

10 ⏻free ⚒🔲Chfree. **Surface:** sand. 🔲 01/01-31/12
Distance: 🚶1km.
Remarks: At sports park.

| | | Piandimeleto | 32C1 |

Via Giacomo Leopardi. **GPS:** n43,72541 e12,41328.⬆➡.

9 ⏻free ⚒🔲Chfree. **Surface:** grassy. 🔲 01/01-31/12
Distance: 🚶100m.

| | | Pietrarubbia | 32C1 |

Vulcangas, Via Montefeltresca 107, Ponte Cappuccini.
GPS: n43,80278 e12,36667.⬆.

2 ⏻free ⚒🔲WCfree. **Surface:** metalled. 🔲 01/01-31/12
Distance: 🚶200m.

| | | Pievebovigliana | 32D2 |

Via Rancia. **GPS:** n43,06583 e13,08526.⬆.

10 ⏻free ⚒🔲Ch ⚡. **Surface:** asphalted. 🔲 01/01-31/12
Distance: 🚶300m.

| | | Pioraco | 32D1 |

Loc. Buchetto, SS361 km77. **GPS:** n43,18010 e12,97422.⬆.

18 (+20) ⏻€13 ⚒ ⚡(16x)WC 🔲included. 🚿 **Location:** Rural,
comfortable, quiet. **Surface:** gravel. 🔲 01/01-31/12
Distance: 🚶700m 🛒on the spot ⊗summer 🏖on the spot.

| | | Pollenza 🌿 | 32D1 |

Contrada Morazzano. **GPS:** n43,26482 e13,34614.⬆➡.

8 ⏻free ⚒🔲free. **Location:** Simple. **Surface:** asphalted.
🔲 01/01-31/12
Distance: 🚶500m.
Remarks: Nearby elevator to centre, max. 48h.

| | | Porto Recanati 🏖🌊 | 32E1 |

Karting Club Pista del Conero, Viale Scarfiotti, loc. Scossicci.
GPS: n43,47067 e13,64246.⬆.

80 ⏻€15/24h ⚒🔲Ch ⚡(80x)WC 🔲included 🔲€1 ⚡free. 🚿
Location: Simple, noisy. **Surface:** gravel. 🔲 01/04-30/09
Distance: ⚓100m ⊗200m.

| | | Porto Recanati 🏖🌊 | 32E1 |

Pro Loco, Viale Scarfiotti, loc. Scossicci. **GPS:** n43,44605 e13,65639.⬆.

40 ⛲€ 10/24h ⟲🗑included Ch ✂(8x)€2 WC 🚽€1. ♨
Location: Simple. **Surface:** grassy. ◯ 01/04-30/09
Distance: 🚶500m 🚴3km 🏖50m ⊗200m 🍴1km.
Remarks: Max. 72h.

Porto San Giorgio 32E1
La Perla Adriatico, Via San Martino 13. **GPS:** n43,16400 e13,80836.
75 ⛲€ 12/18 ⟲🗑Ch ✂WC 🚽 📶. **Surface:** unpaved.
◯ 01/01-31/12
Distance: 🏖beach 200m ⊗300m.
Remarks: Shuttle bus.

Potenza Picena 32E1
Via Togliatti, Porto Potenza Picena. **GPS:** n43,36167 e13,69306. ⬆

45 ⛲€ 7/24h, € 10/48h, € 15/72h ⟲🗑Ch included ✂(12x)€2.
Surface: asphalted. ◯ 01/01-31/12
Distance: 🚶200m 🏖600m ⊗200m 🍴200m.
Remarks: Thursday market.

Recanati 32D1
Camperclub Recanati, Viale Giovanni XXIII.
GPS: n43,40245 e13,55777. ⬆➡

30 ⛲free ⟲🗑✂(22x)free. **Location:** Urban, simple.
Surface: asphalted. ◯ 01/01-31/12
Distance: 🚶500m.

San Benedetto del Tronto 32E2
Viale dello Sport. **GPS:** n42,92312 e13,89527. ⬆

20 ⛲€ 5, Jul/Aug € 8 ⟲🗑Ch ✂included. **Surface:** asphalted.
Distance: 🚴4,3km 🏖500m 🚲on the spot.
Remarks: Along railwayline, under viaduct.

San Ginesio 32D1
Via Ciarlatini. **GPS:** n43,10945 e13,31801.

---

8 ⛲free. **Surface:** gravel. ◯ 01/01-31/12
Distance: 🚶200m ⊗200m 🍴200m 🚲1km.

San Leo 32C1
Via Michele Rosa. **GPS:** n43,89871 e12,34950. ⬆➡

20 ⛲free ⟲🗑Ch ✂free. **Surface:** asphalted. ◯ 01/01-31/12
◉ festivities
Distance: 🚶500m ⊗on the spot.

San Severino Marche 32D1
P7, Viale Mazzini. **GPS:** n43,22757 e13,18836. ⬆➡

12 ⛲free ⟲🗑free ✂(12x)€0,50/4h. **Location:** Simple, quiet.
Surface: asphalted. ◯ 01/01-31/12
Distance: 🚶800m.
Remarks: Parking sports park.

Sant'Agata Feltria 32C1
Piazzale Europa. **GPS:** n43,86386 e12,20549. ⬆➡

40 ⛲€ 8/24h ⟲🗑✂(6x)free. **Surface:** asphalted.
Distance: 🚶100m.

Sarnano 32D2
Via Corridoni. **GPS:** n43,03444 e13,29972. ⬆

15 ⛲free ⟲🗑ChWC free. **Surface:** asphalted. ◯ 01/01-31/12
Distance: 🚶100m ⊗100m 🍴100m.

Sassoferrato 32D1
Via Raffaello Sanzio. **GPS:** n43,43122 e12,85471. ⬆

7 ⛲free ⟲🗑free ✂(6x)€ 1/day. **Location:** Simple.
Surface: asphalted. ◯ 01/01-31/12
Distance: 🚶500m.

Senigallia 32D1
Via F. Podesti 234, SS16, Senigallia-sud. **GPS:** n43,70483 e13,23764. ⬆

14 ⛲free ⟲🗑free. **Location:** Simple, noisy. **Surface:** asphalted.
◯ 01/01-31/12
Distance: 🚶3km 🚴3,3km 🏖150m.
Remarks: Along busy road, next to petrol station, max. 48h.

Tolentino 32D1
Viale Foro Boario. **GPS:** n43,20773 e13,28784.

15 ⛲free ⟲🗑free. **Surface:** asphalted. ◯ 01/01-31/12
Distance: 🚶200m ⊗200m.

Urbania 32C1
Area camper Barco, Loc. Barco Ducale Colonia.
GPS: n43,67916 e12,51277. ⬆➡
65 ⛲free ⟲🗑Ch ✂free. **Location:** Rural.
Surface: gravel/sand.
Distance: 🚶1km.
Remarks: Biking trail, behind former summer residence of dukes of Urbania.

Urbania 32C1
Piazzale Fosso del Maltempo, Viale Michelangelo.
GPS: n43,66482 e12,52191. ⬆➡

50 ⛲free ⟲🗑Ch ✂free. **Surface:** asphalted. ◯ 01/01-31/12
Distance: 🚶500m.
Tourist information Urbania:
🎪 Week market. ◯ Thu.

Urbino 32C1
Via Pablo Neruda. **GPS:** n43,73333 e12,62722. ⬆➡

10 ⛲free ⟲🗑Ch free. **Surface:** asphalted. ◯ 01/01-31/12
Distance: 🚶historical centre 2,5km.
Remarks: Shuttle bus to city centre.

Urbino 32C1
Corte della Miniera, Via Miniera, 10. **GPS:** n43,78336 e12,59091.
5 ⛲guests free ⟲🗑Ch ✂.
Distance: 🚶Urbino 11km ⊗on the spot.
Tourist information Urbino:
🎪 Week market. ◯ Sa.

Urbisaglia 32D1
Abbadia di Fiastra, P4. **GPS:** n43,22111 e13,40722. ⬆

20 🅿free 🚐🅲h ✏free. **Surface:** metalled.
📅 01/01-31/12
Distance: ⬅4km ⊗50m.
Remarks: Parking monastery, archaeological park Urbs Salvia 3km, hiking area.

🅢 Visso 🏔 32D2
Largo Gregorio XIII. **GPS:** n42,93139 e13,09141. ⬆➡.

15 🅿free 🚐🅲hfree ✏€0,80/h. **Surface:** asphalted.
Distance: ⬅800m.

Lazio

🅢 Acquapendente 32C2
Agriturismo Buonomore, SS2 via Cassia km 130.
GPS: n42,73367 e11,88361. ⬆.

8 🅿€ 15, Aug € 30 🚐🅲h ✏ WC included 🧺♻♻
Location: Rural, simple, quiet. **Surface:** grassy/gravel.
📅 01/01-31/12
Distance: ⬅3km ⊗on the spot.

🅢 Acquapendente 32C2
Via Campo Boario. **GPS:** n42,74203 e11,86240. ⬆➡.

20 🅿free 🚐🅲hfree. **Location:** Urban.
Surface: asphalted/metalled. 📅 01/01-31/12
Distance: ⬅250m 🍴250m.
Remarks: At sports park.

🅢 Albano Laziale 32D3
Piazza Guerucci, Via Riccardo Lombardi. **GPS:** n41,73206 e12,65213. ⬆.

8 🅿free 🚐🅲hfree. **Location:** Simple, noisy.
Surface: asphalted.
Distance: ⬅1km �ætrain > Rome 55min.

Remarks: Next to post office and sports park.

🅢 Amatrice 32D2
AgriCamper Amatrice, Località Retrosi. **GPS:** n42,62349 e13,31788.
20 🅿€ 13 🚐🅲h ✏. **Surface:** gravel.
Remarks: Located in national nature reserve Gran Sasso.

🅢 Bolsena 🌿⛱ 32C2
Guadetto, Via della Chiusa. **GPS:** n42,63604 e11,98695. ⬆➡.

60 🅿€ 15/24h 🚐🅲h ✏included WC📶 **Location:** Rural.
Surface: grassy/sand. 📅 01/01-31/12
Distance: ⬅1km ⤢10m ⊗300m 🍴1,5km 🚲on the spot 🚶on the spot.
Remarks: Bread-service, tuesday market.

🅢 Bolsena 🌿⛱ 32C2
Via Santa Maria. **GPS:** n42,63898 e11,98562. ⬆➡.

50 🅿€ 5/12h, € 10/24h. 🚌 **Location:** Urban, simple.
Surface: asphalted. 📅 01/01-31/12
Distance: ⬅800m ⤢100m ⊶on the spot ⊗400m 🍴400m 🚌100m 🚲on the spot 🚶on the spot.

🅢 Bolsena 🌿⛱ 32C2
Agricampeggio Le Calle, Via Cassia km 111,200.
GPS: n42,63029 e11,99716. ⬆.
🅿€ 15-19, 2 pers.incl 🚐🅲h ✏ WC included. 📅 01/04-01/11
Distance: ⬅1km ⊗on the spot.

Tourist information Bolsena:
ℹ️ Citadel and ramparts.

🅢 Bracciano 🌿 32C3
Le Mimose, Via del Lago 25. **GPS:** n42,10856 e12,17893. ➡.

50 🅿€ 14/24h 🚐🅲hincluded ✏(40x)€3/24h 🗑€0,50/time. ♻
Location: Rural, comfortable, quiet. **Surface:** gravel.
📅 01/01-31/12
Distance: ⬅800m ⤢Lago di Bracciano 250m ⊗150m 🍴800m 🚌200m.

🅢 Capodimonte 💧 32C2
Temporanea. **GPS:** n42,55979 e11,88714. ⬆.

50 🅿€ 10/24h 🚐🅲h ✏€3 Ch. ♻ **Location:** Urban, simple, quiet.
Surface: grassy. 📅 01/01-31/12
Distance: ⬅2km ⊗on the spot.
Remarks: At lake Bolsena, check in at bar.

🅢 Cassino 🌿 33B1
Parking Europa, Via Agnone 5. **GPS:** n41,48289 e13,83750. ➡.

20 🅿€ 13,50-16,50, 2 pers.incl 🚐Service €2,50 🅲h ✏€3 WC🗑€1
📶€4/day. ♻ **Location:** Rural, luxurious, quiet.
Surface: grassy/gravel. 📅 01/01-31/12
Distance: ⬅800m 🚲4km ⊗1km 🍴1km 🚌1,5km.
Remarks: Service passerby € 7.

🅢 Castel di Tora 32D3
Via Turano, SP34. **GPS:** n42,21362 e12,96888.
15 🅿€ 5/24h 🚐🅲h ✏. **Surface:** gravel. 📅 01/01-31/12
Distance: ⬅1km ⤢on the spot.
Remarks: At Turano lake.

🅢 Castel Gandolfo 🌿 32D3
Parcheggio Bus Lago Albano, Via Spiaggia del Lago.
GPS: n41,75797 e12,65359. ⬆.

17 🅿€ 10/24h. 🚌 **Location:** Rural, simple, noisy. **Surface:** metalled.
📅 01/01-31/12
Distance: ⤢on the spot ⊗on the spot 🚌800m > Rome.
Remarks: At lake Albano.

🅢 Ciampino 32D3
Il Sassone, Via Doganale 1. **GPS:** n41,78507 e12,62640. ⬆.

70 🅿€ 12/24h 🚐🅲h ✏€2/24h 🗑included. ♻
Location: Rural, comfortable, quiet. **Surface:** grassy.
📅 01/01-31/12
Distance: ⬅3km ⊗1,5km 🍴1,5km 🚌50m.

🅢 Civita Castellana 🌿 32C3
Via Terni. **GPS:** n42,29905 e12,41520. ⬆.

+50 🅿free. **Location:** Simple. **Surface:** asphalted.
📅 01/01-31/12
Distance: ⬅500m 🍴50m.
Remarks: At cemetery.

Tourist information Civita Castellana:
👁 Palazzo Farnese, Caprarola. Pentagonal country house, accessed by winding staircase.

🅢 Colle di Tora 🌿 32D3
Via Maria Letizia Giuliani. **GPS:** n42,20898 e12,94915. ⬆.

25 ⌂€ 10/24h ⚡🚰 Ch 🚿 WC included. **Location:** Rural, simple, quiet. **Surface:** gravel. 🅿 01/01-31/12
Distance: 🚴on the spot 🏊on the spot ⊗on the spot.
Remarks: At Turano lake, pay at restaurant.

📷🆂 **Colleferro** 🌿 **32D3**
Viale Europa. **GPS:** n41,72540 e13,00989.
⌂free 🚰 Ch free.
Distance: 🚲5km 🚆train > Rome.
Remarks: Next to swimming pool.
Tourist information Colleferro:
ℹ Anagni. Region with number of old settlements.

📷🆂 **Farfa in Sabina** **32D3**
Abbazia di Santa Maria, SP41A. **GPS:** n42,22166 e12,71603. ⬆.

20 ⌂free 🚰 Ch free. **Location:** Rural, simple, isolated.
Surface: gravel. 🅿 01/01-31/12
Distance: 🚴4,7km.

📷🆂 **Gaeta** 🌊 **33B1**
Playa Colorada, Località S.Agostino, SS 213, Sperlonga>Gaeta.
GPS: n41,22812 e13,50281. ⬆.

60 ⌂€ 25-30, 2 pers.incl 🚰 Ch 🚿 WC included 💧€1/time 〰
€0,50/h. 🛁 **Location:** Rural, comfortable, central. **Surface:** gravel.
🅿 01/04-30/09
Distance: 🏊50m ⊗bar/restaurant 🛒200m.
Remarks: Shuttle to Gaeta, market Wednesday.

📷🆂 **Gaeta** 🌊 **33B1**
Sosta Camper Internazionale, Via Flacca km 20.500.
GPS: n41,23598 e13,49045.

30 ⌂€ 20-25 🚰 Ch 🚿 WC included 💧€1. **Surface:** gravel.
Distance: 🏊on the spot ⊗on the spot.
Remarks: Monitored parking.

📷🆂 **Gaeta** 🌊 **33B1**
Copacabana Beach, Via flacca Km 20.350, S.agostino Gaeta.
GPS: n41,23743 e13,48781. ⬆.

18 ⌂€ 25-30, 4 pers.incl 🚰€0,50 Ch 🚿 WC €0,50 ⚡€1. 🛁
Location: Rural, simple. **Surface:** gravel/sand.
🅿 01/04-30/09
Distance: 🚴6km 🏊on the spot ⊗on the spot.
Remarks: Shuttle to Gaeta.

📷🆂 **Gradoli** **32C2**
Parcheggio camper San Magno, Strada di Gradoli, SP114 km 6+137.
GPS: n42,59925 e11,86547. ⬆.

50 ⌂€ 15 🚰 Ch 🚿 included. 🛁 **Location:** Comfortable, isolated,
quiet. **Surface:** grassy. 🅿 01/01-31/12
Distance: 🚴7km 🏊on the spot ⊗500m.
Remarks: At lake Bolsena, discount longer stays.

📷🆂 **Ladispoli** 🌊 **32C3**
Area di Sosta Camper Riva di Ponente OT Torre Flavia, Via Roma
139. **GPS:** n41,95954 e12,05282. ⬆.

360 ⌂8-20h € 6, 20-8h € 6 🚰€3/time Ch 🚿€3/24h
WC 💧€1/time 〰. 🛁 🏊 **Location:** Rural, luxurious, quiet.
Surface: grassy/sand. 🅿 01/01-31/12
Distance: 🚴1,2km 🏊on the spot ⊗on the spot 🛒2km.
Remarks: 8% discount on presentation of the guide 2016, at the beach,
swimming pool available.

📷🆂 **Ladispoli** 🌊 **32C3**
Area Sosta Lady Beach, Via Roma 113. **GPS:** n41,95829 e12,05585. ⬆.

60 ⌂€ 12/24h, 01/10-01/03 10/24h 🚰 Ch 🚿€3/24h WC 💧
€0,50/time 〰included. 🛁 **Location:** Rural, simple, quiet, noisy.
Surface: grassy. 🅿 01/01-31/12
Distance: 🚴800m 🏊on the spot ⊗200m 🛒500m 🚌400m.

📷🆂 **Ladispoli** 🌊 **32C3**
Destinazione Sconosciuta Beach, Via Roma 115.
GPS: n41,95784 e12,05673. ⬆.

30 ⌂€ 10-12 🚰€3/time Ch 🚿€3/24h 💧€1.
🅿 01/01-31/12
Distance: 🚴800m 🏊on the spot ⊗200m 🛒500m 🚌500m.
Remarks: At sea.

📷🆂 **Latina** **33A1**
Area Camper Alta Marea, Strada Lungomare 3253, SP39, Loc. Foce
Verde. **GPS:** n41,41043 e12,86008. ⬆.

91 ⌂€ 15 🚰 Ch 🚿 WC included 💧€0,50/time. 🛁 🔍 📷.
Location: Rural, comfortable, quiet. **Surface:** grassy.
🅿 01/04-30/09
Distance: 🚴on the spot 🏊50m ⊗on the spot 🛒200m.

📷🆂 **Latina** **33A1**
Museo di Piana delle Orme, Strada Migliara 43 Mezza.
GPS: n41,44452 e12,98479. ⬆.

25 ⌂free 🚰 Ch. **Location:** Rural, simple, quiet. **Surface:** gravel.
🅿 01/01-31/12
Distance: 🚴Latina 10km ⊗2km.
Remarks: At museum.

📷🆂 **Leonessa** **32D2**
GPS: n42,56436 e12,96172. ⬆.

50 ⌂free 🚰 Ch. **Surface:** asphalted. ⬛ Market day
Distance: 🚴500m ⊗500m 🛒500m 🚌300m.

📷🆂 **Lubriano** **32C2**
Parco Paime, Piazza Palme. **GPS:** n42,63500 e12,10512. ⬆.

17 ⌂€ 5/24h 🚰 Ch 🚿(36x) WC 〰included. 🛁
Location: Comfortable, quiet. **Surface:** grasstiles.
🅿 01/01-31/12
Distance: 🚴1km ⊗on the spot.

IT

Lazio

Remarks: Nights closed with barrier.

Lunghezza 🅢 32D3

Camper Club Antichi Casali, Via Lunghezzina 302/a. **GPS:** n41,93039 e12,70454. ⬆.

40 ⓢ€ 15/24h ⌐🔲Ch🔧WC📶included. 🚿🧺
Location: Rural, comfortable, isolated, quiet. **Surface:** gravel.
🕐 01/01-31/12
Distance: 🚰3km 🏪5km 🚌Rome 20min.
Remarks: Monitored parking 24/24, shuttle bus.

Lunghezza 🅢 32D3

Camper Club Mira Lago Roma, Via Lunghezzina 75. **GPS:** n41,93159 e12,67642. ⬆➡.

60 ⓢ€ 18/24h ⌐🔲Ch🔧WC📋€0,50/time 🔌€4/time 📶included.
Location: Rural, comfortable, isolated, quiet. **Surface:** grassy.
🕐 01/01-31/12
Distance: 🏖700m 🏊on the spot 🎣on the spot ⊗on the spot 🔲on the spot 🚌on the spot.
Remarks: At 2 small lakes, service passerby € 5.

Montalto di Castro 32C3

Via Arbea, Marina di Montalto di Castro. **GPS:** n42,32981 e11,57699. ⬆➡.

50 ⓢ€ 7,50/day, overnight stay free 🔲Chfree. 🅿 **Location:** Rural, simple, quiet. **Surface:** grassy/gravel. 🕐 01/01-31/12
Distance: 🚰250m 🏊200m ⊗200m 🔲200m.
Remarks: Shady, thursday market.

Montalto di Castro 32C3

Via Torre Marina, Marina di Montalto di Castro. **GPS:** n42,32137 e11,59015. ⬆➡.

64 ⓢfree, 01/06-15/09 8-20h € 7,50 ⌐🔲Chincluded. 🅿
Location: Rural, simple. **Surface:** gravel. 🕐 01/01-31/12
Distance: 🚰500m 🏊200m ⊗400m 🔲300m.

Montefiascone 🅢 32C2

Cantina di Montefiascone, Via Grilli 2. **GPS:** n42,53346 e12,04293. ⬆.

30 ⓢfree ⌐🔲Ch🔧free. **Location:** Urban, comfortable, noisy. **Surface:** metalled. 🕐 01/01-31/12
Distance: 🚰1km.

Montefiascone 32C2

Agricamper Bella Cima, Strada Limitone. **GPS:** n42,52241 e12,00767. ⬆➡.

18 ⓢ€ 15/24h ⌐🔲Ch🔧included. **Surface:** gravel.
🕐 01/01-31/12
Distance: 🚰4km ⊗4km 🔲4km.
Remarks: Swimming pool.

Nettuno 33A1

Area Sosta L'Ippocampo, Via Palestrina 9. **GPS:** n41,47354 e12,68916. ⬆.

50 ⓢ€ 15 ⌐🔲Ch🔧WC📋included. 🚿 **Location:** Rural, simple, quiet. **Surface:** gravel. 🕐 01/01-31/12
Distance: 🚰3km 🏊3km.

Oriolo Romano 🅢 32C3

Viale degli Artigiani. **GPS:** n42,16699 e12,13902. ➡.

3 ⓢfree ⌐🔲free. **Location:** Simple. **Surface:** asphalted.
🕐 01/01-31/12
Distance: 🚰850m 🔲on the spot 🚉station 600m Roma-Viterbo.

Pescia Romana 32B3

Area La Pineta, Loc. Marina di Pescia Romana. **GPS:** n42,36552 e11,49389. ⬆➡.

50 ⓢ€ 10-22 ⌐🔲Chincluded 🔧€3 📋€1. **Location:** Rural, comfortable, quiet. **Surface:** grassy. 🕐 Easter-30/09
Distance: 🚰Pescia Romana 5km 🏊100m ⊗100m.
Remarks: Bread-service, monday market.

Rieti 🅢 32D2

Via Fonte Cottorella. **GPS:** n42,39548 e12,86463. ⬆➡.

10 ⓢfree ⌐🔲. **Surface:** asphalted. 🕐 01/01-31/12
Distance: 🚰historical center 100m.

Roma 🅢 32D3

Area Attrezzata per Camper LGP Roma, Via Casilina 700, Rome (Roma). **GPS:** n41,87595 e12,55515. ⬆.

200 ⓢ€ 15/<8m, € 22/8><10m, € 30/10><15m + tourist tax € 2/pp ⌐🔲Ch🔧included 📋🔌Against payment 📶€1/h 📷🚿
Location: Urban, luxurious, central, quiet.
Surface: grassy.
🕐 01/01-31/12
Distance: ⊗100m 🔲100m 🚌bus service to city centre day and night.
Remarks: Accessory shop, trailer/additonal car € 15 on separate parking € 7, repairs.
Exit 18 ring road (G.R.A.), follow Roma centro, ± 4km dir centre, company is on the left side of the road, turning after 2nd lights.

Roma 🅢 32D3

Prato Smeraldo, Via Ardeatina/Via di Tor Pagnotta 424, Rome (Roma). **GPS:** n41,80970 e12,52857. ⬆.

16 ⓢ€ 14 ⌐🔲Ch🔧€2/24h 📶included. 🚿🧺
Location: Highway, simple, noisy. **Surface:** grassy/metalled.
🕐 01/01-31/12, 24/24h
Distance: ⊗on the spot 🔲on the spot 🚌on the spot.
Remarks: Service passerby € 5. Exit 25 ring road (G.R.A.), second light to the right, Via di Tor Pagnotta.

Roma 32D3

Le Terrazze, Via di Fioranello 170, Rome (Roma). **GPS:** n41,79250 e12,54083. ➡.

40 ⓢ€ 20, max. 4 pers.incl ⌐🔲Ch🔧(40x)included. 🚿
Location: Simple, quiet. **Surface:** metalled. 🕐 01/01-31/12
Distance: 🏖750m 🔲1km 🔌on the spot 🚌on the spot.
Remarks: Video surveillance, car rental, excursions. Exit 25 ring road (G.R.A.), dir Santuario Divino Amore.

Roma 32D3

Parcheggio IAT, Air terminal Ostiense, Piazza G. da Verrazzano 9, Zone Mercati Generali, Rome (Roma). **GPS:** n41,86931 e12,48944. ⬆.

🛁€ 1,50, at least € 6, € 27/24h 🚰🗑Ch included ⚡€3,65/24h.
Location: Urban, simple, central, noisy.
Surface: asphalted.
🅿 01/01-31/12
Distance: 🚇metro 1km.
Remarks: Motorhome and Coach Parking.
Tourist information Rome (Roma):
🛈 Città del Vaticano. Domicile of the pope. Independent state since 1929.
🛈 A.P.T. (Azienda di Promozione Turistica), Via Parigi, 11. Capital of the country, a lot of curiosities in the old town centre. Roma Archeologica Card: 7-days ticket € 27,50, free entrance to Roman National Museum, Colosseum, Palatine, Baths of Caracalla, Tomb of Cecilia Metella and Villa of the Quintili.
👁 Piazza del Campidoglio.
👁 Palatino, Via di S. Gregorio, 30. Archeological site.
🅿 9h-sunset. 🎟 € 8, incl. Colosseum.
👁 Subiaco.
Ⓜ Musei Vaticani, Città del Vaticano. Paintings and art objects.
✝ Basilica di San Pietro. Basilica with Sistine Chapel.
⌒ Colosseo, Piazza del Colosseo. Colosseum, anfiteatro, the most important monument of ancient Rome.
🅿 9h-sunset. 🎟 € 8.
⌒ Foro Romane, Via dei Fori Imperiali. Novel Forum, the political, economic, and religious centre of ancient Rome.
🅿 9h-sunset. 🎟 free.
⌒ Pantheon, Piazza della Rotonda. Church of Santa Maria ad Martyres.
🅿 8.30-19.30h, Su 9-18h, Mass Sa 17, Su 10.30h, 16.30h. 🎟 free.
☀ Città del Vaticano. Pope blesses the mob for the window of the library. 🅿 Su 12h.
🛒 Piazza di Spagna.

| 🏕S | **San Felice Circeo** | 33B1 |

Circeo Camper, Viale Europa 1. **GPS**: n41,24095 e13,10426.⬆.

50 🛁€ 23-33, 4 pers. incl 🚰🗑Ch ⚡€3/24h WC 🅿€1 🗑€7 📶included. 📺 **Location:** Rural, luxurious, central. **Surface:** grassy.
🅿 01/04-20/09
Distance: 🏖100m 🏊10m ⊗10m 🛒100m 🛍100m.

| 🏕S | **San Felice Circeo** | 33B1 |

CirceMed, Via Molella 2/A. **GPS**: n41,25684 e13,12089.⬆.

60 🛁€ 18-27 🚰🗑Ch ⚡(50x)WC🅿€1 🗑€1/time ⚡€3 📶included.
📺 **Location:** Rural, comfortable, quiet. **Surface:** grassy.
🅿 01/04-30/09
Distance: 🏊500m ⊗200m 🛍200m 🚇on the spot.
Tourist information San Felice Circeo:
⛵ 🅿 Tue-morning.

| ⚓ | **Terracina** | 33B1 |

Via Amerigo Vespucci. **GPS**: n41,28528 e13,25450.⬆.

20 🛁€ 12. 📶 **Location:** Urban, simple. **Surface:** asphalted.
Distance: 🚇on the spot 🏊100m 🚇on the spot ⊗200m 🛍300m.

| 🏕S | **Tivoli** | 32D3 |

Via Aquaregna. **GPS**: n41,95841 e12,80465.⬆.

30 🛁free 🚰🗑Ch. **Location:** Urban, simple, central, quiet.
Surface: asphalted. 🅿 01/01-31/12 🅿 Wed, market
Distance: 🚇400m.
Remarks: Along the Aniene river.
Tourist information Tivoli:
👁 Villa d'Este. Country house with gardens and fountains, 16th century. ⌒ Villa Adriana. Roman villa.

| 🏕S | **Trevignano Romano** | 32C3 |

Blue Lake Camper, Via della Rena. **GPS**: n42,15877 e12,22411.
🛁🚰🗑Ch⚡. **Surface:** gravel.
Distance: 🏊on the spot 🚇on the spot.
Remarks: At the lake.

| 🏕S | **Tuscania** | 32C2 |

Via Nazario Sauro. **GPS**: n42,42217 e11,87520.⬆➡.

12 🛁free 🚰🗑free. **Location:** Urban, simple.
Surface: grasstiles/metalled. 🅿 01/01-31/12
Distance: 🚇250m ⊗250m 🛍250m.

| 🏕S | **Villa San Giovanni in Tuscia** | 32C3 |

Viale Europa. **GPS**: n42,28160 e12,05282.⬆.

🛁free. **Location:** Rural, simple, quiet. **Surface:** asphalted.
🅿 01/01-31/12
Distance: 🚇200m.

| 🏕S | **Viterbo** | 32C2 |

Piazza Mariano Romiti, loc. Belcolle. **GPS**: n42,40897 e12,11049.⬆.

50 🛁free 🚰🗑free. **Location:** Urban, simple. **Surface:** asphalted.
🅿 01/01-31/12
Distance: 🚇Lazise centre 300m 🚇on the spot.
Remarks: At station.

| 🚻S | **Viterbo** 🏖 | 32C2 |

Bed&breakfast Axia, Strada Procoio 2/C.
GPS: n42,41157 e12,05061.➡.

5 🛁€ 18 🚰🗑Ch ⚡€3 📶included. 📺 **Location:** Rural.
Surface: grassy. 🅿 01/01-31/12
Distance: 🚇Viterbo 4km.
Remarks: 10% discount at entrance Terme dei Papi (900m), bus to Viterbo € 5.

| 🚻 | **Viterbo** 🏖 | 32C2 |

Agriturismo Monteparadiso, Loc. Monterazzano.
GPS: n42,44161 e12,03062.⬆➡.

5 🛁guests free. **Location:** Simple, isolated. **Surface:** gravel.
🅿 01/01-31/12
Distance: 🚇7km.
Remarks: Near Termale Bullicame and Terme dei Papi.

| ♨ | **Viterbo** 🏖 | 32C2 |

Terme dei Papi, Strada Montarone. **GPS**: n42,41487 e12,06351.

100 🛁free. **Surface:** grassy/gravel. 🅿 01/01-31/12
Distance: 🚇3km.
Remarks: At Terme dei Papi.

| 🏕 | **Vitorchiano** | 32C2 |

SP23 Via della Teverina. **GPS**: n42,47152 e12,17212.⬆➡.

10 🛁free. **Surface:** asphalted. 🅿 01/01-31/12
Distance: 🚇500m.

Umbria

| 🏕S | **Amelia** | 32C2 |

Piazzale del Mercato, Via Rimembranze.
GPS: n42,55200 e12,41880.⬆.
10 🛁free 🚰🗑Chfree. **Surface:** asphalted. 🅿 01/01-31/12 🅿 Mo-morning (market)
Distance: 🚇50m ⊗50m 🛍50m.

| 🏕S | **Assisi** 🏖🏛👥 | 32C2 |

Via Giosuè Borsi, loc. Santa Maria degli Angeli.
GPS: n43,05972 e12,58747.⬆.

🅿 € 16/24h, € 1,60/h 🚰🚽Ch⚡. **Surface:** asphalted.
📅 01/01-31/12
Distance: 🚶2km 🚌 bus >Assisi 20min (retour € 1,80).

Assisi 🌊⛱🌳 32C2
Area San Vetturino, SS147. **GPS:** n43,07710 e12,59957.⬆

30 🅿 € 14/24h, € 2/h. **Surface:** asphalted. 📅 01/01-31/12
Distance: 🚶500m.
Remarks: Convento di San Francesco 1km.

Assisi 🌊⛱🌳 32C2
Viale Vittorio Emanuele II/SS147. **GPS:** n43,06864 e12,61420.⬆

10 🅿 € 20/24h. **Surface:** gravel. 📅 01/01-31/12
Distance: 🚶city centre 100m.

Bevagna 🌊⛱ 32D2
Piazza dell'Accoglienza, Via Raggiolo. **GPS:** n42,93417 e12,60639.⬆

50 🅿free 🚰🚽ChWC free. **Surface:** gravel.
Distance: 🚶100m ⊗100m 🚰100m.

Borghetto 32C1
Via Pontile. **GPS:** n43,18415 e12,02372.

4 🅿free 🚰🚽⚡free. **Surface:** asphalted. 📅 01/01-31/12
Distance: ⛵150m 🚶100m.
Remarks: At lake Trasimeno.

Cannara 🌊 32C2
Via Giaime Pintor, Loc. Casone. **GPS:** n42,99272 e12,57840.

20 🅿free 🚰🚽Chfree. **Surface:** asphalted.
Distance: 🚶300m 🚲300m 🚲 on the spot.
Remarks: At sports park XXV Aprile, cycle routes.

Tourist information Cannara:
👁 Assisi. Historical city.

Cascia 32D2
Piazzale Papa Leone XIII, Via della Molinella.
GPS: n42,71968 e13,01605.⬆➡

14 🅿 € 8/day, overnight stay free 🚰🚽Ch🚽free.
Surface: asphalted. 📅 01/01-31/12 🔵 Service: winter
Distance: 🚶300m ⊗300m 🚰300m 🚴100m 🚶100m.
Remarks: Escalator to city centre.

Cascia 32D2
Strada Statale Discascia. **GPS:** n42,72139 e13,01778.
20 🅿 € 7/24h ⚡ included. **Surface:** gravel. 📅 01/01-31/12
Distance: 🚶1km.

Castelluccio di Norcia 32D2
Pian Grande. **GPS:** n42,80045 e13,18947.

🅿free. **Surface:** grassy. 📅 01/01-31/12
Distance: 🚶Castelluccio 5km.
Remarks: Parco Nazionale dei Monti Sibilini.

Castiglione del Lago 🌊 32C2
Viale Divisione Partigiani Garibaldi. **GPS:** n43,12389 e12,05054.⬆

🅿free, summer € 12 🚰🚽Ch⚡included. **Surface:** asphalted/sand.
📅 01/01-31/12
Distance: 🚶800m 🏊on the spot.
Remarks: At lake Trasimeno.

Città di Castello 32C1
Piazzale E. Ferri, Viale Nazario Sauro. **GPS:** n43,45892 e12,23465.⬆➡
🅿free 🚰€0,10/10liter Ch. **Location:** Urban. **Surface:** asphalted.
📅 01/01-31/12
Distance: 🚶300m 🚴1,5km.
Remarks: Escalator to city centre.

Città di Castello 32C1
La Fontana del Boschetto, Via Aretina 38. **GPS:** n43,45737 e12,22882.
20 🅿 € 12 🚰🚽Ch⚡.
Distance: 🚶2km ⊗on the spot.
Remarks: Free shuttle.

Ferentillo 32D2
Loc. Precetto. **GPS:** n42,61802 e12,79347.⬆
5 🅿free 🚰🚽. **Surface:** asphalted.
Distance: 🚶200m.

Ficulle 32C2
Parco Cittadino, Via Orvieto SR 71. **GPS:** n42,83044 e12,06828.⬆➡

25 🅿free 🚰🚽Chfree. **Surface:** gravel.
Distance: 🚶500m 🚴10km ⊗1km 🚰500m.

Gualdo Cattaneo 32C2
Parco Acquarossa, Via Bonifacio 6. **GPS:** n42,89168 e12,53591.⬆
🅿€ 5 🚰🚽Ch⚡🚽WC🔊included. **Location:** Rural.
Surface: gravel.
Distance: 🚴on the spot ⊗on the spot.
Remarks: Excursions, regional products.

Gualdo Tadino 32D1
Piazza Federico II di Svevia. **GPS:** n43,23143 e12,78062.
🅿free 🚰🚽Chfree. **Surface:** asphalted. 🔵 Thu (market)

Gualdo Tadino 32D1
Via Perugia. **GPS:** n43,23756 e12,77235.
100 🅿free 🚰🚽free.
Distance: ⊗400m 🚰20m.
Remarks: Nearby stadium.

Gubbio 🌊 32C1
Camperclub Gubbio, Via del Bottagnone.
GPS: n43,35000 e12,56389.⬆

80 🅿free, 20-8h € 5 🚰🚽Chfree ⚡(8x)€ 1/h. **Surface:** asphalted.
📅 01/01-31/12
Distance: 🚶historical centre 1,5km ⊗100m 🚰200m.
Remarks: Teatro Romano 500m.

Monte Castello di Vibio 🌊⛱🌳🏵 32C2
Via Bartolomeo Jacopo della Rovere. **GPS:** n42,84185 e12,35076.➡

10 🅿free 🚰🚽Chfree. **Surface:** gravel. 📅 01/01-31/12
Distance: 🚶350m ⊗50m.

Montefalco 🌊⛱🏵 32D2
Viale delle Vittoria. **GPS:** n42,89230 e12,64791.⬆

15 🅿free 🚰🚽Ch🚽€1/h WC🔊. **Surface:** grasstiles.
Distance: 🚶100m.

S Montone 32C1

Via Aldo Bologni. **GPS**: n43,36346 e12,32499.
€ 10/24h Ch **Surface**: asphalted. 01/01-31/12
Distance: 200m 250m.
Remarks: At sports park.

S Orvieto 32C2

Area Sosta Camper Orvieto, Strada della Direttissima, Piazza delle Pace. **GPS**: n42,72562 e12,12736.

50 € 18/day Ch WC included. **Surface**: metalled.
01/01-31/12
Distance: funicular (retour € 1,60) 5 min 2,4km 50m pizzeria 50m.

Tourist information Orvieto:
U.I.A.T. (Ufficio Informazioni e di Accoglienza Turistica), Piazza Duomo, 24. City on volcanic plateau.
Del Crocifisso del Tufo. Ruins of Etruscan city.

S Panicale 32C2

Area Camper, Viale della Repubblica. **GPS**: n43,02806 e12,10222.

8 € 8/24h €0,50 Ch €0,50/kWh. **Surface**: grasstiles.
01/01-31/12
Distance: 100m 100m 50m.

S Passignano sul Trasimeno 32C1

Airone Area Camper, Lungolago Giappesi.
GPS: n43,18445 e12,14526.
€ 15 Ch WC €0,50 included. **Surface**: grassy.
01/01-31/12
Distance: 500m beach 200m 50m.
Remarks: At lake Trasimeno.

S Passignano sul Trasimeno 32C1

Via Europa, SS75bis, km 35,8. **GPS**: n43,18509 e12,14348.

4 free €0,30/100liter Ch €0,30/h WC. **Surface**: asphalted.
01/01-31/12
Distance: 400m 100m.
Remarks: At lake Trasimeno.

S Perugia 32C2

Il Bove, Via Giovanni Ruggia. **GPS**: n43,09810 e12,38386.

50 € 5/12h, € 18/24h Ch WC. Location: Urban.
Surface: asphalted. 01/01-31/12
Distance: 1,5km 500m 100m 200m on the spot.

Remarks: Parking police station.

Tourist information Perugia:
Palazzo dei Priori.
Tue.

S San Gemini 32D2

Via della Libertà. **GPS**: n42,61200 e12,54372.

16 Ch WC. **Surface**: metalled. 01/01-31/12
Distance: 300m 100m.

S Sant'Anatolia di Narco 32D2

Purchetta, SP209. **GPS**: n42,73599 e12,83598.
8 free. 01/01-31/12
Distance: on the spot on the spot on the spot.

S Scheggia e Pascelupo 32D1

Camper Scheggia, Via Campo Sportivo. **GPS**: n43,40007 e12,66674.
€ 12/24h Ch included. **Surface**: gravel.
01/01-31/12
Distance: 450m 500m.

S Spello 32D2

Via Centrale Umbra. **GPS**: n42,99371 e12,66730.

70 € 6/24h Ch. **Surface**: asphalted.
Distance: 500m 1,1km 500m 500m.
Remarks: Parking sports park.

S Spello 32D2

Terme Francescane Village, Via Fonte Citerna.
GPS: n43,00619 e12,62116.
30 € 13 Ch €3 WC. **Surface**: gravel. 01/01-31/12
Distance: Spello 6km.

S Spoleto 32D2

Parcheggio Ponciano, Via del Tiro a Segno.
GPS: n42,73687 e12,74212.

20 € 1/h, € 5/24h. **Surface**: gravel. 01/01-31/12
Distance: 500m 500m 500m.
Remarks: Escalator to city centre.

S Spoleto 32D2

Via dei Filosofi. **GPS**: n42,74619 e12,73214.

free free. **Surface**: gravel.
Distance: 800m.
Tourist information Spoleto:

Montefalco. Village worth seeing, parking outside village, narrow streets.
Ponte delle Torri. Aqueduct, 14th century.
Tue, Fri.
Art festival. 01/06-31/07.

S Terni 32D2

Via Lombardo Radice. **GPS**: n42,56634 e12,63577.

€ 4/48h €0,50 Ch included. **Surface**: asphalted.
Distance: 50m 50m.

S Terni 32D2

Piazzale Felice Fatati, SR209. **GPS**: n42,55690 e12,72006.

free. **Surface**: unpaved.
Distance: Terni 7km on the spot.
Remarks: Along river, nearby waterfalls.

S Todi 32C2

Area Porta Orvietana, Viale di Montesanto.
GPS: n42,78120 e12,40168.

16 € 14/24h, € 3/h Ch. **Surface**: asphalted.
Sa-morning market
Remarks: Elevator (free) to centre.

S Torgiano 32C2

Via Perugia. **GPS**: n43,02917 e12,43833.

10 free Ch free. **Surface**: asphalted. 01/01-31/12
Distance: 200m 3,5km 200m 300m.

S Trevi 32D2

Via Costa San Paolo. **GPS**: n42,87829 e12,75221.

20 free Ch free. **Surface**: grasstiles. 01/01-31/12
Distance: 500m 5,1km.
Remarks: At swimming pool.

Abruzzo

[S] Anversa degli Abruzzi — 32E3
Il Sagittario, Loc. Ponte delle Fornaci. **GPS**: n41,99995 e13,80960.⬆.
10 🏕 € 12 🚰🔌Ch 🚿 WC 🛒. **Surface**: gravel. 🔲 01/01-31/12
Distance: 🚶1km ⊗1km 🍴1km.

[S] Anversa degli Abruzzi — 32E3
Bioagriturismo La Porta dei Parchi, Piazza Roma 3.
GPS: n42,00014 e13,79899.⬆➡.

4 🏕 € 10, free with a meal 🚰🔌Ch 🚿 WC 🛒📶included.
Surface: metalled. 🔲 01/01-31/12
Distance: ⊗on the spot.

[S] Campotosto — 32D2
Via Lago, SR557. **GPS**: n42,56208 e13,34805.
🏕 € 5 🚰. **Surface**: grassy. 🔲 01/01-31/12
Distance: 🚶Campotosto 3km 🏊on the spot.
Remarks: At lake Campotosto.

[S] Casalbordino — 32F3
Via Alessandrini. **GPS**: n42,19952 e14,61800.
20 🏕 € 5. **Surface**: grassy/sand. 🔲 01/01-31/12
Distance: 🚶on the spot 🏊on the spot ⊗on the spot.

[S] Casalbordino — 32F3
Area di sosta Ass Villa Sarda, Contr. Piana Sabelli.
GPS: n42,17773 e14,59994.⬆.
20 🏕 🚰🔌Ch 🚿 WC 🛒. **Surface**: grassy. 🔲 01/01-31/12
Distance: 🏊1km ⊗on the spot.

[S] Fossacesia — 32F2
Area Camper, Via Lungomare 16b. **GPS**: n42,24067 e14,52988.⬆➡.

24 🏕 € 10 🚰🔌Ch 🚿included. **Surface**: gravel/sand.
🔲 01/03-30/11
Distance: 🏖6,5km 🏊on the spot.
Remarks: Pebbled beach.

[S] Isola del Gran Sasso — 32E2
S.Gabriele dell Addolorata. **GPS**: n42,51712 e13,65634.⬆.

🏕free 🚰🔌Ch. **Surface**: gravel/sand.
Distance: 🚶on the spot 🏖4km ⊗on the spot 🍴on the spot.
Remarks: Nearby basilica.

[S] Lanciano — 32E2
Area Attrezzata, Strada provinciale Lanciano-Frisa, Lancianovecchia.
GPS: n42,23385 e14,39106.⬆➡.

50 🏕free 🚰🔌ChWCfree. **Surface**: asphalted.
◉ Sa-morning market
Distance: 🚶300m (stairs and elevator).
Remarks: At city walls, upper part of the parking, escalator to city centre.

Tourist information Lanciano:
ℹ Historical city with medieval Jewish district, Ripa Sacca.

[S] L'Aquila 🏔❄ — 32D2
Via porta Napoli. **GPS**: n42,34175 e13,39510.⬆.
10 🏕free 🚰🔌Ch. 🔲 01/01-31/12
Distance: 🚶700m ⊗500m.

[S] L'Aquila 🏔❄ — 32D2
Via Strinella. **GPS**: n42,35323 e13,40708.⬆.

10 🏕free 🚰🔌Chfree. **Surface**: asphalted. 🔲 01/01-31/12
Distance: 🚶500m.
Remarks: In front of Hotel Federico II, adjacent Parco del Castello.

[S] Notaresco — 32E2
Via Martiri della Libertà. **GPS**: n42,65527 e13,89578.⬆➡.
10 🏕free 🚰🔌Chfree 🚿against payment. **Surface**: asphalted.
Distance: 🚶on the spot.
Remarks: At tennis-courts.

[S] Ovindoli — 32E3
Via Statale. **GPS**: n42,14143 e13,51740.⬆.

50 🏕free 🚰🔌Chfree. **Location**: Simple.
Distance: 🚶500m ⊗600m 🚲2km.

[S] Penne — 32E2
Agriturismo Il Portico, Contrada Colle Serangelo 26.
GPS: n42,45592 e13,95165.➡.

15 🏕 € 10, free with a meal 🚰🔌Ch 🚿(7x)€3 WC 🛒included 🧺.
Surface: grassy.

[S] Pescasseroli 🏔❄ — 32E3
Area Camper S.Andrea, Loc. Sant'Andrea.
GPS: n41,79888 e13,79222.⬆.

🏕 € 15, 2 pers.incl 🚰🔌Ch 🚿 WC 🛒included.
🔲 8-13h, 14.30-20h
Remarks: Free shuttle to centre.

Tourist information Pescasseroli:
↓ Parco Nazionale d'Abruzzo. Nature reserve.

[S] Pineto — 32E2
Sand stone beach, Via Tremiti, fraz. Scerne.
GPS: n42,64270 e14,04505.⬆.
🏕 🚰ChWC 🛒. **Surface**: grassy. 🔲 01/05-31/10
Distance: 🏊on the spot 🏖on the spot.

[S] Pineto — 32E2
Ristorante Aria e Sole, Borgo Santa Maria. **GPS**: n42,60891 e14,04341.
Distance: 🏖200m.

[S] Roccaraso 🏔❄ — 32E3
Hotel Park Il Poggio, SS17, C.da Poggio, 1 , Loc Il Poggio.
GPS: n41,82638 e14,10111.⬆➡.

18 🏕 € 20 🚰🔌Ch 🚿(18x)included. 🔲 01/01-31/12
Distance: ⊗on the spot.
Remarks: Shuttle bus to ski-piste.

[S] Roseto degli Abruzzi — 32E2
Area di Sosta Camper Romeo, Via degli Orti 13, loc. Cologna Spiaggia.
GPS: n42,72287 e13,98076.⬆.

40 🏕 € 20/24h 🚰🔌Ch 🚿(40x)WC included 🛒€1. **Surface**: grassy.
🔲 01/01-31/12
Distance: 🚶200m 🏊750m ⊗on the spot 🍴100m.

[S] Roseto degli Abruzzi — 32E2
Area di sosta Isola del Sole, Piana degli Ulivi.
GPS: n42,66902 e14,01189.⬆➡.

11 🏕 € 20 🚰🔌Ch 🚿(11x)€2 WC 🛒included. **Surface**: metalled.
🔲 01/01-31/12
Distance: 🚶3km 🏊3km.
Remarks: Swimming pool (summer).

[S] Roseto degli Abruzzi — 32E2
Palazzo dello Sport. **GPS**: n42,66012 e14,02382.⬆➡.

IT

🚐free 🚰🚽Chfree. **Surface:** asphalted. 📅 Tue
Distance: 🏙200m.
Remarks: Tuesday market.

[S] San Demetrio nei Vestini 32E3

La Grotta di Stiffe, Via del Mulino, Fraz. Stiffe.
GPS: n42,25567 e13,54811.➡.

🚐free 🚰€2,50 🚽Ch🔌€2,50. **Surface:** metalled/sand.
Distance: 🏙l'Aquila 18km.

[S] San Salvo Marina 32F3

Parking on the Beach, Via Amerigo Vespucci 20.
GPS: n42,07233 e14,76945.⬆➡.

35🚐€ 15/30 🚰🚽Ch🔌(30x)€3 WC🚿included 🧺€8.
Surface: asphalted. 📅 01/01-31/12
Distance: 🛣2km 🏖50m sandy beach 🍴50m 🛒Centro Commerciale 2km.

[S] San Salvo Marina 32F3

Area Sosta Communale per Autocaravan.
GPS: n42,07195 e14,76289.⬆.
30🚐€ 16/24h, € 20/48h, € 30/72h 🚰🚽ChWCincluded 🚿cold shower.
Surface: grassy. 📅 01/05-15/09
Distance: 🏙300m 🛣2,2km 🏖300m.

Santo Stefano di Sessanio 32E2

GPS: n42,34706 e13,64545.
🚐free. 📅 01/01-31/12

[S] Santo Stefano di Sessanio 32E2

Ostello del Cavaliere, Piazza Della Giudea.
GPS: n42,34429 e13,64314.⬆.
5🚐guests free 🚰. **Surface:** metalled.
Distance: 🏙300m.

[S] Sant'Egidio alla Vibrata 32E2

Zona industriale. **GPS:** n42,81937 e13,69915.⬆➡.

🚐free 🚰🚽Chfree. **Surface:** asphalted.

[S] Torino di Sangro 32F2

Area camper Vitale, Lido le Morgie. **GPS:** n42,20403 e14,60349.⬆.
100🚐€ 15/24h 🚰🚽Chincluded 🔌€2 WC🚿€0,50.
Surface: grassy/sand.
Distance: 🛣8km 🏖beach 70m 🚲on the spot.

[S] Tortoreto Lido 32E2

Via Napoli. **GPS:** n42,78552 e13,95013.
30🚐€ 12/24h 🚰🚽Ch🔌WC🚿📶. **Surface:** asphalted.
📅 01/01-31/12
Distance: 🏖beach 200m.

[S] Villalago 32E3

SP82b. **GPS:** n41,92255 e13,85621.⬆.

13🚐free 🚰🚽Chfree. **Surface:** asphalted.
Distance: 🏖on the spot.
Remarks: At lake Scanno, nearby beach and kosk.

Molise

[S] Campobasso 32F3

Area di sosta Dominick Ferrante, Contrada Macchie 1.
GPS: n41,56886 e14,65118.⬆➡.

20🚐€ 10/24h, € 15/48h 🚰🚽Ch🔌included.
Surface: gravel.
Distance: 🏙800m.

🍴[S] Monteroduni 32E3

Oasi San Nazzaro. GPS: n41,53448 e14,15924.

40🚐€ 10, free with a meal 🚰🚽Ch🔌(6x)included.
Surface: grassy. 📅 01/01-31/12
Distance: 🎣Fish lake 🍴on the spot.

[S] Petacciato Marina 32F3

Villagio la Torre, SS16 Adriatica km535,5, Termoli ri Vasto.
GPS: n42,02432 e14,88739.⬆.

60🚐€ 10-20 🚰🚽Ch🔌(50x)included WC🚿. **Surface:** gravel/sand.
📅 01/01-31/12
Distance: 🏖on the spot 🍴on the spot 🛒on the spot.
Remarks: Access via gate next to tower ruins.

[S] Petacciato Marina 32F3

Parking spiaggia, Via del Mare, SS16. **GPS:** n42,03543 e14,85337.⬆.

40🚐€ 6, 8-20h 🚿against payment. **Surface:** asphalted.
Distance: 🛣9,5km 🏖50m.
Remarks: Reserved place for motorhomes.

[S] Petacciato Marina 32F3

Parking Tolomei, Via Marinelle, SS 16. **GPS:** n42,03219 e14,85844.⬆.
50🚐€ 15 🚰🚽Ch🔌WC🚿📶. **Surface:** gravel.
📅 01/01-31/12
Distance: 🏖Direct access.
Remarks: Shuttle bus.

[S] Termoli 32F3

Centro Commerciale Sannicola, SS 87 Sannitica, km216-256.
GPS: n41,93880 e14,98754.⬆.

20🚐free 🚰🚽Chfree. **Surface:** asphalted. 📅 01/01-31/12

Puglia

[S] Alberobello 33D1

Parcheggio Nel Verde, Via Cadore. **GPS:** n40,78266 e17,23418.⬆.

60🚐€ 15-18/24h, € 10/12h, € 8/6h 🚰🚽Ch🔌€3 📶included.
Surface: grassy/gravel. 📅 01/01-31/12
Distance: 🏙Trulli-centre 50m 🍴50m 🛒100m.

Tourist information Alberobello:
ℹ Centre of the Trulli-region. Trulli houses are curious houses built without motar.
⛱ 📅 Thu-morning.

[S] Bari 33C1

Area Hobby Park Wash, Via Giovanni del Conte.
GPS: n41,11581 e16,88501.
🚐€ 15/24h 🚰🚽Ch🔌. **Surface:** metalled. 📅 01/01-31/12
Distance: 🏙centre 500m 🏖700m.
Remarks: Monitored parking.

[S] Bari 33C1

Gran Parcheggio Alberotanza, Via Alberotaza, 43A.
GPS: n41,09520 e16,87868.

250🚐€ 15 🚰€0,50/30liter 🚽€2,50 Ch🔌€0,50/kWh 🧺.
Surface: asphalted. 📅 01/01-31/12
Distance: 🛣7,8km 🍴500m 🛒500m.
Remarks: Monitored parking.

[S] Brindisi 33D1

Area Attrezzata, Strada Minnuta 6. **GPS:** n40,63517 e17,91824.

IT

🛏€ 10 🚰🔧Ch 💧€3 WC⌐included. **Surface:** asphalted.
⊙ 01/01-31/12
Remarks: 24/24 surveillance.

| 🏕Ⓢ | Castellana Grotte 🌿 | 33D1 |

Area Sapori & Sapori, Via Turi. **GPS:** n40,88560 e17,15722.⬆.
10 🛏free 🚰🔧Chfree. **Surface:** asphalted.
Distance: 🚶1km.
Remarks: Caves 1,8km.

| 🏕Ⓢ | Castellana Grotte 🌿 | 33D1 |

Le Grotte di Castellana, SS32. **GPS:** n40,87543 e17,14900.⬆.

🛏€ 5. **Surface:** grassy/gravel.
⊙ 01/01-31/12
Remarks: Parking at the caves of Castellana, overnight stay allowed.

| 🏕Ⓢ | Gallipoli | 33D1 |

GPS: n40,06000 e18,03939.
🛏€ 13 🚰🔧Ch 💧€5.
Distance: 🚶5km.

| 🏕Ⓢ | Lesina 〰 | 32F3 |

Oasi, Via Ludovica Ariosto. **GPS:** n41,86472 e15,35806.⬆.

15 🛏€ 12, Sept-Mar-Apr € 15, May/Aug € 18 🚰🔧
Ch 💧WC⌐included. **Surface:** asphalted. ⊙ 01/01-31/12
Distance: 🚶300m ⊗on the spot 🍺500m.

| 🏕Ⓢ | Lucera 🌿 | 32G3 |

Via Montello. **GPS:** n41,49987 e15,33223.⬆.

100 🛏free 🚰🔧. **Surface:** asphalted. ⊙ 01/01-31/12
Remarks: At station.

| 🏛Ⓢ | Lucera 🌿 | 32G3 |

Centro sportivo Casanova, Strada Contrada Casanova.
GPS: n41,48849 e15,26008.⬆.
🛏€ 10 🔧Ch. **Location:** Isolated. ⊙ 01/01-31/12
Distance: 🚶Lucera 9km.

| 🏛Ⓢ | Margherita di Savoia | 32G3 |

Lido Baywatch, Via Barletta. **GPS:** n41,36222 e16,17361.⬆➡.

12 🛏€ 15, Aug € 20 🚰🔧Ch 💧WC⌐included.
Surface: gravel/sand. ⊙ 01/01-31/12
Distance: 🚶2km ⊘on the spot ⊗on the spot.

| 🏕Ⓢ | Massafra | 33D1 |

Area di Sosta La Stella, SS7, SS Appia km 633, Le Forche.
GPS: n40,59201 e17,09904.⬆.

20 🛏€ 10/16-12h, € 20/24h 🚰🔧Ch 💧(18x)WCincluded ⌐€ 1.
Surface: grassy. ⊙ 01/01-31/12
Distance: 🚶1km ⊘500-700m 🍺1km.
Remarks: Beachshuttle € 2.

| 🏕Ⓢ | Mattinata 〰 | 32G3 |

Punta Grugno, SS89dirB. **GPS:** n41,69797 e16,06236.⬆➡.

80 🛏€ 11, Jun € 13, Jul € 16, Aug € 20 🚰🔧Ch 💧€2,50 WC⌐€0,80.
Surface: grassy/sand. ⊙ 01/04-01/10
Distance: 🚶Mattinata 2km ⊘pebbled beach ⊗on the spot 🍺2km.

| 🏕Ⓢ | Mattinata 〰 | 32G3 |

Eden Park, Porto di Mattinata, SP53. **GPS:** n41,70667 e16,06556.⬆.

25 🛏€ 10, Jul/Aug € 20 🚰🔧ChWCincluded ⌐€0,50.
Surface: grassy/sand. ⊙ 01/06-31/08
Distance: 🚶1km ⊘pebbled beach ⊷on the spot ⊗1km 🍺1km.

| 🏕Ⓢ | Melendugno | 33D1 |

Area Camper Salento I Faraglioni, SP366 km 20.5, Sant'Andrea.
GPS: n40,25550 e18,43748.
15 🛏€ 12-27/24h 🚰🔧Ch 💧WC⌐. ⊙ 01/01-31/12
Distance: ⊘700m 🍺on the spot.
Remarks: Shuttle bus to beach.

| 🏕Ⓢ | Melendugno | 33D1 |

Gran Pasha, Strada provinciale Lecce-Melendugno-San Foca, km.18.
GPS: n40,27724 e18,40510.
50 🛏€ 10-15, 20/07-31/08 € 25 + tourist tax 🚰🔧Ch 💧€3 WC⌐.
Surface: unpaved. ⊙ 01/01-31/12
Distance: ⊘1,5km.
Remarks: Free shuttle.

| 🏕Ⓢ | Monopoli | 33D1 |

Area du Sosta Camper Lido Millennium, SP90, Loc. Capitolo, SS16
km850 Uscita Capitolo. **GPS:** n40,90374 e17,35261.⬆➡.

100 🛏€ 12-15-18 🚰🔧Ch 💧6Amp WC⌐included. **Surface:** gravel.
⊙ Easter-30/09
Distance: 🚶500m ⊘50m ⊗50m 🍺50m.
Remarks: Private beach.

| 🏕Ⓢ | Otranto | 33D1 |

Oasy Park, Via Renis. **GPS:** n40,13795 e18,48922.⬆➡.

50 🛏€ 20 3 pers.incl 🚰🔧Ch 💧(70x),16Amp WCincluded ⌐€1 ⊙€4.
Surface: grassy/gravel. ⊙ 01/01-31/12
Distance: 🚶400m ⊘700m ⊗400m 🍺400m.

| 🏕Ⓢ | Otranto | 33D1 |

Area Camper Fontanelle, Sp366, km28. **GPS:** n40,19159 e18,45494.

🛏€ 15, Jul-Aug € 20, 4 pers incl. + tourist tax 🚰🔧Ch 💧€2 WC
included ⌐€0,50.
Distance: 🚶Otranto 5km ⊘beach 200m.
Remarks: Shuttle bus to Otranto.

| 🏕Ⓢ | Peschici 🌿⛱〰 | 32G3 |

Camper Marina Picola, Loc. Pantanello, Baia di Peschici.
GPS: n41,94528 e16,00528.⬆.

45 🛏Apr € 12, May € 13, Jun/Sep € 15, Jul € 20, Aug € 25 🚰🔧
Ch 💧WC⌐included ⌐€0,50. **Surface:** grassy/sand. ⊙ 01/04-30/09
Distance: 🚶2,5km, walking 800m (stairs) ⊘sandy beach 50m.

| 🏕Ⓢ | Peschici 🌿⛱〰 | 32G3 |

AgriCamper Pane e Vino, SS89 km 2,6. **GPS:** n41,92372 e16,01534.
20 🛏€ 10 🚰🔧Ch 💧WC⌐. **Surface:** sand.
Distance: 🚶3,5km ⊗on the spot.

| 🏕Ⓢ | Peschici 🌿⛱〰 | 32G3 |

Area attrezzata per camper Dattoli, Via Spiaggia, SS89.
GPS: n41,94522 e16,01138.
14 🛏€ 15-20 🚰🔧Ch 💧WCincluded ⌐€0,50.
Surface: unpaved.
Distance: 🚶Old city 300m (stairs) ⊘100m ⊗100m.

| 📷 | Putignano | 33D1 |

Grotte di Putignano, SS172. **GPS:** n40,85706 e17,10944.
🛏free. ⊙ 01/01-31/12

| 🏕Ⓢ | Rodi Garganico | 32G3 |

Area sosta camper Isola Bella, Via delle More.
GPS: n41,92444 e15,84166.⬆➡.

30 ⬛€ 15-20, Aug € 25 🚰⚡Ch🚿. WC🚽included.
Surface: grassy/sand. ⬛ 01/06-15/09
Distance: 🏖Lido del Sole 1,5km, Rodi Garganico 3,8km🏊sandy beach 10m🚤on the spot🅿100m🛒1,5km.

| 🏕S | **San Giovanni Rotondo** 🏖⛰ | 32G3 |

Coppa Cicuta, Strada Comunale Pozzocavo-Tre Carrini.
GPS: n41,69599 e15,70423.⬆➡.

30 ⬛€ 12 🚰⚡Ch🚿(30x)€1,50/night WC🚽included 🔲€ 10.
Surface: gravel. ⬛ 01/01-31/12
Distance: 🏖3km ⊗on the spot.
Remarks: Shuttle € 2/pp.

| 🏕S | **San Giovanni Rotondo** 🏖⛰ | 32G3 |

Lo Chalet, Viale Padre Pio. **GPS:** n41,70658 e15,69799.⬆.
⬛€ 15/24h 🚰⚡Ch🚿WC🚽.🚌 **Surface:** metalled.
⬛ 01/01-31/12
Distance: ⊗on the spot.
Remarks: Free shuttle, santuario 300m.

| 🍴S | **San Giovanni Rotondo** 🏖⛰ | 32G3 |

Di Cerbo, Circonvallazione Sud, SP45bis. **GPS:** n41,69725 e15,73097.

20 ⬛€ 5,20/day, € 7,80/night 🚰⚡Ch🚿WC🚽€0,50 🔲€1.
Surface: asphalted. ⬛ 01/01-31/12
Distance: 🏖1km ⊗on the spot 🛒on the spot 🚚on the spot.
Remarks: Shuttle bus.

| P | **San Giovanni Rotondo** 🏖⛰ | 32G3 |

Viale Padre Pio. **GPS:** n41,70679 e15,69927.
150 ⬛€ 2,50, overnight stay free. **Surface:** asphalted.
Remarks: Shrine Padre Pio 200m.

| 🏕S | **San Pietro in Bevagna** 🌊 | 33D1 |

La Salina, SP122, Manduria. **GPS:** n40,30121 e17,72630.⬆.
⬛€ 14-20, 4 pers.incl 🚰⚡Ch🚿€2,50 WC🚽included.
Surface: gravel. ⬛ 01/06-30/09
Distance: ⛱on the spot.

| 🏕S | **San Pietro in Bevagna** 🌊 | 33D1 |

La Marina, Via Favignana, Manduria. **GPS:** n40,30888 e17,67750.⬆.

80 ⬛€ 20/24h. **Surface:** unpaved.
Distance: ⛱300m.

| 🏕S | **Sannicola** 🌊 | 33D1 |

Campo delle Bandiere, Loc. Padula Bianca. **GPS:** n40,09681 e18,01297.
⬛€ 20 🚰⚡ChWC🚽. **Surface:** sand. ⬛ 01/06-01/09

Distance: ⛱Sandy beach.

| 🏕S | **Santa Maria al Bagno** | 33D1 |

Area Camper Mondonuovo, Via Torre Mozza.
GPS: n40,13494 e18,00166.⬆➡.
30 ⬛€ 15 🚰⚡Ch🚿. **Surface:** grassy. ⬛ 01/01-31/12
Distance: ⛱beach 500m.

| 🏕S | **Torre Canne di Fasano** | 33D1 |

Lido Tavernese, SS379, uscita Torre Canne Sud.
GPS: n40,82023 e17,49875.

100 ⬛€ 15-22 🚰⚡Ch🚿(80x)€2 WC🚽included 🚽€1.
Surface: grassy.
Distance: 🏖3,5km ⛱on the spot⬛01/07-31/08.

| 🏕S | **Torre Canne di Fasano** | 33D1 |

Il Privilegio Camper Service, Via Appia, SP90 > Savelletri.
GPS: n40,84363 e17,46359.
⬛€ 15-20 🚰⚡Ch🚿WC🚽. **Surface:** gravel.
Distance: ⊗on the spot.
Remarks: Beach club.

| 🏕S | **Troia** | 32G3 |

Campo della Fiera, Via Sant'Antonio. **GPS:** n41,36158 e15,30616.

12 ⬛free 🚰⚡Ch🚿. **Surface:** asphalted. ⬛ 01/01-31/12
Distance: 🏖200m.
Remarks: Near the cathedral.

| 🏕S | **Vico del Gargano** | 32G3 |

Lido Azzurro. GPS: n41,94208 e15,98303.⬆.

80 ⬛Oct-Apr € 10, May-June € 15, Jul/Aug € 25 🚰⚡Ch🚿€3,(Aug)
WC🚽included 🚽€1. **Surface:** sand. ⬛ 01/01-31/12
Distance: 🏖Valazzo 4km⛱Sandy beach🛒1km (camping).

| 🏕S | **Vieste** 🏖⛰🌊 | 32G3 |

Fusilo Rosina, Contrada S.Lucia. **GPS:** n41,91028 e16,12944.⬆.

70 ⬛Jun-Sep € 15, Jul € 20, Aug € 27,50 🚰⚡Ch🚿(70x)included
WC🚽€0,50. **Surface:** grassy. ⬛ 01/06-15/09
Distance: 🏖4km ⛱300m ⊗50m 🛒100m 🚌50m.

| 🏕S | **Vieste** 🏖⛰🌊 | 32G3 |

Area Eden Blu, Lungomare Enrico Mattei.
GPS: n41,85985 e16,17396.⬆.
40 ⬛€ 22 🚰⚡Ch🚿WC🚽. **Surface:** unpaved. ⬛ 01/04-31/10
Distance: ⛱on the spot.

Tourist information Vieste:
⛺ 📱 Mo.

| 🏕S | **Zapponeta** | 32G3 |

Zapponeta Beach, Via del Mare. **GPS:** n41,45694 e15,96083.⬆➡.

30 ⬛€ 10, 1/7-15/7, 15/8-31/8 €12, 15/7-15/8 € 15/2 pers incl
🚰⚡Ch🚿€2 WC🚽included 🚽€0,50. **Surface:** grassy/metalled.
⬛ 01/04-30/09
Distance: 🏖250m ⛱on the spot 🚤on the spot ⊗500m 🛒500m.
Remarks: Narrow entrance.

Campania

| 🏕S | **Bacoli** | 33B1 |

Sea Oasi Village, Via Strada Romana, loc. Fusaro.
GPS: n40,82194 e14,04791.
± 100 ⬛€ 15/20/24h, 4 pers.incl 🚰⚡Ch🚿€5 WC🚽€1 📶.
Surface: grassy/sand.
Distance: ⛱on the spot.
Remarks: At the beach.

| 🏕 | **Bacoli** | 33B1 |

Sea Oasi Village, Via Strada Romana. **GPS:** n40,82194 e14,04791.
100 ⬛€ 18-20, 4 pers.incl. **Surface:** grassy.
Distance: ⛱on the spot ⊗on the spot.

| 🏕S | **Bacoli** | 33B1 |

Parco Naturale Agriturismo Fondi di Baia, Via Fondi di Baia.
GPS: n40,81132 e14,07518.

20 ⬛€ 10 🚰⚡Ch🚿 included. **Surface:** asphalted. ⬛ 01/01-31/12
Distance: 🏖3km ⊗Baia 700m 🚌100m.

| 🏕S | **Baia e Latina** | 33B1 |

Country Village Il Baglio, Via Sciuliarelle.
GPS: n41,30386 e14,24754.
⬛guests free 🚰⚡Ch🚿WC🚽 📶. ⬛ 01/01-31/12
Distance: 🏖village 2km ⊗on the spot.

| 🏕S | **Benevento** 🏖 | 33B1 |

Sannio Camper Club, Via Domenico Mustilli.
GPS: n41,13141 e14,78960.⬆.

50 ⬛€ 10/24h 🚰⚡Ch🚿 included. ⬛ 01/01-31/12
Distance: 🏖500m 🚲1,8km 🛒300m.

Tourist information Benevento:
⛺ Piazza Risorgimento en Piazza Santa Maria. ⬛ Wed, Sa 8-13h.

| 🏕 | **Casalbore** | 33B1 |

Agriturismo Le Mainarde. GPS: n41,24516 e15,00242.⬆.
30 ⬛€ 15. ⬛ 01/01-31/12
Distance: ⊗on the spot.

| 🏕S | **Cava de' Tirreni** 🏖🌊 | 33B1 |

Via Ido Longo, loc. Sant'Arcangelo. **GPS:** n40,69984 e14,69553.
⬛free 🚰⚡Chfree. **Surface:** grasstiles. ⬛ 01/01-31/12
Distance: 🚲2,3km.

Tourist information Cava de' Tirreni:
ℹ Salerno. City with medieval centre.

IT

M Museo Civico, Amalfi. Museum with Tavole Amalfitane, the old Law of the Sea. ☐ 8-14h, Sa 8-12h ☐ holiday.

Contursi Terme   33C1
Agriturismo Il Giardino, Loc. Prato. **GPS:** n40,64891 e15,23002.
€ 10 Ch **Surface:** metalled.
Distance: 4,4km on the spot.
Remarks: Le Terme Vulpacchio 50m.

Marina di Camerota   33C1
Parcheggio Europa, Via Sirene. **GPS:** n40,00302 e15,36493.
€ 18 **Surface:** unpaved. ☐ Easter-30/09
Distance: 300m.

Mondragone   33B1
Dun Area Camper, Via Domiziana, km 15.250.
GPS: n41,13159 e13,86150.
50 Ch **Surface:** grassy/sand.
Distance: Mondragone 4km on the spot on the spot 3km on the spot.
Remarks: Monitored parking 24/24.

Napoli   33B1
Parking IPM, Via Colli Aminei 27, Naples (Napoli).
GPS: n40,87038 e14,24616.

7-21h € 10 21-8h €10 Ch included €2. **Surface:** asphalted.
☐ 01/01-31/12
Distance: 1,2km bus R4 centre Napoli 30m.
Remarks: Monitored parking.

Napoli   33B1
Parking Patry, Via Nuova Poggioreale 120, Naples (Napoli).
GPS: n40,86788 e14,29436.
€ 24/24h Ch included. **Location:** Urban.
Surface: metalled. ☐ 01/01-31/12
Distance: metro 300m.
Remarks: Monitored parking.

Tourist information Naples (Napoli):
ℹ A.A.C.S.T.(Azienda Autonoma di Cura Soggiorno e Turismo), Palazzo Reale, www.regione.campania.it. Capital of the province with many monuments and cultural treasures.
👁 Vesuvio. Volcano, observatorium on western edge of the crater. Visit with guide possible.
👁 Mergellina. Small peninsula with fishing-port and marina.
👁 Teatro San Carlo. Opera building.
M Museo Nazionale Archeologico di Napoli, Piazza Museo Nazionale 19. Antique hellenic-roman civilisation. ☐ Tue-Su 9-14h.
✠ Palazzo Reale. Royal palace. ☐ 9-13.30h ☐ Mo.
✝ Duomo San Gennaro. Cathedral with original interior.
⌒ Ercolano/Herculaneum. Ancient city buried together with Pompeii.
☐ 9-14.45h, holidays 9-18.15h.
⅄ Mercato Corso Malta. ☐ Mo, Fri.

Paestum   33C1
Camper Village Maremirtilli, Via Linora di Paestum, SP278.
GPS: n40,37607 e15,00119.
70 € 15-25 Ch WC. **Surface:** grassy. ☐ 01/01-31/12
Distance: on the spot.

Paestum   33C1
Camper Park Zone Archeologica, Via Magna Grecia, Capaccio Paestum.
GPS: n40,41851 e15,00697.
30 € 10 Ch included. **Surface:** unpaved. ☐ 01/01-31/12
Distance: 300m 1,6km 50m.
Remarks: Paestum Excavations 200m.

Paestum   33C1
Gli Eucalipti Area di Sosta, Via Linora, 76, Capaccio.
GPS: n40,38565 e15,00308.
25 € 14/17 Ch included. **Surface:** grassy.
☐ 01/05-01/10
Distance: 4km 50m.

Paestum   33C1
Fattoria del Casaro, Via Licinella 5, Capaccio Paestum.
GPS: n40,41504 e15,00505.
100 € 12/24h Ch included.
Distance: 600m beach 1,8km on the spot.

Remarks: Paestum Excavations 300m, regional products and bread.
Tourist information Paestum:
ℹ A.A.C.S.T.(Azienda Autonoma di Cura Soggiorno e Turismo), Via Magna Grecia, 151. Old city, founded by the Greeks. In the surroundings many vestiges from that time. ☐ 9h-sunset.

Palinuro   33C1
Via Palorcio. **GPS:** n40,03722 e15,30944.
€ 20/24h Ch WC included.
Distance: 700m.

Pompei   33B1
Parking Plinio, Via Plinio 98. **GPS:** n40,74710 e14,48756.

30 8-20h € 10, 8-8h € 19, 20-8h € 12. **Surface:** asphalted.
☐ 01/01-31/12
Distance: Archeological site Pompei 250m 300m.
Remarks: Monitored parking.

Pompei   33B1
Camping Pompei, Via Plinio 113. **GPS:** n40,74675 e14,48496.
€ 15,50-20, 2 pers.incl Ch WC included.
Location: Urban.
Surface: grassy.
☐ 01/01-31/12
Remarks: Entrance acient city 150m.

Tourist information Pompei:
ℹ Ancient city at the foot of Vesuvius. ☐ 9h-sunset ☐ holiday.

Pozzuoli   33B1

Castagnaro Parking
Pozzuoli - Napoli

■ **Paved and flat motorhome pitches**
■ **Beautiful view**
■ **Electricity/water/drainage at each pitch**

www.castagnaroparking.it
info@castagnaroparking.it

Castagnaro Park, Via del Castagnaro 1. **GPS:** n40,86939 e14,12150.
85 € 15 Ch (80x)€3/24h WC included €1,50.
Surface: grassy/gravel. ☐ 01/01-31/12
Distance: 300m 4km 300m 300m 200m.
Remarks: Monitored parking, reservation during Christmas period.

Tourist information Pozzuoli:
ℹ Cuma. Archeological site.
☐ 9-14.45h, summer 18h.

Sala Consilina   33C1
Via Santa Maria della Misericordia. **GPS:** n40,41376 e15,56397.
20 € 5/night Ch included. **Surface:** metalled.
☐ 01/01-31/12
Distance: 1,5km 300m 500m 2,5km 1,5km 15km 15km.
Remarks: Behind hotel Vallis Dea.

Tramonti   33B1

Agriturismo Costiera Amalfitana, Via Falcone, 12 - Frazione Pietre.
GPS: n40,69929 e14,61811.
22 01/09-14/06 € 22, 15/06-31/08 - 23/12-06/01 € 30
Ch WC included. **Location:** Rural, comfortable.
Surface: grassy/gravel. ☐ 01/01-31/12
Distance: 50m 15km 6km on the spot 30m 500m on the spot.
Remarks: Amalfi Coast.

Basilicata

Grumento Nova   33C1
Agriturismo Al Parco Verde, Contrada Spineto, Moliterno-Grumento.
GPS: n40,28110 e15,90563.
20 € 20 Ch WC included. **Surface:** grassy
☐ 01/06-01/10
Distance: 8km 2km 5km on the spot 2km 1km.
Remarks: Archeological site 200m.

Metaponto   33C1
Camper parking Nettuno, Viale Magna Grecia, Metaponto Lido.
GPS: n40,35693 e16,83221.

50 € 13/24h, Jul/Aug € 18 Ch WC included €1.
Surface: grassy/gravel. ☐ 01/01-31/12
Distance: 50m on the spot 300m.

Tourist information Metaponto:
ℹ Archeological site. ☐ 9h-sunset.

Calabria

Amantea   33C2
Garden Park Caterina, SS. 18, loc Coreca.
GPS: n39,09383 e16,08508.
10 € 20-25, 4 pers.incl Ch €2,50 WC included €1 €5.
Surface: grassy. ☐ 15/06-15/09
Distance: on the spot on the spot on the spot nearby.

Bova Marina   33C3
Mafalda's Camper Park, Via Sotto Ferrovia, loc. San Pasquale.
GPS: n37,92422 e15,94800.
20 € 10-20 Ch included. **Surface:** gravel/sand.
Distance: 3km on the spot on the spot 200m 500m.
Remarks: Acces via unmetalled road along the beach.

Catanzaro Marina   33C2
Il Chioschetto, Via Carlo Pisacane 24. **GPS:** n38,83321 e16,64862.

10 🛏free 🚰🔌. **Location:** Simple. **Surface:** sand.
Distance: 🏖Sandy beach.

🏕S Cirella 33C1
Area Camper Ulisse, SS 18 km 270, Diamante.
GPS: n39,72500 e15,80930.

130 🛏€ 8-25, 4 pers.incl 🚰🔌Ch🔧 WC🚽included 📶.
Surface: grassy/sand. 📅 01/04-31/10
Distance: 🚶800m 🏖on the spot 🎣on the spot ⊗on the spot 🛒on the spot.

🏕S Cirella 33C1
Lido Alexander, SS 18, Diamante. **GPS:** n39,72168 e15,81097.⬆.

50 🛏€ 8-17 🚰🔌Ch🔧€3 WC included 📶€1 📶€3.
Surface: grassy/gravel. 📅 01/01-31/12
Distance: 🚶1,5km 🏖on the spot 🎣on the spot ⊗on the spot 🛒on the spot.

🏕S Cirella 33C1
Lido delle Sirene, SS 18, Contr. Riviere. **GPS:** n39,71822 e15,81137.➡.

100 🛏 🚰🔌Ch🔧 WC🚽. **Surface:** grassy.
📅 01/06-20/09
Distance: 🚶1km 🏖on the spot 🎣on the spot ⊗on the spot 🛒1km.

🏕S Cirella 33C1
Lido Tropical, Viale Glauco, 9, Diamante. **GPS:** n39,69222 e15,81556.⬆.

200 🛏€ 8-30, 4 pers.incl 🚰🔌Ch🔧 WC🚽📶.
Surface: grassy/sand. 📅 01/01-31/12
Distance: 🚶1,5km 🏖on the spot 🎣on the spot ⊗200m 🛒200m 🚌shuttle to town.

🏕S Cirò Marina 33D2
Via Maddalena. **GPS:** n39,35998 e17,12910.
25 🛏€ 6, 01/06-31/08 € 12 🔧. **Surface:** unpaved.

📅 01/01-31/12
Distance: 🚶1,2km 🏖50m.

🏕S Cittadella del Capo 33C2
Torre Parise, Via Parise. **GPS:** n39,56580 e15,87399.⬆.
16 🛏€ 15, Jul/Aug € 18 🚰🔌Ch🔧 WC included. **Surface:** grassy.
📅 01/01-31/12
Distance: 🚶1,5km 🏖200m 🛒500m.
Remarks: Swimming pool.

🏕S Condofuri Marina 33C3
Agriturismo Antonino Gemelli, Via Salinella 37.
GPS: n37,92372 e15,85150.⬆.
20 🛏€ 15-20 🚰🔌Ch🔧 WC🚽📶. **Surface:** gravel/sand.
📅 01/01-31/12
Distance: 🚶500m 🏖100m.

🏕S Corigliano Calabro 33C1
B&B Club Tepee, Contrada Sant'Agata 42, SS106bis > Cantinella.
GPS: n39,64140 e16,38617.
🛏€ 10 🚰🔌Ch🔧🚽.
Distance: 🚶Corigliano 14km.

🏕S Cropani Marina 33D2
Sena Park, Viale Venezia 34. **GPS:** n38,91143 e16,80963.⬆➡.
25 🛏€ 12-28, 2 pers.incl 🚰🔌Ch🔧 WC🚽€0,50 📶included 📶.
Surface: grassy/sand.
📅 01/01-31/12
Distance: 🚶500m 🏖400m 🎣400m ⊗ristorante/pizzeria 🛒500m.
Remarks: Washing motorhome € 20.

🏕S Crotone 33D2
Hera Lacinia Mare, Via Filippo, 47, Campione III.
GPS: n39,00311 e17,16984.⬆.
10 🛏€ 25 🚰🔌Ch🔧🚽. **Surface:** gravel/metalled.
Distance: 🚶on the spot 🏖on the spot 🎣on the spot ⊗100m 🛒200m.

🏕S Morano Calabro 33C1
Via Gaetano Scorza. **GPS:** n39,84098 e16,13731.⬆➡.

40 🛏free 🚰🚽. **Surface:** asphalted. 📅 01/01-31/12
Distance: 🚶200m 🚲7km ⊗200m 🛒200m.
Remarks: Next to church of San Bernardino, panoramic view.

🏕S Palmi 33C2
Sosta Camper Prajola, Lungomare Donna Canfora.
GPS: n38,39333 e15,86277.⬆➡.

25 🛏€ 15/24h 🚰🔌Ch🔧 WC🚽included 📶. **Location:** Simple.
Surface: gravel. 📅 01/01-31/12
Distance: 🏖on the spot.

🏕S Praia a Mare 33C1
Nuova Playa, Contr. Fiucci. **GPS:** n39,86885 e15,78943.⬆.

15 🛏€ 15, peak season € 30 🚰🔌Ch🔧included. **Surface:** grassy.
📅 01/01-31/12
Distance: 🚶2km 🏖on the spot 🎣on the spot ⊗100m 🛒2km.
Remarks: Black sandy beach, in front of Dino island.

🏕S Praia a Mare 33C1
Punto Mare, Loc. Fiuzzi. **GPS:** n39,87633 e15,78727.⬆.

30 🛏€ 6 🚰€2,50 🔌€2,50 Ch🔧€2. **Surface:** grassy.
📅 01/06-30/09
Distance: 🚶800m 🏖600m 🎣600m ⊗500m 🛒500m 🏖on the spot.

🏕S Rossano 33C1
Sosta Camper Il Faro, C. da Foresta Faro Campo Trionto.
GPS: n39,62148 e16,75146.⬆.

12 🛏€ 13-25 🚰🔌Ch🔧 WC🚽included. **Location:** Comfortable, isolated. **Surface:** grassy. 📅 01/01-31/12
Distance: 🚶2km, Rossano 12km 🏖Sandy beach ⊗on the spot.

🏕S Scalea 33C1
Dolce Vita, Via Fiume Lao 7. **GPS:** n39,79667 e15,79265.⬆.

100 🛏€ 16-21 🚰🔌Ch🔧€5 WC🚽€0,50 📶. **Surface:** grassy.
📅 01/05-30/09
Distance: 🚶on the spot 🏖on the spot 🎣on the spot ⊗on the spot 🛒800m.

🏕S Scalea 33C1
Lido Zio Tom, Corso Mediterraneo km 261,7.
GPS: n39,81306 e15,78917.⬆.

140 🛏€ 10-18 🚰🔌Ch🔧included,4Amp WC🚽hot shower against payment. **Surface:** grassy/gravel. 📅 15/04-15/10
Distance: 🏖on the spot ⊗300m 🛒1km 🚌1,5km.

🏕S Scalea 33C1
Lido Aqua Mar Sosta Camper Martina, Corso Mediterraneo.
GPS: n39,80092 e15,79087.⬆.
🛏€ 20/24h 🚰🔌Ch🔧 WC🚽€0,50.
Distance: 🏖on the spot.

Sardinia

🏕S Aglientu 31G2
Oasi Gallura, Localita'Vignola Mare 19, SP 90 km 53.
GPS: n41,12556 e9,06167.
70 🛏€ 13,50-19 🚰🔌Ch🔧€2,50 WC🚽hot shower € 1 📶€5 📶.
Distance: 🏖50m ⊗on the spot 🛒on the spot.

🏕S Alghero 31F2
Camperpark I Platani, Ss 291 Km 32,5 S.Maria la Palma - Fertilia.
GPS: n40,60693 e8,27522.

🏕 16, Jul €18, Aug € 20 🚰🔌Ch 🚿WC 🛢included 🔲€5.
Distance: 🏖Alghero 7km 🏊1,5km. **Remarks:** Monitored parking 24/24, shuttle bus to beach, swimming pool.

| 📷S | Alghero | 31F2 |

Paradise Park, Loc. Le Bombarde. **GPS:** n40,59180 e8,25610.

100 🏕± € 18 🚰🔌Ch 🚿WC 🛢included.
Distance: 🏖350m 🏊350m 🍴on the spot 🏖on the spot 🚗50m.

| 📷S | Bosa | 31F2 |

S'Abba Drucche Spiagge, SP49 Alghero-Bosa km 38+800.
GPS: n40,31671 e8,47368.
🏕 20-24 🚰🔌Ch 🚿WC 🛢€1 🔲€7 📶. **Surface:** unpaved.
🔲 01/04-30/09
Distance: 🏊on the spot 🍴on the spot.

| 📷S | Buggerru | 31F3 |

Area Terrazze. GPS: n39,40317 e8,40250.

50 🏕€ 20/24h 🚰🔌Ch 🚿€5. **Surface:** sand.
🔲 01/01-31/12
Distance: 🏖200m 🏊on the spot.
Remarks: Beach parking.

| 📷S | Buggerru | 31F3 |

Loc. Cala Domestica. **GPS:** n39,41757 e8,41147.
20 🏕€ 25 🛢cold shower. **Surface:** sand.
Distance: 🏖4km 🏊sandy beach 50m 🍴50m.
Remarks: Beach parking.

| 📷S | Domus de Maria | 31F3 |

Loc. Spartivento, Chia. **GPS:** n38,88962 e8,86437.
🏕 17/24h 🚰🔌Ch 🚿🛢€0,50, cold shower. **Surface:** sand.
🔲 Easter-30/09
Distance: 🏊on the spot 🍴on the spot 🍴on the spot.
Remarks: In front of Hotel Su Giudeu.

| 📷S | Ghilarza | 31F3 |

Via Rosario. **GPS:** n40,12604 e8,83942.
2 🏕free 🚰🔌Ch. **Surface:** forest soil. 🔲 01/01-31/12
Distance: 🏖500m.

| 📷S | Nuoro | 32C2 |

P.le Anfiteatro cittadino, Piazza Veneto. **GPS:** n40,31447 e9,32807. ⬆.
30 🏕free 🚰🔌Ch free. 🔲 01/01-31/12

| 📷S | Oristano | 32D3 |

Stadio Tharros, Via Dorando Petri. **GPS:** n39,89710 e8,58927. ⬆.
🏕free 🚰🔌Ch free. 🔲 01/01-31/12
Distance: 🏖500m 🍴500m 🍴Porta Nuova 650m.

| 📷S | Oristano | 32D3 |

Zona sportiva Sa Rodia, Viale Repubblica. **GPS:** n39,90605 e8,57878.
🏕free 🚰🔌Ch free.
Distance: 🏛historical centre.
Remarks: Parking in front of swimming pool.

| 📷S | San Teodoro | 32B2 |

Via Donat Cattin. **GPS:** n40,76658 e9,66884.

---

30 🏕free. **Surface:** asphalted.

| 📷S | Sorso | 32B2 |

Camp Site, Via degli Oleandri, SP 81 km 13, Platamona Lido.
GPS: n40,81565 e8,46462.
50 🏕€ 12-18 🚰🔌Ch 🚿WC 🛢🔲. 🔲 01/01-31/12
Distance: 🏊300m 🍴nearby 🚗on the spot.

| 📷S | Stintino | 32D2 |

La Pineta, Loc. Pozzo S.Nicola, SP34. **GPS:** n40,86843 e8,23610. ⬆.
🏕 19, Aug € 21 🚰🔌Ch 🚿WCincluded 🛢hot shower €1.
Surface: grassy/sand.
Distance: 🏊3,5km 🍴on the spot.
Remarks: Free shuttle to beach.

| 🛏S | Tonara | 32D2 |

Ostello delle Gioventù, Via Muggianeddu, 2. **GPS:** n40,02855 e9,17542.
🏕 10 🚰🔌Ch 🛢. 🔲 01/01-31/12
Distance: 🏖500m 🍴on the spot.

| 📷S | Valledoria | 32C2 |

Punto Maragnani, Via Cristoforo Colombo, Loc. Maragnani.
GPS: n40,92470 e8,79548.
🏕 18/24h 🚰🔌Ch 🚿WC 🛢included. 🔲 01/01-31/12
Distance: 🏊50m 🍴200m.

| 📷S | Villaputzu | 32C1 |

Area di sosta camper Turimar, Via Nazionale 236, SS125.
GPS: n39,46017 e9,60290.
🏕 🚰🔌Ch 🚿WC 🛢against payment.
Distance: 🏖Villaputzu 6km 🏊50m 🍴on the spot.

| 📷S | Villasimius | 32C1 |

Gli Aranci, Viale dei Carrubi, loc. Pranu Zinnigas.
GPS: n39,14997 e9,51292.
100 🏕€ 22 🚰🔌Ch 🚿WC 🛢included. 🔲 01/05-30/09
Distance: 🏖2km 🏊3km.
Remarks: Shuttle bus to beach.

Sicily

| 📷S | Agrigento 🌸🍃 | 33B3 |

Sosta Camper Quality, Via delle Dune, San Leone.
GPS: n37,24566 e13,61114. ⬆.
50 🏕€ 20 🚰🔌Ch 🚿WC 🛢📶included. **Location:** Comfortable, quiet. **Surface:** sand. 🔲 01/06-31/10
Distance: 🏖Dune 🏊sandy beach 10m 🍴50m.

| 📷S | Agrigento 🌸🍃 | 33B3 |

Valle dei Templi, Viale Caduti di Marzabotto. **GPS:** n37,28881 e13,58181.
50 🏕€ 5. **Location:** Simple. **Surface:** sand. 🔲 01/01-31/12
Remarks: Near entrance and pay-desk of Valle dei Templi.

| 📷S | Augusta | 33C3 |

Area Attrezzata Camper Nelly, SS114 - Km 118,5, Contrada Agnone Bagni. **GPS:** n37,31148 e15,09260.
🏕 13, July € 14, Aug € 15/day 🚰🔌Ch 🚿WC 🛢included.
🔲 01/01-31/12
Distance: 🏖6km.

| 📷S | Caccamo | 33B3 |

SS 285. **GPS:** n37,93410 e13,66115. ⬆.
10 🏕free 🚰🔌Ch 🚿free. **Location:** Simple.
Surface: gravel/metalled.
Distance: 🏖900m 🍴300m.

| 📷S | Caltagirone 🌸 | 33C3 |

Piazzale San Giovanni, Loc. San Giovanni.
GPS: n37,23949 e14,50717. ⬆.
🏕free. **Surface:** asphalted. 🔲 01/01-31/12
Distance: 🏖historical centre 700m.

| 📷S | Caltanissetta | 33B3 |

Via Guastaferro. **GPS:** n37,48959 e14,04515. ⬆➡.
25 🏕free 🚰🔌Ch free. **Location:** Urban, simple, noisy.
Surface: asphalted.
Distance: 🏖2km 🍴on the spot 🍴on the spot.

| 📷S | Castelbuono | 33B3 |

Via Guiseppe Mazzini. **GPS:** n37,93694 e14,09296. ⬆.
10 🏕free 🚰🔌Ch. **Location:** Simple, quiet.
Distance: 🏖700m 🍴700m.

| 📷S | Castellammare del Golfo | 33B3 |

Playtime, Viale Leonardo da Vinci, SS187.
GPS: n38,02494 e12,89086. ⬆➡.
🏕€ 15/24h 🚰🔌Ch 🚿WC 🛢🔲. **Surface:** grassy.
Distance: 🏖200m 🍴1km.

| 📷S | Castelluzzo | 33B3 |

Parcheggio Trinacria, Via Calazza. **GPS:** n38,10694 e12,72861. ⬆➡.

± 40 🏕against payment 🚰🔌🚿. **Surface:** gravel. 🔲 summer
Distance: 🏊400m 🍴500m 🍴500m.
Remarks: Beach parking.

| 📷 | Castelluzzo | 33B3 |

Parking Macari, SP16. **GPS:** n38,13564 e12,73638.

🏕free. **Surface:** sand.

| 📷 | Castelluzzo | 33B3 |

SP16. **GPS:** n38,12166 e12,72666.

🏕free. **Surface:** gravel.
Distance: 🏊on the spot.
Remarks: Beach parking, beach train.

| 📷S | Enna 🏛 | 33B3 |

Ennacamper, C/da S.Giuseppe, Pergusa. **GPS:** n37,52277 e14,29000. ⬆.
30 🏕€ 20/24h 🚰🔌ChService €5 🚿€4 📶.
Location: Simple. **Surface:** sand.
Remarks: Free shuttle, cleaning motorhome € 5.

| 📷S | Francavilla di Sicilia | 33C3 |

Maremonti, Via Cappuccini. **GPS:** n37,90855 e15,14347. ⬆➡.

±50 🏕gift 🚰. **Surface:** unpaved. 🔲 01/01-31/12
Distance: 🏖400m 🏊Riverbed.
Remarks: Gole dell'Alcantara 6km.

| 📷S | Furnari 🏖 | 33C2 |

Tonnarella, Corso Palermo 6. **GPS:** n38,13218 e15,12469. ⬆.

44 🏕€ 13-24 🚰🔌Ch 🚿WCincluded 🛢€0,50 🔲€4.
Location: Simple. **Surface:** gravel. 🔲 01/01-31/12
Distance: 🏖on the spot 🏊on the spot 🍴150m 🍴250m.
Remarks: Monitored parking, excursion to the Eolie-islands.

IT

Gangi 🌺⛰ 33B3

SS14. **GPS:** n37,79203 e14,21079.⬆
15 🛏free 🚰🔌Ch🚿free. **Surface:** gravel/sand.
🅿 01/01-31/12
Distance: 🛒750m ⊗750m.

Gela 33B3

Meridiana Park, Via Torre di Manfria, Contrada Piano Marina.
GPS: n37,11166 e14,12444.⬆➡
80 🛏€ 15/day 🚰🔌Ch🚿WC🗑. **Surface:** grassy.
Distance: 🛒Gela 14km 🏖1,2km.
Remarks: Swimming pool, sandy beach.

Giardini Naxos 🏖🌊 33C3

Parking Lagani, Via Stralcina 22, zona Recanati.
GPS: n37,82092 e15,26753.⬆⬆

30 🛏€ 15-30 🔌Ch🚿WCincluded 🗑€1,(summer) 🔲€5 📶.
Surface: metalled. 🅿 01/01-31/12
Distance: 🛒on the spot 🏖200m 🌊50m 🚰200m 🚌 Bus to Taormina 300m.
Remarks: Special tariff for long stay during the winter, bar, view on Etna and Taormina.

Giardini Naxos 🏖🌊 33C3

Eden Parking, Via Stracina. **GPS:** n37,82188 e15,26701.⬆

30 🛏€ 7-25 🔌Ch🚿€0,35/kWh WC🗑€1 📶. **Surface:** grassy.
🅿 01/01-31/12
Distance: 🏖500m 🚐> Taormina.

Giardini Naxos 🏖🌊 33C3

Holiday Sun, Viale Stracina 20. **GPS:** n37,82109 e15,26784.
30 🛏€ 7-25 🚰🔌Ch🚿WC🗑 📶. **Surface:** grassy/gravel.
Distance: 🏖beach 500m ⊗on the spot 🚐> Taormina.

Tourist information Giardini Naxos:
🚶 🅿 Sa-morning.

Ispica 33C3

Associazione Camper Club Porto Ulisse.
GPS: n36,69761 e14,98647.⬆
🛏🚰🔌Ch🚿. **Surface:** grassy. 🅿 01/01-31/12
Distance: 🏖100m.

Licata 🌊 33B3

Ristorante La Sorgente, Loc. Pisciotto.
GPS: n37,12666 e13,85194.⬆➡

80 🛏Jun € 15, Jul € 20, Aug € 25 🚰🔌Ch🚿WC🗑included.
Surface: gravel.
Distance: 🛒Licata 9km 🏖on the spot ⊗on the spot.
Remarks: Stairs to sandy beach.

Marina di Ragusa 🏖🌊 33C3

Marina Caravan, Via Portovenere 57. **GPS:** n36,78472 e14,56486.⬆

58 🛏€ 10, 01/06-30/09 € 17,50 🚰🔌Ch🚿WC🗑included 🔲€4 📶.
Surface: grassy. 🅿 01/01-31/12
Distance: 🛒500m 🏖300m ⊗100m 🚰100m 🚐200m.
Remarks: Water/drainage at each pitch.

Marina di Ragusa 🏖🌊 33C3

Tanto per Camper, Via Donnalucata. **GPS:** n36,78944 e14,56666.⬆➡

40 🛏15/9-14/6 € 10, 15/6-26/7 € 14, 27/7-30/8 € 18, 2 pers.incl 🚰🔌Ch🚿WCincluded 🗑€1 🔲€4. **Surface:** grassy/gravel.
🅿 01/01-31/12
Distance: 🛒800m 🏖1,5km ⊗100m 🚰800m.
Remarks: Beachshuttle € 0,50.

Marsala 33A3

Beach Sibiliana, Contrada Fossarunza 205/z 14.
GPS: n37,73520 e12,47497.⬆
100 🛏€ 20 🚰🔌Ch🚿WC🗑 📶included. **Surface:** unpaved.
Distance: 🏖50m.

Marsala 33A3

Nautisub Club S. Teodoro, Contrada Birgi.
GPS: n37,91046 e12,46178.⬆➡

± 50 🛏€ 15/20 🚰🔌Ch🚿. **Surface:** grassy. 🅿 01/05-30/09
Distance: 🛒5km 🏖Sandy beach ⊗on the spot.

Marsala 33A3

Via Colonnello Maltese. **GPS:** n37,79497 e12,43270.
🛏free 🚰🔌Ch. **Surface:** asphalted. 🅿 01/01-31/12
Distance: 🛒500m 🏖on the spot.

Mineo 🏛 33C3

Le Bave di Bacco, Strada Provinciale 86. **GPS:** n37,24137 e14,72239.⬆
🛏customers free 🔌📶. **Location:** Rural, simple, isolated.
Surface: grassy. 🅿 01/01-31/12

Montallegro 33B3

Vizzi Parking, Via Lungomare, SP87. **GPS:** n37,38206 e13,30932.
🛏€ 15 🚰€3🔌Ch🚿€2. **Surface:** gravel. 🅿 01/06-01/10
Distance: 🏖100m.

Montallegro 33B3

Agriturismo Torre Salsa, Bove Marina.
GPS: n37,37583 e13,32222.⬆➡

20 🛏€ 17-24 🚰€4🔌Ch🚿according consumption WC🗑€1 🔲€6 📶€1,50/h. **Surface:** grassy. 🅿 01/01-31/12
Distance: 🏖700m.

Remarks: Also pitches on the beach without service, estate 300 acres, hiking and mountain bike trails.

Montevago 33B3

Agricamper Mastragostino - Villa dei Pini.
GPS: n37,70083 e12,98000.
🛏€ 15 🚰🔌Ch🚿included. 🅿 01/01-31/12
Distance: 🛒200m.

Montevago 33B3

Centro Terme Acqua Pia, Loc. Acque Calde. **GPS:** n37,70602 e12,98092.
20 🛏🚰🔌against payment. 🅿 01/04-31/10

Motta Camastra 🌺 33C3

S185, fraz. Ficarazzi. **GPS:** n37,87876 e15,17615.⬆

10 🛏€ 10, Jul/Aug € 15 🚰🔌Ch🚿WC🗑included.
Surface: grassy/gravel.
Distance: ⊗300m 🏖1km.
Remarks: In front of entrance of Gole dell'Alcantara.

Mussomeli 33B3

Piazzale Mongibello. **GPS:** n37,58343 e13,74956.
🛏free 🚰🔌Ch.
Distance: 🛒historical centre.

Noto 33C3

Airone, Via San Corrado, Lido di Noto. **GPS:** n36,85916 e15,11555.⬆➡

50 🛏Jun/Sep € 14-16, Aug € 18 🚰🔌Ch🚿€2 WC🗑hot shower€ 0,50. **Surface:** grassy/sand. 🅿 01/04-30/09
Distance: 🛒100m ⊗100m 🚰750m 🚌Bus to Noto 100m.

Noto 33C3

Il Canneto, Viale Lido di Noto, Lido di Noto.
GPS: n36,86083 e15,11944.⬆➡

55 🛏€ 10-18 🚰🔌Ch🚿€2 WC🗑.
Surface: grassy/sand.
Distance: 🏖on the spot 🚰1,2km.
Remarks: Bread-service and meals, direct access to the sandy beach.

Noto 33C3

NotoParking, Contrada Faldino, Noto. **GPS:** n36,88353 e15,08595.⬆➡

40 🛏€ 18 🚰🔌Ch🚿€3 WC🗑€1. **Surface:** grassy/gravel.
🅿 01/01-31/12
Distance: 🛒1km 🏖3km ⊗200m 🚰200m.
Remarks: Organised excursions in the surroundings, free shuttle bus to Noto.

IT

Noto — 33C3

Oasi Park Falconara, Viale Ionio, Lido di Noto.
GPS: n36,87001 e15,12872.⬆
50 € 15, 01/06-31/10 € 16-20 Ch WC included.
Surface: gravel. 01/01-31/12
Distance: Noto 4km beach 700m pizzeria 50m.
Remarks: Shuttle bus to Noto and beach.

Noto — 33C3

Parcheggio Calamosche, Oasi di Vendicari.
GPS: n36,81611 e15,09888.⬆➡

40-50 € 14 WC included. **Surface:** grassy.
01/06-30/09
Distance: Noto 10km 20 min walking bar/restaurant.

Oliveri — 33C2

Azimut Sosta Camper, Corso Cristoforo Colombo.
GPS: n38,12840 e15,05833.⬆
100 € 12-15-20-22 Ch (100x),6Amp WC included.
Location: Comfortable. **Surface:** grassy/gravel. 01/03-31/10
Distance: 500m, Tindari 1,2km 2,5km beach 50m 50m
50m 200m 10m 100m 100m 200m.

Pachino — 33C3

Dragomar, Strada Marzamemi Portopalo di Capo Passero, Marzamemi.
GPS: n36,72732 e15,12083.⬆➡

30 € 10-15 Ch WC. **Surface:** gravel.
01/01-31/12
Distance: on the spot 400m 600m.
Remarks: Seaview, no beach.

Pachino — 33C3

La Cabana Service, Viale le Aloha, Contrada Granelli.
GPS: n36,70562 e15,00689.⬆➡

200 € 15, Jul/Aug € 20 Ch WC included hot shower € 1.
Surface: grassy/sand. 01/01-31/12
Distance: Pachino 7km on the spot on the spot.
Remarks: Bar, sandy beach.

Palermo — 33B3

Green Car Palermo, Via Quarto dei Mille 11b.
GPS: n38,11016 e13,34307.⬆
€ 20/24h Ch included. **Location:** Simple.
Surface: asphalted.
Distance: piazza Indipendenza 300m.

Palermo — 33B3

Parking Ospedale Cervello, Via Trabucco. **GPS:** n38,15619 e13,31354.
Location: Simple, isolated.
Remarks: Nearby hospital.

Palermo — 33B3

Via Uditore 17. **GPS:** n38,13140 e13,32515.⬆
Ch WC. **Surface:** gravel.
Remarks: Monitored parking, shuttle bus to city centre.

Palermo — 33B3

Piazza Alcide De Gasperi. **GPS:** n38,15170 e13,33944.
free. **Surface:** asphalted.
Distance: on the spot.
Remarks: Nearby stadium.

Palermo — 33B3

Freesbee Parking, Via Imperatore Federico 116.
GPS: n38,14722 e13,35277.⬆
100 € 15-18 Ch WC € 1. **Surface:** asphalted.
Distance: Cathedral Palermo 400m 2km 150m.
Remarks: At motorhome dealer, 24/24 surveillance.

Tourist information Palermo:
U.I.A.T. (Ufficio Informazioni e di Accoglienza Turistica), Piazza Castelnuovo, 34, www.regione.sicilia.it/turismo. Capital of Sicily, port and economical heart of the Island.
San Giovanni degli Eremiti.
Santa Catarina.
Vucciria, Via Cassari-Argenteria. Palermo's most famous, picturesque and historic market.

Piazza Armerina — 33B3

Via G. Lo Giudice. **GPS:** n37,38711 e14,37041.
free. **Location:** Simple. **Surface:** asphalted. 01/01-31/12
Distance: 200m.

Piazza Armerina — 33B3

Agricamper Valle Dell'Elsa, SS65. **GPS:** n37,30173 e14,39605.
12 € 15/24h Ch WC included. **Location:** Rural, comfortable, isolated, quiet. **Surface:** metalled. 01/01-31/12
Distance: Piazza Armerina 20km on the spot.

Piazza Armerina — 33B3

Agriturismo Agricasale, Contrada Ciavarina.
GPS: n37,34032 e14,38840.
40 € 15 Ch included.
Location: Rural, comfortable, isolated, quiet.
Distance: Piazza Armerina 13km bar/restaurant.
Remarks: Swimming pool € 3/pppd.

Piazza Armerina — 33B3

Agriturismo Gigliotto, SS 117bis km60. **GPS:** n37,29051 e14,38721.
20 € 20, 01/04-31/10 € 30 Ch WC included.
Location: Comfortable, quiet. **Surface:** gravel. 01/01-31/12
Distance: Piazza Armerina 13km.
Remarks: Swimming pool incl.

Piazza Armerina — 33B3

SP90. **GPS:** n37,36805 e14,33421.⬆
20 € 15/24h Ch included. **Location:** Simple.
01/01-31/12
Distance: Piazza Armerina 4,5km on the spot.
Remarks: Villa Romana del Casale 400m.

Porto Empedocle — 33B3

Punta Piccola Park, Scala dei Turchi, SP68.
GPS: n37,28916 e13,49250.⬆➡

99 € 15-20, 01/07-31/08 € 23 Ch (65x) WC € 1
included. **Surface:** gravel. 01/01-31/12
Distance: 2,5km on the spot 200m 1km.
Remarks: Shopping service, direct access to the sandy beach.

Tourist information Porto Empedocle:
Valle dei Templi, Agrigento. The Valley of The Temples, archeology.

Portopalo di Capo Passero — 33C3

Cicogna. GPS: n36,68333 e15,13638.➡
20 Jun/Sep € 10, Jul/Aug € 15 Ch (20x) included.
Surface: gravel.
Distance: 50m sandy beach 300m.

Pozzallo — 33C3

Il Giardino di Epicuro, SP67. **GPS:** n36,73128 e14,86240.⬆➡

50 € 8, Jun € 10, Jul/Aug € 13 Ch (22x)€2 cold shower.
Surface: grassy/sand. 01/05-30/09
Distance: 500m on the spot 50m 300m.
Remarks: Sandy beach.

Pozzallo — 33C3

Salvamar, Zona Porto di Pozzallo. **GPS:** n36,71541 e14,82240.⬆

30 € 10-€ 20 (Aug) Ch €3 €1. **Surface:** grassy.
01/01-31/12
Distance: 200m 500m 1km.

Realmonte — 33B3

Sosta camper Zanzibar, C/o Capo Rossello.
GPS: n37,29495 e13,45438.⬆➡

100 € 12-22, 01/10-30/03 € 10 Ch WC included hot shower € 1. **Surface:** gravel. 01/01-31/12
Distance: sandy beach on the spot 150m.
Remarks: Bus to Valle dei Templi (€ 7/pp, min. 4 pers).

Reitano — 33B3

Via Lungomare Colonna. **GPS:** n38,01407 e14,33081.⬆
70 €10 Ch €0,50. **Location:** Simple. 15/07-18/09
Distance: 500m on the spot.

Ribera — 33B3

Kamemi, SS115, Secca Grande. **GPS:** n37,43840 e13,24469.
Camperstop € 8 Ch.
01/01-31/12 01/08-24/08 No Camperstop

Roccalumera — 33C3

Park Jonio, Via Collegio, SS114 Roccalumera > Nizza di Sicilia.
GPS: n37,97943 e15,39752.⬆➡

60 € 13/24h, Jul/Aug € 15 Ch (60x). **Surface:** gravel.
Distance: within walking distance 250m Bar/snack on the spot.
Remarks: In front of Centro Sportivo.

San Giovanni La Punta — 33C3

Entertainmentcity Isivillage, Via Fisichelli 63.
GPS: n37,58929 e15,08612.
guests free. **Surface:** asphalted.

San Vito Lo Capo — 33B3

Via Faro 36. **GPS:** n38,18472 e12,73277.

30 ⌁Jun € 15, Jul € 20, Aug € 25 ⚡🔌Ch🚿included ⬛hot shower €
1. **Surface:** asphalted/grassy.
Distance: 🚶1km 🏖on the spot ⊗300m 🛒1km.
Remarks: Terrace on the sea, no beach, sandy beach 400m.

| 🏕S | San Vito Lo Capo | 33B3 |

Via Savoia 13. **GPS:** n38,16222 e12,73666.⬆.

90 ⌁€ 10, Jun € 12, Jul € 15, Aug € 18 ⚡🔌Ch🚿(90x) WC⬛€0,50
⬛€5. **Surface:** gravel. ◻ 01/01-31/12
Distance: 🚶300m 🏖1,4km ⊗1km 🛒1km.
Remarks: Free shuttle to beach.

| 🏕 | San Vito Lo Capo | 33B3 |

Via la Piana. **GPS:** n38,16886 e12,74307.

⌁free. **Surface:** unpaved.
Distance: 🚶800m 🏖800m.
Remarks: Free shuttle to centre.

| 🏕S | Scicli | 33C3 |

Club Piccadilly, Via Mare Adriatico, Donnalucata.
GPS: n36,74750 e14,66306.⬆.
⌁€ 15-30 ⚡🔌Ch🚿WC⬛📶. ◻ 01/01-31/12
Distance: 🚶3km 🏖sandy beach 100m.

| 🏕S | Scopello | 33B3 |

Fontana Andrea, Contrada Ciauli, SS 187.
GPS: n38,05492 e12,84290.⬆.
⌁€ 12/24h ⚡🔌Ch🚿included. **Surface:** grassy.
◻ 01/04-01/10
Distance: 🏖beach 300m.

| 🏕S | Scopello | 33B3 |

Azienda agricola Plaia Antonella, Fraz. Scopello.
GPS: n38,06777 e12,81777.⬆➡.

50 ⌁€ 20/24h ⚡🔌Ch🚿included ⬛€1. **Surface:** gravel.
◻ 01/05-30/09
Distance: 🚶historical centre 200m 🏖1,5km ⊗100m 🛒400m.
Remarks: Farm products, shuttle to beach and Riserva dello Zingaro
€ 2,50/pp.

| | Siracusa | 33C3 |

Parcheggio Von Platen, Via Augusto Von Platen 38.
GPS: n37,07692 e15,28738.
⌁€ 0,90/h.
Remarks: Near archeological site and museum.

| 🏕S | Siracusa | 33C3 |

Via Procione 6, zona Golfetto, Fontane Bianche.
GPS: n36,96361 e15,22027.⬆.
⌁€ 20 ⚡🔌Ch🚿WC⬛. **Surface:** unpaved.
Distance: 🚶Siracusa 15km 🏖on the spot 🚍on the spot.
Remarks: Bus to Siracusa, natural swimming pool in sea.

| 🏕 | Siracusa | 33C3 |

Area sosta Siracusa, Via Rodi 15. **GPS:** n37,06436 e15,28710.
⌁€ 0,60/h, night € 1. **Surface:** asphalted. ◻ 01/01-31/12
Distance: 🚶Ortigia 500m ⊗50m.

| 🏕S | Sutera | 33B3 |

Piazza Rettore Carruba. **GPS:** n37,52450 e13,72960.⬆.
⌁free ⚡🔌Ch. **Surface:** asphalted.
Distance: 🚶on the spot ⊗on the spot.

| 🏕S | Taormina 🌿 | 33C3 |

Sosta Camper Pier Giovanni, Trappitello, Via Spagnuolo.
GPS: n37,82196 e15,24502.

15 ⌁€ 10-15 ⚡🔌Ch🚿WC⬛included. **Surface:** grassy/metalled.
◻ 01/01-31/12
Distance: 🚶500m 🏖4km 🛒300m 🚍300m.

| 🏕S | Terme Vigliatore 〰 | 33C2 |

Area Trinacria, Via Lungomare Marchesana.
GPS: n38,14018 e15,14596.⬆⬆.

120 ⌁€ 15, Aug € 18 ⚡🔌Ch🚿⬛included. **Surface:** grassy.
◻ 01/01-31/12
Distance: 🏖50m ⊗pizzeria 200m 🛒200m.
Remarks: Excursion to the Eolie-islands.

| 🍴S | Trapani | 33A3 |

Hotel Le Saline, SP21 km4, contrada Nubia-Paceco.
GPS: n37,98304 e12,53106.
20 ⌁€ 15-20 ⚡🔌Ch🚿⬛📶. **Surface:** metalled.

⬛ Luxembourg

Capital: Luxembourg
Government: Grand duchy
Official Language: French, German,
Luxembourgish
Population: 562.000 (2015)
Area: 2,586 km²

General information

Calling code: 00352
General emergency: 112
Currency: Euro

Regulations for overnight stays

Parking overnight and camping by public
road is forbidden. Motorhome-service only on
campsites.

Additional public holidays 2016

May 1 Labor day
June 6 National Holiday
August 15 Assumption of the Virgin Mary
November 1 All Saints' Day

Time Zone

Winter (Standard Time) GMT+1
Summer (DST) GMT+2

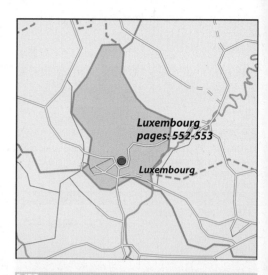

Luxembourg pages: 552-553
Luxembourg

©S Berdorf 15E1

Camperhafen Martbusch, 3, Beim Martbusch.
GPS: n49,82660 e6,34599. ↑→.

9 🅿€ 8-10 ⛽€1/100liter 🚽Ch ⚡€0,50/kWh 🚿€3 📶.
Location: Rural, comfortable, quiet. **Surface:** asphalted.
📅 01/01-31/12
Distance: 🚶500m 🏊on the spot ⚓7km �̲500m 🚲on the spot
🏃on the spot.
Remarks: Max. 2 nights, check in at reception campsite.

©S Bleesbrück 15E1

Camping Bleesbrück, 1, Bleesbreck. **GPS:** n49,87270 e6,18940.

2+2 🅿€ 13 ⛽🚽Ch ⚡WC 📶included.
Location: Rural, simple, noisy. **Surface:** grassy.
📅 01/04-15/10
Distance: 🚶2,5km 🏊on the spot ⚓2,5km.
Remarks: Arrival >18h departure <9h, if not camping tariff.

©S Diekirch 🔀 15E1

Camping de la Sûre, Route de Gilsdorf.
GPS: n49,86597 e6,16489. ↑→.

8 🅿€ 12-€ 15 🚽Ch ⚡WC included,sanitary only summer
📅€3 📶free 🚿. **Location:** Comfortable, central. **Surface:** grasstiles.
📅 01/01-31/12
Distance: 🚶100m 🏊100m 🚲100m (permit € 4/month) 🏊100m
⚓100m.
Remarks: Max. 2 days.
Tourist information Diekirch:
Ⓜ Conservatoire National de véhicules historique, 20-22, rue de
Stavelot. Exhibition of historical vehicles. 📅 10-18h 🚫 Mo.
Ⓜ Musée National de l'histoire militaire, 10, Bamertal. War museum.

📅 01/04-31/10 10-18h, 01/11-31/03 14-18h.
🌞 Rue de Marché. 📅 Tue 8-12h.
🌞 Al Dikkirch. Folk festival. 📅 2nd week Jul.

©S Dudelange 15E1

Parking Gare-Usines. GPS: n49,47176 e6,07772. ↑→.

8 🅿free ⛽🚽Chfree. **Location:** Simple, noisy.
Surface: grasstiles/grassy. 📅 01/01-31/12
Distance: 🚶1km 🏊4,1km ⚓near train station.
Remarks: Well situated for visiting Luxembourg city, 20min by train,
max. 48h.
Tourist information Dudelange:
Ⓜ Musée National des Mines de Fer, carreau de la Mine, Rumelange.
History of the mines. 📅 14-17h. 🎫 € 7,50.

©S Echternach 🔀 15E1

Impasse des Bénédictins. **GPS:** n49,80983 e6,42901.

🅿free ⛽🚽Chfree. **Surface:** metalled.
Tourist information Echternach:
🌞 Sprangprossessioun. Dancing procession. 📅 Tue after Whitsuntide.

⚠S Ermsdorf 🔀 15E1

Neumühle. **GPS:** n49,83917 e6,22503.
🅿€ 16-20,50 ⛽🚽Ch ⚡WC €4 📶included. **Location:** Rural,
comfortable, isolated, quiet. **Surface:** grassy. 📅 15/03-31/10
Distance: 🚶1km 🏊on the spot ⚓6km.

©S Heiderscheid 15E1

Camperhafen Fuussekaul, Fuussekaul 4.
GPS: n49,87806 e5,99278. ↑→.
35 🅿€ 10, Jul/Aug € 15 ⛽🚽Ch ⊞ ⚡(35x),16Amp WCincluded
€1/5minutes 📅€4/2,50 📶€4,90/day 🚿. **Location:** Luxurious,
isolated, quiet. **Surface:** grasstiles/metalled. 📅 01/01-31/12
Distance: 🚶1km 🏊8km 🏊8km 🚲5km 🏊on the spot 🏊on the spot
⚓on the spot 🏃on the spot.
Tourist information Heiderscheid:
🌞 Heischter Mart. Traditional market. 📅 end Jul.

⌂S Hoscheid 🔀 10E3

Hotel-Restaurant Des Ardennes, Haaptstrooss.
GPS: n49,94675 e6,08084. ↑.

4 🅿free with a meal ⛽⚡WC 📶included 📹.
Location: Simple, quiet. **Surface:** asphalted. 📅 01/02-15/12
Distance: 🚶on the spot 🏊on the spot ⚓on the spot.
Remarks: Parking behind hotel.

⌂S Junglinster 15E1

Rue Emile Nilles. **GPS:** n49,70421 e6,25123. ↑→.

LU

3 ⏚free 🚰€0,10/10liter ⚡Ch ☕(4x)€0,50/kWh. **Location:** Simple.
Surface: asphalted. ⬛ 01/01-31/12
Distance: 🚶200m.

Liefrange 15E1

Camperhafen Leifreg, 14, Haaptstrooss. **GPS:** n49,91136 e5,87438. ⬆.

24 ⏚€ 10, Jul/Aug € 16 🚰⚡Ch ☕WCincluded ⏚€1.
Location: Rural, isolated, quiet. **Surface:** grasstiles/metalled.
⬛ 01/04-01/11
Distance: 🚶on the spot ⚓Obersauer Stausee 500m ⊗on the spot.

Luxemburg 15E1

Glacis, Boulevard de la Foire /Av. de la Faiencerie.
GPS: n49,61602 e6,12246.

20 ⏚Mo-Fr € 0,80/h.
Location: Urban, simple, noisy.
Surface: asphalted.
⬛ 01/01-31/12
Distance: 🚶centre 650m 🚌on the spot.
Remarks: Overnight stay allowed.

Tourist information Luxemburg:
🛈 Luxembourg City Tourist Office, Place d'Armes, www.lcto.lu. Citadel and fortifications have been changed in parks and walks, especially in the lower city.
⬛ 01/04-31/10 Mo-Sa 9-19h, Su 10-18h, 01/11-31/03 Mo-Sa 9-18h.
👁 Casemates du Bock, Montée de Clausen. Casemates, 21km.
⬛ 01/03-31/10 10-17h.
Ⓜ Musée National d'histoire et d'art, marché-aux-Poissons. Archeological findings. ⬛ Tue-Su 10-17h.
🏰 Palais Grand Ducal, 17, rue du Marché-aux-Herbes. Ducal palace.
⬛ 01/07-31/08.
✝ Cathédrale Notre-Dame, Rue Notre Dame. ⬛ daily 10-12h, 14-17.30h. 🎫 free.
∩ Crypte Archéologique, Montée de Clausen.
⬛ 01/03-31/10 10-17h.
🎪 Marché-aux-puces, place d'Armes. Bric-a-brac.
⬛ 2nd + 4th Sa of the month.
🎪 Markt, place Guillaume. ⬛ Wed + Sa morning.
☀ Schueberfouer. Folk festival. ⬛ 30/08-15/09.

Mersch 15E1

Um Krounebierg. **GPS:** n49,74403 e6,09075. ⬆.

5 ⏚€ 16,50-20,30 + € 0,75/pp tourist tax 🚰⚡Ch ☕WC⏚◉€6
📶included. **Location:** Rural, comfortable, quiet. **Surface:** gravel.
⬛ 15/03-31/10
Distance: 🚶1km ⊗on the spot ⚐on the spot 🚌on the spot 🚲on the spot ⚲on the spot.

Nommern 15E1

Europacamping Nommerlayen, Rue Nommerlayen.
GPS: n49,78450 e6,16414. ⬆➡.

---

3 ⏚7,50-10, winter free 🚰⚡Ch ☕€2/2kWh WC◉€5,25/4,75
📶included. **Location:** Rural, comfortable, isolated, quiet.
Surface: grasstiles.
⬛ 01/01-13/12 ◉ water disconnected in winter
Distance: 🚶1km ⊗on the spot ⚐on the spot 🚌1,5km ⚲on the spot.

Obereisenbach 10E3

Kohnenhof. **GPS:** n50,01630 e6,13682. ⬆➡.

12 ⏚€ 14 🚰⚡Ch ☕WC⏚included 📶€ 10.
Location: Rural, comfortable, isolated, quiet.
Surface: grasstiles/metalled. ⬛ 01/04-01/11
Distance: 🚶4km ⚓on the spot ⚐on the spot ⊗on the spot ⚲9km 🚌on the spot ⚲on the spot.

Redange/Attert 15E1

Rue de la Piscine 24. **GPS:** n49,76918 e5,89459. ⬆➡.

12 ⏚free 🚰⚡Ch ☕(5x)free. **Location:** Rural, simple, quiet.
Surface: asphalted. ⬛ 01/01-31/12
Distance: 🚶800m ⚲on the spot.
Remarks: Max. 48h.

Schwebsange 15E1

Camport, Rue du Port. **GPS:** n49,51163 e6,36249. ⬆.

18 ⏚€ 10, 2 pers.incl 🚰⚡Ch ☕€2,50 WC⏚◉€2 📶included,at restaurant 🍴. **Location:** Rural, comfortable, quiet. **Surface:** grasstiles.
⬛ 01/04-15/10
Distance: 🚶500m ⚐fishing permit obligatory ⊗on the spot ⚲on the spot 🚌500m.

Tourist information Schwebsange:
Ⓜ A Possen, 1 rue Aloyse Sandt, Bech-Kleinmacher. Folkore and wine museum. ⬛ 01/05-31/10 14-19h, 01/03-30/04, 01/11-31/12 Fri-Su 14-19h ◉ Mo.

Vianden 15E1

39, rue du Sanatorium. **GPS:** n49,93717 e6,20556. ⬆.

3 ⏚free. **Location:** Simple, central, quiet. **Surface:** asphalted.
⬛ 01/01-31/12
Distance: 🚶500m ⚐100m ⊗500m ⚲500m 🚌on the spot 🚲on the spot ⚲on the spot.
Remarks: At the chair-lifts (télesiege).

Tourist information Vianden:
👁 SEO. Large hydro-electric power-station. ⬛ Easter-Sep 10-20h.
🎫 free.
Ⓜ Bakkerij museum, Grand rue 96-98. ⬛ Easter-Oct 11-17h ◉ Mo.
🏰 Château de Vianden. ⬛ 01/04-30/09 10-18h, 01/10-31/03 10-16h
◉ 02/11, 25/12, 01/01.
🎪 Nessmoort. Nuts market. ⬛ 2nd Su Oct.
😀 Télesiège. Chair-lift. ⬛ Easter-Oct.

Wiltz 10E3

Kaul, Rue Joseph Simon. **GPS:** n49,97173 e5,93433. ⬆.

3 ⏚free 🚰€1 ⚡Ch ☕. **Location:** Rural, simple, isolated, quiet.
Surface: gravel. ⬛ 01/01-31/12
Distance: 🚶500m ⊗500m.
Remarks: Recreation park, near campsite.

LU

Montenegro

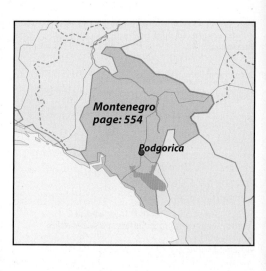

Montenegro
page: 554

Podgorica

Capital: Podgorica
Government: parliamentary republic
Official Language: Montenegrin
Population 650,000 (2014)
Area: 13,812 Km²

General information
Dialling code: 0382
General emergency: 112
Currency: Euro
Credit cards are accepted almost everywhere.

Regulations for overnight stays
Free overnight stay is not allowed.

Additional public holidays 2016
January 7-8 Christmas (Orthodox)
May 1 Labour Day
May 21 Independence Day
July 13 Statehood Day

Time Zone
Winter (Standard Time) GMT+1
Summer (DST) GMT+2

△ S | Bijela | 37C2
Zlokovic. GPS: n42,45768 e18,66873.
50 ⌁ € 21 ⌁ ⌁ Ch included. **Surface:** grassy/sand. ☐ 01/03-01/11
Distance: ⌁2km ⌁on the spot ⌁on the spot ⊗on the spot.

△ S | Dobrilovina | 37C2
Kamp Eco Oaza. GPS: n43,01780 e19,40936.
25 ⌁ € 15 ⌁ ⌁ Ch included.
Location: Rural. **Surface:** grassy. ☐ 01/01-31/12
Distance: ⌁200m ⚹ on the spot.

⌁ | Gusinje | 37C2
Krojet. GPS: n42,55053 e19,82502. ⬆.
15 ⌁ € 10. **Location:** Rural. **Surface:** grassy. ☐ 01/04-30/10
Distance: ⊗on the spot.

⌁ S | Kotor | 37C2
E65. GPS: n42,42761 e18,76881. ⬆.
20 ⌁ € 1/h Ch free.
Location: Urban. **Surface:** gravel. ☐ 01/01-31/12
Distance: ⌁500m ⌁on the spot ⌁on the spot ⊗200m ⌁200m.

△ S | Morinj | 37C2
Naluka. GPS: n42,48694 e18,65214.
40 ⌁ € 20 ⌁ ⌁ Ch included.
Surface: grassy/sand. ☐ 01/05-01/10
Distance: ⌁on the spot ⌁on the spot ⊗600m.

△ S | Petnjica | 37C2
Jatak. GPS: n42,97815 e19,07510.
10 ⌁ € 10 ⌁ ⌁ Ch included. ⌁ € 2 ⌁ € 2.
Surface: grassy. ☐ 01/06-01/09
Distance: ⊗on the spot.

△ S | Petrovac | 37C2
Maslina, Buljarica bb 300. **GPS:** n42,19833 e18,96583.
100 ⌁ € 15,60 ⌁ ⌁ Ch included ⌁ € 3 ⌁.
Surface: grassy. ☐ 01/01-31/12
Distance: ⌁2km ⌁200m ⊗300m.

⌁ S | Podgorica | 37C2
Hostel Izvor. GPS: n42,48363 e19,30621. ⬆.
10 ⌁ € 15 ⌁ ⌁ Ch ⌁ ⌁ included.
Surface: concrete. ☐ 01/01-31/12
Distance: ⊗on the spot.

△ S | Rasova | 37C1
Miro Tara-Regata, Djrdjevica Tara. **GPS:** n43,14862 e19,29217.
20 ⌁ € 15 ⌁ ⌁ Ch included.
Surface: grassy/gravel. ☐ 01/04-30/10

△ S | Ulcinj | 37C3
Miami beach. GPS: n41,90870 e19,24978.
30 ⌁ € 20 ⌁ ⌁ Ch ⌁ included.
Surface: grassy/sand. ☐ 01/05-01/10
Distance: ⌁on the spot ⌁on the spot ⊗on the spot.

△ S | Ulcinj | 37C3
Safari beach. GPS: n41,90466 e19,26533.

---

130 ⌁ € 15, 15/6-15/9 € 30 ⌁ ⌁ Ch ⌁ included ☐ € 3 ⌁.
Surface: grassy. ☐ 01/01-31/12
Distance: ⌁7km ⌁on the spot ⌁on the spot ⊗on the spot.

△ S | Utjeha-Bušat | 37C2
Oliva, Uvala Maslina-Utjeha. **GPS:** n42,01028 e19,15111.
25 ⌁ € 15 ⌁ ⌁ Ch ⌁ included. **Surface:** grassy. ☐ 01/04-30/11
Distance: ⌁on the spot ⌁on the spot ⊗on the spot.

△ S | Utjeha-Bušat | 37C2
Utjeha, Uvala Maslina-Utjeha. **GPS:** n42,01012 e19,15095. ⬆.

20 ⌁ € 14, 20/6-1/9 € 16 ⌁ ⌁ Ch ⌁ included ☐ against payment ⌁.
Surface: grassy. ☐ 15/04-01/11
Distance: ⌁on the spot ⌁on the spot ⊗on the spot.

△ S | Žabljak | 37C1
Kod Boce. GPS: n43,14352 e19,11580.
30 ⌁ € 6 ⌁ ⌁ Ch included ⌁ € 2.
Surface: grassy/gravel. ☐ 15/04/30/10

△ S | Žabljak | 37C1
Razvrsje. GPS: n43,14443 e19,11510.
20 ⌁ € 10 ⌁ ⌁ Ch ⌁ included.
Surface: grassy/gravel. ☐ 01/01-31/12
Distance: ⌁900m ⚹ on the spot.

ME

The Netherlands

Capital: Amsterdam
Government: Constitutional monarchy
Official Language: Dutch
Population: 16,961,000 (2014)
Area: 41, 526 km²

General information

Country dial code: 0031
General emergency: 112
Currency: Euro
Credit cards are not accepted everywhere.

Regulations for overnight stays

Wild camping is forbidden in the Netherlands. Several motorhome-friendly municipalities have regulated facilities where overnight parking is allowed.

Additional public holidays 2016

March 28 Easter Monday
April 27 King's day
May 5 Liberation day
May 16 Pentecost Monday
December 26 Boxing day

Time Zone

Winter (Standard Time) GMT+1
Summer (DST) GMT+2

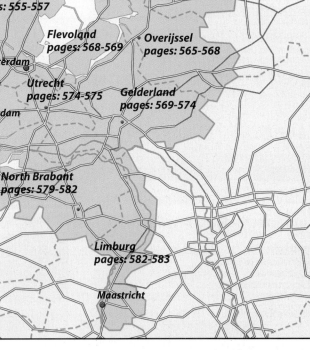

Groningen pages: 561-564
Friesland pages: 557-561
Drenthe pages: 564-565
North Holland pages: 555-557
Flevoland pages: 568-569
Overijssel pages: 565-568
Amsterdam
South Holland pages: 575-577
Utrecht pages: 574-575
Gelderland pages: 569-574
Rotterdam
Zealand pages: 577-579
North Brabant pages: 579-582
Limburg pages: 582-583
Maastricht

NL

North Holland

Abbenes ⚜🏖✈ 8C2

Hoeve 't Groene Hart, Kaagweg 50. **GPS:** n52,22630 e4,61911. ⬆

15 🍴€ 10, Apr-May € 12, 2 pers. incl ⬛🔌Chincluded ⚓(6x) €2/24h,10Amp WC€0,50 🚽€1 📶. 🚿 **Location:** Rural, comfortable, quiet. **Surface:** grassy/gravel. 📅 15/03-01/11
Distance: 🚲4km 🏊900m 🏖1,5km ⛴1,5km ⊗1,5km 🛒4km ⛴Leiden <> Amsterdam 🚌on the spot 🎣on the spot.
Remarks: Bicycle rental € 11/day.

Amsterdam ⚜🏖✈ 8C1

Amsterdam City Camp, Papaverweg 55. **GPS:** n52,39847 e4,90010. ⬆

60 🍴€ 15, Jul/Aug € 20, 2 pers. Incl ⬛€2/100liter 🔌Ch⚓(30x) €3,10Amp 📶included ♻.🚌 **Location:** Urban, comfortable.
Surface: metalled. 📅 01/01-31/12
Distance: 🚲2km 🚌20m ⊗100m 🛒1km 🏪1,5km ⛴500m.
Remarks: Video surveillance, free ferry to city centre.

Amsterdam ⚜🏖✈ 8C1

Fam. Ackermann, Lutkemeerweg 149, Amsterdam-Osdorp.
GPS: n52,36358 e4,77240. ⬆

16 🍴€ 10-12, 2 pers.incl, >7m: +€ 1/m ⬛€3 🔌Ch ⚓€4,50/day. 🚌
Surface: metalled.
📅 01/01-31/12
Distance: 🚲10km city centre 🏪2km 🚋Tram > Amsterdam 1,2km.
Remarks: Via Osdorperweg, special license.

Amsterdam ⚜🏖✈ 8C1

Het Amsterdamse Bos, Kleine Noorddijk 1, Amsterdam-zuid.
GPS: n52,29271 e4,82171.

100 🍴€ 9 + € 5/pp ⬛🔌Ch⚓€4,50 WC🚽 ♻.
📅 15/03-01/12
Distance: 🚲1km 🚌on the spot ⊗on the spot 🏪on the spot 🛒100m.

Tourist information Amsterdam:

ℹ VVV, Stationsplein 10 en Leidseplein 1, www.iamsterdam.com.
City Card gives entrance to museums, public transport, boattrip on the canals etc., 24h/€ 47, 48h/€57, 72h/€ 67, available at VVV.
👁 Canalbus. Boat trip on the canals.
🎫 € 13.
✂ Stelling van Amsterdam. Forts built to protect Amsterdam.
🎡 Albert Cuyp, Albert Cuyp. Market with over 260 stalls.
📅 daily 9-17h 🔘 Su.
🎡 Antiek, Noordermarkt.
📅 Sa 9-17h.
😊 Artis, Plantage Kerklaan 38-40. City-zoo.
📅 9-17/18h.
🛍 Villa Arena, Arena boulevard. Furniture mall, 80 shops.

📅 Tue-Sa 10-18h, Mo 13-18h.

De Rijp ⚓ 8C1

Bloembolbedrijf Stoop, Zuiddijk 34. **GPS:** n52,54813 e4,83416.

4 🍴€ 7 ⬛€1/100liter ⚓(4x)€2/day. 🚌
Location: Rural, simple, quiet. **Surface:** concrete. 📅 01/01-31/12
Distance: 🚲3km 🏖200m 🚌200m ⊗3km 🏪3km.

Den Helder ⚓ 6C3

Willemsoord, Willemsoord 47. **GPS:** n52,96134 e4,76856. ⬆

15 🍴€ 10 ⬛€0,50/80liter 🔌Ch⚓(3x) 🚽€0,50 📶€3.🚌
Location: Simple, central, quiet. **Surface:** metalled.
📅 01/01-31/12
Distance: 🚲400m 🏖300m 🚌300m ⊗400m 🏪1km 🛒600m.
Remarks: Max. 48h, caution key sanitary € 15, ferry boat to Texel 500m.

Den Oever ⚓ 6C3

Haventerrein Oostkade, Oostkade 3. **GPS:** n52,93395 e5,03974. ⬆

10 🛏️€ 10 🚰€0,50/100liter 🗑️€0,50 Ch 💧(8x)WC🚽included.
Location: Highway, simple, isolated, noisy. **Surface:** metalled.
📅 01/01-31/12
Distance: 🚶500m 🚲1,4km 🏊200m 🎣offshore fishing ⊗500m
🍴500m 🛒on the spot.
Remarks: At old harbour, max. 3 days, saturday-morning fishmarket.

🏢S **Enkhuizen** 🌿🪂🚤 **8D1**
Gependam, Dirck Chinaplein. **GPS:** n52,69806 e5,29005.⬆️.

6 🛏️€ 10,50/12-12h 🚰WC€0,20 🗑️€1.🚐
Location: Urban, simple, central. **Surface:** asphalted.
📅 01/01-31/12
Distance: 🚶1km 🏊on the spot 🛒on the spot ⊗100m 🍴1km
☕100m.
Remarks: Max. 48h.

Tourist information Enkhuizen:
Ⓜ Zuiderzeemuseum. Historical little town.
📅 Apr-autumn holiday 10-17/18h.

🏢S **Hoorn** 🌿🚤 **8C1**
Jachthaven Hoorn, Visserseiland 221. **GPS:** n52,63467 e5,05676.⬆️.

20 🛏️€ 13,75 🚰🗑️Ch 💧WC included 🗑️€0,50.🚿🧺
Location: Quiet. **Surface:** metalled. 📅 01/04-31/10
Distance: 🚶500m 🚲2,8km 🏊on the spot ⊗100m 🛒on the spot.
Remarks: Check in at harbourmaster.

🏞️ **Huizen** 🚤 **8D2**
Recreatieterrein Wolskamer, IJsselmeerstraat.
GPS: n52,30860 e5,24046.⬆️.

8 🛏️free. **Location:** Simple, quiet. **Surface:** grassy.
📅 01/01-31/12
Distance: 🚶1km 🏊200m 🛒200m ⊗1km 🍴Lidl 300m
🚤on the spot 🛒on the spot.
Remarks: Max. 48h, service at harbourmaster.

Tourist information Huizen:
⛺ 📅 Sa.

🏞️ **Katwoude** **8C1**
De Simonehoeve, Wagenweg 2. **GPS:** n52,48620 e5,03196.⬆️.

10 🛏️free. **Location:** Simple. **Surface:** asphalted. 📅 01/01-31/12
Distance: 🚶2km 🏊2km 🏊2km 🛒on the spot 🍴2km 🚌100m.
Remarks: Cheese farm, nearby Hotel Volendam, free guided tour.

🏢S **Laren** **8D2**
Sportcomplex De Biezem, Schapendrift 64. **GPS:** n52,25717 e5,23884.

2 🛏️free 🚰🗑️ChWC🚽. **Surface:** metalled. 📅 01/01-31/12
Distance: 🚲1km.
Remarks: Max. 1 night.

🏢S **Medemblik** 🌿🚤 **8D1**
Haven Medemblik, Pekelharinghaven 50. **GPS:** n52,77139 e5,11361.⬆️.

3 🛏️€ 8 + € 0,70/pp tourist tax 🗑️Ch 💧€1,75 🗑️.🚿
Location: Simple, quiet. **Surface:** metalled. 📅 01/01-31/12
Distance: 🚶1km 🏊200m 🛒on the spot ⊗50m 🍴1km 🚤50m
🛒on the spot.
Remarks: Max. 48h, check in at harbourmaster.

Tourist information Medemblik:
Ⓜ Museum Stoomtram. Steam tram museum: Hoorn-Medemblik.

🏢S **Middenmeer** 🚤 **8C1**
Jachthaven Middenmeer, Havenstraat. **GPS:** n52,81236 e4,99112.⬆️.

7 🛏️€ 10 🚰🗑️Ch 💧WC included 🗑️€5/2 🔌€2.
Location: Comfortable. **Surface:** metalled. 📅 01/01-31/12
Distance: 🚶500m 🚲1,7km 🏊50m 🛒50m ⊗500m 🚌150m
🛒on the spot.
Remarks: Max. 48h, check in at harbourmaster.

🏢S **Monnickendam** 🌿🚤 **8C1**
Jachthaven Waterland, Galgeriet 5a. **GPS:** n52,45920 e5,04059.⬆️.

6 🛏️€ 17,50 🚰stay 🗑️Ch 💧€0,50/2kWh WC🚽🗑️€4,50 🔌included.
Location: Urban, simple, quiet. **Surface:** metalled.
📅 30/04-15/10

Distance: 🚶500-800m 🏊on the spot ⊗on the spot.
Remarks: Check in at harbourmaster, caution sepkey € 20, bookings in
peak season.

🏢S **Naarden** 🌿🪂🚤 **8D2**
Jachthaven Naarden, Onderwal 4. **GPS:** n52,30874 e5,14703.⬆️.

10 🛏️€ 12.50 + € 2/pp tourist tax 🚰🗑️Ch 💧WC🚽🗑️€
5/3 🔌included.🚿🧺 **Location:** Rural, comfortable, quiet.
Surface: grassy/metalled. 📅 01/01-31/12
Distance: 🚶Naarden-vesting (fortress) 2,3km 🚲600m
🏊500m lake Gooi ⊗on the spot 🍴on the spot 🚤on the spot.

Tourist information Naarden:
Ⓜ Vestingmuseum. Fortress museum.
📅 01/03-31/10 Tue-Fri 10.30-17h, weekend 12-17h, summer Mo-Fri,
01/11-28/02 Su 12-17h.

🏢S **Nieuw Vennep** **8C2**
Allesonda Hoeve, IJweg 1281. **GPS:** n52,28705 e4,62614.⬆️.
15 🛏️€ 12 🚰🗑️Ch 💧included. **Location:** Rural. **Surface:** metalled.
📅 01/04-01/10
Distance: 🚶1,5km 🏊1,5kmm ⊗1,5km.
Remarks: Only cash payment.

🏞️ **Oosthuizen** **8C1**
Recreatieknooppunt Oosthuizen, Hoornse Jaagweg.
GPS: n52,57609 e4,99719.⬆️.

2 🛏️free. **Location:** Rural, isolated, noisy. **Surface:** asphalted.
📅 01/01-31/12
Distance: 🚶250m 🏊on the spot 🛒on the spot ⊗200m 🍴500m
🚌100m > Volendam 🚤on the spot 🛒on the spot.
Remarks: Max. 48h.

🏢S **Opperdoes** **8C1**
Imkerij de Bijenstal, Zwarte pad. **GPS:** n52,76255 e5,08027.

3 🛏️€ 11,10, 2 pers.incl 🚰stay 💧(2x)€3,50 🔌.🚿
Location: Rural, simple, isolated, quiet. **Surface:** gravel.
Distance: 🚶500m 🚲2km 🏊300m 🍴500m.
Remarks: Boat rental.

Tourist information Opperdoes:
Ⓜ Museum stoomtram, Medemblik. Steam tram museum: Hoorn-
Medemblik. 🎟️ € 12.

🍴 **Oudendijk** **8C1**
Bruin Eetcafé Les Deux Ponts, Slimdijk 2.
GPS: n52,60462 e4,95983.⬆️.

NL

10 �</free, use of a meal obligated. **Location:** Rural, simple, quiet.
Surface: gravel. ◻ 01/01-31/12 ◉ Tue
Distance: ⌂2km ⌂on the spot ⟿on the spot ⊗on the spot

⚓S Purmerend 🌿🚤🍴 8C1

Het Bolwerk, Nieuwstraat. **GPS:** n52,50681 e4,95049.⬆.

5 ⌍€ 6,90 ⟿€1 🛢€0,15/h. 🚐 **Location:** Urban, simple, quiet.
Surface: metalled. ◻ 01/01-31/12 ◉ water: 01/11-01/04
Distance: ⌂200m ⊗200m.
Remarks: Max. 72h, tuesday morning market.

Tourist information Purmerend:
⌖ Centrum. ◻ Tue.

⚓S Schagen 🌿🚤🍴 8C1

Jachthaven Schagen, Lagedijkerweg 2B. **GPS:** n52,79088 e4,78746.⬆.

15 ⌍€ 7 + tourist tax € 0,97/pp ⟿€0,50/100liter 🗑Ch 🛢WC
🗐€0,50 ◉€4/4 🗑€1. 🧹 **Surface:** metalled.
◻ 01/01-31/12
Distance: ⌂500m ⟿on the spot ⊗400m 🗑500m.
Remarks: Check in at harbourmaster, caution key sanitary building
€ 15.

Tourist information Schagen:
⌖ West Friese Folkloremarkt. Folkore market. ◻ Jun-Jul-Aug: Thu.

🏕S Slootdorp 6C3

De Tulpentuin, Wierweg 7. **GPS:** n52,85627 e5,01010.⬆.

10 ⌍€ 10 ⟿🗑Ch 🛢(14x)WC 🗐included. 🧹
Location: Rural, isolated, quiet. **Surface:** gravel. ◻ 01/01-31/12
Distance: ⌂Wieringerwerf 2km 🛵2,6km 🗑Deen 1,9km.
Remarks: At tulip grower.

Stompetoren 8C1

Het Schermer Wapen, Oterlekerweg 3. **GPS:** n52,61285 e4,82096.⬆.

---

4 ⌍free, use of a meal obligated. **Location:** Urban, simple.
Surface: gravel. ◻ 01/01-31/12 ◉ Wed
Distance: ⌂500m ⊗on the spot 🗑500m.

🏕 Texel/De Cocksdorp 6C3

De Krim, Roggeslootweg 6. **GPS:** n53,15110 e4,85996.
10 ⌍€ 16-€ 26. **Surface:** metalled. ◻ 01/01-31/12

⚓S Volendam 🌿🚤🍴 8C1

Marinapark Volendam, De Pieterman 1.
GPS: n52,48944 e5,05972.⬆➡.

36 ⌍€ 6 10-17h, € 14 17-10h ⟿🗑Ch 🛢included ◉€5 🗐. 🧹
Location: Comfortable, quiet.
Surface: grasstiles/metalled.
◻ 01/01-31/12
Distance: ⌂1,5km 🛵50m ⟿50m ⊗300m 🗑300m 🚌300m.

Tourist information Volendam:
ℹ VVV, Zeestraat 37, www.vvv-volendam.nl. Old fishermen's village.
Ⓜ Volendams Museum, Zeestraat 41. Life and Work in Volendam,
1800-1900.
◻ Easter-autumn holiday 10-17h.

Friesland

🏕S Akkrum 6D3

Tusken de Marren, Ulbe Twijnstrawei 31. **GPS:** n53,04853 e5,82577.

20 ⌍€ 12,50 ⟿€0,50/100liter 🗑Ch 🛢€2/night WC 🗐€0,50/time
🗐free. **Surface:** grassy/metalled. ◻ 15/03-01/11
Distance: ⌂200m ⟿on the spot ⟿on the spot 🗑700m 🚌500m.
Remarks: Information at harbourmaster, boat rental.

🏕S Anjum 6E2

It Tún-Hûs, Bantswei 1a. **GPS:** n53,37751 e6,12999.⬆➡.

8 ⌍€ 10 ⟿🗑Ch 🛢🗐. **Surface:** metalled. ◻ 01/04-01/11
Distance: ⌂300m ⊗350m 🗑550m.

🏕S Appelscha 🍴 6E3

De Compagnonshoeve, Vaart Noordzijde 104.
GPS: n52,95222 e6,36278.⬆.

10 ⌍€ 8 ⟿🗑Ch 🛢€1,50 🗐included. 🧹 **Location:** Rural, simple,
quiet. **Surface:** grassy. ◻ 01/01-31/12
Distance: ⌂on the spot 🛵3km ⟿on the spot ⊗200m 🗑400m
◉400m 🚌50m.

⚓S Balk 🚤🍴 6D2

Jachthaven Lutsmond, Sleatemar 1a. **GPS:** n52,90389 e5,59694.

10 ⌍€ 10 excl. tourist tax ⟿🗑Ch 🛢€2,50 WC 🗐.
Surface: grassy. ◻ 01/01-31/12
Distance: ⌂1km ⟿on the spot ⟿on the spot ⊗nearby 🗑1km.

🏕S Bergum 🌿🚤🍴 6E3

Camperterrein Prinses Margriet Kanaal, Opperdijk van Veenweg 22.
GPS: n53,18643 e6,00176.⬆➡.

25 ⌍€ 10/night ⟿🗑Ch included 🛢€2/night 🗐1h free, 1 day €7,50.
🧹 **Location:** Urban, comfortable, quiet. **Surface:** grassy/metalled.
◻ 01/01-31/12
Distance: ⌂2km 🛵2km ⟿on the spot ⊗2km 🗑2km 🚌on the spot
🚲on the spot 🚶on the spot.

⚓S Bergum 🌿🚤🍴 6E3

Jachthaven Burgumerdaam, Bergumerdaam 51.
GPS: n53,18705 e5,99299.⬆.

10 ⌍€ 10 ⟿€0,50/100liter 🗑Ch 🛢€0,50/kWh WC
🗐€0,50/5minutes ◉€3,50/3,50 🗐included. 🧹
Location: Urban, comfortable, central, quiet. **Surface:** metalled.
◻ 15/03-01/11
Distance: ⌂500m 🛵500m 🛵5km ⟿on the spot ⊗500m 🗑500m
🚌500m 🚲on the spot 🚶on the spot.
Remarks: Max. 72h.

🏕S Blesdijke 6E3

Stoutenburght, Markeweg 35a. **GPS:** n52,83850 e6,03339.

12 ⌍€ 10 ⟿🗑Ch 🛢(12x),6Amp WC 🗐included. 🧹
Location: Rural. **Surface:** grassy. ◻ 15/03-01/10
Distance: ⌂5km ⊗2km 🗑2km 🚲on the spot 🚶on the spot.

🏕S Bolsward 🌿 6D3

Camperplaats Half-Hichtum, Hichtumerweg 14.
GPS: n53,07365 e5,52253.⬆.

6 ⟋€ 14 ⊞⬛Ch ⚡WC⟍included ⊡€3,50/time ⟍.⚓
Location: Rural, comfortable, quiet. **Surface:** grassy/metalled.
◻ 01/04-01/11
Distance: 🚶1km ⚓1,3km ⚓6km ⚓500m ⊗1km ⚓1km ⚓200m
🚲on the spot ⚓on the spot.

⚓S **Brantgum** 6E2
Camperplaats Veldzicht, Veldbuurtsterweg 9.
GPS: n53,35556 e5,93632.⬆.

20 ⟋€ 11 ⊞⬛Ch ⚡⟍included. ⚓ **Location:** Rural, comfortable,
isolated, quiet. **Surface:** grassy/metalled.
◻ 01/01-31/12
Distance: 🚶Dokkum 7km ⚓2km ⊗3km ⚓3km 🚲on the spot
⚓on the spot.
Remarks: Ferry boat to Ameland 3km.

⚓S **Burdaard** 6E3
Jachthaven Mouneheim, Mounewei 17. **GPS:** n53,29711 e5,88261.⬆.

12 ⟋€ 10 ⊞⬛Ch ⚡€1/night,10Amp WC⟍€0,50/5minutes ⊡€
4,50/2,50 ⟍included. ⚓ **Location:** Rural, comfortable, quiet.
Surface: grassy/gravel. ◻ 01/01-31/12
Distance: 🚶on the spot ⚓2km ⚓on the spot ⚓on the spot ⊗100m
⚓500m ⚓2km 🚲on the spot ⚓on the spot.
Remarks: Passerby € 1/100l.

⚓ **Dokkum** 🌿 6E2
Kalkhuisplein, Kalkhuisplein. **GPS:** n53,32650 e6,00936.⬆.

3 ⟋€ 5. ⚓ **Location:** Urban, simple, quiet. **Surface:** metalled.
◻ 15/03-31/12
Distance: 🚶500m ⚓1km ⚓20m ⚓20m ⊗1km ⚓1km ⚓1km
🚲on the spot ⚓on the spot.
Remarks: Max. 1 night, only overnight stays 18-9h.

⚓ **Drachten** 6E3
VV Drachten, Gauke Boelensstraat. **GPS:** n53,10289 e6,08832.⬆.

5 ⟋free. **Surface:** asphalted.
Distance: 🚶500m ⚓500m.

⚓ **Earnewâld** 6E3
Eilansgrien. **GPS:** n53,12958 e5,93630.⬆➡.

5 ⟋€ 5,40 + € 0,80/pp tourist tax ⊞⬛Ch ⚡stay WC⟍€0,50 ⊡€
3,50/3,50 ⟍. **Surface:** asphalted. ◻ 01/01-31/12
Distance: 🚶200m ⊗500m ⚓200m.
Remarks: Max. 72h, sanitary/washing machine at tourist office
(Summer season).

⚓S **Harlingen** 🌿 6D3
Tsjerk Hiddesluizen, Nieuwe Vissershaven 17.
GPS: n53,17938 e5,41731.⬆.

10 ⟋€ 7,50 ⊞€1 ⬛Ch ⚡(16x)€1/2kWh WC⟍⊡.⬛
Surface: asphalted.
Distance: 🚶500m ⊗500m ⚓500m ⚓100m.
Remarks: Max. 72h, laundromat/toilets/shower 500m.

⚓ **Heerenveen** 6E3
Thialf, Pim Mulierlaan 1. **GPS:** n52,93843 e5,94495.⬆.

4 ⟋free. **Surface:** metalled.
◻ 01/01-31/12 ⊡ during event
Distance: 🚶2km ⊗2km ⚓2km.
Remarks: On parking ground of skating rink, max. 72h.

⚓ **Heerenveen** 6E3
De Koningshof, Prinsenweg 1. **GPS:** n52,94759 e5,94438.⬆.

4 ⟋free. **Surface:** asphalted. ◻ 01/01-31/12
Distance: 🚶1km ⊗on the spot ⚓4km ⚓500m.
Remarks: Large parking near A32, max. 72h.

S **Heerenveen** 6E3
Gemeentewerf, Venus 4. **GPS:** n52,96663 e5,93502.

⊞⟍free. ◻ Mon-Fri 9-15u

⚓ **Hogebeintum** 6D2
Bezoekerscentrum Terp Hegebeintum, Pijpkedijk 4.
GPS: n53,33612 e5,85266.⬆.

4 ⟋free. **Location:** Simple, isolated. **Surface:** asphalted.
Distance: 🚶4km.
Remarks: Parking information centre/VVV, highest mound in the
Netherlands, max. 2 days, ferry boat to Ameland 3km.

⚓S **IJlst** 🌿⚓🏠⟍ 6D3
De Tsjalk, De Tsjalk. **GPS:** n53,00846 e5,62741.⬆.

4 ⟋€ 7,50 ⚡WC free ⊡€0,50/5minutes. **Location:** Urban, simple,
central, quiet. **Surface:** metalled.
◻ 01/01-31/12
Distance: 🚶200m ⚓on the spot ⊗200m ⚓200m ⚓200m
🚲on the spot ⚓on the spot.

⚓S **Joure** 6D3
Jachthaven, Grienedyk. **GPS:** n52,97210 e5,78836.

4 ⟋€ 16,50 ⊞€0,50/70liter ⬛⚡€3 ⟍€1.
Surface: metalled. ◻ 01/03-01/11
Distance: 🚶500m ⊗50m.
Remarks: Max. 72h.

⚓S **Kollum** 6E3
Jachthaven de Rijd, Cantecleer 2. **GPS:** n53,28727 e6,15139.⬆➡.

12 ⟋€ 9 ⊞⬛Ch ⚡€1,50/night,10Amp WC⟍€1/time ⟍included.
⚓ **Location:** Urban, simple, central, quiet. **Surface:** metalled.
◻ 01/05-01/10
Distance: 🚶on the spot ⚓on the spot ⊗500m ⚓500m ⚓500m
🚲on the spot ⚓on the spot.
Remarks: Max. 72h.

⚓S **Koudum** 🌿⚓🏠⟍ 6D3
De Kuilart, De Kuilart 1. **GPS:** n52,90305 e5,46706.⬆➡.

NL

10 + 2 ⛺ € 10, Quick-Stop € 8 🚰 Ch included 🔌 €1/
night,6 Amp WC 🚿 €0,35/5minutes 🔋€4,40/2,35 📶 📶
Location: Rural, luxurious, noisy. **Surface:** grassy/metalled.
🅿 01/01-07/05, 22/05-05/07, 25/08-31/12 ⬤ holidays
Distance: 🚶1,5km 🏊on the spot 🛒on the spot ⊗on the spot
🔋1km 🚌1km 🚲on the spot 🚶on the spot.

Langweer 🐚 6D3
Brandweerkazerne, Pontdyk. **GPS:** n52,96000 e5,71972.⬆.

4 ⛺free. **Location:** Simple. **Surface:** metalled.
🅿 01/01-31/12
Distance: 🚶500m 🏊500m ⊗500m 🔋500m.
Remarks: Max. 72h.

Langweer 🐚 6D3
Passantenhaven Langweer, Pontsdyk. **GPS:** n52,96091 e5,72240.⬆.

3 ⛺ € 7,50 + € 1/pp tourist tax 🚰€0,20 🍴Ch 🔌€2 WC🚿€0,50 📶€
3,50/3,50 📶. **Surface:** grassy. 🅿 01/04-31/10
Distance: 🚶500m 🏊on the spot 🛒on the spot ⊗500m 🔋500m
🚌500m.

Leeuwarden 🐚 6D3
Prinsentuin, Wissesdwinger 1. **GPS:** n53,20528 e5,79659.⬆.

4 ⛺ € 9,08 🚰🍴Ch 🔌€0,34/kWh,6 Amp WC🚿📶€4,31/3
📶included. 📶
Location: Urban, comfortable, central, quiet. **Surface:** metalled.
🅿 01/01-31/12 ⬤ sanitary building: 01/11-01/04
Distance: 🚶on the spot 🚲2km 🏊on the spot 🛒on the spot ⊗on
the spot 🔋on the spot 🚌on the spot 🚲on the spot 🚶on the spot.

Leeuwarden 🐚 6D3
Harlingertrekweg. **GPS:** n53,19839 e5,77098.⬆.

5 ⛺free. **Location:** Noisy. **Surface:** metalled. 🅿 01/01-31/12

Distance: 🚶1km ⊗1km 🔋1km 🚌500m.

Leeuwarden 🐚 6D3
Leeuwarder Jachthaven, Jachthavenlaan 3.
GPS: n53,19886 e5,83019.⬆➡.

6 ⛺ € 12,50 🚰🍴Ch 🔌WC🚿€1/5minutes 📶included.📶
Location: Urban, comfortable, isolated, quiet. **Surface:** grassy/gravel.
🅿 01/01-31/12
Distance: 🚶2,5km 🚲1km 🏊on the spot 🛒on the spot ⊗500m
🔋500m 📶300m on the spot 🚶on the spot.
Remarks: Check in at harbourmaster.

Leeuwarden 🐚 6D3
Taniaburg, Vierhuisterweg 72. **GPS:** n53,21955 e5,79286.⬆➡.

8 ⛺ € 11,10 🚰🍴Ch 🔌€2,40/night,6 Amp WC🚿📶€
2,50/3 📶included.📶 **Location:** Rural, comfortable, quiet.
Surface: grassy/gravel. 🅿 01/04-01/11
Distance: 🚶3km 🚲1km 🏊on the spot 🛒on the spot 🔋500m
🚌500m 🚲on the spot 🚶on the spot.
Remarks: Canoe and bicycle rental.

Lemmer 🐚 6D3
Jachthaven Lemmer, Plattedijk 4-12. **GPS:** n52,84708 e5,69696.⬆.

29 ⛺ € 13, 2 pers.incl, tourist tax € 1/pp 🚰€0,50 🍴Ch 🔌€0,50
WC🚿€0,50. **Surface:** metalled. 🅿 01/01-31/12
Distance: 🚶1km 🚲2,7km 🏊on the spot 🔋1km.

Lemmer 🐚 6D3
Watersportcentrum Tacozijl, Plattedijk 20. **GPS:** n52,85104 e5,68189.

20 ⛺ € 12 🚰🍴Ch 🔌€3 WC🚿included 📶 📶.
Surface: grassy/metalled.
🅿 01/01-31/12
Distance: 🚶centre 2,2km 🚲3km 🏊on the spot.
Tourist information Lemmer:
👁 Ir. D.F. Woudagemaal. The biggest steam pumpingstation of Europe.

Makkum 🐚 6D3
Gemeentehaven Makkum, Workumerdijk 2.
GPS: n53,05329 e5,40317.⬆. 💙

2 ⛺ € 10 ChWC🚿included 📶€2/2.📶
Location: Urban, simple, central, noisy. **Surface:** metalled.
🅿 01/04-31/10 service: 01/11-01/04
Distance: 🚶100m 🛒on the spot ⊗400m 🔋950m 🚌950m
🚲on the spot 🚶on the spot.
Remarks: Max. 72h.

Mirns 🐚 6D3
De Braamberg, Murnserdyk. **GPS:** n52,85249 e5,48190.⬆.

10 ⛺ € 10 + € 1/pp tourist tax 🚰🍴Ch included 🔌€2 WC🚿📶
Location: Rural. **Surface:** gravel. 🅿 01/01-31/12
Distance: 🏊beach 250m.

Molkwerum 6D3
Camperplaats 't Seleantsje, 't Seleantsje 2.
GPS: n52,90419 e5,39493.⬆.

18 ⛺ € 10 🚰🍴Ch 🔌WC included 🚿€0,50/6minutes 📶€4/2,50
📶€5/day.📶 **Location:** Rural, comfortable, quiet.
Surface: grasstiles. 🅿 15/03-01/11
Distance: 🚶300m 🏊on the spot 🛒on the spot ⊗on the spot 🔋4km
🚌1km 🚲on the spot 🚶on the spot.

Nes 6E3
Manege Nes, Burdineweg 2. **GPS:** n53,05468 e5,85558.⬆➡.

10 ⛺ € 3 🚰🍴Ch 🔌€2/night,16 Amp WC 📶included.📶
Location: Rural, simple, quiet. **Surface:** grassy/metalled.
🅿 01/01-31/12
Distance: 🚶700m 🚲1km 🏊10km 🛒50m ⊗700m 🔋700m
🚌700m 🚲on the spot 🚶on the spot.
Remarks: At manege.

Nijetrijne 6E3
Paviljoen Driewegsluis, Lindedijk 2a. **GPS:** n52,83261 e5,92467.

NL

🛒customers free.
Distance: 🚲on the spot ⊗on the spot.

| ⓘⓈ | Oudega 🚤 | 6E3 |

Jachthaven Oudega, Roundeel. **GPS:** n53,12315 e5,99961. ⬆️▶️.

2 🚐 € 7 🚰€1/100liter ⚡€1 🚽€0,50. **Location:** Simple.
Surface: grassy. ⏰ 01/04-01/11
Distance: 🚲200m ⊗200m 🚉200m.
Remarks: Max. 48h.

| ⓘⓈ | Oudemirdum 🌳 | 6D3 |

Landgoed de Syme, Jan Schotanuswei 106a, via Oude Balksterweg.
GPS: n52,85746 e5,51115. ⬆️▶️.

2 🚐 € 5 🚰included ⚡€2,50/night. 🚽 **Location:** Rural, simple,
isolated, quiet. **Surface:** grassy/metalled.
⏰ 01/01-31/12
Distance: 🚲4km ⚓6km 🚤6km ⊗4km 🚉4km 🚲on the spot
🚶on the spot.

| ⒸⓈ | Oudeschoot | 6E3 |

Minicamping 't Woutersbergje, Van Bienemalaan 15-17.
GPS: n52,93544 e5,96009. ⬆️▶️.

7 🚐 € 10,40 🚰🔌Ch ⚡€2,50/night,6 Amp 🚽🚽📶€3/2 📶included.
🚽 **Location:** Rural, comfortable, central, quiet. **Surface:** metalled.
⏰ 01/01-31/12
Distance: 🚲3,5km 🚉300m 🚲on the spot 🚶on the spot.

| ⓘ | Ried 🚤 | 6D3 |

Jachthaven it Kattegat, Berlikumerweg 13. **GPS:** n53,22416 e5,59330.

3 + 4 🚐 € 9,50. 🚽 **Location:** Rural, simple, quiet.
Surface: grassy/metalled. ⏰ 01/04-01/10
Distance: 🚲on the spot ⚓500m 🚤on the spot 🚲on the spot
🚤500m 🚲on the spot 🚶on the spot.

| ⓘⓈ | Rohel | 6D3 |

Aktiviteitenboerderij, Vierhuisterweg 29. **GPS:** n52,90337 e5,84540.

5 🚐 € 15 🚰🔌Ch ⚡🚽included. **Location:** Quiet.
Surface: metalled. ⏰ 01/01-31/12
Distance: 🚲on the spot 🚤on the spot ⊗on the spot 🚉on the spot.

| ⓘ | Sexbierum | 6D3 |

Restaurant Liauckama State, Liauckamaleane 2.
GPS: n53,22028 e5,47656.

5 🚐 € 10, free for clients. **Surface:** grassy/gravel. ⏰ 01/01-31/12
Distance: 🚲1km 🚉1km 🚤1km.

| 🔲 | Sint Jacobiparochie | 6D3 |

Zeedijk, Zwarte Haan. **GPS:** n53,30915 e5,63051. ⬆️.

25 🚐free. **Surface:** grassy. ⏰ 01/01-31/12
Distance: 🚲Sint Jacobiparochie 8km ⚓Wadden Sea ⊗100m
🚲on the spot 🚶on the spot.

| ⓘⓈ | Sloten 🌿 🚤 | 6D3 |

Jachthaven Lemsterpoort, Jachthaven 7.
GPS: n52,89265 e5,64486. ⬆️▶️.

10 🚐 € 12 🚰€0,50/100liter 🔌Ch ⚡€2,50/24h,6 Amp 🚽🚽€
1/5minutes 📶included. 🚽 **Location:** Urban, comfortable, quiet.
Surface: grassy/metalled. ⏰ 01/01-31/12
Distance: 🚲100m ⚓2km 🚲on the spot 🚤on the spot ⊗100m
🚉100m 🚤500m 🚲on the spot 🚶on the spot.

| ⓘⓈ | Sneek 🚤 | 6D3 |

Jachthaven Holiday Boatin, Eeltjebaasweg 3.
GPS: n53,02184 e5,56702. ⬆️.

4 🚐 € 12 🚰🔌Ch ⚡€1/night,10Amp 🚽📶included.
🚽 **Location:** Urban, comfortable, quiet. **Surface:** concrete.
⏰ 01/01-31/12
Distance: 🚲3,6km ⚓2km 🚲on the spot 🚤on the spot ⊗4km
🚉2km, bakery 300m 🚤300m 🚲on the spot 🚶on the spot.

| ⓘⓈ | Sneek 🚤 | 6D3 |

Amicitia Hotel Sneek, Alexanderstraat.
GPS: n53,02378 e5,67595. ⬆️▶️.

10 🚐 € 7,50, free with a meal 🚰🔌Ch ⚡📶included.
Surface: metalled. ⏰ 01/01-31/12
Distance: 🚲1,5km ⚓400m 🚤8km ⊗on the spot.
Remarks: Reservation during Sneek sailing week:
info@amicitiahotel.nl, 1st week of August.

| ⓘⓈ | Stavoren 🌿 🚤 | 6D3 |

Marina Stavoren, Suderstrand 2. **GPS:** n52,87398 e5,36762. ⬆️.
20 🚐 € 12,50 + € 1/pp tourist tax, dog € 1 🚰🔌Ch ⚡(4x)€2 🚽🚽
📶included. **Surface:** metalled. ⏰ 01/04-31/10
Distance: 🚲300m 🚲on the spot 🚲on the spot ⊗on the spot
🚉300m 🚤500m 🚲on the spot 🚶on the spot.
Remarks: Max. 3 nights, check in at harbourmaster.

| | Sumar | 6E3 |

Recreatiecentrum Bergumermeer, Solcamastraat 30.
GPS: n53,19044 e6,02316. ⬆️▶️.

10 🚐 € 18 🚰🔌Ch ⚡🚽📶included. 🚽 **Location:** Rural,
luxurious, quiet. **Surface:** grassy/metalled. ⏰ 01/04-31/10
Distance: 🚲5km.

| Ⓒ | Sumar | 6E3 |

Recreatiecentrum Bergumermeer, Solcamastraat-30.
GPS: n53,19044 e6,02316.

1 🚐 € 8 17-10h. ⏰ 01/04-31/10

| ⓘⓈ | Surhuisterveen | 6E3 |

Zwembad Wettervlecke, Badlaan 3. **GPS:** n53,17987 e6,16124. ⬆️.

5 🛏 € 5 🚰 €1 💧 €1 WC 🚿 included. **Surface:** grassy.
Distance: 🚲 500m 🛒 500m.

🏕 **S** | **Tersoal** 🚣 | **6D3**

Watersportbedrijf Lege Geaen, Buorren 2.
GPS: n53,07729 e5,74360. ⬆️ ➡️.

6 🛏 € 10 🚰 🔌Ch 💧 €2,50/night WC 🚿 included. 🚿
Location: Rural, comfortable, quiet. **Surface:** grassy/gravel.
⭕ 01/01-31/12
Distance: 🚲 8km 🚤 1,5km ⛱ on the spot 🎣 on the spot ⊗ 1,5km
🛒 8km 🚴 on the spot 🚶 on the spot.

⚓ **S** | **Wartena** 🚣 | **6E3**

Jachthaven Wartena, Stukenwei. **GPS:** n53,15145 e5,90532.

10 🛏 € 10 🚰 €0,50/100 🔌Ch 💧 WC 🚿 €1 🔌 €6 🚿.
Location: Central. **Surface:** grassy/metalled.
⭕ 01/01-31/11
Distance: 🚲 200m ⛱ on the spot 🎣 on the spot ⊗ 500m 🛒 500m
🛒 on the spot 🚴 on the spot.
Remarks: Bicycle rental.

🏕 **S** | **Winsum** | **6D3**

Camperplaats Winsum, Skans 12. **GPS:** n53,15177 e5,63111. ⬆️

4 🛏 € 12 🚰 🔌Ch 💧 included WC 🚿 🔌. **Location:** Simple.
⭕ 01/01-31/12

⚓ **S** | **Wommels** 🚣 | **6D3**

Jachthaven Wommels, Terp 14. **GPS:** n53,10957 e5,58765. ⬆️

5 🛏 € 10 🚰 🔌Ch 💧 WC included 🚿 €0,50. 🚿 **Location:** Simple.
Surface: grassy/metalled. ⭕ 01/04-01/10
Distance: 🚲 300m ⛱ on the spot 🛒 100m.
Remarks: Market 100m, museum 200m.
Tourist information Wommels:

🚶 📧 Tue-morning.

🏕 **S** | **Workum** 🌾🚣🍴🍽 | **6D3**

Jachthaven Bouwsma, Moleburren 11. **GPS:** n52,98230 e5,45518. ⬆️

6 🛏 € 10 🚰 🔌Ch 💧 €2,50/night,6Amp WC 🚿 €1/7minutes 🔌 €8
🚿 included. 🚿
Location: Urban, central, quiet.
Surface: grassy/metalled.
⭕ 01/04-31/10
Distance: 🚲 750m 🚤 1,5km 🎣 on the spot ⊗ 500m 🛒 500m
🛒 200m 🚴 on the spot 🚶 on the spot.
Tourist information Workum
📧 Jopie Huisman Museum, Noard 6. Autodidact, paintings and
drawings. ⭕ 01/04-31/10 10-17h, 01/03-30/11 + Su 13-17h.

🏕 **S** | **Woudsend** 🚣 | **6D3**

Recreatiecentrum De Rakken, Lynbaen 10.
GPS: n52,94649 e5,62732. ⬆️ ➡️

15 🛏 € 17,50 + € 1/pp tourist tax 🚰 🔌Ch 💧 WC 🚿 included
🔌 €4,50/2,50 🚿. **Surface:** grassy/metalled. ⭕ 15/03-15/10
Distance: 🚲 200m 🚤 2,5km 🎣 200m ⊗ 200m 🛒 200m.

🏕 **S** | **Ypecolsga** 🍴 🚣 | **6D3**

Camperplaats Waterloo, Nr. 19. **GPS:** n52,92758 e5,59549. ⬆️

13 🛏 € 10, 2 pers.incl 🚰 🔌Ch 💧 WC 🚿 use sanitary €1,50/pp 🔌 €
4,50/2 🚿 included. **Surface:** grasstiles. ⭕ 01/01-31/12
Distance: 🚲 3km 🚤 1km 🎣 1km ⊗ 3,5km 🛒 3,5km 🛒 nearby
🚴 on the spot.

🏕 **S** | **Zurich** | **6D3**

Camperplaats Zurich, Caspar di Roblesdijk 3.
GPS: n53,11235 e5,39335. ⬆️

3 🛏 € 3. 🚿 **Location:** Urban, simple, central, noisy. **Surface:** metalled.
⭕ 01/01-31/12
Distance: 🚲 on the spot 🚤 1,5km ⛱ on the spot 🎣 on the spot 🚴 on
the spot 🚶 on the spot.
Remarks: Max. 72h.

🏕 **S** | **Zwaagwesteinde** 🚣 | **6E3**

Camperpark Kuikhorne, Kuikhornsterweg 31.
GPS: n53,24124 e6,01875. ⬆️ ➡️

25 🛏 € 9, 2 pers.incl 🚰 €0,50 🔌Ch 💧 €1 WC 🚿 €0,50 🔌 €4/3 🚿 €1.
🚿 **Surface:** asphalted/grassy. ⭕ 15/03-01/11
Distance: 🚲 2km 🎣 on the spot ⊗ 2km, pizzeria within walking
distance 🛒 2km.
Remarks: Max. 72h, boat rental.

Groningen

🏕 **S** | **Appingedam** 🌾🚣🍴🍽 | **6F2**

Camperplaats Appingedam, Farmsumerweg 21.
GPS: n53,32062 e6,86689. ⬆️

10 🛏 free 🚰 free 💧 €1/kWh,10Amp.
Location: Urban, simple, central, noisy. **Surface:** metalled.
⭕ 01/01-31/12
Distance: 🚲 750m 🎣 Damsterdiep ⊗ 500m 🛒 500m 🛒 on the spot
🚴 on the spot 🚶 on the spot.
Remarks: Max. 72h.
Tourist information Appingedam:
🚶 Solwerderstraat. ⭕ Sa 09-16h.

🏕 **S** | **Blijham** | **6F3**

Camperpark Turfstee, Turfweg 28. **GPS:** n53,11118 e7,02912. ⬆️

55 🛏 € 10 + € 0,75 tourist tax 🚰 🔌Ch 💧 WC 🚿 €0,50/5minutes
🔌 €7,50/0 🚿 included. **Location:** Rural, comfortable, isolated.
Surface: grassy/gravel.
Distance: 🚲 3km ⊗ 3km 🛒 3km 🛒 on the spot 🚴 on the spot.

🏕 **S** | **Delfzijl** | **6F2**

Zeebadweg, Zeebadweg. **GPS:** n53,33582 e6,92650. ⬆️

4 🛏 free.
Distance: 🚲 500m ⛱ on the spot 🎣 on the spot ⊗ 100m 🛒 300m.

🏕 **S** | **Doezum** | **6E3**

Landgoed Jonker, Provincialeweg 133a.
GPS: n53,20411 e6,26018. ⬆️ ➡️

NL

60 € 10, 2 pers.incl Ch (20x)€1,50/night WC included.
Location: Luxurious. **Surface:** grassy/metalled.
01/01-31/12
facilities 01/10-31/03
Distance: 1,5km on the spot on the spot on the spot.

Tourist information Doezum:
Abel Tasman Kabinet, Kompasstraat 1, Grootegast. Local archaeological museum seafarer Abel Tasman.
Thu-Sa 13.30-16.30h.

Eenrum 6E2

Jachthaven De Dobbe, Dobbepad. **GPS**: n53,36311 e6,45151.

4 € 3 + € 3/pp + € 1,15/pp tourist tax Ch €2 WC included €0,50.
Location: Rural, simple, quiet. **Surface:** grassy/metalled.
Distance: 500m on the spot 500m 500m.
Remarks: Check in at harbourmaster.

Groningen 6E3

Sportcentrum Kardinge, Bieskemaar. **GPS**: n53,23946 e6,59680.

15 free. **Location:** Rural, simple, quiet. **Surface:** metalled.
01/01-31/12
Distance: 3km 1km on the spot.
Remarks: Max. 72h.

Tourist information Groningen:
Prinsenhof en prinsenhoftuin. 15/03-15/10.

Haren 6E3

De Lijste, Meerweg. **GPS**: n53,16298 e6,57878.
10 free. **Surface:** grassy.
Distance: 1,3km no bathing 250m.

Lauwersoog 6E2

Lauwersmeerplezier, Kustweg 30. **GPS**: n53,40625 e6,20044.

14 € 15, 2 pers.incl WC included €3.
Surface: grassy/metalled. 01/01-31/12
Distance: 500m on the spot on the spot 500m 500m.

Lauwersoog 6E2

Havenkantoor Lauwersoog, Haven 2.
GPS: n53,40819 e6,19768.

2 € 1,50/m Ch WC included. **Location:** Urban, simple, quiet. **Surface:** metalled. 01/01-31/12
Distance: on the spot on the spot on the spot on the spot on the spot.

Lauwersoog 6E2

Jachthaven Noordergat, Noordergat 1.
GPS: n53,40493 e6,20311.

30 € 14 Ch included €2,10/24h €0,50/5minutes €3/2,50. **Location:** Rural, simple, quiet. **Surface:** concrete.
01/01-31/12
Distance: on the spot on the spot on the spot on the spot.

Tourist information Lauwersoog:
Lauwersmeergebied. Breeding area for birds and recreation area.
01/04-31/10 Tue-Su 11-17h.

Leens 6E2

Leenstertillen. GPS: n53,35066 e6,37002.

15 € 6/pp Ch WC included. **Location:** Rural, simple, quiet.
Surface: grassy. 01/01-31/12
Distance: 1,5km 50m 50m 1,5km 1,6km.

Losdorp 6F2

Restaurant Eemshaven, Schafferweg 29.
GPS: n53,37214 e6,84411.

4 consuming is appreciated Ch €5,customers WC free. **Location:** Rural, simple, quiet. **Surface:** metalled. 01/01-31/12
Mo
Distance: 2km 2km 1km on the spot on the spot.
Remarks: Code wifi in restaurant.

Lutjegast 6E3

't Kompas, Kompasstraat 1. **GPS**: n53,23498 e6,25972.

5 free. **Surface:** metalled. 01/01-31/12
Distance: on the spot on the spot 200m on the spot.
Remarks: Behind the club-building.

Midwolda 6F3

Blauwestadhoeve, Hoofdweg 156. **GPS**: n53,19424 e7,00751.
6 € 10 €2,25 €1,50 Ch €1,50 (6x)€1,45 WC €1 €1 € 1,45. **Location:** Rural. **Surface:** grassy/metalled. 01/01-31/12
Distance: 250m 2km 900m 500m 100m 250m 100m on the spot on the spot.

Midwolda 6F3

Jachthaven Midwolda, Strandweg 1. **GPS**: n53,19727 e7,02610.

5 € 12 €0,50 Ch €4/day. **Location:** Rural, comfortable, quiet. **Surface:** grassy. 01/04-31/10
Distance: city centre 1km on the spot on the spot on the spot on the spot on the spot.
Remarks: View at Lake Oldambt.

Musselkanaal 6F3

Jachthaven Spoordok, Havenkade 1. **GPS**: n52,92694 e7,01389.

35 € 9 €0,50/100liter Ch (35x) WC included.
Location: Rural, comfortable, quiet. **Surface:** grassy/metalled.
01/04-31/10
Distance: 500m on the spot on the spot on the spot nearby on the spot on the spot.
Remarks: Max. 72h.

Onderdendam 6E2

Watersportvereniging Onderdendam, Warffumerweg 12.
GPS: n53,33652 e6,58600.

6 € 6 + € 1/pp Ch (6x)€2,50 WC included €0,50.
Location: Simple, quiet. **Surface:** grassy/metalled.
Distance: 500m on the spot on the spot 500m 500m.

Onstwedde 6F3

Holte 9. **GPS**: n53,05021 e7,04459.

5 € 3 Ch included €2. **Location:** Rural, simple.
Surface: grassy. 01/01-31/12
Distance: 1km 1km 1km 1km bike junction.

Sellingen 6F3

Camperpark Westerwolde, Zevenmeersveenweg 1a.
GPS: n52,95412 e7,13174.

NL

10 ⌼€ 8 + € 1/pp tourist tax ⛽€1 🔧Ch WC included 🚰€4.
Location: Rural, simple, quiet. **Surface:** grassy.
📅 01/01-31/12
Distance: 🛒1km ⛽on the spot 🍴1km 🚌1km 🚲on the spot 🏊on the spot.
Remarks: Arrival after 7pm.

Sellingen 🐑 6F3

De Barkhoorn, Beetserweg 6. **GPS:** n52,94617 e7,13421.⬆️.

5 ⌼€ 9 + tourist tax, dog € 3 🚿€3,50.
Location: Rural, simple, quiet. **Surface:** grasstiles.
📅 01/04-31/10 🏠 01/07-22/08

Slochteren 🏛 6F3

Duurswoldje, Edserweg. **GPS:** n53,20051 e6,79020.⬆️➡️.

7 ⌼€ 7 ⛽🔧Ch 🚿included. **Location:** Rural, simple, quiet.
Surface: grassy. 📅 01/01-31/12
Distance: 🛒500m ⛽on the spot ⛽on the spot 🍴1km 🚌on the spot.
Remarks: Covered picnic area, small stock accommodation.

Stadskanaal 6F3

De Roo Campers, Unikenkade 1. **GPS:** n53,03556 e6,87617.⬆️.

10 ⌼€ 5 ⛽🔧Ch WC included 🚰. **L**
ocation: Rural, simple, quiet. **Surface:** grassy.
📅 01/01-31/12
Distance: 🛒8km 🚲 4km ⛽on the spot ⛽on the spot ⛽8km 🍴8km.

Tourist information Stadskanaal:
ℹ️ Pagedal, www.stadskanaal.nl. Daytime recreation.

Ter Apel 🚢 6F3

Jachthaven De Runde, Oosterkade 5. **GPS:** n52,87179 e7,07329.⬆️.

---

10 ⌼€ 7,50 + € 1,50 tourist tax ⛽€0,50 🔧Ch WC 🚿€0,50 🚰€
4/2 💧free,5h. **Location:** Rural, comfortable, quiet. **Surface:** grassy.
📅 01/01-31/12
Distance: 🛒1km ⛽on the spot ⛽on the spot ⛽on the spot 🍴1km 🚌500m 🚲on the spot.
Remarks: Wifi 5h free.

Termunterzijl 6F2

Zeestrand, Schepperbuurt 4a. **GPS:** n53,30173 e7,03085.⬆️.

15 ⌼€ 10 ⛽🔧Ch WC included 🚰€1 🚰€2/2 💧€3 🚲.
Surface: metalled. 📅 01/01-31/12
Distance: 🛒100m 🏊100m ⛽100m ⛽200m 🍴200m.
Remarks: Registration via intercom or phone.

Usquert 🚢 6E2

't Zielhuis, Zijlweg. **GPS:** n53,43203 e6,58396.⬆️.

+10 ⌼free. **Location:** Rural, simple, isolated, quiet. **Surface:** gravel.
📅 01/01-31/12
Distance: 🛒Usquert 4,5km 🏊Wadden Sea ⛽on the spot ⛽on the spot.

Veendam 🚢 6F3

Borgerswold, Flora 2. **GPS:** n53,10637 e6,84826.⬆️➡️.

60 ⌼€ 9/night ⛽🔧Ch 🚿WC 💧included. 🚲
Location: Rural, simple, quiet. **Surface:** grassy.
📅 01/01-31/12
Distance: 🛒2km 🏊beach 50m ⛽on the spot ⛽2km 🍴1km 🚌1,5km 🚲on the spot.

Tourist information Veendam:
Ⓜ️🚂 Museumspoorlijn STAR, Parallelweg 4, Veendam. Museum railway line, tickets available at railwaystation.
📅 01/04-31/10, 27/12-03/01.
🎫 round trip € 9,50.
Ⓜ️ Veenkoloniaalmuseum, Museumplein 5. History of the peat, shipping and industry.
📅 Tue-Fri 11-17h, Sa-Su 13-17h 🏠 01/09-30/06 Mo.

Winschoten 🌺🏖🚢 6F3

Jachthaven de Rensel, Hellingbaan 4. **GPS:** n53,14405 e7,04760.⬆️.

10 ⌼€ 0,75/m, tourist tax € 0,80/pp ⛽€0,50 🔧Ch 🚿WC included.
Location: Simple, quiet. **Surface:** concrete. 📅 01/01-31/12
Distance: 🛒800m 🏊200m McDonalds 🍴200m AH.

Winschoten 🌺🏖🚢 6F3

Hotel Café Restaurant Bowling In den Stallen, Oostereinde 10.
GPS: n53,15371 e7,06528.⬆️.

10 ⌼consuming is appreciated ⛽🚿on demand 💧🚲.
Location: Rural, simple, quiet.
Surface: asphalted/metalled.
Distance: 🛒1km 🏊600m ⛽600m ⛽on the spot 🍴1km 🚌600m.

Tourist information Winschoten:
👁 Stoomgemaal, Winschoter Oostereinde.
Steam-engine 1895.

Winsum 🚢 6E2

Jachthaven/Camping Marenland, Winsumerstraatweg.
GPS: n53,33177 e6,51015.⬆️➡️.

10 ⌼€ 15 ⛽🔧Ch 🚿€3/night,4 Amp WC 🚰 🚰€6,50/0 💧included, at restaurant. 🚲 **Location:** Urban, comfortable, quiet.
Surface: grassy/metalled. 📅 01/04-01/11
Distance: 🛒300m 🏊200m ⛽on the spot ⛽on the spot 🍴500m 🚌200m 🚲on the spot 🏊Pieterpad.

Zoutkamp 🚢 6E2

Jachthaven Hunzegat, Strandweg 17. **GPS:** n53,34114 e6,29406.⬆️.

10 ⌼€ 12,50 + tourist tax ⛽🔧Ch, dump chem.toilet only with biodegradable liquid 🚿(10x),4A WC included 🚰€0,50 🚰€7,40/0 💧. **Location:** Rural, comfortable, quiet. **Surface:** grassy/metalled.
📅 01/01-31/12
Distance: 🛒1km 🏊on the spot ⛽on the spot ⛽500m 🍴500m 🚌300m 🚲on the spot.
Remarks: Bread-service.

Tourist information Zoutkamp:
👁 Zeehondencrèche, Hoofdstraat 94a, Pieterburen. Sanctory to cure sick seals. 📅 9-18h. 🎫 € 4,50.

Zuidbroek 🚢 6F3

De Broeckhof, W.A. Scholtenweg 18. **GPS:** n53,16118 e6,86054.⬆️.

3 ⌼free ⛽🔧Ch WC 🚰🚲💧free.
Location: Rural, simple, central, quiet. **Surface:** metalled.
📅 01/01-31/12 🏠 3rd week Jun
Distance: 🛒500m ⛽on the spot ⛽on the spot 🍴1km 🚌on the spot ⛽on the spot 🚲on the spot.
Remarks: Max. 72h.

NL

Drenthe

Assen 6E3

Van Hobokenstraat 5. **GPS:** n53,00030 e6,57123.⬆.

5 free ⛽€0,50/100 🚿€1. **Location:** Simple. **Surface:** metalled.
📅 01/01-31/12
Distance: 🛒1km ⊗50m 🍴500m.
Remarks: Max. 72h.

Barger Compascuum 8F1

Nationale Veenpark, Berkenrode 4. **GPS:** n52,75504 e7,02546.⬆.

20 €6 + € 1,20/pp tourist tax 🚿included.
Location: Rural, simple, quiet.
Surface: grassy.
📅 01/05-31/10
Distance: ⊗100m 🚲on the spot 🚴on the spot.
Remarks: Max. 3x24h, after visiting Veenpark 2nd night free.
Tourist information Barger Compascuum:
🌐 Veenpark-Wereld van Veen, Berkenrode 4. Life and Work in peat area, 160 acres of nature, peat and villages.
📅 01/04-31/10 10-17h, 01/07-31/08 10-18h. 🎫 >5: € 14, 65+€ 13.

Borger 6F3

Nuuverstee, Rolderstraat 4. **GPS:** n52,92633 e6,77447.⬆➡.

6 €15 ⛽🚿Ch 🚿(6x),10Amp WC 🔌included.🚴
Location: Rural, luxurious. **Surface:** grassy/metalled. 📅 01/02-31/12
Distance: 🛒800m ⚓600m 🏊2km 🚲500m ⊗600m 🍴1km 🚲500m 🚴on the spot 🚶on the spot.

Dwingeloo 8E1

Torentjeshoek, Leeuweriksveldweg 1. **GPS:** n52,81927 e6,36077.⬆➡.

6 €12-14 2p incl. + tourist tax ⛽€1/100liter 🚿Ch 🚿€1/night,10Amp WC 🔌included,on camp site.🚴 **Location:** Rural, luxurious, quiet. **Surface:** grassy/metalled. 📅 01/01-31/12
Distance: 🛒2km ⚓2km 🏊200m 🚲200m ⊗2km 🍴2km 🚲1km 🚴on the spot 🚶on the spot.
Remarks: Arrival >16h, departure <11h.

Eelderwolde 6E3

Scandinavisch Dorp, Oude Badweg 1. **GPS:** n53,16984 e6,55391.⬆.

5 free.
Location: Rural, simple, quiet. **Surface:** asphalted/grassy.
📅 01/01-31/12 🍴 Restaurant: Tue, 01/10-01/04 Mo-Tue
Distance: 🛒2km ⚓5km 🏊500m 🚲on the spot ⊗on the spot 🍴2km 🚲200m 🚴on the spot 🚶on the spot.

Eext 6F3

Schaopvolte, Stationsstraat 60a. **GPS:** n53,00007 e6,72862.⬆.

10 €7,50 + tourist tax ⛽€1 🚿Ch 🚿(6x)€1/4kWh WC 🔌€0,50 🔌€4,50 🔌€2/day. **Location:** Rural, simple, quiet.
Surface: grassy/gravel. 📅 01/04-01/11
Distance: 🛒2km.

Elim 8E1

De Barswieke, Barsweg 9. **GPS:** n52,67144 e6,57821.⬆.

10 €6 🚿🚿Chincluded 🚿€1,50 WC🔌. **Surface:** grassy.
📅 01/01-31/12
Distance: 🛒1km 🍴1km.

Emmen 8F1

Kerkhoflaan- van Schaikweg. **GPS:** n52,78091 e6,90330.⬆➡.

10 free.
Location: Urban, simple.
Surface: gravel/metalled.
📅 01/01-31/12
Distance: 🛒1km ⊗Albert Heijn 600m.
Remarks: Behind hotel Eden, max. 72h, zoo Emmen 900m.
Tourist information Emmen:
🌐 Noorder Dierenpark, Hoofdstraat 18. Zoo.
📅 from 10h.

Erica 8F1

Achter op Erica, Verlengde Herendijk. **GPS:** n52,73006 e6,92256.⬆.
15 €8 + € 1,20/pp tourist tax ⛽🚿Chincluded 🚿€3 🔌€1.
Location: Rural. **Surface:** grassy.
Distance: 🛒3,5km 🚴on the spot 🚶on the spot.

Hoogeveen 8E1

Terpweg 3. **GPS:** n52,72639 e6,50040.⬆.

---

3 free. **Location:** Rural, simple, isolated. **Surface:** metalled.
📅 01/01-31/12
Distance: 🛒2km ⚓2,2km ⊗100m 🍴1km 🚲1km.
Remarks: At sports park, max. 72h.

Matsloot 6E3

Camping Pool, Matsloot 1a. **GPS:** n53,19354 e6,44980.⬆.

10 € 10 ⛽🚿Ch 🚿WC 🔌included.🚴 **Location:** Rural, simple, isolated, quiet. **Surface:** metalled. 📅 01/01-31/12
Distance: 🛒5km 🚲on the spot ⊗on the spot.
Remarks: On Leekster lake.

Meppel 8E1

Jachthaven, Westeinde 32. **GPS:** n52,69615 e6,18096.⬆.

15 € 7,70, 2 pers.incl. ⛽€0,50 🚿Ch 🚿€0,50/kWh WC🔌 🔌€3/3 🔌. **Location:** Urban, comfortable, central, quiet. **Surface:** grassy.
📅 01/01-31/12
Distance: 🛒500m 🏊on the spot 🚲on the spot ⊗on the spot 🍴400m.

Nieuwlande 8F1

Bonenstee, Brugstraat 87. **GPS:** n52,67889 e6,61194.⬆.

20 €6 ⛽🚿Ch 🚿(6x)€1,50 WC🔌€1 🔌included.
Location: Rural. **Surface:** grassy/metalled. 📅 01/04-31/10
Distance: 🛒2km 🏊4km 🚲4km ⊗2km 🍴2km 🚲100m 🚴bike junction 🚶on the spot.
Remarks: Max. 72h.

Noord-Sleen 8F1

De Kalverweide, Zweeloërstraat 1. **GPS:** n52,79330 e6,79475.⬆.

10 €12 ⛽🚿Ch 🚿WC🔌 🔌included. **Location:** Rural, comfortable, quiet. **Surface:** grassy. 📅 01/01-31/12
Distance: 🛒500m 🚲on the spot 🚴on the spot.

Remarks: Use of sauna against payment.

Oosterhesselen   8F1

Sauna Hesselerbrug, Verlengde Hoogeveensevaart 32.
GPS: n52,73535 e6,72029.

⌂use of sauna obligatory. **Surface:** metalled.
Distance: 4km ⚓4km.

Ufelte   8E1

De Blauwe Haan, Weg achter de es 11.
GPS: n52,80220 e6,27264. ⬆➡.

6 ⌂€ 12 ⛽⛃Ch ✎€2,50/night,10Amp WC◻⌖⌃included.
Location: Rural, luxurious, quiet. **Surface:** grassy/metalled.
◷ 01/04-31/10
Distance: 5km 2km ⚓3km 3km ⊗2,5km ⚓5km ⛽2km
⚓on the spot ⛷on the spot.

Westerbork   6F3

Landgoed het Timmerholt, Gagelmaat 4.
GPS: n52,86850 e6,61748. ⬆➡.

4 ⌂€ 10, 19/07-02/08 € 12,50 ⛽⛃Ch ✎included WC€1,50/pppd
⌃€1,50/pppd ⌖€3,90/2,75 ⌃h. **Location:** Rural, luxurious, quiet.
Surface: grassy/metalled. ◷ 01/01-31/12
Distance: 2km 4km ⚓on the spot on the spot ⊗on the spot
⚓2km ⛽2km ⚓on the spot ⛷on the spot.

Tourist information Westerbork:
Ⓜ Herinneringscentrum Kamp Westerbork, Oosthalen 8, Hooghalen.
◷ Mo-Fri 10-17h, Sa-Su 13-17h, 01/07-31/08 11-17h.

Wijster   8E1

Grondsels, Grondselweg 7. **GPS:** n52,80143 e6,49025. ⬆.

10 ⌂€ 5 ⛽⛃Ch ✎€2 WC◻⌃included.
Location: Rural, simple, isolated, quiet. **Surface:** grassy/metalled.
◷ 15/03-31/10
Distance: 3km ⚓on the spot ⊗3km ⛽5km ⚓on the spot.

Overijssel

Almelo   8F1

De Grenzen, Havenkade. **GPS:** n52,36000 e6,65694. ⬆.

3 ⌂€ 4,50 ⛽€2 ⛃Ch ⌃€0,50 ⌖€2,25/2,25. **Surface:** asphalted.
◷ 01/01-31/12
Distance: 300m ⚓on the spot ⊗200m ⛽200m ⚓100m.
Remarks: Max. 72h, check in at harbourmaster.

Tourist information Almelo:
✈ Markt- en Centrumplein. ◷ Thu 8.30-14h, Sa 8.30-17h.

Bathmen   8E2

Prinses Margrietlaan. GPS: n52,25025 e6,29927. ⬆.

2 ⌂free. **Location:** Urban, simple, central, quiet. **Surface:** metalled.
◷ 01/01-31/12
Distance: 1km 2,5km ⊗1km ⛽1km ⚓on the spot
⛷on the spot.
Remarks: Parking gymnasium.

Belt Schutsloot   8E1

Café-Restaurant de Belt, Havezatheweg 4. **GPS:** n52,66774 e6,05189.

10 ⌂free for clients WC ⌂. **Surface:** asphalted.
◷ 01/01-31/12
Distance: 3km ⚓1km ⚓1km ⊗on the spot ⛽3km.
Remarks: North of Zwartsluis, at Belter- and Beulakerwijde.

Beuningen   8F1

De Nijenhaer, Nijenhaerweg 25. **GPS:** n52,34471 e6,99325. ⬆.
15 ⌂€ 10 ⛽⛃Ch ✎included. **Location:** Rural. **Surface:** grassy.
◷ 01/01-31/12
Distance: 3km ⚓on the spot ⛷on the spot.

Borne   8F2

Parking de Koem, De Koem. **GPS:** n52,29957 e6,75800. ⬆.

1 ⌂€ 5/24h. **Surface:** metalled.
◷ 01/01-31/12
Distance: ⚓on the spot ⊗50m ⛽on the spot.
Remarks: Max. 72h, money in envelope in mail box at townhall.

Dalfsen   8E1

Stationsweg 4. **GPS:** n52,49944 e6,25949. ⬆.

5 ⌂free. ⌃ **Location:** Rural, simple, central, quiet.
Surface: grasstiles. ◷ 01/01-31/12
Distance: 500m ⊗500m ⛽800m ⚓on the spot ⚓on the spot
⛷on the spot.
Remarks: Max. 48h, service on campsite.

Dalfsen   8E1

Starnbosch, Sterrebosweg 4. **GPS:** n52,47538 e6,26336. ⬆➡.

7 ⌂€ 10 + € 0,85/pp tourist tax ⛽⛃Ch ✎(8x)WCincluded ⌃€
0,40/5minutes ⌖€5/0,50 ⌃€1/1h. ⌃ **Location:** Rural, comfortable,
quiet. **Surface:** grassy/sand. ◷ 01/01-31/12
Distance: 4km ⊗on the spot ⛽4km ⚓3,3km ⚓on the spot
⛷on the spot.

De Lutte   8F2

Erve Velpen, Beuningerstraat 25. **GPS:** n52,33224 e7,01197. ⬆.

20 ⌂€ 9, 2 pers.incl ⛽⛃Ch ✎€2 ⌃€1/8minutes ⌃included.
⌃ **Location:** Rural, comfortable, isolated, quiet. **Surface:** grassy.
◷ 01/01-31/12
Distance: 4km ⊗300m ⚓bike junction ⛷on the spot.

Dedemsvaart   8E1

Camperplaats Dedemsvaart, Langewijk 112.
GPS: n52,60435 e6,45108. ⬆.

10 ⌂€ 6,50 ⛽€1,50 ✎€2,50 ⌃. ⌃ **Surface:** metalled.
◷ 01/01-31/12
Distance: 700m ⊗300m ⛽200m.
Remarks: Max. 48h.

Diepenheim   8E2

Camperpark Diepenheim, Esweg 6. **GPS:** n52,18307 e6,57872.

30 ⌂€ 12,50 ⛽⛃Ch ✎(30x),6Amp WC⌃€1 included ⌂.
Location: Rural. **Surface:** grassy/metalled. ◷ 15/03-01/11

Distance: ⚓2km ⛵50m ⛴50m ⊗2km ⛽2km 🚲on the spot 🚶on the spot.

| 🛉 S | **Diepenheim** ⛺ 🏕 | 8E2 |

't Holt, Hengevelderweg 1A. **GPS**: n52,19500 e6,59186. 🔼.

3 🛏€ 5, free for clients 🚰Chfree. **Surface:** metalled.
🅿 01/01-31/12
Distance: ⚓3km ⊗on the spot ⛽3km.
Remarks: Golf court (pitch+putt).

| 🛉 | **Diepenheim** ⛺ 🏕 | 8E2 |

In de Kokkerieje, Grotestraat 94. **GPS**: n52,19923 e6,55452. 🔼.

🛏free with a meal. 🅿 Mo-Tue
Distance: ⚓on the spot ⛴1km ⛽500m.
Remarks: Parking behind restaurant.

| 🛉 | **Enschede** ⛺ 🍴 | 8F2 |

Diekmanterrein, Weggelhorstweg. **GPS**: n52,20543 e6,90096.🔼.

5 🛏free. **Location:** Urban, simple, simple, isolated, quiet.
Surface: asphalted. 🅿 01/01-31/12
Distance: ⚓2km ⛽1,4km 🚌on the spot.

| 🛉 S | **Enschede** ⛺ 🍴 | 8F2 |

De Loeks, Moorvenweg 2a. **GPS**: n52,17757 e6,86599. 🔼➡.

15 🛏€ 7, 01/04-31/10 € 15 🚰Ch 🔌WC⊐included. 🚽
Location: Rural, isolated, quiet. **Surface:** grassy/metalled.
🅿 01/01-31/12 🅿 sanitary 01/11-31/03
Distance: ⚓3km ⛽1km 🚲on the spot 🚶on the spot.

| **Enter** 🏕 | 8E2 |

Werfstraat. **GPS**: n52,29808 e6,58271.🔼.

3 🛏free. **Location:** Urban, simple. **Surface:** grassy/gravel.
🅿 01/01-31/12
Distance: ⚓600m ⛵on the spot ⛴on the spot ⊗600m ⛽700m

🚲on the spot 🚶on the spot.
Remarks: Max. 72h.

| 🛉 S | **Geesteren** | 8F1 |

Zalencentrum Spalink, Koelenbeekweg 10. **GPS**: n52,44060 e6,69555.

15 🛏€ 8,50 🚰Ch 🔌 WC. **Surface:** grassy/gravel.
🅿 01/01-31/12
Distance: ⚓3,5km ⊗on the spot ⛽3,5km 🚲on the spot
🚶on the spot.
Remarks: Guests free.

| 🛉 S | **Giethoorn** 🌿 | 8E1 |

Passantenhaven Zuidercluft, Vosjacht 1G. **GPS**: n52,72134 e6,07449.

30 🛏€ 12, 2 pers.incl., 1/11-1/4 € 6 🚰€0,50/100liter 🔌Ch 🔌
€1/2kWh WC⊐€0,50. **Surface:** grassy. 🅿 01/01-31/12
Distance: ⚓1km ⛵on the spot ⛴on the spot.
Remarks: Check in at harbourmaster, water closed during wintertime.

| 🛉 S | **Giethoorn** 🌿 | 8E1 |

Camperplaats Haamstede, Kanaaldijk 17.
GPS: n52,72828 e6,07570.🔼➡.

35 🛏€ 11, 2 pers.incl 🚰€0,50 🔌Ch 🔌€2 WC⊐€0,50. 🚽
Location: Rural, comfortable, central, quiet. **Surface:** grassy.
🅿 01/04-31/10
Distance: ⚓2km ⛵1km ⛴20m ⊗1km ⛽1km 🚲on the spot
🚶on the spot.

| 🛉 S | **Giethoorn** 🌿 | 8E1 |

Camperresort Bodelaeke, Vosjacht 10A. **GPS**: n52,71703 e6,07668.🔼.
99 🛏€ 14 2 pers.incl, dog € 3,50 🚰€0,50/100liter 🔌Ch 🔌€3
WC⊐🔌€6/4 🔌.
Location: Rural, comfortable.
Surface: grasstiles/grassy.
🅿 02/03-31/10
Distance: ⚓1km ⛵on the spot ⛴on the spot.

Tourist information Giethoorn:
ℹ VVV, Eendrachtsplein 1, www.kopvanoverijssel.nl. Village in nature reserve De Weerribben, Dutch Venice, boat trips possible.

| 🛉 S | **Haaksbergen** | 8F2 |

Henk Pen Caravans en Kampeerauto's, Westsingel 2.
GPS: n52,14917 e6,71167.

2 🛏free 🔌free. **Surface:** asphalted. 🅿 01/01-31/12
Distance: ⚓1km ⛵on the spot ⊗on the spot ⛽1km.

Remarks: Motorhome dealer.

| S | **Haaksbergen** | 8F2 |

Camping Scholtenhagen, Scholtenhagenweg 30.
GPS: n52,14820 e6,72467.

24 🛏€ 10 🚰🔌Ch 🔋 🔌(24x),6Amp WC⊐🔌€0,85 🔌€5,25/1
🔌included. **Surface:** grassy. 🅿 01/03-30/09
Distance: ⚓2km ⛵7km ⛴3km ⊗2km ⛽2,5km 🚌1km
🚲on the spot 🚶on the spot.
Remarks: Max. 72h.

| 🛉 S | **Hardenberg** | 8E1 |

De Kuserbrink, Parkweg. **GPS**: n52,57746 e6,62927.🔼.

4 🛏€ 10 🚰€0,50/100liter 🔌Ch 🔌(4x)€1/kWh. 🔌
Location: Rural, comfortable, central, quiet. **Surface:** grasstiles.
🅿 01/01-31/12
Distance: ⚓centre 500m ⛵on the spot 🚶on the spot.
Remarks: Max. 72h.

| 🛉 S | **Hardenberg** | 8E1 |

Fam. Pullen, Allemansweg 1a, Collendoorn.
GPS: n52,58845 e6,59146.🔼.

20 🛏€ 10 🚰🔌Ch 🔌🔌 🔌included. 🚽 **Location:** Rural,
comfortable, isolated, quiet. **Surface:** grassy. 🅿 01/01-31/12
Distance: ⚓3km ⊗3km 🚲bike junction 🚶on the spot.
Remarks: Dog on leads.

| 🛉 S | **Hasselt** 🌿 ⛺ 🍴 | 8E1 |

Jachthaven de Molenwaard, Van Nahuysweg 151.
GPS: n52,59367 e6,08741.🔼➡.

10 🛏€ 8,50 + € 0,70/pp tourist tax 🚰🔌Ch 🔌(10x)€2/1night WC
⊐🔌€0,50/6minutes 🔌€3,75/3,75 🔌included. 🚽
Location: Luxurious, quiet. **Surface:** metalled. 🅿 01/01-31/12
Distance: ⚓500m ⛵on the spot ⛴on the spot ⊗500m ⛽500m
🚌500m 🚲on the spot 🚶on the spot.
Remarks: Check in at harbourmaster.

| 🛉 S | **Heeten** | 8E1 |

De Baanbreker, Speelmansweg 8. **GPS**: n52,36026 e6,31190.🔼➡.

10 🛏€4 🚰€1 💧€0,50 Ch€0,50 💧€1,50. **Surface:** metalled.
⬛ 01/01-31/12
Distance: 🛒2km ⊗2km 🛢2km 🚿 on the spot 🚶 on the spot.

Hellendoorn

Camperplaats Hancate, Zuidelijke Kanaaldijk.
GPS: n52,43418 e6,44060. ⬆➡.

10 🛏€10 🚰💧Ch💧(4x)📶included. 🚿
Location: Rural, simple, quiet. **Surface:** grassy. ⬛ 01/01-31/12
Distance: 🛒5km 🛒on the spot ⊗100m 🛢200m 🚿on the spot
🚶 on the spot.

Hengelo 8F2

Camperplaats Eulerhook, Vöckersweg 19.
GPS: n52,24652 e6,75365. ⬆➡.

15 🛏€8 🚰💧Ch💧🚽WC📶included. 🚿 **Location:** Rural,
luxurious, noisy. **Surface:** grassy/metalled. ⬛ 01/01-31/12
Distance: 🛒4km 🏊2km 🛒500m ⊗4km 🛢3km 🚐1km
🚿 on the spot 🚶 on the spot.
Remarks: Nearby motorway.

Hertme 8F2

Camperpark Rabo Scheele, Hertmerweg 37.
GPS: n52,32663 e6,74691. ⬆➡.

25 🛏€12, 2 pers.incl 🚰💧Ch💧🚽WC📶included. 🚿
Location: Rural, comfortable, quiet. **Surface:** grassy/metalled.
⬛ 01/01-31/12
Distance: 🛒Hertme 500m, Borne 2km 🛒100m 🛢500m 🏊2km
🚐2km 🚿on the spot 🚶 on the spot.

Kampen 8E1

Burgemeester Berghuisplein 1. **GPS:** n52,55268 e5,91356. ⬆.

25 🛏€7,50 🚰💧ChWCincluded 💧€0,50/6minutes. 🛢

Location: Urban, comfortable, central, quiet.
Surface: metalled.
⬛ 01/01-31/12
Distance: 🛒historical centre 500m 🏊1,5km 🛒1,5km ⊗900m
🛢1km 🚿on the spot 🚶 on the spot.
Remarks: Max. 72h,
entrance code sanitary building at town hall.

Tourist information Kampen:
ℹ VVV, Oudestraat 151,
www.vvvkampen.nl. Former Hanseatic town on the Ijssel.

Losser 8F2

Brilmansdennen, Bookholtlaan. **GPS:** n52,26917 e7,01361. ⬆➡.

3 🛏free. **Surface:** metalled. ⬛ 01/01-31/12
Distance: 🛒1km.
Remarks: At sports park, max. 72h.

Nieuwleusen 8E1

Koninging Julianalaan. **GPS:** n52,58213 e6,28076. ⬆.

3 🛏free. **Location:** Urban, simple. **Surface:** metalled.
⬛ 01/01-31/12
Distance: 🛒300m 🚿on the spot 🚶 on the spot.
Remarks: Max. 48h.

Nijverdal 8E1

De Wilgenweard, Sportlaan 6. **GPS:** n52,37118 e6,46538. ⬆➡.

3 🛏€5 + €0,50/pp tourist tax. 🚿 **Surface:** grasstiles/metalled.
⬛ 01/01-31/12
Distance: 🛒500m 🏊on the spot 🛒on the spot ⊗on the spot
🛢500m 🛢200m 🚿on the spot 🚶 on the spot.

Oldemarkt 8E1

Vaartjes partycentrum, Kruisstraat 86-88.
GPS: n52,82095 e5,96698. ⬆➡.

10 🛏free for clients. **Surface:** asphalted. ⬛ 01/01-31/12
Distance: 🛒200m 🏊on the spot 🛒on the spot ⊗on the spot
🛢200m.

Ommen 8E1

Landgoed De Stekkenkamp, Beerzerweg 3.
GPS: n52,51128 e6,43933. ⬆➡.

8 🛏€7,50 + €0,83/pp tourist tax 🚰€0,50/4minutes 💧Ch💧(8x).
🚿 **Location:** Rural, simple, quiet.
Surface: grasstiles/grassy.
⬛ 01/01-31/12
Distance: 🛒1,2km 🏊1,2km 🛒1,2km ⊗1,2km 🛢1,2km 🚐1,2km.
Remarks: At historical farmhouse, max. 72h.

Steenwijk 8E1

Jachthaven, Houthaven. **GPS:** n52,78627 e6,10006. ⬆➡.

20 🛏€10 🚰💧💧€1. **Surface:** grassy. ⬛ 01/01-31/12
Distance: 🛒1km 🏊on the spot 🛒on the spot 🛢300m.
Remarks: Check in at harbourmaster.

Tubbergen 8F1

De Vlaskoel, Sportlaan 3. **GPS:** n52,41043 e6,78316. ⬆.

2 🛏free. **Location:** Simple, simple. **Surface:** metalled.
⬛ 01/01-31/12
Distance: 🛒500m ⊗600m 🛢600m 🚿on the spot 🚶 on the spot.
Remarks: At swimming pool.

Vollenhove 8E1

De Haven. **GPS:** n52,68277 e5,94862. ⬆.

6 🛏€12 🚰💧Ch💧€1 WC🛢0,50. **Surface:** metalled.
⬛ 01/01-31/12
Distance: 🛒100m 🛒100m 🛢1km.
Remarks: Check in at harbourmaster.

Vollenhove 8E1

Recreatiecentrum 't Akkertien, Op de Voorst, Noordwal 3.
GPS: n52,67609 e5,93914.

20 🛏€8 🚰💧Ch💧included. ⬛ 01/01-31/12
Distance: 🛒900m 🏊on the spot 🛒on the spot 🛢400m
🚐peak season.

NL

Wierden 8E1

De Huurne, Zandinksweg 22. **GPS**: n52,34899 e6,57191.

10 € 10 Ch included. ☐ 01/01-31/12
Distance: 2km 3km 2km 700m.
Remarks: Max. 3 nights, max 3,5t.

Wierden 8E1

Wijngaard Baan, Kloosterhoeksweg 15. **GPS**: n52,32172 e6,56709.

24 € 11,50 Ch WC. **Surface:** metalled.
☐ 01/01-31/12
Distance: 3km on the spot on the spot 3km on the spot
on the spot.
Remarks: Vineyard.

Wijhe 8E1

Passantenhaven, Veerweg. **GPS**: n52,38639 e6,12830.

10 € 6 + € 0,45/pp tourist tax Ch WC included.
Location: Simple, central. **Surface:** asphalted/metalled.
☐ 01/04-01/10
Distance: 500m on the spot on the spot 500m 500m
on the spot on the spot.
Remarks: Max. 3 nights.
Tourist information Wijhe:
Marktplein. ☐ Tue-morning.

Zwartsluis 8E1

Voetbalvereniging DESZ, Clingellanden. **GPS**: n52,64437 e6,07810.

10 € 5 Ch. **Surface:** gravel.
Remarks: Service at marina.
Tourist information Zwartsluis:
Stoomgemaal Mastenbroek, Kamperzeedijk 5, Genemuiden.
Pumping-engine, 1856.

Zwolle 8E1
Turfmarkt. **GPS**: n52,51326 e6,10380.

7 mo-sa 8-18h € 4/day, free overnight stay. **Location:** Urban,
simple, central. **Surface:** metalled. ☐ 01/01-31/12
Distance: 800m 1km 650m on the spot on the spot.
Remarks: Max. 72h.

Zwolle 8E1

Jachthaven de Hanze, Holtenbroekerdijk 44.
GPS: n52,53056 e6,07527.

15 € 8 + € 0,60/pp tourist tax Ch (15x)€0,50/kWh
WC included € 1/7minutes.
Location: Rural, comfortable, central, quiet. **Surface:** grassy/metalled.
☐ 01/01-31/12
Distance: 2,5km 2km on the spot on the spot 1km
1km 500m on the spot.
Remarks: Max. 72h.
Tourist information Zwolle:
Sassenpoort, Koestraat 46. Medieval gate building. ☐ Wed-Fri
14-17h, Sa-Su 12-17h.
Ecodrome, Willemsvaart 19. Theme park, history of nature, geology.
☐ 01/04-31/10 10-17, 01/11-31/03 Wed, Sa, Su 10-17h.

Flevoland

Almere 8D2

Marina Muiderzand, IJmeerdijk 4. **GPS**: n52,34302 e5,13521.

10 € 13,50 Ch WC € 5/3 included.
Surface: asphalted. ☐ 01/05-30/09
Distance: 8km on the spot on the spot on the spot
on the spot 1km.
Remarks: Check in at harbourmaster.
Tourist information Almere:
VVV, De Diagonaal 199, www.vvvalmere.nl.
Stadhuisplein. ☐ Wed, Sa 9-16h.
Biologische Boerenmarkt, Kempenhaanpad 14,
www.stadsboerderijalmere.nl. ☐ Sa 9.30-13h.

Almere-Haven 8D2

WSV Almere, Sluiskade 11. **GPS**: n52,33257 e5,21715.

40 € 11, 2 pers.incl Ch (12x)€0,50/2kWh WC € 5
included.
Location: Urban, simple. **Surface:** grassy. ☐ 01/01-31/12
Distance: on the spot on the spot 200m on the spot.

Almere-Haven 8D2

Haven, Sluis. **GPS**: n52,33366 e5,22170.

2 € 1,05/m per night Ch WC € 0,50.
Surface: metalled.
☐ 02/05-04/09
Distance: on the spot 1km on the spot on the spot 1km.
Remarks: Max. 72h, check in at harbourmaster.
Tourist information Almere-Haven:
De Brink. ☐ Fri 9-16h.

Emmeloord 8D1

Camperplaats Emmeloord, Casteleynsweg 1.
GPS: n52,73981 e5,77235.
12 € 9 Ch € 2/day included. **Surface:** grassy.
☐ 11/04-31/10
Distance: 4,9km 150m.
Remarks: 2 bicyclces available.

Lelystad 8D1

P Houtribhoek, Houtribslag. **GPS**: n52,54630 e5,45750.

4 free.
Surface: metalled.
☐ 01/01-31/12
Distance: 2km on the spot on the spot
on the spot 2km.
Remarks: Max. 48h.
Tourist information Lelystad:
Oostvaardersplassen. 6000 acres of lakes, mud fields, reed swamps,
hiking route 5km and cycle route 35 km.
Batavia Stad, Bataviaplein 60. Outlet-shopping.
☐ daily 10-18h.
free, parking € 2,50/4h.

Luttelgeest 8D1

Recreatie en Horeca bedrijf Craneburcht, Kuinderweg 52.
GPS: n52,78304 e5,84331.

10 € 10. **Surface:** metalled.
☐ 01/03-30/11 winter: Mo-Tue
Distance: 200m on the spot 7km.
Remarks: Arrival >17h, departure <10h.

Nagele 8D1

Afslag Nagele, Han Stijkelweg 11. **GPS**: n52,65278 e5,68417.

---

10 🛏 € 12 🔌🚰Ch🚿€2 WC included free.

Location: Comfortable, isolated, quiet. **Surface:** grassy/metalled.

🗓 01/01-31/12

Distance: 3km.

Remarks: Max. 5 days.

Urk 8D1

Haven, Burgemeester Schipperkade. **GPS:** n52,66040 e5,59975.⬆️

24 🛏 € 15 🚰Ch🚿(18x)WC included.

Surface: metalled.

🗓 01/01-31/12

Distance: 200m 100m 🚰 100m, bakery 300m.

Tourist information Urk:

ℹ️ VVV, Wijk 3 2, www.vvvflevoland.nl. Old fishermen's village, former island.

Ⓜ️ Het Oude Raadhuis, Wijk 2 2. Regional museum.

🗓 01/04-31/10 Mo-Fr 10-17h, Sa 10-16h, 01/03-30/11 Mo-Sa 10-16h.

⚓ Urkerhard.

🗓 Sa 8.30-13h.

🚶 Stegentocht/Ginkiestocht. Guided walk, reservation at Touristinfo Urk. Ⓣ € 4.

Zeewolde 8D2

Camperpark De Wielewaal, Wielseweg 9. **GPS:** n52,25981 e5,43727.

50 🛏 € 11 + € 1,50/pp tourist tax 🚰Ch included 🚿€2 WC against payment. **Surface:** metalled. 🗓 01/01-31/12

Distance: 7km on the spot on the spot 🚰7km.

Gelderland

Aalten 8F2

't Noorden, Lichtenvoordsestraatweg 44. **GPS:** n51,93326 e6,58221.⬆️

4 🛏 € 10 🚰€1/80liter Ch included WC free.

Location: Rural. **Surface:** gravel.

🗓 01/01-31/12

Distance: 700m on the spot.

Tourist information Aalten:

👁 Wijngoed De Hennepe, Romienendiek 3, www.wijngoeddehennepe. nl. Guided tour and tastery. 🛒 shop Tue-Fr 13.30h-sunset, Sa 10h, guided tour/tasting Jul/Aug We 15h.

⚓ Hoge Blik. 🗓 Thu 8-12h.

Aerdt 8E2

De Aerdtse Wacht, Heuvelakkersestraat 18.

GPS: n51,88634 e6,08861.⬆️

4 🛏 € 10 🚰€1/80liter Ch🚿🗑

Location: Rural. **Surface:** metalled. 🗓 01/01-31/12

Distance: on the spot on the spot on the spot on the spot.

Almen 8E2

De Nieuwe Aanleg, Scheggertdijk 10. **GPS:** n52,16711 e6,29744.⬆️➡️

12 🛏 € 12 🚰€0,75/100liter Ch🚿(12x)included WC€ 0,75/5minutes. **Location:** Rural, comfortable, quiet.

Surface: metalled. 🗓 01/01-31/12

Distance: 2km on the spot on the spot on the spot 🚰2km on the spot on the spot on the spot.

Remarks: At the Twentekanaal.

Tourist information Almen:

⚓ Dorpsstraat. Small week market. 🗓 Tue 11-13h.

Apeldoorn 8E2

Malkander, Dubbelbeek 38. **GPS:** n52,18305 e5,96673.⬆️

4 🛏 free. **Location:** Simple, isolated. **Surface:** metalled.

🗓 01/01-31/12, 15-09h

Distance: 2km 150m 🚰1km.

Remarks: At swimming pool.

Tourist information Apeldoorn:

⚓ Marktplein. 🗓 Wed 8-13h, Sa 8-17h.

Appeltern 8D3

Herberg 't Mun, Molenstraat 10, Blauwe Sluis.

GPS: n51,84048 e5,56360.

50 🛏 € 5 🚰Ch (12x)€2,6Amp WC included.

Location: Rural, simple, isolated, quiet. **Surface:** grassy/metalled.

🗓 01/01-31/12

Distance: 2km 300m Trout farm on the spot 🚰2km on the spot on the spot on the spot.

Remarks: Show-garden Appeltern 3km.

Arnhem 8E2

Nieuwe Kade. GPS: n51,97327 e5,91593.⬆️

4 🛏 € 9 🚰€2,50/time Ch🚿(4x)€0,50/kWh WC

Location: Urban, simple, central, quiet. **Surface:** metalled.

🗓 01/01-31/12

Distance: 1km 4,7km 200m 🚰1km 1km on the spot on the spot.

Remarks: Along the Rhine river.

Tourist information Arnhem:

⚓ Jansplaats. Small week market. 🗓 Tue 7.30-15h.

Bemmel 8C2

Dijkstraat/Wardstraat. **GPS:** n51,88972 e5,00000.⬆️➡️

3 🛏 free. **Location:** Urban, simple, central, quiet. **Surface:** metalled.

🗓 01/01-31/12

Distance: 400m 400m 🚰400m 400m on the spot on the spot.

Remarks: Max. 72h.

Borculo 8E2

Hambroekplas, Hambroekweg 10. **GPS:** n52,11573 e6,53758.⬆️

4 🛏 € 10 🚰€1/80liter Ch included. **Location:** Rural, comfortable, quiet. **Surface:** gravel. 🗓 01/03-31/10

Distance: 500m 150m 50m on the spot on the spot.

Borculo 8E2

Bruggink Campers, Kamerlingh Onnestraat 19.

GPS: n52,12281 e6,52682.

6 🛏 free 🚿on demand. **Surface:** metalled.

🗓 01/01-31/12, 18-9h

Distance: 1,5km 2km 500m 1,5km 🚰1,5km.

Bredevoort 8F2

P2, recreatieplaats Slingeplas, Kruittorenstraat 10b.

GPS: n51,94749 e6,62346.⬆️➡️

NL

8 € 10 €1/80liter Ch (8x)included.
Location: Rural, comfortable, quiet. **Surface:** metalled.
01/01-31/12
Distance: 200m 100m 400m 500m.
Remarks: Max. 72h.

Tourist information Bredevoort:
VVV, Markt 8. City with half-timbered houses.
Book market. 3rd Sa of the month 10-17.

Culemborg 8D2

Jachthaven de Helling, Beusichemsedijk.
GPS: n51,96117 e5,22148.

20 € 14, 1,55 pers.incl, € 1,55/pp tourist tax €0,50/100liter Ch WC €0,50 €4/4 included. **Surface:** grassy/sand.
01/04-01/11
Distance: 500m on the spot on the spot on the spot 500m 1,5km.
Remarks: Check in at harbourmaster.

De Heurne 8E2

De Haar, Caspersstraat 14. **GPS**: n51,89802 e6,50035.

± 10 € 10 €1/80liter Ch included.
Location: Rural, quiet. **Surface:** grassy. 01/01-31/12
Distance: 1km 8km.
Remarks: Filling station gas bottles 300m.

Doesburg 8E2

Jachthaven Doesburg, Turfhaven. **GPS**: n52,01109 e6,13368.

6 € 7,50 Ch (6x)€0,50/kWh WC included €0,50/4minutes.
Location: Urban, comfortable, central, quiet. **Surface:** concrete.
01/01-31/12
Distance: 500m 4km on the spot 500m 1km 500m on the spot on the spot.
Remarks: Check in at harbourmaster.

Doornenburg 8E2

Kerkstraat. **GPS**: n51,89416 e6,00129.

3 free.
Location: Rural, quiet.
Surface: metalled.
01/01-31/12
Distance: 400m 200m cafetaria 200m 400m on the spot.
Remarks: Max. 3 days, view on castle Doornenburg.

Elburg 8D1

Gemeentehaven Elburg, Havenkade 1. **GPS**: n52,45110 e5,82933.

18 € 7,85 + € 1,05/pp tourist tax Ch €0,50/24h WC €0,50 included. **Location:** Comfortable, central, quiet.
Surface: grasstiles/metalled. 01/01-31/12
Distance: 250m on the spot on the spot 300m 300m on the spot on the spot on the spot.
Remarks: Max. 3 days, water closed during wintertime.

Emst 8E2

De Kievit, Zwarteweg 20. **GPS**: n52,30344 e5,99320.

15 € 10, 2 pers.incl, extra pers € 1,50 Ch €2/night,6Amp included. **Location:** Rural, simple, quiet.
Surface: grassy/metalled. 01/01-31/12
Distance: 3km 1km 1km on the spot on the spot.

Emst 8E2

Recreatiepark 't Smallert, Smallertsweg 8.
GPS: n52,30910 e5,98126.

20 € 5 free. **Surface:** metalled. 01/01-31/12
Distance: 2km on the spot.
Remarks: Check in on arrival.

Epe 8E2

Pastoor Somstraat. **GPS**: n52,34965 e5,98331.

3 free. **Location:** Urban, simple. **Surface:** metalled.
01/01-31/12
Distance: on the spot 3km on the spot on the spot.

Ermelo 8D2

Camperpark Strand Horst, Buitenbrinkweg 82.
GPS: n52,31181 e5,56643.

40 € 10, 2 pers.incl Ch (50x) WC €0,50/6minutes included. **Location:** Rural, comfortable, noisy.
Surface: grassy/metalled. 01/03-31/10
Distance: 4km 50m 200m 200m 500m 4km.

Garderen 8D2

Hotel Restaurant Overbosch, Hooiweg 23.
GPS: n52,22577 e5,70504.

10 € 7,50 €2,50/24h . **Location:** Rural, simple, quiet.
Surface: gravel. 01/01-31/12
Distance: 1km on the spot 1km on the spot on the spot on the spot.
Remarks: Use of a meal desired.

Garderen 8D2

Gasterij Zondag, Apeldoornsestraat 163-165.
GPS: n52,21443 e5,70696.

10 free. **Location:** Rural.
Surface: gravel.
01/01-31/12 Restaurant: Tue
Distance: 2km 3,5km on the spot on the spot on the spot.
Remarks: Max. 1 night, entrance next to restaurant, restaurant visit appreciated.

Geldermalsen 8D2

Kostverlorenkade. **GPS**: n51,88421 e5,28985.

1 free. **Surface:** metalled.
Distance: 100m 3,6km on the spot on the spot on the spot.
Remarks: Parking at departure excursion boat.

Gendringen 8E2

Willem Alexanderplein. **GPS**: n51,86999 e6,37948.

2 free. **Location:** Simple. **Surface:** asphalted. 01/01-31/12
Distance: 200m 100m 500m.
Remarks: Max. 72h.

Gendringen 8E2

Diekshuus, Ulftseweg 4a. **GPS**: n51,87397 e6,38489.

4 ⬛€ 10 ⬛€1 ⬛ ⬛ included. ⬛ **Location:** Rural, simple.
Surface: gravel. ⬛ 01/01-31/12
Distance: ⬛600m ⬛600m.
Remarks: At manege.

Gorssel 8E2

De Vlinderhoeve, Bathmenseweg 7. **GPS:** n52,21825 e6,26255. ⬛⬛

5 ⬛€ 14 ⬛⬛Ch.⬛ WC ⬛⬛€5/1,50 ⬛included.⬛
Location: Rural, luxurious, quiet. **Surface:** forest soil.
⬛ 01/04-31/10
Distance: ⬛8km ⬛on the spot ⬛on the spot ⬛on the spot
⬛on the spot ⬛on the spot.

Groenlo 8F2

Camping Marveld, Elshofweg. **GPS:** n52,03698 e6,63187.⬛

4 ⬛€ 10 ⬛€1/80liter ⬛Ch ⬛. **Surface:** metalled.
⬛ 01/01-31/12

Harderwijk 8D2

P Parkweg, Parkweg. **GPS:** n52,34088 e5,62977.⬛

3 ⬛free. **Location:** Urban, simple. **Surface:** metalled.
⬛ 01/01-31/12
Distance: ⬛1,2km ⬛3km ⬛1,3km ⬛800m.

Hattem 8E1

Jachthaven Hattem, Geldersedijk 20. **GPS:** n52,47699 e6,06945.⬛

Heerde 8E1

Brasserie Meet & Eat, Eperweg 55. **GPS:** n52,37084 e6,02079.

10 ⬛free, use of a meal desired ⬛⬛(2x)included WC ⬛ ⬛.
Surface: grassy/gravel.
⬛ Su (01/10-30/04)
Distance: ⬛3km ⬛1,5km ⬛1,5km ⬛on the spot ⬛2km ⬛100m.

Hengelo 8E2

Elderinkweg 1-9. **GPS:** n52,04457 e6,30377.⬛

2 ⬛free. **Surface:** asphalted. ⬛ 01/01-31/12
Distance: ⬛500m ⬛100m.
Remarks: Next to sports fields, max. 24h.

Heteren 8D2

Steenkuil, N837. **GPS:** n51,95456 e5,73094.⬛

3 ⬛free. **Location:** Rural, simple, isolated, quiet.
Surface: gravel/metalled.
⬛ 01/01-31/12
Distance: ⬛2km ⬛2km ⬛2km ⬛2km ⬛on the spot ⬛on the spot.
Remarks: Max. 72h.

Huissen 8E2

Looveer. **GPS:** n51,93578 e5,94467.⬛⬛

3 ⬛free. **Location:** Simple, central. **Surface:** grasstiles/metalled.
⬛ 01/01-31/12
Distance: ⬛200m ⬛200m ⬛200m ⬛200m ⬛500m
⬛on the spot ⬛on the spot.
Remarks: Max. 72h.

Kerkwijk 8D3

Hippisch Centrum Bommelerwaard, Jan Stuversdreef 1-3.
GPS: n51,78876 e5,19929.⬛

4 ⬛€ 10 ⬛ WC ⬛included. **Surface:** metalled.

⬛ 01/01-31/12 ⬛ Su

Lathum 8E2

Jachthaven 't Eiland, De Muggenwaard 16.
GPS: n51,98819 e6,04462.⬛⬛

20 ⬛€ 8,50 ⬛⬛Ch ⬛(20x)€1,50/day WC included ⬛€
0,50/4minutes ⬛⬛€3/day. ⬛ **Location:** Rural, comfortable, quiet.
Surface: grassy/metalled. ⬛ 01/01-31/12
Distance: ⬛1km ⬛5km ⬛on the spot ⬛on the spot ⬛on the spot
⬛1km ⬛500m ⬛on the spot ⬛on the spot.
Remarks: Max. 48h.

Lichtenvoorde 8E2

't Meekenesch, Kerkhoflaan 5. **GPS:** n51,99305 e6,56831.⬛

3 ⬛free. **Surface:** metalled. ⬛ 01/01-31/12
Distance: ⬛1km ⬛100m.
Remarks: Parking swimming pool, max. 72h.

Maasbommel 8D3

Saletmeubelen, Kapelstraat 30. **GPS:** n51,82459 e5,53193.⬛

5 ⬛€ 10 ⬛⬛Ch ⬛ ⬛included. ⬛ 01/01-31/12
Distance: ⬛300m ⬛1km ⬛1km ⬛1km ⬛300m.

Meteren 8D3

Restaurant den Tol, Rijksstraatweg 80. **GPS:** n51,85759 e5,28009.

5 ⬛free.
Remarks: Use of a meal desired.

Millingen a/d Rijn 8E3

't Crumpse Hoekje, Crumpsestraat 28.
GPS: n51,85624 e6,03145.⬛⬛

6 ⬛€ 6,50 + tourist tax ⬛ 0,75/pp ⬛€1/90liter ⬛Ch ⬛(6x)€2/day
WC free ⬛€1. ⬛ **Location:** Rural, luxurious, quiet. **Surface:** gravel.
⬛ 01/01-31/12

Distance: 🚶1,4km 🚲2km ⊗1,4km 🛒1,4km.

Neede | 8F2

Café restaurant De Olde Mölle, Diepenheimseweg 21.
GPS: n52,14153 e6,61035.

8 💶€ 10 🚰€1/80liter 🔌Ch🚿. **Surface:** metalled.
⚪ 01/01-31/12
Distance: ⊗on the spot.

Neede | 8F2

Partycentrum 't Haantje, Borculoseweg 111.
GPS: n52,13437 e6,59886.⬆️

5 💶€ 5, free with a meal 🚰🔌🚿WCincluded. **Surface:** gravel.
Distance: 🚶600m ⊗on the spot 🛒500m 🚲on the spot.
Remarks: Rental of electric scooters and bicycles.

Neede | 8F2

Den Blanken, Diepneheimseweg 44. **GPS:** n52,18013 e6,58603.⬆️➡️

4 💶€ 10 🚰€1/80liter 🔌Ch🚿included. 🚐 **Location:** Quiet.
Surface: grassy. ⚪ 01/01-31/12 🚲on the spot 🚶on the spot.

Nijkerk | 8D2

Camperplaats Nijkerk, Watergoorweg 31.
GPS: n52,22641 e5,47711.⬆️

2 💶free. **Location:** Urban, simple, noisy. **Surface:** metalled.
⚪ 01/01-31/12
Distance: 🚶500m 🚲2km 🛒2km 🚶500m ⊗500m 🛒500m
🚲200m 🚲on the spot 🚶on the spot.

Nijmegen | 8E3

Lindenberghaven, Waalkade. **GPS:** n51,84889 e5,86936.⬆️

6 💶€ 20 🚰(6x)€0,50/kWh. 🚐
Location: Urban, simple, central, noisy. **Surface:** metalled.
⚪ 01/05-01/09 ⚫ during the Four Days Marche

Distance: 🚶on the spot 🚲on the spot 🚲on the spot.
Remarks: Along the river Waal, max. 72h.

Nunspeet | 8D1

Camperplaats De Zwaan, Hardenbrinkweg 46.
GPS: n52,37901 e5,75363.⬆️➡️

35 💶€ 13 🚰🔌Ch🚿(45x)WC🚽€3/3 📶included. 🚲
Location: Rural, comfortable, luxurious, quiet.
Surface: grasstiles/grassy. ⚪ 01/01-31/12
Distance: 🚶2,5km 🚴3,5km 🚲2,5km 🚲2,5km ⊗1km 🛒2km
🚲900m 🚲Zwanenroute 🚶on the spot.
Remarks: No arrival on Sunday.

Nunspeet | 8D1

Routiers Nunspeet, Rijksweg A28. **GPS:** n52,36199 e5,77061.⬆️

💶free WC🚽. **Surface:** asphalted. ⚪ 01/01-31/12
Remarks: Use of sanitary free with a meal.

Tourist information Nunspeet:
🎋 ⚪ Thu-morning.

Otterlo | 8D2

De Wije Werelt Otterlo

- **Luxurious motorhome stopover**
- **Located in nature reserve**
- **Ideal base for walking and cycling**

www.wijewerelt.nl
info@wijewerelt.nl

De Wije Werelt, Arnhemseweg 100-102. **GPS:** n52,08592 e5,77319.
50 💶€ 18-25 🚰🔌Ch🚿(10x)WC🚽included 🚽€5/2 📶€3,50/day.
🚲 **Location:** Rural, simple. **Surface:** grassy.
⚪ 01/01-31/12
Distance: 🚶500m 🚲500m ⊗on the spot 🛒campsite supermarket
🛒on the spot 🚲on the spot 🚶on the spot.

Tourist information Otterlo:
Ⓜ Kröller Muller Museum. Collection.

Putten | 8D2

Brinkstraat. GPS: n52,26244 e5,60756.⬆️

2 💶free. **Location:** Urban, simple, central. **Surface:** metalled.

⚪ 01/01-31/12
Distance: 🚶200m ⊗300m 🛒300m 🚲250m 🚲on the spot
🚶on the spot.
Remarks: Max. 48h.

Tourist information Putten:
🎋 ⚪ Wed.

Rekken | 8F2

Grensovergang, Oldenkotseweg. **GPS:** n52,09783 e6,75568.⬆️

5 💶€ 5. **Surface:** metalled. ⚪ 01/01-31/12
Distance: 🚶on the spot ⊗on the spot 🛒on the spot.
Remarks: Max. 72h, cycle and hiking routes.

Ressen | 8E2

De Woerdt, Woerdsestraat 4. **GPS:** n51,88867 e5,87215.

15 💶€ 7,50 + € 1/pp tourist tax 🚿(10x)included. 🚲
Location: Rural. **Surface:** grassy/metalled.
⚪ 01/01-31/12
Distance: 🚶2km 🚴3,6km 🛒2km.
Remarks: Regional products, pitches in the orchard.

Ruurlo | 8E2

Camping Tamaring, Wildpad 3. **GPS:** n52,10239 e6,44257.⬆️

2 💶€ 10 🚰€1/80liter 🔌Ch🚿included. 🚐
Location: Simple. **Surface:** forest soil. ⚪ 01/01-31/12
Distance: 🚶2km 🚲on the spot 🚶on the spot.
Remarks: Max. 8M.

Silvolde | 8E2

Parking de Paasberg, Terborgseveld. **GPS:** n51,91633 e6,37194.⬆️

4 💶free. **Location:** Urban. **Surface:** metalled. ⚪ 01/01-31/12
Distance: 🚶city centre 1km ⊗300m.
Remarks: Parking at swimming pool, max. 72h.

Sinderen | 8E2

Natuurlijkbuiten, Toldijk 11. **GPS:** n51,91297 e6,42384.

2 € 12 (2x)included. **Location:** Rural.
Surface: grassy/gravel. 01/01-31/12
Distance: 3km 3km on the spot 3km 3km 2km on the spot on the spot.
Remarks: Bread-service.

Sinderen — 8E2

Biezenhof, Kapelweg 42a. **GPS:** n51,90370 e6,45285.

4 € 10 €1/80liter Ch included.
Location: Rural, simple. **Surface:** gravel. 01/01-31/12

Stokkum — 8E2

Camping Brockhausen, Eltenseweg 20. **GPS:** n51,87778 e6,21167.

4 € 10 €1/80liter Ch included €2,50/day.
Location: Rural. **Surface:** grasstiles. 01/01-31/12
Distance: 800m 500m 2,5km 2km on the spot on the spot.
Remarks: At the edge of the forest, max. 2 nights, bread-service.

Terschuur — 8D2

Camperplaats Groot Westerveld, Leemweg 2.
GPS: n52,16819 e5,53239.

4 € 7,50 Ch €2,50/night,10Amp WC included.
Location: Rural, simple, quiet. **Surface:** grassy/metalled.
01/03-30/09
Distance: 1,5km 4km 2km 3km 2km 1km on the spot on the spot.

Terwolde — 8E2

Dorpsstraat 53, N792. **GPS:** n52,28173 e6,09962.

2 free. **Location:** Simple, central, quiet. **Surface:** metalled.
01/01-31/12
Distance: 100m on the spot on the spot on the spot on the spot.

Tiel — 8D2

Parking Waalkade, Waalkade. **GPS:** n51,88518 e5,44079.

4 € 5,10. **Surface:** asphalted. 01/01-31/12
Distance: 500m on the spot on the spot on the spot 500m on the spot.
Remarks: Max. 2 nights, cash payment.

Toldijk — 8E2

Prinsen, Hardsteestraat 4. **GPS:** n52,04489 e6,21737.

2 € 6 Chincluded (1x)€2,50.
Location: Rural, simple, quiet. **Surface:** grassy. 01/01-31/12
Distance: 1,5km 5km 5km 1,5km 2km 300m on the spot.
Remarks: Max. 3 nights.

Tolkamer — 8E3

Europakade, Europakade. **GPS:** n51,85122 e6,09938.

15 € 7,50 + € 0,80/pp tourist tax (6x)€1/kWh.
Location: Simple, central, quiet. **Surface:** metalled.
01/01-31/12 high water
Distance: 200m 150m 200m 500m on the spot on the spot.
Remarks: Max. 48h.

Tolkamer — 8E3

De Swaenebloem, Bijland 3. **GPS:** n51,86235 e6,07937.

12 € 11,20 Ch (12x)€1,50/day WCincluded.
Location: Rural, comfortable, quiet. **Surface:** grassy.
01/01-31/12
Distance: 3,5km 100m on the spot on the spot 3,5km 3km on the spot on the spot.
Remarks: Max. 2 nights, charging point for electric bicycles.

Twello — 8E2

Jachtlustplein 7. **GPS:** n52,23439 e6,09847.

1 free. **Location:** Urban, simple, central, quiet. **Surface:** metalled.
01/01-31/12
Distance: 100m 100m 100m on the spot on the spot on the spot.

Vaassen — 8E2

Julianalaan. **GPS:** n52,29040 e5,96550.

4 free. **Location:** Simple. **Surface:** asphalted.
Distance: on the spot 100m.
Remarks: Max. 48h.

Varsseveld — 8E2

Pallandtbad, Pallandstraat 4. **GPS:** n51,94444 e6,46639.

3 free. **Surface:** metalled. 01/01-31/12
Distance: 200m 200m 200m 200m.
Remarks: Max. 24h.

Vierakker — 8E2

Hanzestadcampers, Vierakkersestraatweg 19.
GPS: n52,10659 e6,24122.

3 € 7,50 Ch (3x) included.
Location: Rural, simple, quiet. **Surface:** gravel. 01/01-31/12
Distance: 500m 1km 500m 500m.

Voorst — 8E2

De Adelaar, Rijksstraatweg 49. **GPS:** n52,17760 e6,14150.

10 € 12,50 Ch (10x)€2 WC €0,50 €4/4 .
Location: Rural. **Surface:** grassy/metalled. 01/01-31/12
Distance: 500m 7km on the spot on the spot 150m 1km.
Remarks: Incl. use camp-site facilities.

Voorst — 8E2

Boerderij de Kolke, Klarenbeekseweg 30. **GPS:** n52,17355 e6,13318.

NL

16 ⬡€6 ⌁⬡Chincluded ⌁€1. **Surface:** grassy/metalled.
Remarks: Regional products.

Voorthuizen 8D2
Ackersate, Harremaatweg 26. **GPS:** n52,18683 e5,62547.⬆.

5 ⬡€ 14, 2 pers.incl ⌁⬡Ch ⌁WCincluded ⬡€1 ⬡€5,50,on
campsite ⬡.⬡⬡ **Location:** Rural, simple. **Surface:** metalled.
◪ 01/04-27/10
Distance: ⬡1,3km ⬡4,2km ⬡on the spot ⬡on the spot
⬡on the spot ⬡on the spot.

Westendorp 8E2
Recreatieoord Hippique, Doetinchemseweg 141.
GPS: n51,94964 e6,42084.⬆.

4 ⬡€ 10 ⌁€1/80liter ⬡Ch ⌁ included WC ⬡€2 ⬡€5/5 ⬡.⬡
Surface: grasstiles. ◪ 01/01-31/12
Distance: ⬡500m ⬡500m ⬡3km ⬡600m ⬡on the spot.
Remarks: Arrival 9><20h.

Winterswijk 8F2
Landgoed Kreil, Heenkamppieperweg 1. **GPS:** n51,93573 e6,67907.⬆.

2 ⬡€ 10 ⌁€1/80liter ⬡Ch ⌁included ⬡against payment.⬡
Location: Rural, isolated. **Surface:** metalled. ◪ 01/03-31/10
Distance: ⬡Breedevoort 4,5km ⬡Located on estate.

Winterswijk 8F2
Camping Ten Hagen, Waliënsestraat 139A.
GPS: n51,99131 e6,71898.⬆.

4 ⬡€ 10 ⌁€1/80liter ⬡Ch ⌁included.
Location: Rural, simple, isolated, quiet. **Surface:** grassy.
◪ 01/01-31/12
Distance: ⬡city centre 3km ⬡lake.
Remarks: Max. 24h, manufacturer of wooden clogs.

Winterswijk 8F2
Vreehorst, Vreehorstweg 43. **GPS:** n51,95028 e6,69251.⬆.

4 ⬡€ 10 ⌁€1/80liter ⬡Ch ⌁ included. ⬡
Location: Rural, comfortable. **Surface:** gravel. ◪ 01/01-31/12
Distance: ⬡3,6km.

Zelhem 8E2
Carpoolplaats, Stikkenweg/N330. **GPS:** n51,99893 e6,34541.⬆.

2 ⬡free. **Surface:** asphalted. ◪ 01/01-31/12
Distance: ⬡1km.
Remarks: Max. 24h.

Zutphen 8E2
Houtwal. **GPS:** n52,13565 e6,19866.⬆.

8 ⬡€ 10 ⌁€1/80liter ⬡Ch ⌁included.
Surface: metalled. ◪ 01/01-31/12
Distance: ⬡1km.
Remarks: Nearby police station, max. 48h, beautiful view.

Zutphen 8E2
IJsselkade. **GPS:** n52,14037 e6,19119.⬆.

2 ⬡€ 7,80, Sunday free. ⬡ **Surface:** metalled. ◪ 01/01-31/12
Distance: ⬡1km.
Remarks: Motorhome max. 6m, max. 48h.

Tourist information Zutphen:
⬡ Groenmarkt-Houtmarkt-Zaadmarkt. ◪ Thu 8-12h, Sa 8-17h.
⬡ Lange Hofstraat. Farmers market. ◪ Thu 8-13h.

Utrecht

Amersfoort 8D2
Aan de Eem, Klein Koppel. **GPS:** n52,16210 e5,37829.⬆.

3 ⬡€ 1,10/meter ⌁⌁WC ⌁included.⬡ **Location:** Urban, noisy.

Surface: metalled. ◪ 01/01-31/12
Distance: ⬡600m ⬡500m ⬡500m ⬡on the spot.
Remarks: At fire-station, max. 24h.
Tourist information Amersfoort:
⬡ VVV, Breestraat 1, www.vvvamersfoort.nl.

Baarn 8D2
De Zeven Linden, Zevenlindenweg 4. **GPS:** n52,19721 e5,24838.⬆.

3 ⬡€ 10 ⌁€2,50 ⬡Ch ⬡€5/time ⬡.⬡
Location: Simple. **Surface:** metalled. ◪ 01/04-01/11
Distance: ⬡2km ⬡1km ⬡2km ⬡300m ⬡on the spot
⬡on the spot.
Tourist information Baarn:
⬡ Brink. ◪ Tue 8.30-14h.

Bunnik 8D2
Camping de Boomgaard, Parallelweg 9. **GPS:** n52,06065 e5,19943.⬆.

6 ⬡€ 7,50 ⬡ChWC ⬡⬡€2. **Surface:** metalled.
◪ 01/04/31/10
Distance: ⬡3km ⬡800m.
Remarks: Arrival >17h departure <10h check in at reception next
morning, use camp-site facilities allowed.

Bunschoten-Spakenburg 8D2
Jachthaven Nieuwboer, Westdijk 36. **GPS:** n52,26070 e5,37238.⬆.

8 ⬡€ 15, 2 pers.incl ⌁⬡Ch ⌁WC ⬡€3,50/time ⬡included.
Location: Rural, simple, comfortable, quiet. **Surface:** grassy.
◪ 01/01-31/12
Distance: ⬡800m ⬡6km ⬡100m ⬡700m ⬡700m ⬡700m
⬡on the spot ⬡on the spot.

IJsselstein 8C2
Jachthaven Marnemoende, Noord IJsseldijk 107b.
GPS: n52,04583 e5,01861.⬆.

7 ⬡€ 15 ⌁⬡Ch ⌁WC ⬡⬡€4/2 ⬡included.⬡
Location: Rural, comfortable, luxurious, quiet. **Surface:** gravel.
◪ 01/01-31/12
Distance: ⬡2km ⬡on the spot ⬡on the spot ⬡on the spot ⬡2km
⬡2km ⬡on the spot.

Leersum 8D2
Touché, Rijksstraatweg 54. **GPS:** n52,00974 e5,43507.⬆.

5 free. **Location:** Urban, simple. **Surface:** gravel.
01/01-31/12 Mo
Distance: 200m on the spot 200m on the spot on the spot.

Leusden 8D2
De Mof, Arnhemseweg 95. **GPS:** n52,10654 e5,41445.

5 free, use of a meal desired.
Location: Rural, simple. **Surface:** gravel.
01/01-31/12 Mon, Tue
Distance: 4km 4km on the spot on the spot on the spot.
Remarks: First check in at restaurant.

Mijdrecht 8C2
Rondweg. **GPS:** n52,20804 e4,86879.

4 free. **Location:** Urban, simple, noisy. **Surface:** metalled.
01/01-31/12
Distance: 500m 500m 500m 500m.
Remarks: Max. 48h.

Overberg 8D2
De Holle Boom, Dwarsweg 63. **GPS:** n52,02914 e5,50061.

5 free with a meal. **Location:** Rural, simple, quiet.
Surface: gravel.
Distance: on the spot on the spot on the spot on the spot.

Rhenen 8D2
Restaurant 3 Zussen, Kerkewijk-zuid 115. **GPS:** n52,00682 e5,54006.

5 free. **Location:** Rural, simple. **Surface:** asphalted. 01/01-31/12
Distance: 1km Veenendaal on the spot 1km on the spot on the spot on the spot.
Remarks: Use of a meal desired.

Vianen 8D2
Kanaalweg, P1. **GPS:** n51,99549 e5,09620.

4 free. **Surface:** metalled.
01/01-31/12
Distance: 500m.
Remarks: During events: Hazelaarplein, max. 48h.

Tourist information Vianen:
VVV, Voorstraat 97, www.vvv-vianen.nl. Historical centre.
Voorstraat (zuid). Wed 10-16h.

South Holland

Alblasserdam 8C3
Haven 4. **GPS:** n51,86106 e4,65799.

10 € 10 €0,50 ChWC. **Surface:** asphalted.
01/01-31/12
Distance: 500m 1,3km on the spot 500m.
Remarks: At cultural centre 'Landvast', Kinderdijk ± 4,5km, check in at harbourmaster, sanitary in harbour building against payment.

Tourist information Alblasserdam:
Molens, Nederwaard 1, Kinderdijk. World famous mill-area.
01/07-31/08 Sa, 1st Sa of the month.
Wilgenplein.
Mo-afternoon.

Bleiswijk 8C2
Jan van de Heidenstraat. **GPS:** n52,01415 e4,53411.

2 free. **Location:** Urban. **Surface:** metalled. 01/01-31/12
Distance: 300m 5km 500m Jumbo 400m.
Remarks: Next to fire-station.

Bleskensgraaf 8C3
Farm Nescio, Elzenweg 19. **GPS:** n51,85674 e4,75266.

8 € 14 WC included. **Location:** Rural, comfortable, isolated, quiet. **Surface:** metalled. 01/01-31/12
Distance: 2,5km 1,5km 1,5km 1km 2,5km.
Remarks: Possibility of guided tour.

Delft 8C2
Delftse Hout, Korftlaan 5. **GPS:** n52,01772 e4,37945.

20 € 20-28 Ch (20x) €6,50/time included.
Location: Urban, comfortable, central. **Surface:** grasstiles.
01/04-01/11
Distance: 1,5km 1,2km 500m on the spot on the spot on the spot summer > centre on the spot on the spot.
Remarks: Check in at reception campsite.

Tourist information Delft:
VVV, Hippolytusbuurt 4, www.delft.nl. Historical centre with canals and merchant houses. church 01/03-31/10 Mo-Sa 9-18h, 01/11-28/02 Mo-Sa 11-16h.

Den Haag 8C2
Camperpark Den Haag, Valutapad, The Hague. **GPS:** n52,05282 e4,38013.

100 € 19,50, 2 pers.incl Ch (30x) €2/24h,10Amp WC included. **Location:** Urban, comfortable.
Surface: grassy/metalled.
01/01-31/12
Distance: 7km 1,7km 12km 1km 1km 500m.
Remarks: Bread-service.

Tourist information The Hague (Den Haag):
VVV, Hofweg 1, www.denhaag.com. Government city and royal residence.
Bezoekerscentrum Binnenhof, Binnenhof 8a. Guided tours in government buildings. Mo-Sa 10-16h. € 5-10.
Madurodam, George Maduroplein 1. Miniature Holland. 21/03-30/06 9-20h, 01/07-31/08 9-23h, 01/09-21/03 9-18h.

Dordrecht 8C3
Camperplaats Stadswerven, Maasstraat.
GPS: n51,81793 e4,68750.

12 Mo-Sa € 6,50/24h, Su free €1 Ch.
Location: Simple, quiet. **Surface:** metalled. 01/01-31/12
Distance: city centre 3km 5km on the spot on the spot 3km 1km waterbus.
Remarks: Max. 72h, near Noah's Ark.

Dordrecht 8C3
Weeskinderendijk 5. **GPS:** n51,80861 e4,65611.

2 € 1/4h, first 24h free. **Location:** Urban, simple, noisy.
Surface: metalled. 01/01-31/12
Distance: 500m 500m 500m 100m.
Remarks: Max. 72h.

NL

Dordrecht 8C3

Jachthaven Westergoot, Baanhoekweg 1. **GPS**: n51,81518 e4,72467.
⚓€10 Ch ⚡€2 WC €0,50/7minutes €5.
Distance: on the spot.

Giessenburg 8C3

Boerenterras De Groot, A.M.A. Langeraadweg 9.
GPS: n51,85327 e4,92205.

6 €10 Ch ⚡ WC included. **Location:** Rural, simple,
isolated, quiet. **Surface:** concrete. 01/01-31/12
Distance: 1,5km 3km on the spot 1,5km 3,5km
on the spot.

Giessenburg 8C3

Halfomhoeve, Bovenkerkseweg 76/78. **GPS**: n51,84628 e4,87548.

3 €10 ⚡ included WC . **Location:** Rural, simple,
isolated, quiet. **Surface:** concrete. 01/01-31/12
Distance: 2km 3km on the spot 1,5km 1,5km
on the spot on the spot.

Giessenburg 8C3

Landscheiding Giessenburg, Landscheiding 1.
GPS: n51,84753 e4,92294.

6 €10 Ch ⚡ WC included. **Location:** Rural,
comfortable, isolated, quiet. **Surface:** grassy/metalled.
01/01-31/12
Distance: 2km 2km 2km on the spot on the spot.

Gorinchem 8C3

WSV Merwede, Buiten de Waterpoort 8.
GPS: n51,82697 e4,96477.

16 €10 Ch included €0,75 €5/4.
Location: Comfortable, isolated, quiet. **Surface:** gravel/metalled.
01/01-31/12
Distance: 500m on the spot on the spot 300m 1km
on the spot.
Remarks: Max. 72h, check in at harbourmaster.

Tourist information Gorinchem:
VVV, Grote Markt 17, www.gorinchem.nl. Historical centre with city
walls.
Slot Loevestein, Loevestein 1, Poederoijen. Castle, 14th century.
01/05-30/09 Tue-Fri 11-17h Sa-Su-Mo-holidays 13-17h, 01/10-30/04
Sa-Su 13-17h.
Grote Markt.

Mo 8.30-12.30h.

Gouda 8C2

Parking Klein Amerika, Fluwelensingel. **GPS**: n52,01185 e4,71576.

30 €8 Ch (12x) WC included.
Location: Urban, simple, quiet. **Surface:** metalled.
01/01-31/12
Distance: 300m.
Remarks: Max. 3 days.

Tourist information Gouda:
VVV, Markt 27, www.vvvgouda.nl. Historical centre with 300
monuments, famous for its Gouda-cheese.
Kaaswaag, Markt. History of the Gouda cheese. 01/04-30/09
13-17h, Thu 10-17h.
Markt. Thu 8.30-13h, Sa 8.30-17h.
Montmartre, Markt. Antiques and flea market. 01/05-30/09
We 9-17h.

Goudriaan 8C2

Boerderij de Verwondering, De Hoogt 14.
GPS: n51,89150 e4,90741.

2 €10 Ch included.
Location: Rural, simple, isolated. **Surface:** concrete.
Distance: 2,5km 7km.

Hoogblokland 8C2

Landwinkel De Bikkerhoeve, Bazeldijk 66. **GPS**: n51,89716 e4,99563.

6 €10 Ch ⚡ WC included. **Location:** Rural, simple,
isolated, quiet. **Surface:** concrete. 01/03-31/10
Distance: 2km 1,4km 2km 2km on the spot
on the spot.

Leerdam 8C2

De Galgenwaard, Lingedijk 8a, Oosterwijk.
GPS: n51,87451 e5,07311.

3 €8 WC. **Location:** Rural, simple, quiet. **Surface:** metalled.
01/04-01/10
Distance: Leerdam 2km on the spot on the spot 300m
Along the river Linge.
Remarks: Opening hours 7-22h, passenger ferry across the Linge.

Leerdam 8C2

Groenzoom, Lingedijk. **GPS**: n51,88288 e5,08670.

3 free. **Location:** Urban, simple. **Surface:** metalled.
01/01-31/12
Distance: 2,5km 2,5km 2,5km on the spot.
Remarks: In front of Lingedijk 27, small pitches.

Leerdam 8C2

Parking Glasmuseum, Lingedijk. **GPS**: n51,88676 e5,08699.

2 free. **Location:** Rural, simple. **Surface:** asphalted.
01/01-31/12
Distance: 1km on the spot 1km on the spot.

Leerdam 8C2

Jachthaven Oude Horn, Sundsvall 1. **GPS**: n51,88984 e5,09532.

3 free. **Location:** Urban, simple. **Surface:** gravel.
01/01-31/12
Distance: 300m 300m 300m.
Remarks: Max. 72h.

Leiden 8C2

P Haagweg, Haagweg 6. **GPS**: n52,15963 e4,47852.

15 €12/24h.
Location: Urban. **Surface:** metalled.
01/01-31/12
Distance: 800m 800m 800m Free bus to centre.
Remarks: Along railwayline, video surveillance, free shuttle (till 2am).

Nieuwland 8C2

De Grienduil, Geer 25. **GPS**: n51,90106 e5,02622.

4 €10 Ch ⚡ WC included.
Location: Simple, quiet. **Surface:** gravel. 01/01-31/12
Distance: on the spot 2km 4km on the spot on the spot.
Remarks: In winter limited services.

Numansdorp — 8C3

Fort Buitensluis, Fortlaan 10. **GPS:** n51,71727 e4,43866.
5 € 15 Ch included. **Surface:** unpaved.
Distance: 1,5km 5km on the spot on the spot 1,5km
on the spot on the spot.
Remarks: At Hollands Diep, golf court 3km.

Oud Beijerland — 8C3

De Oude Tol, Randweg 31a. **GPS:** n51,82933 e4,39585.

4 free.
Location: Rural, simple, isolated, quiet. **Surface:** asphalted.
01/01-31/12
Distance: 2km on the spot 100m on the spot on the spot.
Remarks: Arrival >16h, max. 24h.

Ouddorp — 8B3

Drive-in Camperpark Klepperduinen, Vrijheidsweg 1.
GPS: n51,81724 e3,89850.

51 € 8-10/12h, € 14,50-18/24h + tourist tax € 0,81/pp, dog € 3,50/day
€3,50/100liter Ch (51x)€3/24h WC included
Location: Rural, luxurious, isolated, quiet. **Surface:** grassy/metalled.
01/01-31/12
Distance: 500m 1km on the spot on the spot
on the spot.

Pernis — 8C2

Casa E Parking, Ring 156 -158. **GPS:** n51,88581 e4,39008.

5 € 8 Ch included €2. **Surface:** metalled.
Distance: Rotterdam 11km 300m 300m 100m.

Poeldijk — 8B2

Booma Recreatie, Vredebestlaan 14b. **GPS:** n52,02464 e4,21242.

10 € 5 Ch included (10x)€2/day. **Location:** Rural,
simple, quiet. **Surface:** gravel. 01/01-31/12
Distance: 800m 50m 800m 800m 800m on the spot
on the spot.

Sassenheim — 8C2

Jachthaven Jonkman, Jonkman 1. **GPS:** n52,22074 e4,54476.

6 € 15 €0,50 Ch €1 WC €0,50 €5 included.
Location: Comfortable. **Surface:** grassy/gravel. 15/03-01/11
Distance: 2km 1km on the spot on the spot on the spot
2km on the spot.
Remarks: Check in at harbourmaster.

Schiedam — 8C2

Doeleplein 1. **GPS:** n51,91972 e4,40111.

2 € 6,60. **Location:** Urban, simple, central, quiet.
Surface: metalled. 01/01-31/12
Distance: 500m 1,5km on the spot on the spot 500m
500m 500m.
Remarks: Max. 72h.

Schiedam — 8C2

Noordvest 40. **GPS:** n51,91926 e4,39372.

6 € 6,60. **Location:** Urban, simple, central, quiet.
Surface: metalled. 01/01-31/12
Distance: city centre 100m.
Remarks: Max. 72h.

Tourist information Schiedam:
M Het Jenever Museum, Lange Haven 74-76. Making distilled spirits.
Tue-Sa 12-17h, Su 13-17h.
Lange Kerkstraat. Fri 9-16h.

Strijensas — 8C3

Jachthaven Strijensas, Sassendijk 6. **GPS:** n51,71472 e4,58735.

6 € 7 €0,50/100liter Ch €2,50 WC €1.
Surface: asphalted. 01/01-31/12
Distance: 500m on the spot on the spot on the spot.
Remarks: Max. 72h.

Vlaardingen — 8C2

Parking Deltabrug, Oosthavenkade 81. **GPS:** n51,90364 e4,34769.

4 free. **Location:** Urban, noisy. **Surface:** metalled.
01/01-31/12
Distance: 1km on the spot 50m 100m 500m.
Remarks: Along railwayline, max. 48h.

Zevenhoven — 8C2

Camperplaats Zevenhoven, Noordeinde 36.
GPS: n52,19475 e4,77305.

5 € 10 Ch included. **Location:** Rural, comfortable.
Surface: grassy/metalled. 01/01-31/12
Distance: 1km 1km on the spot on the spot.

Zealand

Axel — 10B1

P Watertoren, Kinderdijk 4. **GPS:** n51,25972 e3,91028.

2 free. **Location:** Urban, simple, noisy. **Surface:** metalled.
01/01-31/12
Distance: 500m on the spot on the spot 500m
on the spot on the spot.
Remarks: Max. 24h.

Tourist information Axel:
Noordstraat. Sa 8-16h.

Breskens — 8A3

Roompot Recreatie, Nieuwe Sluisweg. **GPS:** n51,40193 e3,54420.

10 € 14 Ch included WC. **Location:** Rural,
comfortable, quiet. **Surface:** metalled. 01/01-31/12
Distance: 500m 400m 100m 100m on the spot
on the spot.
Remarks: Servicepoint at camping Zeebad, ferry to Vlissingen 500m
(pedestrian/bicycles).

Graauw — 10B1

Zandbergsestraat. **GPS:** n51,32519 e4,10420.

NL

7 ☐free. **Location:** Rural, simple, quiet. **Surface:** gravel/sand.
☐ 01/01-31/12
Distance: 🚶400m ⊗400m on the spot.
Remarks: Max. 72h.

| | Groede 🌿⛵🚤 | 10A1 |

De Ploeg, Parking Zuid, Voorstraat 47. **GPS:** n51,38232 e3,51268.⬆.

40 ☐€ 5 17-10h, € 12,50/24h 🚰🚽Ch🚿(35x)€2,50/night WC🚻🔌.
♿ **Location:** Comfortable, central, quiet.
Surface: grasstiles/metalled. ☐ 01/04-01/10 ⦿ 22-7h
Distance: 🚶100m 🏊3km ⊗100m 🍴100m �100m > Terneuzen
🚲on the spot 🚶on the spot.
Remarks: Caution € 10, sanitary/washing machine at campsite.

| | Groede 🌿⛵🚤 | 10A1 |

Strandcamping Groede, Zeeweg 1. **GPS:** n51,39632 e3,48719.⬆.

50 ☐€ 0,80/h. 🚐🚤 **Location:** Rural, simple, quiet. **Surface:** gravel.
☐ 01/01-31/12
Distance: 🚶Groede 3km 🏖sandy beach 200m ⊗60m 🍴on the spot
🚲on the spot 🚶on the spot.

| | Hansweert 🌿⛵ | 8B3 |

Westhavendijk. GPS: n51,44483 e4,00629.⬆.

5 ☐free. **Location:** Rural, simple, isolated, quiet.
Surface: asphalted.
☐ 01/01-31/12
Distance: 🚶250m 🎣4km on the spot 🚲on the spot 🚶on the spot.

| | Hulst 🌿⛵🥨 | 10B1 |

Parkeerterrein Havenfort, Havenfort. **GPS:** n51,27700 e4,04912.

15 ☐€ 0,80/h, mo-sa 9-17h, su 12-18h. 🚐 **Surface:** metalled.
☐ 01/01-31/12
Distance: 🚶on the spot 🚲25m ⊗150m 🍴150m 🚌200m.

Remarks: Max. 72h, shops open on Sunday.
Tourist information Hulst:
ℹ VVV, Grote Markt 19, www.bezoekhulst.nl. Fortified city with
city walls, shops open on Sunday.

| 🚐S | Kamperland 🛥 🚤 | 8B3 |

Camperpark Zeeland, Campensweg 5.
GPS: n51,57495 e3,65236.⬆➡.

102 ☐€ 14,50-19,50 🚰€0,20/min 🚽Ch🚿(75x)€4/24h,16Amp
WC🚻€0,25/min 🚿€6/4 🛜included 🚐🚗 **Location:** Rural,
comfortable, luxurious, quiet. **Surface:** grassy/gravel. ☐ 01/01-31/12
Distance: 🚶3km 🎣2km 🏊50m 🍴50m ⊗100m 🍴4km 🚌2km
🚲on the spot 🚶on the spot.

| 🚐S | Kamperland 🛥 🚤 | 8B3 |

Roompot Beach Resort, Mariapolderseweg 1.
GPS: n51,58972 e3,71666.

20 ☐€ 6 10-17h, € 14 17-10h 🚰🚽Ch🚿WC🚻🔌€4,50/1,20 🛜📷.
Surface: asphalted. ☐ 01/01-31/12
Distance: 🚶3km 🏊500m 🚲500m ⊗500m 🍴500m 🚌1km.

| | Kloosterzande | 10B1 |

Hulsterweg. GPS: n51,36555 e4,02121.⬆.

2 ☐free. **Location:** Rural, simple, central, quiet. **Surface:** metalled.
☐ 01/01-31/12
Distance: 🚶500m ⊗80m 🍴700m 🚲on the spot 🚶on the spot.

| 🚐S | Kruiningen | 8B3 |

Landwinkel de Plantage, Kaasgat 4a. **GPS:** n51,46865 e4,04445.

8 ☐€ 12,50 🚰🚽Ch🚿€2,50/night,10Amp WC🚻included 🔌.
Surface: grassy. ☐ 01/01-31/12
Distance: 🚶3km 🏊3km 🚲3km ⊗3km 🍴on the spot 🚌1km
🚲on the spot 🚶on the spot.

| ⚠S | Kruiningen | 8B3 |

Den Inkel, Polderweg 12. **GPS:** n51,43485 e4,04448.
6 ☐€ 15-21 🚰🚽Ch🚿WCincluded. ☐ 01/01-31/12

| 🚐S | Middelburg 🌿⛵🚤 | 8A3 |

Hof van Tange, Hof van Tange. **GPS:** n51,49688 e3,60474.⬆.

6 ☐€ 9,50, Su/holidays free WC€0,50/time. 🚐 **Location:** Simple,
central, quiet. **Surface:** gravel/sand.
☐ 01/01-31/12 ⦿ 1st week Aug
Distance: 🚶on the spot 🎣5km ⊗500m 🍴300m 🚌on the spot
🚲on the spot 🚶on the spot.
Remarks: Motorhome <6m, max. 48h.

| 🚐S | Middelburg 🌿⛵🚤 | 8A3 |

Oude Veerseweg. GPS: n51,50071 e3,62842.⬆.

5 ☐free 🚰€1 🚽🚿(4x)€1. **Location:** Comfortable, central, quiet.
Surface: metalled. ☐ 01/01-31/12
Distance: 🚶1km 🚲100m ⊗500m 🍴1km 🚲on the spot.

| | Middelburg 🌿⛵🚤 | 8A3 |

Kanaalweg. GPS: n51,49432 e3,61519.⬆.

3 ☐€ 9,50. 🚐 **Location:** Urban, simple, central, noisy.
Surface: concrete. ☐ 01/01-31/12
Distance: 🚶500m 🏊on the spot 🚲on the spot 🍴500m
🚲on the spot.
Remarks: Max. 48h.

| 🚻 | Oosterland 🌿 | 8B3 |

Wok van Zeeland, Rijksweg 6. **GPS:** n51,65767 e4,05336.⬆.

3 ☐free. **Location:** Simple, isolated, noisy. **Surface:** asphalted.
☐ 01/01-31/12
Distance: 🚶2km ⊗on the spot.
Remarks: Only overnight stays.

| 🚐S | Oostkapelle | 8B3 |

De Pekelinge, Landmetersweg 1. **GPS:** n51,55725 e3,55139.⬆.
20 ☐€ 18,50-27,50 🚰🚽Chincluded.🚐🚤 **Location:** Simple,
isolated, quiet. **Surface:** gravel/sand. ☐ 27/03-01/11
Distance: 🚶nearby 🏊nearby ⊗on the spot 🍴on the spot.
Remarks: Arrival >20h departure <10h, max. 1 night.

| ⚓ | Paal | 10B1 |

Jachthaven, Zeedijk van de van Alsteinpolder.
GPS: n51,35331 e4,10937.⬆.

4 🛏free. **Location:** Rural. **Surface:** asphalted/metalled.
🅾 01/01-31/12
Distance: 🚆100m 🏊on the spot 🛒on the spot ⊗on the spot 🍴on the spot 🚶on the spot.
Remarks: Max. 72h.

Camping International, Scharendijkseweg 8.
GPS: n51,74030 e3,78967.⬆➡
20 🛏€ 20, 11/07-22/09 € 35 🚰🚽Ch ⚓(16x)WC 🍴included 🔌€5/3,50 🍶€2. **Location:** Rural. **Surface:** metalled.
🅾 04/03-01/11
Distance: 🚆1,5km 🚲2,5km 🏊on the spot ⊗on the spot 🍴on the spot 🛒1,5km 🍴on the spot 🚶on the spot.

Sas van Gent 10B1

Kanaaleiland, Oostkade. **GPS:** n51,22527 e3,80246.⬆

2 🛏free. **Surface:** metalled.
Distance: 🚆100m ⊗100m 🍴100m.
Remarks: Max. 24h.
Tourist information Sas van Gent:
🏛 Keizer Karelplein. 🅾 Tue 9-16h.

Terneuzen 10B1

Oostsluis, Binnenvaartweg. **GPS:** n51,33555 e3,82117.⬆

4 🛏free. **Location:** Rural, simple, isolated, quiet.
Surface: grassy/metalled. 🅾 01/01-31/12
Distance: 🚆500m 🛒on the spot ⊗500m 🛒200m 🍴on the spot 🚶on the spot.
Remarks: Max. 24h.
Tourist information Terneuzen:
👁 Portaal van Vlaanderen, Zeevaartweg 11. Interactive Visitors Centre at the Terneuzen Locks, guided tour and boat excursions. 🅾 Apr-Jun

---

We, July-Aug Tue-We-Thu, guided tour 13.30h.
🏛 Markt. 🅾 Sa 9-16h.

Tholen 8B3

Jachthaven, Contre Escarpe 4. **GPS:** n51,53112 e4,22390.⬆

4 🛏€ 7,50, service incl. € 10 🚰🚽Ch ⚓WC 📶. **Surface:** metalled.
🅾 01/03-01/10
Distance: 🚆100m ⊗100m 🍴100m.

Vogelwaarde 10B1

Populierenstraat. GPS: n51,32562 e3,97758.⬆

2 🛏free. **Location:** Urban, simple, quiet. **Surface:** metalled.
🅾 01/01-31/12
Distance: 🚆on the spot 🍴on the spot 🍴on the spot 🚶on the spot.

Westdorpe 10B1

De Baeckermat, Bernhardstraat. **GPS:** n51,22917 e3,82167.⬆

2 🛏free. **Location:** Rural, simple, quiet. **Surface:** metalled.
🅾 01/01-31/12
Distance: 🚆500m 🛒on the spot ⊗100m 🍴500m 🛒on the spot 🚶on the spot.
Remarks: Max. 24h.

Wolphaartsdijk 8B3

Camping 't Veerse Meer, Veerweg. **GPS:** n51,54325 e3,81253.⬆

7 🛏€ 15/22 🚰🚽Ch ⚓(5x)WC 🍴on campsite 🔌on campsite 📶included. 🚲 **Location:** Rural, comfortable, isolated, quiet.
🅾 01/01-31/12 ⚡ 15/11-15/12
Distance: 🚆1,5km 🏊100m 🛒100m 🍴100m 🛒on the spot 🚶on the spot.

Zierikzee 8B3

De Zandweg, Zandweg 30. **GPS:** n51,65691 e3,91210.⬆

12 🛏€ 12,50 🚰🚽Ch ⚓(12x),10Amp 📶included. 🚲

Location: Rural, comfortable, central, noisy. **Surface:** asphalted.
🅾 01/01-31/12
Distance: 🚆800m 🏊on the spot 🛒on the spot ⊗350m 🍴1km 🛒350m 🍴on the spot.

North Brabant

Asten 10E1

Camperpark Wetland, Tureluurweg 7. **GPS:** n51,36687 e5,84214.⬆➡

50 🛏€ 9,60, 2 pers.incl 🚰🚽Ch ⚓(37x)€1,50 WC 🍴🔌€2/2 📶included.
Location: Rural. **Surface:** grassy/metalled. 🅾 01/01-31/12
Distance: 🚆2km 🚲4km 🏊9km 🛒5km 🍴2km 🛒1,5km 🍴on the spot 🚶on the spot.
Remarks: Located in nature reserve De Groote Peel.

Bakel 8D3

De Beekakker. GPS: n51,50061 e5,74377.⬆
2 🛏free. **Location:** Simple. **Surface:** metalled.
🅾 01/01-31/12
Distance: 🚆500m 🍴on the spot 🚶on the spot.
Remarks: At gymnasium.

Bergen op Zoom 8B3

De Boulevard Noord. GPS: n51,48735 e4,27708.⬆

5 🛏free. **Surface:** metalled. 🅾 01/01-31/12
Distance: 🚆1km 🚲3,8km 🏊on the spot ⊗on the spot.
Remarks: Max. 72h. On the level of restaurant 'La Playa'.

Tourist information Bergen op Zoom:
🏛🍴 De Markiezenhof, Steenbergsestraat 8. Medieval palace built in the late 15th century. 🅾 Tue-Su 11-17h.

Best 8D3

Carpoolplaats De Wilg. GPS: n51,52106 e5,39423.⬆
3 🛏free. **Location:** Isolated. **Surface:** metalled.
🅾 01/01-31/12
Distance: 🚲 150 m.
Remarks: Max. 24h.

Boxtel 8D3

Dennenoord, Dennendreef 5. **GPS:** n51,59770 e5,28661.⬆

4 🛏€ 12,50, 2 pers.incl 🚰🚽Ch ⚓WC 🍴🔌€4 📶included. 🚲
Location: Rural, simple, isolated. **Surface:** metalled.
🅾 01/01-31/12
Distance: 🚆4km 🚲4km.
Remarks: Max. 3 nights.

Budel 10D1

Camperplaats Budel, Heikantstraat 16. **GPS:** n51,26163 e5,59007.

NL

5 🏕 € 6,50 + € 1/pp tourist tax 🚰🢃ⒸChincluded ⚡€2,50/day,4Amp.
Location: Urban. **Surface:** grassy. ⏹ 01/01-31/12
Distance: 🏊800m ⛵2km ⛽600m ⊗800m 💊800m 🚌600m
🚲on the spot 🅰on the spot.

De Heen 🕮 8B3

Akkermans leisure&golf, Heensemolenweg 23.
GPS: n51,60654 e4,24547.🢁.

10 🏕 € 12,50 🚰🢃Ch ⚡(16x)WC🗋included 📶 📷.
♨ **Location:** Rural, comfortable, isolated, quiet.
Surface: asphalted/metalled. ⏹ 01/01-31/12
Distance: ⊗on the spot 🐾on the spot 🅰on the spot.

Eindhoven 🕮 8D3

P+R Meerhoven, Sliffertsestraat 304. **GPS:** n51,43507 e5,42444.

10 🏕first 24h € 3, € 10/24h 🢃ChWCfree.🗋📷
Location: Simple. **Surface:** metalled. ⏹ 01/01-31/12
Distance: 🏊4km 🚤on the spot ⊗200m 💊500m 💊on the spot
🚲on the spot 🅰on the spot.
Remarks: Free bicycles available.

Escharen 8D3

Bar Bistro De Brouwketel, Hoogeweg 9.
GPS: n51,74152 e5,73376.🢁.

15 🏕free. **Surface:** grassy. ⏹ 01/01-31/12

Etten-Leur 8C3

Jachthaven Turfvaart, Westpolderpad 6. **GPS:** n51,59512 e4,65102.

18 🏕 € 10, 01/03-30/09 € 15 🚰 ⚡€0,50/100liter 🢃Ch ⚡WCincluded
🗋€1 📶free. **Surface:** grassy/metalled. ⏹ 01/01-31/12
Distance: 🏊1,5km ⊗on the spot 💊500m.
Tourist information Etten-Leur:
🅰 ⏹ Mo-morning.

Geertruidenberg 🕮 8C3

Statenlaan 2. **GPS:** n51,70333 e4,86333.🢁.

2 🏕free 📷. **Surface:** metalled. ⏹ 15/03-31/10
Distance: 🏊500m ⛽on the spot ⊗on the spot 💊500m.
Remarks: Max. 24h.

Geertruidenberg 🕮 8C3

WSV Geertruidenberg, Statenlaan 15. **GPS:** n51,70362 e4,86311.🢁.

8 🏕 € 10 🚰🢃Ch ⚡WC🗋📷📶included.
Location: Comfortable, quiet. **Surface:** gravel. ⏹ 01/05-31/10
Distance: 🏊500m 🚤3km ⛽on the spot ⊗on the spot 💊500m.
Remarks: Max. 3 days, max. 9m, only cash payment.

Gemert 8D3

Koksehoeve, Koksedijk 25. **GPS:** n51,57380 e5,65846.

10 🏕free, use of a meal obligated. **Location:** Rural, simple, isolated,
quiet. **Surface:** metalled. ⏹ 01/01-31/12 ⏺ Wed
Distance: 🏊2km.

Grave 🕮 8D3

Koninginnedijk. GPS: n51,76178 e5,73676.🢁🢂.

🏕free. **Location:** Simple, central, quiet. **Surface:** gravel.
⏹ 01/01-31/12
Distance: 🏊100m ⛽100m ⊗150m 💊150m.
Remarks: Max. 72h.

Heeswijk-Dinther 🕮 8D3

De Leygraaf, Meerstraat 45A. **GPS:** n51,66445 e5,47511.🢁.
4 🏕 € 11,20 🚰🢃Ch ⚡included WC🗋€2,50/time.
Location: Rural, comfortable. **Surface:** grassy.
⏹ 01/01-31/12
Distance: 🏊1,5km 🚤6km ⊗on the spot 🐾on the spot 🅰on the spot.

Helenaveen 🕮 8E3

Oude Hoeven, Soemeersingel 99. **GPS:** n51,40951 e5,90594.🢁.

5 🏕 € 6 🚰 ⚡€1,50 📶. **Location:** Quiet. **Surface:** grassy.
⏹ 01/04-01/11 🚲on the spot 🅰on the spot.
Remarks: Max. 72h.

Hoogerheide 8B3

METO parking, Huijbergseweg. **GPS:** n51,42318 e4,33452.
5 🏕free. **Location:** Simple. **Surface:** metalled.
⏹ 01/01-31/12
Distance: 🏊800m ⊗800m 💊800m.

Hoogerheide 8B3

Fa. Broos, Buitendreef 4, De Kooi. **GPS:** n51,42522 e4,34656.🢁.

5 🏕free 🚰 🢃 ⚡(3x)free.♨
Location: Rural, simple, isolated. **Surface:** metalled.
⏹ 01/01-31/12
Distance: 🏊3km 🚤3km ⊗3km 💊3km 🚲on the spot 🅰on the spot.

Hulten 8C3

Restaurant Stad Parijs, Rijksweg 6. **GPS:** n51,56996 e4,96446.

15 🏕free 🗋€0,75. **Location:** Rural, simple, quiet. **Surface:** asphalted.
⏹ 01/01-31/12
Distance: ⊗on the spot.
Remarks: Free, use of a meal obligated.

Linden 🕮 8E3

Jachthaven t'Loo, Hardweg 15. **GPS:** n51,75182 e5,82740.🢁.

11 🏕 € 12,50-15 🚰🢃Ch ⚡€ 2,50 WC🗋€1 📶 incl. **Surface:** grassy.
⏹ 15/04-15/10.
Distance: ⚓on the spot ⛽on the spot ⊗on the spot 💊on the spot.
Remarks: Check in at harbourmaster 9-12h, 15-18h, caution key
sanitary building € 20.

Mierlo 8D3

Boscamping 't Wolfsven, Patrijslaan 4. **GPS:** n51,43888 e5,59000.
6 🏕from € 16 🚰🢃 ⚡WC🗋📷€4,50/1,20 📶 ♨
Surface: asphalted. ⏹ 26/03-21/10
Distance: 🏊3km ⛵150m ⊗150m 💊1km 💊on the spot 🚌1km.

Nuenen 8D3

Oude Landen, Pastoorsmast 12. **GPS:** n51,46429 e5,56023.🢁.
5 🏕free 📷. **Surface:** grassy. ⏹ 01/01-31/12 ⏺ July
Distance: 🏊1,7km 🚤800m 💊900m.
Remarks: Max. 5 days a month.

⊞ S **Oijen** 🏕 **8D3**

Speciaalbierbrouwerij Oijen, Oijensebovendijk.
GPS: n51,81049 e5,53126.

3 🚐 € 10, free with a meal 🚰💧 included. **Location:** Rural, simple, quiet. **Surface:** grassy/gravel. 📅 01/01-31/12
Distance: 🛒on the spot 🚌on the spot ⊗on the spot 🚲on the spot 🏃on the spot.

S **Oirschot** **8D3**

Camperplaats Oirschot, De Rijt. **GPS:** n51,50064 e5,32366.⬆➡.

28 🚐 € 13 🚰💧Ch included. 💧(28x)€2.
Surface: gravel.
Distance: 🛒1km 🚌on the spot ⊗1km 💧900m.
Remarks: Max. 72h.
Tourist information Oirschot:
ℹ VVV, Sint Odulphusstraat 11. www.vvvoirschot.nl. City with 100 monumental buildings, hiking and biking routes.
📅 01/01-31/12.
Ⓜ Museum de Vier Quartieren, Sint Odulphusstraat 11. Regional museum. 📅 Tue-Su 12-16.30h.

S **Oosteind** **8C3**

Camperplaats Oosteind, Ter Horst 19. **GPS:** n51,64705 e4,88326.⬆.

4 🚐 € 8 🚰💧Ch 💧included. **Location:** Rural, comfortable, isolated. **Surface:** grassy. 📅 01/01-31/12
Distance: 🛒2km 🚌1km ⊗500m.

S **Oss** **8D3**

Van Venrooy Motorhomes, Galliërsweg 39.
GPS: n51,75981 e5,55642.⬆.

2 🚐free 🚰💧free. **Surface:** metalled. 📅 01/01-31/12

Oss **8D3**

Sportpark Rusheuvel. GPS: n51,77657 e5,52409.⬆.

🚐free. 🚰 **Surface:** metalled. 📅 01/01-31/12
Distance: 🛒750m ⊗750m 💧AH 500m.
Remarks: Max. 3 nights.

Overloon **8E3**

Van Well, Roosendaalseweg 1. **GPS:** n51,56377 e5,91995.

15 🚐voluntary contribution 🚰💧Ch 💧€2. **Location:** Quiet.
Surface: grassy. 📅 01/01-31/12
Distance: 🛒2,5km 🏊4km ⊗2,5km 💧2,5km 🚲on the spot 🏃on the spot.

S **Raamsdonksveer** **8C3**

De Uilendonck, Lageweg 8, Raamsdonk. **GPS:** n51,68540 e4,91380.⬆.

3 🚐free. **Location:** Rural, simple, isolated, quiet. **Surface:** metalled.
📅 01/01-31/12
Distance: 🛒1km 🚲on the spot.

S **Raamsdonksveer** **8C3**

Kloosterweg 1. **GPS:** n51,68908 e4,87582.⬆.

4 🚐free. **Surface:** metalled.
Distance: 🛒800m ⊗on the spot 💧800m.
Remarks: Parking at sports park.

⊞ S **Reusel** **10D1**

Café-Restaurant de Klok, Turnhoutseweg 32.
GPS: n51,35564 e5,14272.⬆.

3 🚐free 🚰💧WC free. **Location:** Simple. **Surface:** metalled.
📅 01/01-31/12
Distance: 🛒2km.
Remarks: Use of a meal desired.

⊞ **Reusel** **10D1**

De Wekker, Wilhelminalaan 97. **GPS:** n51,36187 e5,17339.

5 🚐Free, use of a meal obligated. **Location:** Simple, quiet.
Surface: sand. 📅 01/01-31/12 ⊙ Wed
Distance: ⊗on the spot.

S **Roosendaal** 🌿 **8C3**

Mobildrôme, Argon 31-33. **GPS:** n51,56333 e4,46278.

8 🚐free 🚰€0,50 💧Ch 💧€0,50.
Surface: metalled.
Distance: 🛒2km 🍴1,1km 💧2km.
Tourist information Roosendaal:
🛒 Rosada, A17, afrit 19. Factory outlet.

© S **Vessem** **8D3**

Eurocamping Vessem, Zwembadweg 1. **GPS:** n51,41197 e5,27490.⬆.
40 🚐 € 7, 19/03-31/10 € 10 🚰💧€1/80liter 💧Ch 💧€0,60/kWh 🔌€0,50
📶€1/day. **Location:** Rural. **Surface:** grassy. 📅 01/01-31/12
Distance: 🛒1,5km 🏊7km ⛵5km 🚌on the spot ⊗1,5km 💧on the spot 🍴300m 🚲on the spot 🏃on the spot.

S **Vianen** **8E3**

Ons Plekske, Berkenkamp 59. **GPS:** n51,71602 e5,84489.⬆.
25 🚐 € 10 🚰💧Ch 💧WC 🔌📶included. **Location:** Comfortable, luxurious, quiet. **Surface:** grassy.
Distance: 🛒on the spot 🏊3,5km ⛵2,6km 🚌2,6km 🚲on the spot 🏃on the spot.
Remarks: Monitored parking 24/24.

S **Wijk en Aalburg** **8D3**

Bakkerij Hardeman, Torenstraat 4. **GPS:** n51,75976 e5,13123.

3 🚐 € 5 🚰💧Ch 💧WC 📶included. 📅 01/01-31/12
Distance: 🛒on the spot 🏃on the spot.

© S **Zundert** 🌿 **8C3**

Museum de Scooter, Heischoorstraat 4. **GPS:** n51,49025 e4,64532.

10 🛏 € 10 🚰🔌Ch🚽WC📶 included. 🅿 01/01-31/12
Distance: 🚲2,8km 🛣 A1 7km 🚴 on the spot 🚶 on the spot.
Remarks: Reservation during flower parade: museum@lambretta-nl.net.

Limburg

Schutterspark P1, Heidestraat 20. **GPS:** n50,94582 e5,98385.

10 🛏 free. **Surface:** metalled. 🅿 01/01-31/12
Distance: 🚲1,5km ⊗100m Schuttershuuske.
Remarks: Max. 72h, barefoot path.

Martinusplein. **GPS:** n51,69985 e5,97206.⬆

5 🛏 free. **Location:** Urban, simple, quiet. **Surface:** metalled.
🅿 01/01-31/12
Distance: 🚲100m 🛣4,6km 🚃200m ⊗150m 🍺bakery 100m,
supermarket 250m 🚴 on the spot 🚶 on the spot.
Remarks: Max. 72h.

A2 Campeercentrum, Veilingweg 13. **GPS:** n50,80632 e5,72201.
4 🛏 free.
Distance: 🚲500m 🛣1,1km.
Remarks: Industrial area, only overnight stays.

Het Kompas, Meerlosebaan 7. **GPS:** n51,42861 e6,12889.⬆

39 🛏 € 12 🚰🔌Ch (39x),4Amp 📶 included. **Location:** Rural.
Surface: grassy/gravel. 🅿 01/03-30/11
Distance: 🚲2km 🚃500m ⊗2km 🍺2km 🚌1km 🚴 on the spot
🚶 on the spot.

Koffieterras De Tump, Heelderweg 13. **GPS:** n51,17698 e5,88315.⬆

5 🛏 € 7. **Surface:** grassy. 🅿 01/05-31/10 ◉ Mo
Distance: 🚲1km 🚃 on the spot.
Remarks: Max. 48h.

Camperplaats Ittervoort, Brigittastraat 31.
GPS: n51,17565 e5,82228.⬆

15 🛏 € 9,10, 2 pers.incl 🚰🔌 included 🔌€2,50 📶€1/day.
Location: Rural, simple. **Surface:** grassy. 🅿 01/01-31/12
Distance: 🚲Ittervoort 500m, Thorn 2km 🛣2,6km
🍺Jan Linders 750m.
Remarks: Vineyard Thorn 600m.

De Watertoren, Kerkveldweg 1. **GPS:** n50,91016 e6,07300.⬆

6 🛏 € 10, peak season € 15 + € 0,90/pp tourist tax 🚰€1/90liter 🔌Ch
🔌 included 📶. **Location:** Simple, isolated, quiet.
Surface: grassy/gravel. 🅿 01/01-31/12

Camperplek IndeVerte, Horsterdijk 97.
GPS: n51,45130 e6,13144.⬆➡

50 🛏 € 12 🚰🔌Ch🔌(50x)🚽€1 ◉€4 📶 included.
Location: Comfortable, isolated, quiet. **Surface:** grassy.
🅿 01/01-31/12
Distance: 🚲3km.

Restaurant Boszicht, Provincialeweg 2. **GPS:** n51,36395 e6,07980.⬆

3 🛏 Free, use of a meal obligated. **Location:** Simple, noisy.
Surface: gravel.
Distance: 🚲2km 🛣2km ⊗ on the spot.

Camperplaats Maastricht, Bosscherweg 35. **GPS:** n50,87553 e5,68018.
100 🛏 € 15 🚰€0,50/50liter 🔌Ch 🔌(67x)€2,50/24h. 🚮
Surface: grassy/gravel. 🅿 01/01-31/12
Distance: 🚲3,2km.

Maastricht Marina, Hoge Weerd 20. **GPS:** n50,82389 e5,69944.

10 🛏 € 17,50 🚰🔌Ch🔌(10x),6Amp WC🚽◉€3,50/2,50 📶 included.
Surface: gravel/metalled. 🅿 01/02-31/12
Distance: 🚲1,5km 🛣2,8km 🚃50m ⊗150m 🍺1,5km 🚌800m
🚴 on the spot 🚶 on the spot.
Remarks: Possibility for reservation.

Nieuwehof, Vieruitersten 25. **GPS:** n51,35410 e5,89717.⬆➡
29 🛏 € 10 + € 1/pp 🚰🔌Ch🔌 WC included 🚽📶 on demand. 🚮
Location: Rural, comfortable, quiet. **Surface:** grassy/sand.
🅿 01/01-31/12
Distance: 🚲1,8km 🛣14km 🚴 on the spot 🚶 on the spot.

Toeristisch knooppunt de Diepen, Zwartweg 60.
GPS: n51,73788 e5,95510.⬆🅿

10 🛏 free. **Surface:** grassy/sand.
Distance: ⊗ on the spot.
Remarks: Next to Eethuis de Diepen.

Jachthaven Hanssum, Hanssum 40b. **GPS:** n51,25778 e6,00361.

5 🛏 € 7,50 🚰Ch🔌WC🚽. **Surface:** grassy/metalled.
Distance: 🚲3km 🚃 on the spot ⊗200m.
Remarks: Max. 48h, service near marina.

Neer 10E1

Café Restaurant Boothuis de Troost, Hanssum 47.
GPS: n51,25964 e6,00380.

4 🗑 € 7,50, guests free. **Surface:** metalled.

Nieuw Bergen 8E3

Camperplaats Bos&Heide, Op de Paal 4. **GPS:** n51,59008 e6,07269.

25 🗑 € 6,50 + € 1/pp tourist tax 🚰included 🗑Ch 🚿(15x)€2 WC.
Surface: grassy. 🅾 01/03-31/10
Distance: 🚶1,5km 🏊2km ⊗1,5km 🛒1,5km.
Remarks: Located in nature reserve Maasduinen.

Ottersum 8E3

Bier-Café Restaurant Old Inn, Siebengewaldseweg 13.
GPS: n51,68935 e6,00728.

20 🗑free. **Surface:** metalled. 🅾 01/01-31/12

Plasmolen 8E3

Eldorado, Witteweg 18. **GPS:** n51,73284 e5,91639.

13 🗑 € 15,50 2 pers.incl, dog € 2 🚰€1/100liter 🗑Ch 🚿(13x)€0,50/
kWh WCincluded 🗑€1 🔲€3 🟰€5/24h.
Location: Rural, comfortable, quiet.
Surface: grassy.
🅾 01/01-31/12 🔧 Service: winter
Distance: 🚶200m 🚲8km 🏊on the spot 🛶on the spot ⊗200m
🛒200m 🚲on the spot ⚓on the spot.
Remarks: Check in at Eldorado Boatshop Witteweg 9, max. 72h.

Sittard 10E1

De Nieuwe Hateboer, Sportcentrumlaan. **GPS:** n51,00794 e5,88150.⬆

10 🗑free 🚰 🗑ChWCuse sanitary facilities at swimming pool 🗑.
Surface: asphalted. 🅾 01/01-31/12
Distance: 🚶2km 🚲6,2km ⊗2km 🛒2km 🚌100m ⚓on the spot.

Remarks: At swimming pool, register via SMS (licence plate number)
+31 6 27 82 55 82, max. 48h.

Thorn 10E1

Waterstraat. **GPS:** n51,15860 e5,84403.⬆

3 🗑 € 2,50/9-18h. **Surface:** gravel. 🅾 01/01-31/12
Distance: 🚶150m ⊗150m.
Remarks: Max. 24h.

Tourist information Thorn:
ℹ VVV, Wijngaard 14, www.lekker-genieten.nl. The white village, with
historical centre and Gothic collegiate church.

Valkenburg 10E2

Camperplaats Valkenburg aan de Geul, Heunsbergerweg 1.
GPS: n50,86037 e5,83148.
30 🗑 € 16-22 🚰€1/100liter 🗑Ch 🚿(30x)€0,60/kWh,16Amp
WCincluded 🗑€0,70/time 🔲€4,75/2,25 🟰€2,50/24h 🚲.
Location: Rural, comfortable, quiet. **Surface:** grassy/metalled.
🅾 01/01-31/12
Distance: 🚶500m 🚲2km 🏊1,5km 🛶1,5km ⊗on the spot 🛒500m
🚌500m 🚲on the spot ⚓on the spot.
Remarks: Maastricht 15km.

🅿 Valkenburg 10E2

Burgemeester Henssingel. **GPS:** n50,86361 e5,83725.

6 🗑 € 1,60/h 10-20h.
Surface: metalled.
🅾 01/01-31/12
Distance: 🚶300m.

Tourist information Valkenburg:
ℹ VVV, Th.Dorrenplein 5, www.vvvzuidlimburg.nl. Popular holiday
resort.
👁 Gemeentegrot, Cauberg 4. Marl caves.
Ⓜ Steenkolenmijn, Daalhemerweg 31. Visiting a gallery of a mine.
🅾 01/04-30/11 10-17, 01/11-07/01 + weekend, guided tour 12h,
13.30h, 15h, remaining 14h.

Venlo 8E3

De Boswesels, Weselseweg/Kikvorstraat.
GPS: n51,39270 e6,19990.⬆➡

16 🗑 € 12 🚰 🗑Ch 🚿(16x)included. 🚲
Location: Simple. **Surface:** grassy. 🅾 01/04-01/11
Distance: 🚶1km 🛒500m ⊗1,8km.

Venlo 8E3

Jachthaven, Jachthavenweg 50. **GPS:** n51,39245 e6,14854.⬆

20 🗑 € 12,50 🚰 🚿10Amp WC🗑included 🔲€3/2 🟰.
Surface: metalled.
🅾 01/04-30/10
Distance: 🚶Venlo centre 4km 🚲3,5km ⊗on the spot 🛒500m.
Remarks: Max. 48h, check in at harbourmaster, free ferry to city centre.

Weert 10D1

Suffolkweg Zuid 30. **GPS:** n51,25435 e5,69283.⬆⬆

20 🗑 € 8, 2 pers incl., 1 pers + € 2 🚰 🗑Chincluded 🚿€2.
Remarks: Max. 72h.

Well 8E3

Camperplaats De Wellsche Hut, Wezerweg 13.
GPS: n51,58687 e6,12344.⬆

18 🗑 € 10 🚰 🗑Ch 🚿 WCincluded 🚲.
Surface: metalled. 🅾 01/01-31/12
Distance: 🚶4km 🏊6km ⊗on the spot.
Remarks: At mountainbike trail, dog on leads, nature reserve
Maasduinen.

Well 8E3

Jachthaven 't Leuken, De Kamp 7a. **GPS:** n51,56361 e6,06360.⬆

30 🗑 € 10 🚰 🗑Ch 🚿 WC🗑included. **Location:** Simple, quiet.
Surface: grassy. 🅾 01/04-01/11
Distance: 🚶Well 2km 🚲11km 🏊on the spot 🛶on the spot
⊗on the spot.
Remarks: Acquatic sports area.

NL

Norway

Capital: Oslo
Government: parliamentary constitutional monarchy
Official Language: Norwegian
Population 5,166,000 (2014)
Area: 323,787 Km²

General information
Dialling code: 0047
General emergency: 112
Currency: Norwegian krone (NOK),
€ 1 = NOK 9,20, NOK 1 = € 0,11 (October 2015)
£ 1 = NOK 12,80, NOK 1 = £ 0,08 (October 2015)
Credit cards are accepted almost everywhere.

Regulations for overnight stays
In general wild camping is allowed, you must hold at least 150 metres from the nearest house or cabin.

Camping Key Europe is obligatory when using campsites: the card can be purchased at any campsite for NOK 160 (± € 16,50/ £ 10,50), valid for one year.

Additional public holidays 2016
March 25 Good Friday
March 28 Easter Monday
May 1 Labor Day
May 16 Pentecost Monday
May 17 Constitution Day
July 29 St. Olaf's Day

Time Zone
Winter (Standard Time) GMT+1
Summer (DST) GMT+2

NO

Nordkapp

Northern Norway
page: 584-585

Trøndelag
page: 585

Trondheim

Western Norway
page: 585-586

Eastern Norway
page: 586-587

Bergen

Stavanger   **Oslo**

Southern Norway
page: 586

Kristiansand

Northern Norway

Båstad — 2A2
Eggumsveien. **GPS:** n68,30729 e13,65160.
30 kr 100 WC. **Location:** Rural, isolated, quiet.
Surface: asphalted.
Distance: on the spot on the spot.
Remarks: Check in at cafe.

Bodø — 2A3
Bobilparkering Sentrum, Hålogalandsgata 11.
GPS: n67,27866 e14,41026.
4 kr 10/h, overnight stay free Chfree. 01/01-31/12
Distance: 500m.

Botnhamn — 2A2
Sjark- Og Småbåtforening. GPS: n69,50743 e17,90753.
5 kr 75 Ch kr50. **Surface:** concrete.
Distance: on the spot on the spot on the spot.

Brønnøysund — 3B1
Brønnøy havn, Havnegata. **GPS:** n65,47271 e12,20725.
free. **Surface:** gravel. 01/01-31/12 snow
Distance: on the spot on the spot on the spot.
Remarks: At shopping centre .

Brønnøysund — 3B1
Statiol, Valveien 48. **GPS:** n65,47919 e12,21634.
kr 130 Ch.
Distance: on the spot on the spot 200m.
Remarks: Behind petrol station.

Fauske — 2A3
Fauske Parkering AS. GPS: n67,25741 e15,38421.
kr 150 Ch included. **Surface:** asphalted. water disconnected in winter
Distance: on the spot on the spot.
Remarks: Max. 24h.

Fiskåbygd — 3A3
Statoil. GPS: n62,09861 e5,55722.
6 free Ch. 01/01-31/12
Distance: on the spot on the spot on the spot 300m

100m.
Remarks: At petrol station, max. 3 days.

Hammerfest — 2A2
Jernbanetrasken. **GPS:** n69,63289 e17,99845.
.
Distance: 300m.
Remarks: Behind the hotel.

Hattfjelldal — 3C1
RV 73. **GPS:** n65,59578 e13,99090.
60 free Chfree. **Surface:** asphalted.
Distance: 100m.

Husøy i Senja — 2A2
Fylkesveg. **GPS:** n69,54522 e17,67056.
6 kr 100.
Distance: on the spot on the spot.

Innhavet — 2A3
GPS: n67,96366 e15,92617.
kr 100 Ch kr30. **Surface:** gravel. 01/01-31/12
Distance: on the spot on the spot 150m.

Jøkelfjord — 2B1
Jøkelfjord Bobilcamping. GPS: n70,06207 e21,92987.
10 kr 100 Ch kr50.
Distance: on the spot on the spot.

Kabelvåg — 2A2
Kabelvåg Feriehus & Camping, Mølnosveien.
GPS: n68,21747 e14,44541.
25 kr 240 Ch kr40 kr50. **Surface:** gravel/metalled.
01/01-31/12
Distance: 2,5km on the spot on the spot.
Remarks: Canoe rental.

Kirkenes — 2C1
Havneveien. **GPS:** n69,72754 e30,07291.
free Ch. **Surface:** asphalted.
Distance: 1km on the spot on the spot 350m.

Kleppstad — 2A2
Lofoten Bobilcamping, Lyngvær. **GPS:** n68,22915 e14,21571.
kr 125 kr40 WC. 01/05-15/09

Distance: on the spot.

Lødingen — 2A2
Båtforeningen. GPS: n68,41249 e16,00871.
kr 120 (18x),kr30 WC kr20. **Surface:** grassy/gravel.
Distance: on the spot on the spot 1km 1km.
Remarks: Money in envelope in mail box.

Melbu — 2A2
Melbu Båtforenings, Neptunveien. **GPS:** n68,49493 e14,81248.
kr 100 included. **Surface:** gravel.
Distance: on the spot on the spot 900m.

Mo i Rana — 2A3
E6. **GPS:** n66,30462 e14,12296.
Ch.

Narvik — 2A2
Turist Parking, Brugata. **GPS:** n68,44172 e17,41705.
free. **Surface:** asphalted.

Oksfjordhamn — 2B1
Oksfjord Båtforening. GPS: n69,90620 e21,32404.
kr 100 ChWC. **Surface:** gravel.

Skaland — 2A2
Senjatrollet, Finnsæter. **GPS:** n69,41020 e17,26334.
20 free Ch. **Location:** Isolated.

Skutvik — 2A3
Skutvik Båtforening. GPS: n68,01368 e15,33414.
kr 100. **Surface:** grassy.
Distance: on the spot on the spot.

Sommarøy — 2A2
Skipsholmvegen. **GPS:** n69,63335 e17,99490.
voluntary contribution Ch. **Surface:** gravel.
Distance: 1km on the spot on the spot 800m.
Remarks: At the beach.

Storforshei — 2A3
Polarsirkel-Senteret, Saltfjellet. **GPS:** n66,55175 e15,32134.
free. **Location:** Isolated, quiet. **Surface:** asphalted.

Stø — 2A2
Stø Bobilcamp. GPS: n69,01984 e15,10762.

Norway

13 🕭kr 180 🖭ChWC🔧🔌. **Surface:** gravel. ⬛ 01/05-15/09
Distance: ⚓on the spot ⛽on the spot ⊗on the spot.

⚓S | Svolvær | 2A2
Vestfjord Hotell Lofoten, Fiskergata 46. **GPS:** n68,22949 e14,56492.

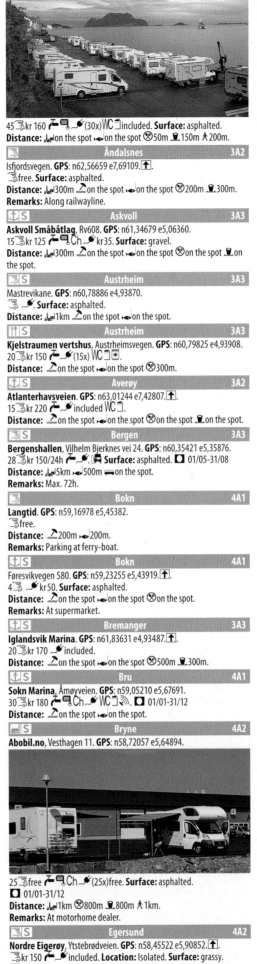

28 🕭kr 250 🚰🔧(34x)WCincluded🚽kr 5.
Distance: 📍200m ⛽on the spot ⊗on the spot 🚂400m 🚌250m
🚲2km 🚶2km.

🕭 | Utskarpen | 2A3
Flostrandveien. **GPS:** n66,31917 e13,31009.
7 🕭free. **Location:** Rural. **Surface:** asphalted/grassy.
Distance: ⚓on the spot ⛽on the spot 🚶on the spot.

🕭 | Vevelstad | 3B1
Steinmo Bobilparkering, Fv17. **GPS:** n65,60550 e12,36637.⬆.
🕭kr 100. **Location:** Isolated, quiet. **Surface:** grassy/gravel.
Distance: ⚓on the spot ⛽on the spot.

Trøndelag

🕭 | Grong | 3B1
Fv391. **GPS:** n64,46587 e12,31143.⬆.
5 🕭free. **Surface:** asphalted.
Distance: 🛁100m ⚓100m 🚂400m.
Remarks: Picnic area.

🍴S | Heimdal | 3B2
Sandmoen Bobilparkering, Sandmoflata 6.
GPS: n63,33155 e10,35678.⬆.
13 🕭kr 200 🚰(10x)🚽kr 20🕭24h,kr 50. ⬛ 01/01-31/12
Distance: 🛁200m ⊗on the spot.
Remarks: Check in at reception, breakfast-service.

🕭S | Inderøy | 3B2
Inderøy Bobilcamp, Øynavegen. **GPS:** n63,87978 e11,26999.⬆.
15 🕭kr 200 🚰🔧Ch🔧included.
Distance: 🛁1,5km ⊗300m.

⚓S | Inderøy | 3B2
Kjerknesvågen Kai, Vågavegen 650. **GPS:** n63,91311 e11,19049.
10 🕭kr 150 🔧WCincluded🚽kr 20. **Surface:** gravel. ⬛ 01/01-31/12
⭕ 1st and 3rd weekend July
Distance: ⚓on the spot ⛽on the spot.

🕭S | Leksvik | 3B2
Hammerbergvegen. **GPS:** n63,66747 e10,61449.
🕭kr 100 🔧🔌included. **Surface:** grassy/gravel. ⬛ 01/01-31/12
Distance: 🛁500m ⚓on the spot ⛽on the spot ⊗on the spot
🚂1km.
Remarks: Pay at restaurant.

🖭S | Oppdal | 3B2
Trollheimsporten Turistsenter, Festa. **GPS:** n62,61610 e9,47695.
🕭kr 150 🔧included. **Surface:** asphalted.
Distance: 🛁12km.

🍴S | Rennebu | 3B2
Berkåk Veikro, Mjukliveien 1. **GPS:** n62,83215 e10,01117.
8 🕭kr 200 🚰🔧WC🔧. ⬛ 01/01-31/12
Distance: ⊗on the spot.

🕭 | Trofors | 3B1
Store Svenningvatn. **GPS:** n65,32528 e13,37714.⬆.
🕭kr 80. **Location:** Rural, isolated, quiet. **Surface:** gravel.
Distance: 🛁Trofors 25km ⚓on the spot ⛽on the spot.
Remarks: Money in envelope in mail box.

🕭 | Trondheim | 3B2
Øya Stadion, Klostergata. **GPS:** n63,42565 e10,38172.⬆.
🕭free. **Location:** Urban.
Distance: 🛁1km ⛽on the spot.
Remarks: At stadium, max. 24h.

Western Norway

🕭S | Ålesund | 3A2
Hjelsetgaarden Motorhome, Sorenskriver Bullsgate.
GPS: n62,47670 e6,16110.

45 🕭kr 160 🚰🔧🔧(30x)WCincluded. **Surface:** asphalted.
Distance: 🛁on the spot ⛽on the spot ⊗50m 🚂150m 🚶200m.

🕭 | Åndalsnes | 3A2
Isfjordsvegen. **GPS:** n62,56659 e7,69109.⬆.
🕭free. **Surface:** asphalted.
Distance: 🛁300m ⚓on the spot ⛽on the spot ⊗200m 🚂300m.
Remarks: Along railwayline.

⚓S | Askvoll | 3A3
Askvoll Småbåtlag, Rv608. **GPS:** n61,34679 e5,06360.
15 🕭kr 125 🚰🔧Ch🔧kr 35. **Surface:** gravel.
Distance: 🛁300m ⚓on the spot ⛽on the spot ⊗on the spot 🚂on the spot.

🕭S | Austrheim | 3A3
Mastrevikane. **GPS:** n60,78886 e4,93870.
🕭🔧. **Surface:** asphalted.
Distance: 🛁1km ⚓on the spot ⛽on the spot.

🍴S | Austrheim | 3A3
Kjelstraumen vertshus, Austrheimsvegen. **GPS:** n60,79825 e4,93908.
20 🕭kr 150 🚰🔧(15x)WC🔧🖭.
Distance: ⚓on the spot ⛽on the spot ⊗300m.

⚓S | Averøy | 3A2
Atlanterhavsveien. **GPS:** n63,01244 e7,42807.⬆.
15 🕭kr 220 🚰🔧included WC🔧.
Distance: ⚓on the spot ⛽on the spot ⊗on the spot 🚂on the spot.

🕭S | Bergen | 3A3
Bergenshallen, Vilhelm Bjerknes vei 24. **GPS:** n60,35421 e5,35876.
28 🕭kr 150/24h 🚰🔧🚗.🍴 **Surface:** asphalted. ⬛ 01/05-31/08
Distance: 🛁5km ⚓500m 🚌on the spot.
Remarks: Max. 72h.

🕭 | Bokn | 4A1
Langtid. **GPS:** n59,16978 e5,45382.
🕭free.
Distance: ⚓200m 🚂200m.
Remarks: Parking at ferry-boat.

⚓S | Bokn | 4A1
Føresvikvegen 580. **GPS:** n59,23255 e5,43919.⬆.
4 🕭🔧kr 50. **Surface:** asphalted.
Distance: ⚓on the spot ⛽on the spot ⊗on the spot.
Remarks: At supermarket.

⚓S | Bremanger | 3A3
Iglandsvik Marina. **GPS:** n61,83631 e4,93487.⬆.
20 🕭kr 170 🔧included.
Distance: ⚓on the spot ⛽on the spot ⊗500m 🚂300m.

⚓S | Bru | 4A1
Sokn Marina, Åmøyveien. **GPS:** n59,05210 e5,67691.
30 🕭kr 180 🚰🔧Ch🔧WC🔧🔌. ⬛ 01/01-31/12
Distance: ⚓on the spot ⛽on the spot.

🖭S | Bryne | 4A2
Abobil.no, Vesthagen 11. **GPS:** n58,72057 e5,64894.

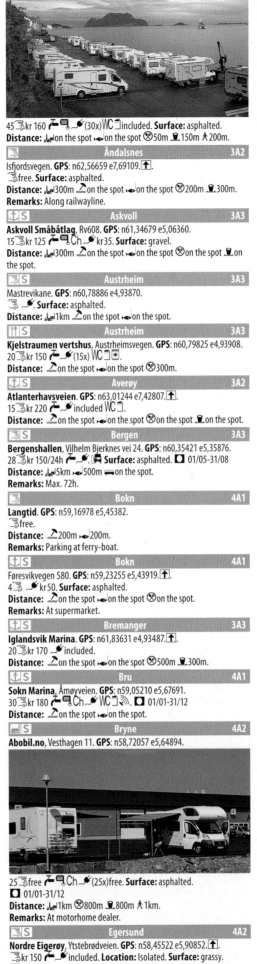

25 🕭free 🚰🔧Ch🔧(25x)free. **Surface:** asphalted.
⬛ 01/01-31/12
Distance: 🛁1km ⊗800m 🚂800m 🚶1km.
Remarks: At motorhome dealer.

🕭S | Egersund | 4A2
Nordre Eigerøy, Ytstebrødveien. **GPS:** n58,45522 e5,90852.⬆.
🕭kr 150 🚰🔧included. **Location:** Isolated. **Surface:** grassy.
⬛ 01/01-31/12
Distance: 🛁5,5km ⚓on the spot ⛽on the spot 🚂5,5km 🚶on the

spot.

🕭 | Egersund | 4A2
Ved taxi-stasjon, Jernbaneveien. **GPS:** n58,45373 e6,00243.
10 🕭free. **Surface:** asphalted.
Distance: 🛁300m ⚓on the spot ⛽on the spot ⊗300m.

🕭 | Erfjord | 4A1
Hålandsosen, Riksveg. **GPS:** n59,34806 e6,23703.
🕭free. **Location:** Isolated, quiet. **Surface:** gravel.
Distance: ⚓on the spot ⛽on the spot 🚂200m.

🕭S | Florø | 3A3
Bobilparkering Florø, Strandvegen 19. **GPS:** n61,60061 e5,02252.
🕭kr 150 WCincluded🖭. **Surface:** asphalted. ⬛ 01/01-31/12
Distance: 🛁600m ⛽on the spot ⊗200m.
Remarks: Pay at tourist office.

🕭S | Fosnavåg | 3A2
Gerhard Voldnes veg. **GPS:** n62,33913 e5,63907.
🕭free 🔧(10x),kr 50.
Distance: 🛁800m ⚓on the spot ⛽on the spot ⊗300m 🚂800m.
Remarks: Coins at town hall.

🖭 | Haugesund | 4A1
Kvalsvik, Skjelavikvegen. **GPS:** n59,43541 e5,24054.
🕭free. **Surface:** gravel/metalled.
Distance: 🛁4km ⚓on the spot ⛽on the spot.

⚓S | Hebnes | 4A1
Joker Vatlandsvåg kai. **GPS:** n59,41009 e6,01843.
🕭kr 100 🚰🔧. ⬛ 01/01-31/12
Distance: ⚓on the spot ⛽on the spot ⊗takeaway restaurant
🚂on the spot.

⚓S | Husnes | 4A1
Husnes Båtlag, Onarheimsvegen. **GPS:** n59,87187 e5,76195.
🕭kr 150 🔧kr 50 WC🔧🔌free.🖭 🔧 **Surface:** metalled.
Distance: 🛁1,5km ⛽on the spot 🚂1,5km.
Remarks: Golf court 300m.

🍴S | Isfjorden | 3A2
Gjerdset Turistsenter, Gjerdsetbygda. **GPS:** n62,57868 e7,56713.
10 🕭kr 100 🚰WC🔌.
Distance: 🛁13km ⚓200m ⛽200m 🚌100m.

⚓S | Jørpeland | 4A1
Jørpeland Bobilparkering. **GPS:** n59,01757 e6,04377.⬆.
🕭kr 150 🔧kr 50 WC🔧. **Surface:** asphalted.
Distance: 🛁500m ⚓on the spot ⛽on the spot ⊗450m.

⚓S | Klokkarvik | 3A3
Kleppe Båtlag. **GPS:** n60,18462 e5,15163.
20 🕭kr 100 🚰🔧Ch🔧kr 50 WC🔧. **Surface:** asphalted.
Distance: 🛁6km ⚓on the spot ⛽on the spot.

⚓ | Kristiansund | 3A2
Kristiansund Småbåtlag, Freiveien 50. **GPS:** n63,11713 e7,73168.
5 🕭kr 7-35, overnight stay free. **Surface:** asphalted.
Distance: 🛁1km ⚓on the spot ⛽on the spot ⊗on the spot.

⚓S | Kulleseid | 4A1
Kulleseidkanalen, Kulleseidkanalen.
GPS: n59,74194 o5,23481.➡.
🕭kr 100 🔧kr 50 🖭🔌
Distance: ⚓on the spot 🚂300m.

🕭S | Måløy | 3A3
Småbåthavn. **GPS:** n61,93361 e5,11316.⬆.
10 🕭kr 150 🚰🔧WCincluded🖭.🖭 **Location:** Central.
Surface: asphalted.
Distance: 🛁on the spot ⛽on the spot ⊗on the spot 🚂on the spot.

⚓S | Matre | 4A1
Matre Havn. **GPS:** n59,84352 e5,98434.
🕭kr 100 🚰🔧Ch🔧kr 50. **Location:** Isolated, quiet.
Surface: asphalted.

🕭 | Nesflaten | 4B1
Fylkesveg. **GPS:** n59,64471 e6,80223.
3 🕭free. **Surface:** asphalted. ⬛ 01/01-31/12
Distance: ⚓on the spot ⛽on the spot.
Remarks: At the quay.

🕭 | Norheimsund | 3A3
Rosselandsvegen. **GPS:** n60,37007 e6,10616.
🕭. **Surface:** asphalted.
Distance: 🛁2,5km ⚓on the spot ⛽on the spot ⊗100m.
Remarks: Nearby waterfalls.

🕭S | Odda | 3A3
Odda bobilcamp, Røldalsvegen. **GPS:** n60,07144 e6,54865.
40 🕭kr 150 🔧included. **Surface:** asphalted.
Distance: ⚓on the spot ⛽on the spot.
Remarks: Max. 3 days.

NO

Rennesøy — 4A1
GPS: n59,13787 e5,59161.
free. **Surface:** asphalted.
Distance: on the spot on the spot.

Rognaldsvåg — 3A3
Rognaldsvåg Bobilparkering. GPS: n61,56494 e4,79580.
8 kr 150 WC. **Surface:** gravel. 01/01-31/12
Distance: 150m 150m on the spot.

Rosendal — 4A1
Skåla Vika, Skålafjæro. **GPS:** n59,98528 e6,00708.
80 kr 175 Ch kr 25. 01/01-31/12
Distance: 200m on the spot on the spot 200m.

Sand — 4A1
Hydrokaien, Nordenden. **GPS:** n59,48516 e6,24756.
6 free WC. **Surface:** asphalted.
Distance: 300m on the spot on the spot 800m 300m
on the spot.
Remarks: At museum.

Sand — 4A1
Stasjon XY. GPS: n59,47590 e6,28913.
Ch.
Remarks: At petrol station.

Sandeid — 4A1
Kai. GPS: n59,54198 e5,86770.
kr 100 kr 25 kr 10. **Surface:** asphalted.
Distance: on the spot on the spot on the spot.
Remarks: Money in envelope in mail box.

Sauda — 4A1
Bobil Havn, Treaskjæret. **GPS:** n59,64480 e6,33716.
15 kr 100 ChWC.
Distance: 1,2km on the spot on the spot 1,2km 1,2km
100m.
Remarks: At the quay.

Skånevik — 4A1
Fylkesveg. **GPS:** n59,73385 e5,92672.
kr 150 ChWC. **Surface:** gravel.
Distance: 500m on the spot on the spot 400m.

Sveio — 4A1
Victors Bobil camping, Fylkesveg. **GPS:** n59,53016 e5,44353.
5 kr 250-300 WC included. **Location:** Isolated.
Surface: grassy. 01/04-31/10
Distance: 9km on the spot on the spot 9km.

Svelgen — 3A3
Svelgen Hotell, Granden. **GPS:** n61,76936 e5,29072.
7 free. **Surface:** grassy.
Distance: on the spot on the spot on the spot 200m.

Sykkylven — 3A2
Sykkylven Småbåthamn, Ullavikvegen. **GPS:** n62,39679 e6,58192.
kr 90 kr 30 WC. **Surface:** asphalted.
Distance: 500m on the spot on the spot 500m 500m.

Sæbøvik — 4A1
Halsnøy Samfunnshus, Riksveg. **GPS:** n59,79431 e5,71196.
12 kr 150 ChWC. **Surface:** asphalted. 01/01-31/12
water disconnected in winter
Distance: on the spot on the spot 200m.

Tau — 4A1
Tau Båtforening, Kvernvegen. **GPS:** n59,06086 e5,91343.
8 kr 150 ChWC included. 01/01-31/12
Distance: on the spot on the spot 1km 1km.

Tjøvåg — 3A2
Laternen Marina. GPS: n62,31388 e5,70805.
kr 100 (4x),kr 45 kr 20 kr 30/20.
Distance: 5km on the spot.
Remarks: Boat rental.

Tresfjord — 3A2
Småbåthamn. GPS: n62,52520 e7,13085.
kr 150 Ch WC.
Distance: on the spot on the spot.

Remarks: At petrol station.

Urangsvåg — 4A1
Fylkesveg. **GPS:** n59,84002 e5,15190.
6 kr 150 ChWC. **Surface:** asphalted.
Distance: on the spot on the spot.

Vikedal — 4A1
Vikedal Båthavn, Riksveg. **GPS:** n59,49656 e5,89000.
kr 150 WC. **Surface:** metalled.
Distance: 200m on the spot on the spot 200m 200m.

Viksdalen — 3A3
GPS: n61,39096 e6,26945.
6 kr 150 Ch included. **Location:** Rural, isolated, quiet.
Surface: gravel.
Distance: 12km on the spot on the spot.

Ølen — 4A1
Fjellstøl Skianlegg. GPS: n59,58853 e5,88857.
kr 30.
Distance: on the spot on the spot.
Remarks: At ski-lift.

Ølen — 4A1
Båtlag, Fylkesveg. **GPS:** n59,60748 e5,81448.
10 kr 140 WC.
Distance: 150m on the spot on the spot 300m 600m.

Ølensvåg — 4A1
Ask Bobilparkering, Gjerdevikvegen 46.
GPS: n59,59728 e5,75857.
30 kr 100 Ch (12x),kr 30. **Surface:** gravel.
Distance: on the spot on the spot.

Southern Norway

Åmli — 4B2
Pan Garden, Tveit 38. **GPS:** n58,74697 e8,50946.
10 kr 100 kr 50 kr 30. **Location:** Isolated, quiet.
Distance: on the spot on the spot on the spot.

Borhaug — 4B2
Lista Fyr, Toppveien 10. **GPS:** n58,10943 e6,56863.
free. 01/01-31/12
Distance: 1,5km.
Remarks: At lighthouse, max. 2 nights.

Borhaug — 4B2
Borshavn. GPS: n58,10081 e6,58335.
kr 200 Ch WC. **Surface:** asphalted.
Distance: on the spot on the spot.
Remarks: Max. 1 day.

Farsund — 4B2
Farsund Bobil Camp, Ferjeveien. **GPS:** n58,09439 e6,81278.
kr 175 . **Surface:** metalled. 01/01-31/12 Service:
winter
Distance: 500m on the spot on the spot 500m 1,5km.

Flekkefjord — 4B2
Tollbodbrygga. GPS: n58,29267 e6,66296.
free kr 50 WC kr 50. **Surface:** gravel.
Distance: 850m on the spot 850m 200m.

Grimstad — 4B2
Sørlandets Caravansenter, Grøm Næringspark 2.
GPS: n58,34011 e8,56658.
3 free Ch free. **Location:** Simple.
Distance: 1km 200m 1km 1km.
Remarks: At motorhome dealer, max. 24h.

Hidrasund — 4B2
Kirkehavn. GPS: n58,22896 e6,52919.
. **Location:** Isolated, quiet. **Surface:** asphalted.
Distance: 2km on the spot 2km 1km on the spot.

Hornes — 4B2
Mineralparken Bobilcamp, Mineralvegen 1.
GPS: n58,54993 e7,77542.
40 kr 200 Ch kr 20 kr 40/40 included.
Surface: grassy.
Distance: 700m on the spot on the spot.
Remarks: Bread-service in summer period.

Lillesand — 4B2
Lillesand gjesthavn, Kokkenes. **GPS:** n58,24745 e8,38349.
25 kr 200 Ch included WC. **Surface:** asphalted.
Service: winter
Distance: 500m on the spot on the spot 200m 500m.

Lindesnes — 4B2
Spangereidveien. **GPS:** n58,03998 e7,15014.

2 kr 150 WC kr 20 kr 45/45.
Distance: on the spot on the spot on the spot.
Remarks: Boat rental.

Mandal — 4B2
Mandal Havn, Havnegata. **GPS:** n58,02440 e7,45566.
10 kr 180 . **Surface:** asphalted.
Distance: 400m on the spot 400m 1km.

Risør — 4C2
Tjenngata. **GPS:** n58,72093 e9,22567.
kr 20/h, kr 100/day kr 10 kr 30/30.
Surface: grassy. Service: winter
Distance: 600m on the spot 500m 600m.

Valle — 4B1
Sanden Såre. GPS: n59,27128 e7,46221.
kr 150-200 Ch. **Location:** Rural, isolated, quiet.
Surface: grassy.
Distance: 10km on the spot on the spot.
Remarks: Nearby waterfalls.

Eastern Norway

Bjørkelangen — 3B3
Bjørkelangen bobilparkering, Stasjonsveien 25.
GPS: n59,88058 e11,57102.
10 free ChWC. 01/03-01/10
Distance: 500m 600m.
Remarks: Next to sports fields.

Brandbu — 3B3
Tegneseriemuseet, Rosendalsvegen. **GPS:** n60,41719 e10,50940.
4 kr 100 kr 50. **Surface:** asphalted. 01/03-01/10
Distance: 500m 400m 300m.
Remarks: At museum.

Bøverdalen — 3A3
Leirvassbu. GPS: n61,54917 e8,24694.
kr 200 WC. **Location:** Isolated, quiet. 20/06-30/09
Remarks: Accessible via toll road (60kr).

Dalen — 4B1
Bobilparkering Dalen Bryggje. GPS: n59,44515 e8,02292.
kr 150 . **Surface:** metalled.
Distance: 900m on the spot on the spot.

Etnedal — 3B3
Sebu Røssjøen, Lenningsvegen. **GPS:** n61,12502 e9,71475.
free.
Distance: on the spot.

Flatdal — 4B1
Kvåle Din gard, Kvålevegen. **GPS:** n59,56042 e8,56248.
5 kr 200 Ch. **Surface:** grassy. 01/01-31/12
Distance: on the spot on the spot.

Fredrikstad — 4C1
Gjestehavn. GPS: n59,21423 e10,92512.
60 kr 250 WC. **Surface:** asphalted.
Distance: on the spot on the spot 150m.

Gjøvik — 3B3
Gjøvik Marina, Bryggevegen. **GPS:** n60,79555 e10,70116.
25 kr 50 Ch. **Surface:** gravel. 15/06-13/09
Distance: on the spot on the spot McDonalds 300m.
Remarks: To be paid at petrol station.

Halden — 4D1
Kiellands gate. **GPS:** n59,11539 e11,38128.
5 kr 150 .
Distance: 800m on the spot on the spot 800m.

Hamar — 3B3
Hamar båtforening, Brygga. **GPS:** n60,78846 e11,07138.
20 kr 120 Ch (6x). **Surface:** asphalted. 01/06-30/09
Distance: 300m on the spot on the spot 1km 400m.

Holmestrand — 4C1
Hagemannsveien. **GPS:** n59,48048 e10,32933.
free. **Surface:** asphalted.
Distance: on the spot on the spot.

Remarks: At harbour.

| ⚓S | **Holmestrand** | 4C1 |

Weidemannsgate 13. **GPS:** n59,48921 e10,32294.
150 ⚡Ch ⚡kWh, kr 2,80. 🗓 01/06-15/09
Distance: on the spot on the spot 100m.

| ⚓S | **Horten** | 4C1 |

Horten Havn. GPS: n59,41302 e10,48695.
14 kr 180 🚰⚡WC. **Surface:** asphalted.
Distance: on the spot on the spot on the spot 100m 600m.

| 🚣S | **Hov** | 3B3 |

Fjordvegen 27. **GPS:** n60,69915 e10,33972.
2 kr 100 ⚡Ch⚡. **Surface:** grassy.
Distance: on the spot on the spot.

| 🏔S | **Høvringen** | 3B3 |

Rondane Haukliseter Fjellhotell. GPS: n61,88853 e9,48745.
kr 200 🚰⚡Ch⚡WC. **Surface:** grassy.
Distance: 1km 1km.
Remarks: Use of sauna against payment.

| 🚣 | **Kongsberg** | 4C1 |

Glabak. **GPS:** n59,67205 e9,64166.
. **Surface:** asphalted.
Distance: on the spot 400m 550m.
Remarks: At swimming pool.

| 🚣 | **Kragerø** | 4C1 |

Allemannsveien. **GPS:** n58,87553 e9,41766.
150. **Surface:** unpaved.
Distance: on the spot 100m.

| 🚣 | **Kvelde** | 4C1 |

Roppestad. **GPS:** n59,15310 e9,90844.
free. **Location:** Isolated, quiet. **Surface:** grassy.
Distance: 50m 50m.
Remarks: Max. 2 days.

| 🚣S | **Langesund** | 4C1 |

Skjærsgårdshallen, Stathelleveien 33. **GPS:** n59,01285 e9,74301.
8 kr 150 ⚡Ch⚡WC. **Surface:** asphalted. 🗓 13/04-11/10
Distance: 2km 700m.
Remarks: At gymnasium.

| ⚓S | **Larvik** | 4C1 |

Indre Havn, Strandpromenaden. **GPS:** n59,04892 e10,03361.
21 € 15/kr 120 🚰⚡Ch⚡included.
Distance: on the spot on the spot 500m 500m.

| 🚣 | **Lillehammer** | 3B3 |

Lysgårdsbakkene, Lysgårdsvegen 55. **GPS:** n61,12431 e10,48914.
70. **Surface:** metalled.
Distance: 250m.

| 🚣S | **Lunde** | 4C1 |

Hogga Sluser, Gamle Strengenvegen. **GPS:** n59,30216 e9,04331.
12 kr 150 🚰⚡Ch⚡included kr 10.
Distance: on the spot on the spot.

| ⚓S | **Moss** | 4C1 |

Bobilhavn, Værftsgata. **GPS:** n59,43486 e10,65141.
14 kr 150 🚰⚡included WC.
Distance: on the spot on the spot 300m 100m.
Remarks: Max. 3 days.

| 🚣 | **Mysusæter** | 3B3 |

Mysuseter Fjellstue. GPS: n61,81161 e9,68463.
40. **Surface:** metalled.

| 🚣S | **Notodden** | 4C1 |

Bobilcamp Nesøya, Heddalsvegen. **GPS:** n59,55876 e9,24851.
13 ⚡(13x)included. **Surface:** unpaved.
Distance: 1km on the spot on the spot on the spot 250m.

| S | **Notodden** | 4C1 |

Heddalsvegen. **GPS:** n59,55981 e9,24834.
🚰kr 2 Ch WC kr 1 kr 2. 🗓 01/01-31/12

| ⚓S | **Oslo** | 3B3 |

Sjølyst Marina, Drammensveien 164. **GPS:** n59,92026 e10,67506.
250 kr 200 🚰⚡Ch⚡WC included. **Surface:** asphalted.
🗓 01/06-20/09
Distance: 6km on the spot on the spot.

| 📷S | **Oslo** | 3B3 |

Bogstad Camp, Ankerveien 117. **GPS:** n59,96293 e10,64203.
38 kr 280, 4 pers.incl WC kr 15. **Surface:** grassy/gravel.
🗓 01/01-31/12
Distance: 700m on the spot.

| 🚣 | **Rauland** | 4B1 |

Raulandsfjell. GPS: n59,71963 e8,00084.

14.
Distance: 5km on the spot on the spot.
Remarks: At ski-lift.

| ⚓S | **Sandefjord** | 4C1 |

Sandefjord Bobil havn, Sandefjordsveien.
GPS: n59,12506 e10,22108.
16 kr 200 🚰⚡included. **Surface:** asphalted.
Distance: 700m on the spot on the spot 700m 1km.
Remarks: Max. 24h.

| 🚣 | **Sarpsborg** | 4D1 |

Tindlund bobilparkering, Østre Greåkervei.
GPS: n59,27398 e11,04709.
100 ⚡(4x). **Surface:** gravel.
Distance: 1,3km.

| 🏭S | **Sarpsborg** | 4D1 |

Stamsaas Fritid, Vogtsvei 40. **GPS:** n59,28532 e11,08414.
free 🚰.
Distance: 350m.
Remarks: Service during opening hours.

| 🚣 | **Seljord** | 4B1 |

Flatin Gard, Flatingrendi 3. **GPS:** n59,50725 e8,63964.
40 kr 100, kr 200 service incl ⚡WC.
Distance: 100m 100m.

| 🚣 | **Siljan** | 4C1 |

Sporevann. **GPS:** n59,38476 e9,69584.
10 free. **Location:** Simple, isolated.
Distance: 11km on the spot on the spot.

| 🏔S | **Skien** | 4C1 |

Fritidspark, Moflatveien 59. **GPS:** n59,18510 e9,59698.
14 kr 200 🚰Ch⚡WC included kr 20. **Surface:** asphalted.
🗓 01/04-01/10
Distance: on the spot.
Remarks: Pay at hotel.

| 📷 | **Skien** | 4C1 |

Teg Seil, Bøleveien 4. **GPS:** n59,19634 e9,62039.
10 kr 150. 🗓 01/05-30/09
Distance: 700m on the spot on the spot 400m on the spot.
Remarks: At sailmaker.

| 🚣 | **Skreia** | 3B3 |

Hersjøen. **GPS:** n60,54498 e11,03309.
kr 45. **Location:** Isolated, quiet. **Surface:** grassy.
Distance: on the spot on the spot 6,5km.

| 🚣 | **Tyristrand** | 3B3 |

Stall Myhre, Holleiaveien 263. **GPS:** n60,11111 e10,07194.
100. **Location:** Isolated, quiet. **Surface:** grassy.
🗓 01/03-01/10
Distance: 3,5km.
Remarks: At horse farm.

| 🚣S | **Tønsberg** | 4C1 |

Storgaten. **GPS:** n59,26323 e10,41569.
8 kr 150 ⚡. **Surface:** asphalted.
Distance: on the spot 100m.
Remarks: Max. 7 days.

| 🚣 | **Tønsberg** | 4C1 |

Fjordgaten. **GPS:** n59,27390 e10,40009.
23 . **Surface:** asphalted.
Distance: 1km 50m 50m.

| 🚣 | **Tønsberg** | 4C1 |

Messeområdet. GPS: n59,28069 e10,41015.
12 free.
Remarks: At the skating rink.

| S | **Tønsberg** | 4C1 |

Shell, Kjelleveien 28. **GPS:** n59,27879 e10,40092.
🚰Ch.

| 🚣 | **Ulefoss** | 4C1 |

Norsjø Golfpark, Romnesvegen 98. **GPS:** n59,30248 e9,26511.
kr 50.
Distance: 4km.
Remarks: At golf court.

| 🚣 | **Uvdal** | 3B3 |

Uvdal resort. GPS: n60,26515 e8,78849.
kr 150. **Surface:** grassy.
Distance: on the spot on the spot.

| 🚣 | **Vågå** | 3B3 |

Steinhole fjellcamp. GPS: n61,62293 e8,99682.
kr 50. **Location:** Isolated, quiet. **Surface:** grassy.

| 🏔S | **Voll** | 4C1 |

Ole"s Kios og gatekjøkken, Svanvikveien 653.
GPS: n59,12797 e9,51008.
150 ⚡included.
Distance: on the spot.
Remarks: Regional products.

| 🐟S | **Ytre Enebakk** | 4C1 |

Holtopp gård, Skiveien 127. **GPS:** n59,72795 e11,00472.
kr 125 ⚡kr30. **Location:** Isolated, quiet. 🗓 01/03-01/10
Distance: 100m.

🇵🇱 Poland

Capital: Warsaw
Government: parliamentary republic.
Official Language: Polish
Population 38,346,000 (2014)
Area: 311,888 Km²

General information
Dialling code: 0048
General emergency: 112
Currency: Zloty (PLN)
€ 1 = 4,24 PLN, 1 PLN = € 0,24 (October 2015)
£ 1 = 6PLN, 1PLN = £ 0,17 (October 2015)
Credit cards are accepted almost everywhere.

Regulations for overnight stays
Free overnight stay is not allowed. On private property with permission of the owner.

Additional public holidays 2016
January 6 Epiphany
May 3 Constitution Day
May 26 Corpus Christi
August 15 Assumption of Mary
November 1 All Saints' Day
November 11 Independence Day

Time Zone
Winter (Standard Time) GMT+1
Summer (DST) GMT+2

PL

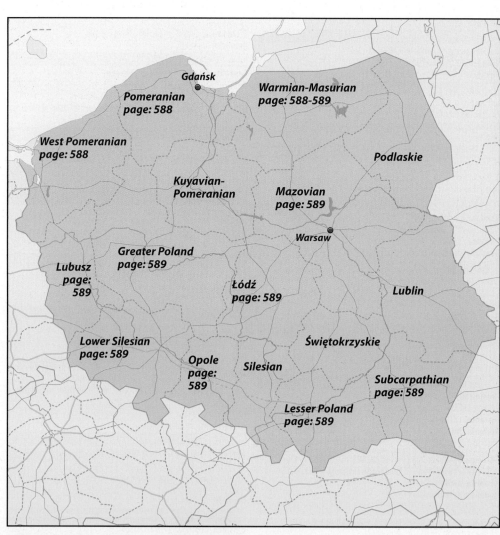

Map labels:
- Gdańsk
- Pomeranian page: 588
- Warmian-Masurian page: 588-589
- West Pomeranian page: 588
- Podlaskie
- Kuyavian-Pomeranian
- Mazovian page: 589
- Warsaw
- Greater Poland page: 589
- Łódź page: 589
- Lublin
- Lubusz page: 589
- Lower Silesian page: 589
- Świętokrzyskie
- Opole page: 589
- Silesian
- Subcarpathian page: 589
- Lesser Poland page: 589

West Pomeranian

🏕	Czaplinek	34A3

Drawtur, Ul. Pieciu Pomostów 1. **GPS:** n53,57671 e16,21984.
30 ⚡€ 12, 2 pers.incl ⚿included ⚿€2,50. **Location:** Rural.
Surface: grassy.
Distance: ⚓50m.

🏕	Miedzywodzie	5H3

Narcyz, Armii Krajowej 35. **GPS:** n54,00376 e14,69290.
⚡€ 12,50 ⚿Ch⚿WC⚿included. **Location:** Rural.
Surface: grassy. 🗓 01/05-01/10
Distance: ⚓100m ⚓800m.

🍴	Miroslawiec	34A3

Hotel Park, Lowic Walecki 60. **GPS:** n53,33081 e16,02333.
30⚡€ 8,50 ⚿€2 ⚿€3,50 Ch included ⚿€4,80/100kWh.
Location: Rural. **Surface:** grassy. 🗓 01/01-31/12
Distance: ⚿100m ⚓500m ⚓50m.

🏕	Szczecin	7H2

Hotel Panorama, Ul.Radosna 60. **GPS:** n53,36420 e14,61550.
10⚡€ 17 ⚿on demand ⚿included. **Surface:** metalled.
🗓 01/01-31/12
Distance: ⚓10km ⚿1km ⚿1,5km ⚿1km ⚿2,5km.

🏕	Wolin	7H1

Fam. Lafrentz, Gogolice 20, Gogolice. **GPS:** n53,83300 e14,62262.
8⚡€ 12 ⚿€2,50 Ch included ⚿€1,50. **Location:** Rural.
Surface: gravel. 🗓 01/01-31/12
Distance: ⚿500m ⚓50m ⚿2,4km.

Pomeranian

🏕	Gdańsk 🌸⚓🍽	34B2

Akademia Muzycna, Lakowa 1-2. **GPS:** n54,34561 e18,66357.
15⚡€ 12. **Location:** Urban. **Surface:** metalled.
🗓 01/01-31/12

🏕S	Malbork	34B2

Nad Stawem, Ul. Solskiego 10. **GPS:** n54,04285 e19,02536.

10⚡€ 12 ⚿Ch ⚿€2,50 WC ⚿included. **Surface:** grassy.
🗓 01/03-01/11
Distance: ⚓200m ⚿50m.

🏖S	Parachowo	34A2

Kalex, Jamnowski Mlyn 15. **GPS:** n54,21853 e17,65753.

20⚡€ 14 ⚿Ch ⚿€2 ⚿included. **Location:** Rural.
Surface: grassy/sand. 🗓 01/01-31/12

Warmian-Masurian

🍴	Mikolajki	34C2

Parking Hotelik Caligula, Ul.Jana Pawla II. **GPS:** n53,80278 e21,57444.
20⚡€ 14 ⚿Ch ⚿on demand ⚿included. **Surface:** gravel.
🗓 01/01-31/12
Distance: ⚓100m ⚿200m ⚓500m ⚿200m ⚿200m.

🏕	Milolyn	34B2

Mazur, Ul Twarda 28a. **GPS:** n53,76583 e19,84639.
5⚡€ 7,50 ⚿€1 ⚿Ch ⚿included. **Surface:** grassy.

🗓 01/01-31/12
Distance: ⚿500m ⚿400m ⚿200m.

🏖S	Osetno	34B3

Osteno 16. GPS: n53,41562 e19,31729.

25⚡€ 5 ⚿Ch included ⚿€1. **Location:** Rural, isolated.
Surface: grassy. 🗓 01/01-31/12
Distance: ⚓800m.

🏕S	Paslek	34B2

Kemping Bezplatny, 526. **GPS:** n53,98052 e19,62524.
100⚡free ⚿free. **Location:** Rural. **Surface:** grassy.
🗓 01/01-31/12

🍴	Piecki	34C2

Restaurant Krutynska, Krutyn 72. **GPS:** n53,68807 e21,43075.
20⚡€ 13 ⚿Ch ⚿included. **Location:** Rural. **Surface:** grasstiles.
🗓 01/01-31/12
Distance: ⚓300m ⚿300m.

🏖	Pieniezno	34B2

Intercamp Pieniezno. GPS: n54,23454 e20,13697.
20⚡€ 8 ⚿Ch ⚿included WC ⚿. **Location:** Rural.
Surface: grassy. 🗓 01/01-31/12
Distance: ⚓1km ⚿800m ⚿800m.

🏖	Sorkwity	34C2

Haus am see, Janowo 1. **GPS:** n53,83495 e21,20284.
5⚡€ 10-15 ⚿Ch ⚿included ⚿. **Location:** Rural.
Surface: grassy. 🗓 01/01-31/12
Distance: ⚿500m ⚓50m ⚿1km.

| | Tolkmicko | 34B2 |

Swietokanska. **GPS**: n54,32367 e19,52264.
4 free. **Surface**: metalled. 01/01-31/12
Distance: 50m 100m.

Lubusz

| S | Owince | 7H3 |

Fisch Camp, Wolności 40. **GPS**: n52,53517 e14,89269.

30 € 12 Ch WC included €1/1day. **Location:** Rural.
Surface: grassy. 01/01-31/12

Greater Poland

| | Biskupice | 34A3 |

WojciechSzczepanski, Jankowo-Mlyn 23. **GPS**: n52,44965 e17,16442.
20 € 20 Ch included. **Location:** Rural. **Surface:** grassy.
01/01-31/12

Mazovian

| | Warszawa | 34C3 |

Parking, 1 Sierpinia, Warsaw (Warszawa). **GPS**: n52,19189 e20,98069.
10 € 10 €2 €2 Ch€3 €5. **Location:** Urban.
Surface: metalled. 01/01-31/12
Distance: city centre 5,5km 2km 100m 500m 300m.

| | Warszawa | 34C3 |

Parking, Wybrzeze Gdanskie, Warsaw (Warszawa).
GPS: n52,25133 e21,01469.
15 € 25. **Location:** Urban. **Surface:** metalled. 01/01-31/12
Distance: city centre 3km 5km on the spot on the spot
250m.

Lower Silesian

| | Karpacz | 35A1 |

Rezydencja Holandia, Ul.Konstytucji 3-go Maja 67.
GPS: n50,77345 e15,74734.
15 € 5 €1 €1 Chfree €1. **Location:** Rural.
Surface: metalled. 01/01-31/12
Distance: 1km 900m.

Opole

| | Gora Swietej Anny | 35B1 |

P Najem Pokoi, Ul.Strzelecka 2A. **GPS**: n50,45785 e18,16895.
20 € 10 Ch included. 01/01-31/12
Distance: 600m 100m.

| | Naklo | 35B1 |

Fam Urban, Ul Strzelecka 91. **GPS**: n50,57790 e18,12715.
10 € 12 Ch WCincluded.
Location: Rural. **Surface:** grassy.
Distance: 400m 100m.

Łódź

| | Lipce Reymontowskie | 34B3 |

Bumerang, Chlebow 3. **GPS**: n51,92795 e19,92847.
8 € 9 Chincluded €3. **Location:** Rural. **Surface:** grassy.
01/01-31/12

Lesser Poland

| | Kraków | 35C1 |

Guesthaus Apis, Ul.Podgorki 60. **GPS**: n49,98885 e19,96210.
5 € 15 Ch WC included.
Surface: metalled.
01/01-31/12
Distance: 50m 400m.

| | Kraków | 35C1 |

Elcamp, Ul.Tyniecka 118e. **GPS**: n50,03418 e19,87658.
10 € 5 €1,20 Ch €1,20. **Surface:** grassy/gravel.
01/01-31/12
Distance: 100m.

| P S | Oswiecim | 35B1 |

Auschwitz Parking, Stanislaw-Leszezynskiej 11.
GPS: n50,02867 e19,20111.
10 € 10 €2,50. **Surface:** metalled. 01/01-31/12
Remarks: Near Auswitz-Birkenau memorial and museum.

| | Wieliczka | 35C1 |

Salt Mine, Edwarda Dembowskiego 22. **GPS**: n49,98542 e20,05338.
20 € 7,50. **Location:** Urban. **Surface:** gravel/sand.
01/01-31/12
Distance: 1,5km 400m 50m 500m.

Subcarpathian

| | Wetlina | 35D2 |

Górna Wetlinka, 38-608. **GPS**: n49,14740 e22,52028.
15 € 15 Chincluded €3. **Location:** Rural. 01/04-01/10
Distance: 200m on the spot on the spot.

Portugal

Capital: Lisbon
Government: Parliamentary democracy
Official Language: Portuguese
Population: 10,813,000 (2014)
Area: 91,642 km²

General information
Dialling code: 00351
General emergency: 112
Currency: Euro
Payments by credit card are accepted almost everywhere.

Regulations for overnight stays
If there is no local prohibition wild camping is allowed, max. 48h, exept in urban areas and drinking water protection areas.

Additional public holidays 2016
January 6 Epiphany
March 25 Good Friday
April 25 Liberationday
May 1 Labor Day
May 26 Corpus Christi
June 10 National Holiday
August 15 Assumption of the Virgin Mary
October 5 Republic day
November 1 All Saints' Day
December 8 Immaculate Conception

Time Zone
Winter (Standard Time) GMT+0
Summer (DST) GMT+1

PT

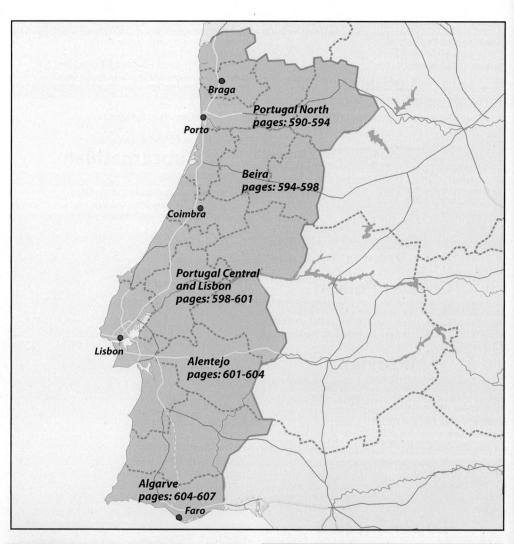

Braga

Portugal North
pages: 590-594

Porto

Beira
pages: 594-598

Coimbra

Portugal Central
and Lisbon
pages: 598-601

Lisbon

Alentejo
pages: 601-604

Algarve
pages: 604-607

Faro

Portugal North

Aguaçadoura   28B3
Aguaçadoura Futebol Clube. GPS: n41,44389 w8,77722. 🖼.

5 🚰free. **Location**: Rural, simple. **Surface**: gravel/sand.
🗓 01/01-31/12
Distance: 🚶500m 🏖50m 🛒500m 🚰500m.
Remarks: Parking at the beach.

Amarante   28C3
Av. Alexandre Herculano. **GPS**: n41,27286 w8,07178.

🚰🚿. **Surface**: metalled.
Distance: 🚶800m 🏖on the spot 🚌on the spot 🚰50m.
Remarks: Parking near sports centre.

Amarante   28C3
GPS: n41,27020 w8,07708.

🚰. **Surface**: metalled. 📍 Wed
Distance: 🍴on the spot 🚰on the spot.
Remarks: Market square along the river.

Amarante   28C3
Penedo da Rainha, São Gonçalo. **GPS**: n41,28031 w8,06925.
🚰🚐🗑Ch🚿. 🗓 01/02-30/11
Distance: 🏊1km 🍴on the spot 🚰on the spot 🚌1km.

Tourist information Amarante:
Ⓜ️✝️ Museu Municipal Amadeu de Souza Cardoso, Alameda Teixeira Pascoaes. Modern art.

Arcos de Valdevez   28C3
N202. **GPS**: n41,84749 w8,41524. 🖼.

10 🚰free. **Location**: Rural, simple. **Surface**: metalled. 🗓 01/01-31/12
Distance: 🚶300m.
Remarks: Along the Vez river.

Avintes   28B3
Parque Biológico de Gaia, Rua da Cunha.
GPS: n41,09730 w8,55414. ⬆️⬆️➡️.

9 🚰€ 4 + € 4 /pp, entrance park incl 🚐🗑Ch🚿included WC
🚰free, at reception. **Location**: Luxurious, quiet. **Surface**: grasstiles.
🗓 01/01-31/12
Distance: 🚶10km 🚌800m 🚗100m.
Remarks: Check in at reception.

Barcelos   28C3
R.Rosa Ramalho. **GPS**: n41,52829 w8,61547. 🖼.

12 🚰free. **Location**: Rural, simple. **Surface**: metalled. 🗓 01/01-31/12
Distance: 🚶centre 800m 🚲3,5km 🏊on the spot.
Remarks: Parking swimming pool.

Tourist information Barcelos:
Ⓜ️ Museu de Olaria de Barcelos, R. Cónego Joaquim Gaiolas. Ceramics and archeology. 🗓 Tue-Su 10-12.30h, 14-18h, Thu 10-18h.

Bico 29B1

R. Vasco da Gama. **GPS:** n40,73016 w8,64747. 🔼.

30 🚐free 🚰free. **Location:** Rural, simple, isolated, quiet.
Surface: metalled. ⬛ 01/01-31/12
Distance: 🚶300m ⚓on the spot ⛽on the spot ⊗on the spot.
Remarks: In fishing port.

Braga 28C3

Bom Jesus do Monte. **GPS:** n41,55278 w8,38137. 🔼.

25 🚐free 🚰ChWCfree. **Location:** Urban, simple. **Surface:** concrete.
⬛ 01/01-31/12
Distance: 🚶6km ⊗20m 🚌100m.
Remarks: Parking at funicular railway.

Braga 28C3

Sameiro. **GPS:** n41,53928 w8,36743.

10 🚐free.
Location: Simple.
Surface: gravel/sand.
Remarks: Parking at place of pilgrimage.
Tourist information Braga:
🕷 Semana Santa. Procession.
⬛ week before Easter.
🌿 Parque Nacional da Peneda-Gerês. Hiking routes.

Bragança 28D3

Parque de Merendas, Rue Miguel Torga. **GPS:** n41,80417 w6,74611. 🔼.

30 🚐free 🚰🍴Chfree.
Location: Rural, comfortable, quiet.
Surface: metalled.
⬛ 01/01-31/12
Distance: 🚶200m ⊗200m 🍺200m.
Remarks: P below the castle, 01/07-15/09, max. 24h, beautiful view.
Tourist information Bragança:
ℹ Medival upper city and castle.
Ⓜ Museu Militar.
⬛ 9-11.45h, 14-18.15h.
🌿 Parque Natural de Montesinho. Nature reserve.

Cabedelo 29B1

R.do Cabedelo. **GPS:** n40,14403 w8,86395.

10 🚐. **Location:** Simple. **Surface:** sand. ⬛ 01/01-31/12
Distance: ⚓on the spot ⊗on the spot.
Remarks: Beach parking.

Caminha 28B3

Largo da Feira. **GPS:** n41,87490 w8,84113. 🔼.

10 🚐free. **Location:** Urban, simple. **Surface:** metalled.
⬛ 01/01-31/12
Distance: 🚶500m 🍺100m.

Carrazeda de Ansiães 28D3

Rua Engenheiro Camilo de Mendonça. **GPS:** n41,24498 w7,30386.
🚐🚰Ch. ⬛ 01/01-31/12
Remarks: Parking swimming pool.

Carregal do Sal 29C1

Quinta de Cabriz. **GPS:** n40,42465 w8,01856.
🚐free. **Surface:** unpaved.
Distance: ⊗on the spot.
Remarks: Portugal Tradicional, max. 24h.

Carregal do Sal 29C1

Luzio, Arruamento Urbano a Sul da Vila. **GPS:** n40,43116 w7,99471. 🔼.

3 🚐free 🚰🍴Chfree. **Location:** Simple. **Surface:** grassy.
⬛ 01/01-31/12
Distance: 🚶1km.
Remarks: Behind petrol station.

Castelo do Neiva 28B3

Av. de Santoinho. **GPS:** n41,67501 w8,78243.
🚐.

Chaves 28C3

Alameda do Trajano. **GPS:** n41,73694 w7,46917. 🔼.

6 🚐free. **Location:** Urban, simple. **Surface:** metalled.
⬛ 01/01-31/12
Distance: 🚶historical centre 300m 🚲 8,6km ⊗100m 🍺100m.
Remarks: Along the Tâmega river.

Chaves 28C3

Quinta do Rebentão, Vila Nova de Veiga. **GPS:** n41,70127 w7,50013.
🚐🚰🍴Ch🔧. ⬛ 01/01-30/11
Distance: ⚓4km ⊗400m 🍺1km 🚌800m.
Tourist information Chaves:
Ⓜ✖ Torre de Mengem. Military museum.

Covas 28C3

Parque Campismo de Covas, Lugar de Pereiras.
GPS: n41,88758 w8,69497.
🚐🚰🍴Ch🔧. ⬛ 01/01-31/12

Covas 28C3

Quinta do Retiro, Lugar Quinta do Retiro s/n. **GPS:** n40,35230 w7,91583.
5 ⬛01/09-30/06 € 17,50, 01/07-31/08 € 22 🚐🚰Ch🔧(5x),10Amp
WC⬛€1/1 📶included. **Surface:** grassy. ⬛ 01/01-31/12
Distance: 🚶800m ⚓3km 🚶3km ⊗3km 🍺8km 🚶on the spot.

Entre-os-Rios 28C3

GPS: n41,08357 w8,29322. 🔼.

4 🚐 WC📶Lunchroom&co. **Location:** Simple, central, noisy.
⬛ 01/01-31/12
Distance: 🚶100m ⚓on the spot 🚶on the spot ⊗100m 🍺100m.
Remarks: Parking along the Douro river.

Espinho 28B3

GPS: n40,98889 w8,64306. 🔼.

40 🚐free 🚰🍴free,beach. **Location:** Rural, simple, isolated, quiet.
Surface: gravel/sand. ⬛ 01/01-31/12
Distance: 🚶1km ⚓25m ⊗1km 🍺1km.
Remarks: Beach parking.

Espinho 28B3

Municipal de Espinho, Zona da Ribeira dos Mochos.
GPS: n41,01402 w8,63743.
🚐. ⬛ 01/01-31/12

Esposende 28B3

Forte de S.João Baptiste, Rue do Farol. **GPS:** n41,54222 w8,79111.

5 🚐free 🚰🍴📶free.
Location: Urban, simple. **Surface:** asphalted.
⬛ 01/01-31/12
Distance: 🚶1,5km ⚓on the spot ⊗on the spot 🍺1,5km.
Remarks: Parking at lighthouse, free wifi for clients restaurant.

Esposende 28B3

Parque de Campismo de Fão, Lírios - Fão. **GPS:** n41,50778 w8,77833.
🚐🚰🍴Ch🔧. ⬛ 01/01-31/12
Distance: ⚓500m ⊗500m 🍺on the spot 🚌500m.

Freixo de Espada a Cinta 29D1

Espaço Multiusos, R. do Samiteiro de Cima.
GPS: n41,08826 w6,81751. 🔼.
12 🚐free 🚰🍴Ch🔧(12x)free. **Surface:** metalled.
⬛ 01/01-31/12
Distance: ⊗900m 🍺900m.
Remarks: Arrival <18h.

Freixo de Numão 29D1

Area de autocaravanas Jean Pierre Rossi, Sebarigos.
GPS: n41,06000 w7,22111. 🔼.

30 🛏️€ 5/night ⛽🔌Ch.🔧🛢️WC included. 🚿 **Surface:** metalled.
Distance: 🚶900m ⊗500m 🛒500m.

Gerês 28C3

Vila do Gerês. GPS: n41,73538 w8,15969. 🔼.

4 🛏️⛽free. **Location:** Rural, simple. **Surface:** asphalted.
🅿️ 01/01-31/12
Distance: 🚶1km ⊗on the spot.

Gondomar 28C3

Medas, Gavinho - Medas. **GPS:** n41,03917 w8,42694.
🛏️⛽🔌Ch. 🅿️ 01/01-31/12

Gosende 29C1

Cooperativa Capuchinhas CRL, Campo Benfeito.
GPS: n40,99799 w7,9269.
🛏️free. **Surface:** unpaved.
🅿️ 01/01-31/12
Distance: 🚴5,1km.
Remarks: Portugal Tradicional.

Guilhufe 28C3

EM594. GPS: n41,19541 w8,31605. 🔼➡️.

8 🛏️free ⛽🔌Chfree. **Location:** Simple, noisy. **Surface:** metalled.
🅿️ 01/01-31/12
Distance: 🚶1km 🚴1,6km ⊗1km 🛒1km.

Izeda 28D3

Largo do Toural. GPS: n41,56750 w6,72333. 🔼➡️.

30 🛏️free ⛽🔌Chfree. **Location:** Rural, simple, central, quiet.
Surface: metalled. 🅿️ 01/01-31/12
Distance: 🚶centre ⊗200m 🛒200m.

Lamego 29C1

Parque Lamego, N2, Lugar da Raposeira.
GPS: n41,09016 w7,82214. 🔼➡️.

40 🛏️€ 5 + € 3/pp ⛽🔌Ch.🔧€4/day WC 📶. **Location:** Luxurious,
isolated, quiet. **Surface:** unpaved. 🅿️ 01/01-31/12
Distance: 🚶1,2km 🚴4,5km ⊗500m 🛒2km ⛽on the spot.
Remarks: Baker every morning, beautiful view, near Caves da Raposeira, sale of wines.

Lamego 29C1

GPS: n41,09501 w7,80372.

🛏️free. **Surface:** metalled. 🅿️ 01/01-31/12
Distance: 🚶on the spot ⊗on the spot 🛒on the spot.
Remarks: At the foot of monumental stairs of the Santuari.

Tourist information Lamego:
👁️ Bodega Raposeira. 🎫 free.
🔆 Nossa Senhora dos Remédios. Pilgrimage in Portugal, most important festivity of the country. 🅿️ end Aug-beginning Sep.

Macedo de Cavaleiros 28D3

Rua das Piscinas. GPS: n41,53756 w6,95715. 🔼➡️.

8 🛏️free ⛽€2/100liter 🔌Ch🔋€2/1h.
Location: Urban, simple, central, quiet. **Surface:** asphalted.
🅿️ 01/01-31/12
Distance: 🚶200m ⊗200m 🛒300m ⛽on the spot.

Macedo de Cavaleiros 28D3

Barragem do Azibo, Frada da Pegada. **GPS:** n41,58333 w6,89944. 🔼.

10 🛏️free. **Location:** Rural, simple, quiet. **Surface:** metalled.
🅿️ 01/01-31/12
Distance: 🚶2km 🏖️Sandy beach ⊗on the spot (peak season).
Remarks: At barrage, guarded during summer period.

Matosinhos 28B3

Av. de Praia. GPS: n41,26044 w8,72434. 🔼.

10 🛏️free. **Location:** Simple, noisy. **Surface:** metalled.

🅿️ 01/01-31/12
Distance: 🚶200m ⊗200m 🛒600m ⛽on the spot.
Remarks: Beach parking.

Matosinhos 28B3

Municipal de Angeiras. GPS: n41,26722 w8,71972.
🛏️⛽🔌Ch. 🅿️ 01/01-31/12
Remarks: Service only € 3,15-5,40.

Melgaço 28C2

Porta de Lamas de Mouro, Lamas de Mouro.
GPS: n42,05202 w8,19413.
🛏️free. **Surface:** metalled.

Melgaço 28C2

Rua do Mercado. GPS: n42,11549 w8,26095. 🔼.

6 🛏️free. **Location:** Rural, simple. 🅿️ 01/01-31/12
Distance: ⊗on the spot.

Miranda do Douro 28E3

Av. Eduardo Quero. GPS: n41,49167 w6,27333.

🛏️free. **Surface:** metalled.
Distance: 🚶25m ⊗200m.
Remarks: Near city wall.

Miranda do Douro 28E3

Largo do Cestelo. GPS: n41,49611 w6,275.

🛏️free. **Surface:** metalled.
Distance: 🚶on the spot ⊗50m 🛒50m.
Remarks: Parking near ruins of castle.

Mirandela 28D3

Largo Cardal. GPS: n41,48685 w7,18391. 🔼.

15 🛏️free 📶Fon. **Location:** Rural, simple, central, noisy.
Surface: metalled.
Distance: 🚶centre ⊗on the spot 🛒on the spot ⛽on the spot.
Remarks: Large parking along the river.

Mirandela 28D3

Três Rios-Maravilha. GPS: n41,50683 w7,19716.
🛏️⛽🔌Ch.
🅿️ 15/05-31/09

Tourist information Mirandela:
🏛️ Museu municipal. Modern Portuguese painting art. 🎫 free.
🏛️ Villa Flôr. Village museum.

T free.

Mogadouro 28D3
Mogadouro, Complexo Desportivo Municipal. **GPS**: n41,33528 w6,71861.
Ch. ■ 01/04-30/09
Distance: ⊗500m ■ on the spot ⌂500m.

Mondim de Basto 28C3
Area Mondim de Basto. GPS: n41,41199 w7,95137. ⬆.

30 free Chfree. **Location**: Urban, simple, central.
Surface: metalled. ■ 01/01-31/12
Distance: 300m ⊗300m ■300m.
Remarks: Friday market.

Montalegre 28C3
Rua João Rodrigues Cabrilho. **GPS**: n41,82280 w7,78684. ⬆.
free Chfree. **Surface**: metalled. ■ 01/01-31/12
Distance: 500m.

Murça 28C3
Murça-Estádio, Variante à N15. **GPS**: n41,40421 w7,44994. ⬆.

free. **Surface**: asphalted. ■ 01/01-31/12
Distance: 500m ⊗300m.
Remarks: At footballstadium.

Nelas 29C1
Paço dos Cunhas de Santar, Largo do Paço, Santar.
GPS: n40,57229 w7,89154.
free.
Remarks: Portugal Tradicional, max. 24h, vineyard/restaurant, awning and generator prohibited.

Parada 28C3
Santuàrio. GPS: n41,68806 w8,20167.

Peso da Régua 28C3
Parque Ovar, Av. de Ovar. **GPS**: n41,16278 w7,79222. ⬆.

4 free (4x)WC free,150m. **Location**: Urban, simple, central, noisy.
Surface: asphalted. ■ 01/01-31/12
Distance: on the spot 4km on the spot ⊗on the spot ■ on the spot.

Ponte de Lima 28C3
Alameda de São João. **GPS**: n41,77052 w8,5847. ⬆.

15. **Location**: Urban, simple. **Surface**: metalled.

■ 01/01-31/12
Distance: 300m on the spot.
Remarks: Along river.

Póvoa de Varzim 28B3
Rio Alto, Estela. **GPS**: n41,46277 w8,77369.
Ch. ■ 01/01-31/12
Remarks: Service passerby € 3,50-6.

Queimadela 28C3
Parque de Campismo do Baragem. GPS: n41,50379 w8,16216.
€ 5 Ch. **Surface**: grassy/metalled. ■ 01/01-31/12
Distance: 100m 100m on the spot.

Santa Maria da Feira 29B1
GPS: n40,91972 w8,54306. ⬆.

5 free. **Location**: Rural, simple, quiet. **Surface**: gravel/sand.
■ 01/01-31/12
Distance: 600m ⊗600m.
Remarks: Parking at castle.

São Romão do Corgo 28C3
Quinta de Bourça, Lugar de Vila Nova. **GPS**: n41,44348 w7,9932.
free €2,50 €2,50. **Location**: Rural.
Distance: 11km.
Remarks: Portugal Tradicional.

São Salvador de Lordelo 28C3
R. da Igreja. **GPS**: n41,23472 w8,41139. ⬆ ➡.

20 free Chfree. **Location**: Simple, quiet.
Surface: gravel/sand. ■ 01/01-31/12
Distance: 400m ⊗400m ■400m.

Soajo 28C3
M530. **GPS**: n41,87197 w8,2633. ⬆.

5 free. **Location**: Rural, simple. **Surface**: metalled.
■ 01/01-31/12
Distance: 100m ⊗100m.
Remarks: Parking near school.

Torre de Moncorvo 29D1
GPS: n41,18083 w7,04167. ⬆.
9 free Ch free. **Surface**: metalled. ■ 01/01-31/12
Distance: 1,5KM.
Remarks: At sports park.

Valadares-SP do Sul 29C1
Cooperativa Mimos, Largo do Cruzeiro 1. **GPS**: n40,75704 w8,19997. ⬆.

3 free. **Location**: Simple. **Surface**: grassy.
■ 01/01-31/12
Distance: on the spot.
Remarks: Portugal Tradicional.

Valpaços 28D3
Do Rabaçal, Rua Gago Coutinho. **GPS**: n41,63222 w7,24778.
Ch. ■ 01/01-31/12

Viana do Castelo 28B3
Rua de Lima. **GPS**: n41,69534 w8,81875. ⬆.

15 free.
Location: Urban, simple. **Surface**: metalled/sand.
Distance: centre 700m.
Remarks: Large parking along the Limia river.

Viana do Castelo 28B3
Cabedelo/Orbitur, Cabedelo - Darque. **GPS**: n41,67862 w8,82611.
€5,40 Ch. ■ 16/01-15/11
Tourist information Viana do Castelo:
Campo do Costelo. Market. ■ Fri.
Romaria da Nossa Senhora da Agonia. Procession with Gigantes (giants). ■ 3rd week Aug.

Vila Chã 28B3
Sol de Vila Chã, Rua do Sol, Facho. **GPS**: n41,29825 w8,73263.
Ch. ■ 01/01-31/12
Distance: 300m ⊗10m on the spot ⌂100m.

Vila do Conde 28B3
Av. Júlio Graça. **GPS**: n41,34476 w8,74541. ⬆.

20 free. **Location**: Urban, simple, central, noisy. **Surface**: metalled.
■ 01/01-31/12
Distance: 400m 150m 150m ⊗200m ■400m.
Remarks: Along the Este river.

Vila do Conde 28B3
Av. Marques de Sa Bandiera. **GPS**: n41,34270 w8,74587. ⬆.

20 free. **Location**: Urban, simple, central. **Surface**: gravel/sand.
■ 01/01-31/12
Distance: 500m on the spot ⊗200m ■400m.
Remarks: Parking at sea.

Vila Nova de Cerveira 28B2
Av. dos Pescadores. **GPS**: n41,93823 w8,74685. ⬆.

4 ⁇free ⚡🍴Ch 💧free. **Location:** Rural, simple.
Surface: asphalted. ⬛ 01/01-31/12
Distance: 🏛historical center 150m ⚓river-beach.
Remarks: Near Minho river and public pool park.

Vila Nova de Foz Côa 29D1

Autocross, N102. **GPS:** n41,06727 w7,15496. ⬆➡.
⁇free ⚡🍴Ch 💧free. **Location:** Isolated, quiet.
Distance: 🏛2km.

Vila Nova de Foz Côa 29D1

Rua Engenheiro Eugénio Nobre. **GPS:** n41,08028 w7,14806. ⬆➡.
+50 ⁇free. **Location:** Rural. ⬛ 01/01-31/12
Distance: 🏛500m ⊗500m.

Vila Nova de Gaia 28B3

Madalena, Rua de Cerro, Praia de Madalena. **GPS:** n41,10750 w8,65556.
⁇🚰🍴Ch.
⬛ 01/01-31/12
Remarks: Service only € 3,15-5,40.
Tourist information Vila Nova de Gaia:
ℹ City of the port wine, at the left bank of the river Douro, Port houses can be visited daily.

Vila Real 28C3

Municipal de Vila Real, Rua Dr. Manuel Cardona, Quinta da Carreira.
GPS: n41,30333 w7,73667.
⁇🚰🍴Ch.
⬛ 01/01-31/12
Tourist information Vila Real:
👁 Solar de Mateus. Baroque country house, 18th century, known from label of the Matheus wine.

Vinhais 28D3

GPS: n41,83381 w7,00271. ⬆.

6 ⁇free ⚡🍴Chfree. **Location:** Urban, simple. **Surface:** gravel.
⬛ 01/01-31/12
Distance: 🏛200m ⊗100m.
Remarks: Nearby swimming pool.

Beira

Aldeia da Ponte 29D1

Caminho do Freguil. **GPS:** n40,41092 w6,87159. ⬆.

4 ⁇free ⚡🍴Chfree. **Location:** Rural, simple. **Surface:** metalled.
⬛ 01/01-31/12
Distance: 🏛300m.
Remarks: Near old Roman bridge.

Almeida 29D1

Rua da Guerreira. **GPS:** n40,72295 w6,90489.

⁇free. **Surface:** metalled. ⬛ 01/01-31/12
Remarks: At fort-castle.

Anadia 29B1

Rua Seabras de Castro. **GPS:** n40,44056 w8,4375. ⬆.

⁇free. **Surface:** asphalted.
Distance: ⊗100m 🍺100m.
Remarks: At restaurants.

Aveiro 29B1

Parcue de S João, Canal São Roque. **GPS:** n40,64328 w8,65859.

10 ⁇free ⚡free. **Surface:** grasstiles. ⬛ 01/01-31/12
Distance: 🏛200m ⚓25m ⊗200m 🍺200m.
Remarks: Parking at the Canal and A25.
Tourist information Aveiro:
Ⓜ Ecomuseu da Troncalhada, Canal das Pirâmides. Salt-making.
☀ summer.
Ⓜ Museu de Aveiro, Av. Sta. Joana Princesa. Collection baroque art.
⬛ Tue-Su 10-17.30h.

Barril de Alva 29C1

EM517-1. **GPS:** n40,28611 w7,96167. ⬆.

50 ⁇free ⚡🍴ChWCfree. **Location:** Rural, simple, quiet.
Surface: unpaved. ⬛ 01/01-31/12
Distance: 🏛500m ⚓river-beach ⊗on the spot.

Barriosa 29C1

Poço da Broca. **GPS:** n40,29366 w7,75376.

⁇free. **Location:** Rural.
Distance: ⚓on the spot ⊗on the spot.
Remarks: Portugal Tradicional, restaurant and regional products for sale.

Belmonte 29C1

Parque de Santiago, N345. **GPS:** n40,27512 w7,35856. ⬆.

4 ⁇free ⚡ChWCfree. **Surface:** metalled. ⬛ 01/01-31/12
Distance: 🏛500m ⊗on the spot 🍺150m 🍴on the spot.

Castelo Bom 29D1

Avenida Santa Maria, N16. **GPS:** n40,61261 w6,83398. ⬆.

3 ⁇free. **Location:** Rural, simple. **Surface:** metalled.
⬛ 01/01-31/12
Distance: 🏛on the spot.
Remarks: Less suitable for motorhomes >6,5m, typical village nearby spanish border.

Castelo Branco 29C2

Municipal de Castel Branco, N18. **GPS:** n39,85815 w7,49351.
⁇🚰🍴Chfree. ⬛ 02/01-15/11
Tourist information Castelo Branco:
⌂ Castelo. Ruins of castle of the Templars.
🌳 Alameda da Liberdade. ⬛ Mo.

Castelo de Paiva 28C3

R. Emidio Navarro. **GPS:** n41,03955 w8,27406. ⬆.

50 ⁇free ⚡🍴ChWCfree. **Location:** Simple, central, quiet.
Surface: metalled. ⬛ 01/01-31/12
Distance: 🏛on the spot ⊗on the spot 🍴on the spot.
Remarks: Market square.

Castelo Mendo 29D1

P5, N16. **GPS:** n40,59444 w6,94833. ⬆.

3 ⁇free ⚡free. **Location:** Rural, simple. **Surface:** grassy/sand.
⬛ 01/01-31/12
Distance: 🏛on the spot 🚲6,8km.

Castelo Rodrigo 29D1

GPS: n40,87778 w6,96611.

🛏free. **Surface:** sand.
Remarks: At the entrance of fort.

Celorico da Beira — 29C1
GPS: n40,63389 w7,40472.

10🛏. **Location:** Isolated. **Surface:** metalled.
Distance: 🚶2km.
Remarks: Parking sports park.

Cinfães — 28C3
GPS: n41,07167 w8,08719.

🛏. **Surface:** metalled. ☐ 01/01-31/12
Distance: 🚶100m ⊗100m 🚰100m.

Coimbra — 29B1
Parque do Choupalinho, Av. Inês de Castro.
GPS: n40,19970 w8,42905.⬆.

20🛏free ⛽🔌Ch🚿free. **Surface:** metalled.
☐ 01/01-31/12
Remarks: Max. 24h.

Tourist information Coimbra:
👁 Portugal dos Pequeninos. Miniature Portugal. ☐ 9-19h.

Coimbrão — 29B2
Praia do Pedrógão. GPS: n39,91500 w8,95.
🛏 ⛽€2,15🔌Ch🛵. ☐ 16/02-15/12
Distance: 🏖50m ⊗on the spot 🚰on the spot 🚌10m.

Condeixa — 29B1
Av. Bombeiros Voluntarios de Condeixa. **GPS:** n40,11291 w8,49336.⬆➡.

6🛏free ⛽🔌Chfree. **Surface:** asphalted. ☐ 01/01-31/12
Distance: 🚶500m ⊗on the spot 🚰300m.
Remarks: Max. 48h, market Friday-morning.

Condeixa — 29B1
Conímbriga, Praça da Republiça Condeixa.
GPS: n40,09895 w8,4894. ⬆.

5🛏free. **Location:** Simple. **Surface:** grassy/metalled.
☐ 01/01-31/12
Remarks: Parking next to archaeological site.

Covas do Monte-SP do Sul — 29C1
Covas do Monte.
GPS: n40,88873 w8,09823.
🛏free ⛽free.
Distance: 🚶250m.
Remarks: Portugal Tradicional.

Escalos de Baixo — 28C2
Hanmar, Estrada National 352. **GPS:** n39,89917 w7,40028.⬆.

20🛏€ 8, May-Aug € 10 ⛽🔌Ch🛵WC⏚included. **Surface:** grassy.
☐ 01/01-31/12
Distance: ⊗1km 🚰1km.

Estarreja — 29B1
R. Dr.Antonio Madureira. **GPS:** n40,75417 w8,56611.⬆➡.

6🛏€ 2/24h ⛽🔌Ch🛵included. **Location:** Urban, simple, central.
Surface: metalled. ☐ 01/01-31/12
Distance: 🚶on the spot ⊗on the spot 🚰on the spot.
Remarks: Max. 48h, check in Cafe Piscina, Ag. Seguros Rebelo, tuesday market 100m.

Estarreja — 29B1
Ribeira do Maurão. **GPS:** n40,81328 w8,61588.⬆➡.

6🛏free ⛽🔌Chfree. **Location:** Rural, simple, isolated, quiet.
Surface: metalled. ☐ 01/01-31/12
Distance: 🏖on the spot 🚶on the spot.
Remarks: Nature reserve.

Figueira da Foz — 29B1
Av. de Espanha. **GPS:** n40,14856 w8,86791.⬆.

30🛏. WC. **Surface:** asphalted. ☐ 01/01-31/12
Distance: 🚶on the spot 🚰on the spot ⊗100m.

Figueira da Foz — 29B1
Gala/Orbitur, Matas Nacias, Gala. **GPS:** n40,11861 w8,85639.
🛏⛽🔌Ch. ☐ 16/01-15/11
Remarks: Service only € 3,15-5,40.

Figueira da Foz — 29B1
Praia de Quiaios. GPS: n40,22083 w8,885.
🛏⛽🔌Ch🛵. ☐ 01/07-30/09
Distance: 🏖500m ⊗on the spot 🚰on the spot 🚌500m.
Remarks: Service only € 2,60-4,40.

Fratel — 29C2
Vila Velha de Ródão. **GPS:** n39,63250 w7,74694.⬆➡.

10🛏free ⛽🔌Chfree. **Surface:** grassy. ☐ 01/01-31/12
Distance: 🚶200m 🚴1km ⊗300m 🚰300m.

Fundão — 29C2
Quinta do Convento. GPS: n40,13276 w7,51205.
🛏 ⛽🔌Ch🛵WC🚿. ☐ 01/01-31/12

Furadouro — 29B1
Praia do Furadouro. GPS: n40,87645 w8,67381.⬆.

30🛏free WC50m. **Location:** Rural, simple, quiet. **Surface:** asphalted.
☐ 01/01-31/12
Distance: 🏖on the spot ⊗300m 🚰300m.
Remarks: Beach parking.

Guarda — 29C1
Parque Pólis, Rua da Direcção Geral de Viação.
GPS: n40,54894 w7,24083.⬆➡.

20🛏free ⛽🔌Chfree. **Location:** Simple. **Surface:** metalled.
☐ 01/01-31/12
Distance: 🚶historical centre 4km 🚴2,4km 🚌700m.
Remarks: Recreation park.

Guarda — 29C1
Rossio de Valhelhas. GPS: n40,40333 w7,40528.
🛏⛽🔌Ch. ☐ 01/05-30/09
Distance: 🏖50m ⊗300m 🚰150m 🚌100m.
Tourist information Guarda:
Ⓘ Medieval city.

PT

⚠S Idanha-a-Nova 29C2

Municipal de Idanha-a-Nova, Albufeira da Barragem Marechel Carmona. **GPS**: n39,95056 w7,18722.
🚐🚰🍽Ch♻ ▢ 01/01-31/12
Distance: 🚶50m ⊗on the spot 🍴on the spot 🚌8km.
Remarks: Service only € 2,60-4,40.

Idanha-a-Velha 29C2

N332. **GPS**: n39,99830 w7,1445.
🚐.

Tourist information Idanha-a-Velha:
⌂ Archeological tour.

Ilhavo 29B1

Av Ns.da Saude. **GPS**: n40,61417 w8,75222.⬆.

7🚐free 🚰ChWC. **Surface:** metalled. ▢ 01/01-31/12
Distance: 🚶on the spot 🏖on the spot.
Remarks: Beach parking.

Ilhavo 29B1

Av. Infante Dom Henrique, Praia da Barra. **GPS**: n40,64375 w8,74456.⬆.

30🚐free. **Surface:** metalled. ▢ 01/01-31/12
Distance: 🚶300m 🏖300m.

Ilhavo 29B1

Costa Nova do Prado. **GPS**: n40,61222 w8,74917.⬆.

7🚐free. **Surface:** metalled. ▢ 01/01-31/12
Distance: 🚶on the spot 🏖on the spot ⊗on the spot 🍴on the spot.
Remarks: Beach parking.

Tourist information Ilhavo:
Ⓜ Museu Histórico da Vista Alegre, Fábrica de Porcelanas da Vista Alegre. Collection of porcelain. ▢ Tue-Fri 9-18h, Sa-Su 9-12.30h, 14-17h.
Ⓜ Museu Marítimo de Ílhavo, Av. Dr. Rocha Madahil. Shipping museum. ▢ Tue-Fri 10-12.30h, 14.30-18h, Sa-Su 14.30-17.30h.

⚠S Lorvão 29C1

Rua do Malhao. **GPS**: n40,25896 w8,31468.

10🚐free 🚰🍽Chfree. **Surface:** metalled.
Distance: 🚶on the spot.

Luso 29B1

GPS: n40,38639 w8,38139.

10🚐free. **Surface:** metalled. ▢ 01/01-31/12
Remarks: Parking next to Hotel de Terme.

Tourist information Luso:
🌿 Mata Nacional do Buçaco. Nature reserve.

⚠S Melo-Gouveia 29C1

Quinta das Cegonhas, Nabainhos. **GPS**: n40,52057 w7,54169.
50🚐 € 14,50-18 🚰🍽Ch🍴WC🚿.

⚠S Mira 29B1

Praia de Mira. **GPS**: n40,44472 w8,79806.
🚐🚰🍽Ch. ▢ 16/01-15/11
Remarks: Service only € 3,15-5,40.

⚠S Miranda do Corvo 29B2

Rua Porto Mourisco. **GPS**: n40,08803 w8,33232.⬆➡.

8🚐free 🚰🍽Chfree. **Location:** Rural. **Surface:** asphalted.
▢ 01/01-31/12
Distance: 🚶700m.

Oleiros 29C2

R. Dr. Barata Relvas. **GPS**: n39,92056 w7,91389.⬆.
🚐free 🚰🍽Chfree. **Surface:** metalled. ▢ 01/01-31/12

⚠S Pardilhó 🌿 29B1

Parque de Merendas, R. Joaquim Maria Resende.
GPS: n40,80111 w8,63472.⬆➡.

15🚐 € 2/48h 🚰🍽Ch🍴 included. **Location:** Rural, comfortable, isolated, quiet. **Surface:** metalled. ▢ 01/01-31/12
Distance: 🚶600m 🏖on the spot 🚌on the spot.
Remarks: Max. 48h, check in at bar (service).

⚠S Penacova 29C1

Bairro de Carrazedos. **GPS**: n40,26722 w8,28306.➡.

10🚐free 🚰🍽ChWCfree. **Surface:** metalled. ▢ 01/01-31/12
Distance: 🚶400m 🍴3km 🏖800m ⊗400m.

⚠S Penamacor 29C2

Benquerença. **GPS**: n40,22938 w7,22136.⬆.

10🚐free 🚰🍽Chfree. **Location:** Rural, simple, quiet.
Surface: gravel/sand. ▢ 01/01-31/12
Distance: 🚶2km 🏖on the spot.

Pinhel 29D1

GPS: n40,77389 w7,06194.

🚐.

Distance: ⊗on the spot 🍴on the spot.
Remarks: At townhall.

⚠S Praia de Mira 🌊 29B1

Praia da Mira. **GPS**: n40,45800 w8,8025.

6🚐 🚰free. **Location:** Simple. **Surface:** metalled.
▢ 01/01-31/12
Distance: 🚶on the spot.
Remarks: Beach parking.

Praia de Mira 🌊 29B1

GPS: n40,44620 w8,80447.

20🚐free. **Surface:** sand.
Distance: 🚶500m.
Remarks: Beach parking.

⚠S Praia de Quiaos 🌊 29B1

Praia de Quiaos. **GPS**: n40,22034 w8,89116.

15🚐 🚰free. **Location:** Simple. **Surface:** metalled.
▢ 01/01-31/12
Remarks: Beach parking.

⚠S Sabugal 29D1

Rua do Cemitério. **GPS**: n40,34843 w7,08653.⬆➡.

6 � free ⟟━⚑Ch free. **Surface:** metalled. ◯ 01/01-31/12
Distance: 500m ⊗400m.

Sangalhos 29B1

R. do Mercado. **GPS:** n40,48639 w8,47528.⬆➡.

20 ⌗free ⟟━⚑Ch free. **Location:** Simple. **Surface:** metalled.
◯ 01/01-31/12
Remarks: At sports centre.

Santa Ovaia 29C1

Ponte das Três Entradas, Avô. **GPS:** n40,30667 w7,87139.
⌗⟟━⚑⚡. **Surface:** grassy.
◯ 01/01-31/12
Distance: ⌂10m on the spot ⊗on the spot ⚡on the spot ⬛10m.

São João da Pesqueira 28C3

Rua General Ramalho Eanes. **GPS:** n41,14682 w7,40187.
10 ⌗€ 10 ⟟━⚑Ch ⚡ WC⌗.
Distance: 400m.
Remarks: At fire-station.

São João da Pesqueira 28C3

Restaurant Carocha, N222. **GPS:** n41,15120 w7,42378.
50 ⌗free ⟟━⚑Ch free. ◯ 01/01-31/12
Distance: 1km ⊗on the spot.
Remarks: Next to restaurant and Port wine cellar Cave Cadão.

São João de Areias 29C1

Terra de Iguanas, Estrada principal 76, Vila Dianteira.
GPS: n40,39045 w8,08574.⬆.

4 ⌗€ 10 ⟟━⚑Ch ⚡ WC⌗⌨⚞included. **Location:** Rural,
comfortable, quiet. **Surface:** sand. ◯ 01/01-31/12
Distance: 2km ⚡1km ⊗1200m ⚡2km ⬛400m ⬥2km
⚲on the spot.
Remarks: Max. 3 nights, swimming pool incl., vegetables and fruit
from the garden.

São Lourenço do Bairro 29B1

Quinta do Encontro, N334. **GPS:** n40,44136 w8,49014.
⌗free. ◯ 01/01-31/12
Remarks: Portugal Tradicional, max. 24h, vineyard/shop/restaurant,
awning and generator prohibited.

São Pedro do Sul 29C1

Termas São Pedro do Sul, N46. **GPS:** n40,74056 w8,08639.⬆➡.

6 ⌗free ⟟━⚑Ch free. **Location:** Simple. **Surface:** asphalted.

◯ 01/01-31/12
Distance: 1km.
Remarks: Max. 48h.

Sertã 29C2

R. Amaro Vicente Martins. **GPS:** n39,79729 w8,09588.⬆.

4 ⌗free ⟟━⚑Ch ⚡free. **Location:** Simple. **Surface:** asphalted.
◯ 01/01-31/12
Distance: 500m ⚡3km ⚡50m.
Remarks: At sports park.

Sertã 29C2

Palácio da Justiça, R. Baden Powell. **GPS:** n39,80028 w8,09944.⬆.

⌗free. **Location:** Simple. **Surface:** gravel/sand.
Distance: 100m ⚡3km ⊗50m ⚡100m.

Sertã 29C2

Albergue do Bonjardim, Nesperal, Sertã. **GPS:** n39,81306 w8,16278.

2 ⌗€ 6 ⟟━⚑⚡€4 WC⌗. **Location:** Luxurious, isolated.
Surface: unpaved. ◯ 01/04-31/10
Distance: 200m ⊗2,5km ⚡1km ⚡50m.
Remarks: Sauna, steam bath and covered pool € 7,50, breakfast € 7,50.

Tábua 29C1

Piscina. **GPS:** n40,36306 w8,03.

3 ⌗free. **Surface:** metalled.

Tábua 29C1

Rua Aurora Jesus Goncalves. **GPS:** n40,36306 w8,02278.

10 ⌗free. **Surface:** metalled.

Trancoso 29C1

Parque Sportivo. **GPS:** n40,77160 w7,35621.

3 ⌗free. **Surface:** metalled.

Trancoso 29C1

Av. Heróis de São Marcos. **GPS:** n40,77583 w7,35056.

10 ⌗. **Surface:** metalled.
Distance: ⊗50m.
Remarks: Note: Friday market day.

Vagos 29B1

Praia da Vagueira. **GPS:** n40,54944 w8,77056.⬆.
20 ⌗€ 7,50, 01/10-31/05 € 5 ⟟━⚑Ch ⚡€2 ⌗€0,50. **Surface:** sand.
◯ 01/01-31/12
Remarks: Service passerby € 2,50.

Vagos 29B1

Vagueira, Gafanha da Boa Hora. **GPS:** n40,55806 w8,74528.
⌗⟟━⚑Ch ⚞. ◯ 01/01-31/12
Distance: ⌂1km ⊗on the spot ⚡1km ⬛500m.
Remarks: Service only € 2,60-4,40.

Vagueira 29B1

Rua Arménio, Praia da Vagueira. **GPS:** n40,56506 w8,76697.⬆➡.

20 ⌗free. **Surface:** metalled.
Distance: 200m ⌂sandy beach 50m.
Remarks: Beach parking.

Vila Nova de Oliveirinha 29C1

Quinta do Tapadinho, Rua dos Brandões. **GPS:** n40,36520 w7,92195.

5 ⌗€ 13,25 ⟟━€2/100liter ⚑Ch ⚡(5x)€5/24h,10Amp WC⌗⌨€4
⚞included. **Surface:** grassy/sand. ◯ 01/01-31/12
Distance: 1km ⚡6km ⊗1km ⚡8km ⬛1km ⚲on the spot.

Vila Pouca da Beira 29C1

Despinheiro, Avenida Principal. **GPS:** n40,30159 w7,9257.

PT

4 🍴 8, 2 pers.incl 🚰 🚿 WC 🗑️€1 🔲€4. **Location:** Rural, isolated, quiet. **Surface:** grassy. 🅾️ 01/01-31/12
Distance: 🚶500m 🏊2km 🚲2km ⊗800m 🚲 on the spot 🎣 on the spot.

Vilar Formoso 29D1

Zaza, Avenida das Tilia's, N332. **GPS:** n40,61528 w6,83833.⬆️.

12 🍴 € 5/24h 🚰€2 🗑️Chincluded 🚿(12x)€1,50/day.🚽
Location: Simple. **Surface:** asphalted/gravel. 🅾️ 01/01-31/12
Distance: 🚶500m 🍺baker on site.

Viseu 29C1

Av. Europa.
GPS: n40,66533 w7,91681.⬆️.
8 🍴free 🚰🗑️Chfree.
Surface: asphalted.
🅾️ 01/01-31/12
Distance: 🚶on the spot 🚲6km.
Tourist information Viseu:
ℹ️ Centre of Vinho do Dão.
🅼 Museu municipal, Castro Daire.Etnographical collection.

Portugal Central

A-dos-Cunhados 29A2

R. Monsenhor José Fialho. **GPS:** n39,15222 w9,30083.⬆️.

🍴free 🚰🗑️Chfree. **Surface:** asphalted. 🅾️ 01/01-31/12
Distance: 🚶100m 🚲6km 🏖️beach 7km ⊗200m.

Abrantes 29B2

Aquapolis, São Joao. **GPS:** n39,45489 w8,18977.⬆️.

🍴free 🚰🗑️Chfree. **Surface:** metalled. 🅾️ 01/01-31/12
Distance: 🚶3km 🚲4,7km ⊗100m 🍺6km.
Remarks: Service 100m.

Abrantes 29B2

Aquapolis, São Joao. **GPS:** n39,45333 w8,19056.⬆️.

10 🍴free 🚰🗑️Ch🔌free. WC 🔲 **Surface:** metalled.
Distance: 🚶3km 🚲4,8km 🏖️Sandy beach.
Remarks: Along the Tagus river.

Abrantes 29B2

Largo do Pralvo. **GPS:** n39,44956 w8,18968.⬆️.

10 🍴free. **Surface:** metalled. 🅾️ 01/01-31/12
Distance: 🚶1km 🚲6,5km ⊗1km 🍺1km.
Remarks: Along the Tagus river.

Abrantes 29B2

Parque Urbano de São Lourenço, São Vincente.
GPS: n39,47530 w8,21541.⬆️.

10 🍴free. **Surface:** grassy/gravel. 🅾️ 01/01-31/12
Distance: 🚶centre 2,4km 🚲4,4km ⊗50m 🍺3,5km.
Remarks: Max. 48h.
Tourist information Abrantes:
⌒ Posto de Turismo, Esplanada 1º de Maio, www.cm-abrantes.pt. City with historical centre.

Alenquer 29B3

Alenquer camping, Casal das Pedras. **GPS:** n39,05917 w9,02833.
4 🍴€ 15,50 🚰€2,50 🗑️Ch. 🅾️ 01/01-31/12
Distance: 🍺on the spot 🚐on the spot.

Almada 29A3

Costa de Caparicia, R. Eduardo Luis. **GPS:** n38,56691 w9,19308.

10 🍴free. **Location:** Simple. **Surface:** sand.
Distance: 🍺on the spot ⊗on the spot 🚐on the spot.

Almourol 29B2

Castelo de Almourol, Praia do Ribatejo. **GPS:** n39,46295 w8,38297.

10 🍴free. **Location:** Simple. **Surface:** metalled.
Distance: 🚶2km 🚲4km ⊗on the spot 🍺2km.
Remarks: On the banks of the Tejo river, parking castle.

Arruda dos Vinhos 29B3

Casal da Pevide. **GPS:** n38,99861 w9,08417.⬆️.

3 🍴free 🚰🗑️Chfree. **Surface:** asphalted. 🅾️ 01/01-31/12

Distance: 🚶2km ⊗on the spot 🍺on the spot.
Remarks: Parking Intermarché.

Assafora 29A3

Pic-nic area, Estr. de São Julião. **GPS:** n38,91167 w9,41138. ⬆️.

4 🍴free. **Location:** Rural, simple, quiet. **Surface:** metalled.
🅾️ 01/01-31/12
Distance: 🚲800m ⊗on the spot.

Baleal 29A2

Estrada do Baleal. **GPS:** n39,37240 w9,33702.

🍴free. **Surface:** asphalted. 🅾️ 01/01-31/12
Distance: 🚶2km 🏖️sandy beach 50m ⊗on the spot 🍺2km.
Remarks: Parking next to bar restaurant in village square, not recommended at the weekend.

Batalha 29B2

Parque Cónego M. Simões Inácio, Rua Cerca Conventual.
GPS: n39,66134 w8,82516.⬆️.

15 🍴free 🚰🗑️Ch🔌🌐free. **Surface:** asphalted. 🅾️ 01/01-31/12
🔘 Mo
Distance: 🚶100m ⊗250m 🍺on the spot.
Remarks: At football ground/tennis, max. 48h.

Cabo Espichel 29A3

P Cabo Espichel. **GPS:** n38,42031 w9,21353.

🍴free. **Location:** Rural, isolated. **Surface:** sand.
🅾️ 01/01-31/12
Distance: 🚶Sesimbra 13km 🏖️At the sea.
Remarks: Beautiful view.

Cascais 29A3

Cap Raso. **GPS:** n38,71134 w9,48498.

🍴free. **Location:** Isolated. **Surface:** sand. 🅾️ 01/01-31/12

Distance: 🚰6km ⊗on the spot 🚰6km.
Remarks: Parking near the cliffs Also possibility for overnight stay at restaurant Maremonte.

⛊S **Cascais** ⚓ ⚑ 29A3

Guincho, Areia, Guincho. **GPS:** n38,72167 w9,46639.
🚐🚰🍽Ch. ⭕ 01/01-31/12
Remarks: Service only € 3,15-5,40.

⛊S **Cerradas** 29A3

Estrada Á-dos-Serrados. **GPS:** n38,91798 w9,38292.⬆️

20 🚐free 🚰🍽Chfree. **Location:** Rural, simple, quiet.
Surface: gravel. ⭕ 01/01-31/12
Distance: 🚰on the spot 🏊5km ⊗on the spot.

⛊S **Constância** 29B2

Estrada National. **GPS:** n39,47670 w8,34365.⬆️

20 🚐free 🚰🍽Chfree. **Location:** Comfortable. **Surface:** metalled.
⭕ 01/01-31/12
Distance: 🚰500m 🚗2,3km 🏊on the spot ⊗500m 🚰300m.
Remarks: Along the Zêzere river.

⛊S **Coruche** 29B3

Area autocaravana, Rua 5 de Outubro. **GPS:** n38,96139 w8,51944.

100 🚐free 🚰🍽Chfree. **Surface:** metalled.
⭕ 01/01-31/12 ◉ last Sa of the month
Distance: 🚰on the spot 🚐on the spot.

⛊S **Costa da Caparica** ⚓ ⚑ 29A3

Caravanismo da Costa da Caparica, Santo António da Caparica.
GPS: n38,65389 w9,23833.
🚐🚰🍽Ch🔧🧹 ⭕ 01/01-31/12
Distance: 🏊500m ⊗on the spot 🚰on the spot 🚐100m.
Remarks: Service only € 3,15-5,40.

⛊S **Dois Portos** 29A3

GPS: n39,03689 w9,18098.

🚐🚰free. **Surface:** metalled. ⭕ 01/01-31/12

⛊S **Ericeira** ⚓ 29A3

Municipal de Mil Regos, N247, Casal do Moinho Velho.
GPS: n38,97778 w9,41861.
🚐🚰🍽Chfree. ⭕ 01/01-31/12
Remarks: Service in front of campsite.
Tourist information Ericeira:

👁 Aldeia Museu de José Franco, Sobreiro. Miniature village. ⭕ 9-19h.
🎫 free.

⛊S **Fátima** 29B2

Rua de Sao Vicente de Paulo. **GPS:** n39,63389 w8,67111.⬆️

10 🚐free 🚰WCfree. **Surface:** asphalted. ⭕ 01/01-31/12
Distance: 🚰1km 🚗3,2km ⊗100m 🚰1km.
Remarks: May 12-13 festivities.

⛊S **Foz do Arelho** 29B2

Av. do Mar. **GPS:** n39,42888 w9,22201. ⬆️

10 🚐free WC. **Surface:** metalled. ⭕ 01/01-31/12
Distance: 🚰1km 🏊50m ⊗on the spot 🚰1,5km.
Remarks: Beach parking.

⛊S **Lisbon** 🚋 ⚑ 29A3

Municipal de Lisboa-Monsanto, Monsanto, Estrada da Circunvalação.
GPS: n38,72472 w9,20805.
🚐🚰🍽Ch🔧WC📷◻🗝
⭕ 01/01-31/12
Distance: 🏊3km ⊗on the spot 🚰on the spot 🚐50m.

Tourist information Lisbon:
ℹ️ Lisboa Card. Card gives entrance to museums, public transport, available at: Rua Jardim do Regedor 50 (10-18), Mosteiros do Jeronimos, Museu dos Coches. 🎫 € 18,50/24h, € 31,50/48h, € 39/72h.
🎪 Market. ⭕ Tue, Sa.
🎪 32 Covered markets, most important market: Av. 24 de Julho.
⭕ 6-14h ◉ Su.
🎪 Campo de Sta Clara. Flea market.
🎪 Rua de São Bento. Antiques market.
🎡 Arena near metro Campo Pequeno. ⭕ 01/05-30/09 Thu.
🎡 Feira Popular. Fairground, opposite the Entrecampos metro.
⭕ 01/05-30/09.
😊 Oceanário, Parque das Nações. Aquarium. ⭕ 10-19h.
🛍 Chiado. Elegant shopping district. ⭕ elevator 7-24h.

⛊S **Mação** 29C2

Campo de Feiras, Av. Vicente Mirrado. **GPS:** n39,55723 w7,99303.⬆️

10 🚐free 🚰🍽Ch🔧WCfree. **Location:** Simple. **Surface:** metalled.
⭕ 01/01-31/12
Distance: 🚰500m 🚗6km ⊗500m 🚰500m.
Remarks: Max. 48h.

⛊S **Mafra** 29A3

R. Arieiro. **GPS:** n38,95451 w9,33555.⬆️

4 🚐free 🚰€1/80liter 🍽Ch. **Surface:** asphalted. ⭕ 01/01-31/12
Distance: 🚰on the spot
Remarks: Max. 24h.

⛊S **Mafra** 29A3

Palacio Nacional. **GPS:** n38,93758 w9,33548.
🚐🚰free. ⭕ 01/01-31/12

Tourist information Mafra:
❌ Posto do turismo, Palácio Nacional de Mafra - Torreão Sul, Terreiro D.
João V, www.cm-mafra.pt/turismo.
😊 Parque Tapada Nacional, Portão do Codeçal. Safaripark. ⭕ 10-19h.

⛊S **Marinha Grande** 29B2

São Pedro de Moel. **GPS:** n39,76974 w9,02752.

🚐free. **Location:** Simple. **Surface:** metalled. ⭕ 01/01-31/12
Distance: 🚰10km 🏊100m ⊗50m.
Remarks: Beach parking.

⛊S **Marinha Grande** 29B2

Parque de Campismo Orbitur, São Pedro de Moel.
GPS: n39,75806 w9,02583.
🚐🚰🍽Ch. ⭕ 01/01-31/12
Remarks: Service only € 3,15-5,40.

⛊ **Montijo** 29B3

GPS: n38,70286 w8,97665.

50 🚐free. **Surface:** metalled.
Distance: 🚰800m 🏊200m ⊗100m 🚰200m ◻2km.
Remarks: Parking at ferry-boat to Lisbon.

⛊S **Nazaré** 29B2

Rua Nossa Senhora da Vitória. **GPS:** n39,64696 w9,06936.
20 🚐free 🚰🍽Chfree 📶. **Location:** Rural, isolated, quiet.
Surface: metalled.
Distance: 🏊on the spot ⊗on the spot.

⛊ **Nazaré** 🚋 29B2

Avenue do Municipio. **GPS:** n39,59741 w9,0696.

7 🚐free. **Surface:** asphalted. ⭕ 01/01-31/12
Distance: 🚰200m 🏊250m ⊗250m 🚰750m.

⛊S **Obidos** 🚋 29B2

Casa Azzurra. **GPS:** n39,39250 w9,16947.⬆️

PT

10 ⊠€6 ⌐⊟Ch ⚡€2 WC ⊟€1 ⊠included.
Location: Comfortable, isolated. **Surface:** grassy. ☐ 01/01-31/12
Distance: ⚐4km ⊶on the spot ⊗4km ⚑4km ⚲on the spot ⚶on the spot.
Remarks: Swimming pool available.

Obidos 29B2
Rue do Ginasio. **GPS:** n39,35628 w9,15672.⬆.

20 ⊠€6/24h ⌐⊟Ch ⚡WC included. **Location:** Simple.
Surface: gravel/sand. ☐ 01/01-31/12
Distance: ⚐500m ⚑1km ⊗500m ⚑500m.

Odivelas 29A3
Rolarlivre, Rua Alm. Gago Coutinho, Póvoa de Santo Adrião.
GPS: n38,79605 w9,16384.⬆.
3 ⊠€5 ⌐⊟Ch ⚡included. **Surface:** metalled. ☐ 01/01-31/12
Distance: ⚑700m ⊗100m.
Remarks: Motorhome dealer, service passerby € 2,50, video surveillance.

Outeiro da Cabeça 29B2
Rua do Pavilhão Gimnodesportivo. **GPS:** n39,19306 w9,1825.⬆.

⊠free ⌐⊟Chfree. **Surface:** gravel. ☐ 01/01-31/12
Distance: ⚐300m ⚑2,5km ⊗300m ⚑300m.

Palmela 29B3
GPS: n38,56664 w8,90032.⬆.

6 ⊠free. **Location:** Urban, simple, quiet. **Surface:** sand.
☐ 01/01-31/12
Remarks: Parking at castle.

Peniche 29A2
Av. Porto De Pesca. **GPS:** n39,35852 w9,37752.⬆.

⊠free. **Location:** Simple, central. **Surface:** metalled.
☐ 01/01-31/12

Distance: ⚐500m ⚑900m ⚑1km ⊗500m ⚑500m.
Remarks: At fire-station and marina.

Peniche 29A2
Farol do Cabo Cavoeiro, Caminho do Farol.
GPS: n39,35989 w9,4082.⬆.

⊠. **Location:** Simple, isolated. **Surface:** metalled.
☐ 01/01-31/12
Distance: ⚑5km ⚑300m ⊗1,5km ⚑3km.
Remarks: At lighthouse.

Peniche 29A2
Praia de Consolação, Avenida do Mar, Consolação.
GPS: n39,32567 w9,35713.⬆.

⊠free. **Surface:** asphalted.
Distance: ⚐on the spot ⚑Sandy beach.
Remarks: Beach parking.

Peniche 29A2
R. de Liberdade. **GPS:** n39,36577 w9,37417.⬆.

⊠. **Location:** Simple. **Surface:** sand. ☐ 01/01-31/12
Distance: ⚐1,7km ⚑50m ⊗200m ⚑200m.
Remarks: Nearby Intermarché.

Peniche 29A2
Peniche Praia, Estrada Marginal Norte. **GPS:** n39,36959 w9,392.⬆.

23 ⊠€15,20, 2 pers.incl ⌐⊟Ch ⚡WC included ⊟⊠.
Surface: grassy. ☐ 01/01-31/12
Distance: ⚑At the sea ⊗on the spot ⚑1,5km ⟺1,5km.
Tourist information Peniche:
M⚑ Fortaleza de Peniche. Bathing resort.
M⚑ Posto de Turismo, Rua Alexandre Herculano,
www.cm-peniche.pt. Bathing resort.

Póvoa e Meadas 29C2
Barragem de Nisa, M1007. **GPS:** n39,48394 w7,5476.⬆.

10 ⊠free ⌐⊟ChWC free. **Location:** Rural, simple, isolated, quiet.
Surface: grasstiles/grassy. ☐ 01/01-31/12
Distance: ⚐4km ⊗4km.

Póvoa e Meadas 29C2
Casa Carita, Rua de Santo Antonio. **GPS:** n39,50532 w7,53139.⬆.

4 ⊠€5 ⌐⊟ ⚡included.⚑ **Location:** Rural, simple, isolated.
Surface: grassy/sand. ☐ 01/01-31/12
Distance: ⚐500m ⊗500m.

Praia de Santa Cruz 29A2
GPS: n39,14418 w9,37482.
⊠free ⌐⊟WCfree. **Location:** Simple. **Surface:** asphalted.
☐ 01/01-31/12
Distance: ⚐300m ⚑20m ⊗on the spot ⚑300m.
Remarks: Parking at the beach or near the cliffs.

Ribamar 29A3
R. do Cacho Longo, São Lourenço. **GPS:** n39,01120 w9,42078.
⊠free. **Location:** Simple, isolated. **Surface:** asphalted.
☐ 01/01-31/12
Distance: ⚑Sandy beach ⊗on the spot ⚑6km.

Santa Susana 29A3
Santa Susana E Pobral. **GPS:** n38,91833 w9,38333.⬆.

20 ⊠free ⌐⊟Chfree. **Location:** Simple. **Surface:** gravel.
☐ 01/01-31/12
Distance: ⊗800m ⚑300m ⟺300m.
Remarks: At gymnasium, max. 48h.

São Martinho do Porto 29B2
Av. Marigal. **GPS:** n39,50176 w9,14132.⬆.

⊠free. **Surface:** metalled. ☐ 01/01-31/12
Distance: ⚐1,4km ⚑5,5km ⚑sandy beach 50m ⊗850m.

Sintra 29A3
Avenida Conde Sucena, São Pedro de Penaferrim.
GPS: n38,78883 w9,37473.⬆.

10 ⌁€5 ⚡🔌Ch included. 🚲 **Location:** Rural, simple, quiet.
Surface: asphalted. 🗓 01/01-31/12
Distance: 🚶2km ⊗on the spot.
Remarks: At footballstadium.

⊟S **Tomar** 29B2

Av. Gen. Bernardo Faria. **GPS:** n39,59972 w8,41306.

⌁free WC.
Location: Simple. **Surface:** gravel/sand.
🗓 01/01-31/12
Distance: 🚶200m ⊗200m 🚰300m.
Remarks: Nearby railway station.
Tourist information Tomar:
Ⓜ Sinagoga de Tomar, Museu Luso-Hebraico, Rua Dr. Joaquim Jacinto, 75. Synagogue and Jewish Portuguese history. 🔲 free.
✝ Convento de Cristo. Fortified monastery.
☀ Festa dos Tabuleiros.
🗓 Whitsuntide.
⊕ Barragem de Castelo de Bode. Artificial lake, 15km east of the city.

△S **Torres Vedras** 29A2

Municipal da Praia de Santa Cruz. **GPS:** n39,13444 w9,37472.
⌁ ⚡🔌Ch against payment. 🗓 01/01-31/12

⊟S **Turcifal** 29A3

Largo Brigadeiro França Borges. **GPS:** n39,04288 w9,26581. ⬆➡

5 ⌁free ⚡🔌Ch free. **Location:** Urban, central, quiet.
Surface: metalled. 🗓 01/01-31/12
Distance: 🚶on the spot ⊗on the spot 🚰on the spot.

⊟S **Vermoil** 29B2

R. Vale de Fojo, Pombal. **GPS:** n39,85080 w8,66125. ⬆

5 ⌁free ⚡🔌Ch free. **Surface:** gravel/sand. 🗓 01/01-31/12
Distance: 🚶200m ⊗300m 🚰300m.
Remarks: At cemetery.

Alentejo

⊟S **Alcácer do Sal** 29B3

Barragem Pego do Altar, Alcácer do Sal > N253 > Montemoro o Novo > N380. **GPS:** n38,42055 w8,39384.

15 ⌁free ⚡Ch WC ⌁free. **Location:** Rural. **Surface:** sand.
🗓 01/01-31/12
Distance: 🚶Alcácer do Sal 13km ⛵on the spot ⊗100m.

⊟ **Alcácer do Sal** 29B3

Rua do Cabo da Vila. **GPS:** n38,36903 w8,50276.
⌁free.
🗓 01/01-31/12
Distance: 🚶Old city 600m ⚓5,6km ⊗400m.
Remarks: Near arena.
Tourist information Alcácer do Sal:
🛈 Little town on the Rio Sado.

⊟S **Almograve** 30B1

Avenida da Praia. **GPS:** n37,65303 w8,80059. ⬆

30 ⌁free ⚡free. **Location:** Simple. **Surface:** grasstiles.
🗓 01/01-31/12
Distance: ⛵on the spot.

⊟ **Alvito** 30B1

Rua de Tapadinha. **GPS:** n38,25917 w7,99222.
⌁free.
Remarks: At swimming pool.

△S **Avis** 29C3

Municipal Albufeira do Maranhão, Barragam Albufeira do Maranhão.
GPS: n39,05682 w7,91145.
⌁ ⚡🔌Ch.
Distance: ⛵on the spot.
Remarks: Service only € 1,90.

⊟ **Campo Maior** 29C3

Barragem do Caia. GPS: n39,00308 w7,14219.

⌁.

⊟ **Castelo de Vide** 29C2

Estr. de São Vincente. **GPS:** n39,41028 w7,44917. ⬆

⌁. **Location:** Rural, quiet. **Surface:** metalled. 🗓 01/01-31/12
Distance: 🚶1km ⊗300m.
Remarks: At stadium.

⊟ **Castelo de Vide** 29C2

Rua Luís de Camões. **GPS:** n39,41583 w7,45778. ⬆

⌁free.
Location: Urban, simple, central. **Surface:** concrete.
🗓 01/01-31/12
Remarks: Near city wall.
Tourist information Castelo de Vide:
🛈 www.cm-castelo-vide.pt. Historical centre with medieval citadel.

⊟ **Cavaleiro** 30B1

Cabo Sardano. GPS: n37,59810 w8,80608. ⬆.

30 ⌁free. **Location:** Simple. **Surface:** sand. 🗓 01/01-31/12
Distance: ⛵on the spot.
Remarks: At lighthouse.

⊟S **Comporta** 29B3

GPS: n38,38308 w8,78712. ⬆.

±6 ⌁ ⚡free. **Location:** Urban, simple, quiet. **Surface:** gravel/sand.
🗓 01/01-31/12
Distance: 🚶250m ⛵1km ⊗300m 🚰500m.
Remarks: Near church.

⊟ **Comporta** 29B3

GPS: n38,37849 w8,78544. ⬆.

40 ⌁free ⚡🔌Ch free. **Location:** Urban, simple, quiet.
Surface: gravel/sand. 🗓 01/01-31/12
Distance: 🚶250m ⛵1km ⊗250m 🚰250m.

⊟S **Elvas** 29C3

Intermarché, Rue Paco Bandera. **GPS:** n38,87458 w7,18429. ⬆.

15 ⌁free ⚡🔌Ch free. **Surface:** asphalted. 🗓 01/01-31/12
Distance: 🚶historical centre 1,7km ⛵on the spot.
Remarks: At petrol station and supermarket, max. 48h.

Elvas · 29C3

GPS: n38,87766 w7,17763.

Surface: metalled.
Remarks: Parking at aqueduct.
Tourist information Elvas:
ℹ️ Fortified city.

Estrela · 30C1

Aldeia de Estrela, Cais. **GPS:** n38,26637 w7,38906.
5 free. **Location:** Rural, simple. **Surface:** gravel/sand.
Distance: on the spot.

Estremoz · 29C3

Rossio Marquês de Pombal. **GPS:** n38,84320 w7,58672.

10 free. **Location:** Urban, simple, central. **Surface:** metalled.
01/01-31/12
Distance: on the spot 50m 50m.
Tourist information Estremoz:
Market. Sa.

Evora · 29C3

GPS: n38,57529 w7,90519.

free. **Location:** Urban, simple, noisy. **Surface:** gravel/metalled.
01/01-31/12
Distance: 1km 500m 500m.
Remarks: Parking university, illuminated.

Evora · 29C3

Avenida Condas De Vilalva. **GPS:** n38,57592 w7,91491.

Location: Urban, noisy. **Surface:** metalled.
01/01-31/12
Distance: 1km.

Evora · 29C3

Lago da Porta de Avis. **GPS:** n38,57672 w7,91096.

free.
Location: Urban, simple, noisy.
Surface: gravel/metalled.
01/01-31/12
Distance: 1,5km.
Remarks: Parking at aqueduct.
Tourist information Evora:
ℹ️ Posto de Turismo,
Praça do Geraldo, www.cm-evora.pt.
City with historical centre.
Igreja de S. Francisco, Capela dos Ossos.
Chapel of the bones.
8-18h
12-14h.
Tue.

Ferreira do Alentejo · 30B1

GPS: n38,05675 w8,11955.

free. **Surface:** asphalted.
Distance: 500m 100m 1km 1,5km.
Remarks: Parking sports park.

Grândola · 30B1

Parque de Grândola. **GPS:** n38,18525 w8,564.

7 free Ch. **Location:** Simple. **Surface:** asphalted.
01/01-31/12
Distance: 1km 7,4km 600m 500m 1,4km.
Remarks: At sports grounds.

Lousal · 30B1

Rua 25 Abril. **GPS:** n38,03591 w8,42908.

6 free Chfree. **Surface:** gravel. 01/01-31/12
Distance: 15km 250m 400m bakery on the spot.
Remarks: At the site of the old mines of Lousal.

Luz · 30C1

R. de Mourão. **GPS:** n38,34278 w7,37389.

free Chfree. **Surface:** metalled.

Marvão · 29C2

N359-6. **GPS:** n39,39434 w7,3736.

12 free Chfree. **Location:** Rural, simple, quiet.
Surface: grassy/gravel. 01/01-31/12
Distance: on the spot 500m.

Melides · 30B1

Praia de Melides. **GPS:** n38,12897 w8,79262.

. **Surface:** metalled. 01/01-31/12
Distance: Melides 6,2km Sandy beach on the spot.

Mértola · 30C1

N122/IC27. **GPS:** n37,64250 w7,65833.

.
Distance: 200m 200m.

Mértola · 30C1

Rua dos Bombeiros Voluntários. **GPS:** n37,64114 w7,66326.
10 free. **Surface:** gravel/sand.
Remarks: At fire-station.

Mértola · 30C1

Rua Doutor Afonso Costa.
GPS: n37,64103 w7,6574.

Remarks: Along river.
Tourist information Mértola:
Convento São Francisco. Former convent, exposition room and atelier.
10-17h.

Messejana · 30B1

GPS: n37,83167 w8,24694.

50 ⌁ € 7 ⌁ ⊡ Ch. **Location:** Rural. ▢ 01/01-31/12
Distance: ⌁ on the spot ⌁ 10km.

⌁ S ━━ Mina de São Domingos ━━ 30C1

Rua Catarina Eufémia. **GPS:** n37,67052 w7,50194.
⌁ free ⌁ € 2 ⌁ Ch.

━━ Mina de São Domingos ━━ 30C1

Praia Fluvial, R265. **GPS:** n37,67228 w7,50418. ⬆.

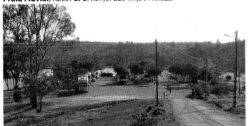

20 ⌁ free. **Location:** Simple. **Surface:** metalled/sand.
Distance: ⌁ 750m ⌁ 50m.
Remarks: At recreation area, marked pitches.

━━ Monsaraz ━━ 29C3

GPS: n38,44250 w7,38003. ⬆.

±15 ⌁ free. **Location:** Quiet. **Surface:** metalled. ▢ 01/01-31/12
Distance: ⌁ 100m ⊗ 100m.
Remarks: Near city wall, beautiful view.

S ━━ Monsaraz ━━ 29C3

Rue da Fonte. **GPS:** n38,45317 w7,38117.

⌁ € 3,50 ⌁ Ch.
▢ Mo-Fr 8-21h, Sa-Su 8-12h
Remarks: Call for the key.
Tourist information Monsaraz:
ℹ www.monsaraz.com.pt/.
Small medieval town.

△ S ━━ Montargil ━━ 29B3

Ponte de Sôr. **GPS:** n39,09972 w8,145.
⌁ ⌁ Ch. ▢ 01/01-31/12
Remarks: Service only € 3-5.

⌁ S ━━ Montemor-o-Novo ━━ 29B3

A6-IP7. **GPS:** n38,61856 w8,07924. ⬆.

2 ⌁ free. **Location:** Highway, simple, quiet.
Surface: asphalted/metalled. ▢ 01/01-31/12
Remarks: Note: toll ticket is valid for 12 hours!.

━━ Odeceixe ━━

GPS: n37,43750 w8,79833. ⬆.

30 ⌁ free. **Location:** Simple. **Surface:** sand. ▢ 01/01-31/12
Distance: ⌁ 6km ⌁ on the spot.
Remarks: Beach parking.

━━ Odemira ━━ 30B1

GPS: n37,59839 w8,64615.

⌁ free. **Surface:** asphalted. ▢ 01/01-31/12
Remarks: Along river.

⌁ S ━━ Pedrogão do Alentejo ━━ 30C1

Alqueva Camping-Car Park, Estrada nacional 258, Km38,5.
GPS: n38,11705 w7,63571. ⬆.

25 ⌁ first night € 7,50, € 6 each additional night ⌁ ⌁ Ch. ⌁
Location: Rural. **Surface:** gravel. ▢ 01/01-31/12
Distance: ⌁ 1km ⌁ 1km ⌁ 1km ⊗ 1km ⌁ on the spot
⌁ on the spot ⌁ on the spot.

━━ Ponte de Sôr ━━ 29C2

Avenida da Liberdade. **GPS:** n39,24996 w8,00824. ⬆.

10 ⌁ free. **Location:** Rural, simple, central, noisy. **Surface:** concrete.
▢ 01/01-31/12
Distance: ⌁ on the spot ⊗ 100m ⌁ 100m.

⌁ S ━━ Porto Covo ━━ 30B1

Rua Francisco Albino. **GPS:** n37,85225 w8,78874. ⬆ ➡.
30 ⌁ free ⌁ ⌁ Ch free. **Surface:** metalled. ▢ 01/01-31/12
Distance: ⌁ centre 250m ⌁ 750m.

Forte do Pessegueiro, Praia da Ilha. **GPS:** n37,49389 w8,47268.

10 ⌁. **Location:** Simple. **Surface:** sand. ▢ 01/01-31/12
Distance: ⌁ 4km ⌁ on the spot.
Remarks: Parking at castle.

⌁ ━━ Porto Covo ━━ 30B1

Praia Grande, Rua do Mar. **GPS:** n37,85054 w8,79299. ⬆.

15 ⌁. **Location:** Simple. **Surface:** gravel.
Distance: ⌁ 1km ⌁ 100m ⊗ 100m ⌁ 1km.
Remarks: Beach parking.

⌁ S ━━ Redondo ━━ 29C3

Zona Industrial. **GPS:** n38,64521 w7,54266. ⬆.

50 ⌁ free ⌁ ⌁ Ch free. **Location:** Urban, simple.
Surface: gravel/sand. ▢ 01/01-31/12
Distance: ⌁ 400m ⊗ 400m ⌁ 100m.

━━ Reguengos de Monsaraz ━━ 29C3

N255. **GPS:** n38,43077 w7,53315. ⬆.

⌁ free. **Surface:** asphalted.
Remarks: Parking at swimming pool.

S ━━ Reguengos de Monsaraz ━━ 29C3

Campo 25 de Abril. **GPS:** n38,42150 w7,53534. ⬆ ➡.

⌁ € 3,50 ⌁ Ch.
Remarks: Next to fire-station.

⌁ S ━━ Santa Clara-e-Velha ━━ 30B1

Barragem de Santa Clara. GPS: n37,51303 w8,44024.

PT

≋free. **Location:** Isolated. **Surface:** metalled/sand.
Distance: ⟂on the spot.
Remarks: Follow 'Pousada/Zona recreitiva balnear'.

🅰🆂 Santiago do Cacém 〰🏖🔦 29A3

Rua das Nogueiras. **GPS:** n38,80437 w9,22871.⬆➡.

7 ≋free 🚰🔌Chfree. **Surface:** grasstiles.
Distance: 🚶600m ⊗100m 🛒600m.
Remarks: At swimming pool.

🅰🆂 Santo André 〰🏖 30B1

Praia de Santo André, Lagoa de Santo Andre.
GPS: n38,10067 w8,78943.

15 ≋🚰. **Location:** Simple. **Surface:** sand.
Distance: 🚶5km ⟂on the spot ⊗on the spot 🛒bakery 1km.
Remarks: Beach parking.

🅰🆂 Santo André 30B1

Lagoa de Santa André. **GPS:** n38,10972 w8,78722.
≋🚰🔌Ch🔦. ⏱ 01/01-23/12
Distance: ⟂1km ⊗500m 🛒on the spot 🚗500m.
Remarks: Service passerby € 2,50.

🅰🆂 Santo António das Areias 〰🏖 29C2

Camping Asseiceira, Asseiceira. **GPS:** n39,41012 w7,34062.
10 ≋€ 15-20 🚰🔌Ch🔌WC📶💡🚿. **Surface:** grassy.
⏱ 01/01-11/11

🅰 São Martinho das Amoreiras 30B1

N503. **GPS:** n37,56250 w8,34139.

≋free. **Surface:** metalled.
Remarks: At barrage.

🅰🆂 Terrugem 29C3

Largo Joaquim Codero Vinaigre. **GPS:** n38,84556 w7,34861.⬆⬆.

10 ≋free 🚰🔌Chfree. **Location:** Rural, simple, quiet.
Surface: asphalted.
Distance: ⊗300m.

🅰🆂 Vila Viçosa 〰🏖 29C3

Avenida do Alandroal. **GPS:** n38,76988 w7,4154.⬆.

10 ≋€ 3 🚰€2🔌Ch. 🐾 **Location:** Rural, simple, quiet.
Surface: asphalted. ⏱ 01/01-31/12
Distance: 🚶1km ⊗100m.
Remarks: At fire-station, monitored parking.

🅰🆂 Vila Viçosa 〰🏖 29C3

Largo Gago Coutinho. **GPS:** n38,77661 w7,42034.⬆.

10 ≋free. **Location:** Urban, simple, central. **Surface:** sand.
⏱ 01/01-31/12
Distance: 🚶250m ⊗25m 🛒100m.

Algarve

🅰🆂 Albufeira 🏖🔦 30B2

Parque da Galé, Rua do Barranco Vale Rabelho.
GPS: n37,09347 w8,31125.

28 ≋€ 6,50 🚰🔌Ch 🚿(28x)📶included. **Location:** Comfortable.
Surface: unpaved. ⏱ 01/01-31/12
Distance: 🚶600m ⟂1,8km ⊗200m 🛒500m.

🅰🆂 Albufeira 🏖🔦 30B2

Parque da Palmeira, Rua da Palmeira. **GPS:** n37,09829 w8,24339.⬆.

90 ≋€ 8 🚰🔌Ch 🚿WC📶💡€4,50 📶included.
Location: Urban. **Surface:** gravel. ⏱ 01/01-31/12
Distance: 🚶Old city 1,7km 🚗7km ⟂1,5km 🛒800m Lidl
🚌bus terminal 300m.

Tourist information Albufeira:

🅘 Posto de Turismo, R. 5 de Outubro,, www.cm-albufeira.pt. ⏱ 10-20h.
🅘 ZooMarine, N125. Attractions park, dolphinarium, aquarium.
⏱ 10-20h.

🅰🆂 Alcoutim 30C2

Estrada da Pousada da Juventude. **GPS:** n37,47500 w7,47472.⬆.
≋free 🚰🔌Chfree. **Surface:** sand.
⏱ 01/01-31/12
Distance: ⊗200m.
Remarks: Next to 'Centro de Saude'.

Tourist information Alcoutim:
🅘 Fortified city. ⏱ 9-17.30h.

🅰🆂 Aljezur 〰🏖 30A1

Largo do Mercado. **GPS:** n37,31611 w8,80278.⬆.

10 ≋free WCfree. **Location:** Simple. **Surface:** metalled.
⏱ 01/01-31/12
Distance: ⊗200m 🛒500m.

🅰 Altura 30C2

Rua de Alagoa. **GPS:** n37,17138 w7,49952.

+10 ≋free. **Surface:** sand.
Distance: 🚶100m ⟂on the spot ⊗100m.
Remarks: Beach parking.

🅰🆂 Alvor 🏖 30B2

Zona para autocaravanas, Praia de Alvor.
GPS: n37,12482 w8,59506.⬆.

150 ≋€ 4 🚰🔌Ch 🔦included. **Location:** Central. **Surface:** sand.
⏱ 01/01-31/12
Distance: 🚶centre 400m ⟂100m ⊗on the spot.

🅰🆂 Ameixial 30B2

Estacionamento de Autocaravannas. **GPS:** n37,36539 w7,97165.⬆.
10 ≋free 🚰🔌Chfree. **Location:** Rural, isolated, quiet.
Surface: unpaved. ⏱ 01/01-31/12

🅰 Cabo de São Vicente 〰🏖 30A2

N268. **GPS:** n37,02361 w8,995.

8 ≋free. **Surface:** metalled. ⏱ 01/01-31/12
Distance: 🚶Sagres 6km.
Remarks: Parking at lighthouse.

PT

Caldas de Monchique 30B2

Parque Rural Autocaravanas Vale da Carrasqueira, Barracão 190. **GPS**: n37,27667 w8,54333.⬆.

14 ⌁ € 12,50/24h ⛽ ⬛Ch ⚡ WC⬛ included ◉ 📶. **Location:** Rural, comfortable. **Surface:** gravel. ⚕ on the spot.

Carrapateira 30A2

Praia de Amado. GPS: n37,19623 w8,90156.⬆.

30 ⌁free. **Location:** Simple. **Surface:** gravel.
Distance: 🚶Carrapateira 2km ⊗100m ⚕on the spot.
Remarks: Beach parking.

Carrapateira 30A2

Praia de Bordeira. GPS: n37,19735 w8,90726.⬆.

10 ⌁free. **Location:** Simple. **Surface:** metalled.
Distance: 🚶Carrapateira 2,5km.
Remarks: Parking near the cliffs.

Carvoeiro 30B2

Casa Long Yin, Sitio nas Travessadas. **GPS**: n37,11547 w8,47011.

5 ⌁ € 10 ⛽⬛Ch ⚡WC⬛ ◉€2,50 📶included.
Surface: grassy. ⬛ 01/01-31/12
Distance: 🚶1,5km ⊿1,5km ⊗300m 🚌600m ⚕on the spot
⚕on the spot.
Remarks: Swimming pool incl.

Carvoeiro 30B2

Estr. do Farol. **GPS**: n37,08774 w8,44285.

8 ⌁. **Location:** Isolated. **Surface:** sand.
Distance: ⊗500m ⚕on the spot.
Remarks: Parking at lighthouse.

Carvoeiro 30B2

Praia Marinha. GPS: n37,09026 w8,41254.

⌁free. **Location:** Isolated. **Surface:** unpaved.
⬛ 04/01-31/12
Distance: 🚶4km ⊿on the spot.
Remarks: Beach parking, beautiful view.

Castro Marim 30C2

Av. Dr. José Afonso Gomes. **GPS**: n37,21984 w7,44434.⬆.

± 20 ⌁free ⛽€2 ⬛Ch. **Surface:** gravel. ⬛ 01/01-31/12 ◉ 2rd Sa of the month
Distance: ⚓1,3km ⊗50m.
Remarks: Coins at the shops in the village.

Falésia 30B2

Algarve Motorhome Park, Praia da Falésia.
GPS: n37,09015 w8,16015.⬆.
55 ⌁ € 8/24h ⛽⬛Ch ⚡€2 📶included. **Location:** Luxurious.
Surface: gravel. ⬛ 01/01-31/12
Distance: ⊿850m ⊗on the spot ⚱250m.

Faro 30B2

Doca de Faro. **GPS**: n37,02551 w7,94657.⬆.

15 ⌁free. **Location:** Urban, simple. **Surface:** metalled.
⬛ 01/01-31/12
Distance: ⚱600m.

Faro 30B2

Parking Largo de São Francisco. GPS: n37,01132 w7,93184.⬆.

±6 ⌁free. **Surface:** metalled. ⬛ 14-08h

Lagos 30B2

Area de servico, Junto ao Estadio Municipal de Lagos.
GPS: n37,11563 w8,678.⬆➡.

20 ⌁€ 3, from 4th night € 2,50 ⛽€2/100 ⬛ChWCfree 📶against payment. **Surface:** gravel. ⬛ 01/01-31/12
Distance: 🚶city centre 2km ⚓7,3km ⊿2,3km ⊗McDonalds 450m.
Remarks: Check in and pay at reception stadio, market 1st Saturday each month.

Tourist information Lagos:
Ⓜ Museu Municipal, Rua General Alberto da Silveira. Regional museum. ⬛ 9.30-12.30h, 14-17h ◉ holiday.

Manta Rota 30C2

Praia de Manta Rota, Quinta Manta Rota 15. **GPS**: n37,16513 w7,52096.

80 ⌁€ 4 ⛽⬛Ch ⚡3h,€2/day 📶included. 🚿
Surface: metalled.
Distance: 🚶on the spot ⚓6,5km ⊿100m ⊗100m ⚱500m.

Moncarapacho 30B2

Far West Style Camp. GPS: n37,08344 w7,76608.⬆➡.
40 ⌁€ 7 ⛽⬛Ch ⚡WC⬛ 📶included. 🚿 **Location:** Rural, comfortable. **Surface:** gravel/sand. ⬛ 01/01-31/12
Distance: 🚶on the spot ⊿3km.

Moncarapacho 30B2

Caravanas Algarve. GPS: n37,09502 w7,77427.

20 ⌁€ 11 ⛽⬛Ch ⚡. **Surface:** gravel. ⬛ 01/01-31/12
Distance: 🚶1km ⊿beach 6km ⊗1km.

Odeleite 30C2

Almada D´Ouro Club-Algarve, M1063, Alcarias-Odeleite.
GPS: n37,33187 w7,46865.⬆.

10 + 20 ⌁€ 4,50 ⛽€2,50 ⬛Ch ⚡€2,50 ◉€5 📶included. 🚿
Location: Isolated, quiet. **Surface:** gravel. ⬛ 01/01-31/12
Distance: 🚶Odeleite 2,3km ⚕on the spot.
Remarks: At hunting club, discount longer stays.

Paderne 30B2

Motorhome Friends. GPS: n37,15643 w8,20972.⬆.

PT

16 ☐ € 4,50 🚰 Ch 🔌(9x)€3 WC 🔲€5 📶included.
Location: Rural. **Surface:** gravel. 🔲 01/01-31/12
Distance: 🚶1km ⛵10km 🏊on the spot.
Remarks: Bicycle rental € 5, car rental € 15.

Paderne 30B2

Cm 1177 920N. **GPS:** n37,16801 w8,20897.

12 ☐ free 🚰 Ch free. **Surface:** metalled. 🔲 01/01-31/12
Distance: 🚶1km ⊗1km.

Pêra 30B2

Mikki's Place, Sitio das Arreias. **GPS:** n37,12781 w8,32305. ⬆️➡️

100 ☐ € 5 🚰 Ch 🔌€2,50/day WC 🔲on demand
📶included. **Location:** Rural, comfortable, isolated, quiet.
Surface: gravel/metalled. 🔲 01/01-31/12
Distance: 🚶2km ⛵3km ⊗on the spot ☎2km.

Pêra 30B2

KM 64 Parque de Autocaravanas, ES125, km64.
GPS: n37,12420 w8,32607.
50 ☐ € 3 🚰 €2 Ch included 🔌€3. **Surface:** asphalted.
🔲 01/01-31/12
Distance: 🚶1,5km ⛵4km.

Pereiro 30C2

Parque de autocaravanismo do Pereiro, Pereiro.
GPS: n37,44695 w7,5924. ⬆️
16 ☐ free 🚰 Ch free. **Surface:** unpaved. 🔲 01/01-31/12
Distance: 🚶500m.

Portimão 30B2

Praia da Rocha, Avenida Rio Arade,. **GPS:** n37,11898 w8,53037. ⬆️

200 ☐ € 2,50 🚰€2/100liter Ch 📶free. 🛒
Surface: metalled/sand.
Distance: 🚶on the spot ⛵100m ⊗on the spot ☎200m 🚌on the spot.

Portimão 30B2

Rue Três Castelos. **GPS:** n37,11969 w8,54723.

25 ☐ free. **Surface:** asphalted.
Distance: 🚶Praia da Rocha 700m ⛵sandy beach 250m ☎1km.

Quarteira 30B2

Estrada Fonte Santa, M527-2. **GPS:** n37,07322 w8,07716. ⬆️➡️

100 ☐ € 2/24h 🚰€2 Ch 🔌€2. 🛒
Surface: gravel.
🔲 01/01-31/12
Distance: 🚶2km ⛵6,8km ⛵sandy beach 2,5km ⊗50m ☎150m
Lidl 🚌on the spot.
Remarks: Tue 17h-Wed 17h adjacent parking because of Gypsy Market.

Sagres 30A2

Fortaleze de Sagres. GPS: n37,00523 w8,94545. ⬆️

50 ☐ free WC. **Surface:** asphalted. 🔲 01/01-31/12
Distance: 🚶500m.
Remarks: At fort-castle.

Sagres 30A2

Rua Comandante Matoso. GPS: n37,00702 w8,93945. ⬆️

10 ☐ free. **Location:** Simple. **Surface:** gravel/sand.
🔲 01/01-31/12
Distance: 🚶400m ⛵on the spot.
Remarks: Parking behind tourist info, service at the left-hand dir harbor.

Salema 30A2

Praia Boca do Rio. GPS: n37,06563 w8,82434. ⬆️

20 ☐ free. **Location:** Simple. **Surface:** sand. 🔲 01/01-31/12
Distance: 🚶2,2km ⛵50m.
Remarks: Forbidden during Summer period.

São Bartolomeu de Messines 30B2

Camperstop Messines. GPS: n37,27979 w8,24133. ⬆️➡️

40 ☐ € 6/night 🚰 Ch WC 🔲€4/4 📶included. 🛒
Location: Rural, quiet. **Surface:** gravel. 🔲 01/01-31/12
Distance: 🚶6,5km ⛵6,4km ⊗1,2km.
Remarks: Shopping service.

São Bartolomeu de Messines 30B2

Rua António Aleixo. **GPS:** n37,25514 w8,2847. ⬆️

4 ☐ free 🚰 Ch free. **Location:** Rural. **Surface:** gravel.
🔲 01/01-31/12
Distance: 🚶centre 150m ⛵2,7km.
Remarks: Monday regional market.

Silves 30B2

Algarve Motorhome Park Silves, N124. **GPS:** n37,18722 w8,45158. ⬆️

50 ☐ € 8 🚰 Ch 🔌 📶included. 🔲 01/01-31/12
Distance: 🚶1km ⛵800m.

Silves 30B2

Club Autocaravana, N124. **GPS:** n37,21834 w8,36924. ⬆️➡️

15 ☐ € 5 🚰 Ch 🔌 WC 🔲 📶included. **Location:** Rural, comfortable. **Surface:** gravel/metalled. 🔲 01/01-31/12
Distance: 🚶9km 🚌100m.

Silves 30B2

Barregem do Arade, N124-3. **GPS:** n37,23960 w8,37699.

10 ☐ free. **Location:** Isolated. **Surface:** sand.
Distance: 🚶Silves 10km.

Tourist information Silves:
Ⓜ Museu Municipal de Arqueologia. Archeological findings.
✠ Castello. 🔲 9-18h.
🎪 Festival da cerveja. Beer festival. 🔲 July.

⊞S Tavira `30B2`

Parque de Autocaravanes. GPS: n37,13637 w7,64013. ⬆.

20 ⬰€ 9,90 ⟷⬱Ch ⚓WC⬲⬛€2 ⬘included. ⬙
Surface: grassy/gravel. ▯ 15/09-15/06 ◉ summer
Distance: ⬰1km.
Remarks: Swimming pool.

Tourist information Tavira:
♜ Castello. ▯ Mo-Fri 8-17.30h.

⊞ Vila do Bispo `30A2`

Praia da Barriga, N1265. **GPS:** n37,09970 w8,94445.

⬰free. **Surface:** asphalted.
Distance: ⬰Vila do Bispo 3,8km ⤋on the spot.
Remarks: Beach parking.

⊞ Vila do Bispo `30A2`

Praia de Ingrina-Zavial. GPS: n37,04667 w8,88057. ⬆.

4 ⬰free. **Location:** Simple. **Surface:** gravel/sand.
▯ 01/01-31/12
Distance: ⬰Vila do Bispo 6,7km ⤋100m ⊗200m ⚲ on the spot.
Remarks: Beach parking.

⚠S Vila do Bispo `30A2`

Sagres, Cerro da Moita. **GPS:** n37,02278 w8,94583.
⬰⟷⬱Ch ⬚. ▯ 01/01-31/12
Distance: ⤋2km ⊗on the spot ⬛on the spot ⬌500m.

⊞S Vila Real de Santo António `30C2`

Avenida de República. **GPS:** n37,19955 w7,4153. ⬆.

70 ⬰€ 4,50 ⟷⬱Ch ⚓€2,50 ⬘included.
Surface: metalled/sand.
Distance: ⬰500m ⊗on the spot.

▮▮Romania

Capital: Bucharest
Government: semi presidential republic
Official Language: Romanian
Population 21,730,000 (2014)
Area: 238,391 Km²

General information
Dialling code: 0040
General emergency: 112
Currency: Leu (RON)
€ 1 = 4,4 RON, 1 RON = € 0,23 (October 2015)
£ 1 = 6,15 RON, 1 RON = £ 0,16 (October 2015)
Credit card are mostly accepted in the main cities.

Regulations for overnight stays
Wild camping is allowed with permission from
land owner/manager or local government.

Additional public holidays 2016
January 6 Epiphany
May 1 Labour Day
August 15 Assumption of Mary
November 1 All Saints' Day
November 30 Saint Andrew's Day
December 1 National Holiday

Time Zone
Winter (Standard Time) GMT+2
Summer (DST) GMT+3

RO

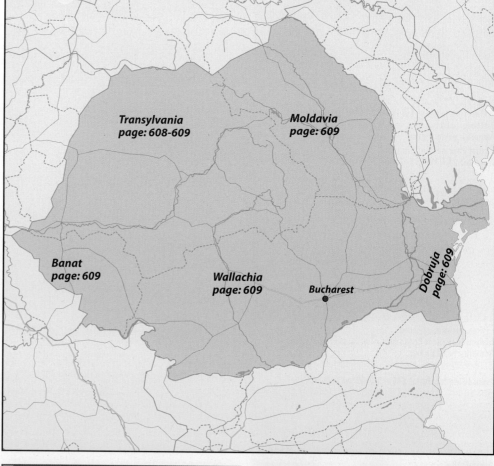

Transylvania
page: 608-609

Moldavia
page: 609

Banat
page: 609

Wallachia
page: 609

Bucharest

Dobruja
page: 609

Transylvania

Aurel Vlaicu — 38B2
Camping Aurel Vlaicu, Str. Pricipala 155. **GPS**: n45,91424 e23,27938.
€ 12,50 Ch €2,50 WC included. **Location**: Rural.
Surface: grassy. 15/4-30-09
Distance: 250m 250m 100m 300m 250m.

Baile Felix — 38A2
Camping Apollo. **GPS**: n46,99608 e21,98056.
€ 14 Ch WC included. 01/01-31/12
Distance: 100m 400m 100m.

Blăjel — 38B2
Camping Doua Lumi, Strada Tudor Vladimirescu 87-89.
GPS: n46,21032 e24,32478.

15 € 13 Ch €3 WC included. **Surface**: grassy.
01/04-15/10
Distance: 10km.

Borşa — 38B1
Borşa Turism, Strada Pietroasa 9. **GPS**: n47,64914 e24,66801.
4 € 9 Ch WC €3,50 included. **Location**: Urban.
Surface: gravel. 01/01-31/12
Distance: 1km 1,5km 900m.

Bran — 38C2
Vampire camping, Soholstr. **GPS**: n45,52787 e25,37183.
€ 15 Ch €3,50 WC included. **Location**: Rural.
Surface: grassy. 01/04-01/11
Distance: 650m.

Cârţa — 38B2
Camping de Oude Wilg, Str. Prundului 311. **GPS**: n45,78332 e24,56700.
€ 11 €2,50 Ch €2,50 WC included €3,50.
Location: Rural. **Surface**: grassy.
Distance: 500m 500m on the spot on the spot.

Gârbova — 38B2
Poarta Oilor, Str. Eminescu 573. **GPS**: n45,85933 e23,72019.
€ 15 Ch WC included. **Location**: Rural.
Surface: grassy. 01/05-30-09

Gilău — 38B2
Camping Eldorado. **GPS**: n46,76748 e23,35381.
€ 13 Ch €2,50 WC included. **Surface**: grassy.
15/04-15/10
Distance: 15km 50m 750m.

Miniş — 38A2
Camping Route Roemenië, Minis 298. **GPS**: n46,13356 e21,59788.

from € 12,50 €1,50 €2,50 Ch €2,75 WC included €4.
Location: Rural. **Surface**: grassy. 15/4-15/9
Distance: 1km.

Mureş — 38B2
Camping Mustang, Câmpu Cetăţii 16/A. **GPS**: n46,66750 e25,00361.
€ 11,50 Ch WC €2,50 included. **Location**: Rural.
Surface: grassy. 01/04-31/10
Distance: 3km 500m 400m.

Nireş — 38B2
Camping Zwaluwnest, Com. Mica 42A. **GPS**: n47,11918 e23,96788.

€ 11 Ch €2,50 WC included €4. **Location**: Rural.
Surface: grassy. 01/04-15/10

Ocna Sibiului — 38B2
Strada Mihai Viteazul 90. **GPS**: n45,88040 e24,04437.
20 € 5 €1 €2. **Surface**: grassy. 01/04-01/10
Distance: 800m.

Remetea — 38A2
Camping Turul, Bihor 8. **GPS**: n46,73443 e22,34436.
€ 10 Ch €2,50 WC included. **Location**: Rural.
Surface: grassy.
Distance: 100m 700m 900m.

Richis — 38B2
Camping La Curtea Richvini. **GPS**: n46,09797 e24,48066.
€ 10 Ch €3 WC included €4. **Location**: Rural.
Surface: grassy.

Vişeu de Sus — 38B1
Gara CFF Mocanita, Strada Cerbului 5. **GPS**: n47,71461 e24,44282.

 �€9 ⟍Ch ⟍WCincluded ⏠according consumption.
Surface: metalled. ◘ 01/01-31/12
Distance: 1,5km.

| △S | Zărneşti | 38C2 |

Alpin Ranch, Strada Pinului 13. **GPS:** n45,57861 e25,34389.

 ⌑€12 ⟍⧉Ch ⟍WC ⏠◙ ⟋included. **Location:** Rural.
Surface: grassy.
Distance: 800m.

Moldavia

| ⟍ | Dărmăneşti | 38C2 |

Camperland, Calea Trotusului 272. **GPS:** n46,40150 e26,48267.
 ⌑€15 ⟍⧉Ch ⟍WC ⏠◙€3,25 ⟋included. **Surface:** grassy.
◘ 15/04-15/10
Distance: ⊗400m.

| △S | Fundu Moldovei | 38B1 |

Camping de Vuurplaats, Strada Principale 130.
GPS: n47,53417 e25,41528.

24 ⌑€14,75 ⟍⧉Ch ⟍€2,75 WC ⏠◙€4 ⟋included.
Location: Rural. **Surface:** grassy. ◘ 01/04-01/10
Distance: ⊗on the spot on the spot.
Remarks: Barbecue place.

Dobruja

| △S | Jupiter | 38D3 |

Camping Popas Zodiac, Gala Galaction str 49.
GPS: n43,85860 e28,59960.⬆.
 ⌑€16,50 - €19,25 ⟍⧉Ch ⟍included ⟋. **Surface:** grassy.
◘ 01/05-31/10
Distance: 200m 200m ⊗100m.

| ⌑S | Murighiol | 38D2 |

La doi Sturioni, Str. Portului 2. **GPS:** n45,03632 e29,16677.

10 ⌑€12 ⟍⧉Ch ⟍included. **Location:** Simple.
Surface: unpaved. ◘ 01/05-01/10
Distance: 200m 200m.

| ⧇S | Murighiol | 38D2 |

Pension Laguna Albastra. GPS: n45,03824 e29,18161.⬆.
25 ⌑€12 ⟍⧉Ch ⟍included. **Location:** Simple. **Surface:** grassy.
◘ 01/04-15/10
Distance: on the spot on the spot ⊗on the spot.

| △S | Navodari | 38D3 |

GPM Camping Holiday. GPS: n44,27467 e28,61774.⬆.
30 ⌑€16 ⟍⧉Chincluded ⟍. ◘ 25/04-30/09
Distance: on the spot on the spot ⊗on the spot.

Banat

| △ | Mehadia | 38B3 |

Camping Hercules, DN6. **GPS:** n44,86918 e22,38774.
5 ⌑€15 ⟍⧉Ch ⟍WC ⏠.

Distance: ⊗on the spot 500m on the spot on the spot.

Wallachia

| △S | Paclele Mici | 38C2 |

Popasul La Hangar, 108. **GPS:** n45,34711 e26,70928.
5 ⌑€7 ⟍⧉Ch ⟍included. **Location:** Simple.
Surface: gravel/sand. ◘ 01/01-31/12
Distance: ⊗on the spot.

Sweden

Capital: Stockholm
Government: parliamentary constitutional monarchy
Official Language: Swedish
Population 9,724,000 (2014)
Area: 450,295 Km²

General information

Dialling code: 0046
General emergency: 112
Currency: Swedish Krona (SEK)
€ 1 = SEK 9,40, SEK 1 = € 0,11 (October 2015)
£ 1 = 13 SEK, 1 SEK = £ 0,07 (October 2015)
Credit cards are accepted almost everywhere.

Regulations for overnight stays

In general wild camping is allowed, not in private gardens and agricultural land.

Camping Key Europe is obligatory when using campsites: the card can be purchased at any campsite for SEK 160 (± € 16,50/ £10,50), valid for one year.

Additional public holidays 2016

March 25 Good Friday
March 28 Easter Monday
May 1 Labour Day
June 6 National day
June 24-25 Midsummer
November 1 All Saints' Day

Time Zone

Winter (Standard Time) GMT+1
Summer (DST) GMT+2

SE

Norrbotten	page: 610-611	
Västerbotten	page: 610	
Västernorrland	page: 613	
Jämtland	page: 613	
Gävleborg	page: 613	
Dalarna	page: 613	
Uppsala	page: 611	
Västmanland	page: 613	
Stockholm	page: 610	
Värmland	page: 613	
Södermanland	page: 611	
Västra Götaland	page: 613	
Östergötland	page: 611	
Jönköping	page: 611	
Kalmar	page: 611-612	
Halland	page: 613	
Blekinge	page: 612	
Skåne	page: 612-613	

Stockholm

Norrtälje — 3D3
Nässelgrundet 7. **GPS:** n59,68147 e18,81752.
3 kr 200 **Surface:** grassy.
Distance: Norrtälje 19km on the spot on the spot.
Remarks: Canoe and boat rental.

Skarpnäck — 4G1
Ställplatsstockholm, Flatens Skogsväg 30.
GPS: n59,24822 e18,16159.
48 kr 180 Ch
Distance: Stockholm 15km.

Stockholm — 4G1
Långholmens Husbilscamping Stockholm, Skutskepparvägen 1.
GPS: n59,32021 e18,03200.
76 kr 250, 19/06-30/08 kr 280 Ch included WC kr 5.
Location: Urban. **Surface:** metalled. 13/05-13/09
Distance: 4km 200m 500m.

Stockholm — 4G1
Tantolundens Husbilscamping Stockholm, Ringvägen 24.
GPS: n59,31241 e18,05299.
14 kr 250, 19/06-30/08 kr 280 WC included.
Location: Urban. **Surface:** gravel. 01/01-31/12
Distance: 5km 2km 350m.

Stockholm — 4G1
Strandvägen. **GPS:** n59,33124 e18,08595.
kr 15/h, overnight stay free. **Surface:** asphalted.
Distance: 1km on the spot 300m.
Remarks: At the quay.

Västerbotten

Byske — 3D1
E45. **GPS:** n64,94809 e21,18009.
free. **Location:** Rural, simple, isolated, noisy.
Distance: 1,7km 1,5km 1,7km.

Klimpfjäll — 3C1
Stekenjokk. **GPS:** n65,09030 e14,45897.

free. **Location:** Isolated, quiet.
Surface: unpaved. With snow
Distance: on the spot on the spot on the spot.

Marsfjäll — 3C1
Trappstegsforsen. **GPS:** n64,95526 e15,46639.
free. **Location:** Isolated, quiet. **Surface:** gravel.
Distance: 7km on the spot.

Sävar — 3D1
Sävar Rastplats, Skomakarvägen. **GPS:** n63,89191 e20,53027.
free Ch free. **Surface:** asphalted.
Distance: 2km 100m 1,7km.

Skellefteå — 3D1
Ställplats Campus, Laboratorgränd. **GPS:** n64,74601 e20,95595.
10 kr 100 WC included.
Location: Urban.
Surface: metalled.
Distance: 1km on the spot on the spot 100m on the spot.

Tärnaby — 3C1
Joeström. **GPS:** n65,74384 e15,08882.
voluntary contribution. **Location:** Rural. **Surface:** grassy.
Distance: 10km on the spot on the spot.

Vilhelmina — 3C1
Meselefors Rastplats, E45. **GPS:** n64,43398 e16,78733.
2 free Ch free.
Distance: on the spot on the spot.
Remarks: Max. 12h.

Vormsele — 3C1
Blåviksjöns, Blå vägen. **GPS:** n64,82994 e18,03335.
free. **Location:** Isolated, quiet. **Surface:** asphalted.
Distance: Vormsele 47km on the spot on the spot.

Norrbotten

Gällivare — 2B3
Lappeasuando. **GPS:** n67,49093 e21,12025.
free Ch WC free. **Location:** Isolated, quiet. **Surface:** asphalted.
Distance: Gällivare 56km 200m 200m.

Jävrebyn — 3D1
Jävrefyrens väg. **GPS:** n65,14339 e21,50862.
kr 50 Ch. **Location:** Rural. **Surface:** grassy/gravel.
Distance: on the spot on the spot 500m.

Jokkmokk — 2B3
Polcirkeln. **GPS:** n66,55058 e19,76375.
kr 100 Ch kr 40 WC included.
Location: Rural. **Surface:** asphalted/grassy.
Distance: 2km on the spot.

Jokkmokk — 2B3
Laponia Rastplats, E45. **GPS:** n66,64258 e19,82465.
free. **Surface:** grassy/gravel.
Distance: 5km 100m.

Moskosel — 2B3
E45. **GPS:** n65,95231 e19,51979.
free Ch free.
Distance: 10km on the spot on the spot.
Remarks: Along river.

Nikkala — 2C3
Båtklubben Bothnia, Haparandahamn 65.
GPS: n65,77154 e23,90442.
kr 100 kr 40. **Surface:** asphalted/grassy.
Distance: on the spot on the spot.
Remarks: Borrow cycles for free, use of sauna against payment.

Övre Soppero — 2B2
Ryssäjoki Naturrastplats. **GPS:** n68,15435 e21,78256.
. **Location:** Rural, isolated. **Surface:** unpaved.
Distance: 8km on the spot on the spot.

Porjus — 2B3
Strömgatan. **GPS:** n66,95671 e19,80798.
free. **Surface:** asphalted.
Distance: 500m.
Remarks: In front of fire-station.

Vittangi — 2B2
Rastplats Suptallen. **GPS:** n67,66938 e21,40521.
free.
Distance: 15km.

Uppsala

⛵S Älvkarleby 3D3
Älvkarleby Turist & Konferenshotell, Västanåvägen 54.
GPS: n60,56518 e17,43796.
20 🏕kr 100 🔌WC📶.
Distance: 🚶100m ⊗on the spot.
Remarks: Pay at reception.

🏭 Öregrund 3D3
Kyrkogatan. **GPS:** n60,33958 e18,43672.⬆.
5 🏕. **Surface:** asphalted.
Distance: 🚶200m ⚓on the spot ⛽on the spot ⊗350m 🚰200m.

⚓ Öregrund 3D3
GPS: n60,34091 e18,44107.⬆.
3 🏕free 🔌free WC🚿. **Surface:** asphalted.
Distance: 🚶on the spot ⚓on the spot ⛽on the spot ⊗100m 🚰200m.

Södermanland

⚓S Eskilstuna 4F1
Sundbyholms Gästhamn, Sundbyholm. **GPS:** n59,44749 e16,62593.⬆.
6 🏕kr 150 🔌kr 40.
Distance: ⚓on the spot ⛽on the spot ⊗on the spot 🏃on the spot.
Remarks: Next to castle.

⚓ Mariefred 4F1
Mariefreds gästhamnen, Gripsholmsvägen.
GPS: n59,25793 e17,22160.⬆.
4 🏕kr 260 🔌WC🚿. **Surface:** asphalted.
Distance: 🚶on the spot ⊗200m 🚰200m.

🏭 Mariefred 4F1
Statoil, Storgatan 18. **GPS:** n59,25944 e17,21805.⬆.
2 🏕. **Surface:** asphalted.

⚓ Oxelösund 4F1
Femöre Marina, Fiskehamnsvägen 12. **GPS:** n58,65830 e17,11123.⬆.
15 🏕kr 150 🔌Ch🔧(10x),kr50. **Surface:** gravel.
Distance: 🚶3km ⚓on the spot ⛽on the spot ⊗on the spot.

⚓ Strängnäs 4F1
Strängnäs Gästhamn, Storgatan 38. **GPS:** n59,37860 e17,02599.⬆.
8 🏕kr 260. ▢ 01/05-30/09
Distance: ⚓on the spot ⛽on the spot ⊗on the spot 🚰200m.
Remarks: Max. 48h.

⚓S Trosa 4G1
Trosa Gästhamn, Uddbergagatan 1. **GPS:** n58,89090 e17,55360.⬆.
8 🏕kr 160 🔌Ch🚿included WC🚿📶.
Distance: ⚓on the spot ⛽on the spot ⊗200m 🚰1km.
Remarks: Use of sauna against payment.

Östergötland

⚓ Borensberg 4F1
Kaffeteriet, Magasinsgatan 7. **GPS:** n58,55885 e15,27995.⬆.
🏕kr 200 🔌🔧included 🚿.
Distance: 🚶550m ⚓on the spot ⛽on the spot ⊗on the spot 🚰550m.

⚓ Motala 4E1
Södra Hamnen, Fabriksgatan 12 H. **GPS:** n58,52979 e15,03811.⬆.
🏕kr 180 🔌Ch 🚿WC🚿📶included. **Surface:** grassy.
▢ 01/01-31/12
Distance: 🚶1km ⚓on the spot ⛽on the spot ⊗500m.

⛵S Motala 4E1
Berggrens Källare, Verkstadsvägen 91. **GPS:** n58,55550 e15,07820.⬆.
6 🏕kr 150 🔧kr50. ▢ 01/05-31/08
Distance: ⛽on the spot ⊗on the spot.
Remarks: Nearby sluices.

⚓ Norrköping 4F1
Albrektsvägen. **GPS:** n58,58403 e16,20064.⬆.
🏕kr 60. **Surface:** asphalted.
Distance: 🚶1km ⊗300m 🚰600m.
Remarks: At swimming pool.

⚓ Ödeshög 4E2
Hästholmens hamn, Hamngatan. **GPS:** n58,27904 e14,63522.⬆.
5 🏕kr 120. **Surface:** asphalted.
Distance: ⚓on the spot ⛽on the spot ⊗on the spot.

🏭 Skänninge 4E2
Gripenbergs gårdsbutik, Gripenberg 1. **GPS:** n58,40659 e15,08026.⬆.
🏕kr 100 🔧kr 25 WC🚿included 🚿. **Location:** Isolated.
Surface: grassy.
Distance: 🚶1,5km 🏊2km ⊗1,5km.

🏭S Söderköping 4F1
Bergaskolan, Tingshusgatan. **GPS:** n58,48033 e16,32952.⬆.
10 🏕kr 120 🔌Ch. 🚜 **Surface:** gravel. ▢ 15/06-15/08
Distance: 🚶350m ⊗350m.
Remarks: At former school, service on campsite.

🏭 Söderköping 4F1
Kanalmagasinet AB, Mem. **GPS:** n58,47923 e16,41422.⬆.
4 🏕kr 185. **Surface:** gravel.
Distance: ⚓on the spot ⛽on the spot.
Remarks: Pay at Kanalmagasinet.

Jönköping

⛵S Gränna 4E2
Gränna Hamn, Hamnvägen. **GPS:** n58,02728 e14,46070.⬆.
30 🏕kr 180 📺Ch🚿(20x)included. 🚐 🚜
Distance: 🚶800m ⚓100m ⛽100m 🚰400m 🚴on the spot 🏃on the spot.
Remarks: Nights closed with barrier.

⚓ Gränna 4E2
Gränna Hamn, Amiralsvägen. **GPS:** n58,02868 e14,45960.
🏕kr 120. **Surface:** asphalted.
Distance: ⚓100m ⛽100m ⊗100m 🚴on the spot 🏃on the spot.

🏭S Hult ⛵🛶(〓) 4F2
Ställplats Lyckarps, Hultvägen. **GPS:** n57,63577 e15,09830.⬆➡.

19 🏕€ 10 🔌according consumption Ch included 🔧(15x) 3.
Location: Rural, isolated. **Surface:** grassy/gravel.
▢ 01/05-31/10
Distance: 🚶8km ⛽on the spot 🚐200m.

🏭 Jönköping 4E2
Statoil Hyltena, Hyltena 50. **GPS:** n57,66554 e14,18237.⬆.
17 🏕kr 99 🔧WC🚿. **Surface:** asphalted.
Distance: 🚶Jönköping 15km 🚰500m.

⛵ Vrigstad 4E3
Timjan Café & Restaurang, Flahult 2. **GPS:** n57,31552 e14,29112.⬆.
6 🏕kr 100 🔧kr50.
Distance: ⊗on the spot 🏃on the spot.

Kalmar

⚓ Bläsinge 4F3
GPS: n56,62015 e16,70076.⬆.
15 🏕kr 120-200.

🏭 Borgholm 4F3
Lindby Boden, Lindby Bygata 23. **GPS:** n56,81571 e16,70548.
35 🏕kr 70 🔧kr30. **Location:** Isolated. **Surface:** grassy.
Distance: 🚶Borgholm 10km 🚴on the spot.

⚓ Borgholm 4F3
Hamnvägen. **GPS:** n56,88301 e16,64790.⬆.
40 🏕kr 130 WC🚿. **Surface:** grassy.
Distance: ⚓on the spot ⛽on the spot.

⚓S Byxelkrok 4F2
Byxelkroks Gästhamn, Neptunivägen. **GPS:** n57,32767 e17,00812.⬆.
🏕kr 130 🔧WC🚿. **Surface:** gravel. ▢ 15/05-30/09
Distance: ⚓on the spot ⛽on the spot ⊗on the spot.
Remarks: Check in at harbourmaster.

⚓ Degerhamn 4F3
Degerhamns Ställplats & Hamn. **GPS:** n56,35697 e16,40940.⬆.
100 🏕kr 120 🔌📺Ch included 🔧kr30. **Surface:** grassy.
▢ 15/04-18/10

⚓ Degerhamn 4F3
Gräsgårds hamn. **GPS:** n56,31722 e16,53167.⬆.
🏕kr 80 🔌kr30. **Location:** Rural. **Surface:** asphalted.
Distance: ⚓on the spot ⛽on the spot.

⚓S Färjestaden 4F3
Brandstationsgatan. **GPS:** n56,65206 e16,46971.⬆.
15 🏕free 🔧. **Surface:** asphalted.
Distance: ⊗500m 🚰on the spot.
Remarks: At shopping centre.

⚓ Figeholm 4F2
Figeholms Båtklubb, Ågatan. **GPS:** n57,37075 e16,55199.⬆.
6 🏕kr 150 🔌kr20 WC🚿. **Surface:** asphalted.
Distance: ⚓1,5km ⛽on the spot ⊗200m.

🏭 Fliseryd 4F3
Ställplats Jungnerholmarna, Jungnerholmarna.
GPS: n57,13050 e16,25596.⬆.
🏕kr 90 🔌kr30 WC🚿. **Surface:** grassy.
Distance: ⚓on the spot ⛽on the spot.

⚓ Grönhögen 4H1
Fiskaregränd. **GPS:** n56,26652 e16,39722.⬆.
30 🏕kr 150. **Surface:** grassy.
Distance: ⚓on the spot ⛽on the spot ⊗500m 🚰500m.

⚓ Hjorted 4F2
Blankaholm. **GPS:** n57,58669 e16,51954.⬆.
8 🏕kr 140 🔧kr40.
Distance: 🚶750m ⚓on the spot ⛽on the spot ⊗750m.

⚓S Kalmar 4F3
Ölandskajen. **GPS:** n56,66030 e16,36130.
9 🏕kr 160 🔧kr40 🚿. **Surface:** asphalted. ▢ 01/01-31/12 ◉ water disconnected in winter
Distance: 🚶200m ⚓on the spot ⛽on the spot ⊗200m 🚰200m.
Remarks: Pay at tourist office.

🏭 Kalmar 4F3
Elevatorkajen. **GPS:** n56,66360 e16,37060.⬆.
6 🏕kr 160.
Distance: 🚶450m ⚓on the spot ⛽on the spot ⊗450m.

🏭 Kalmar 4F3
Svinö. **GPS:** n56,68128 e16,38121.⬆.
20 🏕free 🔌📺Ch. **Surface:** gravel. ▢ 01/01-31/12 ◉ Service: winter
Distance: ⚓on the spot ⛽on the spot 🏃on the spot.

⚓ Köpingsvik 4F3
Kårehamns Fiskaffär. **GPS:** n56,95623 e16,88755.⬆.
30 🏕kr 140 🔧kr20 🚿. **Surface:** gravel.
Distance: ⚓on the spot ⛽on the spot ⊗on the spot.

⚓ Löttorp 4G2
Bödahamnsvägen. **GPS:** n57,24052 e17,07503.
30 🏕kr 140 🔧(10x),kr20 🚿📺. 🚐 **Surface:** grassy/gravel.
Distance: 🚶1km ⚓on the spot ⛽on the spot 🚰1km.

⚓S Mönsterås 4F3
Hamnen Mönsterås, Hamngatan. **GPS:** n57,04151 e16,44874.⬆.
7 🏕kr 125 WC🚿. **Surface:** asphalted.
Distance: 🚶400m ⚓on the spot ⛽on the spot ⊗100m 🚰400m.
Remarks: At the quay.

⚓ Oskarshamn 4F2
Oskarshamns gästhamn, Norra Strandgatan.
GPS: n57,26768 e16,45516.⬆.
10 🏕 🔌📺ChWC🚿📶included. ▢ 01/05-30/09
Distance: 🚶500m ⚓on the spot ⛽on the spot ⊗500m.

🏭 Överum 4F2
Källarbacken 6. **GPS:** n57,98948 e16,31572.
6 🏕kr 100 🔌🔧kr40 WC🚿.
Distance: 🚶on the spot.

⚓ Sandvik 4F3
Gästhamnen Sandvik, Stenhuggarvägen.
GPS: n57,07143 e16,85335.⬆.
40 🏕kr 140 🔧kr20 WC🚿.
Distance: ⚓on the spot ⛽on the spot ⊗on the spot.

🏭 Silverdalen 4F2
Ställplats Viktoria, Bruksallén 3. **GPS:** n57,54539 e15,74915.⬆.
6 🏕kr 40 🔌🚿. ▢ 01/06-30/09
Distance: ⚓on the spot ⛽on the spot.

⚓ Stora Rör 4F3
Stora Rörs Hamn. **GPS:** n56,75654 e16,52817.⬆.
8 🏕kr 140 🔧. **Surface:** gravel.
Distance: 🚶on the spot ⚓on the spot ⛽on the spot ⊗on the spot 🚰100m.

⚓ Timmernabben 4F3
Festplatsen Timmernabben. **GPS:** n56,97350 e16,44028.⬆➡.
🏕kr 150 🔧WC🚿. 🐄 **Surface:** grassy. ◉ With snow
Distance: ⚓on the spot ⛽on the spot.

🏭 Tuna 4F2
Ställplats Tuna, Lillgatan. **GPS:** n57,57716 e16,10351.⬆.
12 🏕kr 100 🔌kr60 🔧Ch🔧(3x) WCkr40 🚿. **Surface:** gravel.
Distance: 🚶500m.

🏭 Västervik 4F2
Ställplats Sågen, Värmeverksgatan. **GPS:** n57,75138 e16,65541.⬆.

SE

45 🍴kr 100 ⛽🍽️ ♨️(15x),kr40.
Distance: 🚶1,5km ⛴️on the spot ⚓on the spot ⊗800m.

Blekinge

| ⚓ | Hasslö | 4F3 |

Garpahamnen Hasslö, Hamnvägen. **GPS:** n56,09990 e15,47368.⬆️.
🍴kr 130 WC⬜.
Distance: ⛴️on the spot ⚓on the spot.

| ⚓ | Hasslö | 4F3 |

Hasslö Stugby, Fiskaregårdsvägen 2, Garpahamnen.
GPS: n56,10227 e15,47770.
🍴 ♨️.

| 🛥️ | Karlshamn | 4F3 |

Hamngatan. **GPS:** n56,16504 e14,86546.⬆️.
6 🍴free. **Surface:** asphalted. 🅾️ 01/01-31/12 🅾️ during event
Distance: 🚶500m ⚓on the spot ⊗on the spot.

| 🛥️ | Karlshamn | 4F3 |

Saltsjöbadsvägen. **GPS:** n56,15835 e14,87974.⬆️.
🍴free. **Location:** Rural, isolated. **Surface:** gravel.
Distance: 🚶2,5km.

| 🛥️ | Karlshamn | 4F3 |

Ställplats Väggaviken, Saltsjöbadsvägen.
GPS: n56,15840 e14,88486.⬆️.
🍴kr 180 ⛽♨️included WC⬜.🏠 **Surface:** gravel.
🅾️ 01/06-31/08

| 🛥️ | Karlshamn | 4F3 |

Stationsvägen. **GPS:** n56,17563 e14,86610.⬆️.
🍴free. **Surface:** asphalted. 🅾️ 01/01-31/12
Distance: 🚶800m ⊗800m 🍺800m ⚓on the spot.

| ⚓🛥️S | Karlshamn | 4F3 |

Svaneviks småbåtshamn. GPS: n56,15649 e14,88870.⬆️.
🍴kr 180 ⛽♨️ WC⬜included. 🅾️ 01/06-31/08
Distance: 🚶3km ⚓on the spot ⚓on the spot ⊗on the spot.
Remarks: Pay at harbourmaster.

| 🛏️ | Karlshamn | 4F3 |

Kreativum Science Center, Strömmavägen 28.
GPS: n56,19288 e14,85211.
🍴free.
Distance: 🚶4km 🚤800m.
Remarks: At museum, check in on arrival.

| ⚓🛥️S | Karlskrona | 4F3 |

Karlskrona Stadsmarina, Skeppsbrokajen.
GPS: n56,16723 e15,58893.⬆️.
24 🍴kr 180 ⛽♨️ WC⬜included 🅾️.
Surface: asphalted.
🅾️ 01/01-31/12
Distance: 🚶1km ⚓on the spot ⚓on the spot ⊗200m 🍺1km.
Remarks: Pay at harbourmaster, out of season less pitches.

| S | Karlskrona | 4F3 |

Argongatan. **GPS:** n56,16988 e15,59426.⬆️➡️.
⛽🍽️Ch.

| 🛥️ | Ramdala | 4F3 |

Brofästet Senoren gårdsbutik, Säby Gård.
GPS: n56,13755 e15,74195.⬆️.
28 🍴kr 100 ⛽🍽️Chincluded ♨️kr50. **Surface:** grassy.
🅾️ 01/04-30/09
Distance: 🚶7km ⚓on the spot ⚓on the spot 🍺1,5km.

| 🛥️ | Ronneby | 4F3 |

Ronneby Golfklubb, Reddvägen 14. **GPS:** n56,18962 e15,29355.⬆️.
6 🍴kr 100 WC⬜.

| ⚓ | Ronneby | 4F3 |

Ronneby Hamn, Östra Piren. **GPS:** n56,17527 e15,30177.
20 🍴kr 150 ♨️. **Surface:** metalled.
Distance: ⚓on the spot ⚓on the spot.

| ⚓ | Sölvesborg | 5H1 |

Hörviks gästhamn, Kustvägen, Hörvik. **GPS:** n56,04139 e14,76556.⬆️.
9 🍴kr 100.
Distance: 🚶12km ⚓on the spot ⚓on the spot ⊗300m.

| ⚓ | Sölvesborg | 5H1 |

Krokås gästhamn, Hörvik. **GPS:** n56,04893 e14,75663.⬆️.
🍴.
Distance: 🚶15km ⚓on the spot ⚓on the spot ⊗1,5km.

| ⚓ | Sölvesborg | 5H1 |

Nogersunds gästhamn, Östra Hamnvägen, Nogersunds.
GPS: n56,00509 e14,73863.⬆️.
🍴kr 160 ♨️included.
Distance: ⚓on the spot ⚓on the spot.

| ⚓ | Sölvesborg | 5H1 |

Torsö gästhamn, Oastensvägen, Västra Torsö.
GPS: n55,99952 e14,64871.⬆️.
6 🍴kr 130 ♨️WC⬜included.
Distance: 🚶7km ⚓on the spot ⚓on the spot.

| 🛥️S | Sölvesborg | 5H1 |

Sölveborgs golfbana, Ljunganabbevägen. **GPS:** n56,04428 e14,59946.
10 🍴kr 150 ♨️WC⬜included.
Distance: 🚶7km ⊗on the spot.
Remarks: At golf court.

| ⚓ | Sturkö | 4F3 |

Ekenabben. GPS: n56,10142 e15,63803.
🍴kr 130 ♨️kr30. 🅾️ 01/04-27/09
Distance: 🚶7km ⚓on the spot ⚓on the spot.

| ⚓ | Sturkö | 4F3 |

Ställplats Sanda, Hamnvägen. **GPS:** n56,11966 e15,65123.⬆️.
🍴kr 130 ♨️kr30. 🅾️ 01/04-27/09
Distance: ⊗1,5km ⚓on the spot.

| ⚓ | Torhamn | 4F3 |

Sandhamn Marine. GPS: n56,09351 e15,85479.⬆️.
🍴kr 100, 01/05-30/09 kr 150 ⛽🍽️Ch ♨️WC⬜ ♨️kr50 🔔included.
Surface: grassy/gravel. 🅾️ 01/01-31/12
Distance: 🚶1km ⚓on the spot ⚓on the spot ⊗on the spot.

Skåne

| 🛥️S | Åhus | 5G1 |

Strandvillan, Kolonivägen 62. **GPS:** n55,94443 e14,32109.

16 🍴kr 150 ⛽♨️WC⬜included 🔔. **Surface:** grassy.
🅾️ 01/01-31/12
Distance: 🚶2km ⊗700m.

| ⚓S | Åhus | 5G1 |

Åhus Gästhamn, Stavgatan 3. **GPS:** n55,92568 e14,30284.⬆️.
🍴kr 50 ⛽WC⬜.
Distance: ⚓on the spot ⚓on the spot.
Remarks: Check in on arrival.

| 🛥️ | Anderslöv | 5G2 |

Sörbyvägen 99. **GPS:** n55,44370 e13,32866.⬆️.
20 🍴kr 100. **Surface:** grassy.
Distance: 🚶900m ⚓1km 🍺900m.

| ⚓🛥️S | Ängelholm | 4E3 |

Ängelholms Föreningshamn, Segelvägen 9.
GPS: n56,26704 e12,84138.
30 🍴kr 150 ♨️(16x)included.
🅾️ 01/06-06/12
Distance: 🚶5km ⚓on the spot ⚓on the spot ⊗on the spot 🍺5km.
Remarks: Max. 48h, pay at harbourmaster.

| ⚓ | Båstad | 4E3 |

Italienska vägen. **GPS:** n56,43383 e12,83132.⬆️.
🍴kr 50. 🏠 **Surface:** grassy. 🅾️ 01/01-31/12
Distance: 🚶1km ⊗400m 🍺500m.

| 🛏️ | Borrby | 5G1 |

Catrinegården. GPS: n55,46673 e14,21090.
🍴kr 100 ♨️kr20. **Location:** Rural. **Surface:** gravel.
🅾️ 01/01-31/12
Distance: 🚶2,5km 🍺2,5km.

| 🛥️S | Bromölla | 5H1 |

Skåneporten Bromölla, Kristiansdasvägen.
GPS: n56,06414 e14,49689.⬆️.
🍴free ⛽🍽️ChWC. **Surface:** asphalted.
Distance: 🚤200m ⚓on the spot 🍺1km.
Remarks: Service to be paid at campsite.

| 🛥️ | Fjälkinge | 5G1 |

Tosteberge Ångar. GPS: n56,01567 e14,45466.⬆️.
🍴. **Location:** Rural. **Surface:** forest soil. 🅾️ 01/01-31/12

| 🛥️S | Höllviken | 5F2 |

Ställplats Foteviken, Museivägen. **GPS:** n55,42810 e12,95237.⬆️.
🍴kr 100 ⛽🍽️Ch ♨️against payment WC⬜. **Surface:** grassy.
Distance: 🚶1km ⚓on the spot ⊗1km 🍺1km.
Remarks: At museum.

| 🍴 | Jonstorp | 4E3 |

Bläsinge Gård, Gamla Södåkravägen 127. **GPS:** n56,23770 e12,65567.
20 🍴kr 150 ♨️kr50. **Surface:** gravel. 🅾️ 01/01-31/12

| 🛥️ | Kristianstad | 5G1 |

Sommarlust, Kanalgatan 100. **GPS:** n56,04442 e14,16646.

🍴free. **Surface:** asphalted.
Distance: 🚶2km 🚤300m 🚐on the spot 🐾on the spot.
Remarks: Max. 24h.

| ⚓🛥️S | Landskrona | 5F1 |

Lundåkrahamnen. GPS: n55,86171 e12,84906.⬆️.
34 🍴kr 150 ♨️WC⬜included. **Surface:** grassy. 🅾️ 01/01-31/12
Distance: 🚶2km ⚓on the spot ⚓on the spot ⊗300m.
Remarks: Arrival <22h, monitored parking.

| 🛥️ | Limhamn | 5F1 |

Lagunen, Vågbrytarvägen. **GPS:** n55,58495 e12,91741.
🍴kr 180 ⛽🍽️Ch ♨️included WC⬜ 🔔. 🏠 **Surface:** asphalted.
🅾️ 15/04-31/10
Distance: 🚶5km.

| ⚓ | Limhamn | 5F1 |

Limhamns Småbåtshamn, Bryggövägen.
GPS: n55,58358 e12,91824.⬆️.
40 🍴kr 200 ⛽♨️WC⬜included. **Surface:** asphalted. 🅾️ 01/01-31/12
🅾️ **Service:** winter
Distance: 🚶700m, Malmö 6km ⚓on the spot ⚓on the spot ⊗on the spot.

| 🛥️ | Simrishamn | 5G1 |

Camping car parking Hammarlunda, Gislövshammar.
GPS: n55,49015 e14,30745.⬆️.
🍴kr 100 ⛽🍽️Ch ♨️. **Surface:** grassy.
Distance: ⚓700m ⚓700m ⊗2,5km.

| ⚓🛥️S | Simrishamn | 5G1 |

Småbåtshamnen. **GPS:** n55,56035 e14,34906.⬆️.
5 🍴kr 200 ⛽🍽️Ch ♨️(4x)kWh,kr2 WC⬜ 🔔. 🏠
Surface: asphalted.
Distance: 🚶500m ⚓on the spot ⚓on the spot ⊗on the spot 🍺on the spot.
Remarks: Tallycard.

| ⚓S | Simrishamn | 5G1 |

Tobisviks Camping, Tobisvik. **GPS:** n55,56693 e14,33750.⬆️.

20 🍴kr 120-200 ⬜. **Surface:** grassy. 🅾️ 01/01-31/12
Distance: 🚶3km ⚓on the spot ⚓on the spot.

| ⚓ | Skanör | 5F2 |

Skanör hamn, Hamnvägen. **GPS:** n55,41608 e12,83168.⬆️.
10 🍴kr 120.
Distance: ⚓on the spot ⚓on the spot ⊗on the spot 🍺1,2km.
Remarks: Max. 24h.

| 🛥️ | Smygehamn | 5G2 |

Smyge strandväg. **GPS:** n55,33978 e13,36172.
🍴kr 150. **Surface:** grassy.
Distance: ⚓on the spot ⚓on the spot.

| 🛥️ | Trelleborg | 5G2 |

Trelleborgs turist Parkering, Västra Trelleborg.
GPS: n55,37536 e13,12004.
🍴free, night kr 80. **Surface:** gravel.
Distance: 🚶2km ⚓on the spot ⚓on the spot ⊗1,5km 🍺800m.

| 🍴🛥️S | Yngsjö | 5G1 |

Gamla skolan, Yngsjövägen 1065. **GPS:** n55,84441 e14,20019.⬆️.
🍴kr 150 ⛽♨️WC⬜included. **Surface:** grassy.
Distance: 🚶1,5km.

SE

Remarks: Breakfast-service.

🏕️Ⓢ Ystad · 5G2
Ystads Marina, Segelgatan 1. **GPS:** n55,42666 e13,81730.⬆️.
🅿️free, night kr 150 🚿 (16x) 🔲. ⬛ 01/06-15/09
Distance: ⚓on the spot ⚓on the spot ►on the spot ⊗on the spot.
Remarks: Caution kr 50.

Halland

🏕️ Fjärås · 4D3
Tjolöholms Slott, Tjolöholms byväg. **GPS:** n57,40173 e12,10161.⬆️.
🅿️kr 100. **Surface:** grassy/gravel. ⬛ 01/01-31/12
Distance: ⊗on the spot.
Remarks: At castle, max. 2 days.

🏕️ Fjärås · 4D3
Skårs Gård, Förlandavägen. **GPS:** n57,40081 e12,26869.⬆️.
6 🅿️kr 140 🚿WC🔲included. **Location:** Rural.
Distance: ⚓11km.

🏕️ Ullared · 4D3
Ställplats Ullared, Värnamovägen. **GPS:** n57,13232 e12,73472.⬆️.
100 🅿️free, night kr 90. 🏪 **Surface:** gravel.
Distance: ⚓1km.
Remarks: Max. 48h.

🏕️Ⓢ Unnaryd · 4E3
Tiraholms Fisk. **GPS:** n56,94263 e13,64560.
🅿️kr 100 🚿. **Surface:** grassy.
Distance: ►on the spot ⊗on the spot.
Remarks: At small lake, check in on arrival.

🏕️Ⓢ Varberg · 4D3
Apelvik Strand, Tångkörarvägen, Apelviken.
GPS: n57,08157 e12,26156.⬆️.
🅿️kr 150 WC🔲.
Distance: ⚓on the spot.
Remarks: Beach parking.

🏕️Ⓢ Varberg · 4D3
Naturum Getterön, Lassavägen 1. **GPS:** n57,12627 e12,25332.
24 🅿️kr 125, 01/06-31/08 kr 200 🚿included. 🏪 **Surface:** gravel.
⚓on the spot.
Remarks: Nature reserve.

🏕️Ⓢ Varberg · 4D3
Getterön Marina, Änggärdev. 1. **GPS:** n57,11399 e12,22588.⬆️.
21 🅿️kr 170-200 🔌Ch🚿🔲📶included. 🏪
Surface: metalled. ⬛ 01/01-31/12
Distance: ⚓on the spot ►on the spot.
Remarks: Monitored parking.

⚓ Värobacka · 4D3
Bua hamn, Hamnvägen. **GPS:** n57,23926 e12,11410.⬆️.
🅿️kr 180, 15/06-15/08 kr 200 🔌Ch🚿WC🔲. 🏪
Surface: asphalted. ⬛ 01/01-31/12
Distance: ⚓1km ⚓on the spot ►on the spot ⊗200m 🛒500m.

Västra Götaland

🏕️Ⓢ Åmål · 4D1
Måkebergsvägen. **GPS:** n59,05615 e12,70862.
🅿️kr 100 🔌kr40 🔌Ch. **Surface:** asphalted. ⬛ 01/04-15/10
Distance: ⚓600m ⚓on the spot ►on the spot ⊗600m 🛒600m.
Remarks: Pay at harbourmaster, servicepoint at Camping Örnäs.

⚓ Bohus-björkö · 4D2
Björkö Hamn, Ljungblomsvägen 7. **GPS:** n57,72812 e11,67751.
🅿️kr 250 🚿included 🔲kr10 🔌kr50. **Surface:** gravel.
⬛ 01/01-31/12
Distance: ⚓on the spot ►on the spot ⊗on the spot 🛒500m.

🏕️ Floda · 4D2
Öjared Golf, Öjaresvägen. **GPS:** n57,85467 e12,39777.⬆️.
🅿️. **Surface:** asphalted.
Remarks: At golf court.

🏕️ Göteborg · 4D2
Lisebergs ställplats Skatås, Skatåsvägen.
GPS: n57,70303 e12,03513.⬆️.
37 🅿️kr 240/24h 🔌Ch🚿included. 🏪 **Surface:** asphalted.
⬛ 30/05-13/09
Distance: ⚓750m ⊗750m 🛒750m.

⚓ Hälsö · 4D2
Tjolmenvägen. **GPS:** n57,73152 e11,65794.
15 🅿️kr 180 🚿WC🔲included. 🏪
Distance: ⚓on the spot ►on the spot.

🏕️ Kungshamn · 4D2
Smögenbrons Rum, Dinglevägen 27. **GPS:** n58,36903 e11,24984.
🅿️kr 100 🔌🔌Ch. ⬛ 01/06-31/08
Distance: ⚓1km ⚓on the spot ►on the spot ⊗1km.

⚓ Öckerö · 4D2
Hönö Klåva Hamn, Öckerövägen. **GPS:** n57,68345 e11,65156.⬆️.
🅿️kr 170, 15/06-15/08 kr 200 🚿included. ⬛ 01/01-31/12
Distance: ►on the spot ⊗500m.

⚓ Öckerö · 4D2
Hönö Röd, Rödvägen. **GPS:** n57,69933 e11,63954.
30 🅿️kr 150 🔌🔌Ch🚿WC🔲included.
Distance: ⚓300m ►300m 🛒500m.

Värmland

🏕️Ⓢ Morokulien · 3B3
Kungsvägen. **GPS:** n59,93089 e12,24181.
🅿️free 🔌🔌ChWC. **Surface:** asphalted/metalled.
Distance: ⊗on the spot.
Remarks: Next to petrol station.

Västmanland

🏕️Ⓢ Västerås · 3D3
Västerås Gästhamn. **GPS:** n59,60190 e16,54648.⬆️.
15 🅿️kr 200 WC🔲included. ⬛ 01/01-31/12
Distance: ⚓500m ⚓on the spot ►on the spot ⊗500m.
Remarks: Pay at harbourmaster.

Dalarna

🏕️ Ludvika · 3C3
Eriksgatan. **GPS:** n60,15020 e15,18936.
🅿️. **Location:** Urban. **Surface:** asphalted.
Distance: ⚓on the spot ⊗200m.
Remarks: Max. 24h.

🏕️ Särna · 3C3
Lägerplats, Byvägen. **GPS:** n61,80383 e12,90931.⬆️➡️.
6 🅿️kr 60. **Location:** Rural. **Surface:** grassy.
Distance: ⚓on the spot ►on the spot.
Remarks: Along river.

🏕️ Säter · 3C3
Säterdalens Folkpark. **GPS:** n60,34854 e15,75439.
🅿️free.
Distance: ⚓650m ⊗650m 🛒850m.

🏕️ Smedjebacken · 3C3
Smedjebackens. **GPS:** n60,13828 e15,41647.
5 🅿️kr 100 🔌🔌Ch🚿🔲. **Surface:** gravel. ⬛ 01/05-01/10
Distance: ⚓500m ►on the spot ⊗200m 🛒500m ⚓on the spot
⚓on the spot.

©Ⓢ Sollerön · 3C3
Sollerö camping, Levnäs. **GPS:** n60,90048 e14,58318.⬆️.
18 🅿️kr 80-100 🚿(8x),kr30. **Surface:** asphalted. ⚓on the spot ⚓on
the spot.
Remarks: Quick-Stop: >18h - <9h.

🏕️ Stjärnsund · 3C3
Villa Solhem, Bruksallén 17. **GPS:** n60,43421 e16,20744.⬆️.
11 🅿️kr 200 🚿(4x),kr 20 WC🔲included.
Distance: ⚓on the spot ⚓300m ►300m.

Gävleborg

🏕️Ⓢ Axmar · 3D3
Axmarbrygga Havskrog, Boskär. **GPS:** n61,04877 e17,15774.⬆️.
30 🅿️kr 90 🔌🔌Ch🚿kr40 WCincluded 🔲kr 10. **Surface:** gravel.
⬛ 03/04-01/11
Distance: ⚓on the spot ►on the spot ⊗on the spot.
Remarks: Bread-service.

🏕️Ⓢ Gävle · 3D3
Hemlingbystugan, Hemlingbyvägen 93. **GPS:** n60,65005 e17,16996.
🅿️free 🔌🔌WC. **Surface:** asphalted.
Distance: ⚓2km ⚓2km 🛒1,8km.
Remarks: Max. 3 days.

🏕️ Gävle · 3D3
Culinarparkeringen, Drottninggatan 47, Anderholmen.
GPS: n60,67810 e17,15493.⬆️.

12 🅿️kr 2/h, overnight stay and weekend free. **Surface:** gravel.

🏕️ Gävle · 3D3
Södra Skeppsbron. **GPS:** n60,67670 e17,15985.⬆️.

2 🅿️free. **Location:** Urban. **Surface:** asphalted. ⬛ 01/01-31/12
Distance: ⚓on the spot ⚓on the spot ►on the spot ⊗on the spot.
Remarks: Max. 48h.

🏕️ Ockelbo · 3C3
Wij Trädgårdar, Vigatan 4. **GPS:** n60,88722 e16,70139.
🅿️free. ⬛ 23/05-06/09
Distance: ⚓1km.
Remarks: Near mill, max. 3 days.

Västernorrland

🏕️ Kvissleby · 3D2
Svartvik. **GPS:** n62,31935 e17,36955.
20 🅿️free. **Surface:** grassy/gravel.
Distance: ⚓on the spot ►on the spot ⊗500m.

🍴 Sandöverken · 3D2
Hotell Höga Kusten AB, Hornöberget. **GPS:** n62,80468 e17,95136.⬆️.
🅿️free. **Surface:** asphalted.
Distance: ⊗on the spot ⚓on the spot.

Jämtland

⚓ Gällö · 3C2
Alma Ångbåt. **GPS:** n62,82794 e15,30652.
🅿️kr 150. **Surface:** grassy.
Distance: ⚓on the spot ►on the spot 🚐300m.

🏕️Ⓢ Hammarstrand · 3C2
Zorbcenter, Dödviken 145. **GPS:** n63,14690 e16,17890.

11 🅿️€ 16 🔌🚿(5x) 2 WC🔲included 🧺. **Surface:** grassy.
⬛ 01/05-31/09
Distance: ⚓15km ►on the spot 🚐1km.
Remarks: Canoe and boat rental.

⚓ Mattmar · 3C2
Ångaren Östersund, Södra Arvesund 516. **GPS:** n63,23573 e14,06810.
🅿️kr 60 🔌🚿kr60 🔲kr20. **Surface:** grassy/metalled.
⬛ 01/01-31/12
Distance: ⚓on the spot ►on the spot ⊗on the spot.

🏕️ Svenstavik · 3C2
Centrumvägen. **GPS:** n62,76731 e14,43496.⬆️.
🅿️kr 100 🔌🔌Chfree 🚿WC. **Location:** Urban. **Surface:** asphalted.
Distance: ⚓on the spot ⊗on the spot 🛒on the spot.

SE

Slovenia

Capital: Ljubljana
Government: parliamentarian republic
Official Language: Slovenian
Population: 1,990,000 (2014)
Area: 20,273 km²

General information
Dialling code: 00386
General emergency: 112
Currency: Euro
Credit card are accepted almost everywhere.

Regulations for overnight stays
There is no regulation against overnight camping, but it is not yet generally accepted. In the National Park Triglav wild camping is forbidden.

Additional public holidays 2016
February 8 Prešern Day - Slovenian cultural festival
April 27 Uprising against the Occupation Day
May 1-2 Labour Day
June 25 National Holiday
August 15 Assumption of the Virgin Mary
October 31 Reformation Day
November 1 All Saints' Day
December 26 Independence Day

Time Zone
Winter (Standard Time) GMT+1
Summer (DST) GMT+2

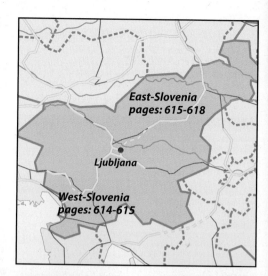

East-Slovenia pages: 615-618

Ljubljana

West-Slovenia pages: 614-615

Slovenia West

Bled 36A1
Old Gardening, Skalickega 3. **GPS**: n45,79536 e15,17039.
10 € 10 Ch (10x)€5 WC included.
Location: Rural, comfortable, quiet. **Surface:** grassy/gravel.
01/01-31/12 with mucht snowfall
Distance: 400m 400m 300m 400m on the spot on the spot.

Bled 36A1
Bled, Kidričeva 10 c. **GPS**: n46,36162 e14,08221.
€ 28,50-€ 31,50 Ch.
01/04-15/10
Distance: on the spot on the spot on the spot on the spot.
Tourist information Bled:
Bled Castle. Exhibition about the history of Bled, during the summer also open-air concerts. 8-17h.
Soteska Vintgar Gorge, TD Gorje, Podhom 0, Gorje. Trail over bridges and galleries along a river.

Bohinjsko jezero 36A1
Zlatorog. GPS: n46,27917 e13,83611.
Ch. 01/05-30/09
Distance: on the spot on the spot 150m.
Tourist information Bohinjsko jezero:
Savica Falls. Water falls.

Bovec 22H1
Kanin Cable Car Station, Dvor. **GPS**: n46,33306 e13,53944.

14 € 9/24h, € 12/36h Ch included.
Location: Rural.
Surface: asphalted.
Distance: on the spot.
Remarks: Max. 36h.
Tourist information Bovec:
Triglav National Park, Dom Trenta, Soča. Information centre.
Kluže Fortress, Trg golobarskih žrtev 8.
Fort above gorge.
Soča Trail, Soča. Hiking trail along the Soca river.

Domžale 36A1
ACG Autocenter Glavan, Češminova ulica 1a.
GPS: n46,14637 e14,60047.

2 free Ch (2x)free,16Amp. **Location:** Urban, simple, central, noisy. **Surface:** asphalted/gravel.
01/01-31/12
Distance: 100m 3km 500m 300m 150m 150m 500m on the spot on the spot 20km 20km.

Dornberk 36A2
Saksida, Zalošče 12a. **GPS**: n45,88963 e13,74751.

15 € 10/pp Ch (15x),16Amp WC included.
Location: Rural, comfortable, isolated. **Surface:** gravel/metalled.
01/01-31/12
Distance: 1km 350m 350m on the spot 1km 300m on the spot on the spot.
Remarks: Covered picnic area, swimming pool available.

DovjeMojstrana 36A1
Kamne. GPS: n46,46444 e13,95778.
Ch. 01/01-31/12
Distance: 1km 1km.

Hruševje 36A2
Penzion & Camp Mirjam, Razdrto 19. **GPS**: n45,75690 e14,06126.

9 € 12 Ch included WC on demand €1
Location: Urban, simple, central, quiet. **Surface:** gravel.
01/05-31/10
Distance: on the spot 1km 10km 10km 50m on the spot on the spot.

Idrija 36A2
Veri Krajnik, Carl Jakoba ulica 9. **GPS**: n45,99879 e14,02595.

3 € 5 Ch included. **Location:** Rural, simple, isolated, quiet. **Surface:** grassy/gravel. 01/01-31/12
Distance: 1,5km 1,5km 1,5km 1,5km on the spot on the spot.
Remarks: Narrow entrance.

Ilirska Bistrica 36A2
Grill Danilo, Bazoviška cesta 46. **GPS**: n45,55846 e14,24340.

6 € 10 Ch (6x),16Amp WC included.
Location: Rural, comfortable, central, quiet.
Surface: asphalted.
01/01-31/12
Distance: 500m 10km 20km 50m on the spot 200m 100m 500m on the spot on the spot 20km 20km.

Izola 36A2
Cankarjev Drevored. GPS: n45,53808 e13,66397.

5 € 15/24h Ch (4x)included,16Amp. **Location:** Urban, simple, quiet. **Surface:** asphalted.
01/01-31/12
Distance: 500m 500m on the spot 500m 500m on the spot on the spot on the spot.

Kamniška Bistrica 36A1
Kamp Alpe. GPS: n46,30510 e14,61110.
10 € 14, 2 pers.incl Ch. 01/05-01/10

Kobarid 22H1
Koren, Drezneske Ravne 333. **GPS**: n46,25083 e13,58667.
Ch. 01/01-31/12
Distance: 500m on the spot on the spot on the spot.

SI

Kobarid 22H1

Lazar, Gregorciceva 63. **GPS:** n46,25530 e13,58720.
Ch. 01/04-31/10
Distance: on the spot on the spot.

Tourist information Kobarid:
Kobariski muzej, Gregorciceva 1. Museum about the first World War.
01/04-30/09 9-18h, 01/10-31/03 10-17h.
Tolmin Chutes, LTO Sotočje, Petra Skalarja 4, Tolmin. Touristic route along the rapid to the thermal source of the river.

Kranjska Gora 36A1

Borovška cesta. **GPS:** n46,48746 e13,77510.
20 15 Ch. included.
Location: Rural. **Surface:** gravel.

Ljubljana 36A1

Alo Camp, Peruzzijeva ulica 105.
GPS: n46,02151 e14,52303.

13 € 10 Ch. (13x)€5 WC included.
Surface: asphalted. 01/01-31/12
Distance: 3km on the spot 500m 50m on the spot on the spot.
Remarks: Check in at hotel, borrow cycles for free, free bus to centre.

Ljubljana 36A1

Pri Kovaču, Cesta II. grupe odredov 82, Dobrunje.
GPS: n46,03162 e14,60386.

10 € 8/night, guests free Ch. (20x)€2/night,16Amp WC € 0,80 included. **Location:** Rural, comfortable, central, quiet. **Surface:** gravel.
01/01-31/12 Restaurant: Tue
Distance: 8km 2,5km 5km on the spot 100m, bakery 200m 20m on the spot on the spot 400m.

Ljubljana 36A1

Sraka, Masarykova cesta 17.
GPS: n46,05740 e14,51870.

15 € 15, park € 10 Ch. included.
Location: Urban.
Surface: gravel.
01/01-31/12
Distance: 1km on the spot 100m on the spot on the spot on the spot.
Remarks: Motorhome washing place.

Tourist information Ljubljana:
Ljubljana Tourist Card. Card offers among other things free public transport, free access at museums and discount in restaurants, shops etc. Available at Tourist Office, railway station and several hotels.
€ 35/72h.
Ljubljana Tourist Information Center, Stritarjeva, www.ljubljana-tourism.si. Capital, historical city with a lot of annual events.
National museum, Muzjeska 1. Archeological and historical museum. 10-18h, Thu 10-20h Mo.
Plecnik museum, Kurunova 4. Architectonic museum in the house of

Joze Plecnik. Tue, Thu 10-14h.
Slovene Natural History Museum, Muzjeska 1. Zoological and botanic museum. daily 10-18h, Thu 10-20h Mo.
Ljubljana Castle. Medieval fortress, tourist train at town centre.
01/10-30/04 10-21h, 01/05-30/09 9-22h.
Vodnikov trg. daily, summer 6-18h, winter 6-16h.
Zoo Ljubljana. Zoo. summer 9-19h, winter 9-16h.

Luče 36A1

Camp Smica, Luče 4. **GPS:** n46,35644 e14,74290.
Ch. 01/05-30/10
Distance: on the spot on the spot 900m.

Lukovica 36A1

Gostilna Furman, Stari trg 19. **GPS:** n46,17026 e14,69233.

10 € 10, € 15 service incl Ch. (10x) WC
Location: Urban, simple, central, quiet. **Surface:** gravel.
01/01-31/12
Distance: on the spot 3km 3km on the spot 200m 100m on the spot on the spot.

Lukovica 36A1

OMV Istrabenz. GPS: n46,16690 e14,69380.
2 free. **Location:** Highway, noisy.
Distance: on the spot on the spot.
Remarks: Parking petrol station OMV Istrabenz.

Portorož 36A2

Marina Portorož, Cesta solinarjev 8. **GPS:** n45,50505 e13,59847.

60 € 16, 11/05-20/09 € 23 + tourist tax € 0,63/pp Ch. (64x),16Amp included. **Location:** Urban, simple, quiet.
Surface: gravel. 01/01-31/12
Distance: 1km on the spot on the spot on the spot on the spot 500m on the spot on the spot.
Remarks: Monitored parking 24/24, swimming pool available.

Tourist information Portorož:
Turistična organizacija Koper, Verdijeva 10, Koper. City with a Venetian past and a lot of curiosities.
Pomorski muzej Sergej Mašera, Cankarjevo nabrežje 3, Piran. Maritime museum. 9-12h, 15-18h, 01/07-31/08 9-12h, 18-21h Mo.

Postojna 36A2

Park Postojnska Jama, Veliki Otok. **GPS:** n45,78066 e14,20322.

20 € 18/24h Ch. (20x)included,16Amp.
Location: Rural, simple, quiet.
Surface: concrete.
01/04-30/09
Distance: 1km 3km 100m 1km on the spot on the spot on the spot.
Remarks: Postojna caves 300m.

Tourist information Postojna:
Križna jama, Bloška polica 7, Grahovo. Largest water caves of Slovenia.
Perdjama Grad. Castle, 16th century and caves.
01/05-30/09 9-18,

01/10-30/04 10-16h.
Postojnska Jama, Jamska cesta 30. Postojna caves.
01/05-30/09 9-18, 01/10-30/04 10-16h.

Šmarje 36A2

Garni Mimosa, Srgaši 38a. **GPS:** n45,50843 e13,70560.

5 € 10 €8/100liter (1x)included,16Amp WC on demand
Location: Urban, simple, central, quiet. **Surface:** gravel.
01/01-31/12
Distance: 6km 50m 50m 100m on the spot on the spot.

Smlednik 36A1

Hotel Kanu, Valburga 7. **GPS:** n46,16927 e14,42228.

20 € 10 Ch. (4x),16Amp WC €5 included
Location: Rural, isolated, quiet. **Surface:** grasstiles. 01/01-31/12
water disconnected in winter
Distance: 300m 5km on the spot on the spot on the spot 300m 300m on the spot on the spot 20km 7km.

Tolmin 36A1

Kamp Siber, Klanec 8. **GPS:** n46,18082 e13,73792.

50 € 6/pp Ch. WC included. **Location:** Rural.
Surface: grassy/gravel. 01/01-31/12
Distance: 1km on the spot on the spot 1km.

Slovenia East

Braslovče 36A1

Najem & Kamping, Preserje 16b. **GPS:** n46,28915 e15,05524.

20 € 5 Ch. (2x)€5/day,16Amp included.
Location: Rural, comfortable, isolated, quiet. **Surface:** gravel.
01/01-31/12
Distance: 1km on the spot on the spot 1km 1km 1km on the spot on the spot 10km 10km.
Remarks: Opening hours 7-22h.

Brestanica 36B1

Bazen Brestanica, Jetrno selo 2. **GPS:** n46,00124 e15,47492.

SI

⌂free ⚡🚰Ch🚿. **Surface:** gravel.
Remarks: At swimming pool.

🛁S Brestanica 36B1

Ribiška družina Brestanica, Raztez 1a. **GPS:** n46,00504 e15,49751.⬆️

5 ⌂free ⚡🚰WC🚿.
Location: Isolated, quiet. **Surface:** gravel.
Distance: 🚲on the spot 🚿on the spot.
Remarks: Fishpond, check in at restaurant.

Celje 🏕🍴♨️ 36B1

Parking Glazija, Ljubljanska cesta 20. **GPS:** n46,23319 e15,25904.
2 ⌂€ 10 🚰🚿included.
Location: Urban. **Surface:** metalled.
Distance: 🍺on the spot.

🏖S Celje 🏕🍴♨️ 36B1

Glavan Center Karavaninga, Gaji 45. **GPS:** n46,24406 e15,30217.⬆️➡️

6 ⌂€ 5 ⚡€1/100liter 🚰Ch🚿(2x)€0,50/kWh,16Amp 🚿.🚐
Location: Rural, simple, isolated, quiet.
Surface: gravel.
🅾️ 01/01-31/12
Distance: 🚲3km 🏊4km 🚿4km ⊗200m 🍺2km 🚌on the spot 🚿on the spot 🏃on the spot.
Remarks: At motorhome dealer.

Tourist information Celje:
👁 Jama Pekel, Šempeter. Caves.
⚔️ Stari Grad Castle. Remainders of castle.
⌒ Rimska Nekropola, Šempeter. Roman Necropolis, archeological park.

🏕S Cirkulane 36B1

Herman Lederhaus, Dolane 8. **GPS:** n46,37114 e15,99682.⬆️

10 ⌂€ 10 ⚡🚰Ch🚿WC included. **Surface:** grassy/gravel.
🅾️ 01/01-31/12
Distance: 🏊on the spot 🚲on the spot ⊗on the spot 🍺50m.
Remarks: Restaurant and leather factory.

🛁S Dolenjske Toplice 🌊♨️ 36A2

Dolenjske Toplice, Meniška vas. **GPS:** n45,76739 e15,05151.⬆️

10 ⌂€ 8, 20/06-24/08, € 12 + tourist tax ⚡🚰Chincluded.
🚿 **Location:** Rural, simple, isolated, quiet. **Surface:** grassy.
🅾️ 01/01-31/12
Distance: 🚲800m 🏊on the spot 🚿on the spot ⊗800m 🍺800m 🚿on the spot 🏃on the spot.
Remarks: Along the Krka river, terme Dolenjske Toplice 800m.

Ivanjkovci 🔥 36B1

Vinoteka Svetinjska Klet, Svetinje 5.
GPS: n46,46220 e16,16990.⬆️➡️

10 ⌂free. **Surface:** metalled.
Remarks: Sale of wines.

🍴S Jesenice na Dolenjskem 36B2

Gostinstvo Strnisa, Jesenice na Dolenjskem 7c.
GPS: n45,85869 e15,68979.⬆️

⌂€ 6 ⚡€2 🚰Ch🚿€2,50 WC🚿. **Location:** Urban.
Surface: concrete.
Distance: ⊗on the spot.

🍴 Kamnica 🔥 36B1

Gostilna Koblarjev Zaliv, Na otok 20. **GPS:** n46,56560 e15,61908.⬆️

20 ⌂free, use of a meal desired 🚿free. **Surface:** grassy.
🅾️ 01/01-31/12
Distance: 🚲Maribor 2km 🏊on the spot 🚿on the spot ⊗on the spot 🍺2km 🚌300m.
Remarks: Walking and bicycle area along the Drava river to Maribor centre.

Kocevje 🏕🍴 36A2

Turistični Kompleks Jezero, Trdnjava 3. **GPS:** n45,64421 e14,87140.⬆️

3 ⌂free. **Location:** Simple, isolated, quiet. **Surface:** asphalted.
🅾️ 01/01-31/12

Distance: 🚲1km 🏊200m 🚿200m 🍺1km 🚌1km 🚿on the spot 🏃on the spot.
Remarks: Nature reserve.

🛁S Krško 36B1

Raceland, Pesje 30. **GPS:** n45,92977 e15,53500.⬆️

50 ⌂€ 12 🚰🚿WC🚿included. **Location:** Rural, isolated, noisy. **Surface:** asphalted.
Distance: ⊗on the spot.
Remarks: Parking at Karting.

Krško 36B1

Stadium Matija Gubec, Cesta krških žrtev 130a.
GPS: n45,94691 e15,48832.⬆️

30 ⌂free. **Surface:** grassy/gravel. 🅾️ 01/01-31/12

🍴 Krško 36B1

Gostilna Stanislava Pečnik, Gunte 8. **GPS:** n45,98645 e15,46572.⬆️

2 ⌂free. 🅿️ Su
Distance: 🏊on the spot 🚲on the spot ⊗on the spot.

🛁S Laško 🌊🏕🍴♨️ 36A1

Thermana Park Laško, Zdraviliška cesta 6.
GPS: n46,16188 e15,23132.⬆️

16 ⌂€ 7-10/pp, dog € 4 ⚡🚰Chincluded 🚿(16x)€4/day,16Amp WC🚿🅿️🚿♨️🚿 **Location:** Urban, simple, central, noisy.
Surface: grasstiles/metalled. 🅾️ 01/01-31/12
Distance: 🚲700m 🏊on the spot 🍺700m 🍴on the spot 🚌on the spot 🏃on the spot 🚿10km 🚿10km.
Remarks: Max. 24h, check in at reception.

🛁S Laško 🌊🏕🍴♨️ 36A1

Zdravilišče Laško, Zdraviliška cesta 4. **GPS:** n46,15761 e15,23224.⬆️

4 ⌂€ 7-10/pp, dog € 4 ⚡🚰Chincluded 🚿(4x)€4/day,16Amp

SI

WC ⧉ ⧉ ⧉ **Location:** Urban, simple, central, noisy.
Surface: asphalted. ▣ 01/01-31/12
Distance: 500m ⊗on the spot 500m on the spot on the spot on the spot on the spot 10km 10km.

Lendava — 36B1

Terme Lendava, Tomsiceve 21A. **GPS:** n46,55396 e16,45813. ⬆➡

90 € 12,50-13,50/pp, dog € 3 Ch €4 WC ⧉ €1/30min-utes. **Surface:** asphalted/grassy. ▣ 01/01-31/12
Remarks: Including access spa resort.

Ljutomer — 36B1

Gostilna Trnek, Mota 76. **GPS:** n46,55516 e16,21929. ⬆➡

25 guests free Chincluded €3 WC ⧉. **Location:** Rural, isolated, quiet. **Surface:** grassy/gravel.
▣ 01/01-31/12
Distance: on the spot on the spot ⊗on the spot 1km.
Remarks: Use sanitary only during opening hours.

Maribor — 36B1

Avtobusna postaja Maribor, Mlinska ulica 1.
GPS: n46,55852 e15,65573. ⬆

4 € 10 Ch . **Location:** Noisy. **Surface:** asphalted.
Distance: on the spot ⊗fast food on the spot on the spot.
Remarks: Nearby bus station P4, check in at tourist office.

Metlika — 36B2

Dependansa sobe Metlika, Cesta bratstra in enotnosti 77.
GPS: n45,64663 e15,31778. ⬆

3 € 10 Ch (3x)€5 included. **Location:** Urban, simple, central, quiet. **Surface:** asphalted.
▣ 01/01-31/12
Distance: 100m 1km 1km ⊗100m 100m 100m on the spot on the spot.

Moravske Toplice — 36B1

Kamp Moravske Toplice, Kranjčeva ulica 12 .
GPS: n46,67862 e16,22151. ⬆➡

€ 3,20 2 pers. Incl., dog € 3 Ch €4 .
Surface: grassy/gravel. ▣ 01/01-31/12
Distance: 400m ⊗100m 200m on the spot on the spot.
Remarks: Including access spa resort 3000.

Tourist information Moravske Toplice:
Goričko Regional Park, Ulica ob igrišču 3, www.park-goricko.org. Information centre.

Novo Mesto — 36B2

Old Gardening, Skalickega 3. **GPS:** n45,79536 e15,17039. ⬆
10 € 10 Ch (10x)€5 WC ⧉ included. **Location:** Comfortable, quiet. **Surface:** grassy/gravel. ▣ 01/01-31/12 with mucht snowfall
Distance: 400m ⊗400m 300m 400m on the spot on the spot.

Novo Mesto — 36B2

Pri Belokranjucu, Kandijska cesta 63. **GPS:** n45,79947 e15,17865. ⬆

3 € 10 Ch (3x)€5/night,16Amp included . **Location:** Urban, simple, central, noisy. **Surface:** asphalted.
▣ 01/01-31/12
Distance: 400m 5km 400m ⊗on the spot 200m on the spot 200m on the spot on the spot.

Obrežje Jug — 36B2

OMV Istrabenz. **GPS:** n45,85517 e15,68513.
2 free. **Location:** Noisy.
Distance: on the spot.
Remarks: Parking petrol station OMV Istrabenz.

Ormož — 36B1

Bar Ribnik, Ob ribniku 1. **GPS:** n46,40588 e16,15963.

3 free included. **Location:** Rural. **Surface:** asphalted.
▣ 01/01-31/12
Distance: on the spot on the spot.

Podbočje — 36B2

Turistična kmetija Hribar, Podbočje 36. **GPS:** n45,86190 e15,47110. ⬆

5 free. **Surface:** gravel.
Distance: 400m on the spot ⊗on the spot on the spot on the spot.

Podčetrtek — 36B1

Golf Klub a Podčetrtek Amon, Olimje 24. **GPS:** n46,14400 e15,56493.

20 € 10 + € 1,25/pp tourist tax WC ⧉ included. **Location:** Isolated, quiet. **Surface:** asphalted/gravel. ▣ With snow
Distance: ⊗on the spot on the spot on the spot.
Remarks: At golf court, bicycle rental.

Podčetrtek — 36B1

Terme Olimia Kamp Natura, Zdravilǐška cesta 24.
GPS: n46,16529 e15,60522.

15 € 16,50-21,50/pp, dog € 3 Ch €4,20 WC ⧉ €3 .
Surface: metalled. ▣ 21/04-30/09
Distance: ⊗on the spot on the spot.
Remarks: Including access spa resort.

Tourist information Podčetrtek:
Sedovška Homestead, Aškercev trg 24, Šmarje pri Jelšah. Traditional farmstead.
Rogatec Open-air Museum, Ptujska cesta 23, Rogatec. Open air museum, 18-20th century.
Božjepotna Marijina cerkev, Sladka Gora, Šmarje pri Jelšah. Pilgrimage church.
Olimje Monastery and Pharmacy, Olimje 82. Monastery and one of the oldest pharmacies in the world.

Podsmreka — 36A2

A2. **GPS:** n45,94805 e14,77065.
5 free free. **Location:** Highway.
Distance: 100m.
Remarks: Guarded parking petrol station Petrol Podsmereka, highway Novo Mesto-Ljubljana.

Prebold — 36A1

Dolina, Dolenja Vas 147. **GPS:** n46,24018 e15,09268.
Ch . ▣ 01/01-31/12
Distance: ⊗200m 200m.

Ptuj — 36B1

Camping Therme Ptuj

- **Located nearby spa**
- **Excellent location for city visit**
- **Medieval town**

www.camping-slovenia.com
kamp@terme-ptuj.si

Terme Ptuj, Pot v toplice 9. **GPS:** n46,42109 o15,85585. ⬆
20 € 20 + € 1,63/registration + tourist tax Ch (2x),16Amp WC ⧉ €5/5 included .
Location: Simple. **Surface:** gravel.
▣ 01/01-31/12
Distance: 800m 3km 500m ⊗100m 1km on the spot 25km.

Tourist information Ptuj:
Maribor Tourist Board, Partizanska 47, Maribor, www.maribor-

SI

tourism.si. Old city with historical centre.

🏛🏴 Mariborski Grad, Maribor. Castle, 15th century, regional museum.
⬛ 01/04-31/12 Tue-Sa 9-17h, Su 9-14h ◼ Mo.
🏛🏴 Ptujski Grad. Castle, 11th century with regional museum.
⬛ 01/05-31/10 9-18h.

🔺S Rečica ob Savinji — 36A1
Menina. GPS: n46,31167 e14,90917.
🛏🚰🔌Ch🧹 ⬛ 01/01-31/12
Distance: 🏊on the spot ⊗on the spot 🛒300m.
Tourist information Rečica ob Savinji:
👁 Mozirski gaj, Hribernikova 1, Mozirje. Botanical garden. ⬛ 01/04-31/10.
🏛 Musej Premogovništva, Stari jašek - Koroška cesta, Velenje. Coal mining museum.

🔲S Rogla — 36B1
Rogla. GPS: n46,45259 e15,33117.⬆.

🛏€ 12 🚰🔌Ch🧹🔌included. Surface: gravel.
Distance: 🏙Zreče 10km 🛒200m on the spot 🚶on the spot 🚵on the spot 🎿on the spot.
Remarks: Altitude 1517m.

🔲S Slovenj Gradec — 36A1
Camperstop Slovenj Gradec, Ozare 18.
GPS: n46,51418 e15,07678.⬆➡.

6 🛏€ 5 🚰🔌Ch🧹(4x)🔌included. Location: Comfortable, quiet.
⬛ 01/01-31/12
Distance: 🏙500m ⊗500m 🛒500m 🚵on the spot.
Remarks: At youth hostel.

Solcava 🏔🏕🌲 — 36A1
Park Logarska Dolina, Logarska Dolina 9.
GPS: n46,41999 e14,64555.⬆.

20 🛏€ 10. 🚽 Location: Rural, simple, isolated, quiet.
Surface: grassy/gravel. ⬛ 01/01-31/12
Distance: 🏙5km 🏊on the spot ⊗5km 🛒5km 🚵on the spot 🚶on the spot 🎿on the spot 🏊on the spot.
Remarks: Entrance park € 7/pp.

🔲S Stahovica 🏔🌲🌲 — 36A1
Pri Jurju, Kamniska Bistrica 5. GPS: n46,32685 e14,58706.⬆.

20 🛏€ 5 🚰🔌Ch🧹(20x)€ 2/day,16Amp WC included 🚿€ 5/day. 🚽 Location: Rural, simple, isolated, quiet. Surface: grassy.
⬛ 01/01-31/12

Distance: 🏙8km ⊗6km ⊗on the spot 🛒8km 🚵300m on the spot 🚶on the spot 🎿3km 🎿3km.

🔲S Tepanje — 36B1
GPS: n46,34776 e15,48695.
5 🛏free 🚰free. Location: Noisy.
Distance: 🚗on the spot.
Remarks: Guarded parking petrol station Petrol Tepanje I, on both sides of the highway Maribor-Ljubljana.

🔲S Visnja Gora 🌿🍴 — 36A1
Mestno kopališče, Kopaliska Ulica 25.
GPS: n45,95268 e14,75097.⬆➡.

20 🛏free 🚰🔌(1x)WC 🔌free. Location: Rural, simple, isolated, quiet. Surface: asphalted/gravel. ⬛ 01/01-31/12
Distance: 🏙on the spot 🚴1,7km 🛒1km 🚵200m on the spot 🚶on the spot 🎿10km 🎿10km.
Remarks: Check in at swimming pool, service during opening hours.

🔲S Žalec 🌿🍴 — 36A1
Camperstop Žalec, Mestni trg. GPS: n46,25418 e15,16274.⬆➡.

4 🛏free 🚰🔌Ch🧹(4x)free,16Amp. Location: Urban, simple, central, quiet. Surface: metalled.
⬛ 01/01-31/12
Distance: 🏙500m 🏊100m 🛒500m 🚵500m on the spot 🚶on the spot.
Remarks: At sports park, caution key service € 20 at hotel.

🍴S Zdole — 36B1
Etnoart tourism Špiler, Kostanjek 18. GPS: n46,01018 e15,54409.⬆.

5 🛏🚰🔌. Surface: grassy.
Distance: ⊗on the spot.

🍴S Zdole — 36B1
Gostilna pri Dularju, Kostanjek 20. GPS: n46,00975 e15,54155.⬆.

10 🛏🚰🔌Ch🧹(3x). Location: Rural, quiet.

🔲S Zgornje Jezersko 🏔🏕🌲 — 36A1
Camperstop Stara Pošta, Zgornje Jezersko 124.
GPS: n46,40240 e14,50673.⬆.

9 🛏€ 12 🚰🔌Ch🧹(16x)€ 3/24h WC 🍴◼€ 4 🔌included. 🚽
Location: Rural, luxurious, quiet. Surface: grassy. ⬛ 01/04-30/09
Distance: 🏙1km 🏊1km 🚴1km ⊗1km 🛒1km 🚵100m on the spot 🚶on the spot.

🔲S Zgornje Jezersko 🏔🏕🌲 — 36A1
Camperstop Šenkova Domačija, Zgornje Jezersko 12.
GPS: n46,40792 e14,51769.

5 🛏€ 10, Jul/Aug € 15 🚰🔌Ch🧹(5x)€ 3/night WC 🍴◼€ 3
🔌included. 🚽 Location: Rural, quiet. Surface: gravel/metalled.
⬛ 01/01-31/12
Distance: 🏙2km 🏊300m 🚴300m ⊗300m 🛒2km 🚵100m on the spot 🚶on the spot 🎿on the spot.

🔲S Zrece — 36B1
Thermal Spa, Cesta na Roglo 15. GPS: n46,37096 e15,39021.⬆.

4 🛏€ 10 + € 1,30/pp tourist tax 🚰🔌🔌included.
Surface: asphalted.
Distance: 🏙300m 🚴300m ⊗on the spot 🛒300m.
Remarks: Check in at hotel, 20% reduction swimming pool.

Slowakia

Capital: Bratislava
Government: parliamentary republic
Official Language: Slovak
Population 5,444,000 (2014)
Area: 49,036 Km^2

General information
Dialling code: 0421
General emergency: 112
Currency: Euro
Credit cards are accepted almost everywhere.

Regulations for overnight stays
Wild camping is not allowed.

Additional public holidays 2016
January 1 Republic Day
January 6 Epiphany
May 1 Labour Day
May 8 End of World War II
July 5 St. Cyril & St. Methodius Day
August 29 National Uprising Day
September 1 Constitution Day
September 15 Day of Lady Sorrows
November 1 All Saints' Day
November 17 Freedom and Democracy Day

Time Zone
Winter (Standard Time) GMT+1
Summer (DST) GMT+2

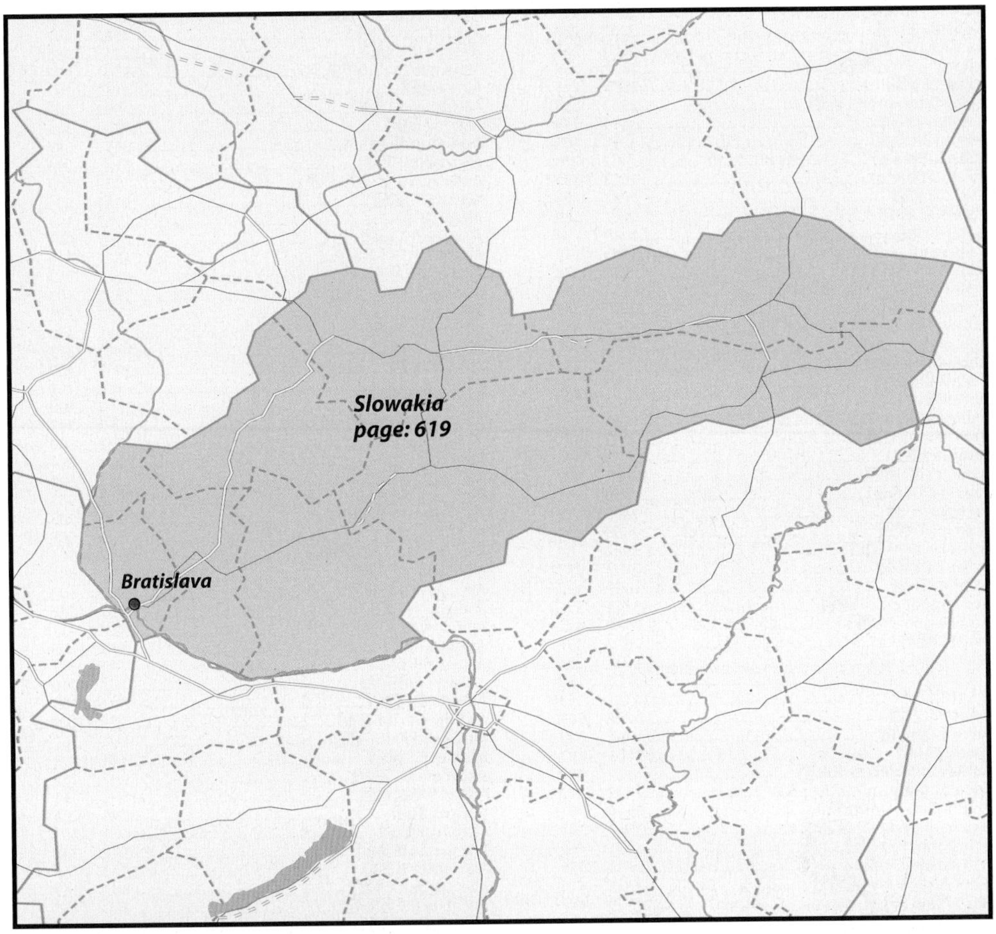

Bratislava 35B3
Camping Zlate Piesky, Senecká cesta 2. **GPS**: n48,18836 e17,18557.
€ 15,80, 2 pers.incl Ch € 3,50 WCincluded .
Location: Urban. **Surface:** grassy. 01/05-15/10
Distance: 8km 100m on the spot 200m.

Banka 35B2
Camping Pullmann Piestany, Cesta Janka Alexyho 921.
GPS: n48,57609 e17,83444.
€ 8 ChWCincluded . **Surface:** grassy.
Distance: 2km on the spot.

Dunajská Streda 35B3
CaravanCamp DS, Kúpelná ulica 21. **GPS**: n47,98689 e17,61150.
15 € 12 Ch WC included. **Location:** Rural.
Surface: grassy. 01/04-01/11
Distance: 1km 350m 900m.

Šamorín 35B3
Stellplatz Čilistov, Čilistov. **GPS**: n48,01364 e17,30850.
25 € 7 Ch € 3 WC included. **Location:** Rural.
Surface: grassy/gravel. 01/04-31/10
Distance: 20km 50m 500m.
Remarks: Golf court 2km.

Liptovský Ján 35C2
Pension Horec, Starojanka. 4
GPS: n49,03709 e19,67526.
15 free. **Location:** Rural. **Surface:** metalled. 01/01-31/12

Varín 35B2
Autocamp Varin, Doktor Jozefa Tisu 13. **GPS**: n49,20833 e18,87861.
€ 12 Ch € 3,30 WC included . **Location:** Rural.
Surface: grassy. 01/05-11/10
Distance: on the spot.

Brezno 35C2
Sedliacky Dvor, Hliník 7, Rohozná. **GPS**: n48,79535 e19,72869.
20 € 13,50 Ch € 3,50 WC € 3,25 included.
Location: Rural. **Surface:** grassy. 15/4-31/10
Distance: 7km on the spot on the spot.

Haligovce 35C2
Camping Goralsky Dvor. **GPS**: n49,37984 e20,43972.
€ 10,50 Ch € 3,50 WC included. **Location:** Rural.
Surface: grassy.
Distance: on the spot.

Snina 35D2
Camping Snina, Rybnícka 4483. **GPS**: n48,97384 e22,18919.
25 € 9 Chincluded € 2,50 € 0,50 . 15/5-30/09
Distance: 3km 50m 50m on the spot on the spot.

Vysoké Tatry 35C2
Pension Slnecny Dom, Tatranská Lomnica 287.
GPS: n49,16664 e20,28169.
4 € 10 Ch included. 01/01-31/12
Distance: on the spot on the spot.

Vyšný Medzev 35C2
Camping Sokol, Hrdinov SNP 64 - 68. **GPS**: n48,71472 e20,90222.
€ 17,50 Ch € 2,50 WC included. **Location:** Highway.
Surface: grassy. 01/04-01/10
Distance: on the spot.

SK

INDEX